Student Manual

The AUTODESK COLLECTION

Professional Design Software for Collegiate Users

Student Manual

The AUTODESK COLLECTION

Professional Design Software for Collegiate Users

Shawna D. Lockhart

with Kevin P. Reagh

Addison-Wesley Publishing Company

Reading, Massachusetts • Menlo Park, California • New York • Don Mills, Ontario
Wokingham, England • Amsterdam • Bonn • Sydney • Singapore • Tokyo
Madrid • San Juan • Milan • Paris

The Autodesk Collection Publishing Team:
Editor: Denise Descoteaux
Assistant Editor: Melissa Honig
Project Manager: Cindy Johnson
Interface Development Team: Frank Nanfara, Tony Uccello,
Mario DeCarolis, Alp Hug and Derek Murphy, TOR Computerized
Systems, Inc.; and David S. Cohn
Senior Production Supervisor: John Walker
Production Coordinator: Kathleen A. Manley
Text Designer: Jean Hammond
Copyeditor: Pamela Mayne
Technical Validators: Jeff Andrews, Kyle Tage, Carl Treadwell, Bill Fletcher
Compositor: Gex, Inc.
Package Designer: Peter Blaiwas
Marketing Manger: Janet Drumm
Senior Manufacturing Manager: Roy E. Logan
Senior Manufacturing Coordinator: Judith Y. Sullivan

ISBN 0-201-96072-9

2 3 4 5 6 7 8 9 10—CRW—9998979695

AutoCAD® is the most widely used design and drafting software for desktop computers in the world. AutoCAD Release 12 provides anyone with a personal computer with the ability to create complex and accurate drawings. Its position as the industry standard makes it an essential tool for anyone preparing for a career in engineering, design, or technology.

The Autodesk Collection: Professional Design Software for Collegiate Users contains fully functioning DOS and Windows™ versions of this best-selling software program. *The Autodesk Collection* also contains a whole range of other design tools that can be used with AutoCAD to create a complete design environment. These tools include AutoVision™, photo-realistic rendering software; 3D Studio®, the most complete rendering and animation software for the PC; and AutoCAD® Designer, new parametric solid modeling software. *The Autodesk Collection* is one of the most complete sets of design tools ever assembled in a single package, allowing the user to take an idea from a sketch to a photo-realistic rendering or animation.

Appropriate for use at home or in class, *The Autodesk Collection* will quickly become indispensable for homework, projects, and day-to-day design problem solving. *The Autodesk Collection* was put together with the student or first-time user in mind. A custom interface written exclusively for this package guides the user through an introduction to each of the various packages contained in The Collection, and through a short piece on how to use the products together to create a design environment. The interface also leads the user to an automated installation procedure and on-line reference material.

This student manual is another essential component of The Autodesk Collection package. This tutorial-based manual can be used in conjunction with a basic engineering graphics course, introductory engineering, introductory architecture and/or design courses, or independently for self-study. In all cases, the novice user will find its step-by-step approach a fast and easy path to proficiency with these design tools.

Features of the Manual

To achieve *The Autodesk Collection*'s objectives, the Student Manual includes

- Step-by-step tutorials written for the novice user
- Tutorials organized to parallel an introductory engineering graphics course
- "Adapting for Architecture" boxes that show architects how they can use AutoCAD for their own needs
- "TIP" boxes that offer suggestions and warnings to students as they progress through the tutorials
- "Going Further" boxes that show students aspects of AutoCAD that they can explore on their own
- Challenging and interesting end-of-tutorial drawing exercises, with applications in mechanical, civil, and electrical engineering, as well as architecture

- Key Terms and Key Commands summaries to recap important topics and commands learned in each tutorial

Organization of the Manual

The Student Manual proceeds in a logical fashion to guide the student from drawing basic shapes to working with AutoCAD's three-dimensional drawing features. It then shows students how to create photo-realistic renderings of their models with AutoVision. Three tutorials on 3D Studio guide the student through the process of creating objects and animations, with one tutorial devoted entirely to architecture. Finally, the student is introduced to AutoCAD Designer's parametric modeling capabilities.

Part 1, Getting Started, introduces the package and its contents, walks the student through installing and configuring the software, and then takes the student on a guided tour of the AutoCAD Release 12 screen display, menus, help facility, and keyboard/mouse usage conventions.

Part 2, Tutorials, introduces the software in *The Autodesk Collection* in the context of technical drawing.

- Tutorials 1 and 2 introduce AutoCAD's basic drawing and editing commands and build proficiency with the menus and drawing aids.
- Tutorial 3 teaches geometric construction techniques and provides instruction on plotting a drawing.
- Tutorials 4 and 5 are devoted to the concepts of drawing orthographic views.
- Tutorial 6 explains prototype drawings and continues work with orthographic views.
- Tutorial 7 instructs the student in basic dimensioning.
- Tutorials 8 and 9 introduce the concepts of three-dimensional solid modeling.
- Tutorial 10 covers section views, using both two-dimensional and solid modeling techniques.
- Tutorial 11 covers creating pictorial drawings, using both two-dimensional and solid modeling techniques.
- Tutorial 12 explains auxiliary views, also using both two-dimensional and solid modeling techniques.
- Tutorial 13 teaches advanced dimensioning techniques, including tolerances.
- Tutorial 14 introduces working drawings in two dimensions.
- Tutorial 15 shows how to create assembly drawings from solid models.
- Tutorial 16 introduces photo-realistic rendering with AutoVision.
- Tutorial 17 explains how 3D Studio can be used to add animation to your AutoCAD models.
- Tutorial 18 teaches the creation and animation of objects in 3D Studio.
- Tutorial 19 demonstrates camera animation in 3D Studio with an emphasis on use by architects.
- Tutorial 20 covers parametric design with AutoCAD Designer.

The Glossary defines key terms used in the tutorials. The Command Grids show where the key commands used in the tutorials can be found. Challenge Exercises provide additional opportunities for students to practice their skills. The Appendix provides more information on using digitizer tablets and working in AutoCAD.

Acknowledgments

I wish to acknowledge the many individuals who contributed to the conceptualization and implementation of the exciting idea that became *The Autodesk Collection*. First, the many teaching colleagues who responded to inquiries and helped to shape the tutorials in this manual. We cannot list all the individuals with whom we spoke in the course of our research, but we are grateful to the reviewers listed below for their help.

Karen Argonza, Autodesk, Inc.

Adrian G. Baird, Ricks College

Steven Combs, Ivy Tech State College

Randy Clark, Autodesk, Inc.

Lamar Henderson, Catholic University of America

John E. Kelly, Arizona State University

Kim Manner, University of Wisconsin - Madison

Gary Hordemann, Gonzaga University

Raymond Stein, Finger Lakes Community College

A heartfelt thank you is extended to Kevin Reagh of the University of Cincinnati, who wrote Tutorial 19 on 3D Studio for architecture and provided important comments on other tutorials. Our thanks also go to David S. Cohn, Senior Editor of CADalyst, who put together the "CAD and the Design Process" section of the interface and who has been an important supporter of student-priced professional design tools.

Our thanks also go to Kyle Tage, for writing the Adapting for Architecture tips, submitting exercises, and creating art files for us; and to Shannon Kyles and James Bethune, authors of previous AutoCAD tutorial guides, from which some material was adapted for this manual.

An extra measure of thanks goes to Frank Nanfara, Tony Uccello, Mario DeCarolis, Derek Murphy, and Alp Hug of TOR Computerized Systems Inc. for their incredible work on the software interface and for helping us to pull the CD-ROM together.

I also wish to thank Richard Cuneo, Vice President U.S. Sales; Jim Purcell, Education Department Manager; Mark Sturges, Education Sales Manager; Jimm Meloy, Education Programs Manager; Wayne Hodgins, Learning Systems Manager; Alan Jacobs, Market Development Manager; and Maureen Barrow, Contracts Administrator, who lent their talents to the partnership between Addison-Wesley and Autodesk. Their commitment to educators was instrumental in making The Autodesk Collection a reality.

Editing, testing, and producing step-by-step tutorials requires a tremendous amount of publishing expertise, and I would be remiss if I did not acknowledge those who worked to make this manual complete, technically accurate, and lovely to look at, especially Melissa Honig, Kathy Manley, John Walker, Denise Descoteaux, and Cindy Johnson for their enthusiasm, efficiency, and professionalism throughout this project. Last but not least, I wish to thank my husband, Bob, children, Catey and Nick, and my family and friends for their support and encouragement.

Shawna D. Lockhart

CONTENTS

TUTORIAL 2

Basic Construction Techniques 37

TUTORIAL 3

Geometric Constructions 73

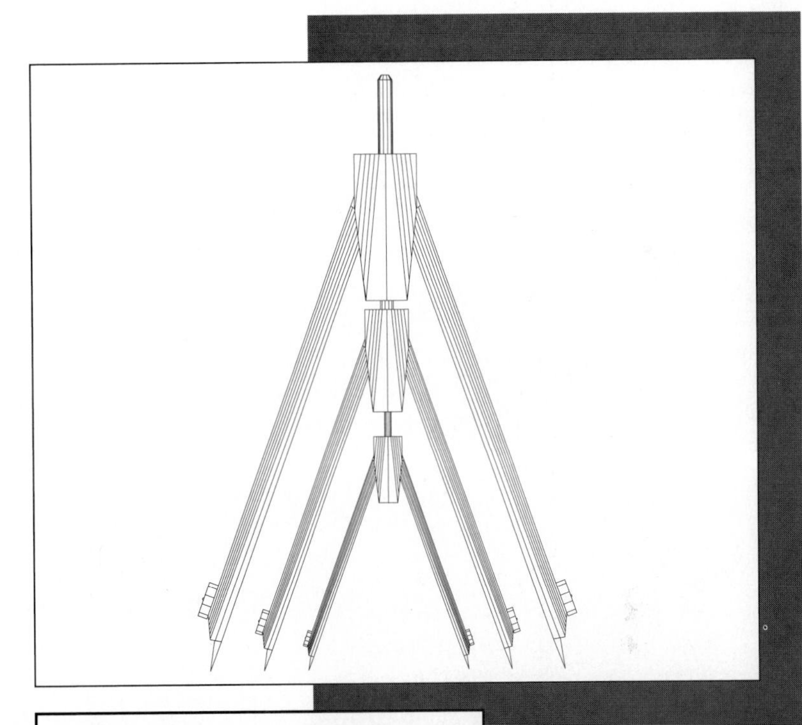

PART ONE

Getting Started

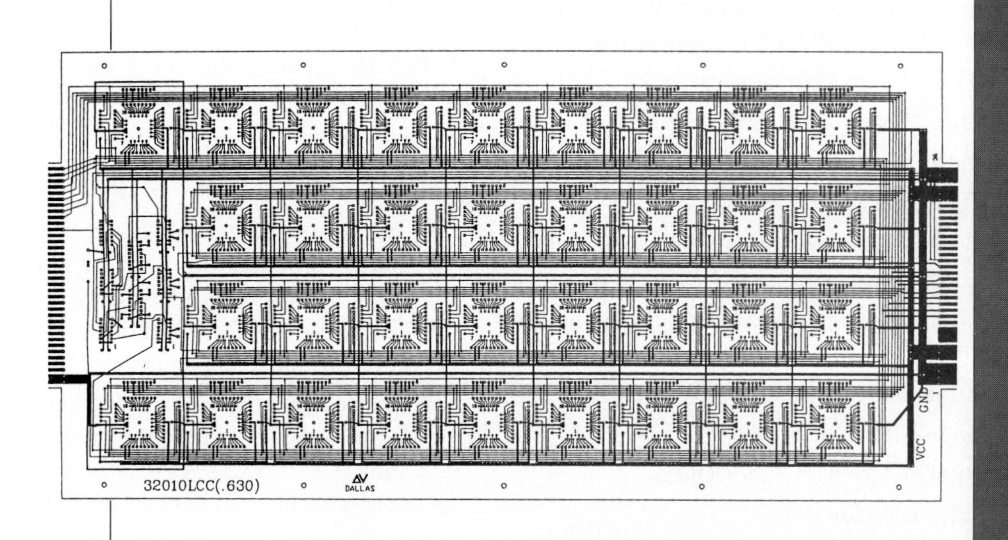

CHAPTER 1

Before You Begin

Objectives

This chapter describes the contents of *The Autodesk Collection*, defines the equipment you'll need to use programs included on the CD-ROM, and previews the types of instructions you'll encounter in the chapters that follow. As you read the chapter, you'll

1. Examine the contents of your Autodesk Collection package.
2. Check your computer system setup.
3. Learn the typographical conventions used in the book.

Checking Your Package

Your package for *The Autodesk Collection* should contain all the following items:

- The Student Manual (this book)
- One 3.5-inch 720K disk
- One CD-ROM
- A License Agreement
- A Warranty and Registration Card

The professional design software that makes up *The Autodesk Collection* and is contained on your CD-ROM includes:

AutoCAD® Release 12 for Windows™
AutoVision™ for Windows
AutoCAD Release 12 for DOS
AutoVision for DOS
AutoCAD Designer
3D Studio® Release 2

Many sample files are also on your CD-ROM, including:

The World Creating Toolkit
Data files for the tutorials in this manual

Checking Your Computer Setup

Before you begin to install the Autodesk Collection software, make sure that your personal computer system is compatible with the minimum system requirements for the software you wish to use. The following list first outlines the minimum configuration common to all software on your CD-ROM; RAM and hard disk requirements for different installations follow.

- COMPAQ® DeskPro 386™, 80386SX, IBM® PS/2® models 70 or 80, Hewlett-Packard® 80386™ systems, or a true 80386 compatible system (the 80386 CPU must be step B0 or higher for AutoCAD; step D0 or higher for 3D Studio). 486-based systems are supported because they are 80386 compatible.

■ ***Warning:*** AutoCAD Release 12 for Windows and 3D Studio Release 2 require a high level of compatibility with the 386 standard. 386SX machines with incompatible ROM bios, older 16-MHz 386 machines, or those using an add-in SX or 386 card might not work properly. AutoCAD Designer requires a 486-based computer system. ■

- The operating system should be DOS version 3.3 or later. AutoCAD for Windows requires Windows 3.1 running in enhanced mode. AutoCAD for Windows does not run in real or standard mode.
- The computer must be equipped with an 80387 or 80487 math coprocessor. For 486 DX and DX2 systems, the 80387 coprocessor is an integral part of the 80486 chip. The 80486SX chip requires an 80487 math coprocessor.

■ ***Warning:*** Older 16-MHz machines with an Intel® 80386 "B Step" processor might wait in an indeterminate state when executing math instructions with paging enabled. This problem occurs most often in machines built during the first year of production. If you have problems running AutoCAD and suspect this may be the reason, see your dealer or the Technical Support section of your CD-ROM under "Solving the 80386 Chip Problem" for more information. ■

- A 720K floppy disk drive and a CD-ROM drive. The MSCDEX driver for your CD-ROM drive must be version 2.10 or greater for proper operation of the interface.
- A video display and adapter of VGA or a higher standard. Other video displays supported by AutoCAD and 3D Studio are listed in the Technical Support section of your CD-ROM under "Video Display Options" (AutoCAD) or "Peripherals and ADI Drivers" (3D Studio).

- A Microsoft® compatible mouse. Other digitizing tablets and mice supported by AutoCAD and 3D Studio are listed in the Technical Support section of your CD-ROM under "Digitizer Options" (AutoCAD) or "Peripherals and ADI Drivers" (3D Studio).
- A printer or plotter is optional but highly recommended. Compatible output devices are listed in the Technical Support section of your CD-ROM under "Plotter Options."
- An asynchronous communications adapter (serial port) is required for digitizers and some plotters.
- At least 485K of free conventional RAM for proper operation of the interface while installing software.
- Minimum requirements for RAM and hard disk space vary by installation and are listed below. If you plan to work on large drawings, more memory will aid performance and is strongly recommended. AutoCAD can access up to 4 gigabytes of memory or use an equivalent swap space.

AutoCAD and 3D Studio read a drawing into memory and page out temporary files to the hard disk when memory is full. Their virtual memory systems need additional disk space beyond the minimums listed below, especially when editing large drawings.

Software	Minimum RAM	Hard Disk Space
AutoCAD for Windows with AutoVision	8 MB plus 4.5 MB for each concurrent AutoCAD session	37 MB for AutoCAD (additional hard disk space will improve performance) plus 12 MB for AutoVision
AutoCAD Release 12 for DOS with AutoVision and AutoCAD Designer 1.0	8 MB (10 MB needed for Designer; 16 MB recommended)	26 MB for AutoCAD plus 12 MB for AutoVision and 7 MB for Designer
3D Studio 2.0	4 MB	12 MB

Obtaining Product Support

If you encounter difficulty installing or using the Autodesk Collection software, first refer to the sections of this manual that contain information on the commands or procedures that you are trying to execute. Additional AutoCAD configuration instructions are in the Appendix to this manual. Information about different system configurations and most supported peripheral devices is located in the "Installation and Technical Support" section of the CD-ROM.

To access the product support on the CD-ROM, select "Installation and Support" from the main menu of the interface and use the menus that appear to locate the technical documentation you need. These text files can also be printed as needed.

If you must ask your instructor for assistance, describe your problem or ask your question in detail. If you encounter a problem, write down what you were doing when the problem occurred (the exact sequence of procedures you followed) and any error messages you received. This will help your instructor understand and respond to your problem.

You are encouraged to follow the steps outlined above to get answers to your questions about the Autodesk Collection software. Telephone support for basic installation questions is provided by Addison-Wesley to purchasers of *The Autodesk Collection* at (617) 944-2630. You may also send your installation questions via email to techsprt@aw.com. Further technical support is available, for a charge, at 1-900-288-6375 ($3 per minute; an average call is 6 minutes).

Disk Exchange

If you have purchased *The Autodesk Collection*, but are unable to use the CD-ROM format with your computer, you may exchange your software for a set of 3.5" 1.44-MB floppy disks from which you can install the programs. These disks will not include the Autodesk Collection Interface, or the World Creating Toolkit files, but will come with complete installation instructions. There is a manufacturing fee for the disk exchange to cover shipping and handling costs, and you should allow four weeks for delivery.

To order a set of floppy disks, call Addison-Wesley Publishing Company, at (617) 944-3700 x2460 to receive further information.

Basic Mouse Techniques

The tutorials in this manual assume you will be using a mouse or pointing device to work with the Autodesk Collection. The following terms will be used to streamline the instructions you are given for using the mouse.

Term	**Meaning**
Pick or Click	To quickly press and release the left mouse button.
Double-click	To click the left mouse button twice in rapid succession.
Drag	To press and hold down the left mouse button while you move the mouse.
Point	To move the mouse until the mouse pointer on the screen is positioned above the item of choice.

■ ***TIP*** Your mouse may have more than one button. To click (or pick) in Windows and in AutoCAD, use the left mouse button. This button is also referred to as the *pick button.* ■

Recognizing Typographical Conventions

When you work with AutoCAD, AutoVision, 3D Studio, and AutoCAD Designer, you'll use your keyboard and your pointing device to input information. As you read this manual, you'll encounter special type styles that will help you determine the commands required and the information you must input.

Special symbols illustrate certain computer keys. For example, the Enter or Return key is represented by the symbol ↵.

The manual also employs special typefaces when it presents instructions for performing computer operations. Instructions are set off from the main text to indicate a series of actions or AutoCAD command prompts. Boldface type is used for letters and numbers to be input by you. For example,

Command: **LINE**

instructs you to select/type/use the command LINE.

From point: ***(select A)***

instructs you to select point A on your screen.

The words "Command" and "From point" represent the AutoCAD prompts you would see on your screen. The AutoCAD prompt line is always in regular type.

Instruction words, such as "pick," "type," and "select," appear in italic type. For example, "type" instructs you to strike or press several keys in sequence. For the following instruction,

Type: **R(4,4)**

you would type "R(4,4)" in that order on your keyboard. Remember to type exactly what you see, including spaces, if any.

"Pick" tells you to pick an object or choose commands from the menu. For example,

Pick: **LINE**

instructs you to use your pointing device or keyboard to select the LINE command from the screen. To select a command, move the pointer until the cursor is over the command and press the pick button (usually the left button on the mouse).

"Press" means to strike or press a key once. For example,

Press: (↵)

means press the Enter or Return key once. Sometimes "press" is followed by two keys that are separated by a hyphen, such as

Press: (ALT)-(F1)

When this occurs, press and hold down the first key, press the second key once and release it, and then release the first key.

Default values that are displayed as part of a command or prompt are represented in angle brackets: <>. For example,

TRACE Trace width <.50>:

is the command prompt when the TRACE command has a default value of .5.

New terms are in italics in the text when they are introduced, and are defined in the Glossary.

Interpreting Text Features

Within the tutorials in this manual, special sections entitled "Adapting for Architecture" are indicated with a small column icon. These sections describe conventions used by architects who work with AutoCAD.

At the end of most tutorials, "Going Further" sections suggest ways in which you can extend what you have learned in the tutorial by exploring additional AutoCAD functions on your own. These sections are designed to be optional and are not referred to in later tutorials.

Exercises at the end of the tutorials are divided into four types, designated by the following icons:

Mechanical Engineering — Exercises in the design of machines and tools

Electrical Engineering — Exercises in the design of electrical systems

Civil Engineering — Exercises in the design of roads, bridges, and other public and private works

Architecture — Exercises in the design of buildings

Additional, more challenging exercises are included in a special section in the appendix.

CHAPTER 2

Installing and Configuring the Autodesk Collection

Objectives

When you have completed this chapter, you will be able to

1. Start the computer.
2. Work with floppy disks.
3. Make backup copies.
4. Install and use the Autodesk Collection Interface.
5. Install the Autodesk Collection on your hard disk.
6. Configure AutoCAD.
7. Start AutoCAD Designer.
8. Configure AutoVision.
9. Start Autodesk 3D Studio.
10. Create a working directory.

Introduction

This chapter shows you how to install the Autodesk Collection software and its dedicated interface (menu system) so that it will work with your equipment. To complete this chapter, you'll need the following items:

- The Autodesk Collection CD-ROM
- The Autodesk Collection Interface Disk
- DOS (and Windows) installed on your hard disk
- 61 megabytes or more of free storage space on your hard disk (this may vary depending on the packages you decide to install; refer to Chapter 1 for hard disk requirements)

The Autodesk Collection contains software for both the DOS and Windows environments. Both versions of AutoCAD Release 12 and AutoVision are on your CD-ROM; you can install them to work within Windows or DOS. 3D Studio Release 2 must be run from DOS and will not operate within a Windows environment (nor in a DOS window). AutoCAD Designer is an AutoCAD application that can only be installed with AutoCAD Release 12 for DOS. If you wish to use AutoCAD Designer, you will need to install and configure AutoCAD for DOS.

This chapter will guide you through the installation of the software needed to complete the tutorials in this manual. The Autodesk Collection Interface that you will install first will make it easy to select and install the software you desire.

Starting Your Computer

To install and use the Autodesk Collection, you must have a computer with a hard disk, a CD-ROM drive, and at least one floppy disk drive. A hard disk is a fixed, permanent disk that can store the contents of many floppy disks. If you're working with a hard disk that has DOS installed on it, begin by turning on the power and, if necessary, the monitor. If your system asks you to enter the date and time, do so and wait for the operating system prompt (usually C:\>) to appear.

Your mouse driver should be installed and loaded. If it is not, refer to the manufacturer's documentation for loading instructions. You may want to add the command sequence to your autoexec.bat file so it is loaded automatically each time you start the computer. See your computer system documentation for instructions on modifying this file.

Before you begin to install or configure your new software, take a moment to identify your system and peripherals.Typing "MSD" at the C:\ prompt will display a list of your system configuration and peripherals.

If you are installing software to run under Windows, your printer, pointing device (mouse), and video display should be configured to work with Windows before you continue.

Video Display

AutoCAD, AutoVision, and 3D Studio allow you to render drawings to the screen or to an output file to achieve a realistic appearance. For good-quality results, your video display and driver should support 256 colors and a screen resolution of 640 × 480 pixels. A standard VGA can support only 16 colors at 640 × 480 resolution, or 256 colors at 320 × 200. Consult your display device documentation for information about the number of colors and screen resolution supported by your system.

If you are installing AutoCAD and AutoVision for Windows and have a display device that will support 256 colors at 640 × 480, use the Windows Setup option to select this driver for your windows display before you continue. Windows Setup is a utility in the Main program group in Windows. Refer to your Windows and video display documentation for details about changing the driver.

■ ***Warning:*** If you select a driver that is not supported by your system, you will be unable to launch Windows. If this occurs, make the Windows directory current (type "cd\windows" at the C:\> prompt) and from that directory, type "SETUP" (C:\WINDOWS>**SETUP**). Select the menu option for setting the video display and reselect the previously installed driver. ■

Backing Up System Files

Changes to your config.sys and autoexec.bat files (in your root directory) may be necessary in the course of configuring your new software. The Autodesk Collection Interface eliminates the need for many of these changes, but it is good practice to print or make a copy of these files before installing software. If you are installing software for Windows, you should do the same for the system.ini and win.ini files (found in your \windows directory).

To copy the files, you can use the Windows File Manager or the DOS COPY command and copy the files to a different but recognizable name. For example, using DOS,

C:\> **COPY CONFIG.SYS CONFIG.OLD** ↵

will cause a copy of the file to be written to the same directory under the name config.old.

To print the files, use the DOS PRINT command or open and print the files in any word processor.

Working with Floppy Disks

The Autodesk Collection's interface comes on a floppy disk in 3.5-inch format. Even though you have a hard disk, you'll be using floppy disks to install the interface menu system and to create backup copies of the drawings you create in AutoCAD and 3D Studio.

Taking Care of Disks

Whenever you work with floppy disks, keep the following precautions in mind:

- Never touch the exposed areas of a disk, and never handle a 3.5-inch disk with its shutter open.
- Be careful when writing on the disk label. Use a felt-tipped pen because a sharp point or hard pressure can damage the disk.
- Keep any disk away from heat, sunlight, smoke, and magnetic fields (telephones, televisions, transformers, etc.).
- If the disk drive's slot is horizontal, slide the disk into the drive with the label facing up. If the drive is mounted vertically, the label should face left. For 3.5-inch disks, insert the metal shutter first. (See Figure G2.1.)
- Insert the disk into the drive as far as it will go, but don't force it.
- Never remove a disk while the drive access light is on.

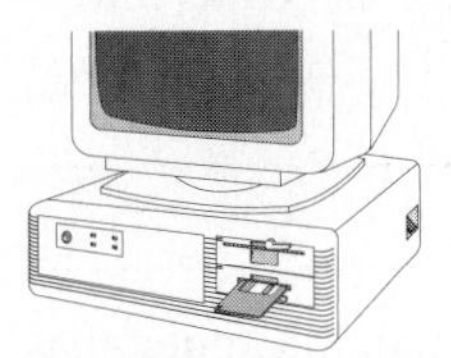

Figure G2.1

Backing Up Disks

A backup is a copy of an original disk. Always work with backups of any software, and store your originals in a safe place. That way, you can always make another copy from the original if anything happens to the backup copy you're using.

Now you'll make a copy of the Autodesk Collection Interface Disk. When you start, your computer should be running and the system prompt C:\> should appear on your screen. The following backup procedure will be slightly different depending on the number of floppy drives you have; the steps below assume you have one 3.5-inch floppy drive. (If you have two 3.5-inch drives, you can substitute B: for the second A: in the following command.) When you are using the DISKCOPY command, both disks must be of the same type; that is, both high-density or both low-density disks. (If your floppy drive is named something other than A:, substitute that drive letter wherever A: appears in the instructions.)

When you see the DOS prompt,

Type: **DISKCOPY A: A:**

Press: (↵)

(If you make a typing error, press the BACKSPACE key to erase the letters and then type the entry correctly.) When you finish, the following prompt should appear:

```
Insert SOURCE diskette in drive A. Press any key to continue...
```

At this prompt, insert the Interface Disk into drive A.

Using a Single Disk Drive

When DOS has copied the contents of the disk, the following message will appear:

```
Insert TARGET diskette in drive A. Press any key to continue...
```

Remove the Interface Disk and insert a blank disk. Then press any key on the keyboard.

The message

```
Formatting while copying
```

may appear. Your system may not be able to copy the entire contents of the source disk into memory in one operation, and you may have to insert the source disk again. Just follow the on-screen instructions for switching disks in the drive. Remember that the original Interface Disk is the source disk, while the blank disk that you are using to create a backup is the target disk.

If you get the error message "Error reading drive A" when A is the drive containing your Interface Disk, check to be sure that the disk is properly inserted in the drive. If the problem persists, and you are able to read other disks in the same drive, the message may indicate a defect on the disk. If so, contact Technical Support.

When your backup copy has been completed, you'll see the prompt:

```
Copy another diskette (Y/N)?
```

Type: **N**

because you don't need to copy another disk. (With some versions of DOS, you must also press (↵).) The system prompt will reappear. Remember to write the disk's title (for example, Interface Disk Backup) on the label.

Using Dual Floppy Drives

If you have a two-disk-drive system, and they are both the same disk format, you will be prompted to place the source diskette (that is, the disk you are copying from) in drive A and the target diskette (the disk you are copying to) in drive B. Then press any key on the keyboard. The drive indicator will light up and a message will tell you what DOS is copying. The message varies according to the type of disk you are using, and the copying process can take a few minutes. When DOS is ready to continue, respond to the prompts to tell DOS whether you wish to copy another disk.

Working with a CD-ROM Drive

The Autodesk Collection software and resources are stored on the CD-ROM that came with your package. The CD-ROM must be in the CD-ROM drive when you are installing software and when you wish to access menu items such as technical support and product information. If you select a menu item that requires the CD-ROM and it is not in the drive, you will be prompted to insert it. You may receive an error message saying that the CD-ROM cannot be located. If so, insert the CD into the drive and try again.

Refer to the manufacturer's instructions for your CD-ROM drive before you begin. Most drives require you to put the CD-ROM into a caddy before it is inserted into the drive. Most caddies have an arrow indicating the side of the caddy to be inserted into the drive first. If you have an external drive, be sure the drive is powered up before you insert the disk. CD-ROMs, like audio compact discs, should be kept clean and free of dust and fingerprints. Take care to handle the CD-ROM only by its edges.

> ■ ***TIP*** When working with a CD-ROM, you may get an error message that a file cannot be found or is unreadable even though the CD-ROM is in the drive. If this occurs, eject and re-insert the disc to be sure it is seated properly. If the problem persists, examine the CD-ROM to see that it is clean and free of fingerprints. Use a soft lint-free cloth to wipe any dirt and smudges from the disc, wiping from the center of the disc outward, not around the disc. After cleaning the disc, reinsert it and try again. If you still encounter difficulties, there may be a problem with the disk drive or its configuration. Contact your computer dealer or technical support person for assistance. ■

Insert the Autodesk Collection CD-ROM into the CD-ROM drive now.

Installing the Interface on a Hard Disk

As stated earlier, the software in the Autodesk Collection must be run directly from your hard disk. You cannot run the programs from the CD-ROM, as the files are compressed and must be installed before use. The Autodesk Collection Interface is a menu system that will help you install and launch the software you install from the CD-ROM. It also includes a graphic introduction to the design environment you have just purchased and access to the World Creating Toolkit, technical information, and related products. The interface, too, must be installed on your hard disk before it is run.

This section will walk you through the process of installing the Autodesk Collection Interface on your computer system so you can use it to install your software.

The instructions for these procedures assume that DOS is installed on your hard disk on drive C and that your CD-ROM drive is drive D. If your hard disk is called by another letter (D, for example), just substitute that letter for C as you follow the instructions. If you need further assistance, consult your computer dealer or the technical resource person at your school.

Running the Install Program

The Autodesk Collection Interface Disk contains a program that completely automates its installation.

Each screen of the install program includes instructions and offers a choice or option and a default response. Press ↵ to accept a default, or type in your own response and press ↵ to enter it. Use the BACKSPACE key to edit a typed response before pressing ↵. If anything goes wrong, or you decide to quit, press (ESC) to return to DOS. If you quit with (ESC) after installation begins, some files are left on the hard disk. You can either delete these files from DOS or restart the install program, which copies over existing files.

Make sure that your backup copy of the Interface Disk is not write-protected (the window in the corner of the disk should be closed). Place it in disk drive A (or whatever your floppy drive is called). You will log on to drive A first. From the C:\> prompt,

Type: **a:** (↵)

Now start the install program. From the A:\> prompt,

Type: **install** (↵)

The first few screens introduce the install program and explain keyboard options. Press any key to continue after you finish reading each screen.

■ ***Warning:*** You must have 485K of conventional RAM free for successful operation of the Autodesk Collection Interface. To check free RAM, type MEM at the DOS prompt; the value listed for "largest executable program size" should be at least 485K. If you do not have 485K free, you must modify your config.sys file to load devices that are running conventional RAM into upper memory. If you have a later version of DOS, you can have the program Memmaker alter your config.sys for you. Refer to your system documentation for more about loading devices into upper memory. ■

Selecting a Hard Disk

When you see a list of the hard disk drives available on your computer, select the drive where you would like to install the interface. Highlight your choice with the arrow keys (the highlighted option is the flashing one) and press (↵).

Personalizing Your Software

The next screen displays your serial number and prompts you to personalize your copy of the Autodesk Collection before you can use it.

Enter your name in the appropriate box. For corrections, use the BACKSPACE key to erase text. The (→) and (←) keys move the cursor along the current line. The program is case sensitive, meaning that there is a difference between capital and small letters. Press (↵) when you are satisfied with your entry.

Enter your school name in the box on the next screen, and press (↵) when it is entered correctly.

The next screen asks you to verify the information you entered. Your serial number, name, and school name appear on the screen and will appear each time you use the software. Make any necessary corrections and take a moment now to fill out and copy the serial number to the registration card that came with your software.

Select Continue to proceed with the installation.

You are next asked to specify whether you have a Super VGA display installed on your computer. If you do, you will be able to view the CD-ROM's introduction to CAD and the Design Process at a higher resolution than VGA. If you are not sure, the interface will use a VGA display.

Several messages are written to your screen as the interface files are decompressed and written to directories on your hard disk. When installation is complete, you are instructed to launch the interface.

■ ***Warning:*** If your autoexec.bat file contains the line, C:\DOS\SHARE.EXE, you will see a message that you must remove it before installing AutoCAD Designer. This line is necessary for certain applications but will interfere with the installation of AutoCAD Designer. Remove this statement and reboot your computer before installing AutoCAD Designer. The statement may be replaced after AutoCAD Designer is installed.

If you do not have an expanded memory manager installed, you will not be able to run 3D Studio. If you see a message asking you to include an EMM driver, you should add the line DEVICE=C:\DOS\EMM386.EXE to your config.sys file before you run 3D Studio. ■

Starting the Autodesk Collection Interface

The files for the interface are stored on your hard disk in a directory called AWCD. Change back to the C drive first.

Type: **C:** ↵

If you are not currently in the AWCD directory, change to it by using the change directory command. At the C:\> prompt,

Type: **cd\AWCD** ↵

At the C:\AWCD> prompt,

Type: **AWCD** ↵

The welcome screen appears, confirming your personalization. Pressing ↵ causes the Interface main menu to appear on your screen, as shown in Figure G2.2.

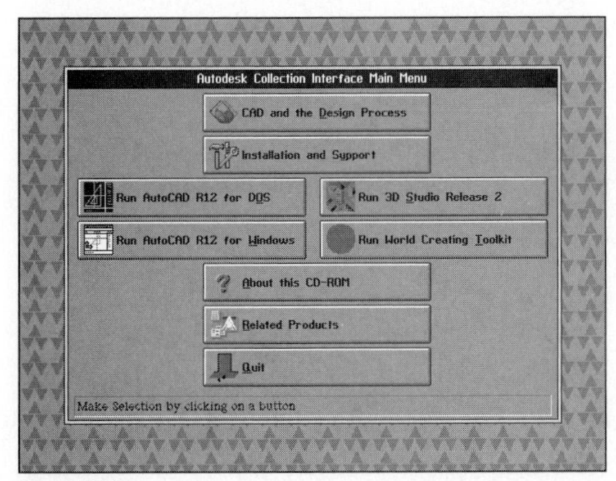

Figure G2.2

The Interface Menu

The Autodesk Collection Interface is designed to be your gateway to AutoCAD Release 12, AutoVision, AutoCAD Designer, 3D Studio Release 2, and the World Creating Toolkit. After you use the interface to install the Autodesk Collection software, you will use the interface regularly to launch the software and to access additional information about the products. You will explore the menu options more fully in the next chapter. In this chapter, you will use primarily the "Installation and Support" section to install your software.

Select menu options by positioning your mouse cursor over the "button" that contains the words "Installation and Support" and pressing the mouse button. (You can also select any option by holding down the ALT while typing the underlined letter in the option.)

Pick: **Installation and Support**

Another menu appears, from which you can choose to install software, get technical support information, or return to the main menu.

Pick: **Install Software**

The next screen allows you to select the software packages you would like to install. You can select one or all of them for installation (depending on the disk space available on your hard drive), but it is strongly recommended that you install and configure one package at a time.

Recommended Installation Procedure

The following instructions are tailored to those packages and data files needed for the tutorials in this manual. Tutorials 1–16 are written for AutoCAD and AutoVision for Windows. (You can use the DOS versions of AutoCAD and AutoVision to complete the tutorials, but you may need to make adjustments for some operations.) Tutorials 17–19 teach you to use 3D Studio Release 2. Tutorial 20 introduces AutoCAD Designer.

Because AutoVision and AutoCAD Designer are ADS applications that work with AutoCAD, you must install and configure AutoCAD before installing them. In this chapter, you will start by installing AutoCAD Release 12 for Windows (or DOS) and configuring it, then installing and configuring AutoVision. If you are installing AutoCAD Release 12 for DOS and wish to install AutoCAD Designer and AutoVision to work together within AutoCAD, it is recommended that you install AutoCAD Designer before you install AutoVision.

Installing 3D Studio and the data files for the tutorials will complete the installation procedure.

The following sections provide valuable information about the installation process for each program. Refer to the appropriate section as the software is being installed for guidance as to the options you should select.

> ■ ***TIP*** AutoCAD Release 12 and 3D Studio Release 2 both require substantial free space on your hard disk for proper operation. If your hard disk is very full and you encounter difficulties in installing or running these applications, exit the interface, free up space on your hard disk, and try the procedure again. ■

Installing AutoCAD Release 12 for Windows

You should still see the Install software window on your screen. (If you wish to install AutoCAD for DOS instead, skip to the next section.) To install AutoCAD Release 12 for Windows, you will click on the box next to its name so that an X appears in it.

Pick: **AutoCAD R12 for Windows**

Pick: **Start Installation**

The installation program for AutoCAD for Windows starts with a reminder to be sure your peripherals are configured to work with Windows. If they are not, you will have to configure them before you can use AutoCAD. AutoCAD for Windows is designed to use the Windows system configuration to simplify the configuration process.

Several messages appear as the installation proceeds. Click Proceed or the OK button until you are asked to select files for installation.

Selecting Files to Install

There are several different types of files included as part of AutoCAD Release 12 with AME for Windows. You can install them all, or you can pick and choose among them. This is especially advantageous if your hard disk is low on space.

The install program lists the following options:

Install all files	Installs the complete release (37 MB).
Executable/ Support files	Required. Installs all the files needed to run AutoCAD.
Bonus/ Sample files	Optional; required for tutorials. Sample AutoCAD drawings and AutoLISP routines.
Source files	Optional; required for tutorials. Standard menu files and source font files.
IGES Font files	Optional; required for tutorials. Initial Graphics Exchange Specification (IGES) text fonts and text source files; AutoCAD drawings of IGES symbols.
Tutorial files	Optional. AutoCAD tutorial files.

ADS/DDE files	Optional; required for tutorials. AutoCAD Development System and Dynamic Data Exchange (DDE) files, including examples of applications developed with AutoCAD for Windows using ADS and Visual Basic.
Render files	Optional; required for tutorials. AutoCAD rendering files.
SQL Extension files	Optional. AutoCAD SQL Extension files.
Advanced Modeling Extension files	Optional; required for tutorials. AutoCAD Advanced Modeling Extension (AME) files.

The Executable/Support files are required in any installation. You can re-run the installation program again if you decide to install more files. *To complete the tutorials in this manual, you must install the Bonus/Sample, Source, IGES font, ADS/DDE, Render, and AME files too.*

Installing all these files requires 37 MB of space on your hard disk drive. The minimum installation for the tutorials in this manual requires 33.4 MB of hard disk space.

Pick with the mouse or use the ↑ and ↓ keys to scroll through the list on screen and use the spacebar to highlight the files you wish to install. If you make a mistake, pick the selection again and press the spacebar again to toggle the selection off. When you have selected the files you wish to install, pick OK. The program displays your selection and gives you the option to make a change, quit, or continue. Press ↵ to continue.

You next have the option of installing all or part of the files needed for the Advanced Modeling Extension (AME). Highlight all files and press ↵. Your selection is confirmed on the next screen. Press ↵ to continue.

Selecting a Hard Disk and Directory

Next you will see a list of the hard disk drives available on your computer. Highlight your choice and press ↵ or pick OK to select the hard disk where AutoCAD will be installed.

At this point the install program checks for space on the hard disk. If not enough free disk space is available, the program will ask if you wish to continue. If you have chosen to install only some of the files and are sure that space is available for them, pick Continue. Otherwise, select another drive or abort the install and free up space on your hard disk.

At the next screen, you name a directory to hold AutoCAD files. The default name is ACADWIN. If you type in a new name and press ↵, you will need to substitute this directory name each time this manual refers to the ACADWIN directory. Press ↵ to accept the default.

Next you are asked to select a directory for your AutoCAD support files. Press ↵ to accept the default to put support files in your AutoCAD directory, \ACADWIN.

The names of files being copied to disk appear on the screen throughout the installation process, along with the names of any new subdirectories.

Now is a good time to fill out your registration card if you haven't already.

When installation is complete, you are returned to the interface. Pick Previous to return to the Installation and Support Menu.

Before you start AutoCAD, you might need to set values for the FILES= and BUFFERS= settings in your config.sys file. DOS limits the number of files a program can have open at once. The FILES= statement in config.sys determines the number of files that can be open at one time. A setting of FILES=40 is optimal for AutoCAD. You should use a setting of BUFFERS=20 when using AutoCAD for Windows. If you are using a disk caching program such as SMARTDrive, use a setting of BUFFERS=10. Refer to your system documentation for help in editing your config.sys file.

If you are not installing AutoCAD for DOS, skip to the section "Configuring AutoCAD for the First Time" on page G-19.

Installing AutoCAD Release 12 for DOS

You should still see the Install software window on your screen. (If you do not, pick "Installation and Support" from the interface main menu, then "Install Software.") To install AutoCAD Release 12 for DOS,

Pick: **AutoCAD R12 for DOS**

Pick: **Start Installation**

Read and continue through the installation screens until you are asked to select files for installation.

Selecting Files to Install

There are several different types of files included as part of AutoCAD Release 12 with AME for DOS. You can install them all, or you can pick and choose among them. This is especially advantageous if your hard disk is low on space.

The install program lists the following options:

Install all files	Installs the complete release (26 MB).
Executable/ Support files	Required. Installs all the files needed to run AutoCAD.
Bonus/ Sample files	Optional; required for tutorials. Sample AutoCAD drawings and AutoLISP routines.
Support Source files	Optional; required for tutorials. Standard menu files and source font files.
IGES Font files	Optional; required for tutorials. Initial Graphics Exchange Specification (IGES) text fonts and text source files; AutoCAD drawings of IGES symbols.
Tutorial files	Optional. AutoCAD tutorial files.
ADS files	Optional; required for tutorials. AutoCAD Development System files.
Render files	Optional; required for tutorials. AutoCAD rendering files.
SQL Extension files	Optional. AutoCAD SQL Extension files.
Advanced Modeling Extension files	Optional; required for tutorials. AutoCAD Advanced Modeling Extension (AME) files.

The Executable/Support files are required in any installation. You can re-run the installation program again if you decide to install more files. *To complete the tutorials in this manual, you must install the Bonus/Sample, Source, IGES font, ADS, Render, and AME files too.*

Installing all these files requires 26 MB of space on your hard disk drive. The minimum installation for the tutorials in this manual requires 23.4 MB of hard disk space.

Use the ↑ and ↓ keys to scroll through the list on screen, and use the spacebar to toggle each selection to Yes or No. If you make a mistake, press the spacebar again to toggle the selection off. When you have selected the files you wish to install, press ↵. The program displays your selection and gives you the option to quit, make a change, or continue. Press ↵ to continue.

You next have the option of installing all or part of the files needed for the Advanced Modeling Extension (AME). Highlight all files and press ↵. Your selection is confirmed on the next screen. Press ↵ to continue.

Selecting a Hard Disk and Directory

Next you will see a list of the hard disk drives available on your computer. Highlight your choice (flashing is highlighted) and press ↵ to select the hard disk where AutoCAD will be installed.

At this point the install program checks for space on the hard disk drive. If not enough free disk space is available, the program will ask if you wish to continue. If you have chosen to install only some of the files and are sure that space is available for them, select Continue. If not, select another drive or abort the installation and free up space on your hard disk.

At the next screen, you name a directory to hold AutoCAD files. The default name is ACAD. Press ↵ to accept the default. If you type in a new name and press ↵, you will need to substitute this directory name each time this manual refers to the ACAD directory.

Next you are asked to select a directory for your AutoCAD support files. Press ↵ to select the default to put support files in a separate subdirectory called SUPPORT in the AutoCAD directory \ACAD.

The names of files being copied to disk appear on the screen throughout the installation process, along with the names of any new subdirectories.

Config.sys Modification

When installation is complete, the install program checks a file on your hard drive called config.sys to see if it contains the statement "FILES=40." If the statement is not present or the number is less than 40, the program will make the suggested change. The program will edit only the FILES statement. Press ↵ to allow this.

If you do not allow the change, the program will create an alternate version of the file called config.cad with the necessary changes. You will have to alter your config.sys file yourself to set FILES to at least 40, and you can use this file as a reference as you do.

Installation is now complete and you are ready to configure AutoCAD. Press a key to return to the interface and pick Previous to return to the Installation and Support menu.

Configuring AutoCAD for the First Time

Now that the necessary files exist on your hard disk, you are ready to configure AutoCAD for your particular computer system. Configuration gives AutoCAD the information it needs to work with the video display, digitizer (mouse), and plotter you will use. (AutoCAD refers to both vector devices, such as pen plotters, and raster devices, such as laser printers, as plotters.) AutoCAD cannot be used until it is configured for the first time. During the configuration process, AutoCAD menus will prompt you for specific information. Unless you are well versed in computer usage, it is suggested that you accept all the default values. Detailed configuration information is included in the Technical Support section under "Changing the AutoCAD Configuration."

Determining Your Hardware Setup

In order for AutoCAD to run properly, it must know the type of plotter, pointing device, and video display your system is using. This chapter assumes that you have already installed this peripheral equipment on your computer.

If you are installing AutoCAD for Windows and wish to use the video display, pointing device, and printer already configured to work with Windows, you can proceed directly to the section "Configuring AutoCAD Release 12 for Windows." If you wish to configure a different pointing device or a pen plotter for AutoCAD for Windows, you should read the following sections.

The AutoCAD configuration procedure will ask you questions about the type of equipment you wish to use with AutoCAD. To make sure that you'll have the answers to these questions when you need them, fill in the following hardware chart:

Pointing device:

Video display:

Plotter/printer:

Plotter/printer port:

Now check the Technical Support section on your CD-ROM for additional information about your system's peripherals by reading about them in the sections "Video Display Options," "Digitizer Options," and "Plotter Options" for the version of AutoCAD you are installing. If your peripheral is not listed, refer to the next section on installing peripheral devices.

To get to the appropriate Technical Support section, from the Installation and Support menu,

Pick: **Technical Support**

Pick: **AutoCAD R12 for Windows *or* AutoCAD R12 for DOS**

Pick: ***(the device you wish to look up)***

If you don't see your device, click on the small arrows to the right of the list of topics to scroll through the list. Picking the topic name will open the file for your review.

If you have any questions about your equipment, consult your dealer or the technical resource person at your school.

Pick the Previous or Main Menu button until you are returned to the interface main menu.

Installing Peripheral Devices

Many peripherals require the installation of a software program called a *device driver* onto your hard disk before the device will operate. Be sure drivers for your peripherals are installed and loaded before you run AutoCAD.

Some peripheral devices mention AutoCAD in their installation instructions and provide help in configuring the device to work most effectively with AutoCAD. Check the user's manuals for these devices for any pertinent installation instructions.

Drivers for devices directly supported in AutoCAD Release 12 are included with your AutoCAD software and explained in the "Device Drivers for AutoCAD Release 12" section of the Appendix. If you are setting up a peripheral device that comes with an ADI driver, check the manufacturer's documentation for information on installing it. General information about ADI drivers is contained in the Appendix, including a discussion of protected-mode and real-mode ADI drivers.

If you do not find your device listed as an option in the configuration menus, see the Technical Support section of the CD-ROM and your user's manual to see if the device will emulate a device supported by an existing driver.

Background Information for the Initial Configuration

Configuration is done with a menu routine that appears automatically when AutoCAD is first started. The configuration routine provides reasonable defaults for all AutoCAD options. In addition, each device can have its own set of choices and defaults. All defaults are displayed within brackets: <default>. It is recommended that you select the defaults during initial installation. To select a default, press the spacebar or ↵, which are equivalent throughout this routine.

AutoCAD must be told the address of the input/output (I/O) ports to which your digitizer (the pointing device), plotter, and sometimes your video display are connected. As you configure each device that connects to an I/O port, AutoCAD asks you to identify the particular port to which the device is connected. You can use the standard DOS names for I/O ports: COM1 and COM2 for serial ports and LPT1, LPT2, and LPT3 for parallel ports. Reasonable defaults are provided.

A plotter can share the same I/O port with a digitizer because AutoCAD doesn't use these devices at the same time. You need to provide a switch or some other means of swapping cables in order to use this type of connection with AutoCAD. If your digitizer and plotter share a port, you must switch between the two at specific times. AutoCAD displays this message before it starts plotting: "Press RETURN to continue or S to Stop for hardware setup." Switch from the digitizer to the plotter at this point. When plotting is finished, you will be prompted to reconnect the digitizer. Don't change the devices at any other time.

■ ***Warning:*** A video display and digitizer can never be connected to the same I/O port. AutoCAD does not permit this configuration. If such a condition is detected, AutoCAD displays the message:

I/O conflict: video display and digitizer are on the same port ■

If you make a wrong choice during configuration, continue to the end. Once AutoCAD is initially configured, you can change your configuration within AutoCAD. Any device can be reconfigured separately without affecting the others. You will learn about this option later in this chapter.

Configuring AutoCAD Release 12 for Windows

Launch AutoCAD from the interface main menu. (If you are configuring AutoCAD for DOS, please skip to the next section.)

Pick: **Previous, Main Menu *(if necessary)***

Pick: **Run AutoCAD R12 for Windows**

Pick: **without AutoVision**

Configuring Your Video Display

Windows and AutoCAD are launched and a list of available video displays appears on your screen. Pick once anywhere on the text window to make it active. Select the default, the Windows Accelerated Display Driver ADI 4.2, by pressing ↵ at the prompt:

Select device number or ? to repeat list <1>: ↵

The Display Driver Configuration dialogue box appears. Press ↵ to accept the defaults.

Many displays have additional options for the graphics window. It is recommended that you accept the defaults for these options during the initial configuration. To accept each default,

Press: ↵

Configuring Your Digitizer or Mouse

A list of available digitizers and mice appears on your screen. A *digitizing tablet* can be used as a screen pointing device. When AutoCAD's drawing editor is active, crosshairs appear on the screen and move in accordance with the movement of the tablet's pointer. Any portion of the tablet's surface can be defined as the screen pointing area; other areas can be reserved for command entry from tablet menus.

A *mouse* is a screen pointing device. When AutoCAD's drawing editor is active, you can move the screen crosshairs in any direction by moving the mouse on the desktop.

Specify the default, the current system pointing device, for the initial configuration unless you are planning to use a digitizing tablet or different pointing device with AutoCAD. To accept the default, press ↵ at the prompt:

Select device number or ? to repeat list <1>: ↵

Various options may appear on the screen, depending on the digitizer selected for your system. Again, it is recommended that you accept the defaults. To accept each default, if any,

Press: ↵

Configuring Your Plotter

A list of available plotters appears on your screen. Type the number of the plotter for your system. If you wish to use the printer currently configured to work with Windows, enter 14 to select the System Printer option. If you wish to use a pen plotter or different device, enter the number for that plotter. If you have no plotter, accept the default, 1, for None. At the prompt,

Select device number or ? to repeat list <1>: ***(type the number that matches your plotter)***

Press: ↵

For all plotters, there are additional options. During the initial configuration, it is recommended that you accept the default values concerning the technical aspects of plotting.

Press: ↵

to accept each default value.

You can enter a name for your printer or press ↵ for none.

Configuring Software Settings

The next prompt is for a login name. This name will appear each time you enter AutoCAD. If you choose not to enter a login name, you will be prompted to enter one each time you open an AutoCAD file. The default is AW Autodesk Collection, as this is a special collegiate edition of AutoCAD. Since this is your own personal copy of AutoCAD, use your name as the login name by typing it at the prompt:

Login name:

Enter default login name or . for none <AW Autodesk Collection>: ***(type your name)*** ↵

The next prompt is for server authorization. This tells AutoCAD how many people will be using the program. Since this is your own personal copy of AutoCAD, and no one else can use it, accept the default, No, when asked whether you want to change this information.

Do you wish to change it? <N>: ↵

The next prompt asks about file locking. It is recommended that you do not enable file locking. Enter "N" at the prompt.

Do you wish to enable file-locking? <Y>: **N** ↵

Completing the Initial Configuration

At the end of the selection process, a screen appears, listing the configuration choices you have just made. To continue,

Press: ↵

The Configuration Menu now appears on your screen. To accept the default <0>,

Press: ↵

The following message appears on your screen:

If you answer N to the following question, all configuration changes you have just made will be discarded. Keep configuration changes? <Y>

You now have the option of saving or discarding the initial configuration. The default option is Y; to complete the initial configuration and save the configuration changes in the file acad.cfg,

Press: ↵

The AutoCAD graphics window appears, as shown in Figure G2.3.

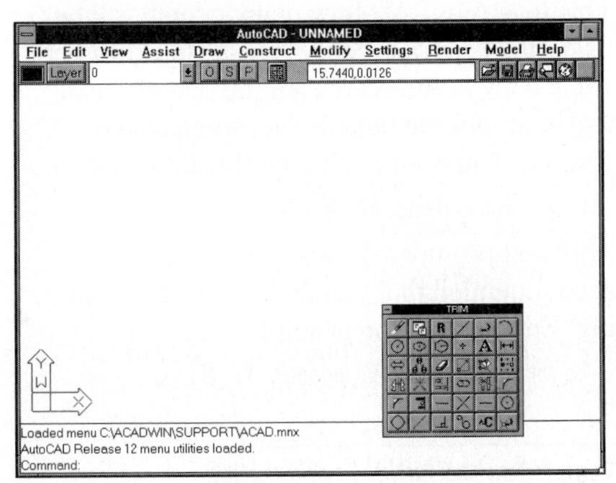

Figure G2.3

You are now ready to test your configuration. Skip to the section "Testing Your Configuration" on page G-25.

Configuring AutoCAD Release 12 for DOS

Launch AutoCAD from the Autodesk Collection Interface main menu.

Pick: **Main Menu *(if necessary)***

Pick: **Run AutoCAD R12 for DOS**

A submenu appears that you may use to load AutoCAD Designer and AutoVision with AutoCAD. Because they are not installed, only the first option "without AutoCAD Designer or AutoVision" is available. Pick it or,

Press: ↵

Configuring Your Video Display

AutoCAD is launched and a list of available video displays appears on your screen. Refer to your hardware chart to determine your display device so that you can type the number of the video display for your system.

Depending on the equipment attached to your computer, AutoCAD can operate in either single-screen or dual-screen mode. In single-screen mode, one display monitor is used both for graphics and as the system console. In dual-screen mode, the graphics are drawn on one monitor, while the other becomes the system console.

At the prompt,

Select device number or ? to repeat list <1>: ***(type the number that matches your video display)***

Press: ↵

A list of options for your graphics display will appear on your screen. These options set your aspect ratio; determine whether you will have a status line, a command prompt area, and a screen menu area; and define the display colors. It is recommended that you accept the defaults for these options during the initial configuration. To accept each default,

Press: ↵

Configuring Your Digitizer or Mouse

A list of available digitizers and mice appears on your screen. A *digitizing tablet* can be used as a screen pointing device. When AutoCAD's drawing editor is active, crosshairs appear on the screen and move in accordance with the movement of the tablet's pointer. Any portion of the tablet's surface can be defined as the screen pointing area; other areas can be reserved for command entry from tablet menus.

A *mouse* is a screen pointing device. When AutoCAD's drawing editor is active, you can move the screen crosshairs in any direction by moving the mouse on the desktop.

Refer to your hardware chart to determine your digitizer or mouse type. Type the number of the digitizer or mouse for your system. At the prompt,

Select device number or ? to repeat list <1>: ***(type the number that matches your digitizer)***

Press: ↵

Various options will appear on the screen, depending on the digitizer selected for your system. Again, it is recommended that you accept the defaults. To accept each default,

Press: ↵

When the selection of your digitizer is complete,

Press: ↵

Configuring Your Plotter

A list of available plotters appears on your screen. Refer to your hardware chart to determine your plotter. Type the number of the plotter for your system. If you have no plotter, enter the default <1> for None. At the prompt,

Select device number or ? to repeat list <1>: ***(type the number that matches your plotter)***

Press: ↵

For all plotters, there are additional options. During the initial configuration, it is recommended that you accept the default values concerning the technical aspects of plotting.

Press: ↵

to accept each default value.

Configuring Software Settings

The next prompt is for a login name. This name will appear each time you enter AutoCAD. If you choose not to enter a login name, you will be prompted to enter one each time you open an AutoCAD file. The default is AW Autodesk Collection, as this is a special collegiate edition of AutoCAD. Since this is your own personal copy of AutoCAD, use your name as the login name by typing it at the prompt:

Login name:

Enter default login name or . for none <AW Autodesk Collection>: ***(type your name)*** ↵

The next prompt is for server authorization. This tells AutoCAD how many people will be using the program. Since this is your own personal copy of AutoCAD, and no one else can use it, accept the default, No, when asked whether you want to change this information.

Do you wish to change it? <N>: ↵

The next prompt asks about file locking. It is recommended that you do not enable file locking. Enter "N" at the prompt.

Do you wish to enable file-locking? <Y>: **N** ↵

Completing the Initial Configuration

At the end of the selection process, a screen appears, listing the configuration choices you have just made. To continue,

Press: ↵

The Configuration Menu now appears on your screen. To return to the main menu, select the default <0> and

Press: ↵

The following message appears on your screen:

> If you answer N to the following question, all configuration changes you have just made will be discarded. Keep configuration changes? <Y>

You now have the option of saving or discarding the initial configuration. The default option is Y; to complete the initial configuration and save the configuration changes in the file acad.cfg,

Press: ↵

The AutoCAD graphics window appears, as shown in Figure G2.4.

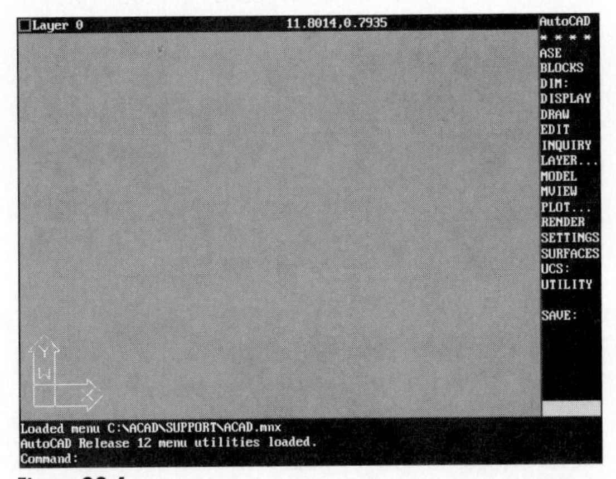

Figure G2.4

Testing Your Configuration

You can test your configuration with the drawing file CHROMA.DWG, which was copied to your hard disk during installation. Be sure that the AutoCAD graphics screen is on your display screen.

At the bottom of the screen, you should see the prompt to enter a command in AutoCAD. You will learn about the various ways to enter commands and work with AutoCAD's menus in the tutorials in this manual. Don't be concerned if you do not understand exactly what you are doing. For now, simply follow these steps and type the commands as specified below.

To open the file,

Type: **open**

Press: ↵

The Open Drawing dialogue box appears on your screen.

If you are using AutoCAD for Windows, the ACADWIN directory is open in the box at right; drawing files in that directory are shown in the box at left. Click on the down arrow on the right-hand box until you see the subdirectory SUPPORT in the ACADWIN directory. Pick twice (double-click) on the word SUPPORT to open the directory. The file CHROMA.DWG should appear in the box at left. Pick on the word Chroma.dwg to highlight it and pick OK.

If you are using AutoCAD for DOS, the directory C:\ACAD should be open. Use the down arrow on the left-hand box until you see the subdirectory SUPPORT in the ACAD directory. Pick twice (double-click) on the word SUPPORT to open the directory. The file CHROMA should appear in the box at right. Pick on the word Chroma to highlight it and pick OK.

Testing the Video Display

You should see an array of colored squares appear on your screen. When it does, you will know that AutoCAD is properly configured for your video display. Your drawing should look similar to Figure G2.5 (the menus will be different, depending on the version of AutoCAD in use).

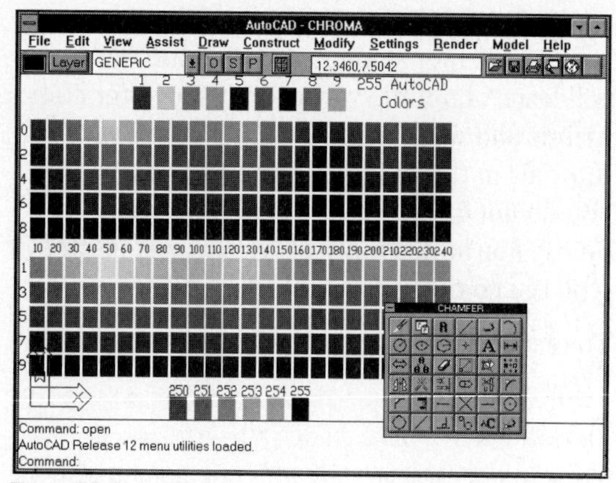

Figure G2.5

Testing the Pointing Device

If you have configured a pointing device, try it. If you have a mouse, move it around the surface of the mouse pad or desktop. If you have a digitizing tablet, move the stylus or puck within the tablet.

Crosshairs should appear on the screen and follow the movements of the pointer.

If your pointing device is not working:

- Verify that it is turned on.
- Verify that the necessary driver has been loaded into memory.
- See if it is connected to the proper port on the computer.
- Make sure that you have configured the right make and model of pointing device and the right options for stylus, puck, or mouse.
- Make sure that the settings match those described in the Technical Support section of the CD-ROM under "Digitizer Options."
- Make sure that you have followed the procedures outlined in your manufacturer's documentation for configuring the device.

Testing the Plotter or Printer Plotter

To see if you have properly configured your plotter, be sure that your plotter is turned on; then

Type: **plot**

Press: ↵

The Plot dialogue box, showing your printing defaults and configuration, appears. Pick OK and press ↵ at the prompts to start printing or plotting.

If your printer or plotter is not working properly:

- Make sure that the cable is connected to the correct port on the computer.
- Make sure that you have configured the right make and model of the plotter or printer plotter.
- Make sure you have selected suitable values for all the prompts in the Plot dialogue box.
- Check the switch settings. Make sure that they are set as indicated in the Technical Support section under "Plotter Options."
- Make sure that you have followed the procedures outlined in your manufacturer's documentation for configuring the device and loading device drivers.
- You may need to reconfigure your peripheral device if you have configured for a Windows system printer. Refer to "System Printer by Autodesk" under "Plotter Options" in the Technical Support section of your CD-ROM.

Error messages such as "Cannot find dgpsumi.dll" indicate a missing device driver. Check your system to be sure the driver for the device you have configured is loaded and located in the AutoCAD path. Refer to the Appendix and the Technical Support section of your CD-ROM for more information about device drivers.

Configuration Problems

If you found that your configuration tests did not work properly, first check your configuration.

Pick: **File *(from the menu bar at the top of your screen)***

Pick: **Configure *(from the pull-down menu that appears)***

AutoCAD will list the current configuration for your review. Press ↵ until you see the Configuration Menu.

Configuration Menu

AutoCAD provides you with the ability to go back in and selectively change the configuration for specific devices. You may need to change a configuration if you add a printer or change the port for an output device. You may also have detected a problem with your configuration when you tested it. This menu gives you the opportunity to correct any problems.

The Configuration Menu should be on your display screen, as shown in Figure G2.6.

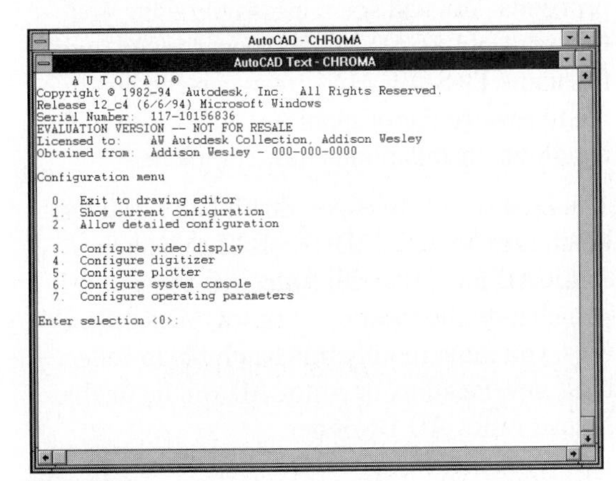

Figure G2.6

To select a configuration task, simply enter the task number and press ↵ or the spacebar. In each task, reasonable defaults are provided for all options.

Allow Detailed Configuration

Tasks 3 – 7 on the Configuration Menu let you adjust many device parameters and select typical modes of operation. Some devices have additional fine-tuning parameters, but the prompts for these are ordinarily suppressed. Select Task 2, "Allow detailed configuration," if you want to specify these additional parameters. Refer to the Technical Support section of your CD-ROM for more information about the detailed configuration options for each device.

Task 0 exits the Configuration Menu and returns to AutoCAD's graphics screen. You will have the option of saving your configuration changes.

Enter selection<0>: **0** ↵

Keep configuration changes? <Y>: **Y** ↵

Exit AutoCAD now to continue with software installation.

Type: **QUIT** ↵

You will be returned to Windows (or the interface, if you are configuring AutoCAD Release 12 for DOS). From Windows, click once on the Program Manager icon to open the Control menu, pick Close, then pick OK to end the Windows session. You will be returned to the interface main menu.

You can now install more software or skip to the section "Installing Data Files" to install the files needed for the tutorials in this manual.

Installing AutoCAD Designer

If you have installed and configured AutoCAD Release 12 for DOS, you are ready to install AutoCAD Designer. If you are using AutoCAD Release 12 for Windows, skip to "Installing AutoVision." AutoCAD Designer cannot be installed with AutoCAD for Windows.

AutoCAD Designer can only be installed on a 486-based computer. If your computer is not 486-based, do not install AutoCAD Designer.

If your config.sys file contains the line C:\DOS\SHARE.EXE, you must remove it before installing AutoCAD Designer.

To install AutoCAD Designer from the main menu of the Autodesk Collection Interface,

Pick: **Installation and Support**

Pick: **Install Software**

Pick: **AutoCAD Designer**

Pick: **Start Installation**

AutoCAD must be installed and configured before you can install AutoCAD Designer. If it is not, you will not be able to select it.

AutoCAD Designer works within AutoCAD and modifies certain files so the Designer menu appears in place of the Model (AME) menu when you run AutoCAD. The interface gives you the option of launching AutoCAD with or without AutoCAD Designer.

Because AutoCAD Designer and AutoVision write to the same files, the interface will automatically create versions of your ACAD.MNU and ACADR12.LSP files that allow AutoCAD Designer and AutoVision to appear on the menu bar at the same time. In order for this to happen, you should install AutoCAD Designer before AutoVision. See the Technical Support section of your CD-ROM for more information about the modifications made to AutoCAD by these ADS applications.

After the initial informational screens, you are prompted to specify the AutoCAD Designer files you wish to install. You must install the Executable/Support files (5 MB) to complete the tutorials in this manual. It is recommended that you select all files for installation (6.5 MB).

Use the ↑ and ↓ keys to scroll through the list on screen, and use the spacebar to toggle each selection to Yes or No. If you make a mistake, press the spacebar again to toggle the selection off. When you have selected the files you wish to install, press ↵. The program displays your selection; press ↵ to confirm it or select the option to redo the selection.

You will be prompted to specify the hard disk where you wish to install AutoCAD Designer. Specify the drive where AutoCAD is installed by highlighting it and pressing ↵.

The installation routine next checks your hard disk to see if there is enough free disk space to install AutoCAD Designer. If there is not, you will be prompted to select another drive or abort to free up disk space and try the installation again at another time.

Select: **Continue**

The following screens ask you to confirm the directory locations for AutoCAD Designer files. Unless you have located AutoCAD elsewhere, accept the defaults by pressing ↵ for each choice.

Files are copied to the hard disk as installation proceeds. You will see a message telling you that your old ACAD.MNU file was saved under the name P9-SAVE.MNU. You can rename this file to restore the original AutoCAD menu headings. Installation is now complete.

The final screen tells you that it has created a batch file called ACADDES.BAT to launch AutoCAD for DOS with AutoCAD Designer. If you change the location of AutoCAD Designer files, you must modify this batch file to reflect their new location, or AutoCAD will be unable to load AutoCAD Designer.

Testing the AutoCAD Designer Installation

To test your installation, return to the interface main menu (if necessary) and launch AutoCAD Release 12 for DOS.

Pick: **Main Menu**

Pick: **Run AutoCAD R12 for DOS**

Pick: **with AutoCAD Designer**

The AutoCAD drawing editor should appear on your screen, as shown in Figure G2.7. If you do not see the Designer menu as shown in the figure below, exit AutoCAD and repeat the process to be sure you launched AutoCAD Release 12 for DOS from the interface main menu. If you did, check to see that the directory names for the AutoCAD Designer files have not been changed.

Select an item from the Designer menu to see that it is properly installed. If it is, you will see the software being initialized. If you are prompted for an authorization code, you need to re-install AutoCAD Designer. Be sure you have at least 485K of free conventional RAM and that DOS\SHARE.EXE is not present in your config.sys before you re-install.

To exit AutoCAD,

Type: **Quit** ⏎

If the Drawing Modification dialog box appears, pick "Discard Changes," as you have no drawing to save.

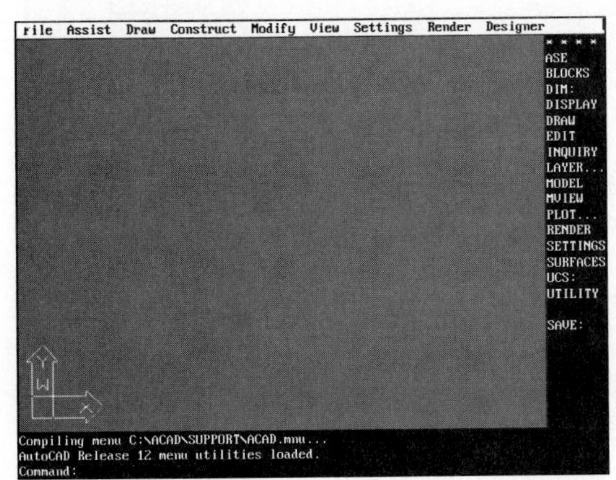

Fig G2.7

Installing AutoVision

If you have configured AutoCAD properly, you are ready to install AutoVision.

From the interface main menu,

Pick: **Installation and Support**

Pick: **Install Software**

Pick: **AutoVision for Windows** *or* **AutoVision for DOS**

Pick: **Start Installation**

If you have not installed and configured AutoCAD, you will not be able to select AutoVision from the menu.

AutoVision modifies certain AutoCAD files so that the standard Render menu is replaced with the AutoVision menu. Each time you launch AutoCAD from the interface, you will have the option of loading it with or without AutoVision.

Because AutoCAD Designer and AutoVision write to the same files, the interface will automatically create versions of your ACAD.MNU and ACADR.12LSP files that allow AutoCAD Designer and AutoVision to appear on the menu bar at the same time. (This applies to AutoCAD Release 12 for DOS only.) It will also create a new batch file for loading AutoCAD that specifies the appropriate paths for the AutoVision and AutoCAD Designer files.

Read the informational screens that appear and proceed until you are asked to specify a disk drive for AutoVision. Highlight your choice and press ⏎ to select it.

The installation routine next checks your hard disk to see if there is enough free disk space to install AutoVision. A minimum of 12 MB is required.

The AutoVision software will be decompressed and installed in a directory named \AUTOVIS unless you choose to change it. If you do, you will have to modify the appropriate path statements to accommodate the change. Accept the default by pressing ⏎. You will see a series of messages as the files are copied to your hard disk.

(If you have already installed the Windows version of AutoVision and are installing the DOS version, or vice versa, allow the installation to re-install to the same directory.)

In order for AutoCAD to find the AutoVision files, certain statements must be executed before you launch AutoCAD (and before you launch Windows if you are using AutoVision with AutoCAD for Windows). The Autodesk Collection Interface automatically creates batch files with these statements when AutoVision is installed. When AutoCAD is launched from the main menu, the interface gives you the option of loading AutoVision or not and executes the appropriate batch file for you. It is important that you use the interface to launch the Autodesk Collection software each time you start a new session, or you will get unexpected results.

If you choose not to use the interface to launch AutoCAD, refer to "Modifying the ACAD Variable for AutoVision" at the end of this chapter for information about executing the necessary statements.

AutoVision installation is now complete. Press any key to return to the interface.

Configuring AutoVision

Launch AutoCAD from the interface main menu to see that AutoVision is properly installed. Return to the interface main menu first, if necessary.

Pick: **Previous, Main Menu**

Pick: **Run AutoCAD R12 for Windows** *or* **Run AutoCAD R12 for DOS**

Pick: **with AutoVision**

The AutoCAD drawing editor should appear on your screen. If you do not see the Autovis menu, as shown in Figure G2.8, be sure you launched AutoCAD from the interface main menu. If you did, check to see that the directory names for the AutoVision files have not been changed. If you are using AutoCAD Release 12 for DOS, you must move your mouse pointer to the top of the screen to see the menu bar.

■ ***Warning:*** If you get the following DOS message: "Out of Environment Space," it means that DOS has not allocated enough space to the environment variables. You can increase the size of the environment by changing the SHELL variable in your config.sys file (see your DOS documentation for more information about changing config.sys). ■

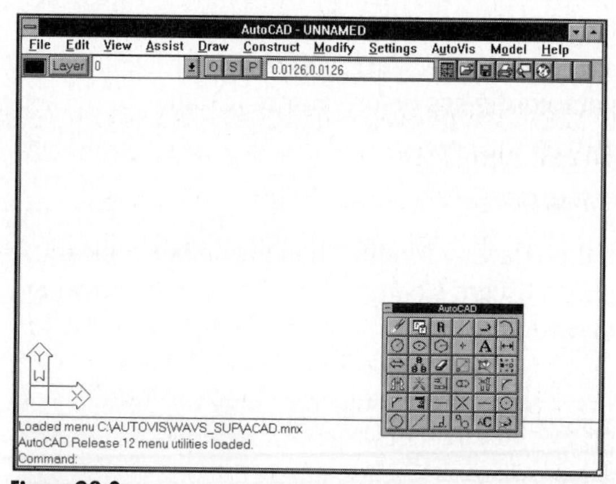

Figure G2.8

The first time you select an AutoVision command, you will be prompted to configure the rendering device. You will choose Render from the Autovis menu to bring up the configuration prompt.

Pick: **Autovis**

Pick: **Render**

The drawing editor disappears and you are prompted to select a rendering display device. Choose the default by pressing ↵.

Rendering selection:<1>: ↵

If you are using AutoVision for DOS, you may see additional prompts. Choose the defaults by pressing ↵.

Press: ↵

Finally, you are prompted to select a hardcopy device or output file format for your renderings. Specify none by choosing the default.

Rendering hard copy selection <1>: ↵

You are returned to the AutoCAD drawing editor and the Render dialogue box.

Pick: **Cancel**

To check your rendering configuration, pick the Autovis menu, then Preferences. Pick the Information option in the AutoVision Preferences dialogue box that appears. This confirms your configuration choices.

Pick: **OK**

You can reconfigure the rendering devices used by AutoVision at any time by picking Reconfigure in the AutoVision Preferences dialogue box. If you change your AutoCAD display driver, you will automatically be prompted to reconfigure the rendering display the next time you access AutoVision.

Pick: **OK *(to exit the dialogue box)***

For more information about the options available to you in configuring AutoVision, refer to the Technical Support section of your CD-ROM. The options are the same as those for the AutoCAD Render function. Select AutoVision for DOS or AutoVision for Windows, then "Configuring AutoCAD Render" to get details about the configuration process.

To exit AutoCAD,

Type: **QUIT ↵**

If the Drawing Modification dialogue box appears, pick "Discard Changes" as you have no drawing to save. AutoVision will still be configured.

You are returned to Windows (or the interface main menu). Return to the interface main menu to continue with software installation. If you wish to start the tutorials now, you must install the data files before you begin. Exit Windows by clicking once on the Program Manager icon, picking Close from the Control menu, and picking OK.

Installing 3D Studio

The installation program for 3D Studio will decompress and install the 3D Studio Release 2 files on your hard disk. In the course of the installation process, you will be asked to specify which math coprocessor you have installed on your system: Intel (or Intel compatible) or Weitek. If you are unsure of the math coprocessor you have or make a mistake, you can re-run the installation at a later time and specify the other option. (For more about math coprocessors and 3D Studio performance, see "Perfomance and Memory Management" in the Technical Support section of your CD-ROM.)

The 3D Studio installation stores the location of the 3D Studio files, video display settings, and other defaults in a file called 3ds.set. The default display is standard VGA, using a screen resolution of 640 × 480 for the user interface and 320 × 200 for rendering. If you wish to modify this file after installation, refer to "Configuring with the 3ds.set File" in the Technical Support section of your CD-ROM.

If you have optional peripherals, such as a digitizing tablet, frame buffer, or super VGA display, read "Peripherals and ADI Drivers" in the Technical Support section of the CD-ROM about installing these devices.

The Install Program

If you are not continuing with an installation, start the interface as you did at the beginning of this chapter and proceed to the main menu.

Pick: **Installation and Support**

Pick: **Install Software**

Pick: **3D Studio Release 2**

Pick: **Start Installation**

The first few screens are informational. Read and respond to the prompts. When you are asked whether this is your first installation, highlight Yes and press (↵).

Next you will see a list of the hard disk drives available on your computer. Highlight your choice and press (↵) to select the hard disk where 3D Studio will be installed.

3D Studio, like AutoCAD, uses a virtual memory program to write to disk when it runs out of available RAM. You will be asked to specify a disk drive to be used for the swap file. (For more information about the swap file, refer to "Virtual Memory Management" under "Performance" in the Technical Support section of your CD-ROM.) Specify your hard disk when prompted, and press (↵).

■ ***TIP*** 3D Studio recommends that you have at least twice the installation space (12 MB) free on your hard disk for the new files you will create. ■

Accept the default directory name, 3DS2, by pressing (↵).

Specify the Intel or Weitek math coprocessor on your system. If you are unsure, specify Intel and press (↵).

The installation program tells you where the files will be installed, checks the disk space available, and proceeds to copy the files to your hard disk.

The install program next reports that it is configuring the virtual memory drive and the values for a variety of switches that appear on your screen. If 3D Studio conflicts with any other programs on your system, you may need to modify these switch settings with the help of a technical support person or your dealer. Refer to "Using CFIG386.EXE" under "Performance" in the Technical Support section of your CD-ROM for more information.

When installation is complete, you are returned to the interface.

Starting 3D Studio

Autodesk 3D Studio can be launched from the interface main menu or by typing "3ds" from the \3DS2 directory in DOS. (See "Using 3dshell.com" under "Performance" in the Technical Support section of your CD-ROM for an alternative means of launching 3D Studio.)

To launch 3D Studio from the interface,

Pick: **Previous, Main Menu *(if necessary)***

Pick: **Run 3D Studio Release 2**

When 3D Studio starts up, it looks for the 3ds.set file in the same directory as the program. Your screen should look like Figure G2.9 below after 3D Studio is launched. If it does not, or you see an error message upon start-up, see the Technical Support section of the CD-ROM for information related to the error message.

■ ***Warning:*** 3D Studio requires an extended memory manager for proper operation. If your config.sys file does not include the line DEVICE=C:\DOS\EMM386.EXE you must add this driver before you run 3D Studio. Consult your system documentation and the Technical Support section of the CD-ROM for more information about 3D Studio and memory managers. ■

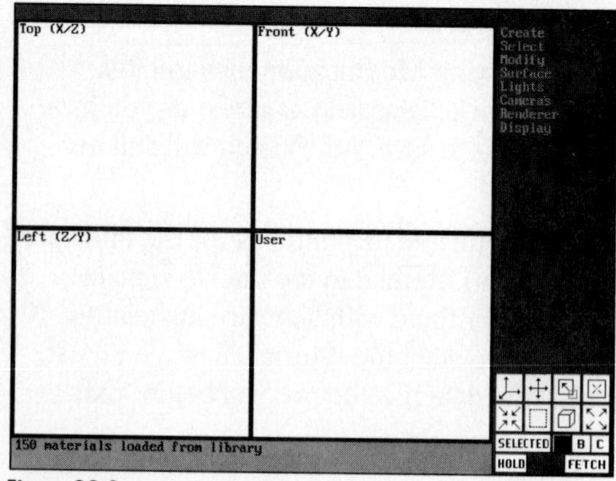

Figure G2.9

Move your cursor to the top of the screen until a menu bar appears.

Pick: **File**

Pick: **Quit**

Pick: **Yes *(to confirm your exit)***

You have completed the 3D Studio installation and are returned to the Autodesk Collection Interface. You must install the data files for 3D Studio before starting Tutorials 17–19 in this manual.

Installing Data Files

To complete the tutorials and exercises in this manual, you must also install the data files provided on the CD-ROM. The AutoCAD files should be in the directory where you plan to store all AutoCAD drawings. In the tutorial manual, this directory is assumed to be C:\DRAWINGS. If you use a directory (or subdirectory) other than DRAWINGS, you must substitute that directory each time this manual refers to the DRAWINGS directory.

3D Studio files will be installed in the PROJECTS subdirectory within the 3DS2 directory.

The interface will automatically create a directory called C:\DRAWINGS and copy the AutoCAD data files to it, then copy the 3D Studio files to the PROJECTS subdirectory.

Pick: **Installation and Support**

Pick: **Install Software**

Pick: **Data Files for Tutorials**

Pick: **Start Installation**

Pick: **Proceed**

You have the option of installing just AutoCAD or just 3D Studio data files. Accept the default, all files.

Press: (↵)

The AutoCAD drawing files are copied to the C:\DRAWINGS directory on your hard disk, and the 3D Studio files are copied to the PROJECTS subdirectory in the 3DS2 directory.

If you have not installed 3D Studio yet, you will see a message telling you that the PROJECTS directory cannot be located. Pick Abort installation and repeat the data file installation process after you have installed 3D Studio.

You are returned to the Install Software menu. Continue to install software or return to the main menu.

Batch Files Created by the Interface

To simplify the installation and loading of the Autodesk Collection, the interface installation routine created batch files that include path statements and environment variable settings needed by AutoCAD. Some or all of the following files now exist on your hard disk in the root directory:

AutoCAD Release 12 for Windows: ACADWIN.BAT

AutoCAD Release 12 for Windows with AutoVision: AVWIN.BAT

AutoCAD Release 12 for DOS: ACADR12.BAT

AutoCAD Release 12 for DOS with AutoVision: ACADAVIS.BAT

AutoCAD Release 12 for DOS with AutoCAD Designer: ACADDES.BAT

AutoCAD Release 12 for DOS with AutoCAD Designer and AutoVision: ACDESAV.BAT

If you need to modify your installation, you should use these batch files as the platform for doing so. (Be sure to make a back-up copy before you make any changes.) Refer to your system documentation for more information about editing and saving batch files.

READ.ME Files on Your Hard Disk

Several read.me files were copied to your hard disk when the Autodesk Collection was installed. These files include additional information that was unavailable when the original product documentation was released. In most cases, you will not need to refer to these files, but they can be opened and printed from any word processor as an additional reference. Cross-references to the original documentation may not be relevant, although many of the documents referred to will be found in the Technical Support section of your CD-ROM.

Modifying the ACAD Variable for AutoVision

If you choose not to use the interface to launch AutoCAD Release 12 for Windows, you must modify the ACAD variable in order to access AutoVision. (For AutoCAD Release 12 for DOS, use the batch files listed on page G-33.) This variable is a file path statement used by AutoCAD and AutoVision to locate support files. From the interface main menu,

Pick: **Run AutoCAD R12 for Windows**

When the AutoCAD graphics screen appears, you will use the Preferences dialogue box to modify the path statement.

Pick: **File *(from the menu bar at the top of your screen)***

Pick: **Preferences *(from the pull-down menu that appears)***

The Preferences dialogue box appears. You will select Environment to call up the dialogue box that controls the AutoCAD environment variables.

Pick: **Environment**

You will add the drive names and paths for AutoVision in the text box to the right of Support Dirs. These paths must precede the paths for AutoCAD. Pick in the box so your cursor is positioned immediately after the equal sign in SET ACAD=. (If you have installed AutoVision and its support files on a drive other than C: or in different directories, you must substitute those directory and drive names in the path statement you type.)

Type: **C:\AUTOVIS\WACAD;C:\AUTOVIS\WAVS_SUP**

The complete path statement for AutoCAD for Windows should now read:

ACAD=C:\AUTOVIS\WACAD;C:\AUTOVIS\WAVS_SUP;C:\ACADWIN\FONTS;C:\ACADWIN\SAMPLE;C:\ACADWIN\SUPPORT.

Close the dialogue box:

Pick: **OK**

Then save the changes you made by picking the radio button next to Save to ACAD.INI in the Preferences dialogue box.

Pick: **Save to ACAD.INI**

Pick: **OK**

Now exit AutoCAD.

Type: **Quit** ↵

Your autoexec.bat file should also be altered to include the location for the AutoVision texture maps. Add the following line to this file with any word processor, taking care to save it as a text-only file. If you have installed AutoVision in a directory other than AUTOVIS, you must substitute the name of that directory.

SET AVEMAPS = C:\AUTOVIS\MAP;C:\AUTOVIS\TUTORIAL

You must reboot your computer for these autoexec.bat changes to take effect.

The next time you launch AutoCAD from the Windows icon, you will see the AutoVision menu (Autovis) in place of the Render menu on the menu bar at the top of your screen.

These changes are only necessary if you do not use the interface to launch AutoCAD.

CHAPTER 3

AutoCAD Basics

Objectives

When you have completed this chapter, you will be able to

1. Load the Autodesk Collection Interface.
2. Access the information on your Autodesk Collection CD-ROM.
3. Load AutoCAD Release 12 for Windows from the interface main menu.
4. Learn basic techniques for the Windows operating system.
5. Recognize the menus and commands used in AutoCAD.
6. Use the mouse to pick commands, menu options, and entities.
7. Work with a dialogue box.
8. Access AutoCAD's on-line help facility.
9. Exit from the graphics window and return to the Windows operating system.

Introduction

In this chapter, you will learn how to load the Autodesk Collection Interface and use it to access the information on your Autodesk Collection CD-ROM. You will learn to use the interface to start AutoCAD Release 12 for Windows on your computer system. This chapter assumes that you have installed the Autodesk Collection Interface and installed and configured AutoCAD as described in Chapter 2. It also assumes that you are using AutoCAD Release 12 for Windows. If you prefer to use AutoCAD Release 12 for DOS, you can still use the tutorials in this manual, but you may have to make some minor adjustments.

After loading AutoCAD, you will learn how to enter commands and access menu options, the basics of using a mouse, and how to work in dialogue boxes. You will also learn how to access on-line help in AutoCAD. Some key differences between AutoCAD Release 12 for DOS and AutoCAD Release 12 for Windows are also explained.

IMPORTANT: The instructions in this manual are written with the assumption that you are using AutoCAD's standard configuration. If you are using AutoCAD on a network at your school, ask your professor or system administrator about how the software is configured. Unique changes might have been made that differ from AutoCAD's standard configuration; for example, the program might be under a different directory name or require a special command or password to get started.

Loading the Autodesk Collection Interface

To launch any of the software you installed in Chapter 2, you will use the Autodesk Collection Interface. Using this interface ensures that the appropriate batch files are run before you load AutoCAD or 3D Studio.

■ ***Warning:*** If you do not use the interface to launch your Autodesk Collection applications, you will need to modify your system yourself to be sure the environment is set for proper operation. Refer to Chapter 2 for more about installing and configuring your Autodesk Collection software. ■

Before you begin, be sure your computer is on and you are at the DOS prompt. First, you will change to the directory where the interface is installed; then you will load the interface.

C:\> **cd \ AWCD** ↵

C:\AWCD> **AWCD** ↵

The opening screen appears. Your name and school name as you entered them during installation appear on the opening screen. Refer to the serial number on this screen whenever you need the registration number for the software in your Autodesk Collection.

The Start button on your screen takes you to the interface main menu. The dark outline around the button indicates that it is the default and can be activated by pressing ↵. You can also activate it by picking it with the mouse.

Press: ↵

The interface main menu appears. Your screen should look like Figure G3.1.

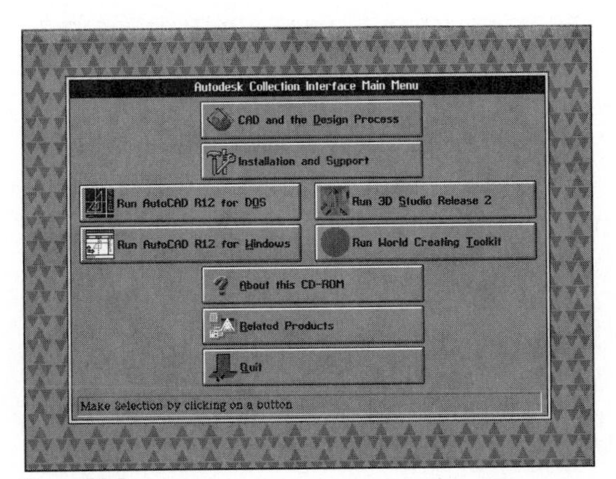

Figure G3.1

Accessing Information on Your CD-ROM

You used the interface main menu in Chapter 2 to install and launch your software. In this section, you will explore the other information contained on your CD-ROM.

A brief explanation of the options displayed in the main menu appears along the bottom of the window on your screen. Move your mouse over the various menu buttons (without pressing the mouse button) and notice the description change.

The first menu item is "CAD and the Design Process." This brief overview introduces you to the Autodesk Collection as a complete design environment. David S. Cohn, Senior Editor of *CADalyst* magazine, presents the Autodesk Collection, using text and graphics to show you how the tools work together toward a polished, presentation-quality result.

Take a few moments now to read his introduction. Remember that you can choose a menu item by holding down (ALT) and pressing the underlined letter in the menu item, or you can pick an item by clicking it with the mouse. You will choose the top menu item.

Pick: **CAD and the Design Process**

Use the arrow buttons to move forward and back through the Introduction. When you are finished, return to the main menu.

Accessing Technical Support

The next menu item is "Installation and Support." You have used this option to install the Autodesk Collection and look up information about your system's devices.

Pick: **Installation and Support**

Pick: **Technical Support**

The Technical Support section of your CD-ROM contains additional information about configuring your system and peripherals for best performance. If you encounter difficulty with any Autodesk Collection product, refer to the indexes included in this section for topics related to your problem.

To do so, you must first choose the product about which you would like additional information. Do so now to see how Technical Support information is displayed.

Pick: **AutoCAD R12 for Windows**

The Technical Support index for AutoCAD for Windows appears, as shown in Figure G3.2.

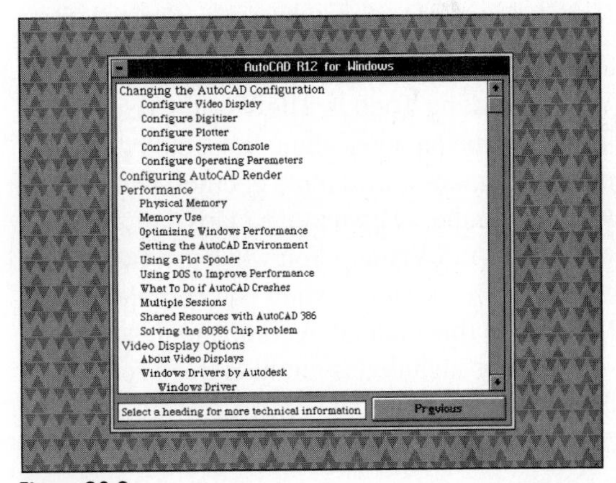

Figure G3.2

From this window, you can select topics of interest by picking them with the mouse.

Pick: **Performance**

Information about this topic appears on your screen. Once you have located the item you need, you can print the file by picking the Print button. This option activates the DOS PRINT command and prints the underlying text file on your CD-ROM. If your system is not configured for the PRINT command, this may not work for you. If not, you can open the relevant text file in any word processor. Technical Support files are located in the directory AWCD\TXTFILES\TECHSUPP on your hard disk. Use the .IDX file for a given product in this directory to identify the file name for the section you need.

Return to the interface main menu.

Pick: **Main Menu**

Accessing the World Creating Toolkit

The next group of menu items launch the Autodesk Collection software after installation, as you saw in Chapter 2. Because AutoVision and AutoCAD Designer run within AutoCAD, you have the option to launch them when you launch AutoCAD (if they have been installed).

This group also includes a button for the World Creating Toolkit. The World Creating Toolkit is not an application, but a collection of texture maps and sample geometry for use with 3D Studio. (The texture maps can also be used with AutoVision.) You will learn how to access these elements when you complete the tutorials in this manual. A complete description of the maps included is found in the Technical Support section for the World Creating Toolkit on your CD-ROM.

In addition, the World Creating Toolkit contains a number of images and sample "flics" (animations) to show you what you can create with 3D Studio. You can explore these images from the submenu that appears when you select "Run World Creating Toolkit." Explore some of these now, if you wish. The second option on the menu gives you a VGA preview of 3D Studio animations.

Pick: **Run World Creating Toolkit**

Type: **2** (↵)

A preview of the animations begins. Press (ESC) at any time to cancel the preview and return to the menu. Type "EXIT" to return to the interface main menu.

Additional Information

"About this CD-ROM" provides information about the Autodesk Collection, using the interface, and getting technical support. "Related Products" presents a number of Addison-Wesley and Autodesk products you may find useful in working with the Autodesk Collection.

Explore these options now on your own before you continue.

Loading AutoCAD Release 12 for Windows

The rest of this chapter will introduce you to AutoCAD Release 12 for Windows and some basic operations in Windows and AutoCAD. If you are using AutoCAD Release 12 for DOS, you will encounter several places where the screen display is different. This chapter points out the major differences you will encounter, but the tutorials in this manual do not. If you are planning to use AutoCAD Release 12 for DOS with the tutorials, you should use AutoCAD's on-line help for guidance when your screen display differs from that in the tutorials.

You will load AutoCAD Release 12 for Windows as you did in Chapter 2. You should be at the interface main menu.

Pick: **Run AutoCAD R12 for Windows**

Pick: **with AutoVision**

The AutoCAD graphics window is displayed on your screen, as shown in Figure G3.3.

■ ***Warning:*** If AutoCAD does not appear, or you see a message stating that AutoCAD must be configured, refer to the appropriate sections of Chapter 2 to be sure you have installed and configured AutoCAD properly for your system. ■

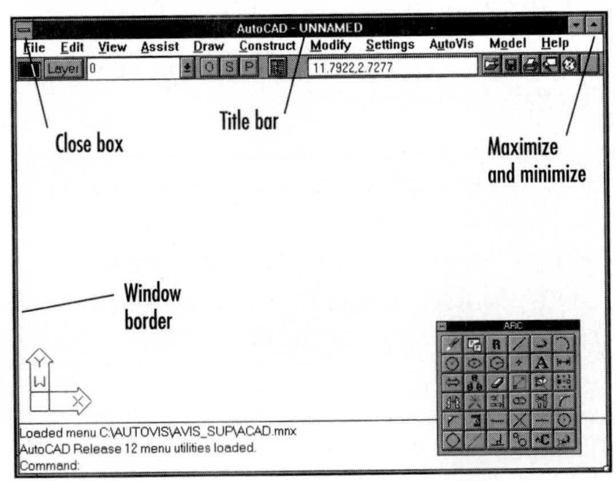

Figure G3.3

Note: If you are using AutoCAD Release 12 for DOS, your screen display will be slightly different.

Microsoft Windows and AutoCAD

AutoCAD Release 12 for Windows uses many of the same conventions as other applications that run within Windows. This section will identify some of the techniques that you will be using to complete the tutorials in this manual.

The tutorials in this manual assume you will be using a mouse or pointing device to work with the Autodesk Collection. Refer to Chapter 1 to review language used for basic mouse techniques.

Basic Elements of a Graphics Window

The AutoCAD graphics window is the main workspace. It has elements that are common to all applications written for the Windows environment that you will use as you complete the tutorials in this manual. These elements are labeled in Figure G3.3 and described below.

- The *Close,* or *Control menu, box* is in the upper-left corner of each window. This box is referred to as the *close box* in the tutorials, as it can be used to close a window. Picking it once reveals a menu that can be used to close, move, or resize a window. Double-clicking it closes the window.
- The *title bar* shows the name of the application (in this case, AutoCAD) followed by the document name (in this case, UNNAMED). AutoCAD for Windows allows you to have more than one AutoCAD drawing open at any given time. If more than one window is open, the title bar for the active window (the one in which you are working) is usually a different color intensity than the other title bars.
- The *window border* is the outside edge of a window. You can change the window size by moving the cursor over the border until it becomes a double-ended arrow. Holding the mouse button down while you move the mouse (dragging) resizes the window.
- The *Maximize and Minimize buttons* are in the upper right corner of the window. Clicking the Maximize button with the mouse enlarges the active window so that it fills the entire desktop; this is the default condition for AutoCAD. You will learn to use the Minimize button in the next section.

Minimizing and Restoring AutoCAD for Windows

There may be occasions when you want to leave AutoCAD temporarily while you are in the middle of a work session, perhaps to access another application. Minimizing AutoCAD allows you to reduce the application to an icon and return to it more quickly than would be the case if you had to exit and start AutoCAD all over again. (This section does not apply to AutoCAD Release 12 for DOS.)

Picking the Minimize button (the downward pointing arrow) reduces the window to an icon and makes the Windows desktop accessible. (You can also choose Maximize and Minimize from the Control menu.)

Pick: ***(the Minimize button)***

AutoCAD is reduced to an icon at the bottom of your screen. (In a working AutoCAD session, you should always save your work before minimizing AutoCAD.)

AutoCAD is still running in the background, but other applications are accessible for your use. When you are ready to return to AutoCAD, double-click the AutoCAD program icon or pick the AutoCAD icon once and choose Restore from the menu that appears.

Restore AutoCAD on your own now.

Basic Keyboard Techniques for Windows

Using a mouse is usually easier and faster than using the keyboard, although a combination of mouse use and keyboard shortcuts is the most efficient way to navigate. If you prefer using the keyboard to do common tasks, such as selecting commands on menus and moving around in dialogue boxes and lists, you can use these basic techniques throughout Windows and AutoCAD for Windows. In addition to these basic techniques, you will learn keyboard shortcuts for specific AutoCAD functions later in the tutorials. For more on keyboard commands in Windows, see your *User's Guide* for Windows.

Using Menus

To	Press
Activate the menu bar	ALT or F10
Select a menu	ALT+the underlined character in the menu name
Open the close box menu for an application window	ALT-spacebar
Choose a menu command	An arrow key, ↵, or the underlined character in the command name

■ ***TIP*** Although you can choose any menu command by using this method, many commands have faster keyboard equivalents, which are usually shown next to the command on the menu. ■

Moving Around

To move	Press
Between menu commands, characters in a text box, or items in a list	An arrow key
To the next or previous dialogue box item	TAB or SHIFT-TAB
To a dialogue box item	ALT+the character underlined in the item name
Right or left one word in a text box	Ctrl-← or Ctrl-→
To the beginning or end of a line, list, or screen	HOME or END
Up or down one screen	PGUP or PGDN

Pointing Techniques in AutoCAD

A drawing is made up of separate elements, called *entities*, that consist of lines, arcs, circles, text, and other elements that you access and draw through AutoCAD's commands and menu options.

The pointing device (assumed in this text to be a mouse) is the most common tool used to pick commands and menu options, select entities, or locate points in AutoCAD.

Entering Points

You can specify points in a drawing either by typing in the coordinates from the keyboard or by using your mouse to locate the desired points in the graphics area.

When you move the mouse around on the mouse pad or table surface, *crosshairs* (the intersecting vertical and horizontal lines on the screen) follow the motion of the mouse. These crosshairs form the AutoCAD cursor in the drawing editor. When you are selecting points during execution of some commands, the location of the intersection of the crosshairs will be the selected point when you press the left mouse button. This is how you pick a point. There are other modes in AutoCAD in which the crosshairs change to arrows or boxes with target areas during the execution of certain commands. You will learn about these modes in the tutorials. The cursor on the screen always echoes the motion of the mouse.

Picking Commands and Menu Options

The AutoCAD menus let you enter a command simply by pointing to the command and pressing the left mouse button to "pick" it. The left mouse button is often referred to as the *pick button*. In this way you are instructed to *Pick:* specific commands.

The right mouse button is often referred to as the *return button* and duplicates the action of the ↵ key when you are selecting objects or repeating commands and options from menus.

Dragging

Many AutoCAD commands permit dynamic specification, or *dragging*, of an image of the object on the screen. You can use your mouse to move an object, rotate it, or scale it graphically. You will learn about DRAG mode in the tutorials. Once an object is selected in DRAG mode, AutoCAD draws tentative images as you move your pointing device. When you are satisfied with the appearance of the object, press the pick button to confirm it.

Entity Selection

Many of AutoCAD's editing commands ask you to select one or more objects for processing. This collection of objects is called the *selection set*. You can use your mouse to add objects to, or remove objects from, the selection set. AutoCAD has various tools and commands to work with when selecting objects; you use the cursor to point to objects in response to specific prompts. AutoCAD highlights the objects as they are selected. You will learn about the various ways to select objects in the tutorials.

AutoCAD Commands and Menu Options

AutoCAD gives you several options for entering commands. Commands can be typed at the command prompt or picked from the pull-down menu bar, from the toolbox, or from the screen menu. These elements are labeled in Figure G3.4, although you will not see the screen menu on your screen yet. You will learn to display the screen menu later in this chapter.

Note: AutoCAD Release 12 for DOS displays the screen menu as a default, but does not include the toolbox. Also, the pull-down menu bar is not visible unless the cursor is moved to the top of the screen.

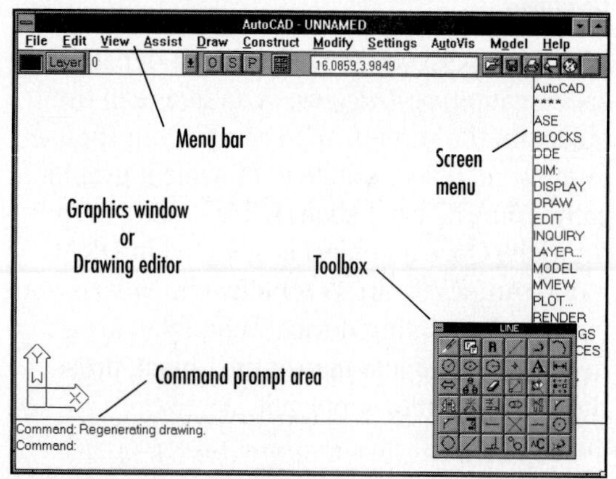

Figure G3.4

Most AutoCAD commands can be typed at the command prompt, but it is easier to pick them from a menu or the toolbox in most instances. How a command is invoked may affect the order and wording of the prompts you see on the screen. These differences offer you options for more efficient use of AutoCAD. For the purposes of the tutorials in this manual, you should pick or type commands as instructed. The menu location you should use will be indicated in parentheses after the command. For example, *Pick:* **CIRCLE *(toolbox)***. As you progress through the tutorials, you will learn about the benefits of choosing commands in different ways in different situations.

Typing Commands

The command line area at the bottom of your screen is one means of interacting with AutoCAD. Commands that you enter are echoed there, and AutoCAD responds there with additional prompts that tell you what to do next. "Command:" on the command line is a signal that AutoCAD is ready for a command. Watch the command prompt area as you type "LINE" and press (↵).

Command: **LINE** (↵)

The LINE command is activated when you press (↵) and the LINE command prompt "From point:" is in the command prompt area. This prompt tells you to enter the first point from which a line will be drawn. You will learn about the LINE command in Tutorial 1. For now,

Press: (Ctrl)-C

to cancel the command and return to the "Command:" prompt.

■ ***Warning:*** You cannot type menu names that are not also AutoCAD commands, such as DRAW, at the "Command:" prompt. If you do, you get an error message and your cursor is returned to the "Command:" prompt, as follows:

Unknown Command. Type ? for list of commands.

Command: ■

The tutorials in this manual explain each of the ways you can access a command. The command reference at the end of this manual also lists these locations with the command names that can be entered at the command line.

Repeating Commands

You can press the spacebar or (↵) at the "Command:" prompt to repeat the previous command, regardless of the method you used to enter that command. You can also press the right mouse button to repeat the command. Some commands, especially those that prompt you for settings when first invoked, assume default settings when repeated in this manner.

Backing Up and Backing Out of Commands

When you type a command name or any data in response to a prompt on the command line, the typed characters "wait" until you press the spacebar or ↵ to instruct AutoCAD to perform the command or enter and act upon the entered data.

If you have not already pressed ↵ or the spacebar, use the BACKSPACE key (generally located above and to the right of the ↵ key on standard IBM PC keyboards and represented by a long back arrow) to delete one character at a time from the command/prompt line. Pressing Ctrl-H has the same effect as pressing BACKSPACE.

Pressing Ctrl-C terminates the currently active command (if any) and reissues the "Command:" prompt. You can cancel a command at any time: while typing the command name, during command execution, or during any time-consuming process. A short delay may occur before the cancellation takes effect and the prompt "*Cancel*" confirms the cancellation.

Pressing Ctrl-C is also useful if you wish to cancel a selection process. If you are in the middle of selecting an object, press Ctrl-C to cancel the selection process and discard the selection set. Any item that was highlighted because you selected it will return to normal.

If you complete a command and the result is not what you had expected or wanted, use the U or UNDO command to reverse the effect. You will learn more about UNDO in Tutorial 3.

Using the Toolbox

The most common AutoCAD commands are represented in the toolbox. A single pick on the icon for a command invokes it. Additional prompts and options appear at the command line, as they do for commands that are typed.

Pick the CIRCLE command from the toolbox to see the options that appear. The CIRCLE icon is in the first column of the second row of the toolbox. It looks like a circle. As you move your mouse over the icon, its name is confirmed at the top of the toolbox.

Pick: **CIRCLE *(icon in toolbox)***

Note: If you are using AutoCAD Release 12 for DOS, type "CIRCLE" at the command line and press ↵.

You will see the following options appear at the command line:

Command: _circle 3P/2P/TTR/<Center point>:

3P/2P/TTR are command options for the CIRCLE command. Subcommands and options work properly only when entered in response to the appropriate prompts on the command line. When a subcommand or option includes one or more uppercase letters in its name, it is a signal that the letters can be typed at the prompt as a shortcut for the option name (for example, "X" for eXit).

Type: **Ctrl-C**

Using Pull-Down Menus

The menu bar and its associated pull-down menus provide another means of executing AutoCAD commands. The menu bar in AutoCAD for Windows operates in the same way as menus in other applications for Windows.

You open a menu in the menu bar by picking its name. To practice,

Pick: **Draw *(menu bar)***

Picking a menu item executes the commands associated with it, opens a submenu of options, or opens a dialogue box of options to be used to control the command. A triangle to the right of a menu item indicates that there is a submenu associated with it. Pick Circle to see its submenu.

Pick: **Circle *(from the pull-down menu)***

The submenu shown in Figure G3.5 should appear next to the Draw pull-down menu.

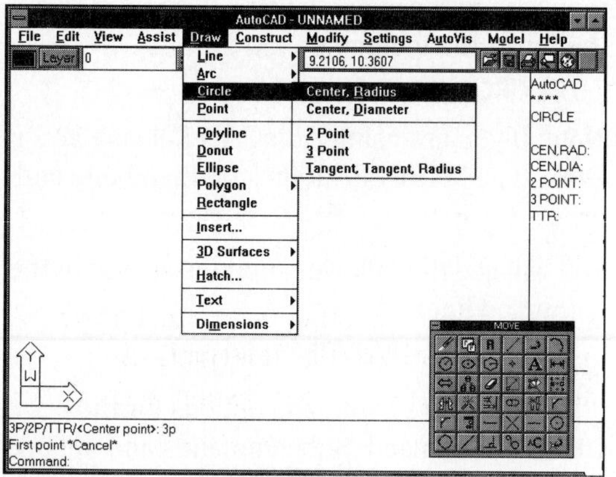

Figure G3.5

A pulled-down menu remains displayed until you

- Pick an item from it
- Pull down another menu by picking it from the menu bar
- Remove the menu by picking an unused area of the menu bar
- Pick a point on the graphics screen
- Type a character on the keyboard
- Pick an item from a tablet or button menu
- Move your pointing device into the regular screen menu area and click

To remove the Draw pull-down menu from the screen,

Pick: ***(a point on the graphics window)***

Working with Dialogue Boxes

An ellipsis (. . .) after a menu item indicates that it will open a dialogue box. Several commands let you set AutoCAD modes or perform operations by checking boxes or filling in fields in a dialogue box. When a dialogue box is displayed, the cursor changes to an arrow that points up and to the left. This arrow is used to select items from the dialogue box.

Open the Drawing Aids dialogue box by picking the Settings menu on the menu bar, then picking Drawing Aids from the menu.

Pick: **Settings *(menu bar)***

Pick: **Drawing Aids. . .**

The dialogue box shown in Figure G3.6 should appear on your screen.

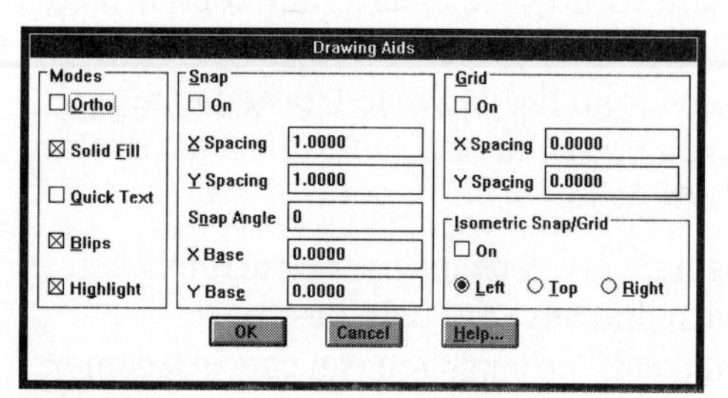

Figure G3.6

Drawing Aids is a typical dialogue box. Every dialogue box has an OK button that is used to confirm the settings or options you have selected in the dialogue box. It is analogous to pressing (↵) to send a command to AutoCAD. The Cancel button is used to disregard all changes made in the dialogue box; pressing it has the same effect as pressing (Ctrl)-C or (ESC). The Help. . . button is used to get more information about a particular command.

■ ***Warning:*** The term "button" used in conjunction with a dialogue box refers to these input boxes and should not be confused with the buttons on your mouse or digitizer. ■

Some dialogue boxes have sub-boxes that pop up in front of them. When this occurs, you must respond to the top dialogue box before the underlying one can continue.

Most dialogue boxes have several types of buttons that control values or commands in AutoCAD. Refer to Figure G3.6.

- Check buttons: A check button is a small rectangle that is either blank or shows an X. Check buttons control an on/off switch, for example turning GRID on or off; or control a choice from a set of alternatives, for example determining which modes are on. A blank check button is off.
- Radio buttons: A radio button also turns an option on or off. The Isometric grid is indicated by radio buttons labeled Left, Top, and Right in this dialogue box. A filled-in radio button is on.
- Action buttons: An action button doesn't control a value but causes an action. The OK action button causes the dialogue box to close and all the selected options to go into effect. When an action button is highlighted (outlined with a heavy rule), you can press ⏎ to activate it.
- Input buttons: An input button specifies a value, such as the snap spacing in Figure G3.6. Picking an input button puts the cursor in it and lets you type values into it or alter values already there. If you enter an invalid value, the OK button has no effect; you must highlight the value, correct it, and select OK again.

  Sometimes input buttons have a small arrow at the right end of the button. Picking the arrow causes the value area to expand into a menu of options that you can use to select the value for the button.

You can also use the keyboard to move around in dialogue boxes. Pressing TAB moves you among the options in the box. Once you have highlighted an option, you can use the arrow keys to move the cursor in input boxes, and the spacebar to toggle among on/off options.

Another common feature of dialogue boxes is the *scroll bar*. A dialogue box may contain more entries than can be displayed at one time. The scroll bars are used to move (scroll) the items up or down. You will use a scroll bar in the section "Accessing On-Line Help."

To return to the drawing editor,

Pick: **Cancel**

Picking from an Icon Menu

An icon menu is another type of menu you will encounter in AutoCAD. This menu displays choices as graphic images (icons) rather than words. Select the hatch pattern icon menu as follows:

Pick: **Draw *(menu bar)***

Pick: **Hatch. . .**

Pick: **Hatch Options. . .**

Pick: **Pattern. . .**

Your screen should look like Figure G3.7.

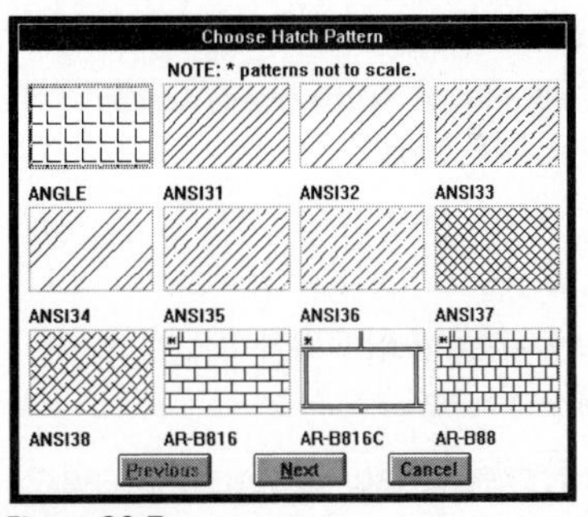

Figure G3.7

Using Next

Many menus contain more items than can fit on one screen listing. If there are more menu items than can be listed, a Next button appears at the bottom of the menu. The next part of the menu will appear if the word Next is activated.

Pick: **Next**

A new screen of hatch patterns appears. Pick Previous to go back. If you wanted to choose a hatch pattern, you would move the arrow (using your pointing device) over the desired icon and press the left mouse button (the pick button).

Pick: ***(a hatch option)***

That hatch pattern is now active and you are returned to the previous screen. Exit the Hatch Options dialogue box without confirming this change by picking the Cancel button or pressing Ctrl-C or ESC in each dialogue box until you return to the graphics window.

Using the Screen Menu

The screen menu is yet another way you can pick commands. Figure G3.4 showed the "root" page of the screen menu, which is organized in a hierarchical fashion. To display the screen menu, in AutoCAD for Windows,

Pick: **File**

Pick: **Preferences . . .**

Pick: ***(the check button next to the words Screen Menu in the top left corner)***

Pick: **OK**

Pick: **Continue**

The screen menu should now be visible on the right side of your screen.

Options are picked from the screen menu as they are from the menus on the menu bar. When you pick an item from the screen menu, however, the root page disappears and is replaced by the appropriate submenu or listing of command options. To see how,

Pick: **DRAW**

Pick: **LINE**

These command options are similar to those that appear at the command line and those that appear on submenus or in dialogue boxes when you use the pull-down menus. Next and LAST are used to navigate among the menus, and you can pick the word AutoCAD at the top of the screen menu at any time to return to the root page of the screen menu.

■ ***TIP*** Click and drag the title bar of the toolbox to move it out of the way, if necessary. ■

Accessing On-Line Help

AutoCAD has a context-sensitive on-line help facility. If you have a question about how a command operates, you can get help in a number of ways.

- If you need help with a menu, press F1 while the menu is pulled down.
- If you need help as you are using a command, press F1 to get help for that command.
- Click the Help button in any dialogue box to get help about that dialogue box.
- Pick Help from the menu bar, then Contents from the Help menu to see the table of contents for the help system. Pressing F1 or typing "HELP" when no command is active or menu pulled down will also access the main help index.

Note: In AutoCAD Release 12 for DOS, you can access context-sensitive help by activating a command and typing "'help" (help preceded by an apostrophe) while the command is active, or by picking Help from the Assist pull-down menu at the top of the screen. The function key F1 will not work; it is used to toggle to the text screen and back.

Pick: **Help *(menu bar)***

Pick: **Contents**

Your screen should resemble Figure G3.8.

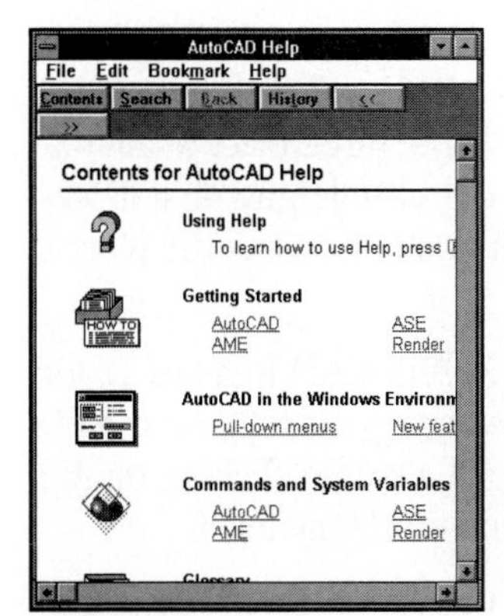

Figure G3.8

From the Help dialogue box, you can pick any of the underlined topics in the Contents listing, or you can search through the index to look at the Help screens for different commands.

Pick: **Search**

You will see an alphabetical list of AutoCAD commands and a scroll bar.

Using a Scroll Bar

A *scroll bar* allows you to access items on lists that are too long to be fully displayed in the box. Pick the up or the down arrow to scroll in the desired direction. A *slider box* is located between the up and down arrows on the scroll bar. You can pick the slider box and drag it to move the entries up and down; with long lists this is often faster than using the arrows.

Use the up and down arrows now to move through the list. Then place the cursor on the slider box and click and drag it up and down to move more quickly through the list. Choose CIRCLE to get information about the Circle command. (You can also type the word in the box above the list of topics.)

Pick: **CIRCLE**

Pick: **Show Topics**

Your choices show up in the bottom portion of the Search dialogue box.

Pick: **CIRCLE Command**

Pick: **Go To**

AutoCAD displays a text screen of information about the CIRCLE command; your screen should look similar to Figure G3.9.

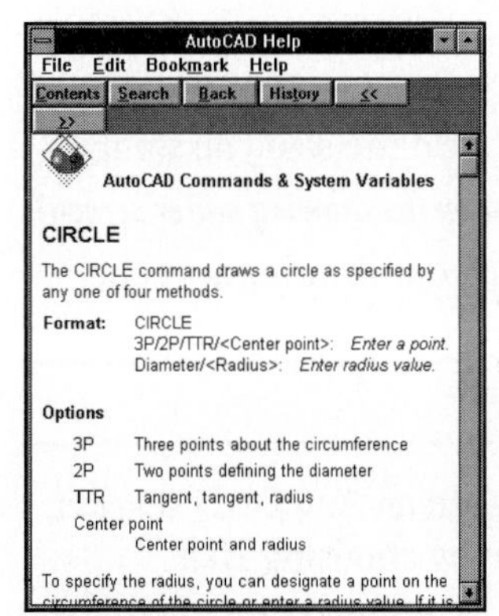

Figure G3.9

If there is additional information that will not fit on the screen, use the scroll bar to move through it.

To return to the graphics window,

Pick: ***(double-click on the close box)***

Accessing On-Line Help in the Middle of a Command

The HELP command can also be used while you are in the middle of another command. This is called *transparent help*. If you need additional help while in the middle of a command, press F1 or use the transparent command ' help. Try this now for the CIRCLE command by activating the command, then pressing F1.

Pick: **CIRCLE icon *(toolbox)***

Press: F1

AutoCAD displays a help screen of information about the command you are currently using, in this case, the CIRCLE command.

After you exit the Help dialogue box, the command function that you are using resumes.

Pick: ***(double-click on the close box)***

You are still in the CIRCLE command. Use your mouse to

Pick: ***(any point in the graphics area)***

As you move your mouse, you will see a circle on the screen getting larger and smaller. When you have made the circle the size you want,

Pick: ***(any second point on the drawing editor screen)***

A circle should be on your drawing screen.

Exiting AutoCAD

When you have finished an AutoCAD session, you exit the program by choosing Exit AutoCAD from the File menu on the menu bar.

Pick: **File *(menu bar)***

Pick: **Exit AutoCAD**

Because quitting AutoCAD unintentionally could cause the loss of a lengthy editing session, AutoCAD prompts you to save the changes if you wish to. The Drawing Modification dialogue box appears, which contains a "The current drawing has been changed" message and gives you three options: Save Changes; Discard Changes; and Cancel Command.

Pick: **Save Changes**

The Save Drawing As dialogue box appears, as shown in Figure G3.10.

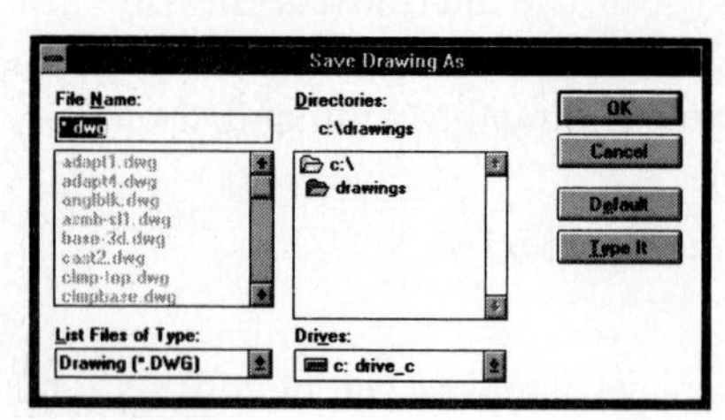

Figure G3.10

This dialogue box is similar to other Windows dialogue boxes for managing files. Along the right side you see a list of directories available on your system. By double-clicking on a directory, you can open it and select it as the place to store your file.

Note: If you are using AutoCAD Release 12 for DOS, the directories are on the left and the file names are on the right. Double-clicking on the .. moves you back one directory level.

When you installed the data files for the tutorials, you created a directory called DRAWINGS shown in Figure G3.10.

It is good practice to use a separate directory for your drawing files, and you will be instructed to save your files to the DRAWINGS directory throughout the tutorials in this manual. The DRAWINGS directory was created in your root directory, usually C:\.

Double-click on C:\ to reveal the directories in it. Use the arrow buttons on the scroll bar to locate the DRAWINGS directory. Double-click on DRAWINGS to open it. Your screen should look like Figure G3.10, with the data files for the tutorials appearing in the list at left. You will repeat this procedure each time you save a file so that all of your drawings will be in the DRAWINGS directory.

> ■ ***TIP*** If you want to save your file to a disk, below the directory list you will see an input box labeled Drives; pressing the down arrow displays the disk drives available on your machine. Double-click on the disk drive and directory where you wish to save your drawing. ■

Now you need to give your file a name. Your file name cannot be longer than eight characters and cannot contain any spaces or periods. Since you have been testing the CIRCLE command, name the file TESTCIRC. Click on the File Name: box and drag to highlight all the text in the box. When the text is highlighted,

Type: **TESTCIRC**

Pick: **OK**

Your file is saved, and AutoCAD automatically returns you to the Windows Program Manager.

■ ***TIP*** If you did not wish to save your drawing, you would have picked Discard Changes. If you have made some irreversible error and wish to discard all changes made in an AutoCAD session, you can choose Exit AutoCAD from the File menu (or type "QUIT" at the "Command:" prompt) and select Discard Changes so the changes are not saved to your file. ■

If you wish to restart AutoCAD again before you turn off your computer, you can do so from the Program Manager. Open the AutoCAD program group (if necessary) and double-click the AutoCAD icon. If you restart your computer, you must launch AutoCAD from the Autodesk Collection Interface so the appropriate batch files are loaded.

You are now ready to complete the tutorials in this manual. Double-click the close box on the Program Manager window to exit Windows.

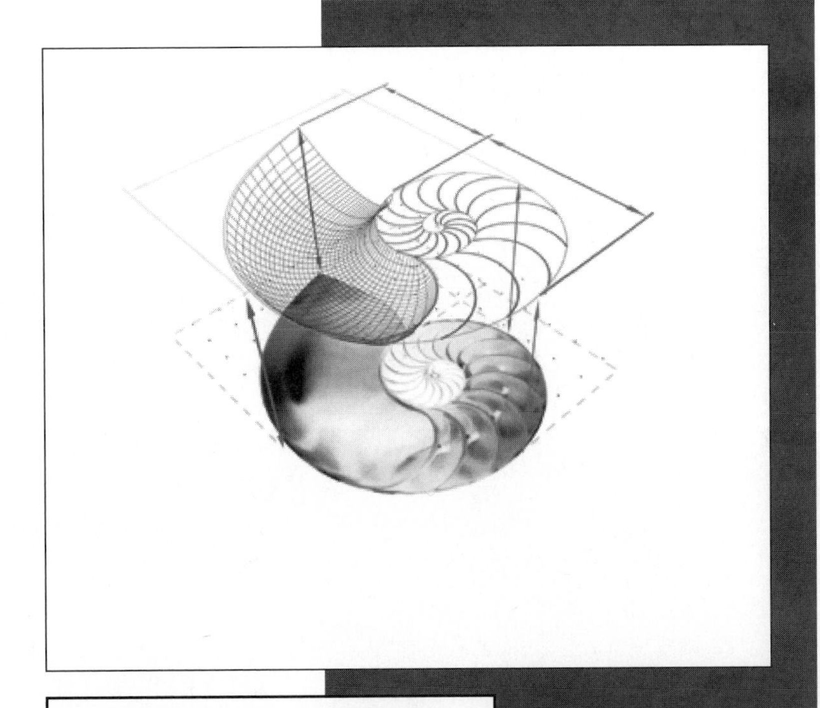

PART TWO

Tutorials

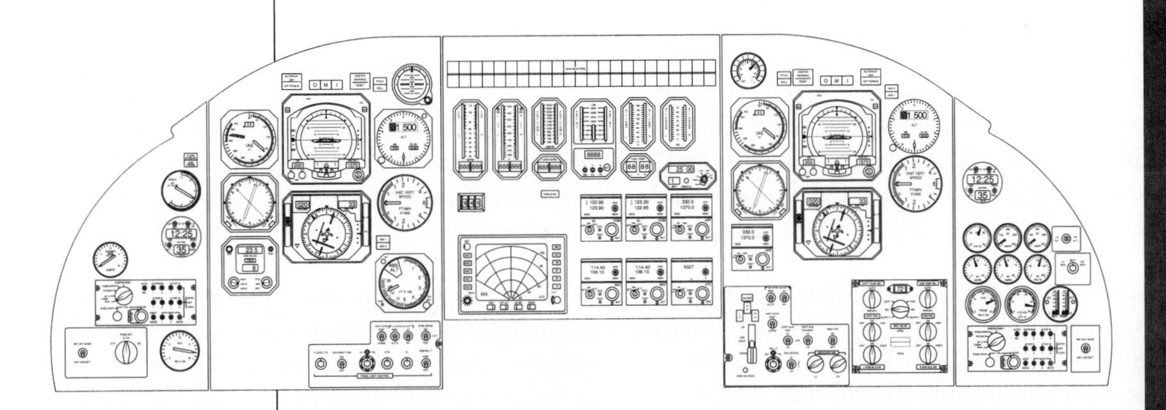

TUTORIAL 1

Introduction to AutoCAD

Objectives

When you have completed this tutorial, you will be able to

1. Create a drawing using AutoCAD.
2. Set up and use a screen background.
3. Draw lines, rectangles, and circles.
4. Use absolute, relative, and polar coordinates.
5. Use AutoCAD's HELP command.
6. Erase drawing entities.
7. Select drawing entities, using implied Window and Crossing.
8. Set Drawing Units control and LIMITS.
9. Add text to a drawing with DTEXT and edit it with DDEDIT.
10. Select fonts and create text styles.
11. Save a drawing and transfer a drawing from one drive to another.

Introduction

This tutorial introduces the fundamental operating procedures and drawing tools of AutoCAD. It explains how to create a new drawing, how to draw circles and lines, and how to name a new drawing and save a drawing. You will learn how to erase items and how to select groups of entities. This tutorial also explains how to add text to a drawing. As you are working through the tutorial, keep in mind that one of the advantages of using AutoCAD over drawing on paper is that you are creating an accurate model of the drawing geometry. In later tutorials you will see how to use this accurate drawing database to find areas, lengths, and other information. You will also learn to use basic two-dimensional shapes as a basis for three-dimensional solid models.

■ ***TIP*** If you are using AutoCAD Release 12 for DOS, you will find some discrepancies between your software and the operations of AutoCAD in the Windows environment. Chapter 3, AutoCAD Basics, in Part 1, Getting Started, presents common Windows-based operations as well as basic AutoCAD operations. Reading this chapter before you begin will help you identify areas where you will need to substitute DOS-based AutoCAD operations for those in the tutorial. ■

Starting

You will launch AutoCAD Release 12 for Windows as you learned in Chapter 3, by using the Autodesk Collection interface you used to install the program. From the DOS prompt, change to the AWCD directory (if you are not already there).

C:\> **cd\AWCD** ↵

C:\AWCD> **AWCD** ↵

Pick Start from the opening screen (or press ↵) and the main menu will appear. Select Run AutoCAD R12 for Windows to launch the program. If you need help, please review Chapter 3, AutoCAD Basics, in Part 1, Getting Started.

■ ***Warning:*** There are batch files that must be executed before Windows and AutoCAD are launched. If you do not use the interface for launching the programs you have installed, you will get error messages indicating that your system is not set up properly or that AutoCAD cannot find the files it needs to operate. Refer to Chapter 2, Installing and Configuring Your Software, for more information about the batch files you need for each program. ■

The AutoCAD Screen

Your computer display screen should look similar to Figure 1.1, which shows AutoCAD's drawing editor. When you are first starting out, it is important to familiarize yourself with the six important screen areas.

■ ***Warning:*** If your screen does not look similar to Figure 1.1, be sure that you have configured AutoCAD properly for your computer system. Refer to Chapter 2, Installing and Configuring Your Software, in Part 1, Getting Started. ■

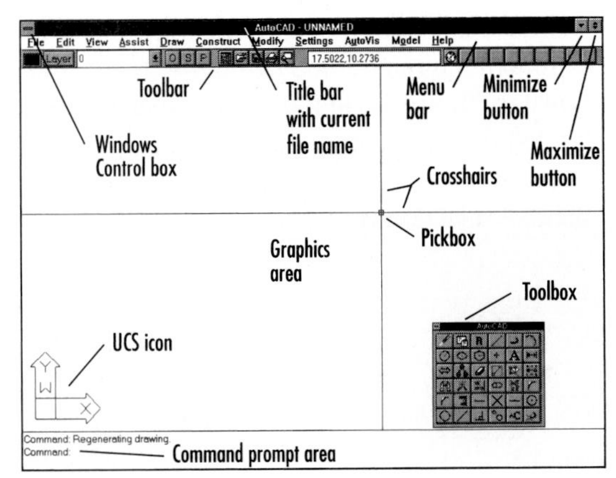

Figure 1.1

The Graphics Area: The *graphics area* is the central part of the screen, which you use to create and display drawings.

The Graphics Cursor or Crosshairs: The *cursor*, or *crosshairs*, shows the location of your pointing device in the graphics area of the screen. You use the graphics cursor to draw, select, or pick menu items. The cursor is displayed differently depending on the command or option selected.

The Command Prompt Area: The *command prompt area* takes up one or three lines at the bottom of the screen, depending on your hardware configuration. Pay close attention to this area because this is where AutoCAD prompts you when you need to enter information or make selections.

The User Coordinate System (UCS) Icon: The *UCS icon* helps you keep track of the current X, Y, Z coordinate system that you are using and the direction from which the coordinates are being viewed in 3D drawings.

The Toolbar Area: The top of the screen displays the *toolbar*. The toolbar shows the current drawing layer, any special modes in effect, and the X, Y coordinates of the crosshairs, as well as *buttons* for frequently used commands. From left to right on your screen you can see a box to the left of the layer name that shows the current color, which will be used for newly created drawing entities. The current layer is listed next, in this case 0. The boxed letters O, S, and P that appear to the right of the layer name are buttons you can pick to turn on the special modes Ortho, Snap, and Paper space. When one of these modes is in effect, its button is *highlighted*. To the right of the special modes buttons is the toolbox icon. You will read about the toolbox in the next section. The coordinate reference of the crosshairs location appears in a box near the center of the toolbar as two numbers with the general form *X.XXXX, Y.YYYY*. The specific numbers displayed on your screen tell you the location of your crosshairs. The remaining buttons are quick ways to invoke commonly used commands that you will learn about later. You may see fewer buttons and the buttons may be displayed in different locations on the toolbar, depending on the resolution of your computer monitor. You can customize the toolbar to make the commands you use frequently appear on the buttons. You will learn how to do this in Tutorial 5.

The Toolbox: The *toolbox* contains buttons for commonly used commands. When the cursor is positioned over an item (or button) on the toolbox, the name of the item appears in its title bar. You can move the toolbox around on your screen by picking on its title bar where you see the word AutoCAD and holding the mouse button down as you *drag* the toolbar to its new location. You can also change the shape of the toolbox by picking on the toolbox icon that appears on the toolbar at the top of the drawing area. Try picking once on the toolbox icon shown on the toolbar. Figure 1.2 shows the toolbar as a vertical strip along the left side of the screen, instead of a *floating* square. Click the toolbox icon on the toolbar once again. The toolbox strip disappears from the screen entirely. Picking the toolbox icon a third time moves it to the right-hand side of the screen. Pick it once again to return it to the floating toolbox that you can position on the screen. The toolbox is very useful because you can quickly pick commands and because it is *heads-up*; in other words, you are looking at the monitor the entire time you are using it. This usually increases the speed with which you can select commands. You can customize the toolbox to show the commands you use most frequently. You will learn to do this in Tutorial 5.

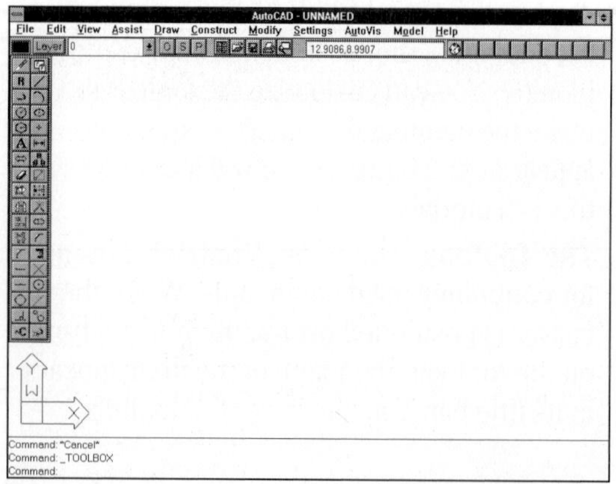

Figure 1.2

Next you will select the LINE command from the toolbox.

To draw a line you will position the cursor over the fourth item in the top row of the toolbox as shown in Figure 1.3 and press the pick button (the left mouse button).

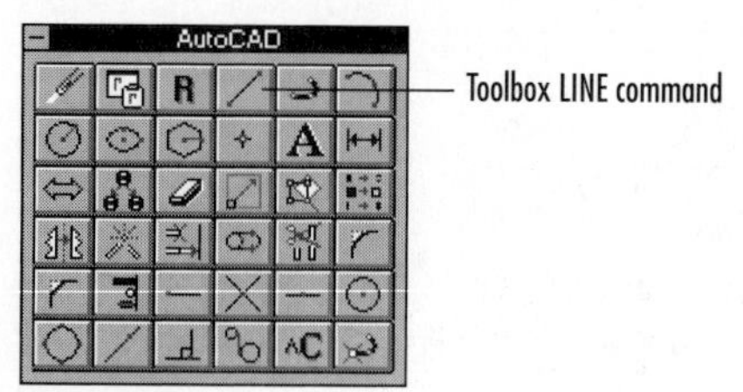

Figure 1.3

Pick: **LINE**

Your screen displays the prompt "Command:_line From point:" in the command prompt area. You can pick points from the screen or type coordinate values for a given point from the keyboard in response to command prompts. You will learn more about drawing lines later in this tutorial.

At the prompts,

From point: ***(select a point near the center of the screen by moving the crosshairs there and pressing the pick button)***

To point: ***(move the crosshairs near the upper left corner of the screen and press the pick button)***

Notice that a line is stretching from the first point to the crosshairs location while you are moving the cursor. This is called *rubberbanding*.

To point: ***(press the ↵ key or right mouse button to end the command)***

The Menu Bar

The row of words at the top of the screen is called the *menu bar*. The menu bar allows you to select commands. You pick commands by moving the cursor to the desired *pull-down* menu heading and pressing the pick button on your pointing device to pull down the available choices. To select an item from the selections that appear, position the cursor over the item and press the pick button. Use your mouse or tablet device to move the cursor to the menu bar.

Pick: **Modify**

Your screen should look similar to Figure 1.4.

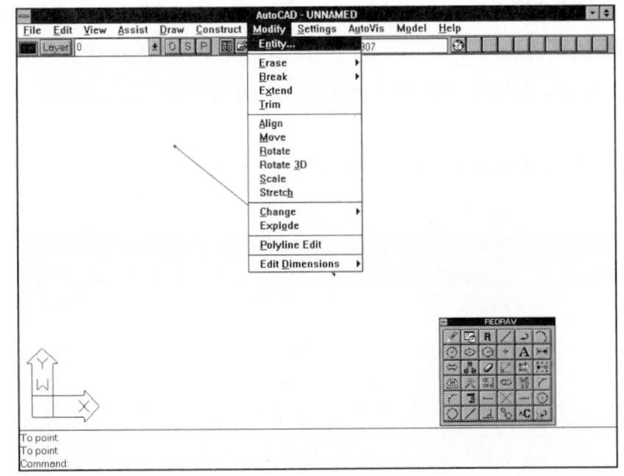

Figure 1.4

Figure 1.4 shows the results of activating the Modify selection from the menu bar. Menu bar items with a triangle after the name activate another menu when picked. Items on the menu with three dots after them cause a dialogue box to appear on the screen when picked.

To remove the menu from the screen,

Pick: ***(any area on the screen off the menu)***

Activating and Using the Screen Menu

A *screen menu* is also available. Before you can use it, you must turn it on by selecting File from the menu bar and then Preferences from the list of options that appear, as shown in Figure 1.5.

Pick: **File, Preferences**

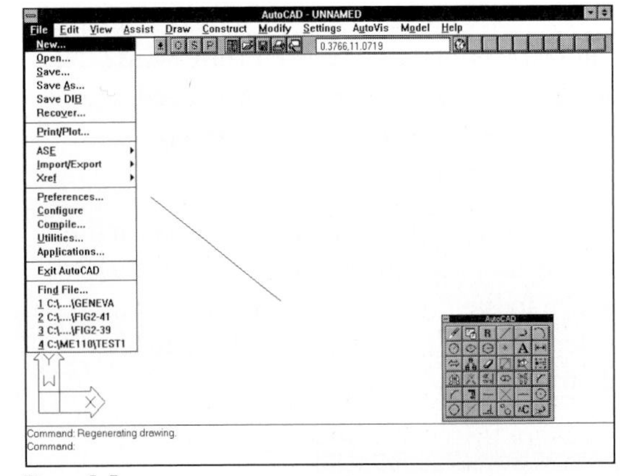

Figure 1.5

The Preferences dialogue box appears on your screen, as you see in Figure 1.6.

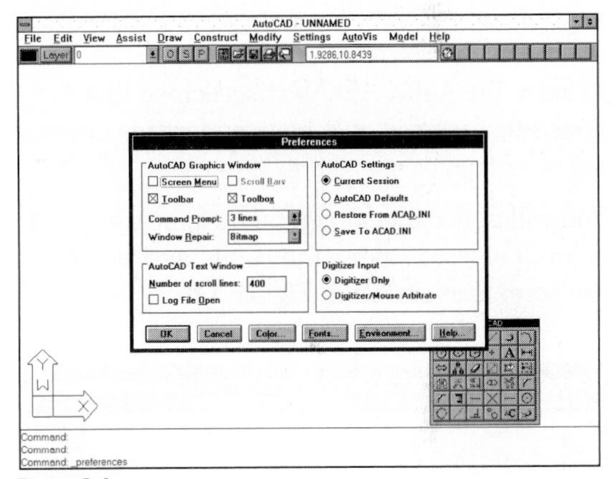

Figure 1.6

The Preferences dialogue box lets you set the size for the command prompt, turn the toolbar and toolbox on and off, turn the screen menu on and off, and set various other defaults. The Settings options in the dialogue box offer various means of handling the changes you make. The default selection makes your change for this drawing session only. The AutoCAD Defaults option clears any changes you have made and brings back the defaults shipped with the program. Save To ACAD.INI saves your changes so they will be in place each time you start AutoCAD. Restore From ACAD.INI brings back the settings you last saved.

Pick: ***(the box to the left of Screen Menu)***

Pick: **OK**

The AutoCAD Alert message appears on the screen, as shown in Figure 1.7. If you wish to return to the Preferences dialogue box in order to save the changes you have made, choose Edit Preferences.

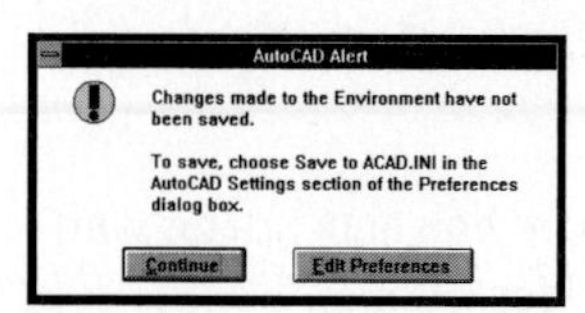

Figure 1.7

Pick: **Continue**

to leave the AutoCAD Alert screen so that your selection will only be used for this drawing session.

You will notice the screen menu appearing as a column of words along the right-hand side of the screen, as shown in Figure 1.8.

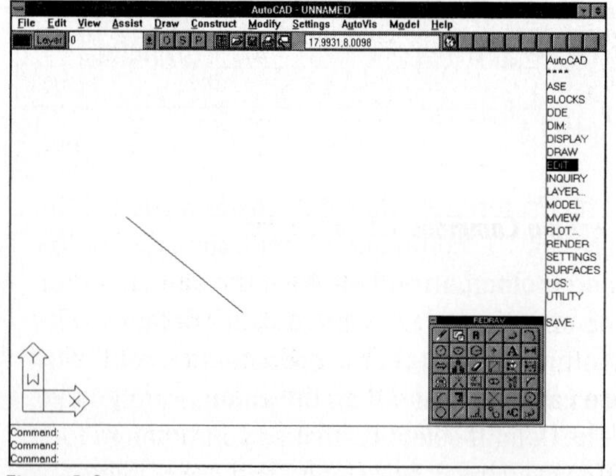

Figure 1.8

To select an item, position the cursor over the name of the item you wish to select, just as you did when using the menu bar. Notice that the selections on the screen menu appear in alphabetical order. Items that do not have a colon (:) after them are menu names, not command names. When you select a menu name, a new list of items will replace the previous list of words in the right-hand column.

Pick: **EDIT**

Notice the new items that appear on the screen menu. They are shown in Figure 1.9. You will select the ERASE command and erase the line that you drew previously.

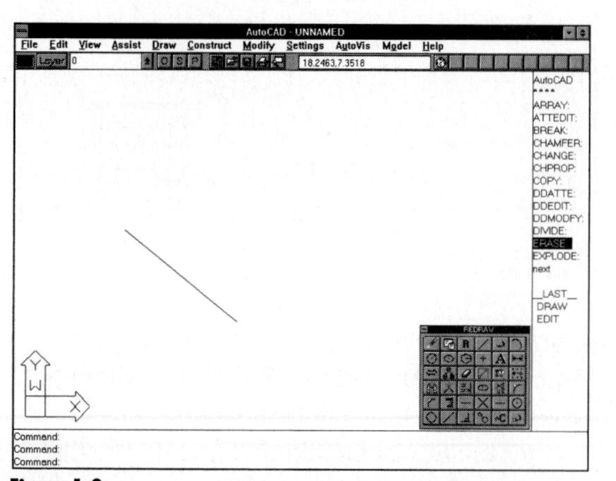

Figure 1.9

Pick: **ERASE**

The Command prompt area echoes the command you have selected and displays the prompt, "Select objects:".

Select objects: ***(pick the line by positioning the pickbox on the line entity as shown in Figure 1.10. and pressing the pick button)***

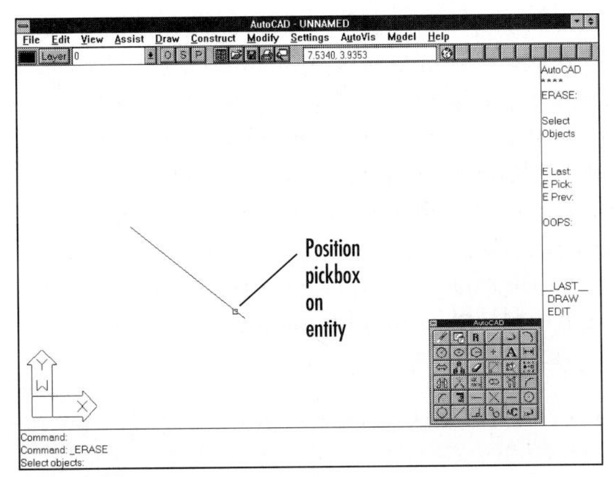

Figure 1.10

The line you have selected becomes highlighted but is not erased. When using AutoCAD, you can select more than one item to create a *selection set*. You will learn more ways to do this in Tutorial 3. When you are done selecting, you press the ↵ key or return button (right mouse button) to tell AutoCAD that you are done selecting and want the command to act on the items.

Press: ↵ ***(or the right mouse button)***

The selected line is erased from the screen. Some marks may remain on the screen; these are called *blipmarks*. Blipmarks indicate where you have selected a point from the screen. These are removed by using the REDRAW command, which you will pick from the toolbox.

Pick: **R *(the third item on the top row of the toolbox)***

Your screen is redrawn, eliminating the marks.

The word AutoCAD at the top of the screen menu has a special function. It can be highlighted and picked to bring back the original screen menu selections. This set of selections, shown in Figure 1.8, is called the *root page* of the menu. Picking AutoCAD also cancels any current command. This function is very helpful when you are first learning AutoCAD. If you are lost or confused, picking AutoCAD allows you to start with the root page of the menu again.

Pick: **AutoCAD**

Typing Commands

You can type commands directly in the command prompt area. To do this you must type the exact command name. Remember that many of the words on the menu bar are *submenu* names, not commands. Only the actual command name, not submenu names, can be typed to activate a command. Try the LINE command again, but this time type the word LINE in the command prompt area. You can type all capitals, capitals and lowercase, or all lowercase letters.

> ■ ***TIP*** Whenever you see the ↵ key in an instruction line, you must press the ↵ key, sometimes referred to as the **Enter** or **Return** key, on your keyboard to enter the command or response. ■

Command: **LINE** ↵

You will see the prompt "From point:" in the command prompt area of your screen.

Press: **Ctrl-C**

to cancel the command.

> ■ ***TIP*** You can also pick Ctrl (^C) from the last row of the toolbox. ■

Typing a Command Option Letter

If, after you have selected a command, a number of *options* are displayed at the command prompt, you can type the letter or letters that are capitalized and then press the ↵ key to select the option you wish. The options will usually also appear on the screen menu and can be highlighted and picked using the mouse.

Command Aliasing

Typing commands can be done more quickly through *command aliasing*. Any command can be given a shorter name, called an *alias*. Some sample commands already have aliases assigned to them to help you get started. These are stored in the file ACAD.PGP, which is part of the AutoCAD software, usually found in the directory \ACADWIN\SUPPORT. You can create your own command aliases by editing the file ACAD.PGP with a text editor and inserting lines that give the new, shorter names. These lines take the form *ALIAS, *COMMAND* in the ACAD.PGP file. After editing ACAD.PGP, you can use the shortened name at the AutoCAD command prompt. The following commands already have aliases created for them. When you need one of the following commands, you can type the given alias at the command prompt instead of the entire command name to save time.

Alias	Command
A	ARC
C	CIRCLE
CP	COPY
DV	DVIEW
E	ERASE
L	LINE
LA	LAYER
M	MOVE
MS	MSPACE
P	PAN
PS	PSPACE
PL	PLINE
R	REDRAW
Z	ZOOM

AutoCAD has many different ways to select any command. After you have worked through the tutorials in this book, find the methods that work best for you by experimenting. When you are working through the tutorials it is important to select the commands from the locations specified, because the command prompts and options may differ depending on how the command was selected. Hereafter, the menu will be indicated in parentheses after the item to be selected.

■ ***TIP*** If you have a digitizing tablet instead of a mouse, you may want to pick commands from the tablet menu by moving the tablet puck crosshairs over the desired menu command and pressing the pick button. Using the tablet menu can save time in selecting because you can start the command you want directly, without having to make multiple picks from the screen menus. ■

Starting a New Drawing

When AutoCAD is started, it opens a new, unnamed drawing file. You could begin drawing in this file (which is the current file you now have open) and save the drawing to a file name later. Or you can start a new file at any time. When you do, AutoCAD closes the current file and opens the one you specify. You will start a new file now and specify its file name. Select the menu bar option File and then the item New from the list that pulls down on the screen.

Pick: **File *(menu bar)*, New**

AutoCAD queries you about the current file before closing it and opening a new one, as it recognizes that changes have been made to the file that is open. You will not save this file.

Pick: **Discard Changes**

The Create New Drawing dialogue box appears on the screen. It should look like Figure 1.11.

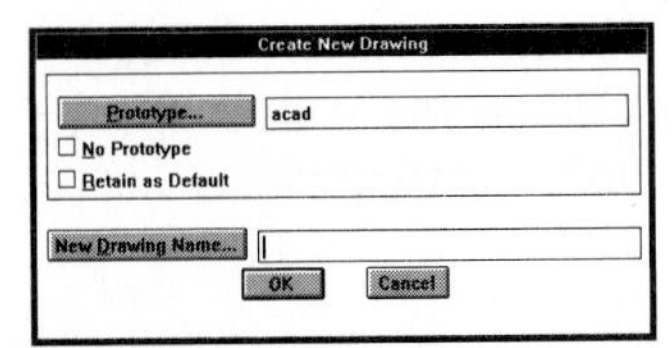

Figure 1.11

The Create New Drawing dialogue box lets you start a new drawing. You can begin the new drawing from scratch or from a *prototype drawing*. Any drawing that has already been created can be used as a prototype drawing. It can contain drawing entities or just basic settings. (You will learn more about creating and using prototype drawings in Tutorial 6.) A drawing called ACAD.DWG is the default prototype drawing provided with the AutoCAD software. A default drawing or setting is the one that is used unless you specify otherwise. The name ACAD appears in the box next to the word Prototype. . . . For your new drawing you will use the prototype drawing ACAD. Make sure that the No Prototype box is turned off (i.e., no X should appear in the box). If you start from no prototype, your drawing will lack even the basic settings that are included in ACAD.DWG. If the box is already checked, click in the box again to unselect it. Make sure the prototype drawing name, ACAD, appears in the box to the right of Prototype. . . .

Naming Drawing Files

The drawing name SHAPES will serve as a good name for this sample drawing. Move the cursor to the empty box next to New Drawing Name. . . and click the pick button on your mouse. The I-beam-shaped *typing cursor* appears in the empty box.

Type: **SHAPES**

Drawing names can contain letters, numbers, and certain other characters, such as underscore (_) and dash (-). You can use either upper- or lowercase letters. Most punctuation marks, such as comma (,), period (.), and number sign (#), are not allowed. No spaces are allowed in a file name. The tutorials in this book use drawing names that are descriptive of the drawing being created. For example, the drawing you will create for this first tutorial consists of basic shapes. Descriptive names make it easier to recognize completed drawings.

Drawing names can include a drive and directory specification. If no drive is specified, the drawing will be saved on the computer's hard drive (usually the C drive) in the *default directory.*

If a drawing is to be saved on a disk in drive A, the drawing name A:SHAPES will automatically send the drawing file to the A drive. If you choose to name your drawing so that it is sent to a floppy drive, such as drive A, it is a good practice to make sure to exit the AutoCAD program before you remove your disk from the drive. Always leave the same disk in the drive the entire time you are in AutoCAD. Otherwise, you can end up with part of your drawing not saved, which will result in an unrecoverable, corrupted drawing file. The best procedure is to create files on the hard drive, especially as it runs faster and has more space.

When you installed the data files for these tutorials, you should have already created a default working directory for AutoCAD called C:\DRAWINGS, where you will save your drawing files.

Picking the item New Drawing Name will display a dialogue box that you can use for naming your file and selecting the drive and directory from the list provided. (It can also be used to confirm the current drive and directory.)

You will use this to select your drawing directory.

Pick: **New Drawing Name**

Pick: ***(twice on C:\)***

Use the scroll arrows to locate the DRAWINGS directory, then double-click on it to open it.

Pick: ***(twice on drawing)***

Pick: **OK**

> ■ ***TIP*** If your drawing cannot be opened for use with the AutoCAD program because it is corrupted, you may be able to recover it with the selection File, Recover. . . from the menu bar. ■

AutoCAD follows the DOS rules for naming a file. Drawing file names can consist of 1 to 8 characters, followed by a *file extension*. The file extension is composed of a period, followed by 1 to 3 characters that help identify the file. All AutoCAD drawing files are automatically assigned the file extension .DWG. The .DWG drawing extension usually need not be typed with the drawing name; AutoCAD automatically adds it when the drawing is opened or saved. Unless you are using a different working directory on your system, the entire name of your drawing is C:\DRAWINGS\SHAPES.DWG.

Pick: **OK *(from the box near the bottom of the Create New Drawing dialogue)***

This returns you to the drawing editor, where you can begin work on your drawing called SHAPES. Notice that the name SHAPES now appears in the title bar area as the current file name.

■ ***Warning:*** It is suggested that all drawings be initially stored on the C or hard drive. As a drawing is being created, more and more data is being stored in the drawing file. If the file size exceeds the remaining capacity of a disk (say a floppy in drive A), a **FATAL ERROR** may occur, resulting in the loss of the entire drawing file. To prevent problems with files that may become too large for a floppy, create all drawings on the C or hard drive and then transfer the drawings to a floppy disk for storage. After completing the drawing for this tutorial, you will learn how to transfer drawings from the hard drive to a floppy disk. ■

Getting Ready to Draw

Using GRID

It is often helpful to add a *grid* to the drawing area to act as a reference for your drawing. A grid is a background area on the graphics display screen covered with regularly spaced dots. The grid does not show up in your drawing when you print or plot. You can add a grid background to the drawing area by typing the word GRID after the prompt:

Command: **GRID** ↵

The next prompt is "Grid spacing(X) or ON/OFF/Snap/Aspect <0.0000>:". This prompt displays the options available for the command, as do all AutoCAD prompts. The *default option* appears within *angle brackets*. For GRID, the starting default value is 0.0000. To set the size of a grid, type in the numerical value of the spacing and press ↵.

Grid spacing(X) or ON/OFF/Snap/Aspect<0.0000>: **.5** ↵

> ■ ***TIP*** If the chosen grid size is too small, the error message "Grid too dense to display" appears in the command prompt area and you must re-enter the GRID command to change to a larger value. If the grid values are too large, nothing appears on the screen, because the grid is beyond the visual limits of the screen. ■

Your screen should look similar to Figure 1.12, which shows a sample background grid drawn with .5-inch spacing.

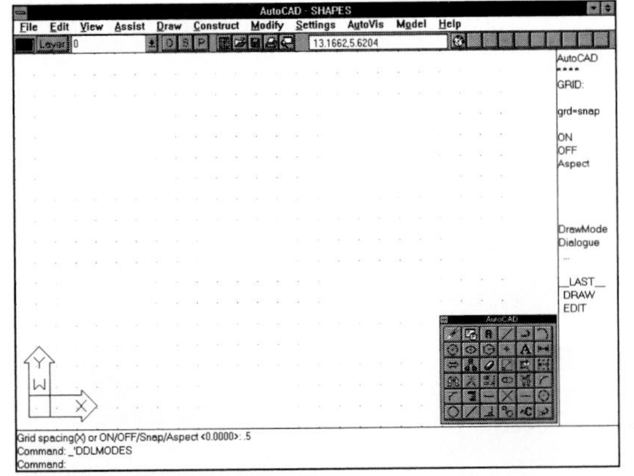

Figure 1.12

Using SNAP

The SNAP command is used to limit the movement of the cursor to make it easier to select points with a specified spacing. You can activate the SNAP command by typing the word SNAP in the command prompt area.

Command: **SNAP** (↵)

It is useful to align the SNAP function with the grid size so the snap spacing is the same as the grid spacing. Since the grid spacing is .5, as shown in Figure 1.12, specify a numerical value of .5 at the prompt to align the SNAP function with the grid.

Snap spacing or ON/OFF/Aspect/Rotate/Style <1.0000>: **.5** (↵)

> ■ ***TIP*** Notice that the SNAP button (boxed letter S) on the toolbar becomes highlighted to let you know that the SNAP mode is in effect. ■

Move the crosshairs around on the screen. Notice that instead of the smooth movement that you saw previously, the crosshairs jump or "snap" from point to point on the snap spacing. SNAP is a very helpful feature when you are locating points or distances on a drawing. If each dot on a grid is exactly .5 inch from the next dot (horizontally or vertically only, not diagonally), a line 2.00 inches long could be drawn by moving the cursor four spaces along the grid dots.

GRID and SNAP Toggles

You can turn GRID and SNAP on and off quickly by picking their respective buttons from the toolbar. The buttons on the toolbar act as a toggle: that is, when picked once the function is turned on; when picked a second time the function is turned off. GRID and SNAP can be toggled on and off during other commands.

Pick: **SNAP button *(toolbar)***

Move the crosshairs around on the screen. Notice that they have been released from the snap constraint. To turn SNAP on once again,

Pick: **SNAP button *(toolbar)***

The crosshairs jump from snap location to snap location again. Notice how the command line keeps a visual record of all the commands. Use (F7) to toggle on and off the grid.

Press: (F7)

The grid is removed from your screen. To show the grid again,

Press: (F7)

> ■ ***TIP*** GRID and SNAP can also be toggled on or off, using the (F7) and (F9) function keys respectively. Pressing (Ctrl)-G also toggles the grid on and off. ■

■ ***TIP*** If you set the snap spacing first, leaving the grid spacing at 0.0000, and then activate GRID by pressing (F7), the grid spacing is automatically set to the same value as the snap spacing. ■

Using LINE

The LINE command is used to draw straight lines between endpoints that you specify. The LINE command is located under the Draw selection on the menu bar. AutoCAD arranges menu sequences according to general spoken English syntax. This is helpful when you are trying to remember where commands are located. For example, you might say, "I want to draw a line." Since commands can be selected many different ways, the menu you are to use will be indicated in parentheses after the menu name. This will help you avoid confusion that might occur because some command choices and options are different when picked from different menus.

■ ***TIP*** If you are unsure which selection from the menu bar may contain the command you wish to use, move the cursor to the menu bar area and hold down the right mouse button. Keeping the mouse button down, move from menu to menu as you check for the location of the command. ■

■ ***TIP*** Using the toolbox and typing command aliases at the prompt are two of the fastest methods of selecting commands. ■

Pick: **Draw *(menu bar)*, Line, Segments**

Your screen should look similar to Figure 1.13, which shows the LINE command options on the screen menu.

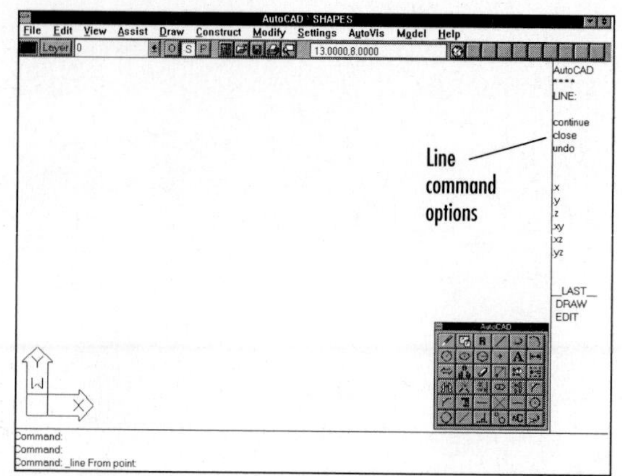

Figure 1.13

AutoCAD prompts, "Command: LINE From point", asking for the starting point of the line. Prompts requesting the input of a point can be answered in different ways: you can move the cursor into the drawing area and choose a screen location by pressing the pick button, you can set up a grid and snap alignment and use the cursor to locate specifically defined points, or you can enter X, Y, and Z *coordinate values* for the point.

■ ***TIP*** If you make an error when using any of the menu commands, press the (Ctrl) key and the letter C key simultaneously and the system will return to the command prompt. ■

Getting Help

During any command you can get help, using AutoCAD's transparent help command. A *transparent command* is one that can be executed during another command. In AutoCAD these commands are preceded by' (apostrophe). If you type "'?" at the command prompt during a command, you will enter the help dialogue box showing help for the command you are currently using. Type "'HELP" while you are at the LINE command prompt:

From point: 'HELP ↵

The AutoCAD Help dialogue shown in Figure 1.14 appears on your screen. Notice that it is already showing help for the LINE command. (Depending on your display resolution there may not be room for all of the help information; if so, use the scroll bar at the right of the help window to scroll down through the information.)

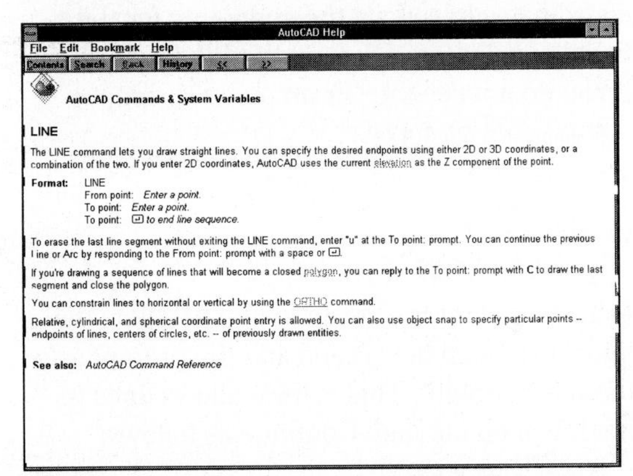

Figure 1.14

The dialogue box has a menu bar of its own that is used to access on-line help.

Pick: **Search**

The Search dialogue box shown in Figure 1.15 appears on your screen. Notice that the list of items begins with LINE, because it was the current command when you invoked transparent help. The up and down arrows at the right of the list in the middle of the dialogue box let you scroll the index list so that you can see the names that will not currently fit in the display area. The empty box above the display area allows you to type in a selection. As you type, the list in the scroll box updates to show the choices that contain the letters you have typed. For example, typing "R" displays the index items that begin with the letter R. When you have typed in "RE" of the word REDRAW, the list will begin with items that start with the letters RE. When you see the topic you would like to select, pick it so that it is highlighted and then pick inside the box containing the words Show Topics. Then select the topic from the list that appears in the box near the bottom of the screen. Highlight the desired topic and then pick inside the box with the words Go To in order to see the help for that item.

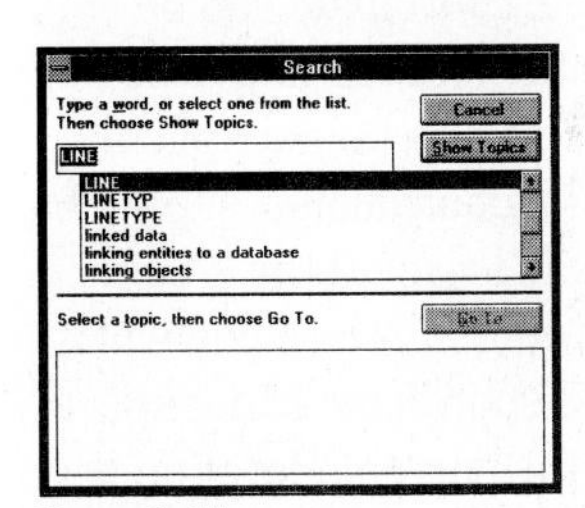

Figure 1.15

As with other windows applications, use the *Windows Control box* to close the help window.

Pick: ***(twice in the box in the top left corner of the help window)***

Double-clicking the control box in the corner of the window should close it. Try again if the window does not disappear.

You can also select HELP from the extreme right side of the menu bar. Although HELP when selected here is not context sensitive, by selecting Contents, you can see a list of the major help topics. Clicking on any of the words displayed in the highlighting color will display a further list of topics or help for the item picked.

■ ***TIP*** Pressing F1 also pops up the transparent Help dialogue box. ■

Entering Coordinates

AutoCAD stores your drawing geometry using World Coordinates, AutoCAD's default Cartesian coordinate system, where X, Y, and Z coordinate values specify locations. The UCS icon near the bottom left of your screen shows the positive X and positive Y directions on the screen. The default orientation of the Z coordinate can be thought of as specifying the location above or below the monitor. You specify a point explicitly by entering the X, Y, and Z coordinates, separated by a comma. You can leave off the Z coordinate when you are drawing in 2D, as you will be in this tutorial. If the Z coordinate is not specified, it is assumed to be the current elevation in the drawing, for which the default value is zero. For now type only the X and Y values, and the default elevation of zero for Z will be assumed.

Using Absolute Coordinates

It is often necessary to type the exact location of a specific point. When you are creating a drawing, you will want to represent the geometry of the object you are creating exactly. This is often done by typing the X, Y, and Z coordinates to locate the point. These are called the *absolute coordinates*. Absolute coordinates specify a distance to move along the X, Y, and Z axes from the origin (point 0,0,0 of the coordinate system).

■ ***TIP*** When typing in coordinates, do not enter a space between the command and the next coordinate. In AutoCAD the spacebar acts the same way as the ↵ key, to end the command. Using the spacebar as the ↵ key lets you enter commands quickly. ■

Resuming the LINE command, use absolute coordinates to specify the endpoints for the line you will draw. (Restart the LINE command if you do not see the "From point:" prompt.)

From point: **5.26,5.37** ↵

The next prompt, "To point:", asks for the endpoint of the line.

To point: **8.94,5.37** ↵

Once you enter the second point of a line, the line appears on the screen and the prompt asks for another point. This feature allows lines to be drawn end to end. Continue as follows:

To point: **8.94,8.62** ↵

To point: **5.26,8.62** ↵

The Close option listed in the Line menu joins the last point drawn to the first point drawn, thereby closing the lines and forming an area. To close the figure, type "c" in response to the prompt. (You can also pick Close from the screen menu.)

To point: **c** (↵)

Using GRID and SNAP

Use the grid and snap settings to draw another rectangle to the right of the one you just drew, as shown in Figure 1.16. (Be sure Snap is highlighted on the toolbar. If it is not, pick the boxed S from the toolbar or press (F9) to turn on SNAP.)

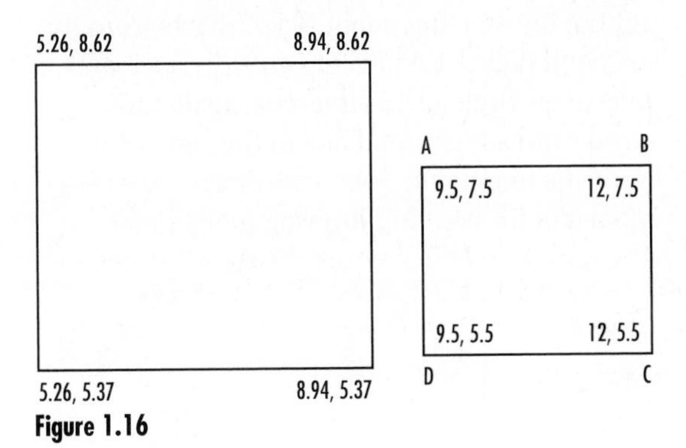

Figure 1.16

Pick: **LINE (*toolbox*)**

■ ***TIP*** You can **restart** the last command by pressing the (↵) key, the spacebar, or the right mouse button. Since LINE was the last command used, you could have pressed (↵) or the spacebar to restart the LINE command. Using these shortcuts will help you produce drawings in less time. ■

On your own, choose a starting point on the grid by moving the cursor to point A, as shown in Figure 1.16, and pressing the pick button.

Create the 2.5" horizontal line by moving the cursor 5 spaces to the right and pressing the pick button to select point B.

Complete the rectangle on your own by drawing a vertical line 4 spaces (2.00") long to point C, and another horizontal line 5 spaces (2.5") long to point D. Then use the Close command option to return to the first point.

Using Last Point

AutoCAD always remembers the last point that was specified. Often you will find it necessary to specify a point that is exactly the same as the previous point. The @ symbol on your keyboard is AutoCAD's name for the last point. Try using last point entry with the LINE command.

Pick: **LINE (*toolbox*)**

From point: **2,5** (↵)

To point: **4,5** (↵)

To point: (↵)

Press: (↵) **(or the right mouse button to restart the LINE command)**

From point: **@** (↵)

■ ***TIP*** Once in the LINE command, you can also press the spacebar, right mouse button, or (↵) at the "From point" prompt to start your new line from the last point. ■

Your starting point is now the last point that you entered in the previous step (4,5).

Using Relative X, Y Coordinates

Relative coordinates allow you to select a point at a known distance from the last point specified. To do this, you must precede your X, Y coordinate values with @. Continuing the LINE command from above,

To point: **@0,3** ↵

Notice that your line is drawn 0 units in the X direction and 3 units (6 spaces on the grid) in the positive Y direction from the last point specified, which was 4,5. To complete the shape,

To point: **@–2,0** ↵

To point: **@0,–3** ↵

To point: ↵ ***(to end the command)***

Your screen should look similar to Figure 1.17.

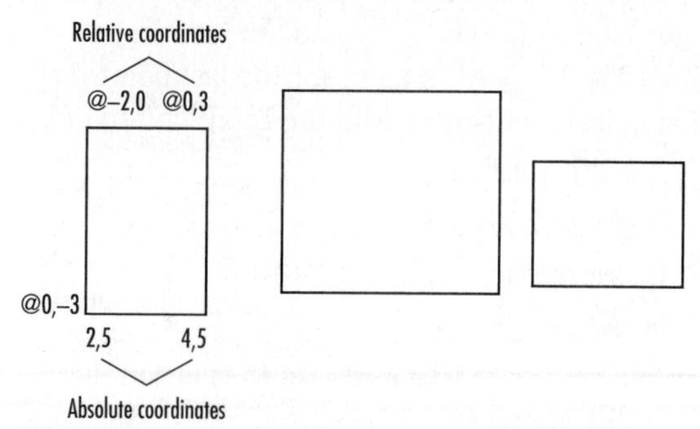

Figure 1.17

Using Polar Coordinates

When prompted to enter a point, you can specify the point using *polar coordinates.* Polar coordinate values use the input format *@DISTANCE<ANGLE.* When you are using the default decimal units, no units for the angle and length need be specified. Later in this tutorial you will learn how to select different units of measure for lengths and angles. When you are using relative coordinates, each new input is calculated relative to the last point entered. The default system for measuring angles in AutoCAD is that a horizontal line to the right of the current point is defined as zero degrees. As shown in Figure 1.18, angular values are positive in the counterclockwise direction. Both distance and angle values may be negative. Figure 1.18 also shows an example of lines drawn using relative polar coordinates. Using relative coordinate entry, a line is drawn from the starting point at the distance and angle specified. In the figure, the line labeled 1 goes from the start point a distance of 3 units at an angle of 30 degrees. Notice that the default is that the angle is measured from a horizontal line to the right of the starting point. Line 2 starts from the last point of line 1 and is drawn a distance of 2 units at an angle of 135 degrees, again measured from a horizontal line to the right of the line's starting point. Polar coordinates are very important for creating drawing geometry.

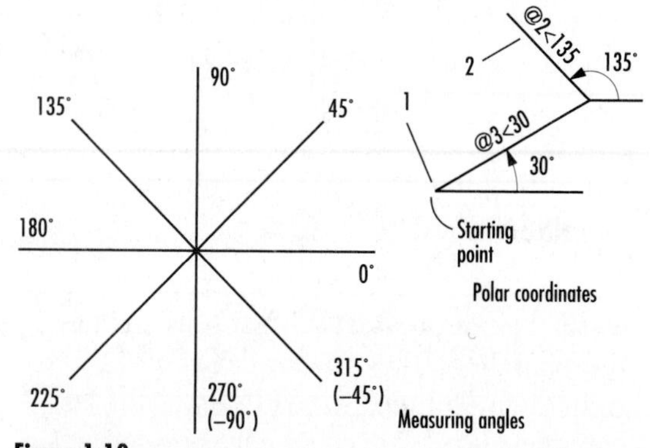

Figure 1.18

You will now draw a rectangle, using polar coordinate values. The starting point for this rectangle is specified in Figure 1.19. Use the menu bar to select the LINE command. Draw a horizontal line 3.5" to the right of the starting point by responding to the prompts:

Pick: **Draw *(menu bar),* Line, *Segments***

From point: ***(pick point A, coordinates 1.0,4.0)***

To point: **@3.5<0** ↵

Complete the rectangle, using polar coordinate values.

To point: **@2<–90** ↵

> ■ ***TIP*** Picking once on the coordinates displayed on the toolbar toggles the display so that the coordinates do not change when you move the crosshairs. If you are in a command, like the LINE command, the second time you pick on the coordinate display changes to show the length and angle from the last point picked. This can be very useful in helping to determine approximate distances and angles for polar coordinate entry. The F6 function key or Ctrl D also toggles the coordinate display. ■

To point: **@3.5<180** ↵

To point: **c** ↵ ***(to select the Close option)***

> ■ ***TIP*** If you select a wrong point while in the LINE command, you can back up one endpoint at a time by selecting the UNDO option on the LINE command or typing "U" ↵. Make sure you are in the "To point:" prompt. ■

■ ***Warning:*** UNDO functions differently if picked as a command. If you select UNDO when you are in the "Command:" prompt, entire command sequences may be undone. If necessary, you can use REDO to return something that has been undone; however, REDO only restores the last thing undone. ■

Your drawing should look like Figure 1.19.

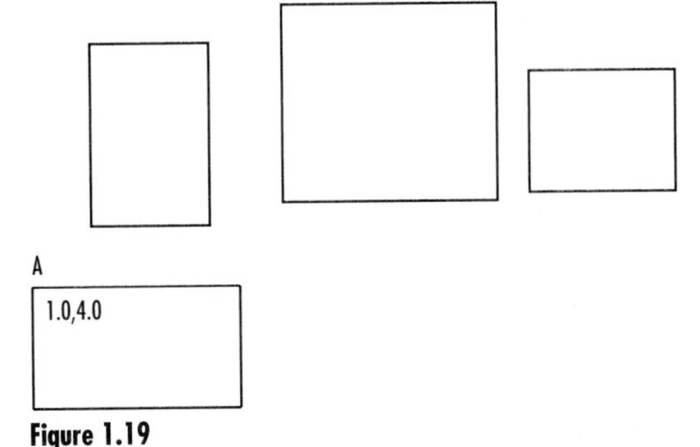

Figure 1.19

Using the ERASE Command

The ERASE command is used to remove entities from a drawing. The ERASE command is located under Modify on the menu bar and on the EDIT screen menu (the EDIT screen menu is completely different from the Edit selection on the menu bar). Also, you can select the icon (or picture symbol) of an eraser from the toolbox to start the ERASE command.

> ■ ***TIP*** Typing "E" and pressing ↵ will start the ERASE command using the command alias. ■

Pick: **ERASE *(from the third row and third column of the toolbar)***

The prompt "Select objects:" appears in the command area. The select cursor, a small rectangle, replaces the crosshairs. You identify *entities* (or individual drawing elements) to be erased by placing the cursor over them and pressing the pick button. Each line that you have drawn is an entity.

You will erase the entities labeled A and B in Figure 1.20. Turn SNAP off (by picking the SNAP button from the toolbar) to make selecting easier.

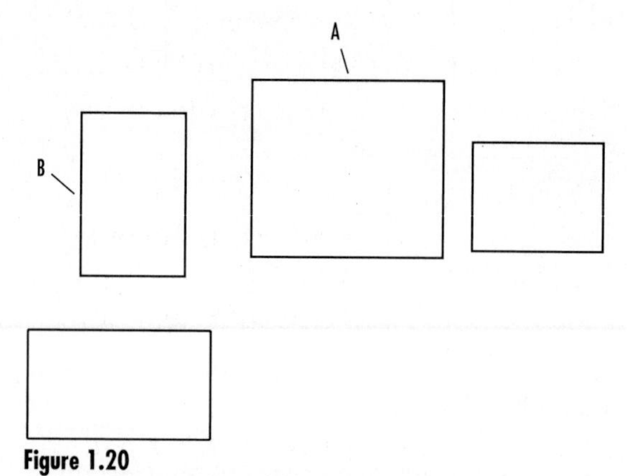

Figure 1.20

Select objects: ***(pick on line A)***

Select objects: ***(pick on line B)***

Select objects: ↵

Pressing ↵ or the right mouse button completes the selection set and erases the selected entities.

> ■ ***TIP*** Don't position the selection cursor at a point where two entities cross because you cannot be certain which will be selected. The entire entity is selected when you point to any part of it, so select the entity at a point that is not ambiguous. ■

If an entity is erased by mistake, activate the OOPS command from the ERASE screen menu.

Pick: **OOPS *(screen menu)***

The lines are restored on your screen. OOPS restores only the most recently erased entities. It will not restore entities beyond the last ERASE command. However, it will work to restore erased entities even if other commands have been used in the meantime.

Erasing with Window or Crossing

You need to clear your drawing editor to make room for new shapes. You will erase all the rectangles and squares on your screen. You can pick large groups by using the Window and Crossing selection modes.

To use AutoCAD's *implied windowing mode*, at the "Select objects:" prompt, pick a point on the screen that is not on an entity. A window-type box rubberbands from the point you picked. If the box is drawn from left to right, a window is formed that selects everything that is entirely enclosed in the box. However, if the box is drawn from right to left, the Crossing mode is used. This means that everything that either crosses the box or is entirely enclosed in the box is selected for erasure. You can use implied windowing to select entities for use with many other commands besides ERASE when you are prompted to select objects.

Implied windowing can be turned on and off. Before using it, check to see that implied windowing is turned on by picking Settings, Selection Settings. . . from the menu bar.

Pick: **Settings *(menu bar)*, Selection Settings**

The dialogue box you see in Figure 1.21 appears on your screen. For implied windowing to work, an X must appear in the box to the left of Implied Windowing. Select this mode if it is not currently selected, then pick OK to exit the dialogue box.

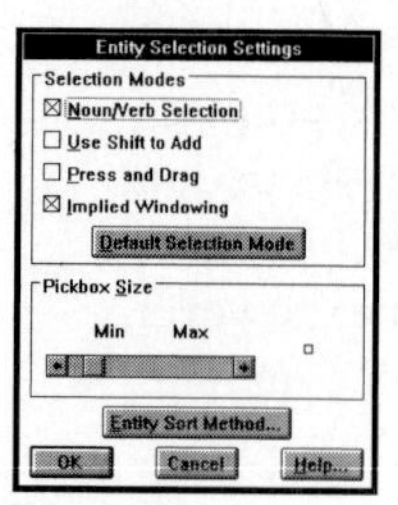

Figure 1.21

Pick: **ERASE (*toolbox*)**

Select objects: ***(pick point A in Figure 1-22 above and left of your rectangles)***

Other corner: ***(pick a point below and to the right of the rectangles, near the point labeled B)***

Select objects:

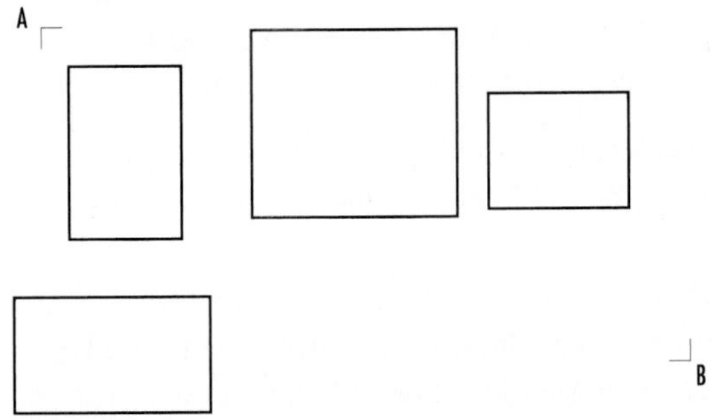

Figure 1.22

You will notice that a "window" box formed around the area specified by the upper left and lower right corners. Your screen should look like Figure 1.23.

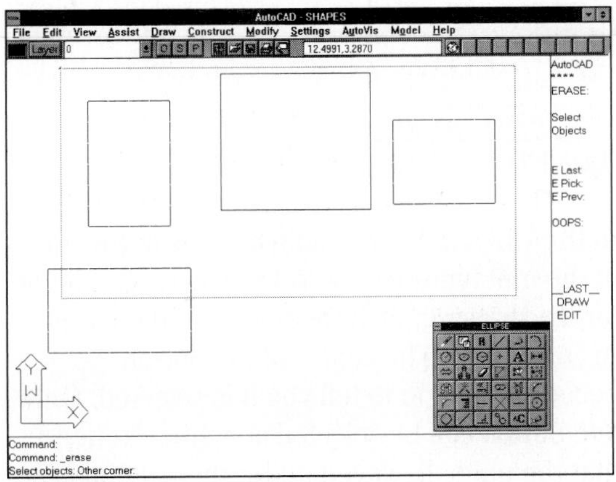

Figure 1.23

End object selection by pressing the ↵ key, erasing the selected entities:

Select objects: ↵

Only entities that are entirely within the window are erased. The fourth rectangle was not completely enclosed and was not erased.

Next, use the ERASE command with Crossing to erase the fourth rectangle.

Pick: **ERASE (*toolbox*)**

Select objects: ***(pick a point below and to the right of the remaining rectangle)***

Other corner: ***(pick a point above and to the left of the rectangle)***

Select objects: ↵

The remaining rectangle is erased from the drawing.

Using REDRAW

The REDRAW command removes the excess marks added to the drawing screen when you are drawing objects and restores objects partially erased while you are editing other objects. REDRAW is the R on the toolbox. The REDRAW command is also located under the DISPLAY screen menu and under View on the menu bar. The REDRAW command has no prompts; it is simply activated by the pick button.

Pick: **R (*toolbox*)**

Notice how the grid and lines are refreshed on your screen.

> ■ ***TIP*** You can also just type "r" at the command prompt. R is the command alias for REDRAW. ■

Next you will create a new drawing that will use engineering units. Save SHAPES first, then begin a new drawing. Use the File selection from the menu bar to do both.

Pick: **File *(menu bar)*, Save**

AutoCAD will use the QSAVE command to quickly save your drawing to the default file name. QSAVE can be used whenever you wish to save the file to the existing default file name. When you create a new drawing with the File, New option, you assign the file name at that time. Because the name is already created, you do not need to tell AutoCAD the name of the file again at the time you save, so you can use the QSAVE command. If no default file name exists, AutoCAD displays the Save Drawing As dialogue box, which you can then use to name and save your drawing. Your drawing will be saved to the file name SHAPES, which you specified when you started the drawing. Now start a new drawing:

Pick: **File *(menu bar)*, New**

Name your new drawing C:\DRAWINGS\PLOTPLAN in the empty box to the right of New Drawing Name. . . in the Create New Drawing dialogue box. Use the default prototype drawing ACAD.

Pick: **OK *(to leave the dialogue box)***

Setting the Units

AutoCAD allows you to work in the type of *units* that are appropriate for your drawing. The default units are decimal. You can change the type of units for lengths to *architectural units* that appear in feet and fractional inches, *engineering units* that appear in feet and decimal inches, *scientific units* that appear in exponential format, or *fractional units*. When you use architectural or engineering units, one drawing unit is equal to one inch; to specify feet you must type the feet mark after the numerical value (examples: 20.2' or 20'2" or 20'-2"). For the other types of units, you can think of them as representing any type of "real-world" measurement you wish: decimal miles, furlongs, microns, or anything else you desire. When the time comes to plot the drawing, you determine the final relationship between your drawing database, in which you create the object the actual size it is in the real world, and the paper plot.

Angular measurements can be given in decimal degrees; degrees, minutes and seconds; gradians; radians; or surveyors' units, such as the bearing N45d0'0"E.

Use the Settings selection from the menu bar to select the Units Control dialogue.

Pick: **Settings *(menu bar)*, Units Control. . .**

The Units Control dialogue should appear on your screen, as shown in Figure 1.24.

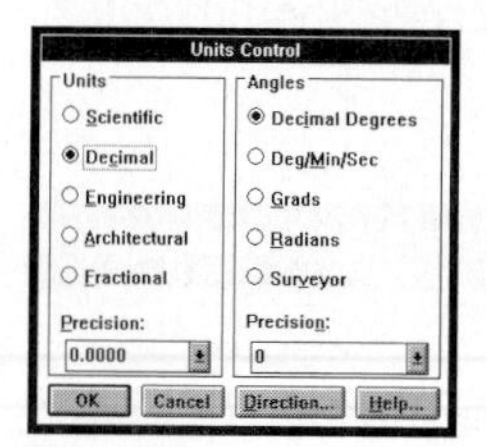

Figure 1.24

In the Units area, the radio buttons to the left of the unit types let you select the type of units for the drawing. Pick the button to the left of Architectural. The center of the button becomes filled in to tell you it is selected. Only one button can be selected at a time. Notice that the units displayed under the heading Precision: on the left side of the dialogue box change to architectural units. Pick the button for Decimal once again. Notice that the units in the Precision: area change back to decimal units. The dimensions for the plot plan you will create will be in decimal feet. Next, pick on the number 0.0000 displayed in the box below Precision:. The choices for length unit precision pull down below where you picked, as shown in Figure 1.25.

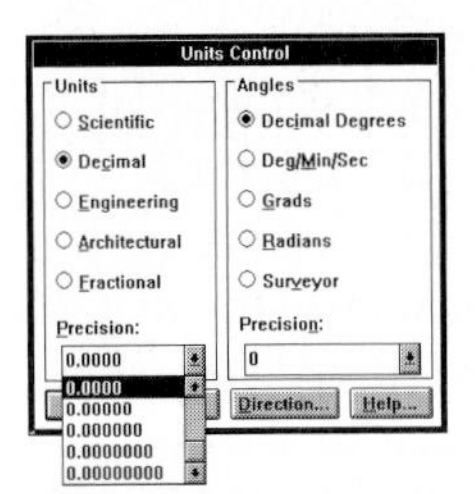

Figure 1.25

Pick on the up arrow, or use the slider box, in order to scroll the list of precisions to show more selections. Pick on the selection **0.00** to set the display to show two decimal places. When specifying coordinates and lengths, you can still type a value from the keyboard with up to 14 decimal places of precision and AutoCAD's drawing database will keep track of your drawing with this accuracy. Units precision determines the display of the units on your screen and in the prompts, not the accuracy internal to the drawing. Though AutoCAD keeps track internally to at least 14 decimal places, only eight decimal places of accuracy can appear on the screen.

The right side of the dialogue box controls the type and precision of angular measurements. Select the button for **Surveyor angles**. Notice that the display in the Precision: area in the right side of the dialogue box changes to list the angle as a bearing. When this mode is active, you can type in surveyors' angles. AutoCAD will measure the angle from the specified direction, North or South, toward East or West, as specified. If you wish to see more precision for the angles, pick on the box containing the precision N 0d E. The list of the available precisions shown in Figure 1.26 pulls down, allowing you to select to display degrees, minutes, and seconds.

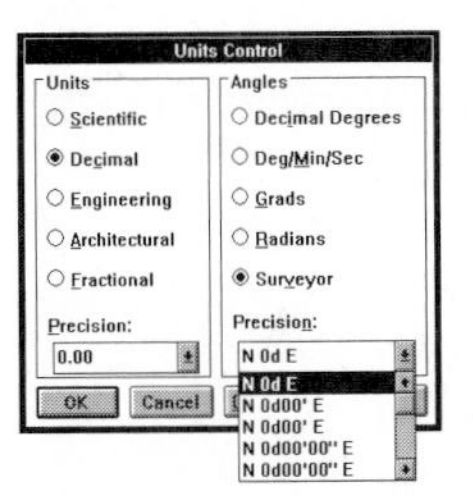

Figure 1.26

The default direction of North is straight toward the top of the screen. Angles are measured in a counterclockwise direction, starting from a horizontal line to the right as 0 degrees. You can change this by picking on the Direction selection. Leave the direction set at the default of 0 degrees towards East. Be sure your angles are set to Surveyor before you go on.

Pick: ***OK (to exit the dialogue box)***

Look at the toolbar. You will see that the coordinate display near the top of the screen has changed to show two instead of four places after the decimal.

Sizing Your Drawing

In AutoCAD you always create your drawing geometry in *real-world units.* This means that if the object is 10' long, you make it exactly 10' long in the drawing database. If it is a few millimeters long, you create the drawing so that it is in millimeters. After the drawing geometry has been created, then you can decide on the scale in which you wish to plot your final hardcopy drawing on the sheet of paper. This is one of the powerful features of CAD. You can create very exact drawings, from which you can make accurate measurements and calculations using the computer. Also, you can plot the final drawing to any scale, saving a great deal of time because you don't have to remake drawings just to have different scaling, as you would with paper drawings.

For your plot plan drawing, you need to create a larger drawing area to accommodate the site plan shown in Figure 1.27.

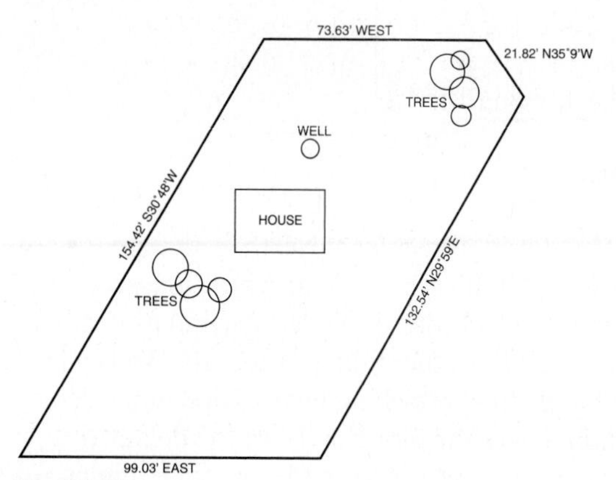

Figure 1.27

Using LIMITS

The AutoCAD command LIMITS sets the size of your drawing. LIMITS can also be turned off if you do not want to preset the size of the drawing. Use LIMITS from the Settings menu bar to change the overall size of the drawing to reflect the metric drawing units.

Pick: **Settings *(menu bar)*, Drawing Limits**

Reset Model Space Limits

ON/OFF/<Lower left corner> <0.00,0.00>: ↵

(to accept default of 0,0)

Upper right corner <12.00,9.00>: **300,225** ↵

Notice that the prompt read, "Reset Model Space Limits". The default space where you create your drawing geometry or model is called model space. This is where you accurately create real-world-size models. Later, in Tutorial 3, you will learn to use paper space, where you lay out views like you do on a sheet of paper. Model space and paper space can have different sizes set with the LIMITS command.

Using ZOOM

The ZOOM command is used to enlarge areas of the drawing on your screen. It is different from the SCALE command, which actually makes the selected items larger or smaller in your drawing database. You can use the ZOOM command when you wish to enlarge something on the screen so that it is easier to see the details. You can also zoom out so that objects appear smaller on your display. ZOOM is located on the DISPLAY screen menu and on the View pull-down menu, although all of the options of the command are not available from the pull-down selection.

ZOOM, All

The ZOOM, All function displays the drawing limits, or shows all of the drawing entities on the screen, depending on which is larger. You can select View, ZOOM, All from the menu bar to show this larger area on your display.

Pick: **View *(menu bar)*, Zoom, All**

Your display redraws with a larger area. Move the crosshairs to the upper right-hand corner of the screen. You will see that the toolbar displaying the location of the crosshairs indicates that the size of the drawing area has changed to reflect the limits of the drawing.

■ ***TIP*** If the toolbar does not display a larger size, check to see that you set the limits correctly and that you picked Zoom, All. Make sure that the coordinates are turned on by pressing F6 until you see them change as you move the mouse. ■

Now set the grid spacing larger so that you can see the grid on your screen.

Command: GRID ↵

Grid spacing(x) or ON/OFF/Snap/Aspect <0.00>: 10 ↵

Adapting for Architecture

Unlike decimal engineering drawings, where typical grid assignments are 10, 5, 1, and .5, a grid spacing of 2' and snap spacing of 6" are good default values to use in starting new architectural drawings. The snap and grid can be changed as better values become apparent. ■

You will draw the site boundary shown in Figure 1.27, using absolute and polar coordinates as directed. The starting point for the lower left corner of the site will be 50,30. Using the toolbox,

Pick: **LINE *(toolbox)***

From point: 50,30 ↵

To point: @99.03<E ↵

To point: @132.54<N29d59'E ↵

To point: @21.82<N35d9'W ↵

To point: @73.63<W ↵

To point: c ↵

Your screen should look like Figure 1.28.

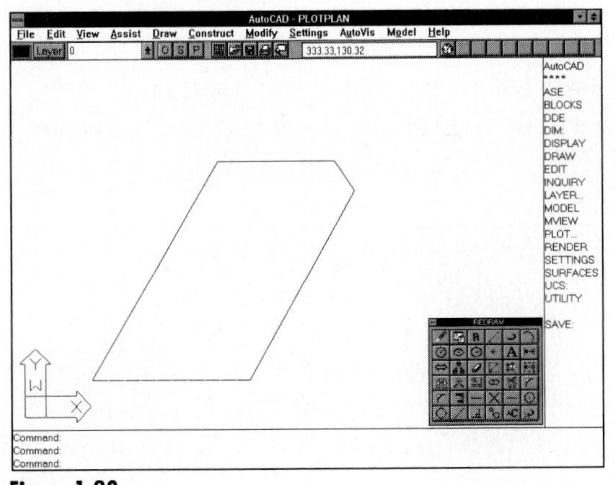

Figure 1.28

Using RECTANGLE

Next you will draw a rectangle using AutoCAD's RECTANGLE command, found under Draw on the menu bar.

Pick: **Draw *(menu bar)*, Rectangle**

Type in the coordinates for the corners of the rectangle. In the command line area you will see the prompt:

First corner: 120,95 ↵

The first point acts as an anchor for the first corner of the rectangle. As you move the crosshairs away from the point, a box stretches from the first point to the current location of the crosshairs. The screen displays the prompt:

Other corner: 150,115 ↵

Your screen should look similar to Figure 1.29.

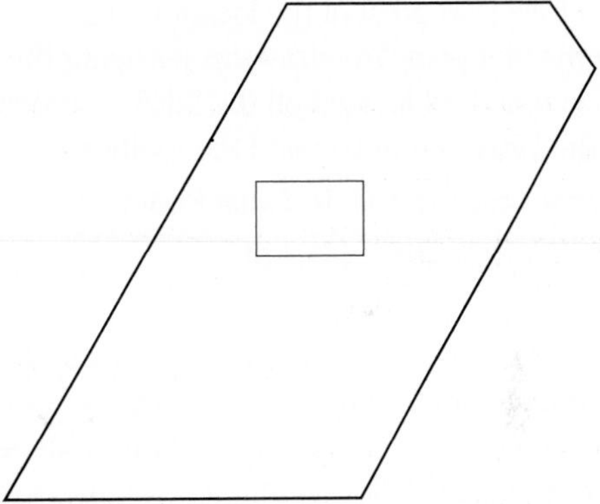

Figure 1.29

Adapting for Architecture

The RECTANG command is useful in creating simplified spaces for quick spatial analysis in architectural drawings. Accurate room sizes can quickly be generated to study various configuration possibilities. Floor plans can even be developed from these early drawings by editing them with techniques you will learn in Tutorial 2. ■

Saving Your Drawing

Having completed the site boundary, you should now save the drawing on your disk. It is a good practice to save your drawing any time you have completed a major step or every 10 to 15 minutes. This way, if your computer crashes, you will not have lost more than a few minutes of work. Also, if you make a mistake that you don't know how to correct, you can discard your drawing changes and start from the saved version.

Pick: **File *(menu bar)*, Save**

AutoCAD saves your file to the name you assigned when you began the new drawing, PLOTPLAN.DWG.

Drawing Circles

Draw a circle to represent the location of the well on the plot plan. You draw circles using the CIRCLE command located on the DRAW screen menu, the Draw menu bar, and the toolbox.

Pick: **Draw *(menu bar)*, Circle, Center Radius**

3P/2P/TTR/<Center point>: **145,128** ↵

As the cursor is moved away from the center point, a circle continually reforms, using the distance from the center you selected to the cursor location as the diameter value. Type the value to specify the exact size for the circle's radius.

Diameter/<Radius>: **3** ↵

Now draw some circles to represent trees or shrubs in the plot plan. You will specify the locations for the trees by picking from the screen.

Pick: **CIRCLE *(toolbox)***

■ ***TIP*** The icon for the CIRCLE command is the second symbol in the first column on the toolbox. As you would expect, the icon looks like a circle; notice that it shows the center and a point on the radius. This indicates that the default method circles are drawn by is to specify their center and radius. ■

3P/2P/TTR/<Center point>: ***(pick a point for the center of circle 1, as shown in Figure 1.30)*** ↵

Diameter/<Radius>: ***(move the crosshairs away from the point you picked, until the circle appears similar to Figure 1.30, and press the pick button)*** ↵

On your own, draw the remaining circles representing trees, using the method you have learned.

Your drawing should look similar to Figure 1.30.

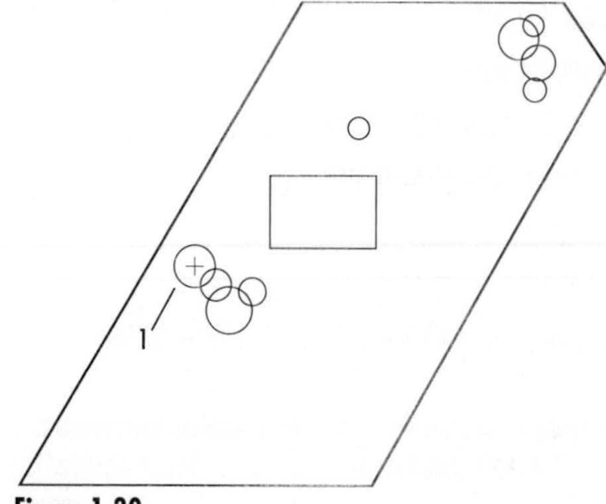

Figure 1.30

Using DTEXT

The DTEXT command is used to add text, words, or numbers to a drawing. DTEXT is located on the Draw menu. You can select Draw from the menu bar or from the screen menu by picking the word DRAW at the lower end of the screen menu. DTEXT appears as the letter "A" on the standard toolbox.

Pick: ***DTEXT (toolbox)***

The prompt "Justify/Style/<Start Point>:" is in the command prompt area. Unless you specify otherwise, text is added to the right of a designated starting point. Text can also be centered about a point or added to the left of a point through the use of the Justify option. To enter text in response to the DTEXT prompt, specify a starting point, using the cursor and pick button. You will add text labeling the lengths and bearings of the lot lines shown in the plot plan. Start with the bottom lot line by picking a point below the lot line.

Command: DTEXT Justify/Style/<Start Point>: ***(select a point below the bottom lot line)***

The prompt is "Height<0.20>:". The .20 value is the default text height. Since the current drawing must be scaled to fit on a piece of paper, this height is much too small. A height of 3 will create text that is in proportion with the drawing.

> ■ ***TIP*** To determine the necessary text height, you must know the size of paper and the scale at which you will plot the final drawing. In Tutorial 3 you will learn to use paper space to set up scaling and text for plotting. If you are unsure what text height to use, move the crosshairs on the screen and read the coordinate display on the toolbar. Use the lengths shown to get an idea of an appropriate size for your text. ■

Height<0.20>: **3** ↵

The default value of E in the "Rotation angle <E>:" prompt generates horizontal (East) text. You can specify any angle. Text on technical drawings is usually drawn horizontally and is called unidirectional text. Unidirectional dimensioning will be explained further in Tutorial 10. To accept the default rotation angle,

Rotation angle <E>: ↵

AutoCAD is now ready to accept the typed-in text.

Text: **99.03′ EAST** ↵

Text: ↵

You can type the text just as you would with a word processing program. AutoCAD does not wrap text, so you must designate the end of each line by pressing the ↵ key. If you make a mistake before exiting DTEXT, backspace to erase the text. After exiting the DTEXT command, you can use the command DDEDIT to make corrections to lines of text. The "Text:" prompt always appears after every line of text. Press the ↵ key without entering any text (a null reply to the prompt) to clear the DTEXT command. When you exit DTEXT, AutoCAD recreates the text as a permanent entity. Your screen should look like Figure 1.31.

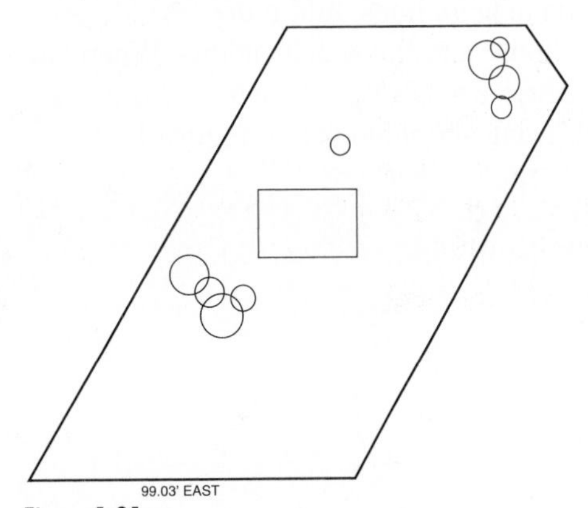

Figure 1.31

Add the text labeling the length and angle for the right-hand lot line. You will type the special text item %%d to create the degrees symbol. Type the line of text with %%d in place of the degree symbol. When you finish typing in the text and press (↵), AutoCAD replaces %%d with a degree symbol. You will also specify a rotation angle for the text so that it is aligned with the lot line.

Pick: **DTEXT *(toolbox)***

Justify/Style/<Start Point>: ***(pick a point slightly to the right of the right-hand lot line)***

Height <3.00>: (↵)

Rotation angle <E>: **N29d59'E** (↵)

> ■ ***TIP*** You can also specify the rotation by picking when the line rubberbanding from the point you picked for the text location is oriented at the rotation angle you desire. ■

Text: **132.54' N29%%d59'E** (↵)

Text: (↵)

The text should appear in your drawing aligned with the lot line.

On your own, use the techniques that you have learned to add the bearings and distances for the remaining lot lines. Add more text identifying the house and the well locations. When you are finished, use QSAVE to save your drawing. Your drawing should look like Figure 1.32.

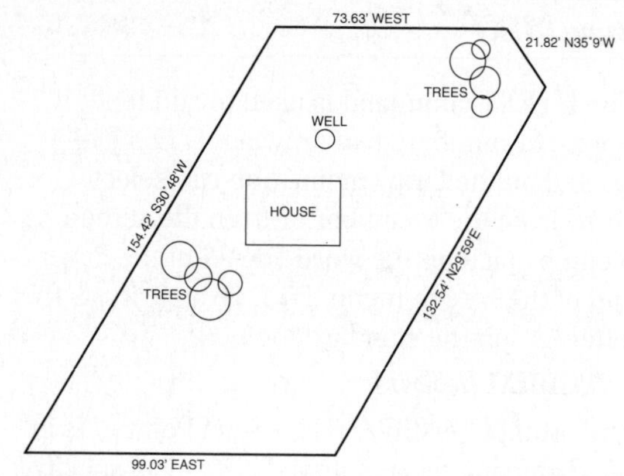

Figure 1.32

DDEDIT

The DDEDIT command allows you to edit text using a dialogue box. DDEDIT is located under EDIT on the screen menu.

Pick: **EDIT *(screen menu)*, DDEDIT**

Pick: ***(a line of text)***

After you activate the command, you are prompted to select a text entity (line of text) by pointing. The selected text appears in a dialogue box like the one in Figure 1.33. You can add or change text without erasing the entire line. Use the arrow keys on your keyboard to move within the line of text without deleting. Use the (DEL) key to delete the letter to the right of the cursor. Use the BACKSPACE key to delete the letter to the left of the cursor. You can also retype the entire line.

Pick: **OK**

to exit the DDEDIT dialogue box when you have made any necessary corrections to your text.

<Select a TEXT or ATTDEF object>/Undo: (↵) ***(to exit the command)***

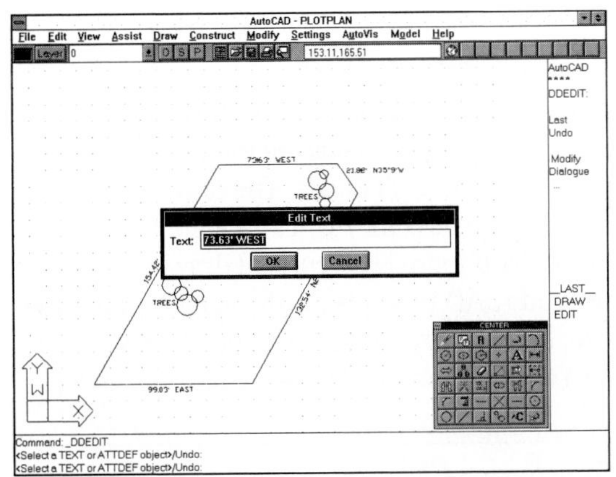

Figure 1.33

Adapting for Architecture

Text can be simplified and abbreviated in the design development phase, then as information becomes more concrete, you can use DDEDIT to alter the text accordingly. For example, room names can be supplemented with numbers or square footage as that information becomes available, without the bother of aligning new text. ■

Setting the Text Style

The STYLE command allows you to select the font you wish to use prior to adding text to your drawing. A text font determines the shapes used to draw text characters. AutoCAD supplies several fonts that can be used to create "text styles." These fonts are illustrated when you select Draw, Text, Set Style. . . from the menu bar. A text style is composed of several characteristics that will be presented after you select a new font from the list of available fonts. Once you create a style, that style remains current for all text until you set a new style as the current one. The font that appears the best for engineering drawings is called Roman Simplex. You will set it as the current font.

Pick: **Draw *(menu bar)*, Text, Set Style**

The dialogue box shown in Figure 1.34 appears on your screen. Pick ROMAN SIMPLEX as the font to make current. Pick OK to return to the command prompt for the remaining selections.

■ ***Warning:*** You will accept the default text height of 0.00. Setting the text height in the STYLE command means that you are not prompted for the height of the text in the DTEXT command. Setting the height to something other than zero can also make it difficult to size text correctly when you add dimensions to your drawing. ■

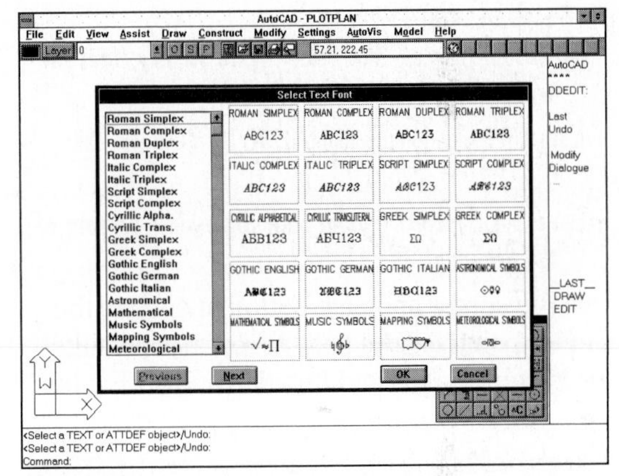

Figure 1.34

Font file <txt>: romans Height <0.00>: (↵)

Width factor <1.00>: (↵)

Obliquing angle <0d0'>: (↵)

Backwards? <N>: (↵)

Upside-down? <N>: (↵)

Vertical? <N>: (↵)

ROMANS is now the current text style.

Adapting for Architecture

AutoCAD comes with two architectural lettering fonts, country and city blueprint. These hand-lettering style fonts can be used to make drawings appear more hand-crafted. Keep in mind that architectural and engineering drawings rarely use slanted fonts as a convention; therefore you will usually set the obliquing angle to 0 in the STYLE command. ■

Any new text added to your drawing will use the current text style until you set a different style as current. You will add a title to the bottom of the drawing.

Pick: **DTEXT *(toolbox)***

DTEXT Justify/Style/<Start Point>: ***(pick Justify from the screen menu)***

Align/Fit/Center/Middle/Right/TL/TC/TR/ML/BL/BC/BR: **C** ↵

Center point: ***(select a point near the middle bottom of the drawing)***

Use the cursor and pick button to specify the Center point: for the text. Accept the defaults for Height <3.00>: and Rotation angle <E>: by pressing ↵.

Height <3.00>: ↵

Rotation angle <E>: ↵

Text: **PLOT PLAN** ↵

Text: ↵

> ■ ***TIP*** At any time you can use the UNITS command to change the measurements for lengths and angles to a different setting. If you find it awkward to enter surveyor's angles when inputting text, change the units so that angles are measured in degrees. ■

To save your drawing,

Pick: **File *(menu bar)*, Save**

The default file name is always the current drawing name. When you started the new drawing, you named it PLOTPLAN. The drawing will be saved in the directory you specified when you named it. If there is no current drawing name set, AutoCAD prompts for the name you wish to use. Remember, AutoCAD automatically adds a .DWG extension to all drawing file names.

Transferring Files

■ ***Warning:*** To complete this section you will need a blank formatted floppy disk. ■

Files can be transferred from one drive to another. To transfer a file, place a blank formatted disk in drive A. To transfer the file named PLOTPLAN from the hard drive to a floppy disk in the A: drive, you will use AutoCAD's File, Utilities pull-down menu.

Pick: **File *(menu bar)*, Utilities**

The File Utilities dialogue shown in Figure 1.35 appears on your screen. Position the arrow cursor on the selection Copy file. . . and press the pick button to select it.

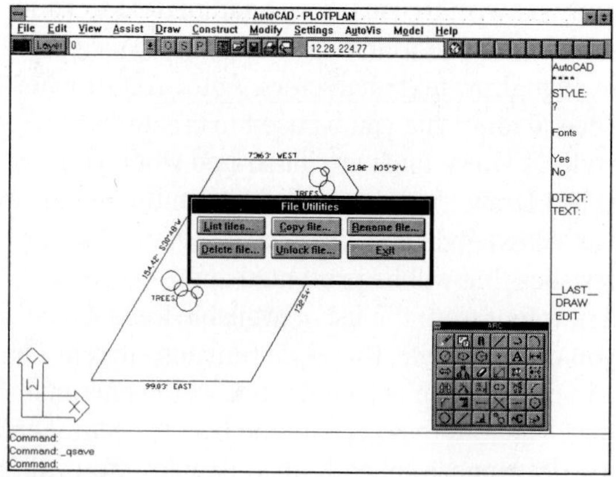

Figure 1.35

The Source File dialogue box shown in Figure 1.36 replaces the previous dialogue box on your drawing screen. Use this dialogue box to select the file you wish to copy, PLOTPLAN.DWG. Use the list of directories in the middle of the dialogue box to change to the directory where you have saved your file PLOTPLAN.DWG. To change the directory selection, position the arrow cursor over the name of the directory you wish to select and double-click the pick button. The selected directory name appears near the top of the dialogue box. If you need to step back out of a subdirectory to the root, or main, directory, double-click on the C:\ selection. If you need to select a different drive, pick inside the box under the heading Drives:. The list of available drives pulls down. If you need to select a different drive, click on its name, such as A:, B:, or C:. Once you have selected the drive and directory where your file is stored, you will see the name of your file, PLOTPLAN.DWG, in the left-hand list. Holding down the pick button while it is positioned over the arrow scrolls the directory selections down to the bottom of the list. You can also pick on the slider box and hold down the left mouse button, dragging the box up and down the scroll bar. This is a faster way to move among a long list of files. Select your drawing file as the file to copy by picking it from the list. It appears in the box near the top of the dialogue box under the heading File Name:. When you have completed this,

Pick: **OK**

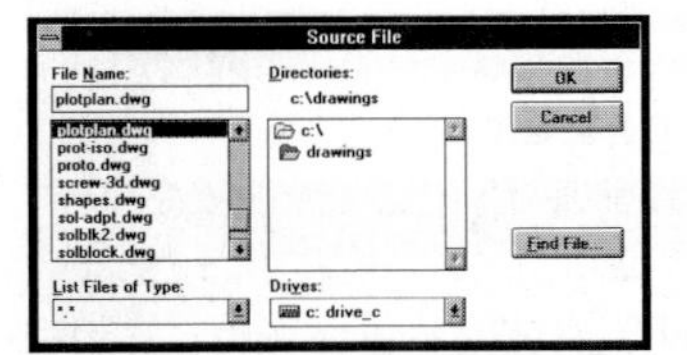

Figure 1.36

The Destination File dialogue appears on your screen, as shown in Figure 1.37. Use the procedure you have just learned to select the destination drive and directory, if needed. When you are done, position the arrow cursor over the box for File Name:, near the top of the dialogue box, and press the pick button. You will see the typing cursor appear in the box. Replace the current selection *.* (wildcard) with the name you wish the file to have, including the three-letter extension .DWG.

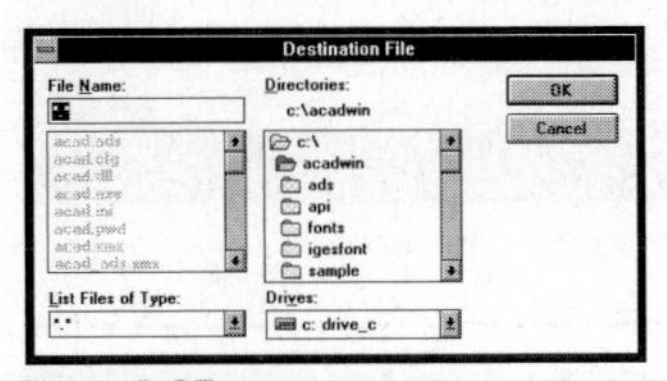

Figure 1.37

Pick: **OK** ***(to copy the file)***

The File Utilities dialogue returns, containing the message "Copied ____ bytes." The number of bytes is the file size of the drawing you copied, in this case PLOTPLAN.DWG.

Pick: **Exit** ***(to leave the File Utilities dialogue box)***

Going Further

Use the commands LIMITS and UNITS to set up some standard sheet sizes and scales for architectural drawings. You can save these drawings and call them up later to save time in starting new drawings. Example: a 24 × 36-inch drawing at 1/8"=1' would have limits of 192' × 288'. Set the grid to 2' and the snap to 6". Use the STYLE command to select the country blueprint font. Save the drawings with descriptive names that allow you to easily recall the proper file, for example, A24361-8.DWG. When starting a new drawing using this format, pick File, Open and select the appropriate drawing. Then pick File, Save As and save the drawing with a new name. When you have created some architectural default drawings, try creating a default drawing for metric mechanical drawings on an 8.5 × 11-inch format.

Exiting AutoCAD

The Exit AutoCAD selection from the File menu is used to return to the Windows Program Manager, or you can type "QUIT" in response to the "Command:" prompt. If you have not previously saved your drawing, the File, Exit AutoCAD selection prompts you to save changes, discard changes, or cancel. If you have already saved your drawing, it exits immediately. If you have not saved your changes and would like to, highlight the words Save Changes. . . in the dialogue box and press the pick button. This will save your drawing to the file name PLOTPLAN.DWG that you selected when you began the new drawing.

The system returns to the Windows Program Manager.

■ ***TIP*** The END command in AutoCAD saves the file to the current default file name and directly exits the program. However, the Save and Exit AutoCAD series eliminates unused and erased items from the drawing database, resulting in smaller file sizes. The Save, Exit AutoCAD series is thus a better practice. ■

■ ***TIP*** You can also double-click the *Windows Control box*, which you see above the File selection on the menu bar, to exit the program. ■

Now you have completed Tutorial 1.

KEY TERMS

absolute coordinates
alias
angle brackets
architectural units
blipmarks
buttons
command aliasing
command prompt area
coordinate values
cursor (crosshairs)
default option
default directory
drag
engineering units
entities
file extension
floating
fractional units
graphics area
grid
heads-up
highlight
implied windowing mode
menu bar
options
polar coordinates
prototype drawing
pull-down menu
real-world units
relative coordinates
root page
rubberbanding
scientific units
screen menu
selection set
submenu
toolbar
toolbox
transparent command
typing cursor
UCS icon
units
Windows Control box

KEY COMMANDS

Circle
Dynamic Text
Dynamic Dialogue Edit Text
End
Erase
Grid
Help
Limits
Line
New Drawing
Oops
Quit
Rectangle
Redraw
Save
Snap
Style
Undo
Zoom

EXERCISES

Redraw the following shapes. If dimensions are provided, use the dimensions and create your drawing to show the exact geometry of the part shown. The letter M after an exercise number means that the given dimensions are in millimeters (metric units). If no letter follows the exercise number, the dimensions are in inches. The Ø symbol indicates that the following dimension is a diameter. Do not include dimensions or centerlines on the drawings.

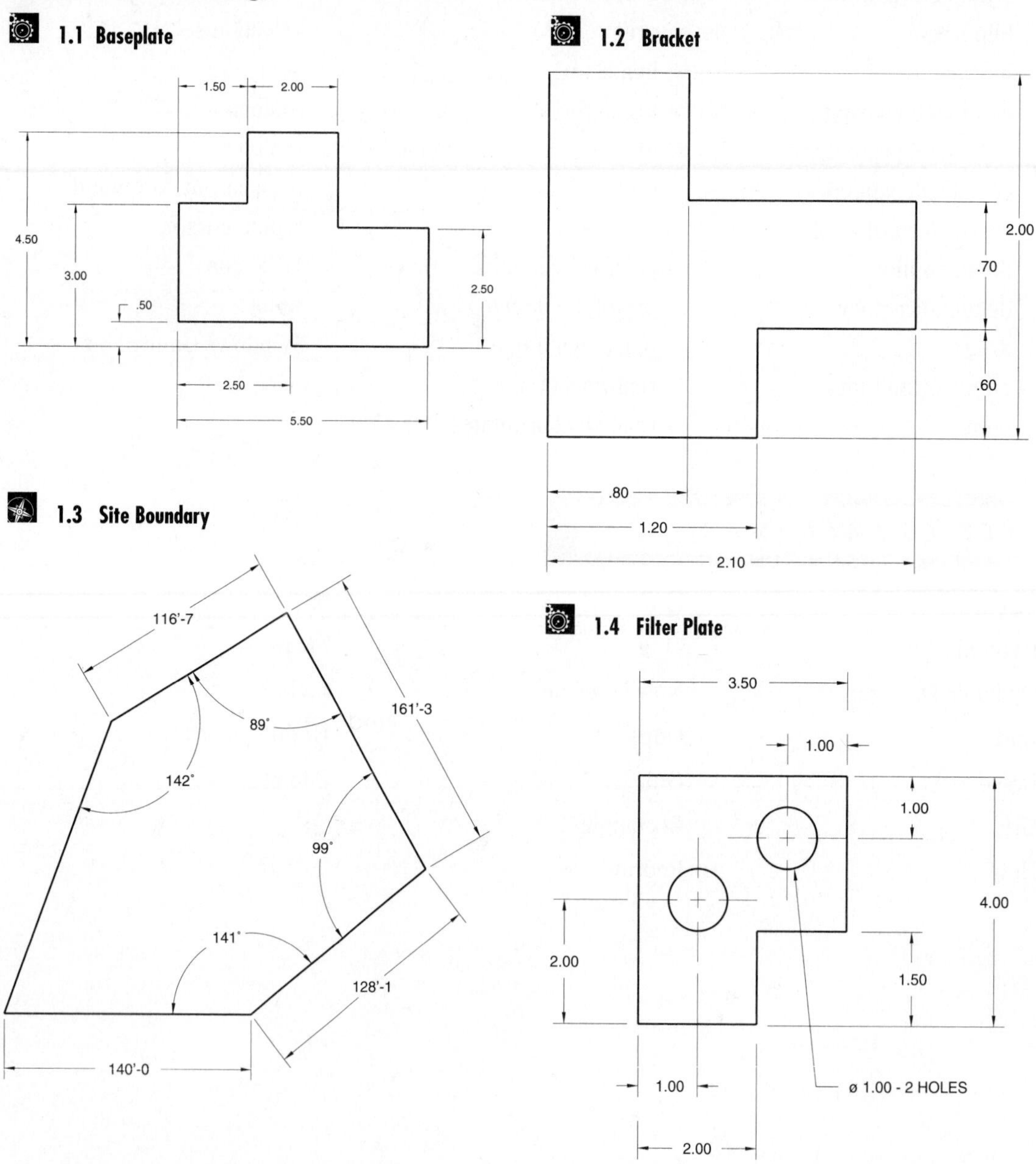

1.5M Gasket

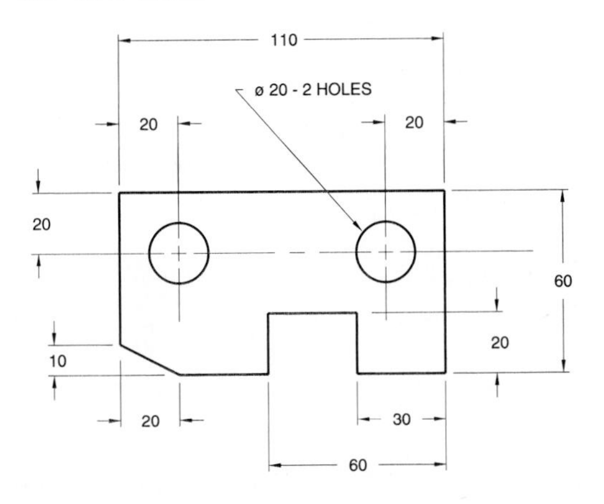

1.6 Spacer

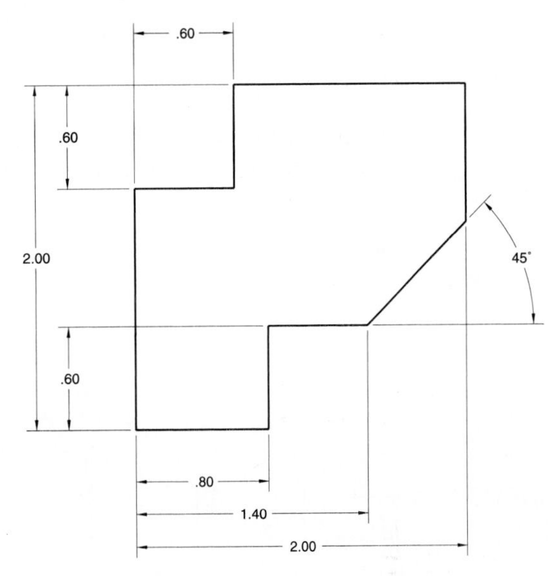

1.7M Guide Plate

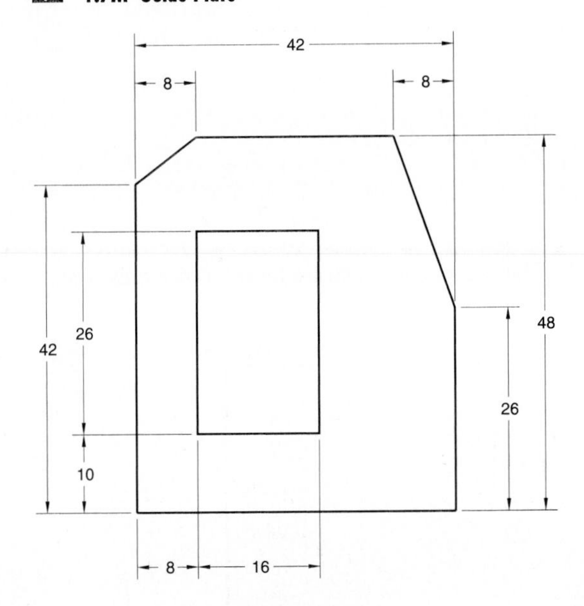

1.8 Amplifier

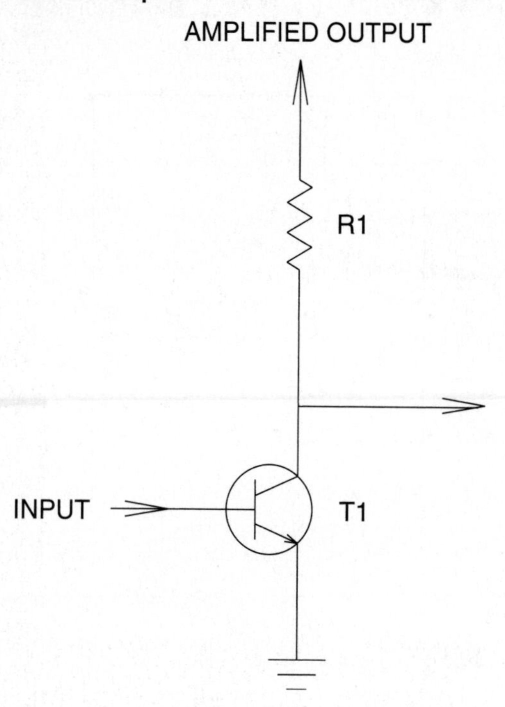

1.9 Dorm Room

Reproduce this drawing using SNAP and GRID set to 0.25. The numerical values are for reference only. Use DTEXT to label the items.

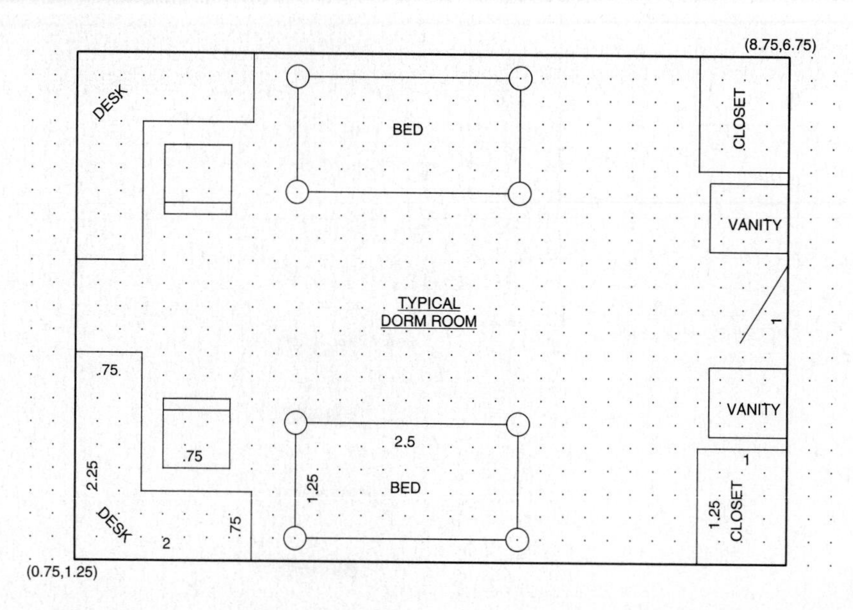

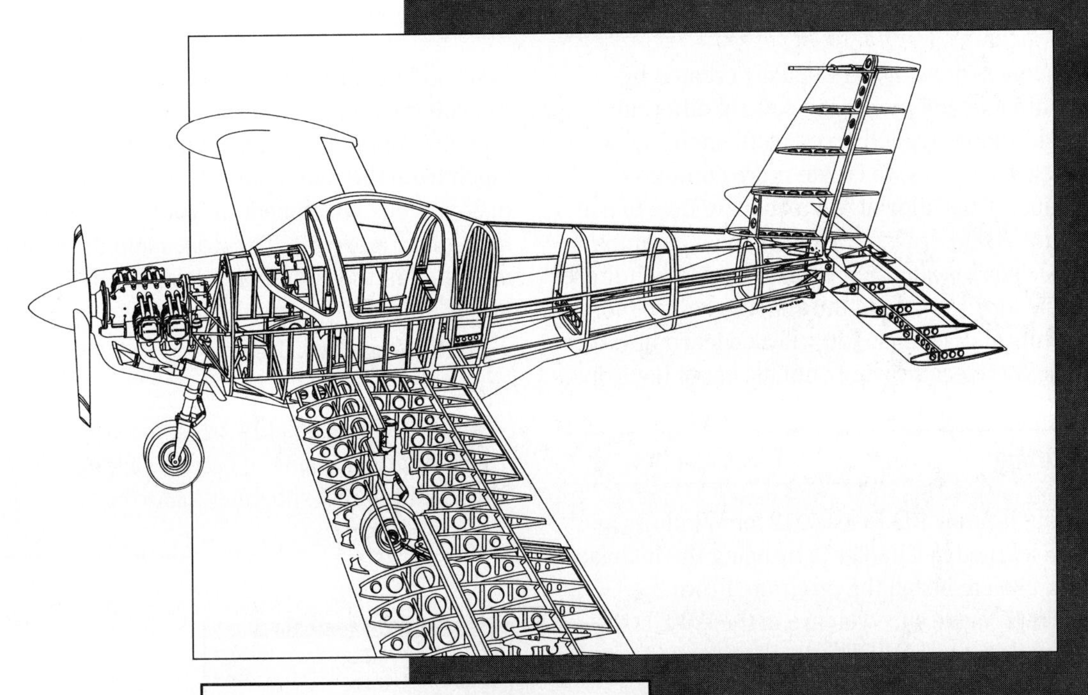

TUTORIAL 2

Basic Construction Techniques

Objectives

When you have completed this tutorial, you will be able to

1. DRAW, using the ARC, DONUT, and OFFSET commands.
2. EDIT your drawing, using the FILLET, CHAMFER, and TRIM commands.
3. Change the display, using ZOOM and PAN.
4. Load and use linetypes, change linetype scale.
5. Use SAVEAS.
6. Use hot grips to select, STRETCH, MOVE, MIRROR, ROTATE, and SCALE entities.
7. Use dimension commands to create a center mark.
8. MIRROR, COPY, and ARRAY objects in your drawing.

Introduction

Technical drawings are usually created by combining and modifying several different basic shapes (called *primitives*), such as lines, circles, and arcs, to create more complex shapes. This tutorial will teach you how to use AutoCAD to draw more of the most common basic shapes and then explain how to edit these basic forms to create the shapes required for technical drawings. You will also learn how to quickly select drawing entities, using hot grips.

Starting

Launch AutoCAD Release 12 for Windows as you learned in Chapter 3, by using the interface you used to install the program. From the DOS prompt, make sure you are in the AWCD directory; then type AWCD(↵).

Pick Start from the opening screen (or press (↵)) and the main menu appears. Select Run AutoCAD R12 for Windows to launch the program. If you need help, review Chapter 3, AutoCAD Basics, in Part 1, Getting Started.

■ ***Warning:*** If you do not use the interface for launching, you will get error messages. Refer to Chapter 2, Installing and Configuring Your Software, for more information. ■

■ ***Warning:*** If the main AutoCAD screen, including the drawing area, toolbar, toolbox, command prompt area, and menu bar, is not on your display screen, check to be sure that you have configured AutoCAD properly for your computer system. If you are still having difficulty, ask your technical support person for help. ■

Opening a File

You will begin this tutorial with the SHAPES file you created in Tutorial 1. To open a file that you have previously saved, you will select File, Open from the menu bar. The Open Drawing dialogue box will appear on your screen, as shown in Figure 2.1. The drives and directories are listed in the right-hand column; the files are listed in the left-hand column.

Pick: **File *(menu bar)*, Open**

■ ***TIP*** You can quickly select the Open Drawing File dialogue box by picking the symbol of an opening folder from the toolbar. ■

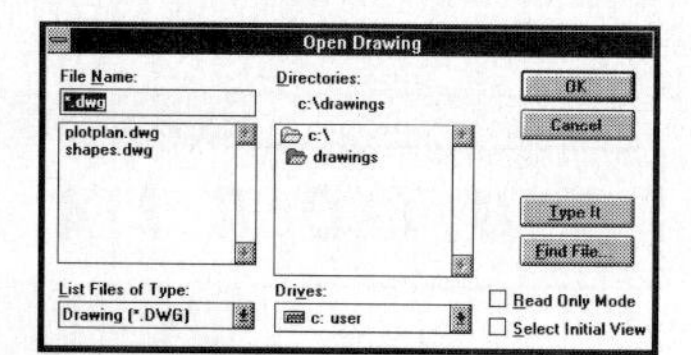

Figure 2.1

Use the Open Drawing dialogue box to open files that you have previously created. If the file you want is not in the list on the left-hand side of the dialogue box, you can change directories by clicking on the directory name that appears in the right-hand column. If you are in a subdirectory and you wish to return to the main or root directory, click on C:\ near the top of the column at the right. If the name you wish to select is not visible on the list, it may be because there are too many files to show all of them at once. If so, move the cursor over the downward pointing arrow and press the pick button. The list of files or directories should scroll on the screen. You can also *grab* the slider bar (the little box on the vertical bar along the list of names) to move the list of names. To do this, position the arrow cursor over the box on the slider bar, hold down the pick button and move your pointing device to drag the file list up or down. Practice these methods and experiment with the various options. If you need to change the drive, the drive names are at the very bottom of the dialogue box on the right-hand side. Pick inside the box beneath the heading Drives: and the list of available drives pulls down. You can also move directly to the File Name: box and type in "SHAPES". To type in the name directly, you may have to include the drive and directory names preceding the file name; for example, "C:\DRAWINGS\SHAPES". You do not need to include the .DWG file extension.

Use the scroll bars in the dialogue box to locate the file SHAPES. Select it and pick OK to exit the dialogue box. The main AutoCAD screen should appear on your display once again. SHAPES does not contain any lines because you erased all of them before you saved it in Tutorial 1.

Use the menu bar to select File, Preferences and turn on the screen menu if it is not already on. If you wish, pick the button next to Save to ACAD.INI to save the preferences so that you do not need to turn on the screen menu each time you start AutoCAD. After this point, you will not be instructed to turn on the screen menu. If you start AutoCAD and the screen menu is not available, use the above procedure to turn it on.

Using ARC

The ARC command can be used in 11 different ways to create an arc in your drawing. The ARC command is located on the DRAW screen menu and the Draw pull-down menu. You can also select it quickly by using the toolbox. The arc icon is in the upper right-hand corner of the toolbox. It appears as an arc with three points marked, because the default method is to specify three points through which the arc will pass.

Pick: **Draw *(menu bar)*, Arc**

The ARC command selections pull down on your screen. Each of the ARC command options requires you to input point locations. You can define point locations by defining the coordinate values of the points or by locating the points with the cursor and pressing the pick button on your pointing device. For the exercises presented in this tutorial, it is suggested that you select points from the screen, using the pick button. Where specific point locations are required, the coordinates will be specified.

3-point

To draw an arc with the 3-point option,

Pick: **3-point**

At the prompt:

Center/<Start point>: ***(select any point as the first point)***

Center/End/<Second point>: ***(select a second point)***

AutoCAD enters DRAG mode. When you are in DRAG mode you can see the arc move on the screen as you move the cursor, as shown in Figure 2.2. (You should remember this feature from drawing circles in Tutorial 1.) Many AutoCAD commands permit dynamic specification, or dragging, of the image on the screen.

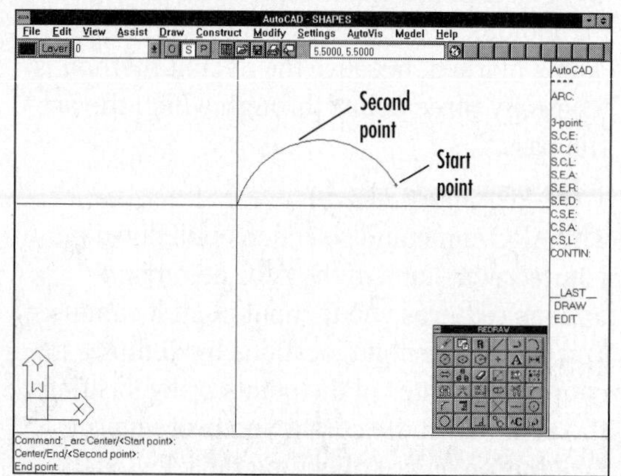

Figure 2.2

Move the cursor around the screen and see how it affects the way the arc would be drawn.

End point: ***(select a third point)***

The third point defines the endpoint of the arc. The radius of the arc is calculated based on the locations of the three points. Your screen should now show the completed arc.

Start, Center, End

Next, you will draw an arc with the Start, Center, End (S,C,E) function.

Pick: **Draw *(menu bar)*, Arc, Start, Center, End**

Figure 2.3 shows the points that you will select to create this arc. You can locate the arc anywhere on your drawing screen.

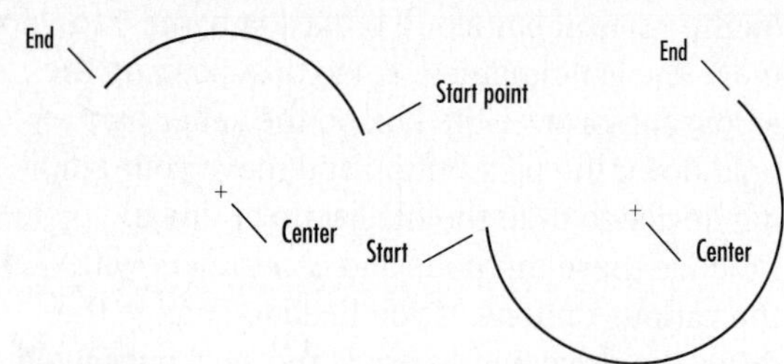

Figure 2.3

At the prompt:

Center/<Start point>: ***(select the start point)***

AutoCAD prompts that the next point is the center point.

Center: ***(select the center point)***

The distance between the start point and the center point is used as the radius for the arc. You must pick the endpoint location, which defines the end of the arc. You are in DRAG mode.

Angle/Length of chord/<End point>: ***(select the endpoint)***

An arc is always drawn in a counterclockwise direction from the start point. It is therefore important to correctly define the start point and the center point. Figure 2.4 shows the point locations needed to draw a concave corner arc. If the start point was located where the endpoint is, a convex arc outside the corner would have been drawn.

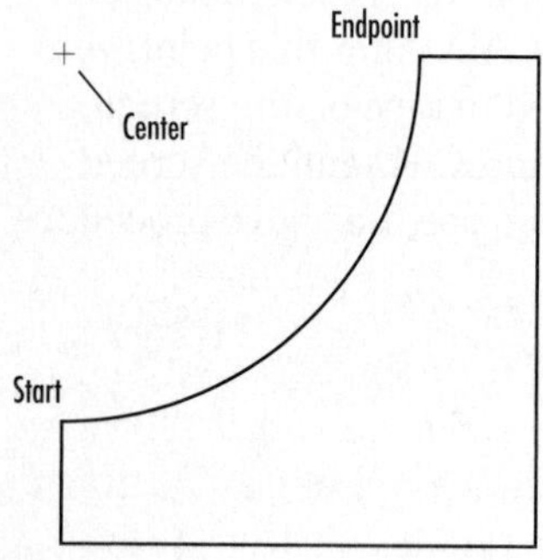

Figure 2.4

Try drawing another arc with the Start, Center, End option, this time locating the start point to the left of the center point. The resulting arc should be concave, as is the one shown in Figure 2.4.

If your screen is getting too crowded, use ERASE with implied windowing on your own to clear entities from it. Use REDRAW (R) to remove leftover blips.

Start, Center, Angle

To draw an arc with the Start, Center, included Angle (S,C,A) function,

Pick: **Draw *(menu bar)*, Arc, Start, Center, Angle**

Figure 2.5 shows the points that you will select.

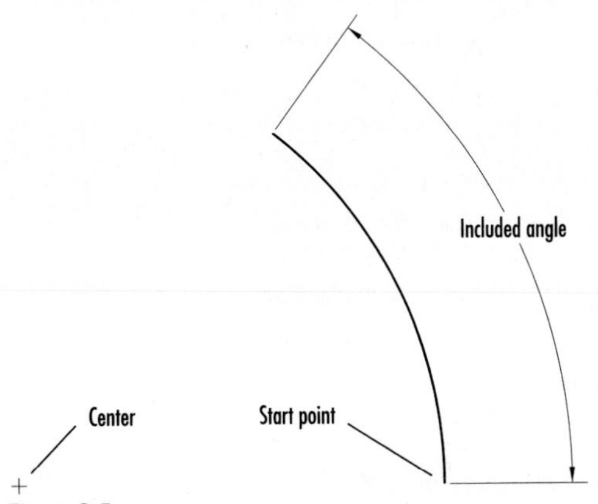

Figure 2.5

Center/<Start point>: ***(select a start point)***

Next, specify the center point for the arc.

Center: ***(select a center point)***

See Figure 2.5. The endpoint of the arc is defined by the included angular value from the start point to the endpoint. Angular values are positive in the counterclockwise direction. Negative values can be used and result in an arc drawn in the clockwise direction.

Included angle: **75** ↵

Start, Center, Length

Draw an arc, using the Start, Center, Length of chord (S,C,L) function. The points are shown in Figure 2.6.

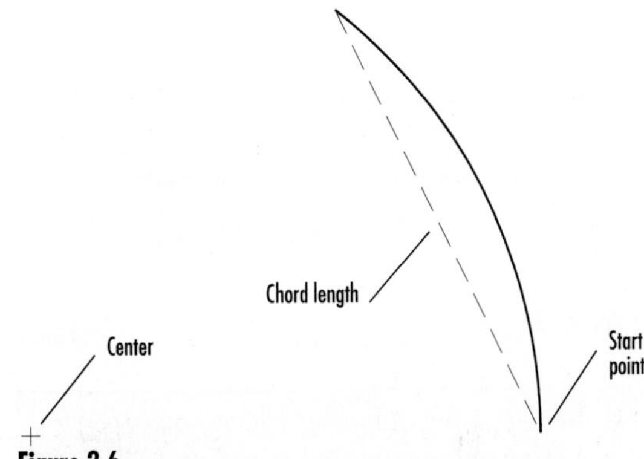

Figure 2.6

Pick: **Draw *(menu bar)*, Arc, Start, Center, Length**

Center/<Start point>: ***(select a start point)***

Center: ***(select a center point)***

Select the endpoint, as defined by a *chord length*. A chord length is a straight line from the start point to locate the endpoint of the arc. Negative values can be entered.

Length of chord: **2** ↵

The arc on your screen should look similar to Figure 2.6.

Start, End, Radius

Draw an arc, using the Start, End, Radius (S,E,R) function. The locations of the start and end points are shown in Figure 2.7.

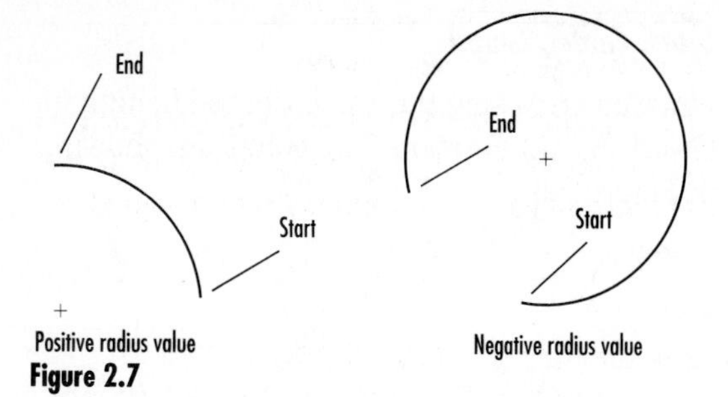

Figure 2.7

Pick: **Draw *(menu bar)*, Arc, Start, End, Radius**

Center/<Start point>: ***(select a start point)***

End point: ***(select an endpoint)***

Radius: **2** ↵

> ■ ***TIP*** Negative radius values can be used to create a major arc, as shown in Figure 2.7. ■

Contin

The Contin option allows an arc to be joined to a previously drawn arc or line. The Contin option is not on the Draw toolbar menu. To select it, pick from the screen menu. To draw an arc that is the continuation of an existing line, first draw the line.

Pick: **LINE icon *(toolbox)***

and on your own draw a line anywhere on your screen. Once you have a line drawn,

Pick: **DRAW *(screen menu)*, ARC, Contin**

The last point drawn for the line becomes the first point for the arc. AutoCAD is in DRAG mode and an arc appears from the end of the line. Pick an endpoint.

End point: ***(select an endpoint)***

Use the screen menu to select S,C,E and draw another arc. Use Contin to draw an arc from the endpoint of the arc that was created.

Pick: **S,C,E *(screen menu)***

Center/<Start point>: ***(select a start point)***

Center: ***(select a center point)***

Angle/Length of chord/<End point>: ***(select an endpoint)***

Pick: **Contin *(screen menu)***

End point: ***(select a location for the endpoint)***

> ■ ***TIP*** At the first prompt of the LINE or ARC commands, pressing ↵ or the spacebar, or clicking the right mouse button, starts your new entity from the last point entered. This is faster than picking Contin from the screen menu. ■

Your drawings should look similar to Figure 2.8.

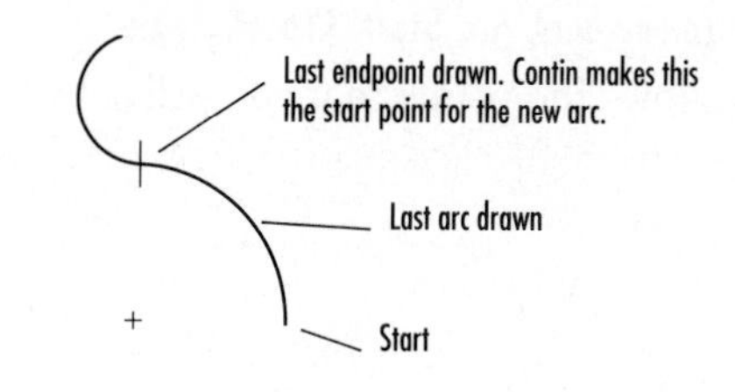

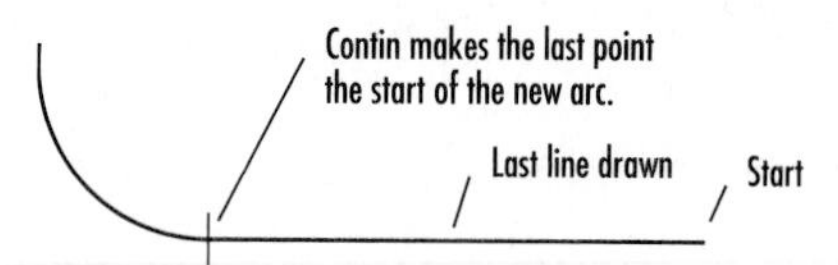

Figure 2.8

Quick Selections for ARC

If you wish to quickly select the ARC command, you can type the command alias, A. When you start the ARC command this way (and also when you use the ARC icon in the toolbox), the default for drawing the arc is the 3-point method you learned earlier in this tutorial. If you wish to use any of the other methods, you can type the command option letter at the prompt.

Pick: **ARC icon *(toolbox)***

The ARC command is echoed at the command prompt, followed by the prompt:

Center/<Start point>: **C** ↵ ***(to enter the center point first)***

Center: ***(pick a center point for the arc)***

Start point: ***(pick a start point)***

Angle/Length of chord/<End point>: ***(pick an endpoint)***

The arc is added to your drawing. Notice that you could have used A or L to enter the angle or length of chord instead of the endpoint at the last prompt.

Using DONUT

The DONUT command is used to draw filled circles and concentric filled circles. DONUT is very useful for creating filled connection dots for electrical diagrams. It is also useful for creating pads for circuit board layouts. See Figure 2.9.

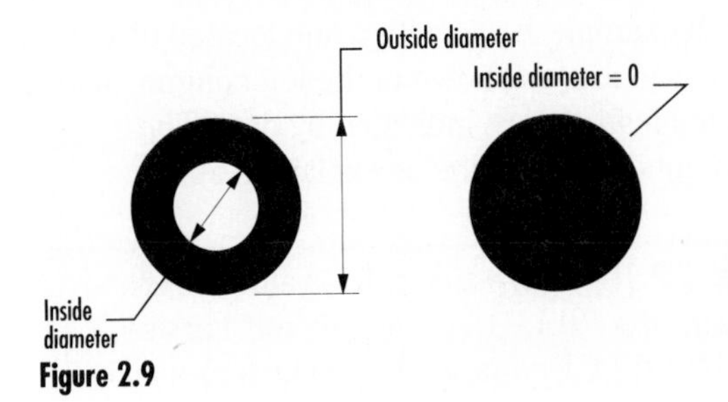

Figure 2.9

The DONUT command is located on the DRAW screen menu and Draw menu bar. The DONUT command requires numerical values for the inside and outside diameters of the concentric circles, as well as a point location for the center point. If you enter a zero value for the inside diameter, a solid dot appears on the screen. The diameter of the dot equals the stated outside diameter value.

Pick: **Draw *(menu bar)*, Donut**

Inside diameter<0.5000>: ↵

Outside diameter<1.0000>: ↵

Notice that a doughnut-like shape is now moving with your cursor. The "Center of doughnut" prompt is repeated so that more than one donut can be drawn. Select points on your screen:

Center of doughnut: ***(select a point)***

Center of doughnut: ***(select a point)***

Draw as many donuts as you wish. When you have finished drawing all donuts of the same size, you will exit the command by pressing the ↵ key.

Center of doughnut: ↵

Using the methods you learned in Tutorial 1, erase and redraw your screen on your own.

Using FILLET

The FILLET command is used to connect lines, arcs, or circles with a smoothly fitted arc, or *fillet*. The FILLET command is located on the second page of the EDIT screen menu, under Construct on the menu bar, and in the fourth row of the toolbox.

Use the LINE command on your own to draw a rectangular shape. Use SNAP and GRID to help you draw the rectangle as shown in Figure 2.10.

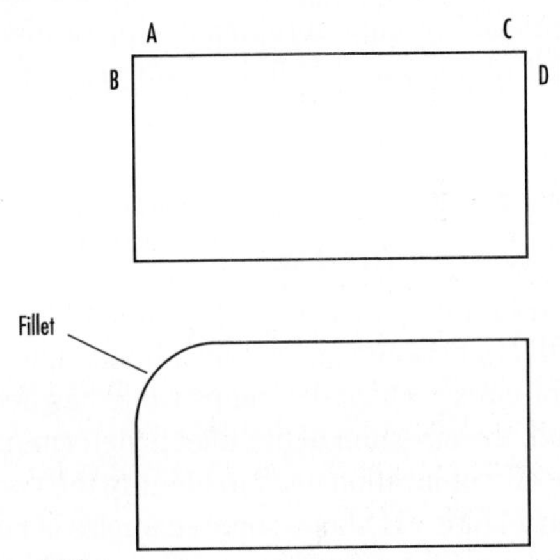

Figure 2.10

Pick: **Construct *(menu bar)*, Fillet**

Polyline/Radius/<Select first object>: **r** ↵

Typing "r" tells AutoCAD you want to enter a radius value for the fillet. Enter a radius value of 1.00.

Enter fillet radius <0.0000>: 1 (↵)

Command: (↵) *(to restart the command)*

> ■ ***TIP*** If you select the Radius option from the screen menu instead of typing it after you select FILLET, the command is automatically repeated, saving you the step of restarting the command. ■

AutoCAD prompts you to select the two objects. Refer to Figure 2.10 to select the lines.

Command: FILLET Polyline/Radius/<Select first object>: *(select line A)*

Select second object: *(select line B)*

A fillet should appear between the two lines, as shown in Figure 2.10.

Command: (↵)

AutoCAD repeats the previous command when you press (↵) or the right mouse button at the "Command:" prompt. It returns to the original FILLET prompt, which allows you to repeat the selection process, drawing additional fillets of the same radius.

Polyline/Radius/<Select first object>: *(select line C)*

Select second object: *(select line D)*

The FILLET command can be used to fit a smooth arc between any combination of lines, arcs, or circles. Once the radius value has been defined, the direction of the fillet is determined by the cursor location used to identify the two objects. Figure 2.11 shows some examples of how you can use FILLET to create different-shaped fillets by choosing different point locations.

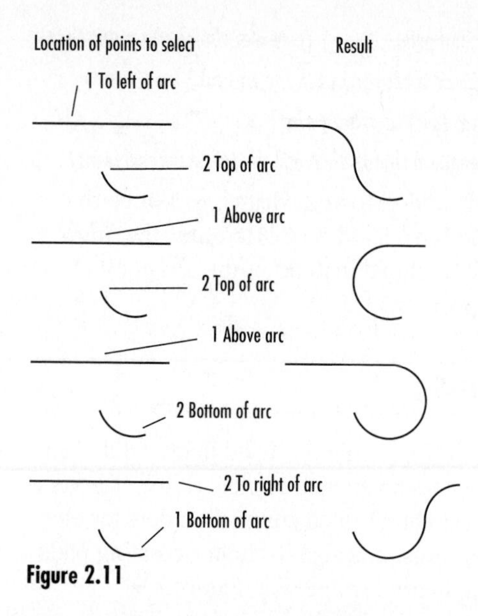

Figure 2.11

Each example starts with a line located directly above an arc, as shown in the left column. The point locations are indicated by dots. The prompts are the same as explained above.

> ■ ***TIP*** If you use the radius value of zero with the FILLET command, you can use the FILLET command to make a clean corner from two lines that would intersect if they were extended. This also works to make a neat corner from lines that extend past an intersection. You can also do this with the CHAMFER command (which you will learn next) by setting both chamfer distances to zero. ■

Adapting for Architecture

When you are developing site plans, the FILLET command is useful in creating curbs that require smooth corners at a known radius. ■

Using CHAMFER

The CHAMFER command is used to draw a straight line segment (called a *chamfer*) between two given lines. Chamfering is the name for the machining process of flattening off a sharp corner of an object. The CHAMFER command is located on the EDIT screen menu, under Construct on the menu bar, and in the fifth row of the toolbox.

So that you will have an object to chamfer, use the LINE command on your own to draw another rectangle, as shown in Figure 2.12.

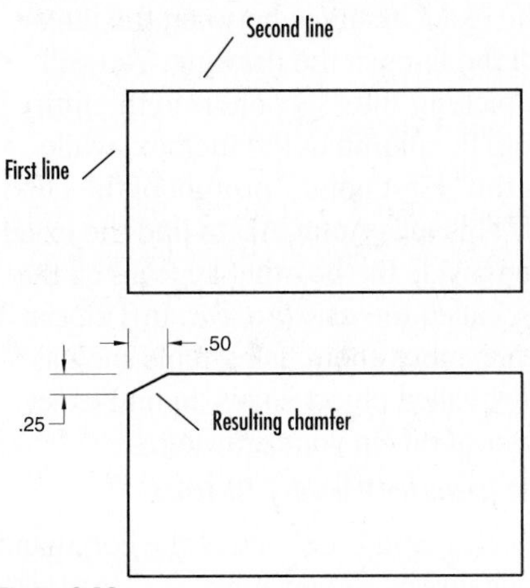

Figure 2.12

Pick: **Construct *(menu bar)*, Chamfer**

Polyline/Distances/ <Select first line>: **d** ↵

Typing "d" tells AutoCAD you want to enter distance values.

Enter first chamfer distance <0.0000>: **.25** ↵

Enter second chamfer distance <0.2500>: **.5** ↵

■ ***TIP*** In the previous step, if you pick Distance from the screen menu, the command is repeated automatically. ■

Command: ↵

AutoCAD returns to the CHAMFER command and prompts for selection of the first and second lines to add the chamfer between. Refer to Figure 2.12 to select the lines.

Polyline/Distances/<Select first line>: ***(select the first line)***

Select second line: ***(select the second line)***

A chamfer should appear on your screen that looks similar to the one shown in Figure 2.12. The size of a chamfer is defined by the distance each end of the chamfer is from the corner. As with the FILLET command, once these distances have been entered, you can draw additional chamfers of the same size by pressing ↵ after each chamfer is completed to restart the command.

FILLET and CHAMFER can also be picked from the toolbox, as shown in Figure 2.13. This is especially useful if you have already set the fillet radius or the chamfer distances you wish to use, because the toolbox is easily available from the screen.

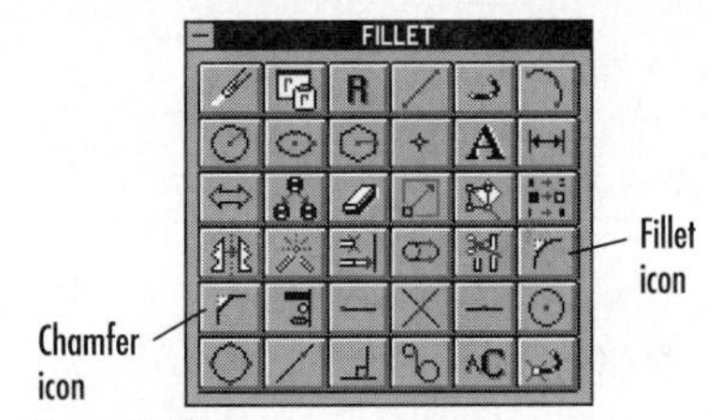

Figure 2.13

You have now finished with the practice drawing SHAPES. You will save this drawing and begin another.

Pick: **File *(menu bar)*, Save**

■ ***TIP*** You can select the icon that looks like a floppy disk from the toolbar. This executes the QSAVE command and saves your drawing to the current file name. ■

Now select File from the menu bar and then select the option New. . . to begin a new drawing. As you learned in Tutorial 1, start your new drawing from the prototype drawing named ACAD. Call your new drawing WRENCH. Your new drawing file will be created in the default directory on your system; you should change it to the directory DRAWINGS that you created in Getting Started. You may include a directory name before the file name, or select New Drawing Name. . . and pick the directory where you wish to store your file. Be sure to select OK to exit the Create New Drawing dialogue box.

Begin the Wrench Drawing

You will draw the basic shapes required for a wrench in this tutorial and then complete the drawing in Tutorial 3. The first lines you must draw are the figure's center lines. Refer to Figure 2.14.

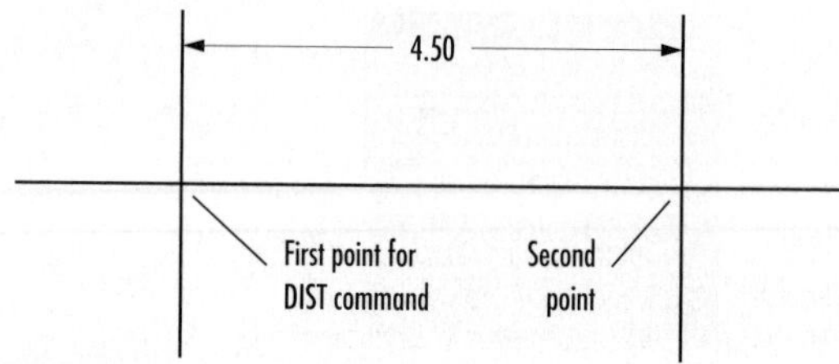

Figure 2.14

First use LINE on your own to draw a horizontal line that extends 7.5 inches across the center of your drawing screen. Use GRID and SNAP with .5-inch spacing. Then draw two vertical lines that are 3 inches long and 4.5 inches apart. Make sure you complete these steps before continuing.

Using DISTANCE

The DISTANCE command reads out the value for the distance between two points you select in your drawing. This is often helpful to double-check that your drawing is correct. It can also be used to graphically solve problems involving distances, as in descriptive geometry. The DISTANCE command is located on the Assist pull-down menu, under Inquiry. It can also be found on the INQUIRY screen menu. When using DISTANCE, it is important to pick exact points in the drawing. Otherwise, the distance measured is just that of the screen and not necessarily the exact distance between the intersections of the lines in the drawing. You will do this by picking Intersection from the fifth row and fourth column of the toolbox, while you are at the "First point:" prompt of the DIST command. This tells AutoCAD to find the exact intersection inside the box that appears on the crosshairs, called the *aperture box*. In Tutorial 3 you will learn more about using tools such as Intersection, called object snaps, to find exact geometric locations in your drawing.

Pick: **Assist (menu bar), Inquiry, Distance**

The DIST command is echoed at the command prompt, followed by the prompt:

First point: ***(pick the Intersection icon from the toolbox)***

of ***(place the aperture box over the intersection of the left vertical line and the horizontal line and pick)***

Second point: ***(pick the Intersection icon from the toolbox)***

of ***(place the aperture box over the right vertical line and the horizontal line and pick)***

Distance=4.5000, Angle in XY Plane =0, Angle from XY Plane=0

Delta X=4.5000, Delta Y=0.0000, Delta Z=0.0000

AutoCAD prints the information listed above on your screen. You should see that the distance between the points is exactly 4.5000. If you have some other value, check to make sure that you have drawn the lines correctly.

Make corrections to your drawing as necessary, turning SNAP on and redrawing the lines if necessary. It is extremely important that you create accurate drawing geometry. Picking a point from the screen can never be done exactly unless SNAP or the Object Snap modes, like Intersection, are used. Object snaps can also be used in combination with the DISTANCE command to solve simple engineering problems by measuring accurate distances from your drawing.

Now use CIRCLE on your own to draw a circle with a 2-inch diameter. The center point of the circle should be the intersection of the horizontal line and the right vertical line. It is on the snap interval so you can pick the point accurately. (Refer to Tutorial 1 if you need to review the CIRCLE command.)

Using COPY

The COPY command is used to copy an entity or group of drawing entities within the same drawing. The original entities remain in place and the copies can be moved to a new location. The COPY command is located on the EDIT screen menu and under Construct on the menu bar. It can also be quickly picked from the toolbox, as shown in Figure 2.15.

You will pick the COPY command from the toolbox to draw a second circle on your drawing. Refer to Figure 2.15.

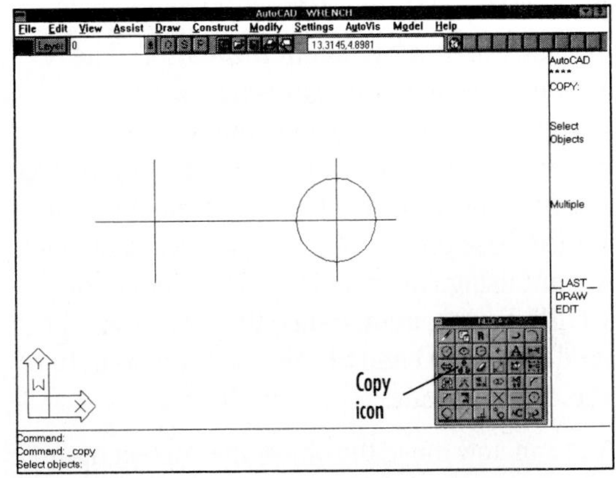

Figure 2.15

Pick: **COPY icon *(toolbox)***

> ■ ***TIP*** It might be difficult to get the cursor to select the circle. You might find that turning SNAP off makes it easier to select the circle. Be sure to turn it back on again before selecting the base point or displacement, or your drawing may become inaccurate. ■

Select objects: ***(select the circle)***

Select objects: (↵)

Pressing (↵) tells AutoCAD you are done selecting things and want to go on with the command. Be sure SNAP is on again so you can accurately select the center point of the circle, which was created at a SNAP location.

Pick: **S button *(from the toolbar to turn on SNAP if needed)***

Press: (F7) ***(to turn on GRID if needed)***

<Base point or displacement>/Multiple: ***(select the center point of the circle)***

AutoCAD switches to DRAG mode so you can see the object move about the screen. The prompt "Second point of displacement:" asks you to choose a point somewhere on the screen. You can define the new location by typing new absolute or relative coordinate values for the base point. You can also accurately pick a point using GRID and SNAP to define the COPY displacement. Since this object was created with GRID and SNAP, use them to define the displacement.

You can now move the object the correct number of spaces to the left to achieve an accurate copy. The second circle must be centered at the intersection of the horizontal and left vertical lines.

Second point of displacement: ***(pick the left intersection)***

Your drawing should now look like Figure 2.16.

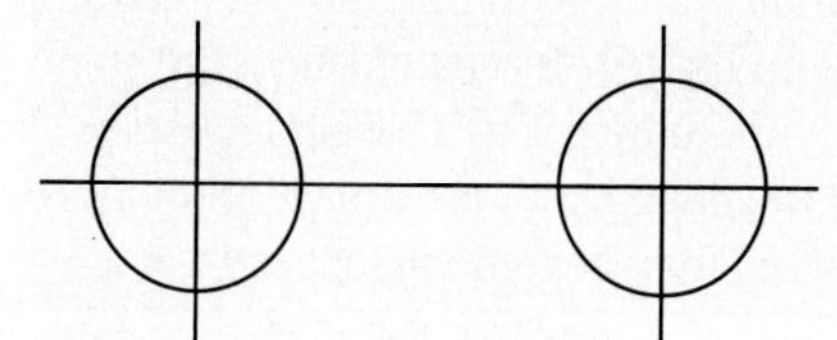

Figure 2.16

Using OFFSET

The OFFSET command is used to create a new entity parallel to a given entity. The OFFSET command is located on the DRAW screen menu and under Construct on the menu bar. You will use OFFSET to draw two parallel lines 0.5 inch from the horizontal line. See Figure 2.17.

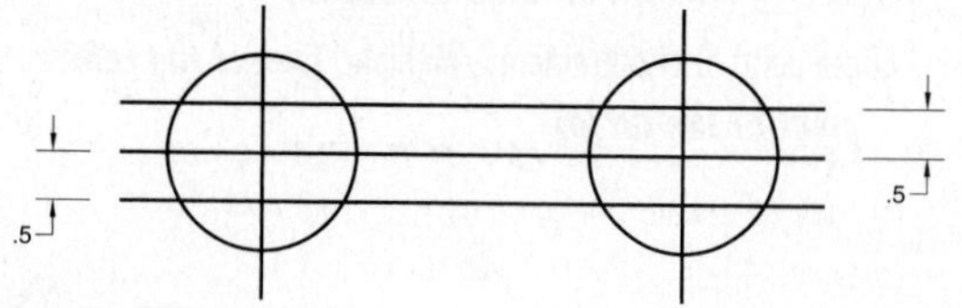

Figure 2.17

Pick: **Construct *(menu bar)*, Offset**

To draw an offset line, you need to determine the offset distance (the distance away from the original line) or the through point (the point through which a line is to be drawn). To specify the offset distance indicated in Figure 2.17,

Offset distance or Through <Through>: .5 ↵

Select object to offset: ***(select the horizontal line)***

Side to offset? ***(select a point above the horizontal line)***

Once you have defined the offset distance, AutoCAD repeats the prompt "Select object to offset:", allowing you to create additional parallel lines.

On your own, create a second line offset .5 inch below the original horizontal line, as specified in Figure 2.17, by repeating the preceding two steps. Press ↵ to exit the command when you are finished.

Adapting for Architecture

The OFFSET command can be used to quickly generate wall thicknesses from single-line architectural drawings. Try to use standard architectural distances for construction (such as 6", 8", or 1') to maintain drawing clarity. ■

Using ZOOM Window

To zoom in on an area of the drawing, use the Window option of the ZOOM command to specify the area to be enlarged.

Pick: **View *(menu bar)*, Zoom, Window**

The ZOOM command is echoed at the command prompt and then followed by the prompts,

All/Center/Dynamic/Extents/Left/Previous/Vmax/Window/ <Scale(X/XP)>: _window"

You will specify a window to define the area to be enlarged. Notice that the ZOOM command has an ' (apostrophe) in front of it in the command prompt area. This means that it is a transparent command and can be selected during another command. You will zoom in on the left circle. To create the window, first select a point at the top left corner of the area to be zoomed, then select a point on the diagonal in the lower right corner, as shown in Figure 2.18.

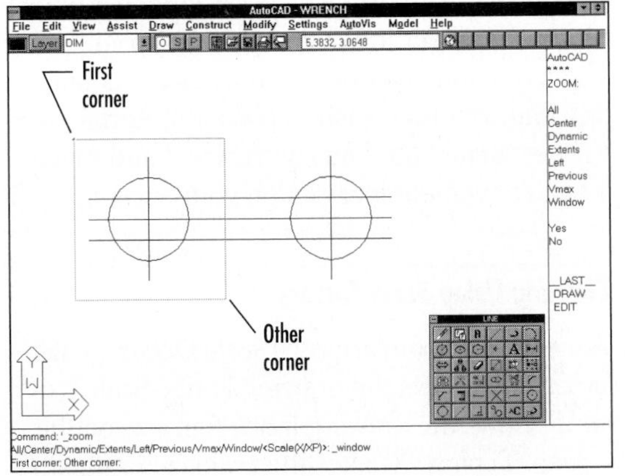

Figure 2.18

First corner: ***(select the first point)***

Other corner: ***(select the other point)***

The defined area is enlarged to the full screen size, as shown in Figure 2.19.

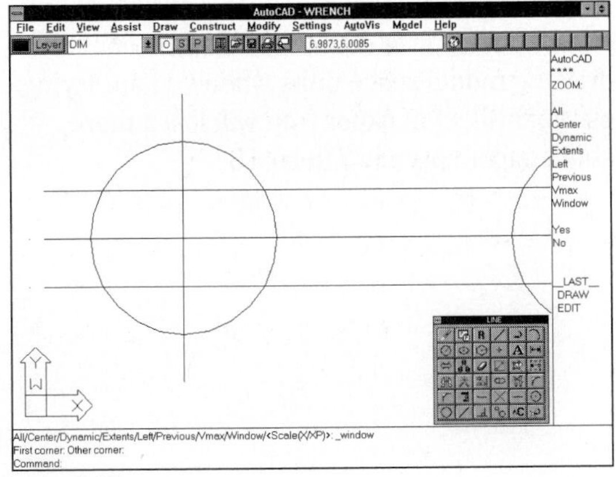

Figure 2.19

To return an area to its original size,

Pick: **View *(menu bar)*, Zoom, Previous**

Your drawing is returned to the previous size. Areas can be repeatedly zoomed; that is, you can zoom in on a zoomed area. In fact, you can continue to zoom until the portion shown on the display is ten trillion times the size of the original.

Using the Aerial Viewer

To allow you to quickly zoom in and move around in a large drawing, AutoCAD provides the Aerial Viewer. To select the Aerial Viewer, pick the icon that looks like a compass from the toolbar. The Aerial Viewer appears on your screen, as shown in Figure 2.20.

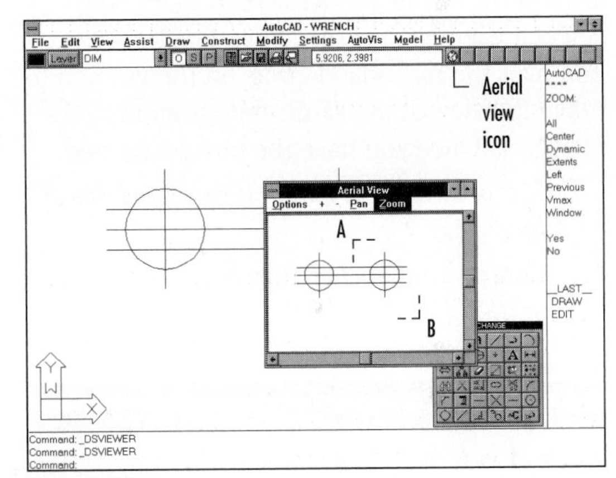

Figure 2.20

■ ***Warning:*** You cannot use the Aerial Viewer with AutoCAD unless you have selected the Windows Accelerated Display Driver ADI 4.2 in the AutoCAD Display Configuration. If you need to make this change, refer to Part 1, Chapter 2, Installing and Configuring AutoCAD. If you need additional help, ask your technical support person or refer to the Display Device information provided on the CD-ROM. ■

You will use the crosshairs in the Aerial Viewer to form a window around the area in the drawing you would like to enlarge on the screen.

Pick: ***(point A, indicated in Figure 2.20)***

Pick: ***(point B)***

Once you have selected point B, the area enclosed in the window in the Aerial Viewer is enlarged to fill the screen. Next you will select the Pan option from the menu bar on the Aerial Viewer. The Aerial Viewer should remain available on your screen. If it does not, press the (ALT) and (ESC) keys simultaneously to cycle through your applications until you see both AutoCAD and the Aerial Viewer on the screen.

Pick: **Pan *(from the menu bar on the Aerial Viewer)***

The Pan selection becomes highlighted. Notice that now instead of crosshairs that move around the Aerial Viewer screen to let you select a window, you see a box. Position the box over the right-hand circle on the wrench to move the view at the same enlargement to the new area. Once you have the box positioned,

Pick: ***(to position the box near the right-hand side of the wrench)***

The view on your screen moves so that it is similar to Figure 2.21.

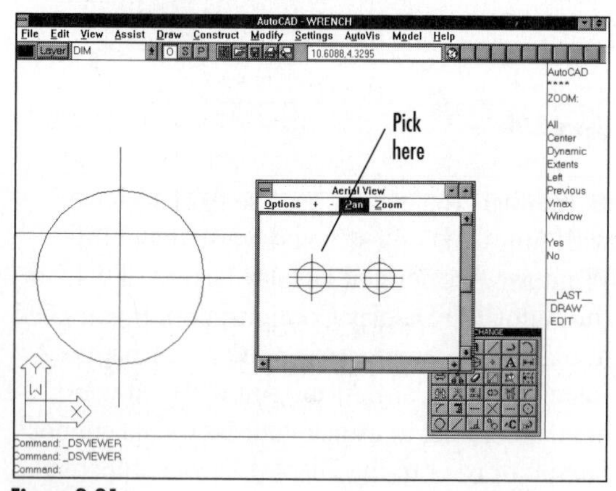

Figure 2.21

You can reposition the Aerial Viewer on your screen by grabbing its title bar (picking on its title bar with the right mouse button and keeping the button held down) and dragging it to a new location. To resize the Aerial Viewer, move the arrow pointer near the upper left corner of the Aerial Viewer window until you see the cursor change to a double arrow. While the cursor is a double arrow, grab the corner of the window and drag it to enlarge or reduce the size of the window. To remove the Aerial Viewer from your screen, double-click the Windows Control box in the upper left corner of the Aerial Viewer. If you are working on a large, detailed drawing, you may wish to leave the Aerial Viewer turned on. You can resize it and move it to a convenient location on your screen.

Zooming Using Scale Factors

You can also zoom areas by *scale factors*. Scale factor 1.00 shows the drawing limits. Scale factor .5 shows the drawing limits half size on the screen. Typing "X" after the scale factor means the zoom scale will be relative to the previous view. For example, entering "2X" causes the new view to be shown twice as big as the view established previously. A scale factor of .5X reduces the view to half its previous size. Typing "XP" after the scale factor means the new view will be relative to *paper space*. A scale factor of .5XP means that the object will be shown so that one paper space unit is equal to two of the current drawing model space units when you are laying out your sheet of paper. You will learn more about paper space in Tutorial 3.

You will use the toolbar to select the ZOOM command this time. The ZOOM icon appears as a magnifying glass near the top of your screen in the upper right corner of the toolbar.

Pick: ***(the ZOOM icon from the toolbar)***

All/Center/Dynamic/Extents/Left/Previous/Vmax/Window/
<Scale(X/XP)>: **2X** ↵

The entities are enlarged on the screen to twice the size of the previous view.

Command: ↵

All/Center/Dynamic/Extents/Left/Previous/Vmax/Window/
<Scale(X/XP)>: **.5** ↵

The drawing limits appear on the screen at half their original size. The area shown on the screen is twice as big as the drawing limits.

ZOOM, Left and ZOOM, Center let you specify a fixed point, the center point or the lower left corner respectively, before you enter the zoom scale factor. You will learn more about these options in Tutorials 8 and 9. ZOOM, Scale uses the current left corner or 0,0 coordinates as the base point.

Command: ↵

All/Center/Dynamic/Extents/Left/Previous/Vmax/Window/
<Scale(X/XP)>: **A** ↵

The drawing should return to its original size, the way it was before you began the ZOOM command. Experiment on your own with the other options of the ZOOM command. The Vmax option lets you zoom out as far as possible without causing AutoCAD to *regenerate* the drawing. AutoCAD uses a *virtual screen*, a file from which the screen display is created. If you try to zoom out to areas that are not calculated in the current virtual screen file, the drawing has to be regenerated to calculate the display for the new area. Depending on your hardware configuration, regenerating a complex drawing can take quite a while, so it is useful to zoom out without causing a regeneration.

Using PAN

As you saw using the Aerial Viewer, the PAN command lets you move the drawing around on the screen without changing the zoom factor. The PAN command prompts you to select two points. The first point you select is a base point; the second point is the new location you wish that point to have on the screen.

Pick: **View *(menu bar)*, Pan**

Displacement: ***(pick a point near the center of the screen)***

Second point: ***(pick a point about 1 inch to the right of the first point)***

The drawing should shift over to the right on the screen by about 1 inch. Notice that the PAN command can be transparent, or used during another command.

Using TRIM

The TRIM command is used to remove part of an entity. The TRIM command is located on the second page of the EDIT screen menu and under Modify on the menu bar. TRIM has two steps. You are first prompted to select the entities that will be used as *cutting edges*. The cutting edges are drawing entities that are used to cut off the portions that you wish to trim. The cutting edge entities you select must cross the entities to be trimmed at the appropriate point. When you are done selecting cutting edges, you are prompted to select the portions of the entities that you want to trim.

Pick the TRIM command from the toolbox (it appears as a pair of scissors cutting a shape) to remove the excess lines inside the circles. First you will select the cutting edges so they are highlighted.

Pick: **TRIM icon *(toolbox)***

Select cutting edge(s)... Select objects: ***(select a circle)***

1 selected, 1 found

Select objects: ***(select the other circle)***

Select objects: ⏎

Now you are done selecting the cutting edges. Use Figure 2.22 as your guide to selecting all the excess lines to remove. By selecting lines in the order shown, you can use TRIM to remove them all in one step. (You can use ERASE to remove remaining portions if you select the lines out of order.)

<Select object to trim>/Undo: ***(select the lines to trim)***

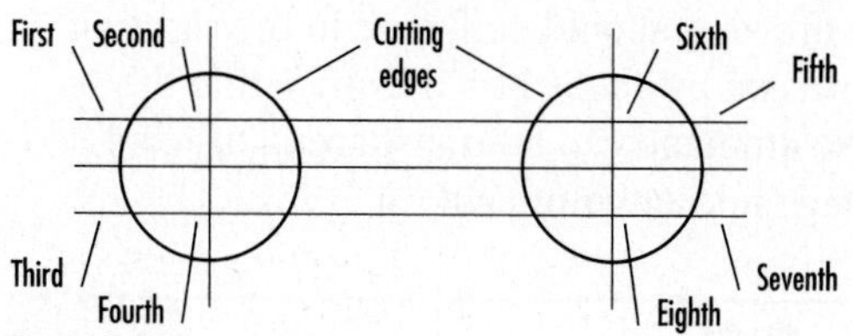

Figure 2.22

When you are done, your figure should look similar to Figure 2.23.

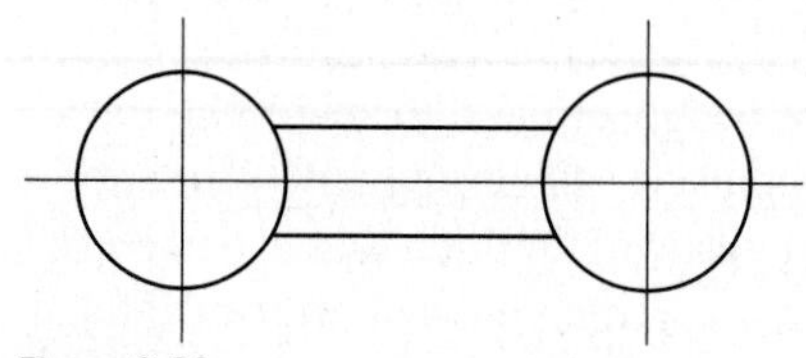

Figure 2.23

To end the command,

Press: ⏎

Refer to Figure 2.24 to understand how the cutting edge works in relation to the object to be trimmed.

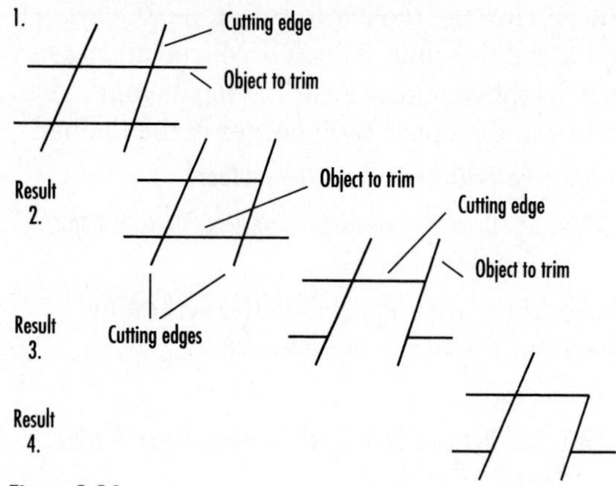

Figure 2.24

When lines come together, such as at a corner, one or both of the lines can be selected as cutting lines, as shown in Figure 2.24, parts 1 and 3. Again, the cursor location determines which portion of the line is removed.

Adapting for Architecture

The TRIM command and the EXTEND command are invaluable for creating floor plans. You can easily generate wall openings by trimming between the two lines that define the rough openings. Early design development lines can be offset, extended, and trimmed to develop final drawings. ■

Loading Linetypes

Once you have finished removing the excess lines, you will want to add the center lines in your drawing. Center lines are one of several different types of lines used in technical drawings. Each type of line has a specific use. Figure 2.25 shows the most common types of lines.

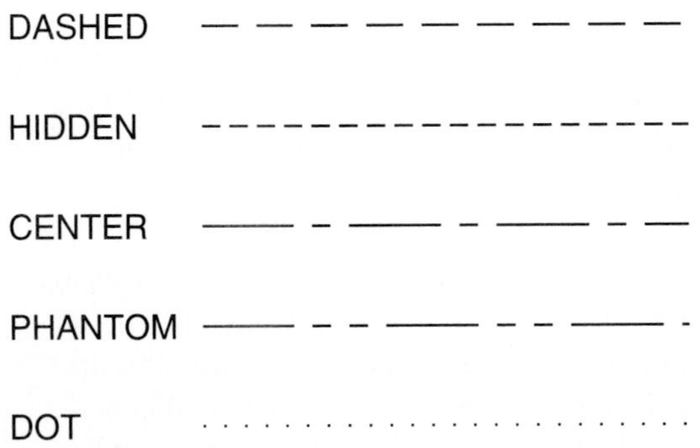

DASHED — — — — — — — — —

HIDDEN - - - - - - - - - - - - - - - - -

CENTER ——— - ——— - ——— - —

PHANTOM ——— - - ——— - - ——— -

DOT . . . .

Figure 2.25

Before you can use various linetypes in AutoCAD, you must load them into the drawing. You will use * (asterisk) or wildcard for the name(s) of the linetypes; this loads all of the available linetypes from the file.

■ ***TIP*** You can do this in a prototype drawing to prevent having to do it each time. You will learn how to do this in Tutorial 6. The LINETYPE command is found on the SETTINGS screen menu. Be sure to select the screen menu, because the Settings pull-down menu is different, or you can type "LINETYPE". ■

Pick: **SETTINGS *(screen menu)*, LINETYP**

?/Create/Load/Set: **L** ↵

Linetype(s) to load: * ↵

The Linetype File dialogue box appears on your screen, as shown in Figure 2.26. You can use the LINETYPE command to create your own linetypes and store them in a linetype file with the file extension .LIN. The default AutoCAD linetypes are stored in a file called ACAD.LIN. Since that file is the default in the File Name box, you can either press ↵ to select it or pick OK.

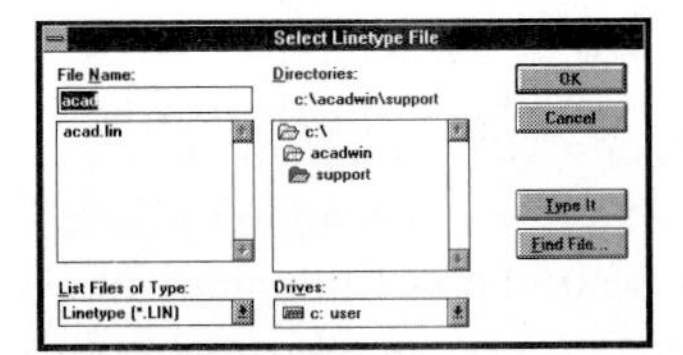

Figure 2.26

You will see the names of the linetypes scroll by on your screen and then the prompt returns:

?/Create/Load/Set: ↵ ***(to end the command)***

Now the linetypes are loaded and ready for use in other commands. Press F2 to display AutoCAD's text screen. You will see the names of the linetypes that were loaded. Press F2 again to return to the drawing screen.

■ ***TIP*** The transparent command 'TEXTSCR can be used if you wish to look back to see a command prompt, message, or previous entry that is no longer displayed in the "Command:" prompt area and to return from the text screen to the drawing screen. You can select 'TEXTSCR by picking Edit, Text Window from the menu bar. When the text screen is on your display, use the arrow keys and slider box to move up and down the list of previous commands. You can set the number of lines that are saved and in the 'TEXTSCR command using the File, Preferences dialogue box. ■

Modifying Entities

You can use the Modify, Entity dialogue box selection from the menu bar to change the lines you have drawn to center lines. Changing entities in this way is not always a good practice. In Tutorial 4 you will learn to use *layers* to set the linetypes and colors of lines, as well as other properties. In general it is better to use layers to set the color and linetype. The default method for setting the color of entities is BYLAYER, which means that the color set for the layer is used as the color for the entities.

Pick: **Modify *(menu bar)*, Entity. . .**

The command prompts you to select a single object. You will select the middle horizontal line.

Select object to modify: ***(select the middle horizontal line)***

The Modify Line dialogue box appears on your screen. This dialogue box, shown in Figure 2.27, lets you change a number of properties of the entities that you have drawn. You can change the color, layer, linetype, and thickness (this gives the entity thickness in the Z direction to create a 3D wireframe), and the X, Y, or Z coordinates by typing or picking a new point. The handle number for the entity, its length, and the angle at which it is drawn appear as information in the box also.

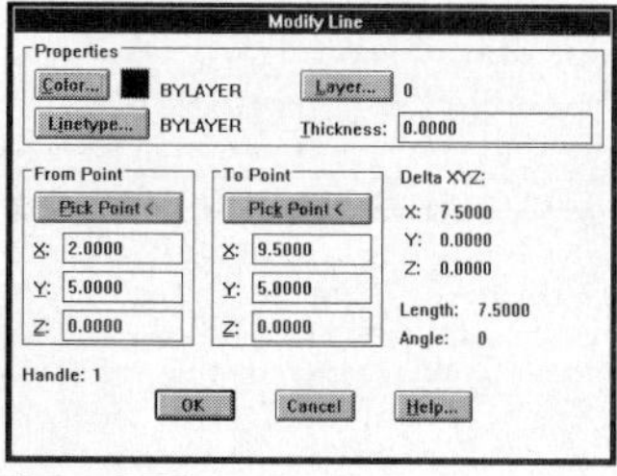

Figure 2.27

■ ***Warning:*** Changing the color or linetype of a layer does not affect entities on that layer that have had their color or linetype set with the Modify, Entity; COLOR; LINETYPE; or CHANGE commands. ■

Move the arrow cursor over the box enclosing the word Linetype. . .. (Remember, any menu item that has an . . . (ellipsis) after it pops up a dialogue box when it is selected.) When you have selected, you will see the Select Linetype dialogue box on the screen, as shown in Figure 2.28.

Pick: **CENTER**

Pick: **OK *(to exit the Linetype dialogue box)***

Pick: **OK *(to exit the Modify Line dialogue box)***

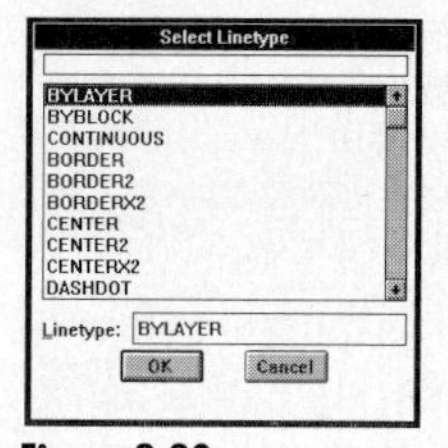

Figure 2.28

Since only one entity at a time can be modified in this way, go back and select the left vertical line and repeat this process on your own to turn it into a center line. Repeat the process for the right vertical line too. Your drawing should look like Figure 2.29.

■ ***TIP*** You can also pick the CHPROP (change properties) command from the EDIT menu, or the Change Properties (DDCHPROP) dialogue box from the Modify selection on the menu bar. When using the CHPROP command, you must type in the letter(s) of the property you wish to change. At the prompt "Change what property (Color/Elev/LAyer/LType /Thickness)?:", type "LT" and press ↵. The advantage of the CHPROP and DDCHPROP commands is that you can select a group of entities to change at the same time unlike the Modify, Entity command which lets you select only one item at a time. ■

Adjusting the Linetype Scaling Factor

To make the center lines line up better in the circles, use LTSCALE under the SETTINGS menu option to adjust them.

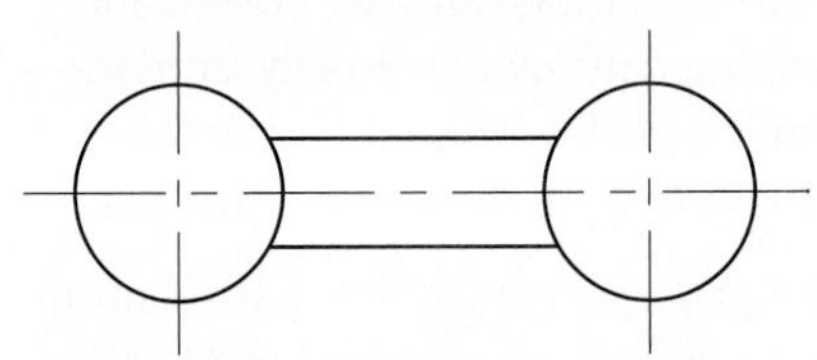

Figure 2.29

Pick: **SETTINGS *(screen)*, next, LTSCALE**

New scale factor <1.0000>: ***.75*** ↵

The center lines should now create a center mark in each circle. If they do not, select a different scale factor for your drawing until they do. Later in this tutorial you will learn another method to add center marks to circles. Save your drawing before continuing.

You will continue your drawing by using FILLET between the handle and the heads of the wrench in the next steps. In order to select the objects to fillet more effectively, use ZOOM Window to enlarge your drawing.

Pick: **View *(menu bar)*, Zoom, Window**

Pick the first and second corners of the window box, enclosing the area you wish to enlarge on your screen. Refer to Figure 2.30 for the area you will be working in.

Pick: **Construct *(menu bar)*, Fillet**

Polyline/Radius/<Select first object>: **r** ↵

Enter fillet radius <1.0000>: **.5** ↵

Command: ↵

Command: FILLET Polyline/Radius/<Select first object>: ***(pick point 1, referring to Figure 2.30)***

Select second object: ***(pick point 2)***

The fillet should appear. On your own, create the remaining fillets referring to Figure 2.30 for the pairs of points you need to select. When you are filleting objects to an arc or circle, more than one fillet may be possible. To help in selecting the correct fillet, pick points 1, 3, 5, and 7 as close to the 45-, 135-, 225-, and 315-degree positions on the circles as possible. AutoCAD selects the fillet closest to the two points used to select the objects to be filleted. (If you make a mistake, type "U" for Undo and press ↵ at the prompt to remove the last action.)

■ ***TIP*** When you are filleting between two intersecting lines, the fillet is always drawn in the direction of the longer segment of the line, no matter where you pick. If this is a problem, use the Modify menu bar command BREAK @ and the Intersection selection from the toolbox and follow the prompts to break the long line at the intersection before you insert the fillet. ■

Your drawing should look like Figure 2.30.

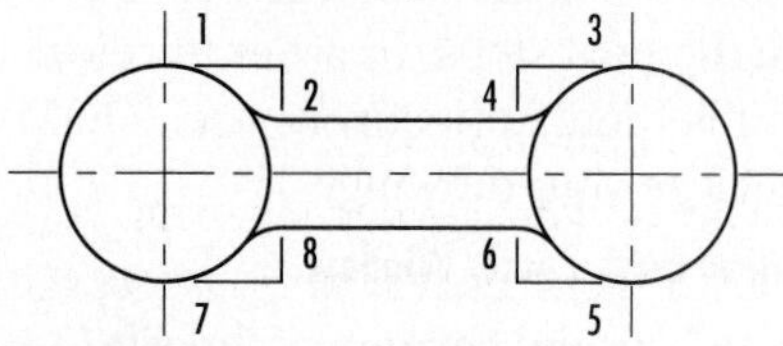

Figure 2.30

You have now completed the first part of the drawing WRENCH. Save this drawing to be completed in Tutorial 3.

Pick: **File *(menu bar)*, Save...**

Using SAVEAS

The SAVEAS command allows you to save a drawing to a new file name. After you have used SAVEAS, the current drawing assumes the new name and future saves are made to this new file. You will save your WRENCH drawing under a different name before you continue so that you may make changes without affecting the WRENCH drawing you will complete later. Select the SAVEAS command from the FILE screen menu or from File on the menu bar.

Pick: **File *(menu bar)*, Save As...**

The Save Drawing As dialogue box appears on your screen, as shown in Figure 2.31. You will use it to specify the new drawing name, WRENCH2. (You can also select a different drive and directory for this new file as you name it.)

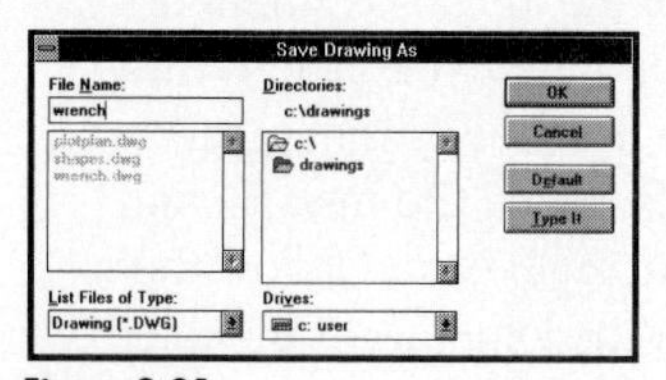

Figure 2.31

To save the drawing to the file name WRENCH2, you will type over the default filename, WRENCH. Be sure WRENCH is highlighted in the File Name: box. (If not, click and drag to highlight it.)

Type: **WRENCH2** ↵

Pick: **OK**

Your drawing is saved as you have specified. You are returned to the drawing editor. Notice that the drawing name displayed in the title bar is now WRENCH2.

Making Changes with Hot Grips

Now that you've renamed your file, you will use the WRENCH2 drawing to demonstrate some of AutoCAD's powerful editing commands. As you have seen with COPY and TRIM, AutoCAD's editing commands can save large amounts of time in drawing creation and editing.

A quick way to make changes to your drawing is by using *hot grips*. Hot grips let you grab an entity that is already drawn on your screen and use certain editing commands directly from the mouse or pointing device without having to select the command from the menu or keyboard.

To use the hot grips you must have a two-button mouse as your minimum hardware configuration. Grips must be enabled or they cannot be used. Pick Settings, Grips from the menu bar and use the dialogue box to be sure an X appears in the box to the left of Enable Grips. Exit the dialogue box by picking OK. You are returned to the drawing editor.

Selecting

Move the crosshairs over the center line of the wrench drawing and press the pick button to select the line. The line becomes dashed and small boxes appear at the center and end points, as shown in Figure 2.32.

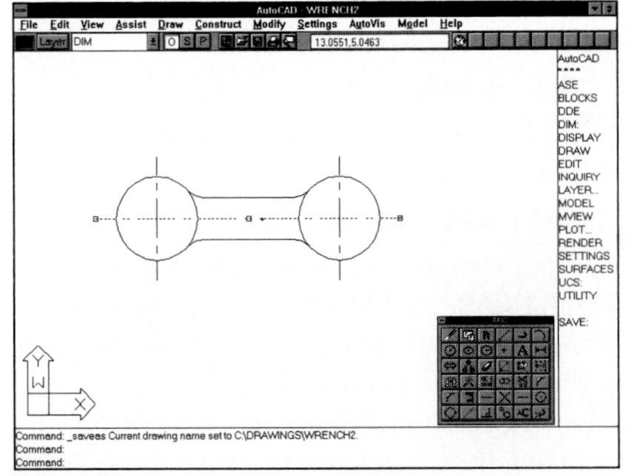

Figure 2.32

These boxes are the hot grips. You can use them to stretch, move, rotate, scale, and mirror the object.

Using STRETCH with Hot Grips

Move the crosshairs to the grip at the right endpoint of the line and press the pick button on your mouse or pointing device to select it. You will see it change to the highlighting color and become filled in solid. This is now the *base grip*. It will act as the base point for the command you will select by pressing the buttons on your pointing device.

In the command line area, you should see the prompt for the STRETCH command:

STRETCH

<Stretch to point>/Base point/Copy/Undo/eXit:

The right end of the line, where you picked the base grip, rubberbands from the position of the crosshairs. Move the crosshairs to a point to the right of the old endpoint and press the pick button. The point you selected should move to the new stretched location, as shown in Figure 2.33.

■ ***TIP*** If you want to stop using the hot grips, press Ctrl-C twice to eliminate the selection of entities with hot grips. ■

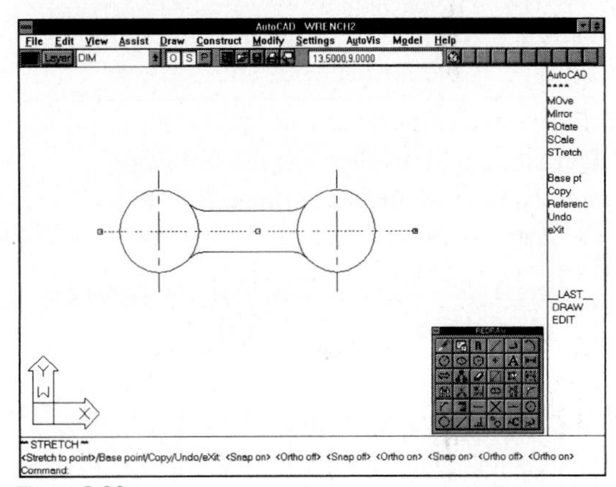

Figure 2.33

Using MOVE with Hot Grips

Now use implied windowing to select the entire wrench (by picking the upper left corner of the wrench and then stretching the box that appears to the lower right until all the lines are enclosed). The hot grips now appear as small boxes on each entity that makes up the wrench. Select the left end of the center line as the base grip by moving the crosshairs over the box and picking. You will see the prompt for the STRETCH command in the command line area. Press the right button, or enter button, on your pointing device. You will see the command prompt cycle to the MOVE command.

> ■ ***TIP*** You can also press the ↵ key to cycle through the command choices that are available for use with hot grips. ■

The command prompt has the following options for the MOVE command:

MOVE

<Move to point>/Base point/Copy/Undo/eXit: ***(move the crosshairs down and to the left)***

You will see the faint outline of the object attached to the crosshairs. Move it to a new location down and to the left and press the pick button when you have it positioned where you want it.

Using MOVE with the Copy Option

Now pick the grip on the top of the left circle as the base grip. Press the enter button on your pointing device once to cycle to the MOVE command. Type "c" to pick the Copy option when you see the prompt:

MOVE

<Move to point>/Base point/Copy/Undo/eXit: **c** ↵

A new prompt appears, similar to the previous one. Move the crosshairs to a location where you would like to make a copy of the object and press the pick button. You can continue to pick points and make several copies of an object. When finished, press ↵ or the right mouse button to end the command.

MOVE (multiple)

<Move to point>/Base point/Copy/Undo/eXit: ***(pick a point)***

<Move to point>/Base point/Copy/Undo/eXit: ↵

On your own, pick the command sequence EDIT, ERASE, Select Objects, ALL from the screen menu to erase everything from your screen. Be sure to press the ↵ key after choosing ALL to tell AutoCAD you are done selecting things and now you want them erased. Once the entities are erased, pick R from the toolbox to redraw the screen, removing the blipmarks.

Using ROTATE with Hot Grips

In order to have some objects to use with the ROTATE command, you will use the pull-down Draw menu and pick LINE, Double Lines to draw the figure you see in Figure 2.34. Use GRID (F7) and SNAP (F9) to help you pick points.

Pick: **Draw, Line, Double Lines**

Break/Caps/Dragline/Offset/Snap/Undo/Width/<Start point>: ***(pick four corners to draw the rectangle shown in Figure 2.34)***

Figure 2.34

The DLINE command is useful for drawing architectural floor plans and other items that require parallel lines. It will also draw the cap across the end of an open line, change the width separating the lines, and perform other useful functions. Experiment with these options on your own to draw a floor plan. The double line is set to either side of the points that you select as endpoints, so you must draw the center line of the walls to use DLINE effectively.

Now you will use implied windowing to activate the hot grips for these lines. Refer to Figure 2.34.

Pick: ***(point A)***

You will see a window box form as you move the crosshairs away from the point you selected. Move downwards and to the right to enclose all of the lines in the drawing in the window. When you have the window sized correctly,

Pick: ***(a point below and to the right of the rectangle)***

You will see the hot grips appear on the lines, as shown in Figure 2.35.

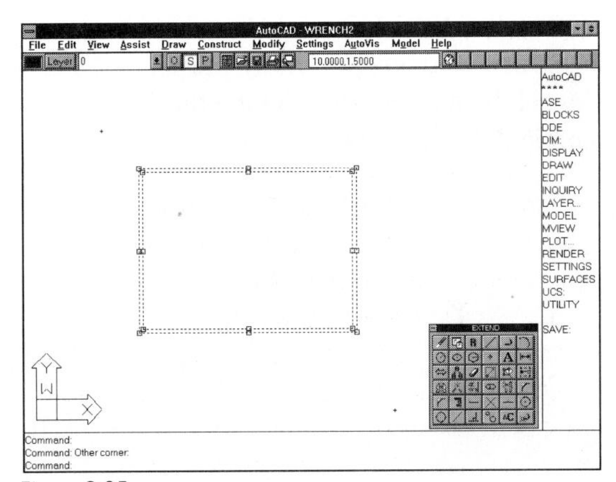

Figure 2.35

On your own, select the middle grip on the bottom line as the base grip by positioning the crosshairs over it and pressing the pick button. You will see it turn the highlighting color and be filled in solid. The STRETCH command appears at the command prompt. Press the right mouse button, or enter button, once to cycle to the MOVE command. Press it again to cycle to the ROTATE command. If SNAP is turned on, press the F9 key to turn it off so you can see the effect of the rotation command clearly.

You will see the faint object rotating as you move the crosshairs around on the screen. You can press the pick button when the object is at the desired rotation, or type in a numeric value for the rotation. Keep in mind that 0 degrees is to the right and positive values are measured counterclockwise.

ROTATE

<Rotation angle>/Basepoint/Copy/Undo/Reference/eXit: **45** ↵

Notice that the object rotated so that it is at an angle of 45 degrees, as shown in Figure 2.36. Cancel the hot grips by clicking the CTRL-C icon in the toolbox twice.

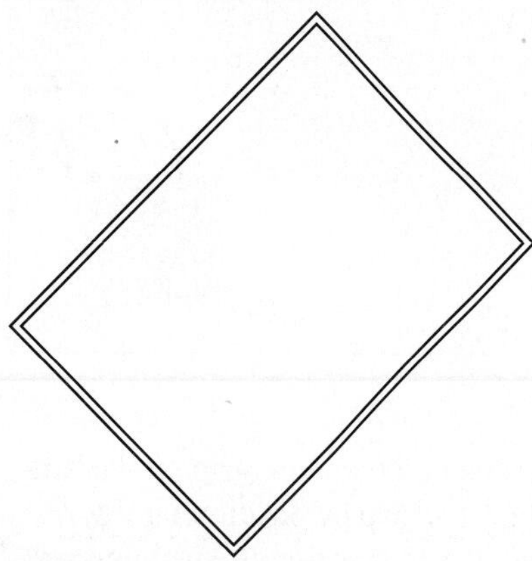

Figure 2.36

Using SCALE with Hot Grips

The SCALE command changes the size of the object in your drawing database. You should only use this when you want to make the actual object larger or smaller. (For example, when converting a drawing from feet to inches, you could use a scale factor of 12.) Use ZOOM, Window when you just want to enlarge its display on screen to show more detail.

On your own, use hot grips to scale the object. Activate the hot grips, using implied windowing again. This time, however, use the Crossing option. In order to use Crossing instead of Window, start your window box in the lower right corner of the drawing and select the first point. Move the crosshairs with the window up and to the left, drawing the box from right to left. This specifies a crossing box. Unlike Window, which selects only the entities that are entirely enclosed in the box, Crossing selects anything that crosses the box or is enclosed. When you have done this successfully, you will see the hot grips appear at the corners and midpoints of the lines.

Pick: ***(the lowest grip as the base grip)***

It becomes solid, filled with the highlighting color. You will see the STRETCH command in the command prompt area. Cycle through the commands until the SCALE command appears.

Press: ***(the right mouse button three times)***

When you see the SCALE prompt, the faint image of the object becomes larger as you move the crosshairs away from the base point; as you get closer to the base point it appears smaller, as demonstrated in Figure 2.37. When you are happy with the new size of the object, press the pick button.

SCALE

<Scale factor>/Base point/Copy/Undo/Reference/eXit: ***(pick a point)***

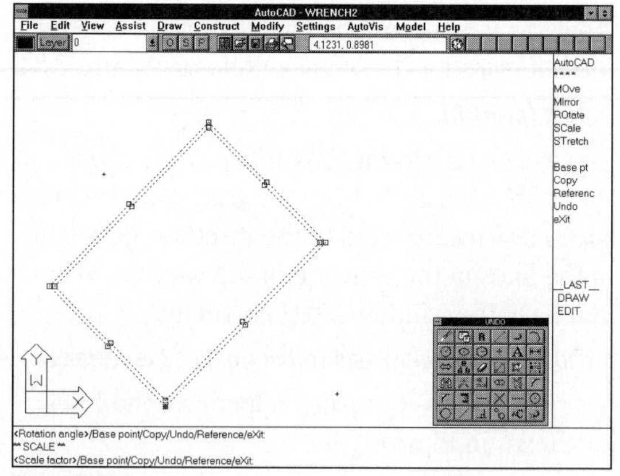

Figure 2.37

■ ***TIP*** To change the scale to known proportions, you can type in the scale factor. A value of 2 makes the object twice as large; a value of .5 makes it half its present size. ■

Using MIRROR with Hot Grips

The MIRROR command creates a mirror image of the selected entities, using a *mirror line* that you specify. To use the MIRROR command with hot grips, once again activate the hot grips by implied windowing (if they are not active). When you see the grips appear on the object, select the lower right-hand grip as the base grip. Press the right mouse button to cycle through the commands STRETCH, MOVE, ROTATE, and SCALE until the MIRROR command appears in the command prompt area.

The MIRROR command uses a mirror line and forms a symmetrical image of the selected objects on the other side of the line. You can think of this line as rubberbanding from the base grip to the current location of the crosshairs. Notice that as you move the crosshairs to different positions on the screen, the faint mirror image of the object appears on the other side of the mirror line. You will see the prompt:

MIRROR

<Second point>/Base point/Copy/Undo/eXit: **B** ↵

The Base point option lets you specify some other point besides the hot grip you picked as the first point of the mirror line for the object. Refer to Figure 2.38.

Base point: ***(pick point A)***

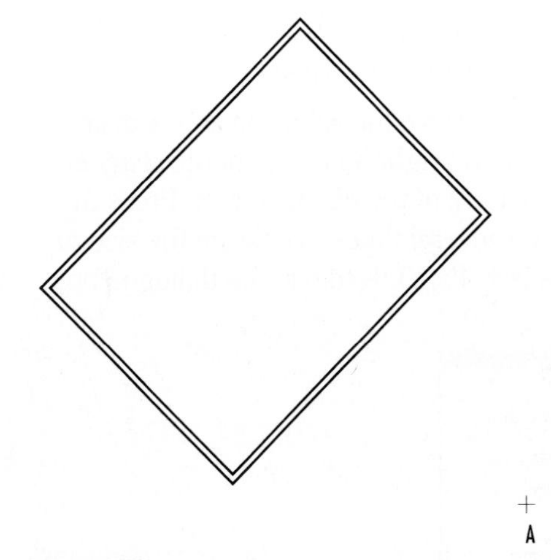

Figure 2.38

Move the crosshairs on the screen and notice the object being mirrored around the line that would be between the base point and the location of the crosshairs. When you are happy with the location of the mirrored object, press the pick button to select it. The old object disappears from the screen and the new mirrored object remains. Use ZOOM, All to see the new object.

Pick: **ZOOM icon *(toolbar)*, All *(screen menu)***

Changing the Grips

AutoCAD allows you to turn grips on or off in your drawing and to change their color and size. To do this,

Pick: **Settings *(menu bar)*, Grips. . .**

You will see a dialogue box like the one in Figure 2.39 appear on your screen.

On your own, move the selection arrow over the arrow at the right-hand end of the *slider bar* near the bottom of the dialogue box. Press the pick button several times to enlarge the size of the grips box. Pick OK to exit the dialogue box.

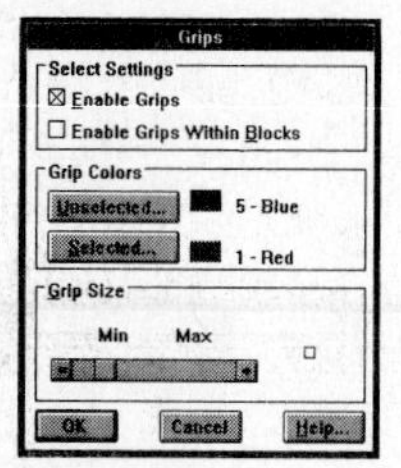

Figure 2.39

Position the crosshairs over one of the lines in your drawing and press the pick button to activate the grips for that line. You will notice that the grip is now larger than it was during the previous exercise. If it appears too large, return to the dialogue box by picking Settings, Grips. . . and reset to a smaller size. You will notice you can also change the color of the grips, and the base or activated grip, and turn grips off completely if you do not want to use them.

Noun/Verb Selection

You may have noticed that Noun/Verb selection was on when you used implied windowing. Hot grips can also be used with other commands for *Noun/Verb selection.* When you use Noun/Verb selection, you select the entities that will be affected by a command first, instead of first selecting the command and then the group of entities. Think of the drawing entities as nouns, or things, and the commands as verbs, or actions. Next you will use Noun/Verb selection with the ERASE command to clear your screen.

Pick: ***(a point below and to the right of all your drawing entities)***

Other corner: ***(pick a point above and to the left of the drawing entities)***

You will see the hot grips for the entities that were crossed by the implied crossing box appear in your drawing.

Pick: **ERASE icon *(toolbox)***

Notice that you do not have to select the items. They were pre-selected with the hot grips and as soon as you pressed (↵), they were erased.

Creating the Geneva Cam

You will use many of the editing commands you have learned in this tutorial, plus one more, to create the geneva cam you see in Figure 2.40. You will use the ARRAY command to create rectangular and radial patterns.

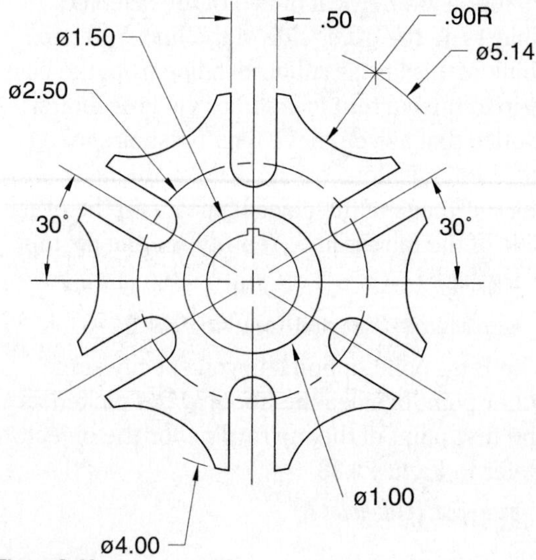

Figure 2.40

Before you begin set SNAP to .25. Make sure that SNAP is turned on by checking to see whether the SNAP button on the toolbar is highlighted. If it is not, pick on the SNAP button or press F9 to turn SNAP on. If you do not have a grid displayed in the drawing, press F7 to turn GRID on.

You will first use the CIRCLE command to create the innermost circle of diameter 1. Locate the center of the circle at coordinates 5.5, 4.5.

Pick: **Draw *(menu bar)*, Circle, Center, Diameter**

3P/2P/TTR/<Center point>: **5.5,4.5** ↵

Diameter<2.0000>: **1** ↵

On your own draw the 1.5-diameter circle and the outer 4-diameter circle concentric to the circle you just drew.

Using DIM to Draw Center Lines

The center points of circles are located on a drawing using center lines. Because center lines need to be positioned exactly over the center point of the circle to form a neat cross, then a gap and a line that extends past the edge of the symmetrical part, AutoCAD includes a special tool for drawing center lines. To draw center lines for the circles, you must first set the variable named DIMCEN to define the style of center line you wish to draw.

When you use DIMCEN, you are prompted to enter its new value. A positive value results in a center mark only; a negative value results in a full set of center lines. Figure 2.41 shows the results of adding center marks with DIMCEN set to –.125 and +.125. The absolute value of the entry determines the length of the lines that make up the center mark. You will enter a negative value to set the mode to a full set of center lines for each circle in the drawing.

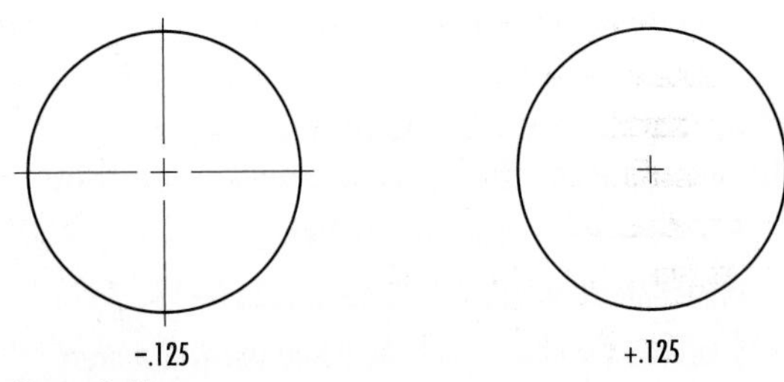

Figure 2.41

Type "DIMCEN" at the prompt:

Command: **DIMCEN** ↵

New value for DIMCEN <0.0900>: **–.125** ↵

Once the variable value has been entered, use the Dimension command CENTER and select the center points to be marked. You can select DIM, DIM, next, CENTER from the screen menu; select Dimensions, Radial, Center Mark from the Draw pull-down menu; or type the CENTER command at the prompt. You may want to turn off SNAP temporarily to make it easier to select the circle. If you do so, turn it back on when you have finished the command. (If you use DIM, you must use EXIT or Ctrl-C to return to the command prompt. You will learn more about dimensioning in Tutorial 7.)

Pick: **Draw *(menu bar)*, Dimensions, Radial, Center Mark**

Select arc or circle: ***(pick on the outer 4-diameter circle)***

Your drawing should look similar to Figure 2.42.

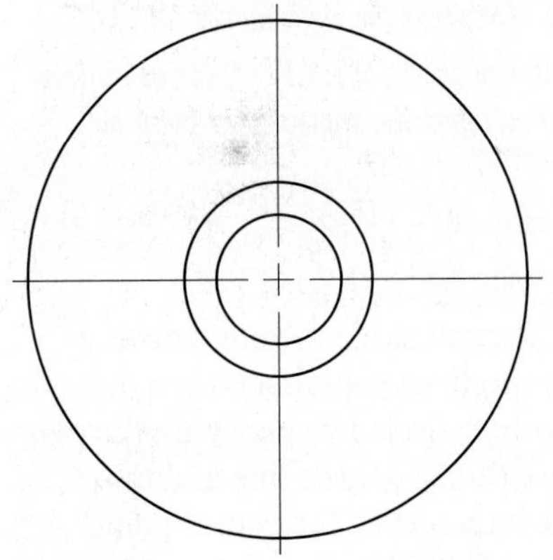

Figure 2.42

You will continue adding the other features according to the dimensions given in Figure 2.40. Use the OFFSET command to create lines parallel to the upper vertical center line.

Pick: **Construct *(menu bar)*, Offset**

Offset distance or Through <Through>: **.25** ↵

Select object to offset: ***(pick the upper vertical center line)***

Side to offset? ***(pick on the right side)***

Select object to offset: ***(pick the same vertical center line)***

Side to offset? ***(pick on the left side of the line)***

Select object to offset: ↵

Next you will use the alias L to select the LINE command to draw a line angled at 60 degrees, as you see in Figure 2.43.

Command: **L** ↵

From point: **5.5,4.5 *(or pick the center point of the circles, using SNAP)***

To point: **@3<60** ↵

To point: ↵

Use the CIRCLE command to add the construction circles to your drawing.

Pick: **Draw *(menu bar)*, Circle, Center, Diameter**

3P/2P/TTR/<Center point>: **5.5,4.5** ↵ ***(or use a snap increment to select the same center point as before)***

Diameter<4.0000>: **5.14** ↵

Command: ↵ ***(or press the right mouse button)***

3P/2P/TTR/<Center point>: **5.5,4.5** ↵ ***(or use a snap increment to select the same center point as before)***

Diameter/<Radius>: **d** ↵

Diameter<5.1400>: **2.5** ↵

You will add a small circle to your drawing between the two lines you offset, then draw the final construction circle by specifying the coordinates where the 60-degree line and the largest circle intersect as the center point. Refer to Figure 2.43. (You may also pick Intersection from the toolbox, as you did when finding the distance between the intersections on the wrench.)

Command: ↵

3P/2P/TTR/<Center point>: ***(pick 1, the point where the upper vertical center line crosses the 2.5-diameter construction circle)***

Diameter/<Radius>: **d** ↵

Diameter<2.5000>: **.5** ↵

Command: ↵

3P/2P/TTR/<Center point>: **6.7850,6.7257** ↵

Diameter/<Radius><0.2500>: **.9** ↵

Your drawing should look like Figure 2.43.

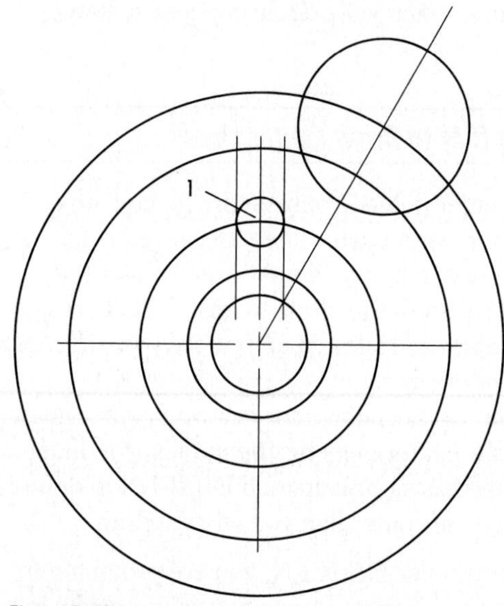

Figure 2.43

The next step is to remove the portions of the lines and circles that you will not need in the ARRAY command.

Use the TRIM and ERASE commands on your own to remove the unwanted portions of the figure until your drawing looks like Figure 2.44.

■ ***TIP*** If you use the implied crossing method to select all of the entities in the drawing as the cutting edges and then press ↵, you can quickly trim the object to the shape shown by picking on the extreme ends of the entities you wish to have removed. Use ERASE to remove any of the entities that no longer cross a cutting edge. ■

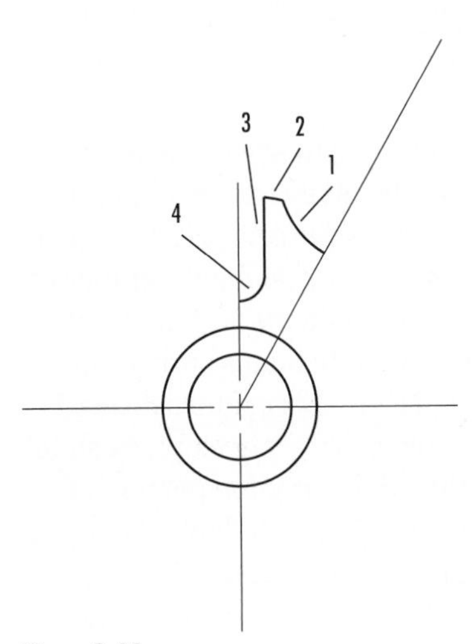

Figure 2.44

Next you will use the MIRROR command to mirror the lines and arcs labeled 1-4 in Figure 2.44 around to the left side of the vertical center line.

Using MIRROR

You have seen how the MIRROR command is used with hot grips to create mirror images of shapes. The MIRROR command is also located on the EDIT screen menu, on the Modify pull-down menu, and in the fourth row and first column of the toolbox. Its icon is the mirror image of a shape. Unlike the MIRROR hot grips command, this MIRROR command asks you whether or not to delete the old entities.

To MIRROR an object, you must specify a mirror line. A mirror line is used to define both the angle and distance at which the mirrored image is drawn. The mirrored image is drawn perpendicular to the mirror line. You can use slanted mirror lines. The mirrored object is the same distance from the mirror line as the given object, but on the other side of the mirror line. The mirror line does not have to be drawn before you use the MIRROR command; when asked to specify the mirror line, you can pick two points from the screen that define the line.

The vertical center line will serve as the mirror line as you mirror the lines and arcs. Refer to Figure 2.44 as you pick points. Be sure SNAP is turned on before picking the points for the mirror line.

Pick: ***MIRROR icon (toolbox)***

Select objects: ***(pick entities 1, 2, 3, and 4)***

■ ***TIP*** If you select entities that you do not wish to mirror, you can use the Remove option of the object selection modes to remove them from the selection. To do this, type "R" or pick Remove while still at the "Select objects" prompt. Pick the entity to be removed from the selection. If you wish to Add more entities after using Remove, pick Add or type "A" while still at the "Select objects" prompt. Press ↵ when you have the objects you want selected. This tells AutoCAD you are done selecting and want to continue with the command. You will learn more about selection methods in Tutorial 3. ■

Select objects: ↵

First point of mirror line: ***(select the center of the concentric circles)***

Your cursor is now dragging a copy of the entities around the screen.

Second point: ***(select a point straight down from the center point)***

Delete old objects? <N> ↵

> ■ ***TIP*** Had you typed "Y" at the prompt "Delete old objects? <N>", the original object would have disappeared. ■

Your screen should look like Figure 2.45.

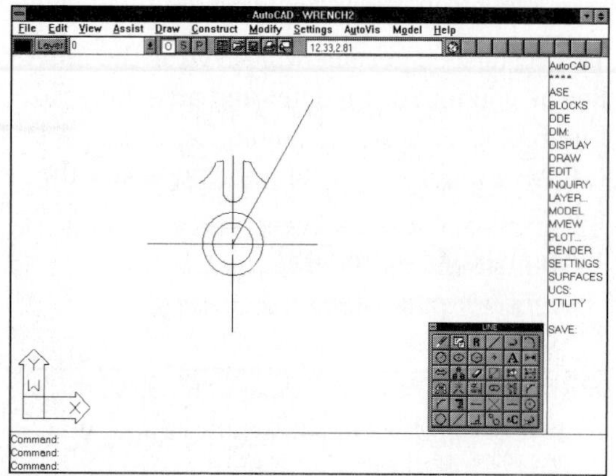

Figure 2.45

> ■ ***TIP*** Figure 2.46 shows an object mirrored about one of its own edge lines. If you wish, mirror lines can be added to the drawing and then erased after the construction is complete, or you can pick any two points from the screen that would define a line. ■

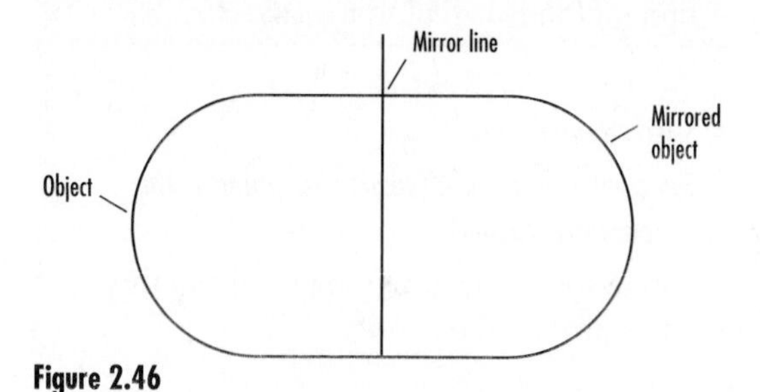

Figure 2.46

Using ARRAY

The ARRAY command can be used to copy an object multiple times to form a regularly spaced rectangular or circular pattern. Any time that you have a regularly spaced pattern of objects or entities in your drawing, you can use the ARRAY command to quickly create the pattern. Examples are creating a circular pattern of holes in a circular hub, creating rows of desks in laying out a classroom, or creating the teeth on a gear.

The ARRAY command is located on the EDIT screen menu and the Construct pull-down menu. You are prompted to select the items you wish to array. The array can be either a *rectangular array* or a *polar array*. A rectangular array is composed of a specified number of rows and columns of the items with a specified distance between them. In a polar array, the items are copied in a circular pattern around the center point you specify. The copies can fill 360 degrees of the circle or some portion of 360 degrees. You can choose to have the items rotated as they are copied with the ARRAY command so that the copied items have the proper orientation.

You are now ready to use the ARRAY command to copy the lines and arcs around in a radial pattern to finish creating the geneva cam.

Pick: **Construct *(menu bar)*, Array**

Select objects: ***(pick the items 1–4 that you mirrored and the mirrored copies of them)***

Select objects: ↵

Rectangular or Polar array (R/P) <R>: **P** ↵

Center point of array: ***(use SNAP to pick the center of the concentric circles)***

Number of items: **6** ↵

Angle to fill (+=ccw, -=cw) <360>: ↵

Rotate objects as they are copied? <Y>: ↵

On your own use ERASE to erase the angled line from the drawing. Your drawing should look like Figure 2.47.

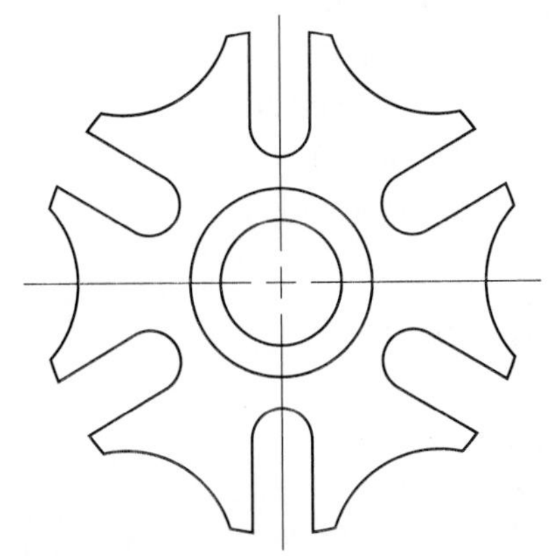

Figure 2.47

Adapting for Architecture

The ARRAY command is useful in architectural drawings. Rectangular arrays can be used to easily generate column bays for large buildings or framing members on structural plans. Spiral stairs or plant symbols can be generated using the polar array command option. ■

Your drawing is now complete. Use the File, Save As. . . selection to save your drawing to a new file name.

Pick: **File *(menu bar)*, Save As. . .**

The Save Drawing As dialogue box appears on your screen. Be sure that WRENCH2 is highlighted in the box below File Name, then

Type: **GENEVA *(for the name of the drawing)***

Pick: **OK *(to exit the dialogue box and save your drawing)***

Going Further

Use the Rectangular option of the ARRAY command to create a pattern showing six copies of the geneva wheel drawing you created. Select Construct, Array from the pull-down menu. Pick the entire object, using the implied crossing method, and then press ↵. At the next prompt, type "R" to create a rectangular array. At the prompt, "Number of rows (---)<1>:", type "2" and press ↵. At the prompt, "Number of columns (|||)<1>:", type "3" and press ↵. Finally, you are prompted for the distance between the rows and columns. You can either specify the distance on screen or type a response at the prompt. At the "Unit cell or distance between rows (----):" prompt, type "6" and press ↵. You will see the prompt, "Distance between columns (|||):". Type "6" and press ↵. Use the ZOOM, All command to have the copies you created fill the screen area. Use File, Save As. . . from the menu bar to save your drawing with the name GEN-ARRY.

Pick: **File *(menu bar)*, Exit AutoCAD**

You are returned to the Windows Program Manager. Close the AutoCAD Program Group by double-clicking the Windows Control box in the upper left corner of the AutoCAD Program Group window.

KEY TERMS

aperture box
base grip
chamfer
chord length
cutting edges
fillet
grab
hot grips
layer
mirror line
Noun/Verb selection
paper space
primitives
polar array
rectangular array
regenerate
scale factors
slider bar
virtual screen

KEY COMMANDS

Arc
Array
Center Marks
Chamfer
Change Properties
Copy
Dimensions
Distance
Donut
Double Line
Dynamic Dialogue Change Properties
Fillet
Linetype
Linetype Scale
Mirror
Move
Offset
Open
Pan
Quick Save
Rotate
Save As
Scale
Stretch
Text Screen
Trim

EXERCISES

Redraw the following shapes. If dimensions are given, create your drawing geometry exactly to the specified dimensions. The letter M after an exercise number means that the given dimensions are in millimeters (metric units). If no letter follows the exercise number, the dimensions are in inches. Do not include dimensions on the drawings. The ∅ symbol means diameter; R indicates a radius.

2.1 Clearance Plate

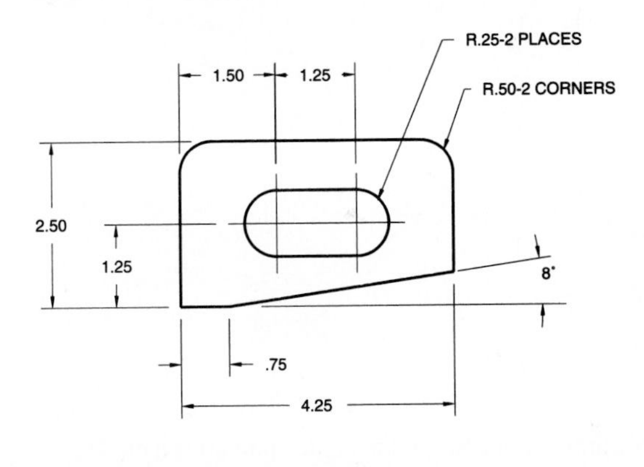

2.2M Bracket

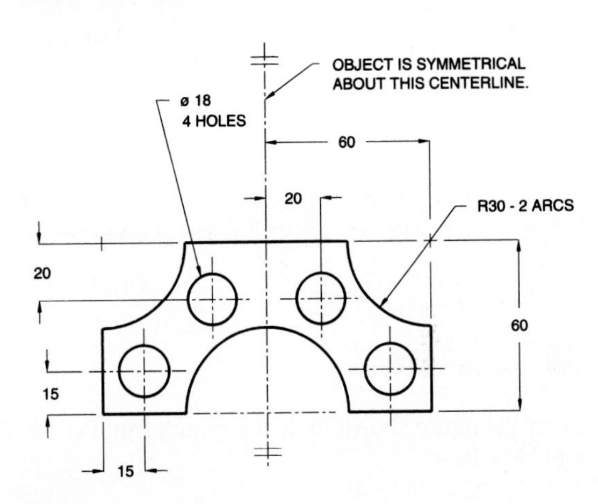

2.3 Gasket

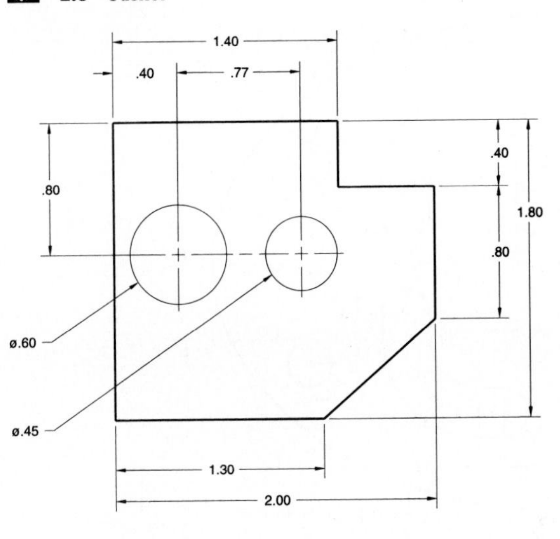

2.4 Plot Plan

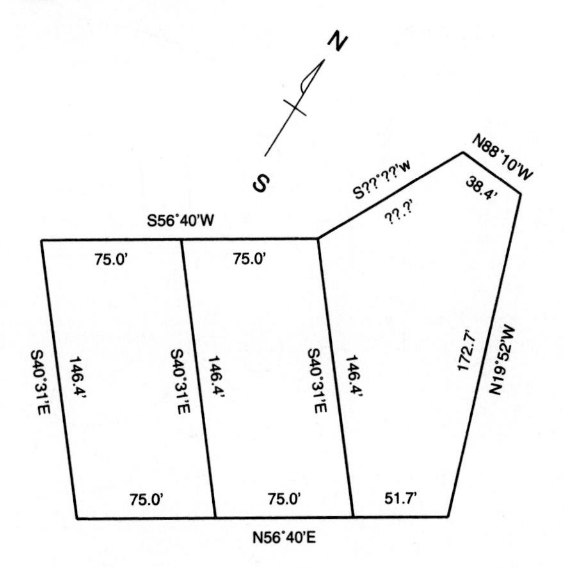

2.5M Puzzle

Draw the figure shown according to the dimensions provided. From your drawing determine what the missing distances must be (hint: use DIST).

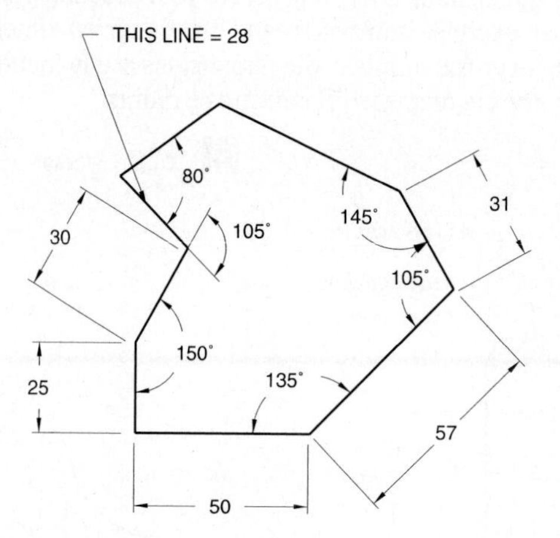

2.6 Slotted Ellipse

Draw the figure shown (note the symmetry). Do not show dimensions. Show the center line on the circles and the ellipse.

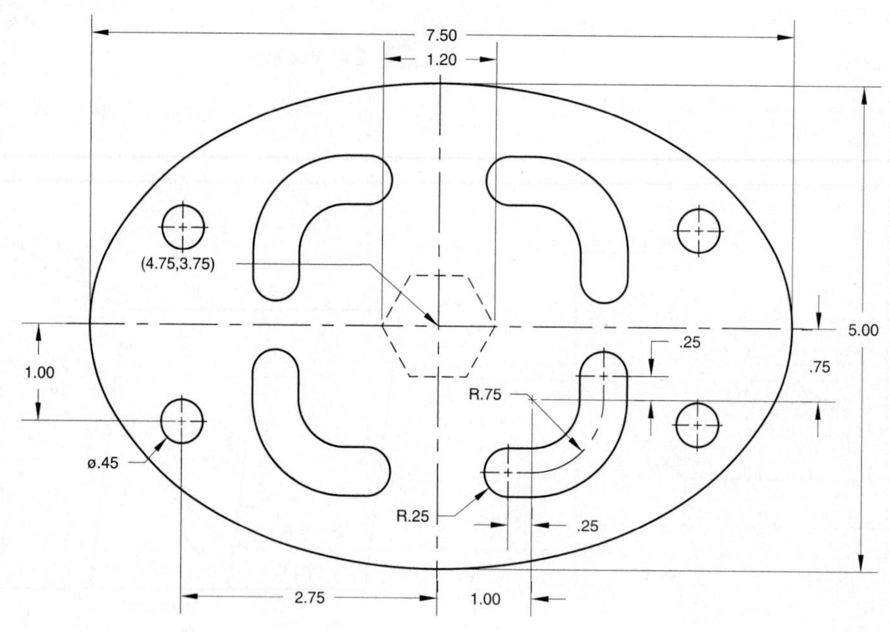

2.7 Roadway

Shown is a center line for a two-lane road (total width is 20 feet). At each intersection is a specified turning radius for the edge of pavement. Construct the center line and edge of pavement. Use Dim: Center to label the radius points with a +. Do not show any of the text. Scale is 1" = 20'.

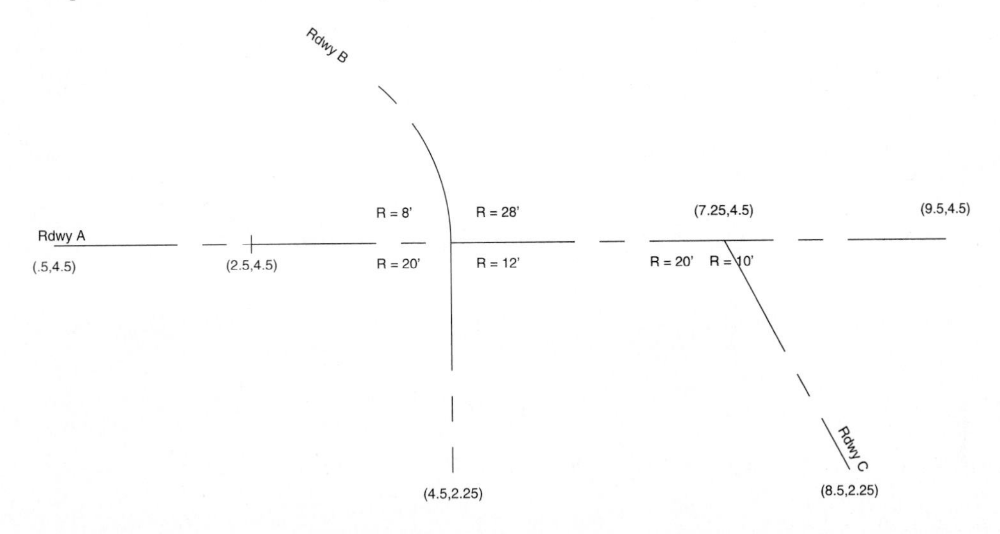

2.8 Power Supply

Draw this circuit using the techniques you have learned.

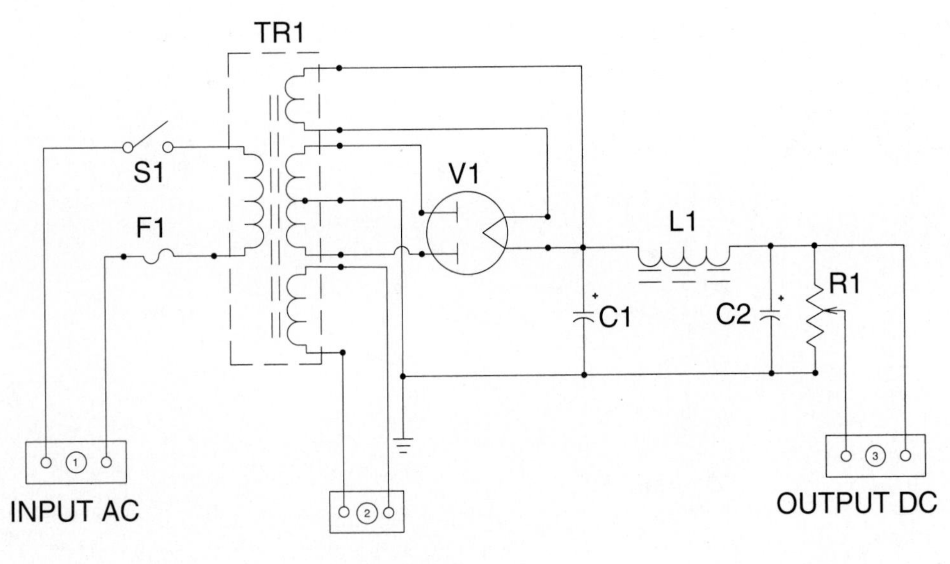

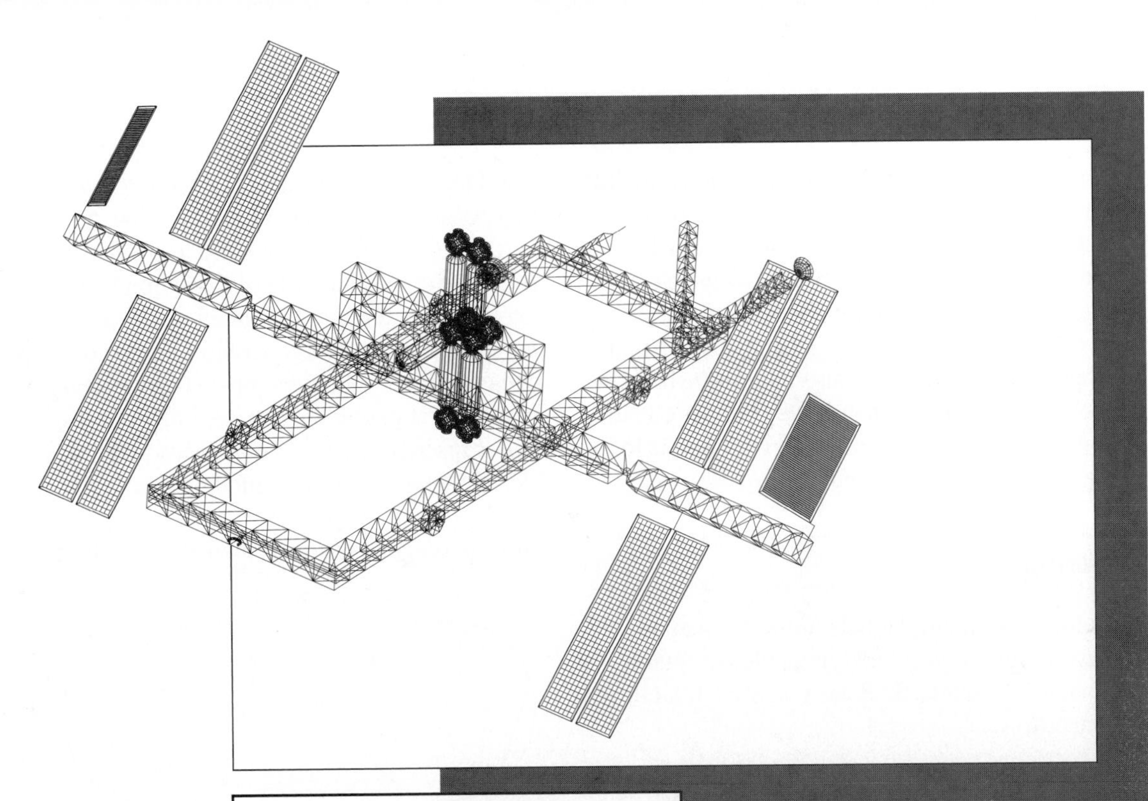

TUTORIAL 3

Geometric Constructions

Objectives

When you have completed this tutorial, you will be able to

1. Draw objects, using the POLYGON, PLINE, CIRCLE (2P, 3P, TTR), and ELLIPSE commands.
2. Correct mistakes with UNDO and REDO.
3. Use the OSNAP command and its related functions to pick geometric locations.
4. Use the PEDIT, EXTEND, ROTATE, MOVE, and BREAK editing commands.
5. Set the TILEMODE variable and print or plot a drawing, using paper space and viewports.
6. Use DIVIDE to insert points or entities.

Introduction

This tutorial expands your skills by introducing several of the AutoCAD drawing techniques used for geometric constructions. You will learn to use object snaps (OSNAP) to select locations, such as intersections, endpoints, and midpoints of lines, based on your existing drawing geometry. The tutorial synthesizes the techniques you have learned by showing you how to coordinate the drawing commands to create technical drawings.

Starting

Before you begin, launch AutoCAD as you have before. If you need help, please review Chapter 3, AutoCAD Basics, in Part 1, Getting Started.

Your computer display shows AutoCAD's drawing editor. Notice that at the top of the screen the word UNNAMED appears instead of the current file name. This tells you that you are starting out in a new AutoCAD drawing, and that you have not yet assigned a name for the drawing. Later, when you save your drawing, you will be prompted for a file name. If you use QSAVE without specifying a file name first, the drawing is saved as 1.DWG in the current directory.

■ ***Warning:*** If the main AutoCAD screen, including the drawing editor, toolbar, toolbox, menu bar, command prompt area, and screen menu, is not on your display screen, check to be sure that you have configured AutoCAD properly for your computer system. ■

Using POLYGON

The POLYGON command is used to draw regular *polygons* with from 3 to 1024 sides. A regular polygon is one in which the lengths of all sides are equal. The size of a polygon is usually expressed in terms of a related circle. This derives from the classic straight edge/compass construction techniques most students learn in their first geometry course. Polygons are either *inscribed* in or *circumscribed* about a circle. A pentagon is a five-sided polygon. Figure 3.1 shows a pentagon inscribed within a circle and a pentagon circumscribed about a circle.

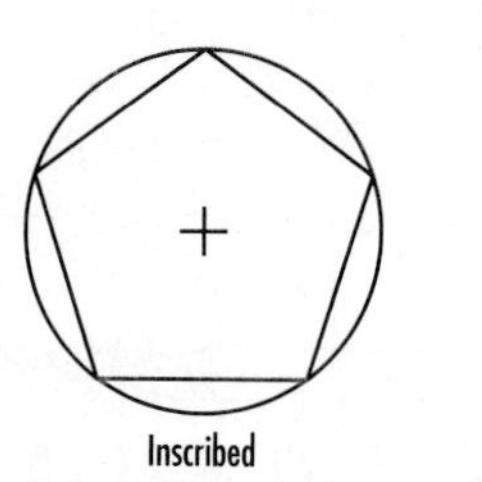

Figure 3.1

The POLYGON command is located on the DRAW screen menu, on the Draw menu bar, and in the second row and third column of the toolbox. You are going to circumscribe the pentagon about a circle. To draw a pentagon,

Pick: **POLYGON *(toolbox)***

Number of sides <4>: **5** ↵

Edge/<Center of polygon>: ***(select a point for the center)***

Inscribed in circle/Circumscribed about circle (I/C)<I>: **C** ↵

If you had wanted to inscribe the pentagon, you would have selected I for Inscribe. You must specify the radius of the circle, either by picking with the pointing device or typing in the coordinates. For this example,

Radius of circle: **1.5** ↵

A five-sided regular polygon (a pentagon) is drawn on your screen. Your screen should look similar to Figure 3.2.

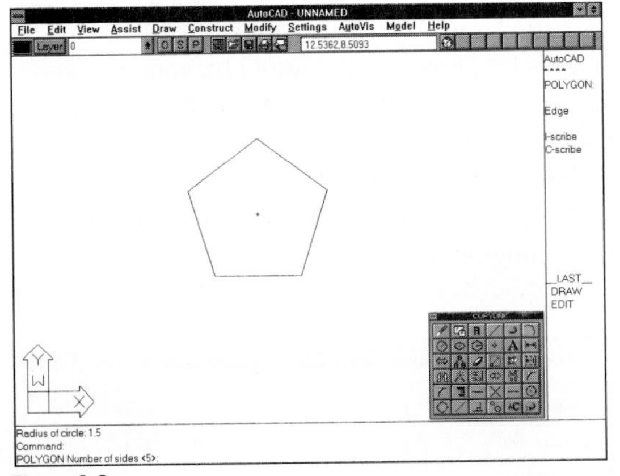

Figure 3.2

Drawing Hexagons

Hexagons are a very common shape in technical drawings. Hexagons are six-sided polygons. The heads of bolts, screws, and nuts often have a hexagonal shape. The size of a hexagon is sometimes referred to by its *distance across the flats*. This is because the sizes of screws, bolts, and nuts are defined by the distance across their flat sides. For example, a 16mm hexhead screw would measure 16 mm across its head's flats and would fit a 16mm wrench. The distance across the flats of a hexagon is not the same as the length of one of the edges making up the hexagon. Figure 3.3 illustrates the difference between the two distances. If a hexagon is **circumscribed** about a circle, the diameter of the circle will equal the distance across the hexagon's flats. If a hexagon is **inscribed** in a circle, the diameter of the circle will equal the distance across the corners of the hexagon.

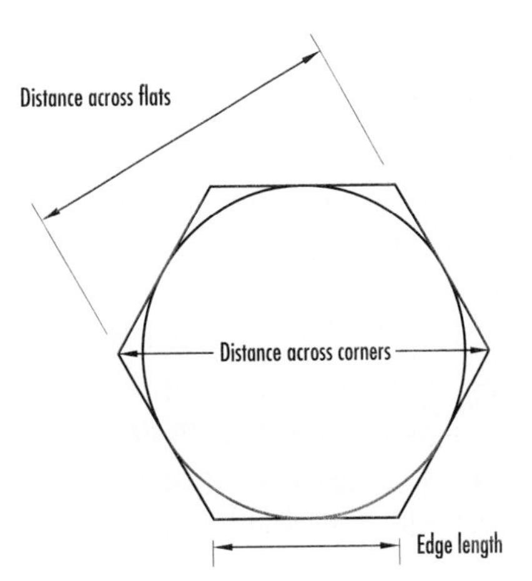

Figure 3.3

You can also use the POLYGON command to draw regular polygons by specifying the length of the edge. This function is helpful when you are creating side-by-side hexagonal patterns (honeycomb patterns). Next, you will draw a hexagon based on a specified edge length. AutoCAD draws polygons in a counterclockwise direction. This means that the sequence in which you select points will affect the position of the polygon. See Figure 3.4.

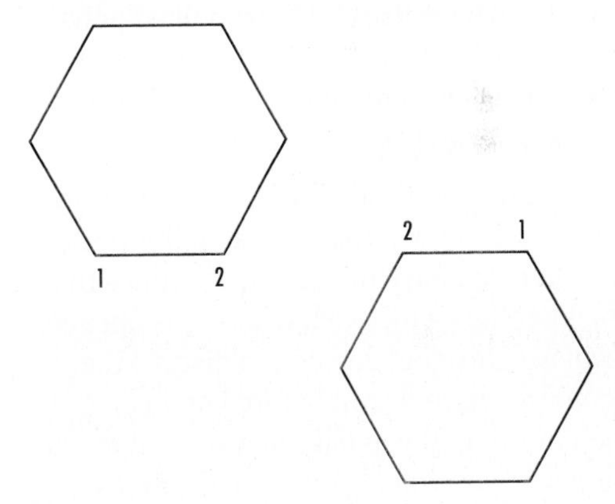

Figure 3.4

Command: ↵ ***(or press the right mouse button)***
Number of sides <5>: **6** ↵
Edge /<Center of polygon>: **e** ↵
First endpoint of edge: ***(select a point)***

AutoCAD is in DRAG mode. You can see the hexagon move on your screen as you move your cursor. This helps you place the hexagon in your drawing. To complete the hexagon,

Second endpoint of edge: ***(select a second point)***

A hexagon with the edge length specified by your selection of points should appear on your screen.

Adapting for Architecture

The POLYGON command can be used to make a wide variety of architectural symbols in drawings. Window, door, and material callout symbols can be made easily by using four- , five- , and six-sided polygons. ■

Completing the Wrench

Now that you have learned how to draw polygons, you can complete the WRENCH drawing that you began in Tutorial 2.

Pick: **File *(menu bar)*, Open**

The Drawing Modification dialogue box shown in Figure 3.5 is on your screen, alerting you to the fact that you have drawn some entities that will be lost when a different drawing is opened. You will use this dialogue box to discard the polygons you have drawn before you open the wrench drawing. If you did not want to discard the drawing, you would pick Save Changes, and then the Save Drawing As dialogue box would appear, allowing you to name and save the drawing.

Pick: **Discard Changes**

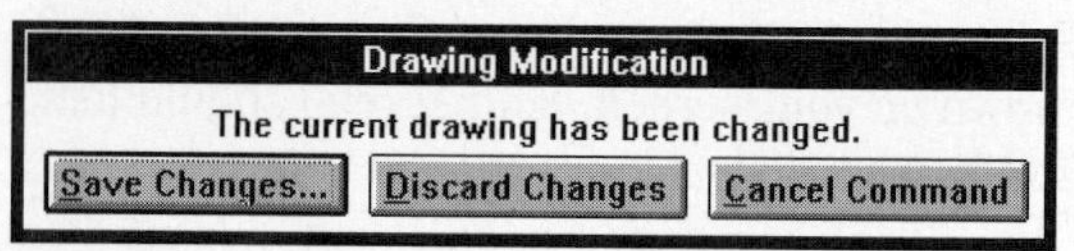

Figure 3.5

The Open Drawing dialogue box appears on the screen, as shown in Figure 3.6. Use it to locate the WRENCH drawing that you started in Tutorial 2 and pick OK to exit the dialogue box. (Refer to Tutorial 2 if you need help using the dialogue box.)

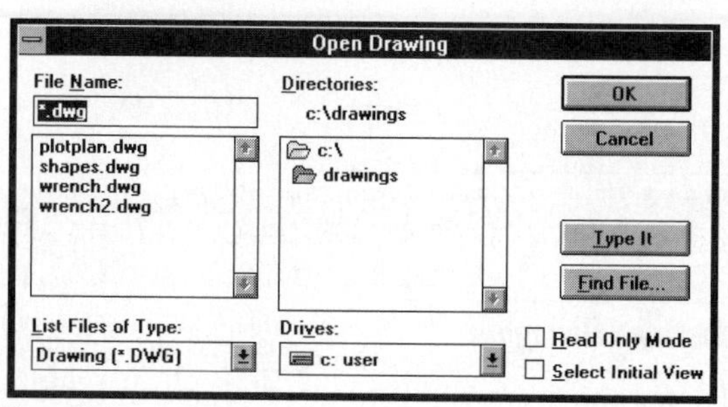

Figure 3.6

When you have successfully opened the WRENCH drawing, your screen should look similar to Figure 3.7.

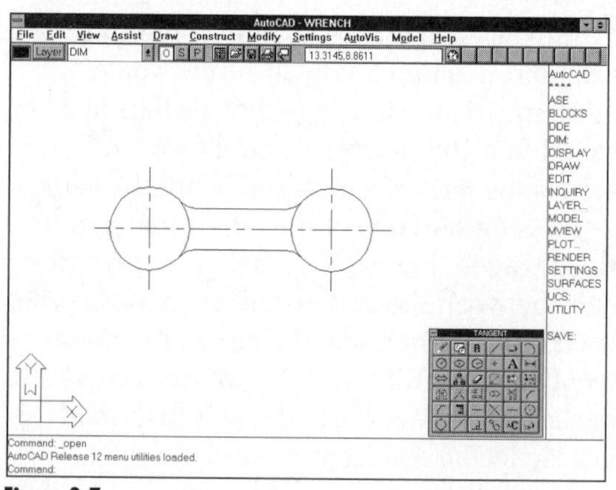

Figure 3.7

To complete the drawing, you need to draw two polygons.

■ ***TIP*** Use SNAP and GRID with .5 spacing to help you with this drawing. When you load a file, SNAP and GRID are set as they were when you saved the drawing. If they are not set to .5, use SNAP and GRID to reset them now. (Refer to Tutorial 1 if you need help.) ■

First, you will circumscribe a pentagon about a .5-radius circle in the right circle of the wrench. You will need SNAP turned on to pick points.

Pick: **POLYGON icon *(toolbox)***

Number of sides <4>: **5** ↵

Edge/<Center of polygon>: **(select the center point of the right circle)**

Inscribe in circle/Circumscribe about a circle (I/C)<I>: **C** ↵

Radius of circle: **.5** ↵

Next, you will circumscribe a hexagon that is 1.00 across the flats in the left circle of the wrench. Use ↵ to repeat the POLYGON command.

Command: ↵

POLYGON Number of sides <5>: **6** ↵

Edge/<Center of Polygon>: ***(select the center point of the left circle)***

Inscribe in circle/Circumscribe about a circle (I/C) <C>: ↵

Radius of circle: **.5** ↵

A hexagon measuring 1.00 across the flats should appear in your wrench. The final drawing should look similar to Figure 3.8.

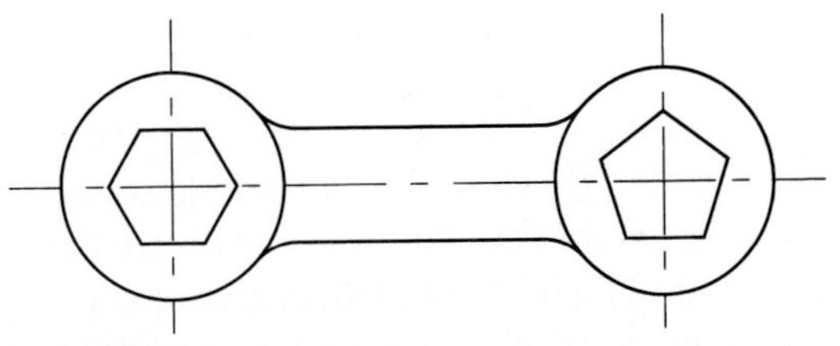

Figure 3.8

You have now completed your wrench. You will save this drawing and begin the next drawing to continue this tutorial.

Pick: **File *(menu bar)*, Save...**

In this next section, you will practice with additional drawing commands. You will start a new drawing, as you did in the previous tutorial, but you will leave the drawing name portion of the dialogue box empty, which will result in an unnamed drawing (like when you drew the polygons).

Pick: **File *(menu bar)*, New...**

Remember to leave the drawing name portion of the dialogue box empty.

Pick: **OK**

You are returned to the drawing editor. Notice that UNNAMED appears in place of the drawing name.

Using PLINE (Polyline)

The PLINE (Polyline) command is used to draw a series of connected entities (lines or arcs) that are treated as a single entity by AutoCAD, called a *polyline*. A hexagon drawn using the POLYGON command is an example of a polyline: six connected lines that function as a single entity. The PLINE command is used on technical drawings to draw irregular (French) curves, and lines that have a width. An irregular curve is any curve that does not have a constant radius (a circle and an arc have a constant radius). The PLINE command is located on the DRAW screen menu, the Draw menu bar selection, and on the toolbox. The PLINE icon on the toolbox is the one to the right of the LINE icon. It appears similar to an arc, except that the lines are thick.

To draw an irregular curve,

Pick: **Polyline *(toolbox)***

From point: ***(select any point)***

Current line-width is 0.0000

Arc/Close/Halfwidth/Length/Undo/Width/<Endpoint of line>:
(select 9 more points)

You will use the Close option as you have done in past tutorials when drawing closed figures with the LINE command.

Arc/Close/Halfwidth/Length/Undo/Width/<Endpoint of line>:
c ↵

Your screen should show a line made of multiple segments, similar to that shown in Figure 3.9.

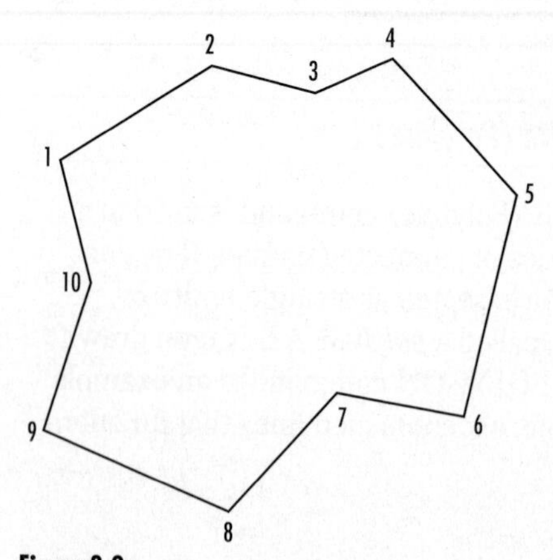

Figure 3.9

A shape drawn using PLINE is different from a shape created by using the LINE command, in that AutoCAD treats the pline as one line. You cannot ERASE one of the pline segments. If you try, the entire line is erased. Other PLINE options allow you to draw an arc as a polyline segment (Arc), specify the starting and ending width (or half-width) of a given segment (Width, Half-width), specify the length of a segment (Length), and remove segments already drawn (Undo).

PEDIT

Once a polyline has been created, it and its individual segments can be changed with PEDIT. The PEDIT (Polyedit) command is located on the EDIT menu, the Modify, Polyedit and in the bottom right hand corner on the toolbox. You will use PEDIT to change the segmented line you just created to a smooth curve.

The PEDIT command has two different methods of fitting curves. The Fit option joins every point you select on the polyline with an arc. The Spline option produces a smoother curve by using either a cubic or a quadratic B-spline approximation (depending on how the system variable SPLINETYPE is set). You can think of the spline operation as working like a string that is stretched between the first and last points of your polyline. The vertices on your polyline act to pull the string in their direction, but the resulting spline does not necessarily reach the point.

Pick: **PEDIT *(toolbox, bottom right corner)***

Select polyline: ***(select any part of the pline)***

Open/Join/Width/Edit vertex/Fit/Spline/Decurve/Ltype gen/ Undo/eXit <X>: F ↵ *(or Fit curve from the menu)*

> ■ ***TIP*** PEDIT can be used to convert entities into plines. At the "Select polyline:" prompt, pick the line or arc you wish to convert to a pline. You will see the message, "Entity selected is not a polyline. Do you want to turn it into one? <Y>:" Press ↵ to accept the yes response to convert the selected entity into a pline and continue on with the prompts for the PEDIT command. ■

The straight line segments change to a curved line, as shown in Figure 3.10.

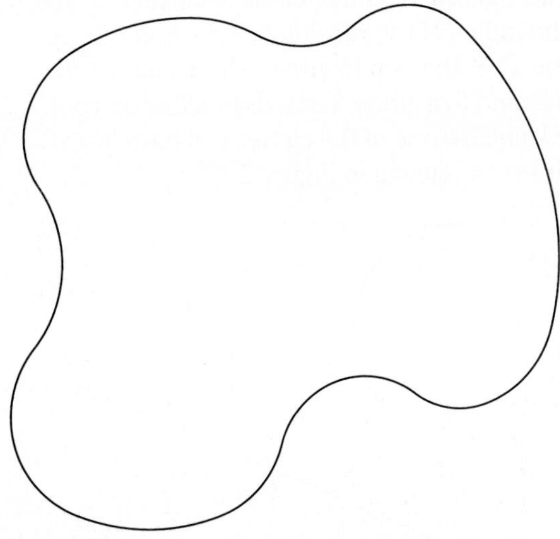

Figure 3.10

Fit curve connects all the vertices of a 2D polyline by joining each pair of vertices with an arc. Use the Undo option of the command to return the polyline to its original shape.

Open/Join/Width/Edit vertex/Fit/Spline/Decurve/Ltype gen/ Undo/eXit <X>: U ↵

The original polyline returns on your screen. Now try the Spline option:

Open/Join/Width/Edit vertex/Fit/Spline/Decurve/Ltype gen/ Undo/eXit <X>: S ↵

You should see a somewhat flatter curve, similar to the one shown in Figure 3.11, replace the original polyline. Among other things, splined polylines are useful for creating contour lines on maps.

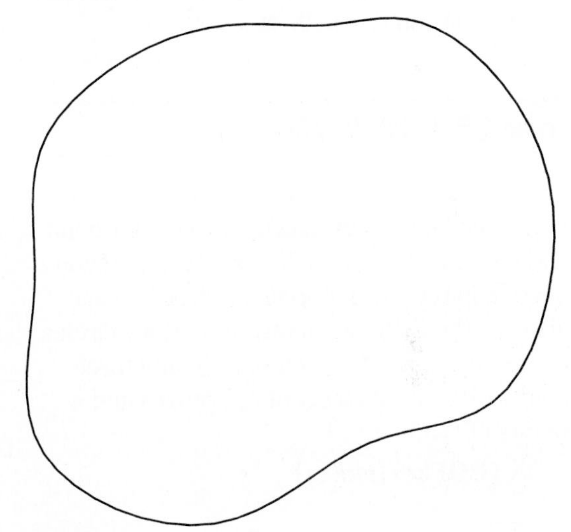

Figure 3.11

Now try the width option:

Open/Join/Width/Edit vertex/Fit/Spline/Decurve/Ltype gen/ Undo/eXit <X>: W ↵

Enter new width for all segments: **.2** ↵

The splined polyline is replaced with one that is .2 units across. You will accept the default by pressing ↵ to exit the PEDIT command.

Open/Join/Width/Edit vertex/Fit/Spline/Decurve/Ltype gen/ Undo/eXit <X>: ↵

> ■ ***TIP*** If you have a polyline that has already been curved with Fit or Spline, Decurve returns the original polyline. ■

Adapting for Architecture

You can use the PLINE command in conjunction with OFFSET to quickly create floor plans. With a pline, the perimeter walls can be created and then offset the required distance to form the interior of the wall, without any further editing. Make sure to close the perimeter pline when you create it. ■

Using CIRCLE 2P, 3P, TTR

You have already seen how the CIRCLE command can be used by specifying a center point and either a radius or a diameter value. If you need help refer to Tutorials 1 and 2. You can also use the CIRCLE command to draw circles by specifying any two points (2P), any three points (3P), or two tangent references and a radius (TTR).

Pick: **CIRCLE icon *(toolbox)***

2P

First you will draw a circle, using the 2P (2-point) function of the CIRCLE command. The two points that you select are the endpoints of the circle's diameter.

Pick: **2 Point *(from the screen menu)***

First point on diameter: ***(select a point)***

You are in DRAG mode and you can see the circle move around on your screen with your cursor.

Second point on diameter: ***(select a point)***

The circle is drawn, using the two points that you selected as the endpoints for the diameter of the circle.

3P

To draw a circle with the 3P (3-point) function of the CIRCLE command, specify three points on the circle's circumference.

Pick: **3 Point(screen menu, to restart the CIRCLE command and use the 3 point option)**

First point: ***(select a point)***

Second point: ***(select a point)***

You are in DRAG mode again; you can see the circle being created on your screen as you move the cursor.

Third point: ***(select a point)***

The circle has been defined by three points on its circumference.

TTR

The TTR function of the CIRCLE command stands for Tangent, Tangent, Radius. It requires that you specify two lines and/or circles that the resulting circle is tangent to, and the radius of the resulting circle. You will use the TTR function to draw a circle tangent to a line and to a circle. First, draw a line on your own below one of the circles you have just drawn, as shown in Figure 3.12.

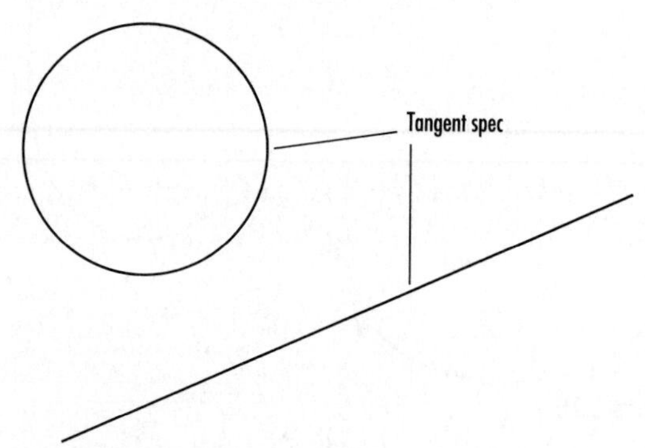

Figure 3.12

Pick: **CIRCLE *(toolbox)*, TTR *(screen)***

You will notice that your cursor now resembles a small box, called an *aperture*, with the horizontal and vertical lines crossing through it. Refer to Figure 3.13. You can select either the circle or the line first.

Enter Tangent spec: ***(select the circle)***

Enter second Tangent spec: ***(select the line)***

Radius <default>: **.9** ↵

A circle with a radius of .9 is drawn that is tangent to both the original circle and the line, as shown in Figure 3.13. If you selected points on the opposite side of the line and circle, your circle may be positioned differently, although it is still tangent to both. If you get the message, "Circle does not exist," the .9 radius may be too small or too large to be tangent to both the line and the circle. Try again, using a different value for the radius.

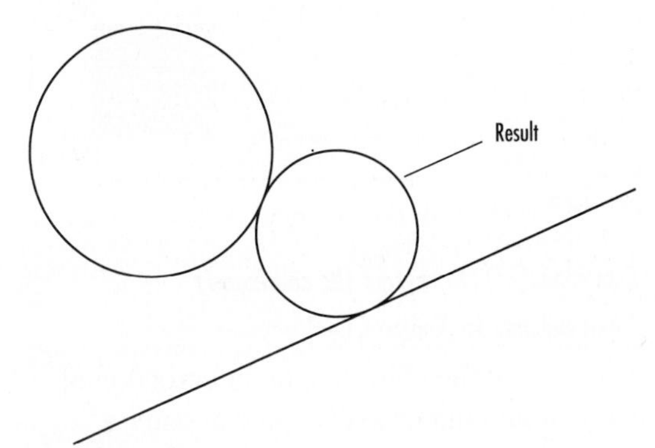

Figure 3.13

You can also use the TTR function to draw a circle tangent to two circles, as shown in Figure 3.14.

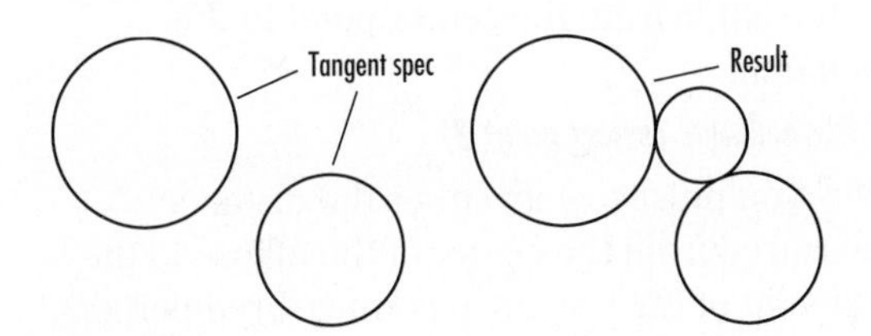

Figure 3.14

Draw two circles on your own, using 2P for the first one and 3P for the second. Then you will draw a circle tangent to them.

Pick: **TTR *(screen menu)***

Enter Tangent spec: ***(select one of the circles)***

Enter second Tangent spec: ***(select the other circle)***

Radius<0.9000>: **1** ↵

A circle with a radius of 1 is drawn that is tangent to both circles.

On your own, ERASE the circles to make room in your drawing to create ellipses.

Using ELLIPSE

The ELLIPSE command is used to draw ellipses. AutoCAD approximates the shape of an ellipse by drawing 4 connected pline arcs. There are four different ways to specify an ellipse using AutoCAD, not including the isometric ellipse, which will be explained in Tutorial 11. The ELLIPSE command is located on the DRAW screen menu, the Draw menu bar, and is available from the toolbox (just to the right of CIRCLE). To draw an ellipse by specifying three points,

Pick: **ELLIPSE icon *(toolbox)***

<Axis endpoint 1>/Center: ***(select a point)***

Axis endpoint 2: ***(select a point)***

<Other axis distance>/Rotation: ***(select a point)***

An ellipse is created on your screen, using the three points that you selected. The ellipse has a *major axis*, the longest distance between two points on the ellipse, and a *minor axis*, the shorter distance across the ellipse. AutoCAD determined which axis was major and which was minor by examining the distance between the first pair of endpoints and comparing it to the distance specified by the third point.

AutoCAD provides several methods for drawing ellipses to make it possible to draw an accurate shape with the information at hand. One way to describe an ellipse is to create a circle and then tip the circle away from your viewing direction by a rotation angle. This is the method you use when you specify the angle of rotation instead of the endpoint of the second axis.

You will draw an ellipse, using two endpoints and an angle of rotation. The rotation angle must be between 0 and 89.4 degrees.

See Figure 3.15 to determine the location of the points.

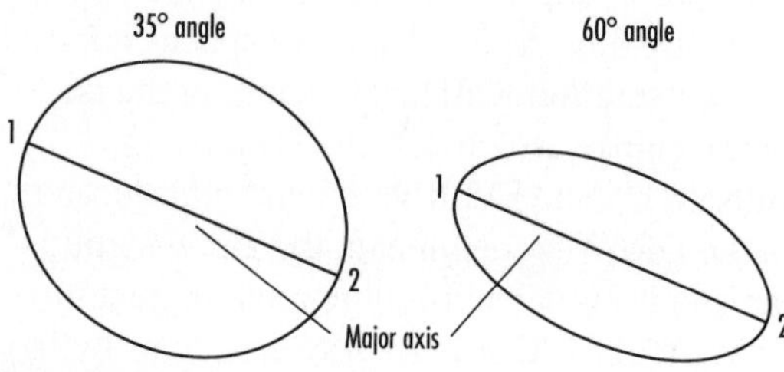

Figure 3.15

Pick: **ELLIPSE *(screen menu)***

<Axis endpoint 1>/Center: ***(select point 1)***

Axis endpoint 2: ***(select point 2)***

This construction method defines the distance between points 1 and 2 as the major axis (diameter) of the ellipse. This circle will be rotated into the third dimension by the specified rotation angle.

<Other axis distance>/Rotation: **R** ↵

Rotation around major axis: **35** ↵

On your own, erase the objects from your screen.

The other two construction methods for ellipses are analogous to the two methods already described, but they use radius values rather than diameter values. That is, the center point of the ellipse is known and is used as a starting point instead of an endpoint. Next, you will draw an ellipse by specifying a center point and two axis points; refer to Figure 3.16 for the locations of the points.

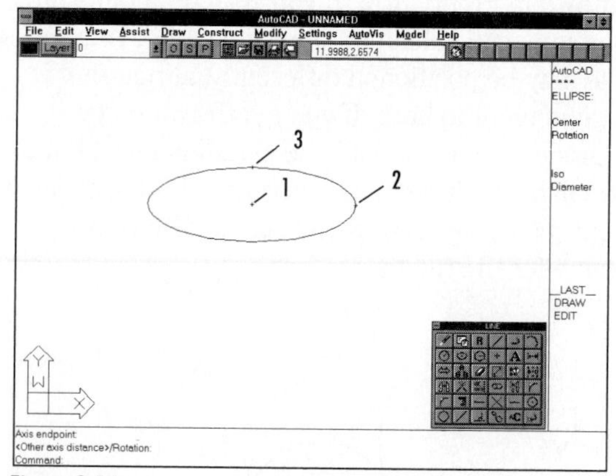

Figure 3.16

Command: ↵ ***(to restart the command)***

<Axis endpoint 1>/Center: **C** ↵

The center of the ellipse is the intersection of the major and minor axes. You can enter a coordinate or use the cursor to select a point on the screen.

Center of ellipse: ***(select point 1)***

Next, you must provide the endpoint of the axis. The angle of the ellipse is determined by the angle from the center point to this endpoint.

Axis endpoint: ***(select point 2)***

Now you must specify either the distance measured from the center of the ellipse to the endpoint of the second axis (measured perpendicular to the first axis), or a rotation angle.

<Other axis distance>/Rotation: ***(select point 3)***

AutoCAD used the point that you selected to decide whether the first axis was a major or minor axis. The ellipse is drawn on your screen.

Next you will draw an ellipse by specifying a center point, one axis point, and an angle of rotation. (See Figure 3.17.) When you select the command from the pull-down menu, you pick one of the two basic approaches from the menu, eliminating the need to specify Center in another step.

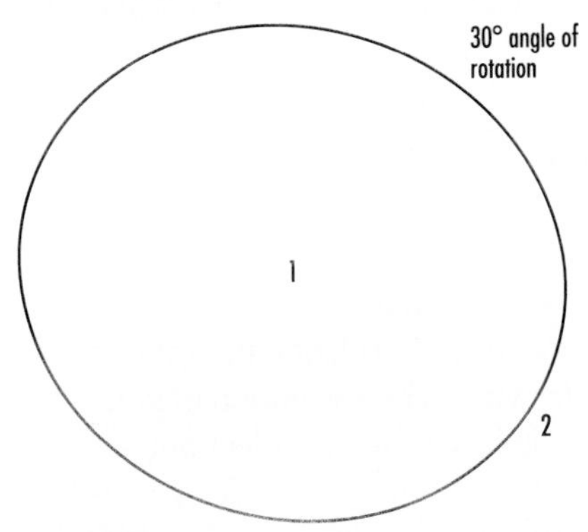

Figure 3.17

Pick: **Draw *(menu bar)*, Ellipse, Center, Axis, Axis**

Center of ellipse: ***(select point 1)***

Axis endpoint: ***(select point 2)***

<Other axis distance>/Rotation: **R** ↵

Rotation around major axis: **30** ↵

Your ellipse should look like the one in Figure 3.17.

UNDO

The UNDO command is used to remove the effect of previous commands. If you make a mistake, pick the UNDO command from the upper left corner on the toolbox, from the EDIT screen menu, or under Edit on the menu bar, and the effect of the previous command disappears.

Try this now to see the last ellipse you drew disappear.

Pick: **EDIT *(menu bar)*, UNDO**

> ■ ***TIP*** If you UNDO the wrong entity, there is a command, REDO, which lets you restore the last item you have undone. ■

As you saw with PLINE, several commands also include Undo as an option within a command. LINE, TRIM, DIM, EXTEND, and others include Undo as a command option that allows you to undo the last action within the command. This Undo subcommand appears on the screen menus for these commands. Notice the difference between these uses.

Pick: **LINE *(toolbox)***

From point: ***(pick a point)***

To point: ***(pick a point)***

To point: ***(pick a point)***

To point: **undo *(screen menu)(to undo the last endpoint picked)***

To point: ↵

One line segment disappears and you remain within the LINE command. Now undo the entire LINE command with the UNDO command.

Pick: **Edit *(menu bar)*, UNDO**

All the line segments drawn with the last instance of the command disappear.

UNDO picked from the toolbox (or typed at the command line or picked from the EDIT screen menu) offers more options for undoing your work. You will draw some lines to have some entities to undo.

On your own, use ERASE from the toolbox to clear your drawing editor and then pick LINE to draw six parallel lines anywhere on your drawing screen. Use SNAP and GRID as needed.

In the next step you will use the UNDO command to remove the last three lines that you drew.

Pick: **Undo *(toolbox)***

Auto/Back/Control/End/Group/ Mark/<number>: **3** ↵

The last three lines drawn should disappear, corresponding to the last three instances of the LINE command. You could have selected any number, depending on the number of command steps you wanted to undo.

> ■ ***TIP*** Often it is easier to back up one step at a time, by typing "U" at the command prompt and pressing the ↵ key, or by using Undo from the menu bar. Some commands do several steps in one sequence and you may not be sure of the number you want to back up. ■

REDO

If the last command issued was UNDO and you really did not want to undo it, you can use the REDO command to reverse the effects of the last UNDO.

Command: **REDO** ↵

The three lines should reappear. REDO reverses only the last UNDO; it must follow immediately after the UNDO command.

Back

The Back option of the UNDO command takes the drawing back to a mark that you set with the Mark option or to the very beginning of the drawing session if you haven't set any marks. Be careful selecting these options or you may undo too much.

Pick: **UNDO *(screen menu)*, BACK**

This will undo everything. OK?<y>: ↵

All the lines should disappear.

Command: **REDO** ↵

All the lines should reappear. Use UNDO to erase all entities in this drawing session from the screen on your own. Use REDRAW to clean up the screen.

Using OSNAP

The Object Snap feature in AutoCAD, activated with the OSNAP command, is used to accurately select locations in relation to other entities in your drawing. The resolution of your screen makes it impossible to select points with the accuracy at which AutoCAD stores the drawing geometry in the database. You have seen how SNAP makes it possible to pick an accurate point on the screen by "snapping" to a grid point. OSNAP makes it possible to accurately pick points on your drawing geometry by snapping to an entity's Center point, Endpoint, Midpoint, and so on. Whenever you are prompted to select a point, you can use an OSNAP mode to help make an accurate selection. Without this command, it is virtually impossible to locate two entities with respect to each other in a way that gives you correct and useful geometry. OSNAP is one of the most important tools that you have available to you when using AutoCAD. The many specialized OSNAP modes are listed on the Assist pull-down menu shown in Figure 3.18. Many of the Object Snap override modes can also be selected from the toolbox.

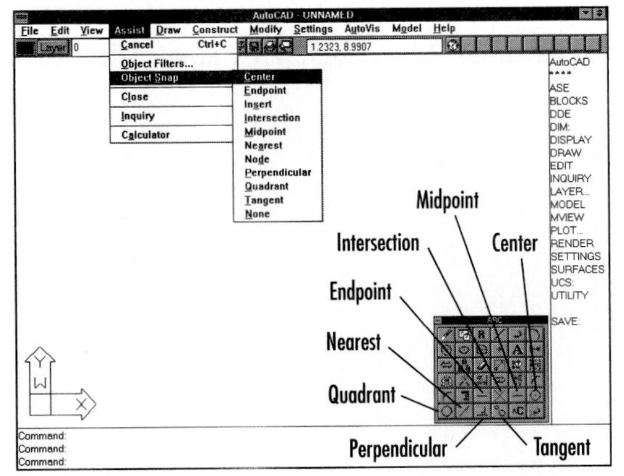

Figure 3.18

To use OSNAP, you must specify the mode you want to use. As you can see from the Assist menu, the selected mode determines the specific location on the drawing entity you will find when you press the pick button and select an entity. This section of the tutorial will explain those modes used most often to create technical drawings.

OSNAP can operate in two different ways. The first is called *override mode*. In this method, you select the OSNAP mode **during** a command. The OSNAP acts as a modifier within the command string to target the next point you select. When OSNAP is activated from within another command in this manner, it is active for one pick only. Remember, this method can only be used during a command that is prompting for the selection of points or objects.

You activate OSNAP from within other commands by picking the appropriate icon from the toolbox, selecting the four asterisks (****) beneath AutoCAD on the screen menu, and selecting one of the modes listed; by selecting one of the modes under Assist, Object Snap on the menu bar; or by typing the three-letter mode name any time you are prompted to enter points or select objects. The OSNAP icons are located in the last two rows of the toolbox; the entity locations they select are indicated with red dots on the icons. You will use a variety of methods to invoke OSNAP in this tutorial. Thereafter, you may use whichever method suits your style.

■ ***TIP*** The OSNAP overrides are used so frequently that many AutoCAD configurations use the middle mouse button on a three-button mouse to activate the menu. If you have a three-button mouse, try the middle button. If you are using a digitizing tablet, press the fourth button, to cause the OSNAPs to appear on the screen at your current cursor location. ■

When an OSNAP mode is active, AutoCAD has a special cursor, the aperture, shown in Figure 3.19. You saw the aperture box in Tutorial 2 when you used the object snap mode INTERSECTION from the toolbox to find the distance on the WRENCH drawing, and again in this tutorial when using the CIRCLE, TTR command.

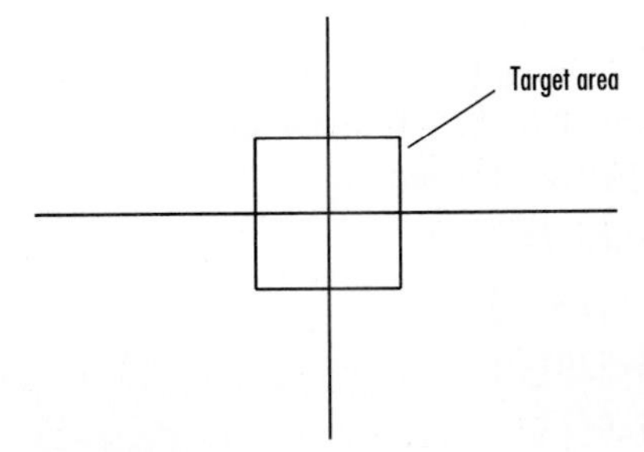

Figure 3.19

The square area around the horizontal and vertical lines is called the *target area*. When you are selecting an entity in an OSNAP mode, the entity need only be within the target area.

OSNAP Overrides

You will draw the coupler shown in Figure 3.20, using the OSNAP overrides. You will use the OSNAP override modes to position lines and circles relative to this figure. (You may see other ways that you could use editing commands to create parts of this figure, but in this example OSNAPS will be used as much as possible. When you are working on your own drawings, you will use a combination of the methods you have learned.)

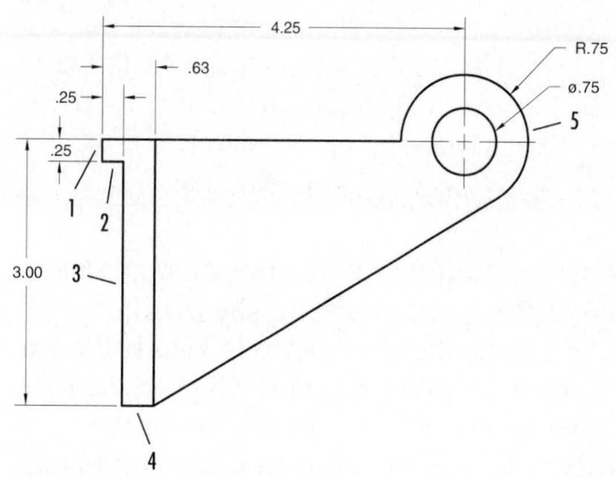

Figure 3.20

Next you will use the LINE and CIRCLE commands to create lines 1–4 and circle 5. On your own set your grid to .25 and make sure that GRID and SNAP are turned on.

Pick: ***LINE (toolbox)***

From point: **3.75,6.5** ↵

To point: **@.25<270** ↵

To point: **@.25<0** ↵

To point: **@2.75<270** ↵

To point: **@.375<0** ↵

To point: ↵

Pick: ***CIRCLE (toolbox)***

3P/2P/TTR/<Center point>: **8,6.5** ↵

Diameter/<Radius><1.0000>: **.75** ↵

When you have finished drawing these entities, your drawing should look like Figure 3.21.

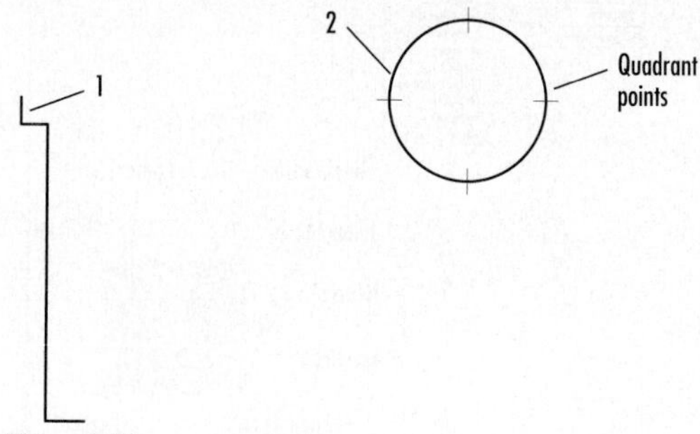

Figure 3.21

Turn SNAP off by pressing F9 or picking the SNAP button on the toolbar. You will use the OSNAP modes to accurately locate points. Leaving SNAP turned on may interfere with selection.

The Endpoint Mode (END)

The Endpoint mode snaps to the closest endpoint of an arc, line, or polyline vertex. You will draw a line from the endpoint of line 1, shown in Figure 3.21, to touch the circle, at the *quadrant point.* The quadrant points are at 0, 90, 180, and 270 degrees of a circle or arc. You will use the object snap modes Endpoint and Quadrant to locate the exact points.

> ■ ***TIP*** Remember that you can also type the three-letter code for the OSNAP (listed in parentheses) at the "Select objects:" prompt instead of picking it from the menu. However, instead of typing the three-letter code, END, for Endpoint, it is better to use four letters, ENDP. Otherwise, if you are at the "Command:" prompt instead of the "Select objects:" prompt, the command END to end your drawing may be selected. ■

Pick: ***LINE (toolbox)***

From point: ***(pick Assist, Object Snap, Endpoint)***

Notice that the cursor changes to the aperture and the command line reflects the OSNAP mode chosen.

endp of: ***(place the aperture box on the upper end of line 1 and press pick)***

Notice that the cursor has jumped to the exact endpoint of the line. The endpoint you wish to select does not have to be inside the aperture box; the box merely has to be positioned on the entity nearer to that endpoint than the other one. Positioning the aperture box slightly away from the point you wish to pick is useful because then you can see when the cursor "jumps" to the object snap location. This way you are able to determine that the OSNAP has worked.

The Quadrant Mode (QUA)

The Quadrant mode attaches to the quadrant point on a circle nearest to the position of the crosshairs. The quadrant points are the four points on the circle that are tangent to a square that encloses it. They are also the four points where the center lines (when shown) intersect the circle. Next you will finish the line, using the Quadrant override to pick the quadrant point of the circle as the second endpoint for your line. You should see the "To point:" prompt for the LINE command.

To point: ***(pick Assist, Object Snap, Quadrant)***

qua of ***(pick on the circle near point 2 in Figure 3.21)***

To point: ↵

Your drawing should look similar to Figure 3.22.

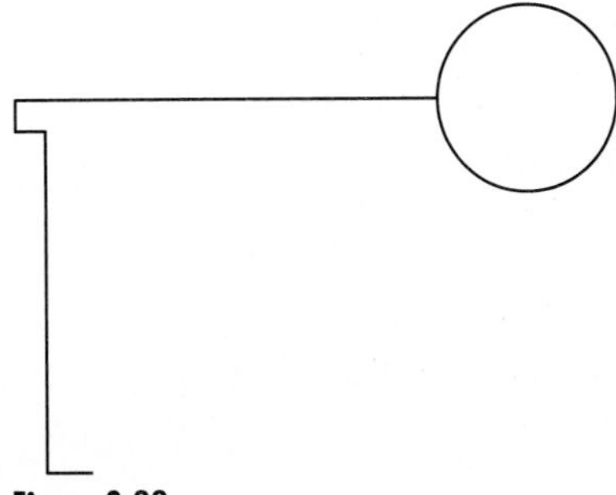

Figure 3.22

The Center Mode (CEN)

The Center mode snaps to the center of a circle or an arc. You will use it to create concentric circles by selecting the center of the circle you have drawn as the center for the new circle you will add.

Pick: ***CIRCLE (toolbox)***

3P/2P/TTR/<Center point>: ***(pick CENTER from the toolbox)***

center of: ***(pick on the edge of the circle)***

> ■ ***TIP*** A point on the circle must be within the target area of the aperture box. Do not position the target area over the center point. ■

AutoCAD finds the exact center of the circle and a circle rubberbands from the center to the location of the crosshairs. Notice that the aperture box disappears once the circle is picked. OSNAP stays active for only one pick in override mode. You are now prompted to pick a point to specify the radius or diameter; in this case, you will type in the diameter.

Diameter/<Radius><0.7500>: **d** ↵

Diameter<1.5000>: **.75** ↵

The circle should be drawn concentric to the original circle in the drawing, as shown in Figure 3.23.

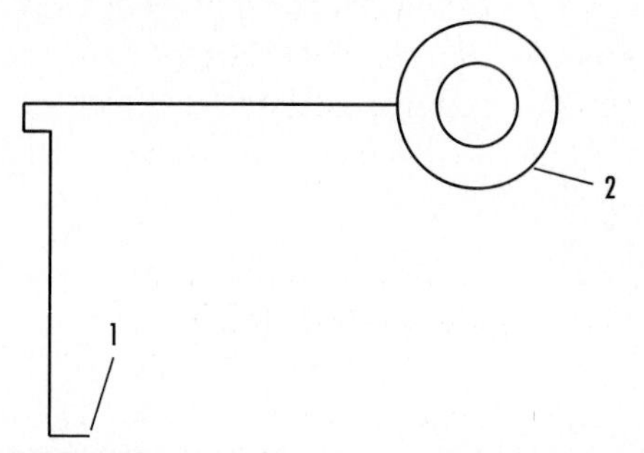

Figure 3.23

To position the next line from the endpoint of line 1, shown in Figure 3.23, tangent to the outer circle, you will use the Endpoint override and then the Tangent override.

Pick: **LINE *(toolbox)***

From point: ***(pick Endpoint from the toolbox)***

end of: ***(pick near the right endpoint of line 1)***

A line should rubberband from the endpoint of line 1 to the location of the crosshairs. Next you will use the Tangent override to locate the second endpoint tangent to the circle.

The Tangent Mode (TAN)

The Tangent object snap attaches to a point on a circle or an arc; a line drawn from the last point to the referenced arc or circle is drawn tangent to the arc or circle at that point.

From point: ***(pick TANGENT from the toolbox)***

tan to: ***(pick 2 near the lower right side of the circle)***

To point: (↵)

Your screen should look similar to Figure 3.24.

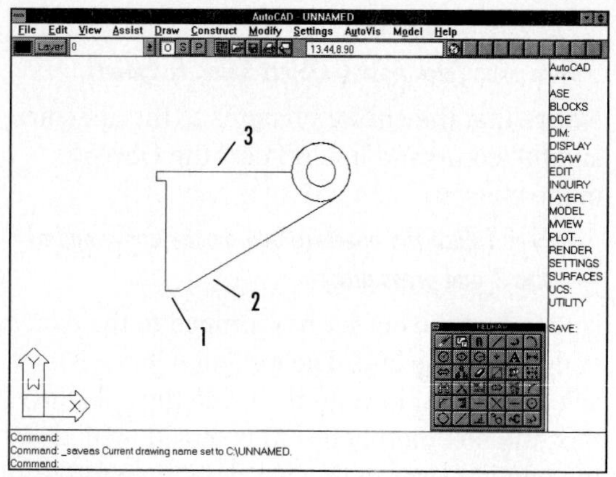

Figure 3.24

Next you will draw the line from the intersection of the short horizontal line and the angled line perpendicular to the upper line of the object. You will use two more OSNAP override modes to draw this line.

The Intersection Mode (INT)

The Intersection mode locks onto the intersection of two drawing entities. These entities can be two lines, a line and a circle or arc, or two arcs or circles, as well as some other types of entities. When you are using 3D solids modeling later in the book, remember when you are looking for the intersection of two entities that they must intersect in 3D space, not just apparently intersect on the screen (one line may be behind the other in the 3D model). You will pick the OSNAP override from the screen menu by selecting on the row of asterisks (****).

Pick: **LINE *(toolbox)***

From point: ***(pick **** (screen menu), INTersec)***

INTERSEC of ***(pick so that the intersection of lines 1 and 2 in Figure 3.24 is anywhere inside the box)***

A line rubberbands from the intersection to the current position of the crosshairs. To select the second endpoint of the line, you will use the Perpendicular override to draw the line perpendicular to the top horizontal line.

The Perpendicular Mode (PER)

The Perpendicular mode is used to attach to a point on an arc, a circle, or a line; a line drawn from the last point to the referenced entity forms a right angle with that entity.

This time, invoke the OSNAP by typing its first three letters at the command line.

To point: **PER** (↵)

to: ***(pick on line 3 in Figure 3.24)***

To point: (↵)

The new line is drawn at a 90-degree angle, perpendicular to the line, regardless of where on the line you picked. Your screen should look similar to Figure 3.25. Although this example draws a perpendicular line that touches the target line, it need not touch it. If you select to draw perpendicular to a line that does not intersect at an angle of 90 degrees, the perpendicular line is drawn to a point that would be perpendicular to the target line if it were extended.

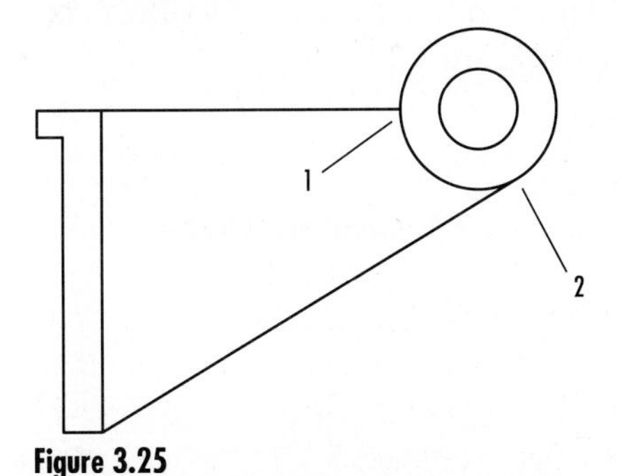

Figure 3.25

> ■ ***TIP*** Remember that in order to draw a perpendicular line, you must define two points. If you want to draw a perpendicular line from a line, and you select the line first, nothing is drawn until you define the second point, because there are an infinite set of perpendicular lines to a particular line. There is only one line perpendicular to a line through a given point. ■

Use the techniques you have learned to save your drawing now. Name your drawing COUPLER.

Practice on your own with each of the OSNAP override modes. Try selecting the rest of the override modes from the toolbox. Erase any extra lines you have added to your screen before going on.

Practicing with Running Mode OSNAPs

OSNAP can also be used in what is called the *running mode*. When you use OSNAP this way, the command is turned on and left on. Any time a command calls for the input of a point or selection, the current OSNAP mode is used when you pick. The running mode OSNAPs are very useful, as they reduce the number of times you must pick from the menu to achieve the desired drawing results. Any of the OSNAP modes can be used in running mode or in override mode. When you are creating drawings, you will decide which OSNAP mode is more helpful to you at the time.

The OSNAP running mode is activated from Object Snap on the Settings pull-down menu. More than one mode can be active at the same time, and the modes remain active until you use the dialogue box (or command line) to turn them off.

■ ***Warning:*** When using running mode OSNAPs, make sure to turn them off when you are done. If you forget, you may have trouble with certain other commands. For example, if you turn on Perpendicular and leave it on and later try to erase something, you may have trouble selecting entities because AutoCAD will try to find a perpendicular point to every entity you pick on. ■

Pick: **Settings *(menu bar)*, Object Snap**

You will see the Running Object Snap dialogue box appear on the screen which looks like Figure 3.26.

Pick in the empty box to the left of Intersection. An X appears in the box to indicate that Intersection has been selected. Pick OK to leave the dialogue box and keep your selection.

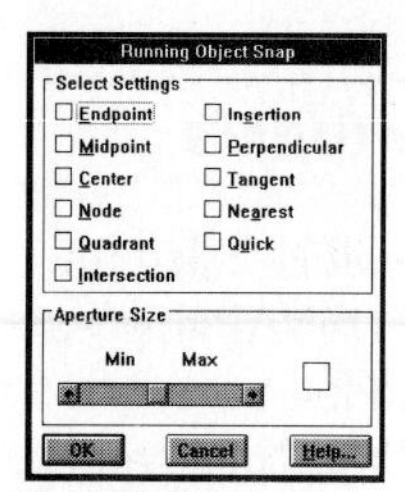

Figure 3.26

The Intersection Mode (INT)

Now Intersection is turned on. Any time you are prompted to select, you will see the aperture box on the crosshairs. If the intersection of two entities is inside the aperture area when you press the pick button, the exact intersection is selected. If you do not have an intersection inside the box, the closest point to the center of the crosshairs is selected. Unlike override mode, running mode does not display a message to tell you no intersection was found.

■ ***Warning:*** Because the closest position to the center of the crosshairs is returned when there is no intersection in the box, you must be careful when using OSNAP running modes. If your drawing geometry does not intersect properly, you will not be made aware of this fact when using the running mode OSNAPs. For a beginner, the safest method is to use the override modes. Then you will be prompted if the OSNAP condition is not met. ■

The Intersection mode locks onto the intersection of two drawing entities. These entities can be two lines, a line and a circle or arc, or two arcs or circles, as well as some other types of entities.

You will use the BREAK command to break the circle between intersection 1 and intersection 2 shown in Figure 3.25. As you break the lines, notice that the aperture appears each time you are prompted to select a point—you do not have to select the OSNAP mode each time. You will use the running mode object snap to select points during the break command. (Notice that you could also accomplish this by using TRIM.)

Using BREAK

The BREAK command is used to erase part of a line or entity. The BREAK command is located on the EDIT menu, the toolbox, and the Modify pull-down menu. The BREAK command options, selected from the Modify menu, are shown in Figure 3.27.

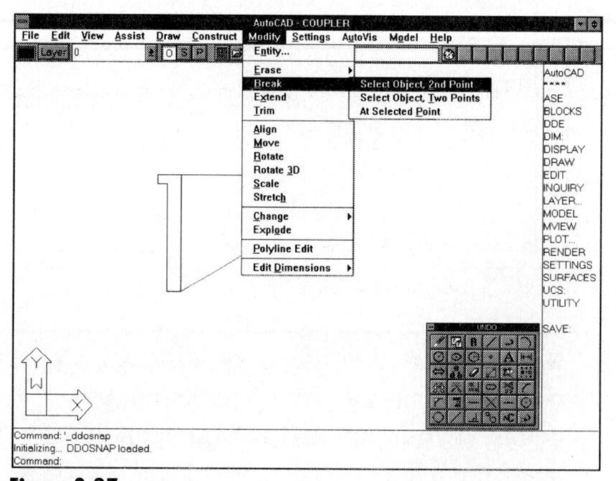

Figure 3.27

Pick: **Modify *(menu bar)*, Break, Select object, Two points**

Select object: ***(pick on the circle)***

Enter first point: ***(target intersection 1 in Figure 3.25)***

Enter second point: ***(target intersection 2)***

Notice that while you are prompted to select points, the aperture box automatically appears on the crosshairs. The running mode Intersection is in effect. After you select the second break point, the portion of the circle between the two selected points is removed. Your drawing should look similar to Figure 3.28.

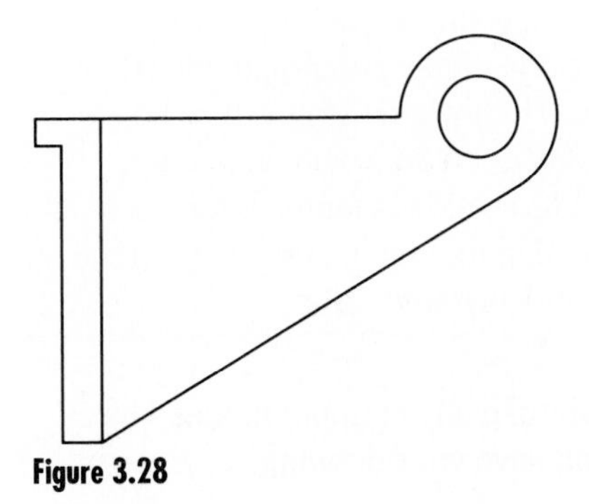

Figure 3.28

> ■ ***TIP*** When you are in running mode, you may still use a different OSNAP within a command. The override mode takes precedence over the running mode for that pick. ■

Sizing the Aperture Box

You can resize the aperture box that is used with the OSNAP modes. Sometimes it is helpful to have a smaller box when you have many things on the screen and you do not want to accidentally pick the wrong one. A larger box can also be useful, because you do not need to position so carefully when there are few objects on the screen.

Pick: **Settings *(menu bar)*, Object Snap**

Move the cursor over the right-hand arrow on the slider bar in the Aperture Size area of the Running Object Snap dialogue box. Press the pick button several times. You will see the size of the box on the screen change. Make the aperture box smaller by picking on the left arrow. You can also grab the box on the slider bar by holding down the pick button and moving your pointing device. Re-size the aperture box until you are happy with the size and pick OK to exit the dialogue box.

The other Object Snap modes are described below. Try them on your own until you are familiar with how they work. When you are finished, return to the Object Snap dialogue box and turn off any modes you may have left on.

The Nearest Mode (NEA)

The Nearest mode attaches to the point on an arc, circle, or line, or to the point entity, that is closest to the middle of the target area of your cursor.

A line drawn using the Nearest function may look similar to a line that could have been drawn simply using the LINE command, but there is a subtle difference. Many of AutoCAD's operations require an enclosed area: all lines that define the area must intersect (touch). This is particularly true when you are working with three-dimensional functions. When you draw lines by picking two points on the screen, sometimes the lines are not really touching. They appear to touch on the screen, but when you zoom them sufficiently, you will see that they don't touch. They may only be a hundredth of an inch apart, but they don't touch. This means that you do not have an enclosed area and many of AutoCAD's functions will not recognize the apparent area as an area. When creating a drawing with AutoCAD, you should always strive to create the drawing geometry accurately. The Nearest function ensures that the lines touch and therefore define an enclosed area acceptable to AutoCAD. You can use ZOOM, Window to zoom the area if you wish to see that the lines meet exactly.

The Node Mode (NOD)

The Node mode finds the exact location of a point entity in your drawing. Later in the tutorial you will use Node to locate points put into the drawing with the DIVIDE command.

The Quick Mode (QUICK)

This can be used in conjunction with the other modes you have learned to limit the search through the database, making selection using OSNAP modes faster. For example, if you have Intersection and Quick turned on, the search through the drawing database stops as soon as one intersection is found, even if there are several within the aperture box. When using Quick, it is best to have just one of the type of entity you are trying to locate within the aperture box.

The Insert Mode (INS)

The Insert mode finds the insertion point of text or of a block (you will learn about blocks in Tutorial 14). This is useful when you wish to determine the exact point where existing text or blocks are located in your drawing.

■ ***TIP*** The ID command lists the coordinates of a selected point. To find the exact insertion point of text or a block, pick Inquiry, ID, and then use the OSNAP mode Insert and pick on the text or block. Similarly, you can find the coordinates of an endpoint or intersection by combining those modes with the ID command. ■

■ ***TIP*** You can turn on more than one OSNAP mode at the same time. For instance, you could select both Intersection and Nearest from the running modes dialogue box. Then when the aperture box is positioned over an area with an intersection, the intersection is found; but if there is no intersection in the box, the point on the nearest entity is found. ■

On your own turn any running modes object snaps off and save your drawing.

Begin the Adapter Drawing

You will draw the basic shapes needed for an adapter, a typical part for a technical drawing.

On your own, begin a new drawing from the ACAD prototype. (Save COUPLER first if you haven't already done so.) Name your drawing ADAPTER and locate it in the Drawings directory. Use LINE to draw two horizontal lines 3 units long connected to a 1.5-unit vertical line, as shown in the top part of Figure 3.29. Use SNAP and GRID as needed. Set up .5-inch spacing. Draw a vertical line 1 unit to the right of the horizontal lines that is longer than the vertical line you have drawn to the left.

Using EXTEND

The EXTEND command is used to extend the lengths of existing lines and arcs to end at a selected boundary line. It works something like the opposite of TRIM. Like TRIM, EXTEND has two parts: first you select the entity to act as the boundary, then you select the entities you wish to have extended. EXTEND is located on the EDIT screen menu and on the Modify pull-down menu. As EXTEND is a frequently used command, it is also located on the toolbox. The toolbox icon for EXTEND is in the fourth row and third column of the toolbox.

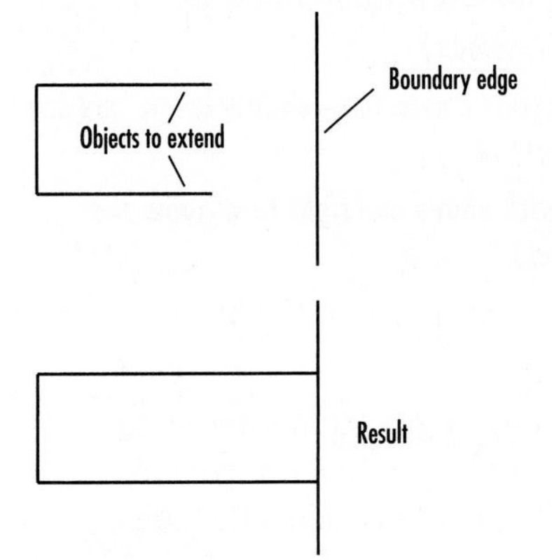

Figure 3.29

> *Pick:* **EXTEND *(toolbox)***
>
> Select boundary edge(s)... Select objects: ***(select the vertical line on the right)***
>
> Select objects: ↵

You are finished selecting boundary lines. To extend the horizontal lines, select them by picking points on them near the end closer to the boundary line. (If the points are picked closer to the other end, the lines are not extended.)

> <Select object to extend>/Undo: ***(select the two horizontal lines)*** ↵

On your own, use TRIM to remove the excess vertical lines. The two horizontal lines will be the cutting edges.

The rectangle is complete.

> ■ ***TIP*** Remember that the command FILLET: 0 (a fillet with a radius of 0) can be used to neaten up corners that do not meet or that extend past each other. Pick EDIT, Next, FILLET: 0 from the screen menu and then select the two lines that should meet at the corner. Instead of putting a rounded arc in, FILLET: 0 trims or extends the corners so that they meet neatly. FILLET: 0 acts both as EXTEND and TRIM when used this way. You can also use CHAMFER with the distances both set to zero. ■

The EXTEND command is very helpful when you are changing the shape of a drawing. If you draw a rectangle that is too short in the horizontal direction, rather than erase the rectangle and start over, you can easily extend the shape. Refer to the rectangle shown in Figure 3.30.

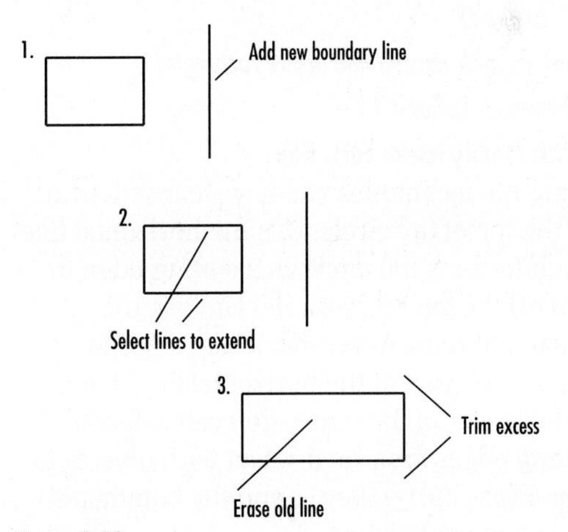

Figure 3.30

The object is too short in the horizontal direction. A vertical line drawn to the right of the rectangle is used to define the new edge of the rectangle. EXTEND extends the two horizontal lines, and the ERASE and TRIM commands remove the old vertical edge line and trim the excess from the added vertical line.

Completing the Adapter

You will finish the basic adapter shape so that the object is similar to the one shown in Figure 3.31. You will draw the circle with the center point located in the middle of the top horizontal line of the rectangle. You will use the Midpoint OSNAP to select the middle point.

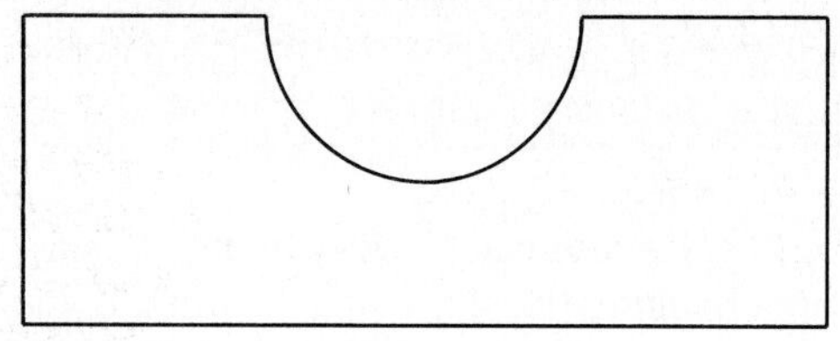

Figure 3.31

Pick: **CIRCLE (*toolbox*)**

3P/2P/TTR/<Center point>: ***(pick MIDPOINT from the toolbox)***

mid of: ***(pick the top line of the rectangle)***

Diameter/<Radius>: **1** ↵

Pick: **Modify (menu bar), Trim**

Using the techniques you have learned, trim off the top of the circle. Use the horizontal line that intersects the circle as a cutting edge to trim off the top of the circle, and use the remaining semicircle as a cutting edge to remove the part of the horizontal line that is in the center of the circle. You can select both cutting edges first, then select both objects to trim. Press the ↵ key to end the command when you are finished.

Pick: **Redraw (*toolbox*)**

Using ROTATE

You used the ROTATE command with hot grips in the last tutorial to rotate a drawing entity or group of entities to a new orientation in the drawing. ROTATE is located on the EDIT screen menu, the Modify menu bar, and in the third row and fifth column of the toolbox. It appears as a rectangular shape, with a rotated shape also shown. Notice that the toolbox icon for ROTATE shows it using the hot grips. This can be a very effective way to select the objects you wish to rotate. In this section, you will learn to use the command without hot grips.

Pick: **ROTATE (*toolbox*)**

Select objects: ***(start a selection window below and left of the object)***

Other corner: ***(pick above and right to window the entire object)***

6 found:

Select objects: ↵

You will select the lower left corner of the object as the base point. Use Endpoint or Intersection to accurately select the point.

> ■ ***TIP*** The base point need not be part of the object chosen for rotation. You can use any point on the screen; the object rotates about the point you select. It is often useful to select the base point for rotation in the center of the object you wish to rotate, so that as the object rotates it stays in a position similar to the original. ■

Base point: ***(pick Intersection from the toolbox)***

int of: ***(select the lower left corner of the object)***

<Rotation angle>/Reference: **30** ↵

Your adapter should be rotated 30 degrees, as shown in Figure 3.32. Angles are positive in the counterclockwise direction. A horizontal line to the right of the base point is defined as 0 degrees. Negative values can also be entered.

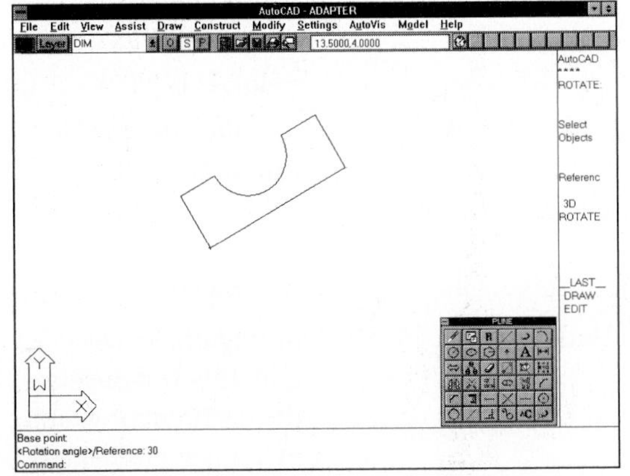

Figure 3.32

Using MOVE

The MOVE command is used to move an existing shape from one area on the drawing to another area. You used the MOVE command with hot grips; it is also located on the second page of the EDIT screen menu, on the Modify menu bar, and in the third row and first column of the toolbox.

Pick: **MOVE *(toolbox)***

Select objects: ***(cross the entire original adapter)***

Select objects: ↵

Base point or displacement: ***(pick ENDPOINT from the toolbox)***

endp of ***(select the lower corner of the adapter)***

> ■ ***TIP*** The base point does have to be on the object. ■

AutoCAD switches to DRAG mode so you can see the object move about the screen.

Second point of displacement: ***(select a point so the adapter is centered on the screen)***

> ■ ***TIP*** You can also define the new location by using absolute or relative coordinate values for the base point. For example, if you want the adapter to be moved 3.5 inches to the right of the original location, you could type in "@3.5, 0". You can also use GRID and SNAP to help accurately define the MOVE displacement. For example, if an object is to be moved horizontally to the right 3 inches, set up GRID and SNAP with 1-inch spacing. You can then move the object 3 snaps to the right to achieve an accurate 3-inch move. ■

Methods of Selecting Objects

An advantage of AutoCAD software is the versatile way that drawing entities can be selected for use with a command. You have already seen how you can use Window and Crossing. Lots of time can be saved in creating and editing your drawing by clever use of the selection modes. Some of the available modes for building a selection of drawing entities are listed below. During any command that prompts, "Select objects", you can type the option letter to use the indicated method of selection. You can also select the Select Objects option from the screen menu to display the list of object selection methods on the screen menu. AutoCAD allows you to continue selecting, using any of the following methods, until you indicate that you are ready to stop selecting by pressing the ↵ key. Then the command will continue or take effect on the items that you have selected.

Name	Option Letter	Method
Picking entities	none	pick entities by placing selection cursor and pressing pick button
Window	W	specify diagonal corners of a box, which only selects entities that are entirely enclosed
Crossing	C	specify diagonal corners of a box, which selects entities that cross or are enclosed in the box
Window Polygon	WP	similar to Window, except you draw an irregular polygon instead of a box around the items to select
Window Crossing	WC	similar to WP, except that all entities that cross or are enclosed in the polygon are selected
Fence	F	similar to WC, except that you draw line segments through the items to select
All	ALL	selects all the entities in your drawing unless they are on a frozen layer
Last	L	selects the last entity created
Previous	P	reselects the previously used selection set
Remove	R	selects entities to remove from the current selection set; removal continues until Add or ↵ is selected; you can use Window, Crossing, etc. while selecting items to remove
Add	A	use after Remove to Add more entities to selection set; can continue with any of the selection modes
Undo	U	during object selection, this will unselect the last item or group of items you selected.

Additional methods of selecting are AUto, Box, SIngle, and Multiple. Consult AutoCAD's online Help for definitions of their use.

On your own, save the ADAPTER drawing before continuing.

Printing/Plotting Drawings

AutoCAD, Release 12 uses a method similar to hand drafting to create plots to any exact scale on your paper.

Up to this point you have been working in *model space*, where you create your drawing geometry. When you are ready to plot, you use paper space, where you lay out the views of your drawing on the "sheet of paper." Paper space is basically two dimensional; model space is three dimensional. Your drawing geometry is created in model space, whereas paper space contains things like the border, title block, and viewports.

Using TILEMODE

To switch from model space, where you have been creating your drawing model, to paper space, where you will get the drawing ready to plot, you use the TILEMODE variable. As you will learn in Tutorial 8, you can create multiple *viewports* (effectively splitting your screen into several separate displays) in order to show several views at once on the screen, or on the paper. These viewports act differently depending on whether they are in model space or paper space. In three-dimensional model space, you can create multiple viewports on your screen. The number you can create depends on your hardware configuration. These viewports cannot overlap each other. They must meet exactly at the edges. They are called *tiled viewports*, because they are like floor tiles that you would lay edge to edge. Tiled viewports are created when the TILEMODE variable is set to ON or 1.

You can also create multiple viewports in paper space. These viewports can be overlapping or separated from each other, as you wish. You can create any number of these viewports to lay out your drawing on the paper sheet in the way you want. Each viewport contains a view of the model space drawing at the zoom factor and direction of sight that you specify. Paper space viewports are very useful for plotting the drawing, adding drawing details, showing an enlarged view of the object, or showing multiple views of the object.

Before you can use paper space and create viewports that are not tiled, you must set TILEMODE to OFF or 0. From View on the menu bar, Tilemode acts like a switch. Picking the command turns it OFF if it is ON, and ON if it is OFF. The default is ON, signified by a check mark next to the command on the menu. When you pick the command, the check mark disappears and Tilemode is OFF.

Pick: **View *(menu bar)*, Tilemode**

Don't be alarmed when your drawing disappears from the screen. This is normal. When you enter paper space you are effectively holding up a piece of paper between you and the model you created in model space. To see through the paper to your model or drawing geometry, you must create a hole, called a viewport.

Notice also that the UCS icon, which was previously in the lower left of your display, has been changed to the Paper space icon, which looks like a triangle. Your screen should look similar to Figure 3.33.

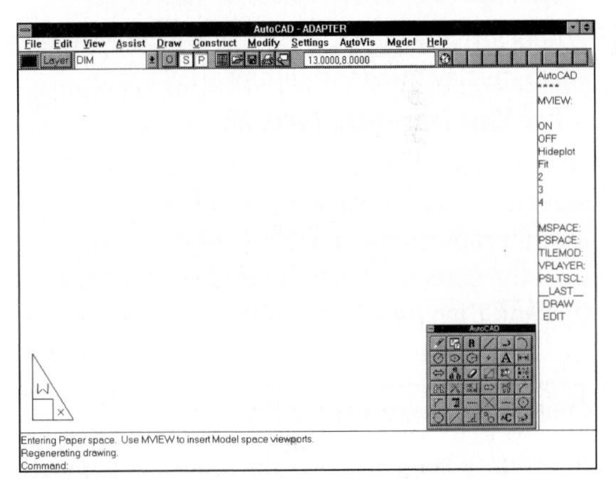

Figure 3.33

Plotting Using Paper Space

There are many advantages to using paper space for plotting your drawing, although you can plot single viewports from model space. Paper space can have its own grid, snap, and limits, independent of those you have set in model space. You can set the limits for paper space to the size of the paper you are using, and lay out the views, title block, border, etc. in paper space the size you want them on the sheet, using the units and dimensions of the paper. In model space, these things must be sized relative to the scale that will be used to plot the drawing. For instance, if you are using model space to plot a drawing of a football field that will be shown on the final plot at a scale of 1"=10', you must make the text in the border 15", or 1'-3", tall in your drawing if you want it to be 1/8" tall on the paper.

You will set the limits for paper space next. Access the LIMITS command this time by typing. Because most printers and plotters cannot print right to the very edge of the paper, set the limits slightly smaller than the paper.

Command: LIMITS ↵

ON/OFF/<Lower left corner> <0.0000,0.0000>: ↵

Upper right corner <12.0000,9.0000>: 10.5,8 ↵

Limits are now reset. Next you will use Zoom, All to display the entire limits area.

Pick: **View *(menu bar)*, Zoom, All**

Notice that the grid area may not fill the entire screen. This is because your grid may have different proportions or a different *aspect ratio* than the screen. (Turn the grid on to check this and then turn it back off.)

Creating a Viewport in the Paper

In order to see your drawing model in paper space, you must create a viewport. This is similar to cutting a hole in the sheet of paper that was put in front of your model space drawing when you entered paper space. You can look through the viewport and see your drawing model again. AutoCAD provides a program, MVSETUP, written in the LISP programming language, that helps you set up the size and relationships for viewports. You will use MV Setup from the View menu bar to help you create the viewport and set up your drawing for plotting. (You can also type the command at the command prompt.)

Pick: **View, Layout, MV Setup**

Align/Create/Scale viewports/Options/Title block/Undo: C ↵

Delete objects/Undo/<Create viewports>: ↵

AutoCAD switches to the text screen and you see the choices listed in Figure 3.34 displayed on your screen. You will select number 1.

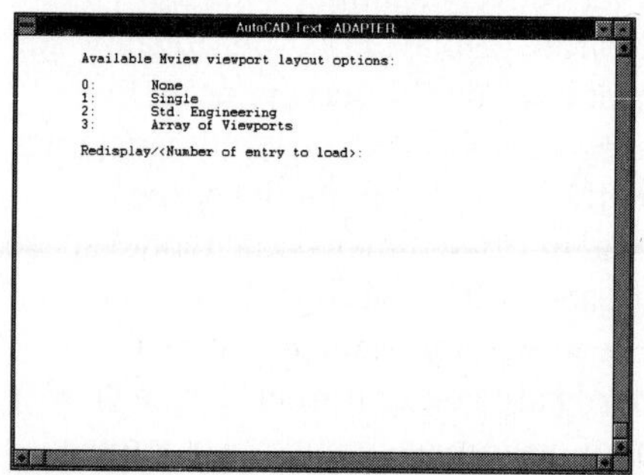

Figure 3.34

Redisplay/<Number of entry to load>: 1 ↵

Since most printers and plotters cannot print right up to the edge of the sheet, make your viewport 1" smaller in both directions than your 8.5 × 11 paper. Starting at point .25,.25 will center the viewport within the limits. Type the coordinates for the corners of the viewport.

Bounding area for viewports. First point: .25,.25 ↵

Other point: 10.25,7.75 ↵

You will see the viewport lines drawn on your screen and your model will show through the viewport hole that you have created. You can have many viewports in the same sheet of paper space if you wish and the views in the viewports can be at different scales. You will see how to use this in later tutorials to create multiple-view drawings from a single 3D solid model. This can also be useful for creating a detailed or enlarged view on the sheet.

Plotting Scales and Paper Space

MV Setup also contains an option to scale the viewport. Many times your entire drawing is too large to plot full size on the paper. Remember that you create the drawing model to be the real-world size. If you were drawing a football field, your drawing model would be 300' or longer. The Scale option lets you scale your model in the viewport relative to your sheet of paper (paper space).

Align/Create/Scale viewports/Options/Title block/Undo: S ↵

Select objects: *(pick on one of the lines forming the edge of the viewport)* ↵

Number of paper space units. <1.0>: ↵

Number of model space units.<1.0>: ↵

Align/Create/Scale viewports/Options/Title block/Undo: ↵

This makes your drawing full scale on the plot. In engineering drawing you often need a lot of space for notes and dimensions, so this size is realistic. Don't forget to scale the drawing for paper space before plotting. If you do not set a scale for the model space to paper space units, the scale is randomly determined based on what fits in the viewport when it is created. Most engineering and architectural drawings are created to known scales. You can repeat the MVSETUP command and change to a different scale at any time.

Next, switch back to model space by picking the boxed P on the toolbar.

Pick: ***P (toolbar)***

You will see that the UCS icon has returned and is positioned inside the viewport you created. Whenever you need to make a change to the original drawing geometry, you will need to return to model space in order to edit the drawing. Your drawing should look similar to Figure 3.35.

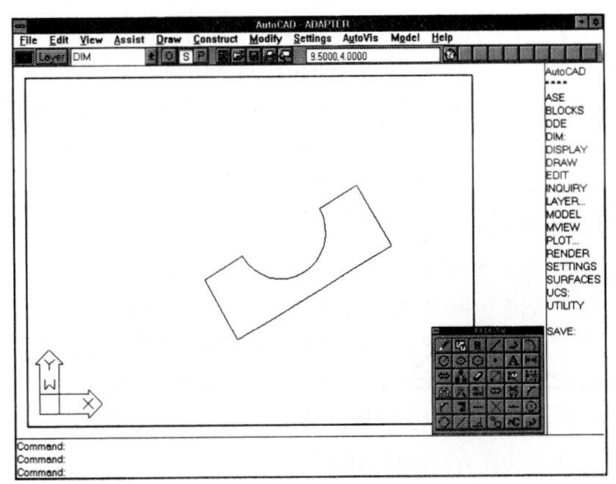

Figure 3.35

Pick: *P* (toolbar, to return to paper space)

Next you will add a title block to the bottom of the drawing. You will add it in paper space because it is basically a notation on the paper, not a part of the drawing geometry. Using paper space makes it easy to size the title block and text on the paper, regardless of the scale of the model space drawing.

Adding Notes and a Title Block

You will use the viewport boundary as a border for your sheet. The lines of the viewport border will plot on the paper unless the border is turned off. (You will learn how to use layers to turn groups of entities on and off in Tutorial 4.) Next you will add some lines and text for a title block.

Now set the snap to .125; this will be useful for positioning lettering and the lines for the title block. Use the LINE command and draw a line across the bottom of the viewport .375 units (three snap increments) up from the bottom line of the viewport on your own. Refer to Figure 3.36. You may also wish to reposition the toolbox if it is in your way. Do this by grabbing its titlebar and dragging it to a new location.

Using DIVIDE

The DIVIDE command places points along the entity you select, dividing it into the number of segments you specify. You can also choose to have a block of grouped entities placed in the drawing, instead of points. You will use the DIVIDE command to place points along the line you just drew, dividing it into three equal segments. DIVIDE is found on the EDIT screen menu and the Construct menu bar.

Pick: **EDIT *(screen)*, DIVIDE**

Select object to divide: ***(pick the line you drew to form a title strip)***

<Number of segments>/Block: **3** ↵

Because the Point Display mode is set at just a dot, you will probably not be able to see the points that mark the equal segment lengths. You will use the Settings pull-down menu to change the display of points in the drawing to a larger style so you can see them easily.

Pick: **Settings *(menu bar)*, Point Style. . .**

The Point Style dialogue box is on your screen. Select one of the point styles that has a circle or target around the point so it is easier to see. Pick OK to exit the dialogue box.

You will need to tell AutoCAD to recalculate the display file for your drawing in order to see this change. This is done with the REGEN command. Type the command at the prompt.

Command: **REGEN** ↵

The points should appear larger on the screen now. Your drawing should look like Figure 3.36.

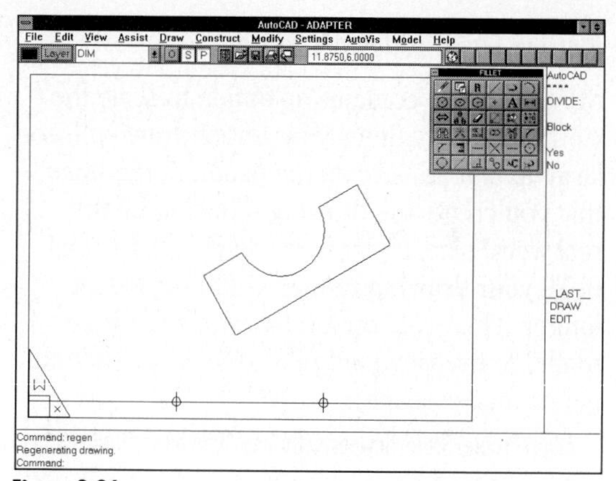

Figure 3.36

You can use the OSNAP mode Node to find point entities in your drawing. To draw lines dividing the title area exactly into thirds,

Pick: **LINE *(toolbox)***

From point: ***(pick Assist, Object Snap, Node)***

node of: ***(target one of the points)***

Draw a line straight down from the point by using OSNAP Perpendicular.

To point: ***(pick Assist, Object Snap, Perpendicular)***

perpendicular to: ***(pick the bottom line of the viewport)***

To point: ↵

Now repeat this process to draw another line at the other point, then use the Point Style dialogue box to change the point style back on your own. Use REGEN to regenerate the points on the screen, or you can erase the points instead.

■ ***TIP*** The MEASURE command is similar to the DIVIDE command, except that instead of specifying the number of segments into which you wish to have a line divided, with MEASURE you specify the length of the segment you would like to have. Like DIVIDE, the MEASURE command puts points or groups of entities called blocks (which you will learn about in Tutorial 14) the specified distances along the line. ■

Adapting for Architecture

The MEASURE and DIVIDE commands are very useful in architectural applications. You can use the DIVIDE command to place points at window center lines in a wall that is difficult to measure, or use the MEASURE command to place points at regular intervals along a length. The MEASURE command works well when creating parking lots. By using the MEASURE command on a line with an 8' interval, you can quickly lay out parking spaces, even along a curvilinear path (if you made it with the PEDIT command). ■

Pick: **Draw *(menu bar)*, Text, Set Style**

The text fonts dialogue box appears on your screen. It should look like Figure 3.37.

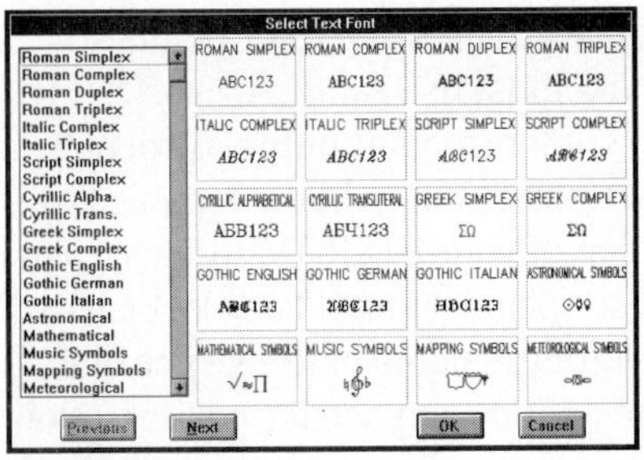

Figure 3.37

Pick: ***(on the name or icon for Roman Simplex)***

Pick: **OK *(to exit the dialogue box)***

The prompts for the Style command appear on the screen.

Text style name (or ?) <STANDARD>:romans

New style.

Font file <txt>: romans Height <0.0000>: ↵

Width factor <1.0000>: ↵

Obliquing angle <0>: ↵

Backwards? <N>: ↵

Upside-down? <N>: ↵

Vertical?<N>: ↵

ROMANS is now the current text style.

Pick: **Draw *(menu bar)*, Text, Dynamic**

Justify/Style/<Start point>: **C** ↵

Center point: **5.125, .375** ↵

Height <0.2000>: **.125** ↵

Rotation angle <0>: ↵

Text: **ADAPTER** ↵

Text: ↵

The word ADAPTER appears, centered around the point you selected. The centering is only horizontal; otherwise the letters appear above the point selected for the center. If you wish both horizontal and vertical centering, pick the Middle option of Justify text.

Now repeat this process, using the Left justified option of the TEXT command to position the words DRAWN BY: YOUR NAME in the left-hand area of the title block. The default Start point option prompts you for the bottom left starting point for the text you will enter. Use the Right justified option to right justify the words Scale: 1:1 in the right-hand area. The Justify, R option prompts you for the bottom-rightmost point for the text you will enter.

Now you have completed a simple title block for your drawing and are ready to plot. Your drawing should look like Figure 3.38.

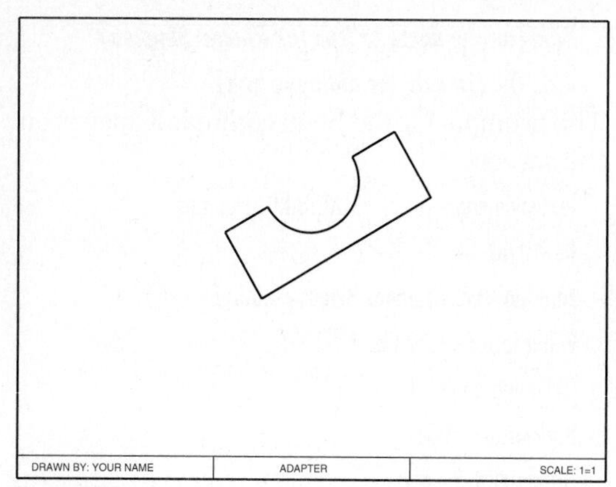

Figure 3.38

Make sure you are still in paper space for plotting your drawing. If you are not, your plotted drawing may not fit on the sheet correctly and the title block will not be shown.

If you have the grid on, turn it off by pressing (F7) on your own. Save your drawing before you go on.

> ■ ***TIP*** You should always save your drawing before you plot. If for some reason the plotter is not connected or there is another problem, AutoCAD may not be able to continue. To go on, you would have to re-boot the computer and would lose any changes you had made to your drawing since the last time you saved. ■

Options of the Plot Configuration Dialogue Box

Depending on the types of printers or plotters you have configured with your computer system, the PLOT commands cause your drawing to be either printed on your printer or plotted on the pen plotter that you configured to use with AutoCAD. The PLOT command causes the Plot Configuration dialogue box to be displayed on your screen. It appears similar to Figure 3.39.

Pick: **File, Print/Plot *(menu bar)***

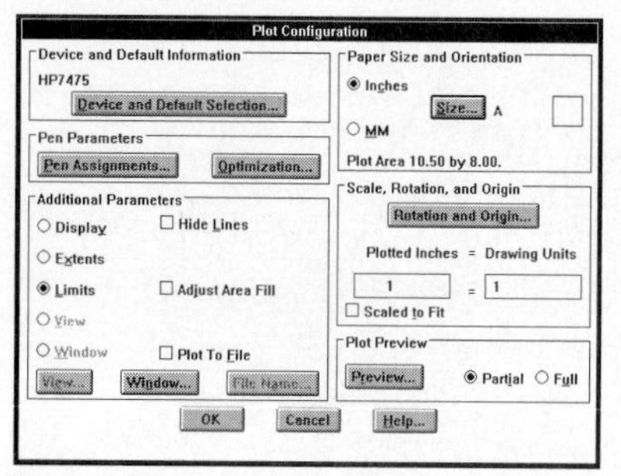

Figure 3.39

The Plot Configuration dialogue box lets you choose what portion of your drawing you wish to plot or print, the plotter or printer where you will send the drawing, the pen or color selections for the plotter or printer, the scale at which the finished drawing will be plotted, whether you want to use inches or millimeters as the plotter units, where your plot starts on the sheet, and whether it is rotated, among other things. Because there are so many factors, take care when you are starting out not to change too many things about the plotter at once. That way you can see the effect that each option has on your plot.

Device and Default Selection

Click on the box for device and default selection. A dialogue box appears that lets you select from among the plotters you have configured. If there are no printers or plotters listed, then you must use AutoCAD's CONFIG command to configure your output devices. See Detailed Configuration in the technical support section of your CD-ROM for an explanation of these specifications. To select a listed device, highlight the name of the device and pick OK. The options you see for pen selection and other items depend on your particular output device. If an item in the Plot Configuration dialogue box appears grayed instead of black, it is not available for selection. You may not be able to choose certain items, depending on the limitations of your printer or plotter.

Additional Parameters

This area of the dialogue box lets you specify what area of the drawing will be printed or plotted. Display selects the area that appears on your display as the area to plot. Extents plots any drawing entities you have in your drawing. Limits plots the predefined area set up in the drawing with the LIMITS command. View plots a named view you have created with the VIEW command. (Notice that if you have not made any views, this area is grayed.) Window lets you go back to the drawing display and create a window around the area of the drawing you want to plot. You will select Limits by picking on the button to its left, because you have previously set up the exact size of the area you wish to plot. If you have not set up the size with LIMITS, then Extents is often useful.

Hide Lines is used to hide the back lines in a 3D drawing. You will not need this for your 2D plot of drawing ADAPTER. When Adjust Area Fill is turned on in a drawing that contains areas solidly filled with color, they are adjusted for the width of the plotter pen so that it does not draw over the boundary line for the area. Plot To File sends your plot to a file rather than directly to the plotter or printer. If you wish to do this, check the box to the left of the words and the File Name item will turn black, indicating that it can now be used to display a dialogue box where you can enter the file name. The plot file will be created in the format of whatever output device you have selected in the Device and Default Selection. . . area.

Paper Size and Orientation

Select either Inches or MM (millimeters) by picking the appropriate button to the left of the measurement you wish to use for your paper. For the drawing you have just set up, pick Inches. A solid circle fills the center of the button to indicate that it is selected. Pick on Size. . . to see the dialogue box where you can set the paper size. The paper sizes that you can select depend on your printer. Standard 8.5 × 11 paper is called size A. 11 × 17 paper is size B. Drawing ADAPTER is set up to be plotted on size A paper. (If you have a laser printer and specified that the drawing be rotated when you configured the printer, the paper sizes shown may reflect this.)

Scale, Rotation, and Origin

You set the scale for the drawing by entering the number of Plotted Inches for the number of Drawing Units in your drawing. If you do not want the drawing plotted to a particular scale, you can **fit** it to the sheet size by picking the button to the left of Scaled to Fit. Most of the time it is useful to have your engineering drawing plotted to a known scale. You have already used paper space to create a viewport where you scaled your drawing to full size. This is convenient because you can plot paper space at a scale of 1 Plotter Unit = 1 Drawing Unit, or full size, in order to plot the model full-size. If Scaled to Fit is on, turn it off, and type in "1" for Plotted Inches and "1" for Drawing Units if they do not appear in the boxes already.

Depending on whether you have a printer or plotter, your drawing may need to be rotated to fit on the sheet correctly. Most printers will need to have a horizontal-shape drawing, such as ADAPTER, rotated 90° to print it out correctly. Most plotters will not need to have the drawing rotated. You may have to experiment to find out what will work for your particular printer or plotter.

Use the Rotation and Origin. . . option to place the 0,0 coordinates or lowermost left point in the drawing at the location you specify on the paper. You can move the drawing to the right 1/2" by using a value of .5 for the X Origin on the paper; move the drawing up on the paper by specifying a positive value for the Y Origin. (Keep in mind that selecting to rotate your plot will affect the directions for X and Y Origin.) Also you should be aware that moving the origin for the paper may cause the upper line and right line of the drawing not to print if they are outside the printer limits.

Preview

You may choose to have a partial preview, where you see only the overall border of your drawing area as it will appear on the paper, or a full preview, where your entire drawing as it will fit on the paper is shown on the screen. If you have a very detailed drawing, it may take some time to do a full preview. The drawing ADAPTER is relatively small, so pick the button next to Full so that you can see approximately how the drawing will appear on the sheet. Click on Preview to show the drawing on the screen. Your screen will look similar to Figure 3.40.

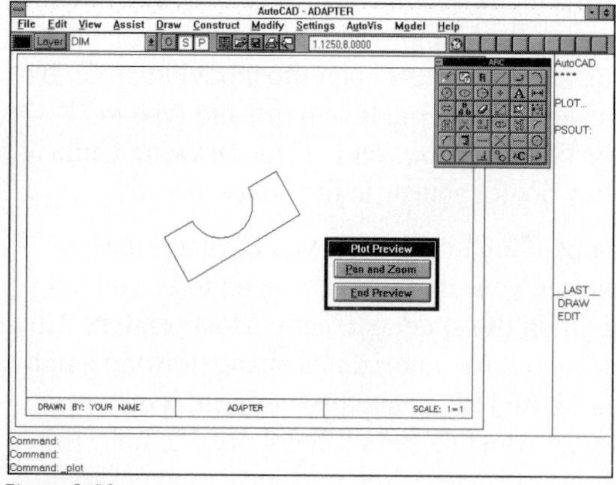

Figure 3.40

> ■ ***TIP*** You can move the Plot Preview message box shown in Figure 3.40 around on your screen by picking on its title bar and dragging it to a new location with the pick button held down. ■

If the drawing appears to fit the sheet correctly, pick End Preview to return to the Plot Configuration dialogue and then pick OK to plot your drawing.

You will see a prompt similar to the following, depending on your hardware configuration.

Effective plotting area: 10.50 wide by 8.00 high

Position paper in plotter.

Press RETURN to continue or S to stop for hardware setup.

Press ↵ if you are ready to print or plot.

If the drawing does not fit on the sheet correctly, review this section and determine which setting in the plot dialogue needs to be changed. You should have a print or plot of your drawing that is exactly full scale. The lines and text of the title block should be exactly the same size you specified when creating them. This is useful because standards for engineering drawing specify the minimum size for text and other items on the plot. You can use paper space to get exactly the sizes you want in your drawing.

On your own, return to model space by typing "MS" at the "Command:" prompt and save your drawing. Exit AutoCAD.You have completed Tutorial 3.

KEY TERMS

aperture
aspect ratio
circumscribed
distance across the flats
inscribed
major axis
minor axis
model space
override mode
polygon
polyline
quadrant point
running mode
target area
tiled viewports
viewport

KEY COMMANDS

Break
Divide
Ellipse
Extend
Identify
Measure
Model Space
MV Setup
Object Snap
Paper Space
Plot
Polyedit
Polygon
Polyline
Redo
Regenerate
Tilemode
View

EXERCISES

Redraw the following objects according to the given dimensions. The letter M after an exercise number means that the given dimensions are in millimeters (metric units). If no letter follows the exercise number, the dimensions are in inches. Do not include dimensions on the drawings.

3.1 Roller Arm

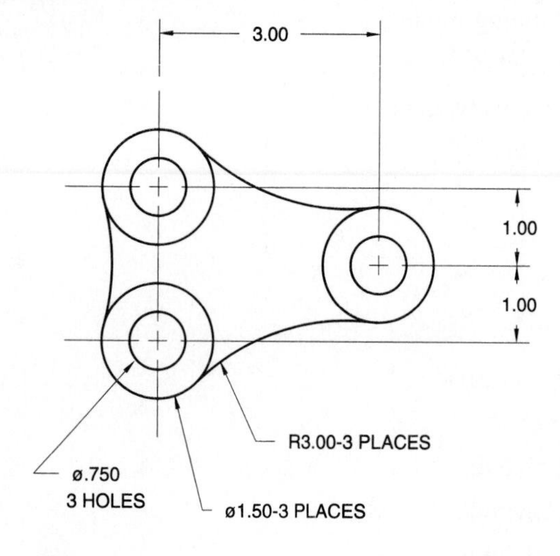

3.2 Starboard Rear Rib

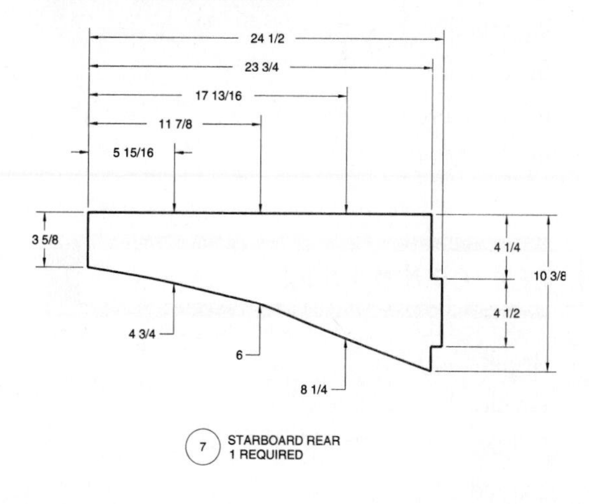

3.3M Flange

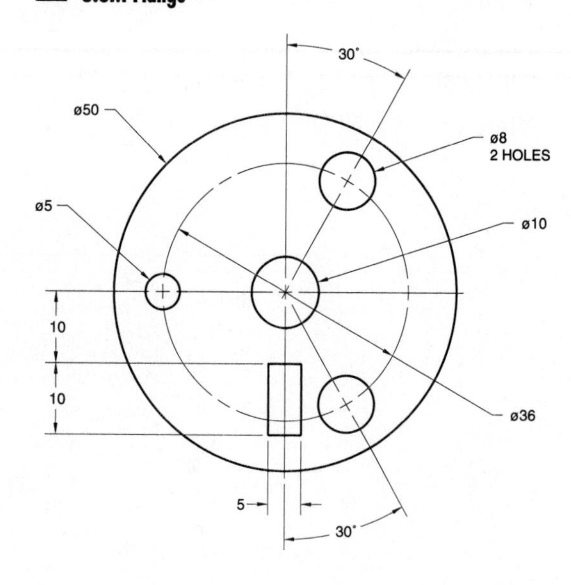

3.4 The Cycle

Starting with the parallelogram shown, use Osnap to draw the lines, arcs, and circles indicated in the drawing. Osnap commands needed are Int, End, Cen, Mid, Per, and Tan.

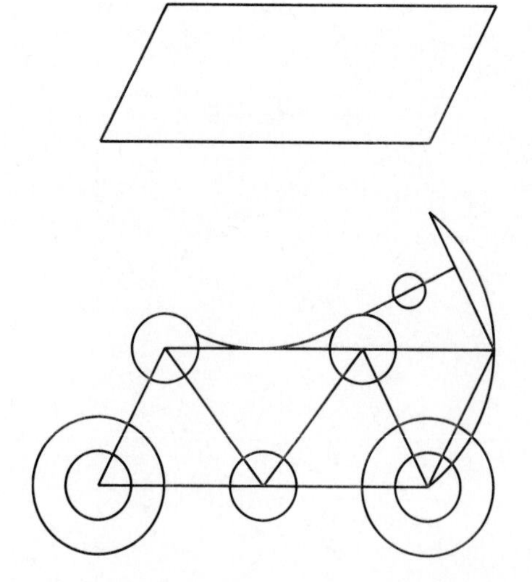

Redraw the following objects according to the given dimensions. The letter M after an exercise number means that the given dimensions are in millimeters (metric units). If no letter follows the exercise number, the dimensions are in inches. Do not include dimensions on the drawings.

3.5 Roller Support

2.96
.56
R1.16
R1.16
2.00
ø1.52

3.6M Gasket

45°
45°
R50
R20
R35
10
2 SLOTS
45°
45°

3.7 Park Plan

Create a park plan similar to the one shown here. Use PLINE and PEDIT, Spline to create a curving path. Note the symmetry. Add labels with DTEXT.

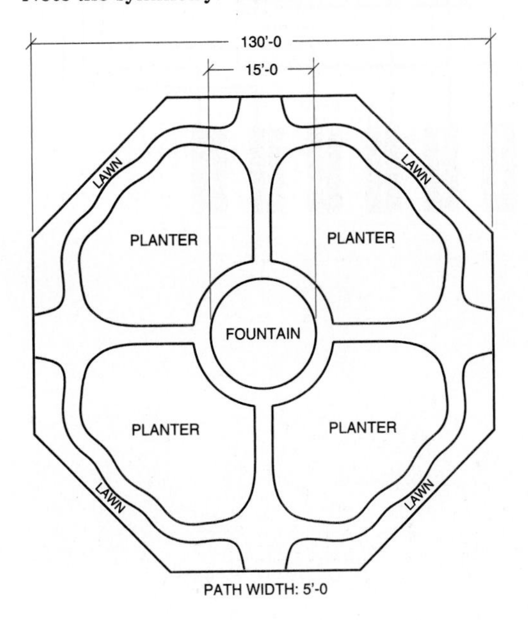

3.8 Circuit Board

Draw circuit board below, using PLINEs with the width option to create wide paths.

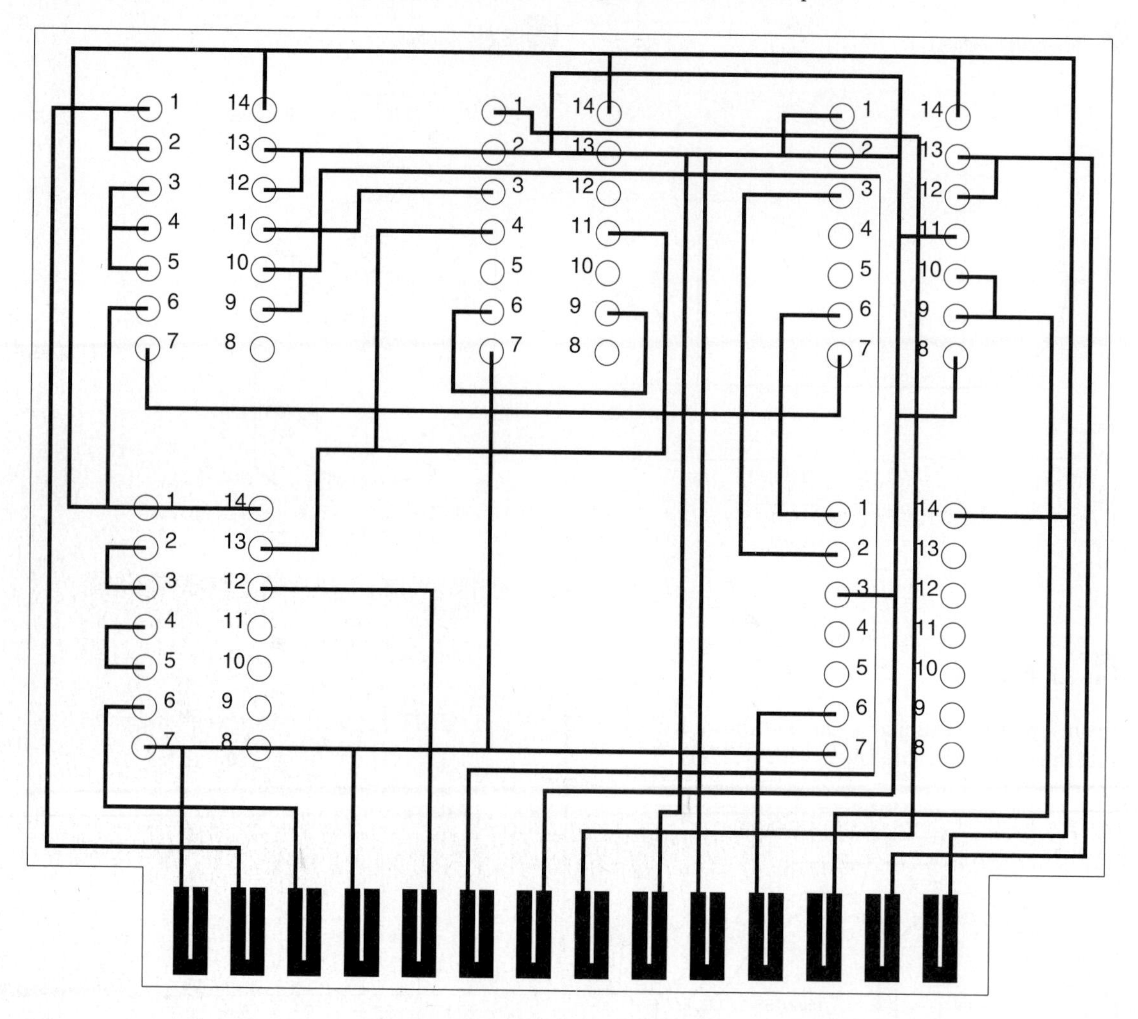

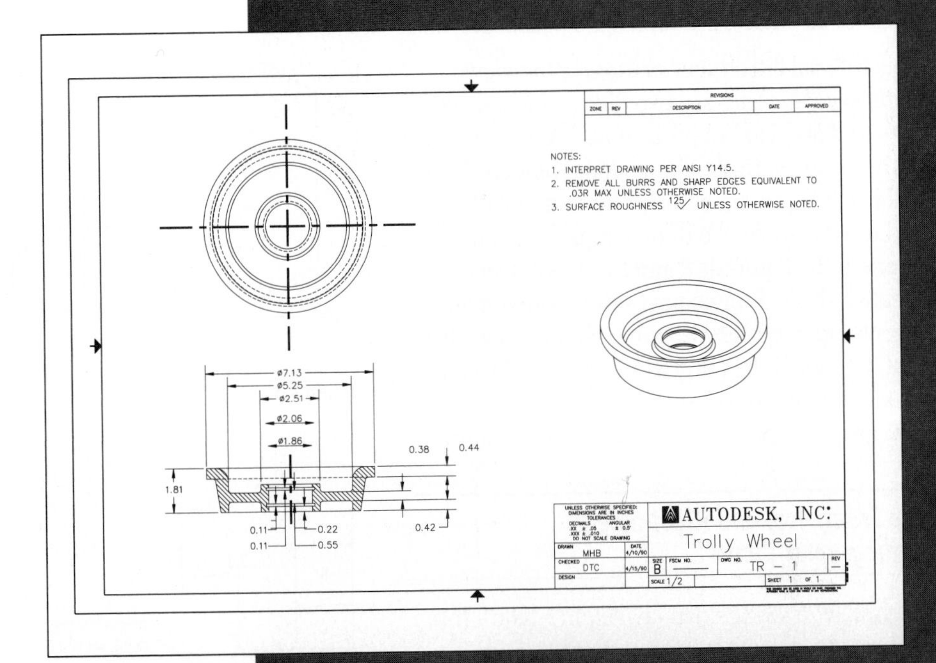

TUTORIAL 4

Introduction to Orthographic Views and Projection Theory

Objectives

When you have completed this tutorial, you will be able to

1. Project orthographic views of objects.
2. Draw 2D orthographic views.
3. Use the ORTHO and LAYER commands.
4. Understand and draw hidden, projection, center, and miter lines.
5. Use the Change Properties dialogue box.
6. Adjust the LTSCALE factor.

Introduction

This tutorial introduces orthographic views. *Orthographic views* are two-dimensional drawings that are used to present an accurate picture of the shape of three-dimensional objects. You will learn to look at a three-dimensional object and draw a set of two-dimensional drawings that define it. In Tutorials 8 and 9 you will learn to create a three-dimensional solid model of an object and generate two-dimensional views from that 3D model. In Tutorial 11, you will learn to create 2D drawings called isometric drawings that give the appearance of three dimensions.

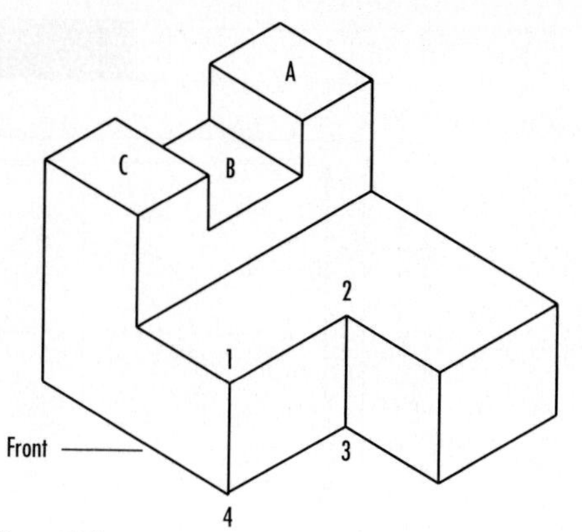

Figure 4.1

The Front, Top, and Right-Side Orthographic Views

Technical drawings usually require front, top, and right-side orthographic views to completely define the shape of an object. Some objects can be done with fewer views and others require additional views. All the objects in this tutorial require three views. Each orthographic view is a two-dimensional drawing that shows only two of the three dimensions (height, width, and depth). This means that no individual view contains sufficient information to completely define the shape of the object. You must look at all the views together to get a complete understanding of the object's shape. Figure 4.1 shows an object, and Figure 4.2 shows the front, top, and right-side orthographic views of the object.

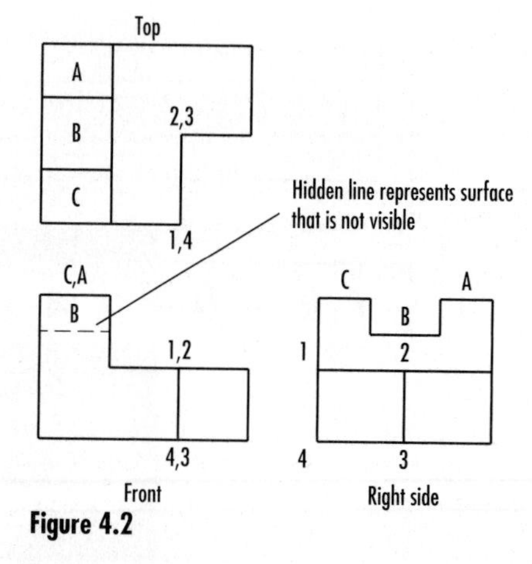

Figure 4.2

There are three rectangles, labeled A, B, and C, located on the left side of the top view. Each rectangle represents a plane. Which plane is the highest? The top view alone is not sufficient to answer this question. The three planes must be located on the other views for you to get a complete understanding of the relationships among the planes. The right-side view (usually just called the side view) shows that planes C and A are at the same height, and that plane B is lower.

The side view shows the relative locations of planes A, B, and C, but the planes appear as straight lines; therefore the top view is needed to get the overall shape of the planes. Both the top view and the side view are needed to define the size, shape, and location of the planes.

Look at plane 1-2-3-4 in Figure 4.2. You see its shape in the right-side view but it appears as a straight line in the front and top views, because it is perpendicular to the views—like a sheet of paper viewed looking onto the edge. A plane appears as a straight line when viewed from a direction where the plane is perpendicular to the viewing plane. Surfaces that are perpendicular to two of the three principal orthographic views are called *normal surfaces* (normal meaning 90 degrees). All surfaces in the object shown in Figure 4.1 are normal surfaces.

Plane B is shown in the front view, using a *hidden line*. All surfaces must be drawn in all views. Hidden lines are used to represent surfaces that are not directly visible; that is, that are hidden from view by some other surface on the object.

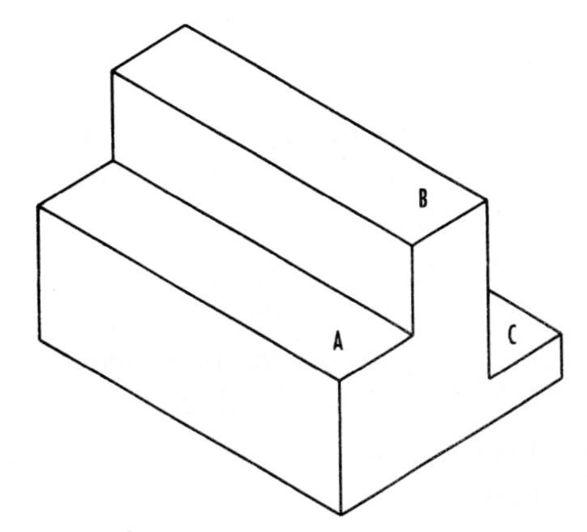

Figure 4.3

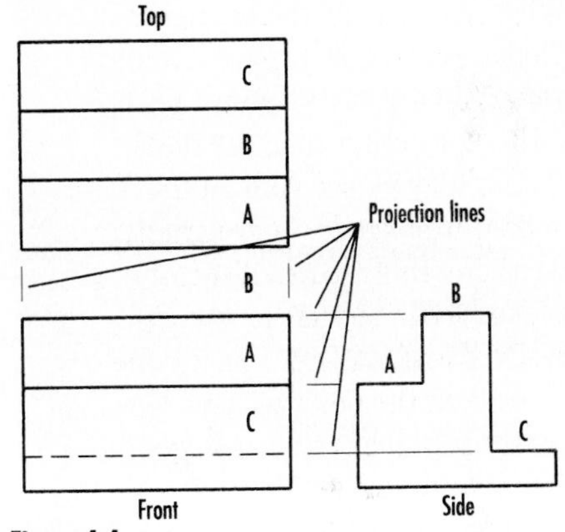

Figure 4.4

View Location

The locations of the front, top, and side views on a drawing are critical. The top view must be located directly above the front view. The side view must be located directly to the right of the front view. By aligning the views with each other precisely, you can *project* information from one view to another. Refer to Figures 4.3 and 4.4.

Planes A, B, and C in Figure 4.3 appear as three straight lines in the side view. Which line represents which plane? Because the front and side views are aligned, horizontal lines can be drawn from the planes in the front view to the lines in the side view. These lines are called *projection lines* and each plane is located between its projection lines in both views. Lines and surfaces can be matched between the front and top views, using vertical projection lines. Without exact view alignment, it would be impossible to accurately relate the lines and surfaces of one view to those of another view, making it difficult or impossible to understand the drawing.

Starting

Before you begin, launch AutoCAD. If you need help, please review Chapter 3, AutoCAD Basics, in Part 1, Getting Started.

Your computer display shows AutoCAD's drawing editor. You will begin this tutorial by drawing an orthographic view for the adapter in Figure 4.5. To begin a new drawing,

Pick: **File *(menu bar)*, New**

Type: **ADAPTORT**

Pick: **OK**

> ■ ***TIP*** When you specify the file name, be sure to include the disk drive and directory name if you are saving your files to a drive or directory other than the hard disk and directory where your AutoCAD program files are located. For example, if you are saving this file to a directory called DRAWINGS, be sure to specify C:\DRAWINGS\ADAPTORT as the file name. Or pick on the box that says New File Name. . . and then you can select the directory name you wish to save the file to before you type in the file name. You will see the directory name appear near the top of the dialogue box when you have selected it successfully. ■

The main AutoCAD drawing editor should appear on your display screen. Figure 4.5 shows the adapter you will create. All dimensions are in inches.

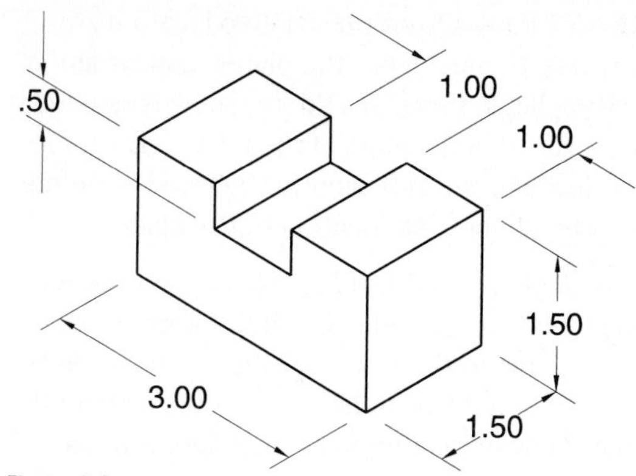

Figure 4.5

Before drawing front, top, and right-side orthographic views of the object, you should study the object for overall size. The adapter is 3 inches wide, 1.5 inches high, and 1.5 inches deep. The slot in the top of the adapter is .5 inches deep. Therefore, you will set up a background grid with .5 spacing and align SNAP with the same .5 spacing.

Using the Drawing Aids Dialogue Box

You have learned how to set the grid and snap spacing, using the GRID and SNAP commands, and how to toggle GRID on and off by using the (F7) function key, as well as how to toggle SNAP by picking on the toolbar or pressing the (F9) function key. You can also use the Drawing Aids dialogue box to perform these functions.

Pick: **Settings *(menu bar)*, Drawing Aids. . .**

The Drawing Aids dialogue box should appear on your screen, as shown in Figure 4.6.

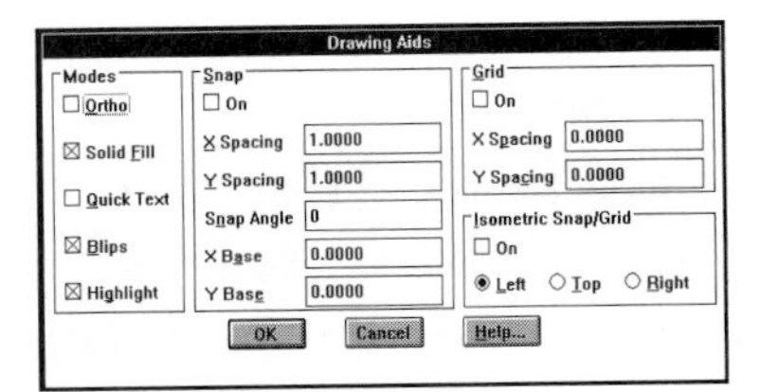

Figure 4.6

This dialogue box allows you to control some of AutoCAD's drawing aids, such as GRID and SNAP. The input buttons allow you to specify the X and Y spacing. You will pick the button to turn on the grid.

Pick: ***(the box under Grid labeled On)***

An X should appear in the box. Next move the cursor to the column under the heading Snap and pick the box to the left of On:

Pick: ***(the box under Snap labeled On)***

GRID and SNAP are now turned on. You will highlight the text in the box to the right of X Spacing under SNAP. (Position your cursor before the 1 and drag with the left mouse button down until 1.0000 is highlighted.) Next you will type the new x spacing for SNAP.

Type: **.5** ↵

> ■ ***TIP*** The Snap Y spacing adjusts to match the X. If you want to pick different X and Y spacing in the dialogue box, enter the X spacing first, then enter the Y spacing. ■

Move the cursor to highlight the text in the GRID X Spacing box.

Type: **.5** ↵

The GRID Y spacing changes to match the X spacing.

Pick: **OK**

> ■ ***TIP*** If you leave the grid spacing set to 0, it will automatically match the snap spacing when you leave the dialogue box. ■

The grid should be on your screen and the Snap indicator should be highlighted on the toolbar.

Using ORTHO

You can use the ORTHO command to restrict LINE and other commands to operate only horizontally and vertically. This feature is very handy when you are drawing orthographic views and when you are projecting information between the views. The ORTHO command is toggled on and off with the F8 function key, or with the O on the toolbar, so it is easy to activate when you are in a different command. Pressing F8 turns ORTHO on; pressing it again turns ORTHO off. Or pick the O button from the toolbar:

Pick: ***O (toolbar)***

<Ortho on>

Pick: ***O (toolbar)***

<Ortho off>

You can also use the Drawing Aids dialogue box to toggle the ORTHO command.

Pick: **Settings *(menu bar)*, Drawing Aids...**

Pick: ***(the empty box to the left of Ortho under the heading Modes)***

An X should appear in the Ortho box.

Pick: **OK *(to return to the drawing editor)***

The Ortho indicator should be on the toolbar of your screen. Next, draw the horizontal and the vertical line, as shown in Figure 4.7.

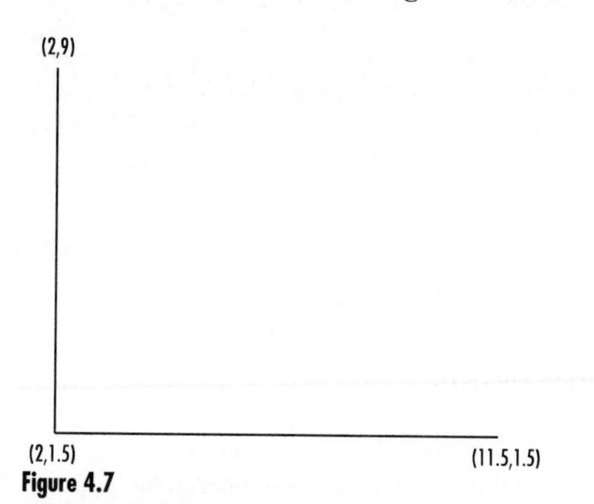

Figure 4.7

Pick: **LINE *(toolbox)***

From point: **2,9** ↵

To point: **2,1.5** ↵

To point: **11.5,1.5** ↵

To point: ↵

Next, you will use the OFFSET command to create a series of parallel horizontal and vertical lines, as shown in Figure 4.8. If you need to, review the OFFSET command in Tutorial 2.

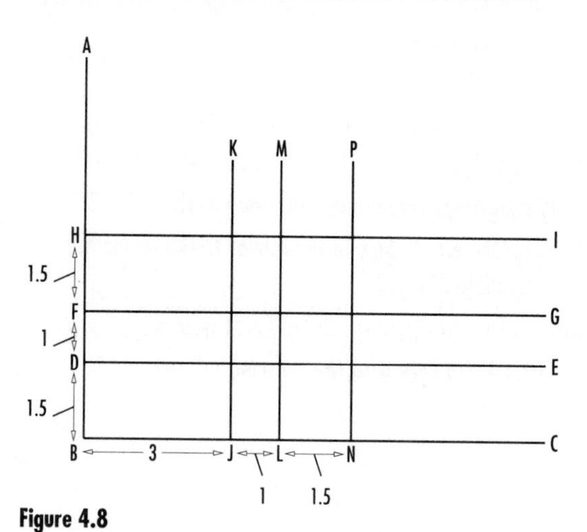

Figure 4.8

For the horizontal lines,

Pick: **Construct *(menu bar)*, Offset**

Offset distance or Through<Through>: **1.5** ↵

Select object to offset: ***(pick the horizontal line)***

Side to offset? ***(pick any point above the horizontal line)***

A new line is created, parallel to the bottom line and exactly 1.5 units away. End the command with the ↵ key because the next line will be a different distance away.

Select object to offset: ↵

Restart the OFFSET command by pressing ↵ so that you are prompted again for the offset distance.

Command: ↵

Offset distance or Through<1.5000>: **1** ↵

Select object to offset: ***(pick the newly created line)***

Side to offset? ***(pick any point above the line)***

A line appears 1.00 unit away from the line you selected.

Select object to offset: ↵

Now repeat this process on your own until you have created all of the horizontal and vertical lines that are shown in Figure 4.8. The lines are parallel to the horizontal line at distances of 1.5 (the given height of the object), 2.5 (the 1.5-inch height and an arbitrary 1-inch spacing between the front and top views), and 4 (the 1.5 plus 1 plus the 1.5-inch depth of the object). Your screen should look similar to Figure 4.8.

You will define the areas for the front, top, and side views by using the TRIM command to remove excess lines. Use Figure 4.9 to determine the lines to select. First, you will use the TRIM command and select all of the lines as cutting edges. Use implied crossing to do this in one step.

Pick: **TRIM *(toolbox)***

Select cutting edges(s)...

Select objects: ***(start your selection at corner A, shown in Figure 4.9, then pick corner B)***

Select objects: ↵

<Select object to trim>/Undo: ***(select segments 1–16 in the order in which they are numbered in Figure 4.9)*** ↵

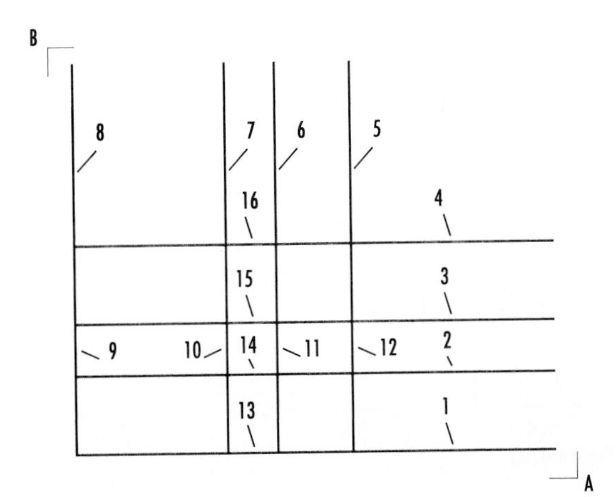

Figure 4.9

■ ***TIP*** Turn SNAP off while trimming to make it easier to select. ■

Next, use the ERASE command to remove the unwanted lines, as shown in Figure 4.10.

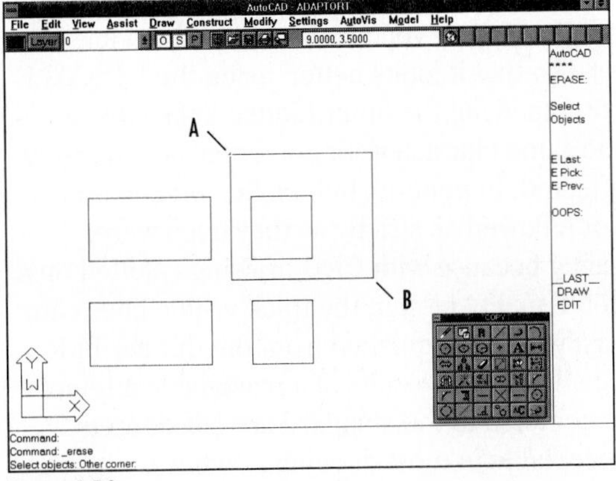

Figure 4.10

Pick: **ERASE *(toolbox)***

Select objects: ***(pick corner A as shown in Figure 4.10)***

Other corner: ***(pick corner B)***

Select objects: ↵

Your screen should look similar to Figure 4.11.

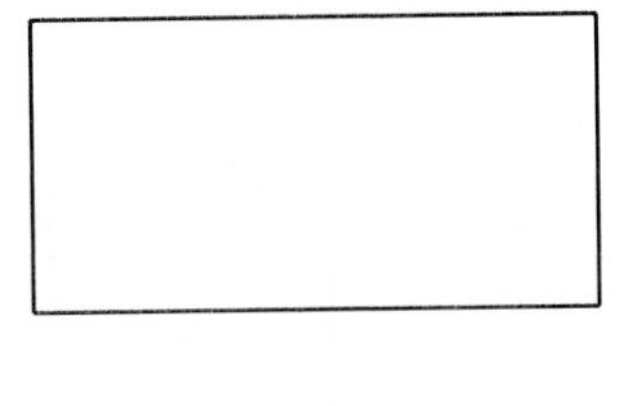

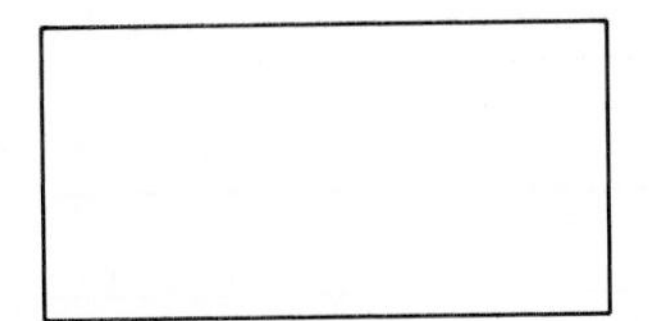

Figure 4.11

The views are aligned correctly and information can now be projected between them. Before continuing, you will redraw the screen.

Type: **R** ↵

You can now draw the slot in the front view, using the dimensions specified on the original object in Figure 4.5.

Pick: **LINE *(toolbox)***

From point: **3,3** ↵

To point: **3,2.5** ↵

To point: **4,2.5** ↵

To point: **4,3** ↵

To point: ↵

On your own, use the TRIM command from the toolbox and remove the center portion of the top horizontal line.

Now your drawing should look like Figure 4.12.

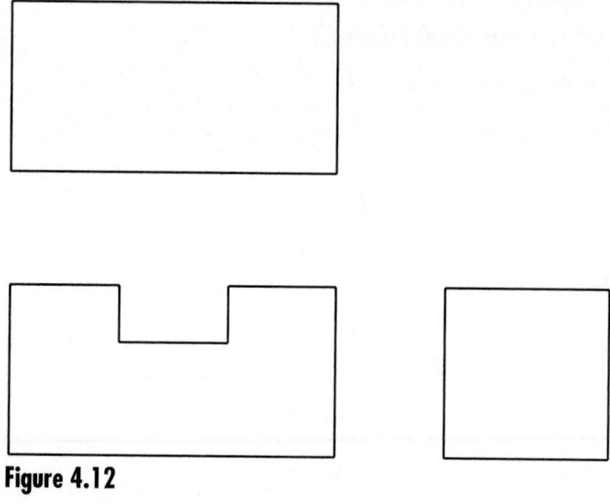

Figure 4.12

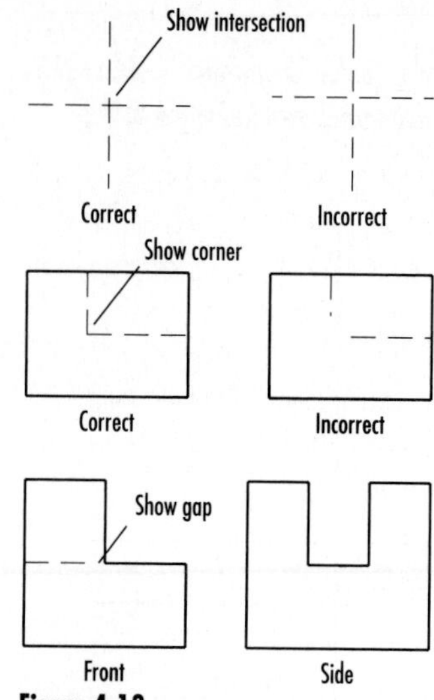

Figure 4.13

Hidden Lines

You will use hidden lines to represent the lines that are not visible on the side view. Remember, each view is a view of the entire object drawn from that line of sight. All surfaces are shown in every view. A hidden line in the drawing represents one of three things:

1. An *intersection* of two surfaces that are behind another surface and therefore not visible.
2. The *edge view* of a hidden surface.
3. The outer edge of a curved surface that is hidden. This is also called the *limiting element* of a contour.

There are a few general practices to use when drawing hidden lines. They are used to help prevent confusion and to make the drawing easier to read. See Figure 4.13.

Clearly show intersections, using intersecting line segments.

Clearly show corners, using intersecting line segments.

Leave a noticeable gap between aligned continuous lines and hidden lines.

These hidden line practices are sometimes difficult to implement because the hidden line pattern in AutoCAD is a fixed mathematical relationship. If you change one hidden line pattern so that it looks better, using the LTSCALE command, all the other hidden lines take on the same characteristics and may be adversely affected. In general, hidden line practices are not followed as strictly as they once were, partly because with CAD drawings plotted on a good-quality plotter, the thick visible lines can easily be distinguished from the thinner hidden lines. The results of a reasonable attempt to conform to the standard are considered acceptable in most drawing practices.

> ■ ***TIP*** If you draw hidden lines with a polyline (PLINE), you can set the PLINEGEN variable to 1 to make the linetype a continuous pattern over the length of the polyline. When this variable is set to 0, each segment of the polyline begins and ends with a dash. Use the PEDIT, Ltype gen command option to set this variable. You can use this method to improve the appearance of intersecting hidden lines. ■

Hidden lines are usually drawn using a different color than the continuous object lines on the AutoCAD drawing screen. This helps to create a visual difference between the different types of lines and makes them easier to interpret. Also, printers and plotters are controlled by using different colors in the drawing to represent different thicknesses of lines on the plot. You can use any color, but be consistent. Make all hidden lines the same color. It is best to set the color and linetype by drawing the hidden lines on a separate layer that has the correct properties set. This is why BYLAYER is the default choice for color in AutoCAD.

Using LAYER

A layer can be thought of as a transparent sheet that you place over the drawing and that you can remove at will. You can create an infinite number of layers within the same drawing. The LAYER command controls the color and linetype associated with a given layer, and allows you to control which layers are visible at any given time. Layers allow you to overlay a base drawing with several different layers of detail (such as wiring or plumbing schematics over the base plan for a building). By using layers, you can also control which portions of a drawing are plotted, or remove dimensions or text from a drawing to make it easier to add or change entities on another layer. You can also lock a layer so that it is visible on the screen, but nothing in that layer can be changed while it is locked.

Current Layer

The *current layer* is the layer you are working on. Any new entities you draw are added to the current layer. The default current layer is Layer 0. You have been using this layer when drawing. (Notice that Layer 0 is displayed on the left side of the toolbar.) The Layer Control dialogue box is located under Settings on the menu bar. To create a new layer,

Pick: **Settings *(menu bar)*, Layer Control. . .**

The Layer Control dialogue box appears on the screen, as shown in Figure 4.14.

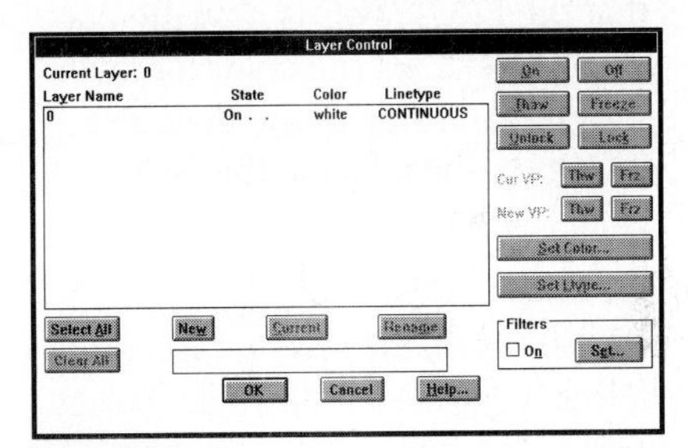

Figure 4.14

There should be one name listed in the Layer Name column, 0. Layer 0 is a special layer that is provided in AutoCAD. It cannot be renamed or deleted from the list of layers. Layer 0 has special properties when used with the BLOCK and INSERT commands, which you will learn in Tutorial 14. Layer 0 is presently the current layer. There can be only one current layer at a time.

You will now create a layer named PROJ for projection lines and make PROJ the current layer.

You will see the typing cursor in the empty box (above the word OK), ready for you to type in the layer name. Layer names cannot have spaces in them, nor can they have any illegal DOS characters, such as a period (.), comma (,) pound sign (#), or other similar characters. Letters and numbers and the characters dollar sign ($), _ (underscore), and - (hyphen) are valid.

Type: **PROJ**

Pick: ***(the word New in the box just above where you typed PROJ)***

The layer name PROJ appears on the list near the top of the screen, below the 0 layer.

To make PROJ the current layer,

Pick: ***(the name PROJ in the layer name list; it becomes highlighted)***

While the name is highlighted,

Pick: ***(the Current box below the layer names)***

This means that the PROJ layer is now the current drawing layer. Next, set the color for layer PROJ. On the right-hand side of the dialogue box is the Set Color. . . box. While the layer name PROJ is highlighted,

Pick: **Set Color**

A dialogue box pops up on the screen that contains color choices. Figure 4.15 shows the Select Color dialogue box you will see on your screen.

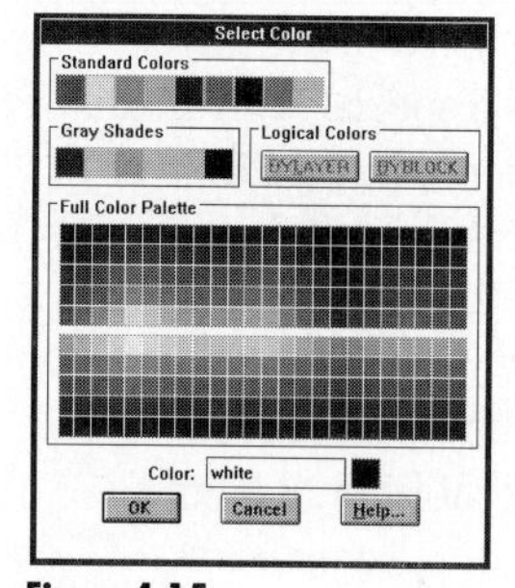

Figure 4.15

Color in Layers

The box allows you to specify the color for entities drawn on a layer. For example, you could create a separate red layer just for center lines. The color helps you visually distinguish center lines from other types of lines in the drawing. It can also be used to select the pen and pen width for your printer or plotter.

AutoCAD has two different ways of selecting the color for entities. The best way is to set the layer color and draw the entities on the appropriate layer. The other method is to use the COLOR command and set the drawing color. When you do this, the color stays set to whatever color you have selected, regardless of what layer is current, until you change it again with the same command. The default option for the COLOR command and the LINETYPE command is BYLAYER. This is the best selection, because then when you draw a line, the color and linetype will be those of the current layer. Otherwise the color in your drawing can become very confusing.

The Select Color dialogue box is used for selecting color in other dialogue boxes, as well as in the Layer Control dialogue. It has the choices BYLAYER and BYBLOCK on the right-hand side. Since you are specifying the color for layer PROJ only, these choices cannot be selected, so they are shown *grayed*. Move the arrow cursor into the box that contains the color magenta, the purplish color sixth from the left in the top row of colors labeled Standard Colors.

Pick: ***(the magenta box from the Standard Colors list)***

You will see the name of the color you have selected appear in the box next to the word Color: at the bottom of the screen. (If you select one of the standard colors, the name appears in the box; if you select one of the other 256 colors, the color number appears.)

Pick: **OK**

Now the color for layer PROJ is set to magenta. You will see that magenta has replaced white (the default color) in the Color column to the right of the layer name PROJ. Check the listing of layer names and colors to see that this is displayed.

> ■ ***TIP*** If you selected dark lines on a light background (the default) when configuring your video display, white lines will be black on your monitor and color boxes indicating white will be black. ■

Pick: **OK**

to return to the drawing editor screen.

The word PROJ is now indicated as the layer on the left side of the toolbar and the color magenta appears in the square at the left of the toolbar.

Use the LINE command to draw a few random lines on the screen. These lines are on the PROJ layer; they will appear magenta on your color monitor.

Layer Visibility

One of the advantages of using layers in the drawing is that you can choose not to display selected layers. This way, if you want to create projection lines, or even notes about the drawing, you can draw them on a layer that you will later turn off so that it is not displayed or plotted. Or you may want to create a complex drawing with many layers, such as a building plan that contains the electrical plan on one layer and the mechanical on another, as well as separate layers for the walls, windows, etc. All of the information can be stored in a single drawing, and then different combinations of layers can be plotted to create the electrical layout, first-floor plan, and any other combination you wish. Use the Layer Control dialogue to turn off Layer 0. This time you will activate the Layer Control dialogue by picking on the word Layer on the toolbar.

Pick: **Layer *(from the left-hand side of the toolbar to activate the Layer Control dialogue)***

The Layer Control dialogue appears on your screen.

Pick: ***(Layer 0 to highlight it)***

Pick: ***(the Off button at the top right-hand side of the dialogue box)***

The word On next to the layer name 0 disappears. Layer 0 is turned off.

Pick: **OK**

to return to the drawing editor screen.

The original drawing is gone and only the lines drawn on the PROJ layer remain.

Pick: **Layer *(toolbar)***

Pick: **0**

Pick: ***(the On box)***

The word On next to layer name 0 reappears. The On check button toggles layers between visible (on) or invisible (off). More than one layer can be visible on the screen at the same time, although drawing can only be done on the current layer. Invisible (off) layers are not printed or plotted, but objects on these layers are still part of the drawing.

Freezing Layers

The Freeze option is used not only to make the layer disappear but also to cause it to be skipped when the drawing is regenerated. This feature can noticeably improve the speed with which AutoCAD regenerates a large drawing. The current layer can never be frozen.

Highlight the layer name 0 and

Pick: ***(the Freeze box)***

Pick: **OK**

Your original drawing is still on, but Frozen and therefore invisible. You will use the LAYER command on the screen menu to Thaw the 0 layer.

Pick: **AutoCAD (screen menu), LAYER**

Pick: ***(CANCEL or press Ctrl-C to get rid of the Layer Control dialogue box so you can use the screen menu)***

Pick: **LAYER, Thaw**

Layer name(s) to Thaw: **0** ↵

?/Make/Set/New/ON/OFF/Color/Ltype/Freeze/Thaw/LOck/Unlock: ↵

AutoCAD regenerates the drawing and the 0 layer reappears.

You will type "LA", the alias for the LAYER command, at the prompt.

Command: **LA** ↵

?/Make/Set/New/ON/OFF/Color/Ltype/Freeze/Thaw/LOck/Unlock: **C** ↵

Color: **red** ↵

Layer name(s) for color 1 (red) <PROJ>: ↵

?/Make/Set/New/ON/OFF/Color/Ltype/Freeze/Thaw/LOck/Unlock: ↵

Your lines will not turn red until you exit the LAYER command.

Linetype in Layers

The Linetype column in the LAYER command allows you to change the type of line drawn on a layer. You could, for example, create a layer that not only drew all lines in red, but also drew only hidden lines. Until the linetypes are loaded with the LINETYPE, Load command (which you used in Tutorial 2), they are not available in the Layer Control dialogue. However, using the LAYER command from the screen menu or typing it allows you to select linetypes that are loaded automatically as you use them. You will load the linetypes later in this tutorial. Restart the LAYER command.

Command: ↵

?/Make/Set/New/ON/OFF/Color/Ltype/Freeze/Thaw/LOck/Unlock: **L** ↵

Linetype (or ?) <CONTINUOUS>: **hidden** ↵

Layer name(s) for linetype HIDDEN <PROJ>: ↵

?/Make/Set/New/ON/OFF/Color/Ltype/Freeze/Thaw/LOck/Unlock: ↵

AutoCAD regenerates your drawing and the lines on the PROJ layer assume the characteristics you specified.

■ ***TIP*** You may want to call up the drawing ACAD.DWG that is provided with the AutoCAD program (usually in the directory \ACADWIN\SUPPORT) and load the linetypes you use frequently into that drawing. This way when you use it as a prototype to start a new drawing, the linetypes will already be loaded. ■

Now use the Layer Control dialogue box to see the changes you made. Turn the PROJ layer off. Make Layer 0 the current layer. Do these steps on your own at this time.

Drawing Hidden Lines

Now you will create a hidden line in the side view of your drawing to represent the bottom surface of the slot.

On your own, use the layer commands you have learned to make a layer for hidden lines. Name the layer HIDDEN and assign the color blue and the linetype HIDDEN. Set this new layer as the current layer.

You will draw a horizontal line from the bottom edge of the slot in the front view into the side view. This line will be used to project the depth of the slot into the side view. Check to see that the Ortho button (O) on the toolbar is highlighted.

Pick: **LINE *(toolbox)***

From point: ***(pick* INTERSECTION *from the toolbox)***

int of ***(target the lower right corner of the slot in the front view of the object)***

To point: ***(pick any point to the right of the side view)***

To point: ↵

Your drawing should look like Figure 4.16.

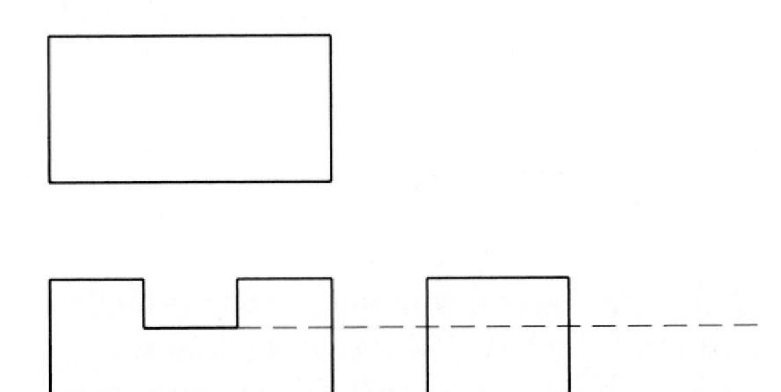

Figure 4.16

You will trim the projection line so that only the portion within the side view remains.

Pick: **Modify *(menu bar)*, Trim**

Select cutting edge(s)...

Select objects: ***(select the left and right vertical lines of the side view)***

Select objects: ↵

<Select objects to trim>/Undo: ***(select the extreme left and right ends of the slot projection line)*** ↵

<Select objects to trim>/Undo: ↵

Your screen should look like Figure 4.17.

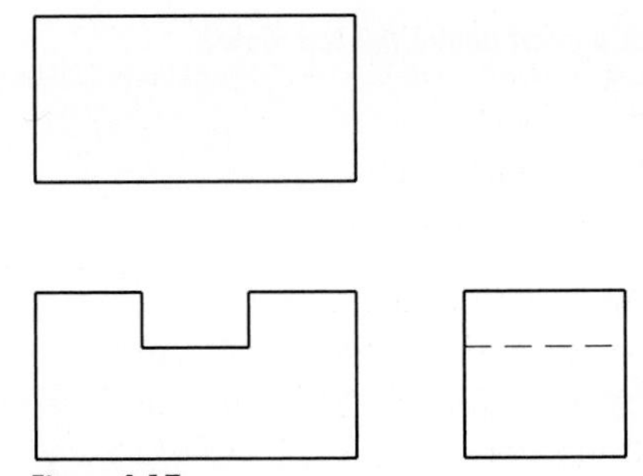

Figure 4.17

The LTSCALE Factor

The linetype scale factor for any line pattern can be changed using the LTSCALE command located on the SETTINGS menu. All standard AutoCAD line patterns are defined in the file ACAD.LIN. Each line pattern is defined by the distance to draw each dash and gap, as well as dots, if they are used. Because these are defined using specific distances, you may need to adjust the lengths of the dashes and gaps for use in your drawing. The LTSCALE command lets you adjust the line pattern lengths by the scaling factor you specify. A setting of 2 for LTSCALE makes the dashes and gaps twice as long as the original pattern; a setting of .5 makes them half as long. When you are plotting your drawing to a particular scale, you usually set the LTSCALE factor to the reciprocal of the plot scale. For instance, if you are going to plot the drawing at 1"=10", then you set LTSCALE to 10. LTSCALE affects all line patterns in your drawing at the same time (although you can adjust differently for paper space and model space).

Adjust the LTSCALE factor for the lines in your drawing. Often you need to adjust the scaling for the hidden lines to meet the standards for drawing hidden lines that were described earlier in this tutorial.

Pick: **AutoCAD *(screen menu)*, SETTINGS, next, LTSCALE**

The prompt asks for a scale factor. Try some different values to see the effect; .7 often works well for engineering drawings that will be plotted full scale. Be sure to select the default value, 1, before you go on.

New scale factor <1.0000>: **1** ↵

■ ***Warning:*** When you are working in metric units, the line patterns sometimes may not appear correctly. A line may appear to be the correct color, but not the correct pattern. This is because the line pattern is defined in terms of inches, AutoCAD's default unit system. The line has the correct pattern, but the spacing is so small it can't be seen. Use LTSCALE to adjust the spacing. The value for LTSCALE is usually the reciprocal of the scale that you will use to plot the drawing. For metric units, try a value of 25.4. ■

Adapting for Architecture

The standard AutoCAD line patterns often produce dashes in architectural drawings that are too large, if you use the recommended settings of the reciprocal of your plot scale. Generally, halving the recommended values will allow you to create a drawing with a crisp, more exact appearance. ■

Next, you will use the LINE command to project the width of the slot into the top view, using vertical lines.

First, you will set the current layer back to Layer 0 for these lines. You can quickly select the current layer by picking on the layer name displayed on the toolbar. The list of available layer names pulls down. You can use the list that appears to pick on the layer you wish to set as current.

Pick: ***(HIDDEN from the toolbar)***

Pick: ***(0 from the list of layers that pulls down, as shown in Figure 4.18)***

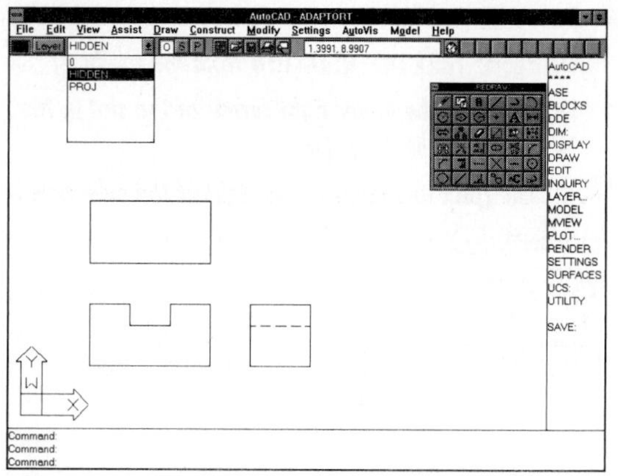

Figure 4.18

Notice that Layer 0 now appears on the toolbar as the current layer. Now you can draw the lines for the slot in Layer 0. To help make the projection lines straight, turn ORTHO on (by picking the O button from the toolbar) if it is not already highlighted on the toolbar at the top of the screen.

Since you will be drawing a number of lines from intersections, use the Settings (pull-down) menu, Object Snap. . . option to turn on the running mode Intersection.

Pick: **Settings *(menu bar),* Object Snap. . .**

Pick: **Intersection**

Pick: **OK**

Pick: **LINE *(toolbar)***

From point: ***(target the upper left corner of the slot in the front view)***

To point: ***(pick a point above the top view)***

To point : ⏎

Command: ⏎

From point: ***(target the upper right corner of the slot in the front view)***

To point: ***(pick a point above the top view)***

To point: ↵

Use the TRIM command to remove the excess lines. Your screen should look similar to Figure 4.19.

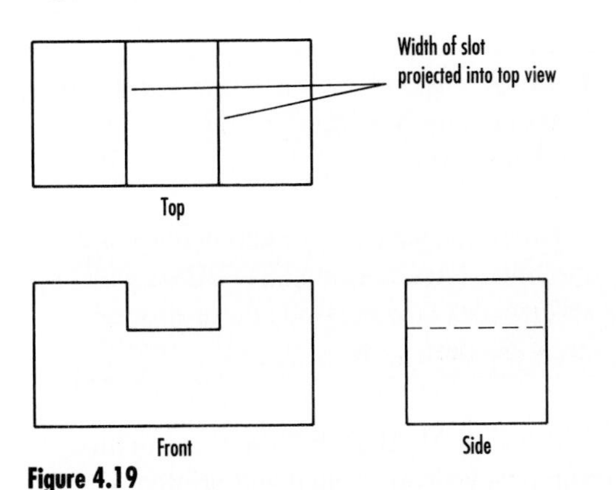

Figure 4.19

Type: **SAVE** ↵

ADAPTORT should appear as the file name in the dialogue box. If it does not, make the correction and then pick OK. The drawing is now saved on your disk. If you gave your file a directory and drive prefix when you created it, the complete file name should appear in place of ADAPTORT as the default. If you want to change the file name, enter it before pressing ↵. You have now drawn the front, top, and side orthographic views of Figure 4.5. Check your work by matching each line in the orthographic views with its equivalent in the drawing shown in Figure 4.5.

Line Precedence

Different types of lines often line up with each other within the same view, as illustrated in Figure 4.20.

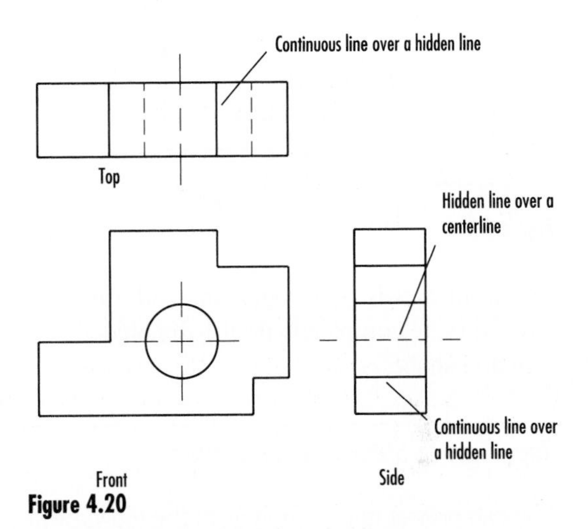

Figure 4.20

The question arises, which type of line takes *precedence*; that is, which type do you draw? The rule is that continuous lines take precedence over hidden lines, and hidden lines take precedence over center lines. Note that in the side view of Figure 4.20, the short-end segments of the covered-up center line show beyond the edge of the object.

Slanted Surfaces

Orthographic views can only distinguish *inclined* lines from normal lines if the lines are drawn in profile. Inclined lines are parallel to one of the principal views, but tipped away, or foreshortened, in the other views. As illustrated in Figure 4.21, there is no way to tell by looking at the top and side views which lines are inclined and which are normal.

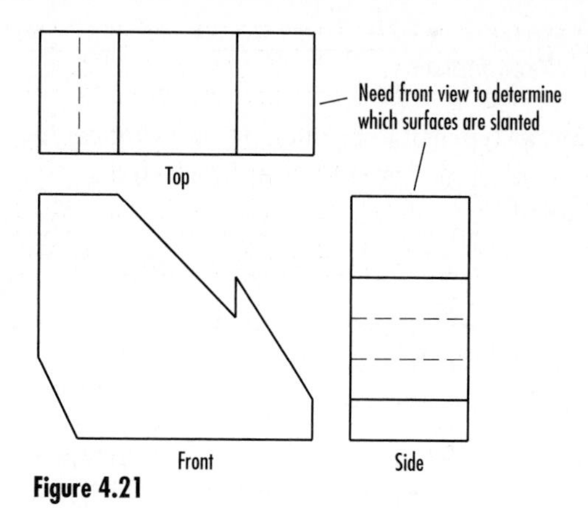

Figure 4.21

The front view is required, along with the other two views, to completely define the object's size and shape.

Top-View to Side-View Projection

You can project information from the top view to the side view and vice versa by using a 45-degree miter line. The miter line can be drawn anywhere above the side view and to the right of the top view, but is often drawn from the top right corner of the front view, as shown in Figure 4.22.

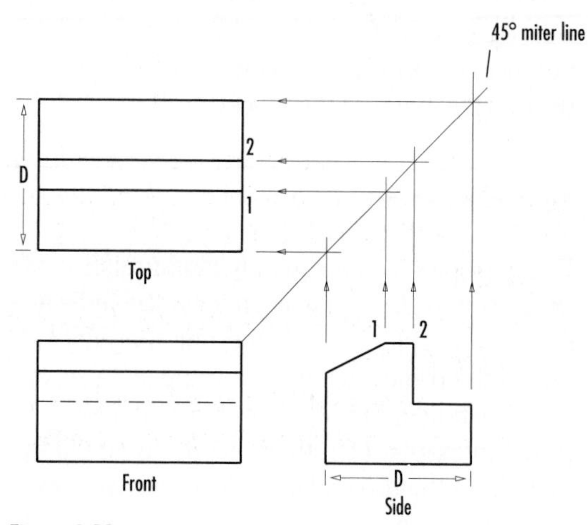

Figure 4.22

To project information from the side view to the top view, you would draw vertical projection lines from the points in the side view so that they intersect the miter line. In the example in Figure 4.22, points 1 and 2 are projected. Then horizontal lines would be projected from the intersection of the vertical lines and the miter line across the top view. Remove all excess lines.

■ ***TIP*** When you are drawing vertical and horizontal lines to intersect the miter line, the command OSNAP, Intersection will help to capture the intersection points between the vertical projection lines and the miter line. Turning ORTHO on will ensure that only vertical and horizontal lines are drawn. ■

The drawing ADAPTORT, the three orthographic views you created and printed, should still be on your screen. You will now modify the object by adding a slanted surface. The object you need to draw is shown in Figure 4.23.

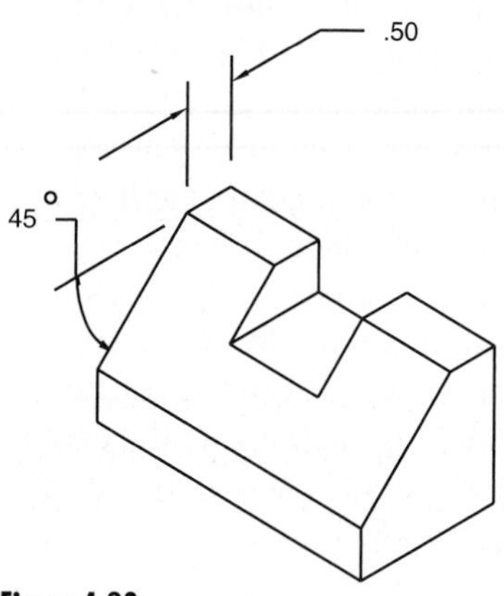

Figure 4.23

To modify the orthographic views so that they represent the drawing that includes the slanted surface, begin by using the LINE command to add the slanted surface to the side view.

Locate a point .5 inches to the left of the top right corner of the right-side view, and draw a slanted line from this point, using relative coordinates:

Pick: **LINE *(toolbox)***

From point: **7,3** ↵

To point: **@3<–135** ↵

To point: ↵

The distance 3 was chosen because the exact distance is not known and 3 is obviously longer than needed.

Your screen should look similar to Figure 4.24.

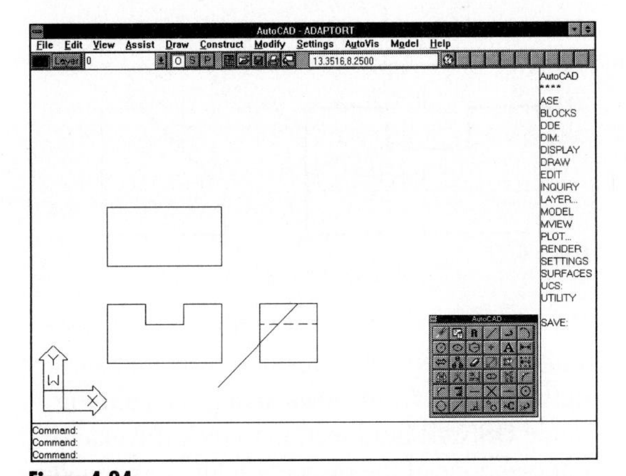

Figure 4.24

Before continuing, use the TRIM command on your own to trim this line and remove any lines above the slanted surface, and then set the current drawing layer to PROJ. When you are finished, your drawing should look like Figure 4.25.

■ ***TIP*** Use Zoom, Window to zoom the side view to help you locate the points to trim. Return to your drawing with Zoom, Previous when all the excess lines are removed. You may want to turn SNAP off to help you trim the lines. ■

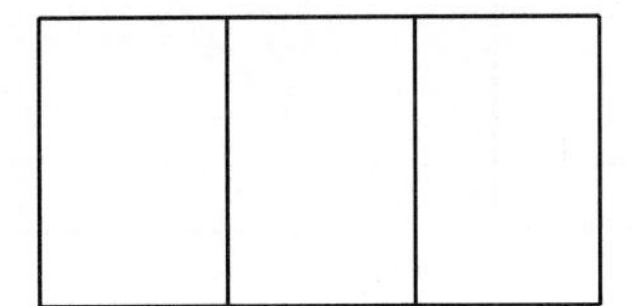

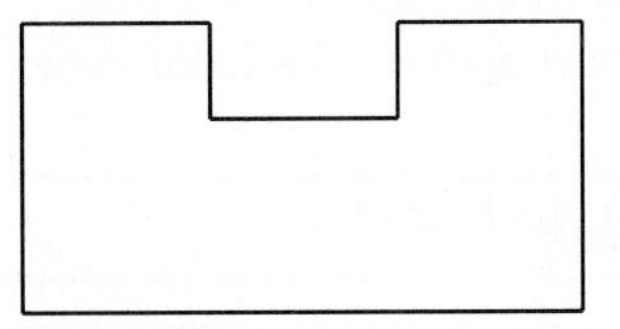

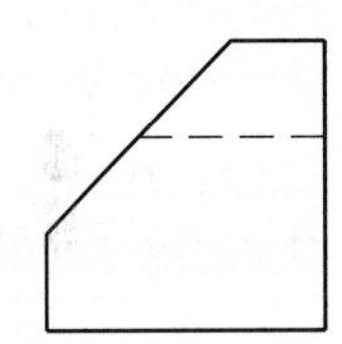

Figure 4.25

Next, use the LINE command to project a horizontal line into the front view to locate the line formed between the slanted surface and the front surface.

Pick: **LINE *(toolbox)***

From point: **6,2** ↵

To point: **2,2** ↵ ↵

Draw vertical line up from the same point in the right side to begin to locate the projection of the right-side view into the top view.

Pick: **LINE *(toolbox)***

From point: ***(pick point 1 on the right-side view shown in Figure 4.26)***

To point: ***(make sure ORTHO is on and draw the line to extend up past the first horizontal line in the top view)***

To point: ↵

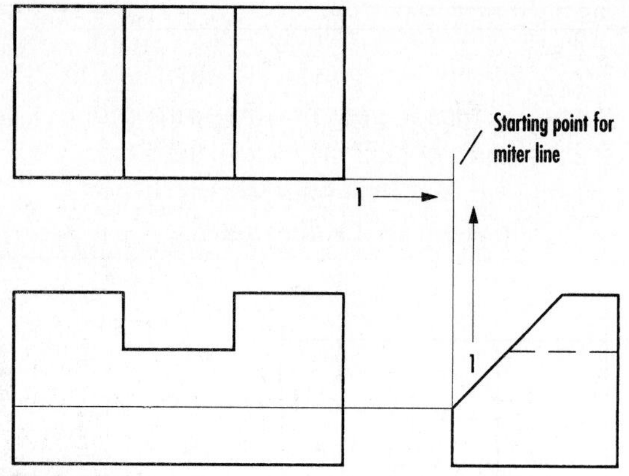

Figure 4.26

On your own project the point labeled 1 in the top view horizontally to the right until it intersects the line you drew up from the front view.

Drawing the Miter Line

You will use the LINE command to draw a 45-degree line 3.5 inches long, starting at the intersection between the two projection lines you just drew from the points marked 1. Turn SNAP on and ORTHO off to draw this line. You will want to use relative polar coordinates once you have selected the intersection where the line is to begin. Refer to Figure 4.26.

Pick: **LINE *(toolbox)***

From point: ***(target the intersection point of the projection lines from the 1 points)***

To point: **@3.5<45** ↵

To point: ↵

Now turn ORTHO on and project the corner point, point 2 in Figure 4.27, created by the slanted surface in the side view, into the top view on your own. Draw the vertical projection line from where the hidden line intersects the slanted surface.

Double-check to make sure that the running mode OSNAP, Intersection is still turned on before you draw the horizontal lines across the top view. When you have finished, your screen should look similar to Figure 4.27.

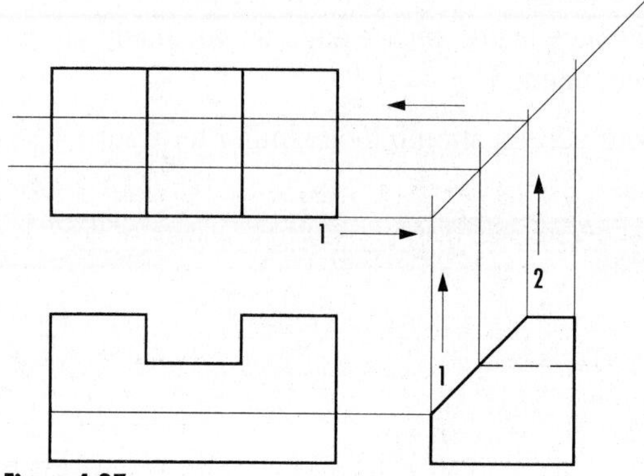

Figure 4.27

On your own, set Layer 0 as the current layer and draw the visible lines of the slanted surface in the top and front views, using the running mode OSNAP, Intersection to pick the exact intersections of the projection lines. When you have completed the visible lines, use the techniques you have learned to freeze layer PROJ so that your drawing looks like Figure 4.28.

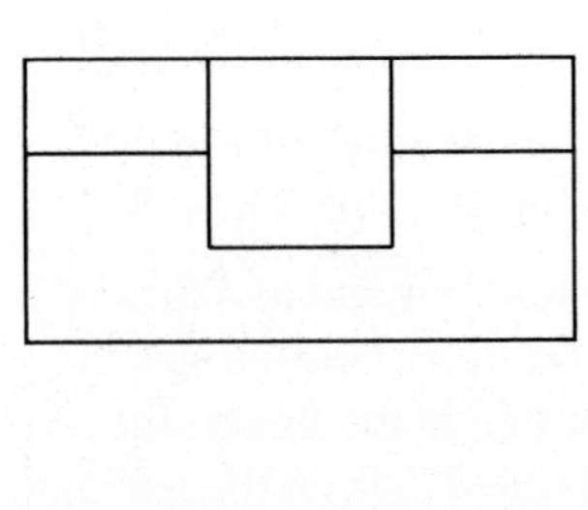

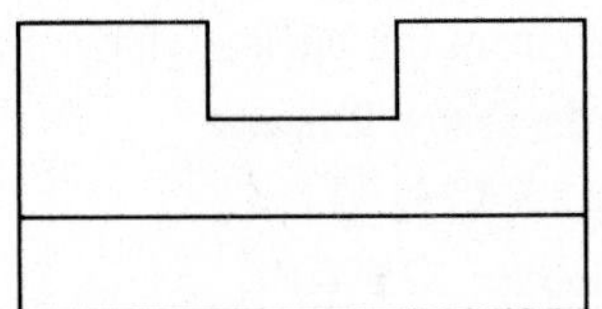

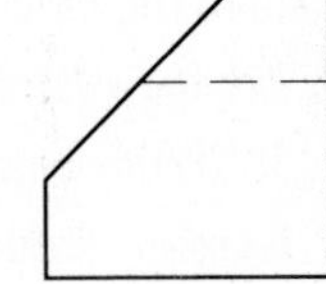

Figure 4.28

Turn the running mode OSNAP, Intersection off using the Settings selection from the menu bar. Remember that leaving this mode turned on can cause difficulty with other commands. When you are finished projecting lines from intersections, you should always turn the OSNAP running mode back off in order to avoid problems.

■ ***TIP*** It is good practice to frequently SAVE your drawings on your disk. If your system experiences a power failure and you lose the drawing in memory, you can always retrieve a recent version from your disks. ■

Command: **SAVE** ↵

You should see the file name ADAPTORT in the file name box. Make corrections to the file name, if necessary, and pick OK.

Check your figure by matching each line in the orthographic views with its equivalent on the object shown in Figure 4.23.

Drawing Holes

Figure 4.29 shows an object with two holes and the way they are represented in front and top views.

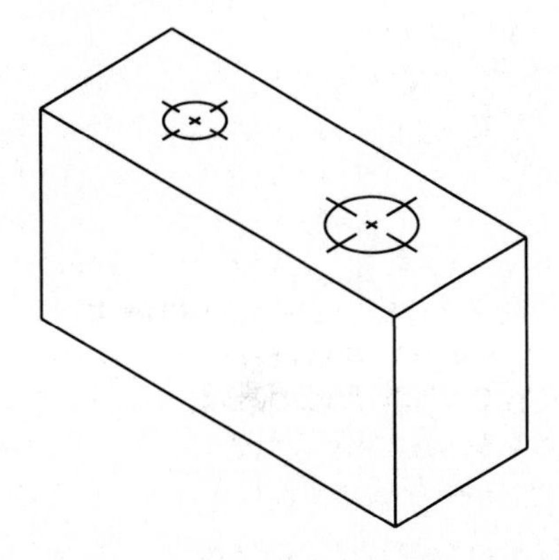

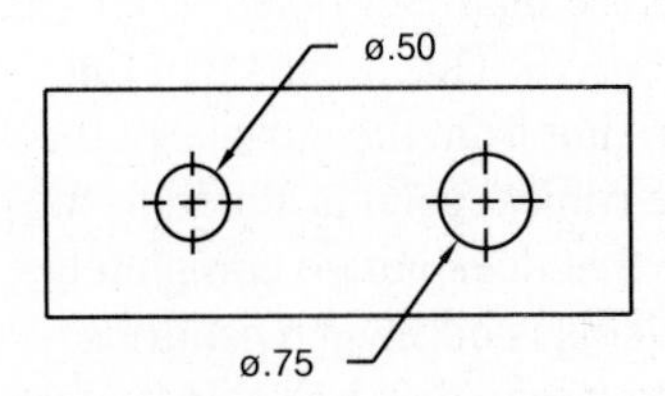

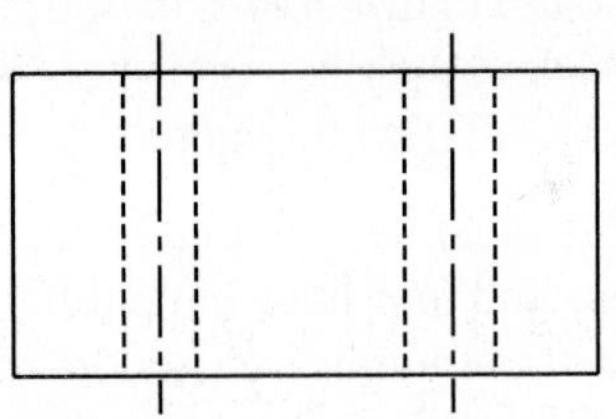

Figure 4.29

The *diameter symbol* ∅ is used to indicate a diameter value. If no depth is specified for a hole, it is assumed that the hole goes completely through the object. No depth is specified for the holes, so the hidden lines in the front view go from the top surface to the bottom surface.

You will add two holes to the orthographic views you have drawn to represent the adapter, as shown in Figure 4.30.

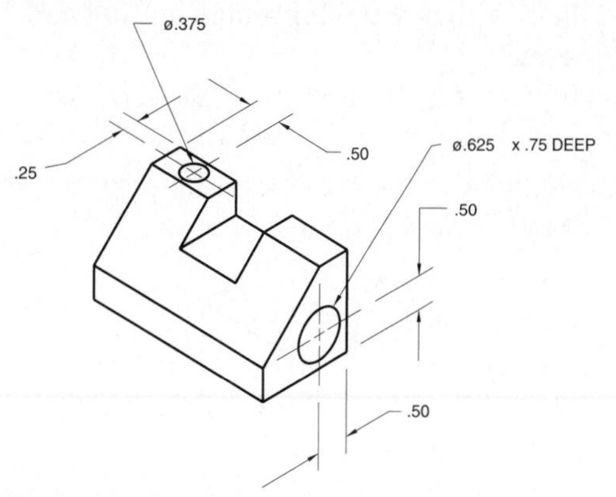

Figure 4.30

In Figure 4.30, the .625-diameter hole has a depth specification of .75. This means that the hole is .75 deep, drilling from the surface of the object. A 30-degree conical point is added to the bottom of any hole that does not go completely through an object. This is because twist drills, the type used most often to drill holes, have a conical point. The 30-degree drill point is not included as part of the depth of the hole.

Center lines for holes must be included in all views. A center cross and four lines extending beyond the four quadrant points are used to define the center point of a hole in its *circular view* (the view where the hole appears as a circle). A single center line, parallel to the two hidden lines, is used in the other views, also called the *rectangular views* because the drill hole appears as a rectangle.

Return to the orthographic views of the adapter on the screen.

Use the Drawing Aids dialogue box from the Settings pull-down menu on your own to turn SNAP on and change the spacing to .25.

You will start with the top view and add the circular view of the .375 diameter hole, as specified in Figure 4.30. As indicated in the figure, the hole's center point is located .5 from the left surface of the view and .25 from the back surface.

Pick: **Draw *(screen)*, Circle, Center, Diameter**

3P/2P/TTR<Center point>: **2.5,5.25** ↵

Diameter/<Radius>:_D Diameter: **.375** ↵

Next, you will draw the center lines for the circle. Engineering drawings use two different thicknesses of lines. Thick lines are used for visible lines, cutting plane lines, and short break lines. Hidden lines, center lines, dimension lines, section lines, long break lines, and phantom lines are drawn with thin lines. In AutoCAD, color can be used to tell the plotter or printer which thickness of lines to use.

Since center lines in the circular view should be thin, you need to make a new layer to draw them on. You will assign it a color other than white, because the color white has already been used to draw the object outline, and object lines are thick. You will use linetype CONTINUOUS, rather than linetype CENTER, because the cross at the center of the circular view center lines will be drawn by using AutoCAD's DIM: CENTER command. You will not want additional dashes drawn along the center lines, which you would get when using linetype CENTER.

Make a new layer, called THIN, and make it current on your own. Use COLOR to set the layer's color to red. Leave the linetype set to CONTINUOUS. Refer to the section on LAYER earlier in this tutorial if you need help.

Next you will use the menu bar selection Draw, Dimensions, Radial, Center Mark to draw the circle's center lines in layer THIN. Use this command sequence whenever you are drawing a center line in the circular view. (Remember from Tutorial 2 that a negative value for DIMCEN results in a full set of center lines. The absolute value of the variable determines the size of the center mark. Usually the cross at the center should appear 1/8" wide, but since this hole is relatively small, you will need a smaller center mark, so use the value –.05.)

Command: **DIMCEN** ↵

New value for DIMCEN <0.0900>: **–.05** ↵

Command: **Draw *(menu bar)*, Dimensions, Radial, Center Mark**

Select objects: ***(pick on the outer edge of the circle)***

Select objects: ↵

You should see the circular view center lines appear in the drawing. Next, you will project the width of the hole into the front view, using OSNAP, Intersection. Since the hole will be hidden in the front view, first set the current layer to layer HIDDEN. Pick Layer from the toolbar and use the Layer Control dialogue box to set HIDDEN as the current drawing layer on your own. You will draw a vertical line from the point at which the edges of the hole intersect with the horizontal center line, and project the vertical center line into the front view.

■ ***TIP*** Use Zoom Window and turn SNAP off, if you need to make it easier to target the intersections. ■

Now turn running mode OSNAP, Intersection on, using the Settings pull-down menu on your own. Because you are going to project straight lines, make sure you have ORTHO turned on.

Pick: **LINE *(toolbox)***

From point: ***(pick the intersection of the circle's horizontal center line with the left edge of the circle)***

To point: ***(pick ****, PERpend and pick any point on the lowest horizontal line in the front view)***

To point: ↵

Repeat this procedure to draw the projection line for the right side of the hole and for the center line. Use Zoom Previous if needed to return your screen to full size.

Now that you have finished this step, your screen should look similar to Figure 4.31.

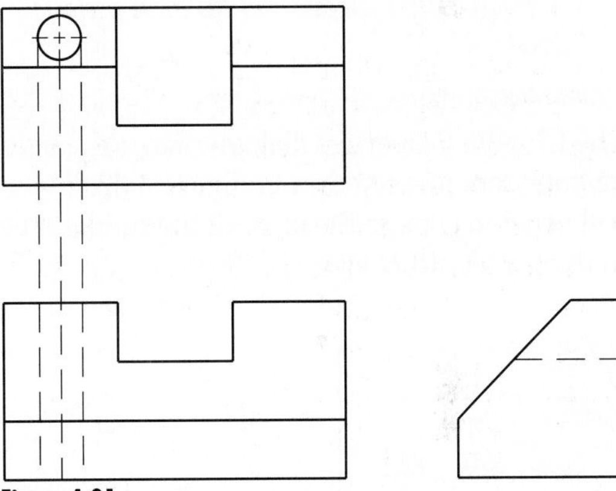

Figure 4.31

You will need a center line in the rectangular view of the drill hole. For this, a new layer will be necessary.

Type the LAYER command and use the option New to make a new layer. Name this layer CENTERLN and give it the color green and the linetype CENTER. This time **don't** set this as the current layer. You will use a new command to change the line onto this layer after you have constructed it.

■ ***Warning:*** Do not use the Layer Control dialogue in the previous step because the linetype CENTER is not loaded and therefore is not available in the dialogue box. ■

Using the Change Properties Dialogue Box

Next you will change the properties of the center line so that it is on layer CENTERLN, using the Change Properties dialogue box. The Change Properties dialogue box is very similar to the Modify, Entities dialogue box that you used in Tutorial 2. The Change Properties dialogue box lets you change fewer features, but it has the advantage of allowing you to select multiple entities to change with one use of the command.

Pick: **Modify *(menu bar)*, Change, Properties**

Select objects: ***(select the center of the three projected lines)***

Select objects: ↵

The Change Properties dialogue box appears on your screen, as shown in Figure 4.32. You will use it to change the layer of the hidden line to the CENTERLN layer.

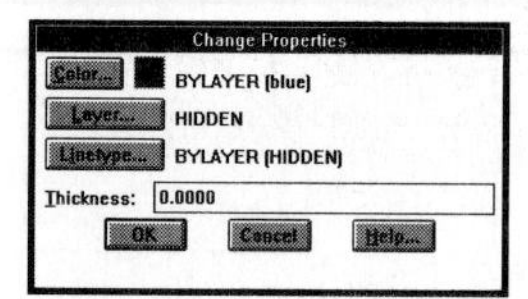

Figure 4.32

Pick: ***(the box with the word Layer. . .)***

From the list of layers that appears on your screen, select the layer CENTERLN.

Pick: **OK *(to exit the dialogue box)***

Pick: **OK *(to exit the Change Properties dialogue box)***

You will see the line change to color green and linetype CENTER, indicating that its layer has changed as selected. Next you will break the line so that it is the right length for a center line in the front view.

Before continuing, turn the OSNAP, Intersection running mode off on your own.

Breaking the Center Line

Pick: **Modify *(menu bar)*, Break, Select object, Two points**

You will be breaking the middle vertical line so that it can be used as a center line. If you need help with the BREAK command, refer to Tutorial 3. Center lines should extend at least .375" past the edge of the cylindrical part when the drawing is plotted. You will extend the center line .5" past to meet this criterion.

Select object: ***(select the middle vertical line)***

The first point of the break is the point that you want to use as the top of the center line. The second point is past the end where the line extends into the top view, so that all of the center line extending into the top view is broken off. Refer to Figure 4.33. On your own make sure that SNAP is turned on to make selecting easier.

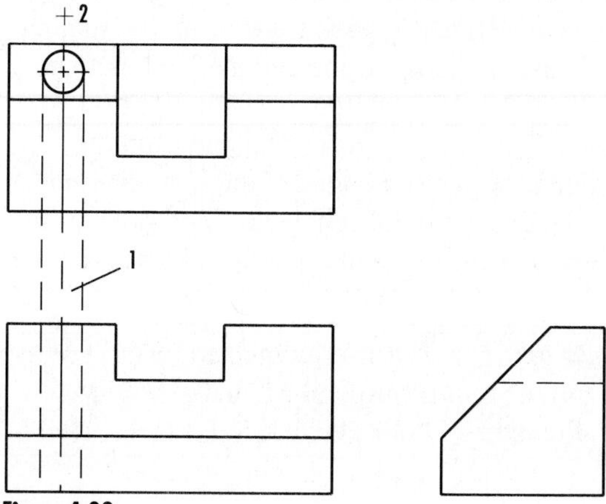

Figure 4.33

■ ***TIP*** If you pick on the end of the line, you may not get a location past the end of the line for the second point of the break; instead, short segments of the line may remain and look like random points in your drawing. ■

Enter first point: ***(select break point 1, on the line, .50 units away from the top of the object in the front view)***
Enter second point: ***(select point 2, past the top end of the line)***

Adapting for Architecture

Often when drawing, you will need to break a line along its length. If you use a pline to develop a parking scheme, and want to use the MEASURE command to quickly generate the spacing for cars, sometimes you will have to break the polyline to give the correct distance. Use the BREAK command, and pick the First option. Choose a point along the length of a line you want to break and then choose @ to pick that point. This will create two separate entities instead of one continuous line. ■

■ ***TIP*** To break a line without removing a piece of it, pick Break, Single point from the Modify menu. ■

Now use the hot grips with the STRETCH command to stretch the center line down .5" past the bottom of the front view. Refer to Tutorial 2 if you need to review using hot grips and the STRETCH command.

Click on the center line to activate the hot grips. Pick the grip on the bottom endpoint. You will see the prompt for the STRETCH command. Place the new point about .5" past the bottom of the front view. Your drawing should look like Figure 4.34.

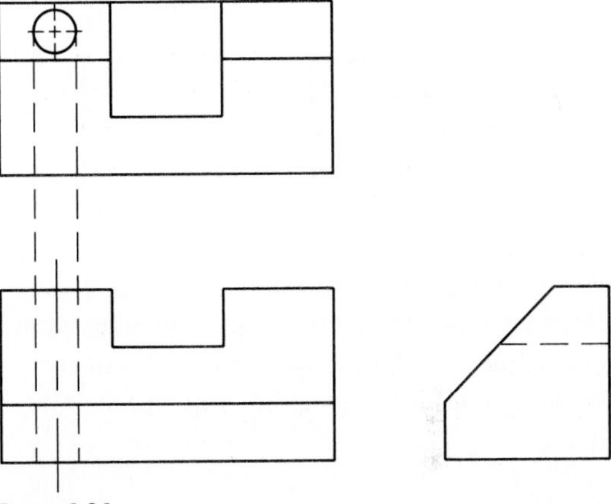

Figure 4.34

Trim the hidden lines forming the rectangular view of the hole where they extend past the top of the front view.

To complete the projection into the side view, you will project the location of the hole into the side view. Then you will use the hot grips with the MOVE, Copy command to copy the lines from the front view to the side view.

On your own, thaw layer PROJ, set it as the current layer, and draw a projection line from the point on the circle where the vertical center line intersects it and project it out past the miter line. Turn on OSNAP, Intersection and ORTHO. Make sure that SNAP is off. Refer to Figure 4.35. Then project the intersection of the horizontal projection line with the miter line into the side view, creating a vertical projection line.

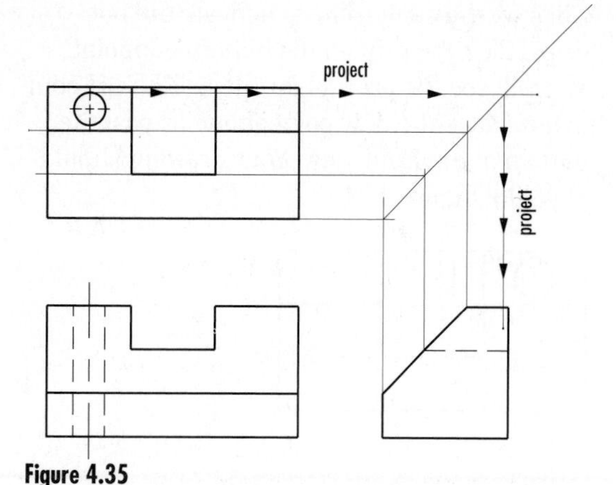

Figure 4.35

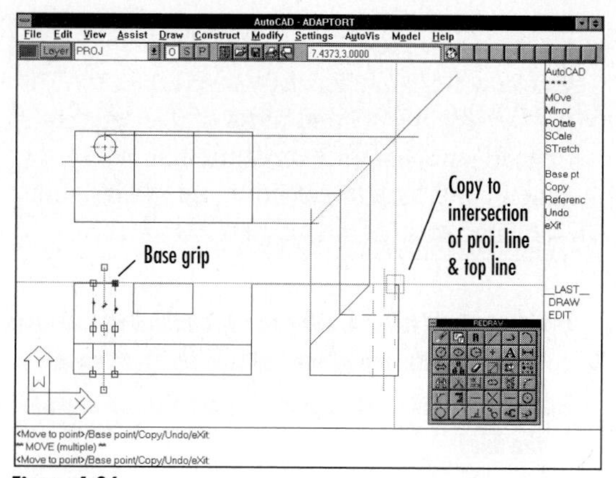

Figure 4.36

Because holes are symmetrical, the side view of the hole will appear the same as the front view, except for the location. You will use the hot grips with the MOVE, Copy command to copy the two hidden lines and the center line from the front view to the side view.

Activate the hot grips for the two hidden lines and the center line by picking on them.

Pick: ***(the grip on the top endpoint of the right-hand hidden line as the base grip)***

STRETCH

<Stretch to point>/Base point/Copy/Undo/eXit: ⏎

MOVE

<Move to point>/Base point/Copy/Undo/eXit: **C** ⏎

A faint copy of the lines you selected appears, attached to the crosshairs. (You should still have the running mode OSNAP, Intersection active.) Target the intersection between the top line in the side view and the projection line locating the side of the hole, as you see in Figure 4.36. You may want to use ZOOM, Window to help you choose the correct intersection. The three lines are copied to this location. Press ⏎ to exit the Copy command.

Leave the projection lines and the miter line, as you will need them to project the other hole from the side view. Your drawing will look like Figure 4.37. Redraw your screen before you continue.

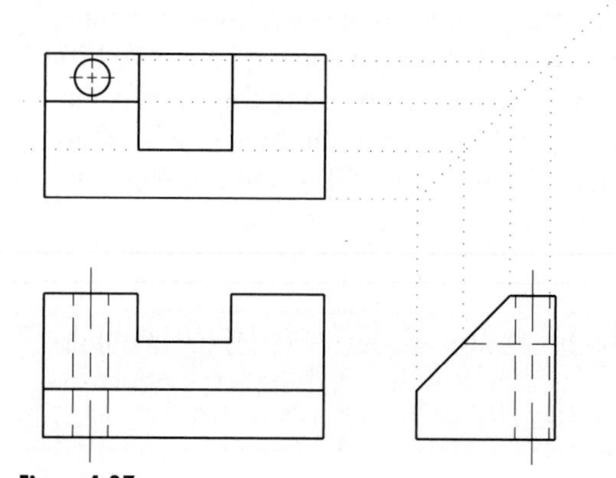
Figure 4.37

Next you will add the circular view of the .625 hole to the side view and then project the width and center line of the hole into the front view, as presented above.

Pick: **PROJ *(layer name from toolbar)***

Pick: ***(layer 0 to make it the current layer)***

Pick: **Draw *(menu bar)*, Circle, Center, Diameter**

The center point of the hole is 6.75,2 and the diameter is .625. Complete the circle on your own.

Now make layer THIN current and use Draw, Dimensions, Radial, Center Mark to add center lines. Once you have completed this step, return to the HIDDEN layer and use OSNAP, Intersection to project the hole's edge lines into the front view on your own, as shown in Figure 4.38.

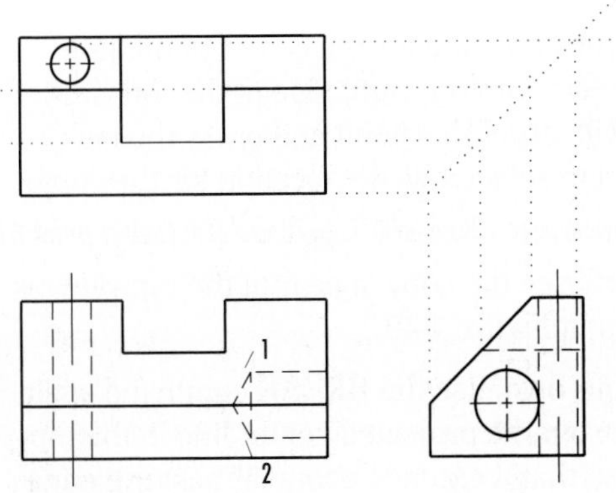

Figure 4.38

Add the .75 depth of the hole by using OFFSET to create a vertical line parallel to the right surface of the front view on your own. If you need help using OFFSET, refer to Tutorial 2. Then use the TRIM command to remove the excess lines. Refer to Figure 4.38.

Next you will add the 30-degree conical point to both views. First you will enlarge the area you are working on so that it fills your screen.

Pick: **View *(menu bar)*, Zoom Window**

Zoom the front view so that you can add the conical point. Select the corner points necessary to enlarge the front view.

Pick: **LINE *(toolbox)***

From point: ***(target intersection 1 in Figure 4.38)***

To point: **@.75<240** ↵

To point: ↵

Command: ↵

Line from point: ***(target intersection 2)***

To point: **@.75<120** ↵

To point: ↵

Pick: **View *(menu bar)*, Zoom Previous**

to return to your original display screen area.

Use the TRIM command to remove any excess lines on your own.

Now use the Modify, Entity selection to change the line you offset to the layer named HIDDEN on your own. If you need help, refer to Tutorial 2. Pick Layer, not linetype, in the dialogue box and choose layer HIDDEN from the list that appears.

Then use Settings, Layer Control to change the current layer to the layer named CENTERLN. Project a line from the side view, where the center line crosses the edge of the circle, to the front view on your own.

Notice that the horizontal center line in the front view is covered by an edge line. Refer to the section at the beginning of this tutorial and Figure 4.18 on line precedence. The object line takes precedence over the center line, but AutoCAD displays the last line drawn.

On your own, use BREAK to remove the excess center line, as you learned earlier, so that only a short tail remains at each end of the hole.

To get rid of the excess blip marks,

Pick: **REDRAW icon *(toolbox)***

Now project the center of the hole from the side view to locate it in the top view so that you can copy it from the front view. Be sure that OSNAP, Intersection is turned on.

Pick: **LINE** ***(toolbox)***

From point: ***(select the point where the center line touches the top of the hole in the side view)***

To point: ***(select a point slightly past the miter line)***

To point: ↵

Command: ↵

Line from point: ***(select the point where the projected line intersects with the miter line)***

To point: ***(select a point near the middle of the top view)***

To point: ↵

Your lines may need to be adjusted with LTSCALE to make the center line pattern visible and the hidden pattern have shorter dashes.

Pick: **AutoCAD** ***(screen menu)*****, Settings, next, LTSCALE**

New scale factor <1.0000>: **.65** ↵

Your drawing should look like Figure 4.39.

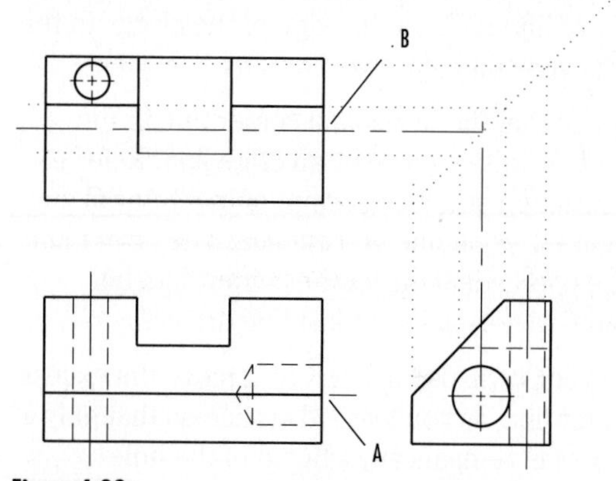

Figure 4.39

Now you are ready to use the hot grips and MOVE, Copy to copy the hidden lines from the front view into the top view. You will use a procedure similar to last time, except that you will change the base point. When prompted for the base point, you will select the intersection of the center line with the right edge of the object in the front view. Refer to Figure 4.39.

Pick: ***(on the hidden lines forming the hole and drill point in the front view to activate the hot grips)***

Pick: ***(any grip as the base grip)***

Press: ↵ ***(or the spacebar, to cycle past STRETCH to the MOVE command)***

** MOVE **

<Move to point>/Base point/Copy/Undo/eXit: **B** ↵

Base point: ***(target point A)***

<Move to point>/Base point/Copy/Undo/eXit: **C** ↵

You will see a faint copy of the lines you have selected attached to the crosshairs. Move the crosshairs to the point in the top view where the projection line for the center of the hole intersects with the right side of the top view. You will target this point and press the pick button to select it as the location for the copy.

<Move to point>/Base point/Copy/Undo/eXit: ***(select point B)***

You will see the copy appear in the top view, as shown in Figure 4.40.

On your own, use the BREAK command again to shorten the projected center line in the top view so that it extends about .5" past the edge of the circular part. Then freeze layer PROJ containing the projection and miter lines. Redraw your screen.

Your screen should look like Figure 4.40.

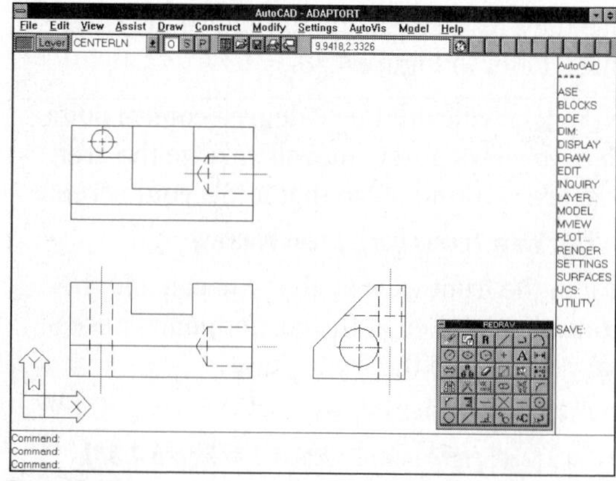

Figure 4.40

Saving Your Drawing

You have completed this orthographic drawing. Save the drawing on your disk as ADAPTORT.

Going Further

Using AutoCAD's LINETYPE command, you can create your own line patterns. Try it for yourself.

Select AutoCAD (screen menu), SETTINGS, LINETYP, Create. You will be prompted, "Name of linetype to create:". Type "MYLINE" and press ↵ to give this name to the new linetype that you will define in the next steps. The Create or Append Linetype File dialogue box appears on your screen. Replace the file ACAD with the new name CUSTOM to store your new linetype separately from the linetype patterns that come with the AutoCAD program. Pick OK to continue the command when you have typed "CUSTOM" in the box provided. AutoCAD checks to see if the name MYLINE already exists. If it does, you will be given the chance to replace it. If it does not exist, you will see the prompt, "Descriptive text:". This is the text that is displayed when you list the linetypes on the screen. Enter "Dash dot dot dash" ↵ as the descriptive text for your linetype. (You could also make a simple pattern from the underscore (_) and period (.) characters to represent this type of line.)

Now you will define the pattern. A positive value specifies the length of a dash in the line pattern. A negative value specifies the length of a gap. You define a dot by typing a zero (0) in the line pattern. The pattern starts automatically with the alignment designation A to indicate that the lines drawn will start and end with a dash. This is the only alignment currently allowed. You will see the prompt, "Enter pattern (on next line): A". Enter ".25,–.125,0,–.125,0,–.125,.25" ↵ to define the dash dot dot dash pattern.

AutoCAD responds, "New definition written to file. ?/Create/Load/Set:". Type "L" ↵ to load the line pattern that you created. At the prompt, "Linetype(s) to load:", type "MYLINE" ↵. Use the dialogue box that appears to select the file CUSTOM.lin where your line pattern is stored. Pick OK to exit the dialogue box. You see the message "Linetype MYLINE loaded," and the LINETYPE command prompt returns. Press ↵ to end the command.

Once you have created and loaded the linetype, it is available for you to use. Create a layer called TEST that has the color green and linetype MYLINE. Set it as the current layer. Use the LINE command to draw lines using your new linetype. Adjust the LTSCALE factor to see the effect that it has on the linetype you created.

Adapting for Architecture

The DOT1 and DOT2 linetype patterns defined in ACAD.LIN can be used with a small LTSCALE value to create stippled patterns in drawings. You can make site lines appear stippled by using either of these linetypes. ■

Exit AutoCAD; you have completed Tutorial 4.

KEY TERMS

- circular view
- current layer
- diameter symbol ∅
- edge view
- grayed
- hidden line
- inclined
- intersection
- limiting element
- normal surface
- orthographic view
- precedence
- project
- projection lines
- rectangular view

KEY COMMANDS

- Layer
- Ortho

EXERCISES

Draw front, top, and right-side orthographic views of the following objects. The letter M after an exercise number means that the problem's dimensional values are in millimeters (metric units). If no letter follows the exercise number, the dimensions are in inches.

4.1 Base Block

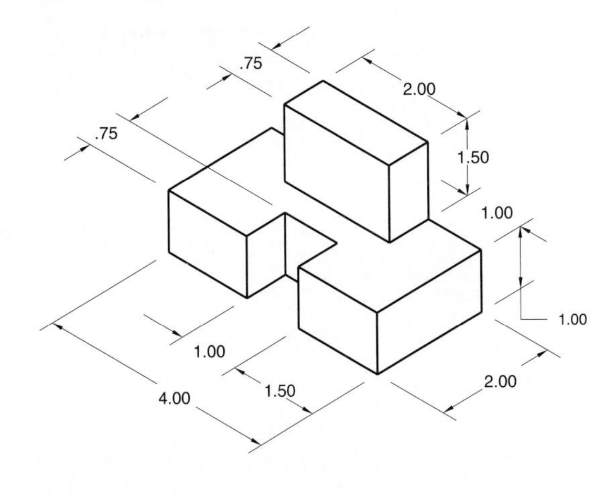

4.2M Shaft Block

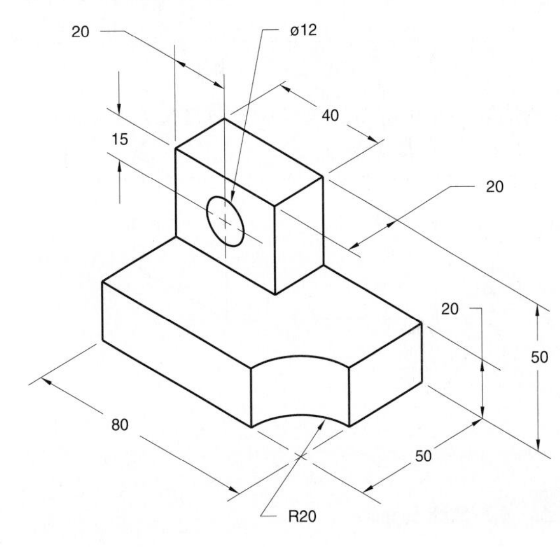

4.3 Piston Guide

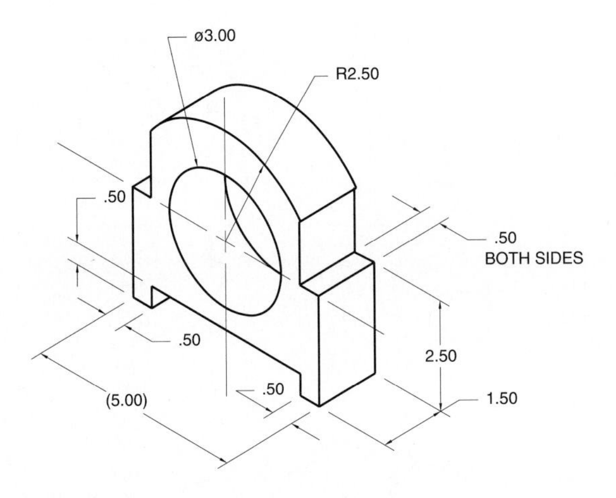

4.4 Stress Test Circuit

Create this layout using GRID and SNAP set to 0.2.

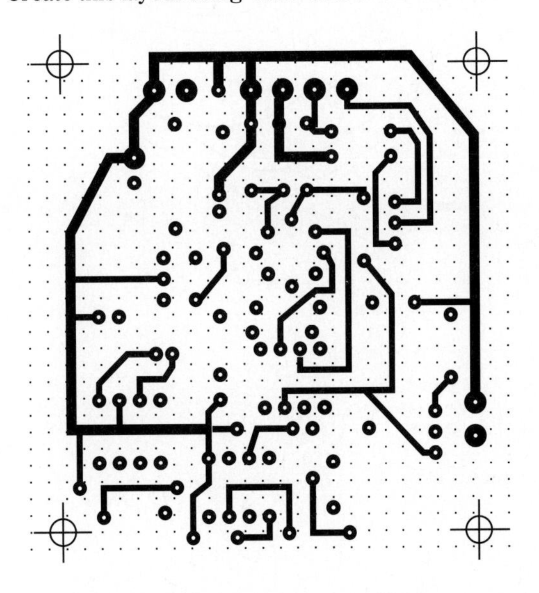

Draw front, top, and right-side orthographic views of the following objects. The letter M after an exercise number means that the problem's dimensional values are in millimeters (metric units). If no letter follows the exercise number, the dimensions are in inches.

4.5 Bearing Box

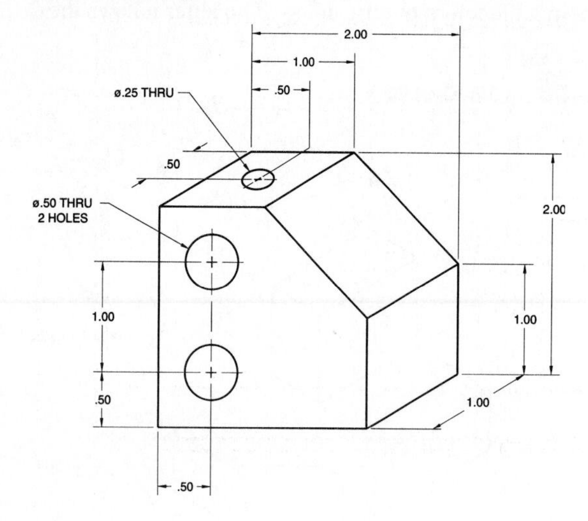

4.6M Bushing Holder

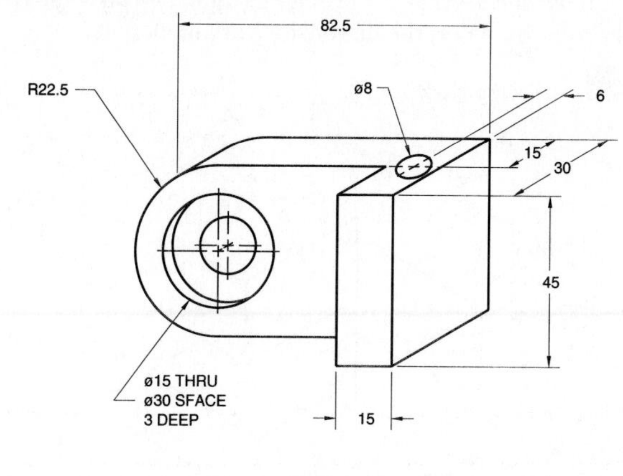

4.7 Shaft Support

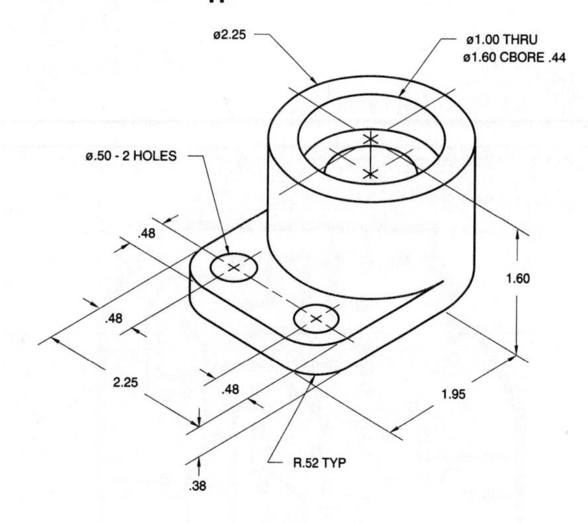

4.8 Floor Plan

Draw the floor plan according to the dimensions shown. Use separate layers for walls, windows, and doors. Add text, border, and title block.

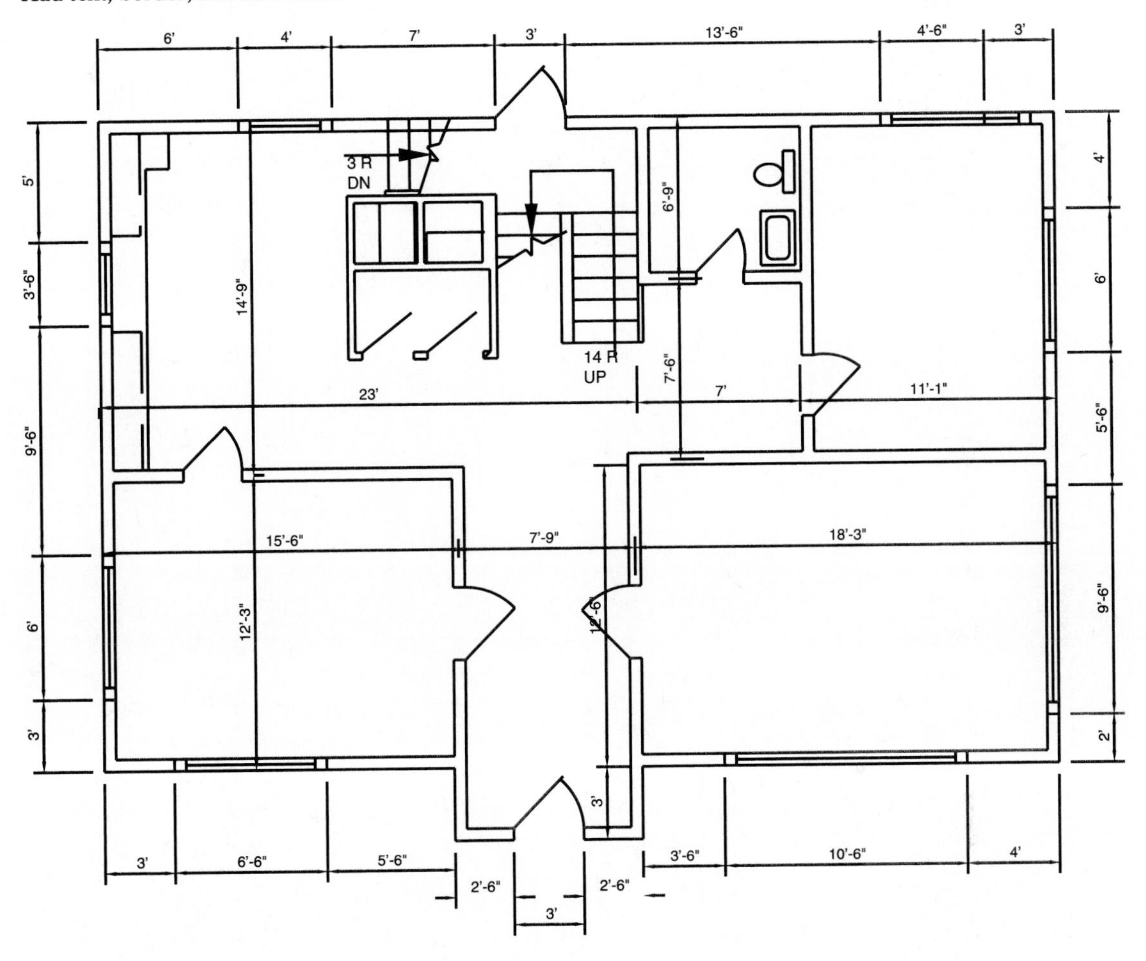

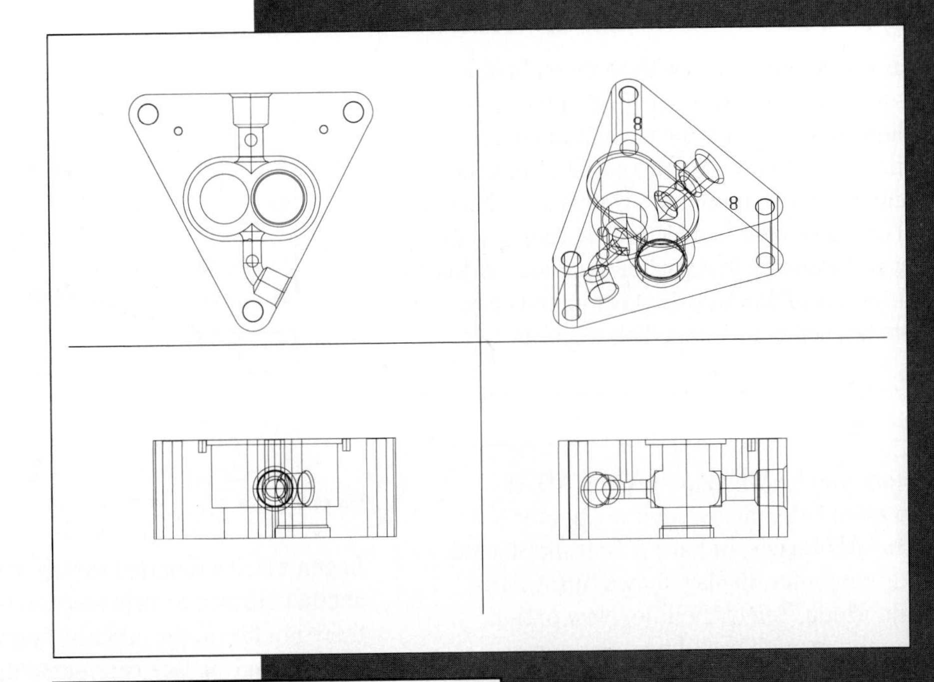

TUTORIAL 5

More Practice in Drawing Orthographic Views

Objectives

When you have completed this tutorial, you will be able to

1. Draw orthographic views of cylinders.
2. Create orthographic views of oblique lines and oblique surfaces.
3. Project information needed to define the intersection of two objects.
4. Project slanted surfaces on cylinders.
5. Identify points and find areas of surfaces.
6. Plot from model space.
7. Program the toolbox and toolbar.

Introduction

This tutorial continues with more techniques associated with drawing orthographic views, oblique lines, oblique surfaces, and intersections between two objects, as well as projecting slanted surfaces on rounded surfaces. This tutorial develops your knowledge of projection theory and assumes that you have a good working knowledge of the AutoCAD commands you have learned in the preceding tutorials.

Starting

Before you begin, launch AutoCAD. If you need help, please review Chapter 3, AutoCAD Basics, in Part 1, Getting Started. Your computer display shows AutoCAD's Main Menu. Select the File, New option from the menu bar and type the name "CYL1ORTH" (for Cylinder 1 orthographic).

Rounded Surfaces

Figure 5.1 shows the orthographic views of several objects that contain rounded surfaces.

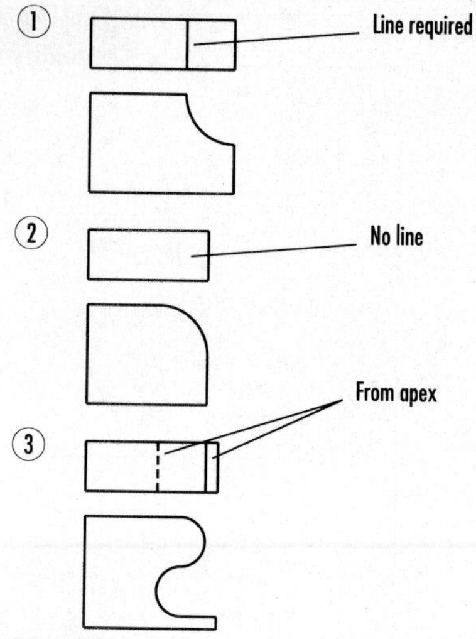

Figure 5.1

In general, if a rounded surface intersects another surface to form an edge (see example 1), there is a line in the other orthographic views. If the rounded surface runs smoothly into another surface (see example 2), then no line is required in any of the views. If the included angle of a curved surface is greater than 90 degrees (see example 3), then the vertex of the surface generates a line in the other orthographic views.

Figure 5.2 shows a cylinder.

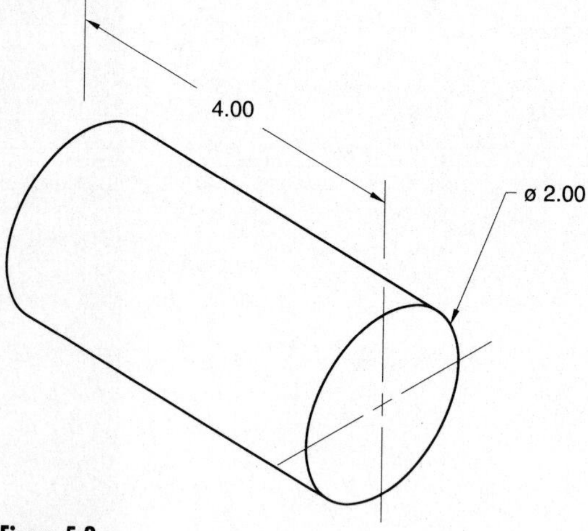

Figure 5.2

The front and top views of this cylinder are referred to as its rectangular views. The side view is referred to as the circular view.

To draw the front, top, and side orthographic views of the cylinder, you will first define the center line locations for each view.

On your own, set the grid and snap with .5 spacing. Use either the Settings (menu bar), Drawing Aids dialogue box or the GRID and SNAP commands.

Use the LINE command to draw two horizontal lines across the screen and the vertical line on the right side of the screen, as shown in Figure 5.3.

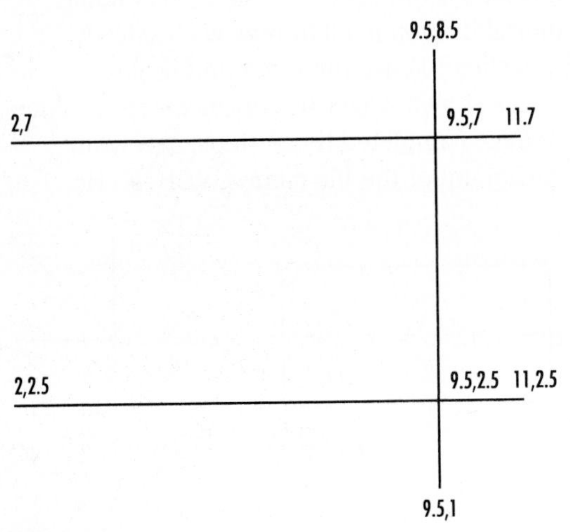

Figure 5.3

The cylinder has a 2-inch diameter. You will draw a 2-inch diameter circle centered about the lower intersection point,

Pick: **CIRCLE *(toolbox)***

3P/2P/TTR/<Center point>: ***(select the center point, 9.5,2.5; use SNAP or Intersection)***

<Radius>: **1** ↵

Now create layer THIN with color red and linetype CONTINUOUS. Set it as the current layer. Set the variable DIMCEN and set the magnitude and style of the center mark to –.125. Next use the Draw, Dimensions, Radial, Center Mark selection to add the center line for the circle. Reset Layer 0 as the current layer before you proceed.

Next you will draw a 45-degree miter line through the upper intersection point. Refer to Figure 5.4 as you select the points.

Pick: **LINE *(toolbox)***

From point: **8,5.5** ↵

To point: **11,8.5** ↵

To point: ↵

> ■ ***TIP*** The grid background and SNAP can be used to draw 45-degree lines because the grid pattern is a square. A diagonal line across the corner of a grid square is 45 degrees. ■

The length of the line should exceed the width of the circle. This line will be used to project information between the top and side views. To help project the width of the cylinder into the front and top views,

Pick: **Settings *(menu bar)*, Object Snap. . .**

Use the dialogue box that appears to turn on the running mode Intersection. When you have finished, pick OK to exit the dialogue box. Next you will use the toolbar to turn on the ORTHO mode.

Pick: **O button (toolbar)**

Now draw the projection lines so your drawing looks like Figure 5.4.

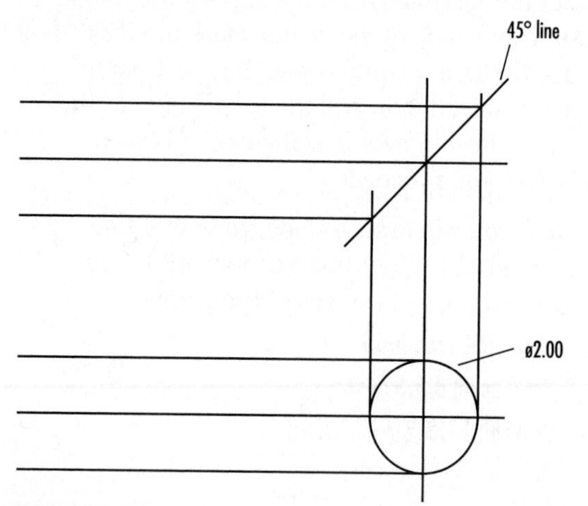

Figure 5.4

Next, draw two parallel vertical lines 4 inches apart that cross the front and top views. The vertical lines define the length of the cylinder. Their placement is somewhat arbitrary, as long as they are 4 inches apart. Your screen should look similar to Figure 5.5.

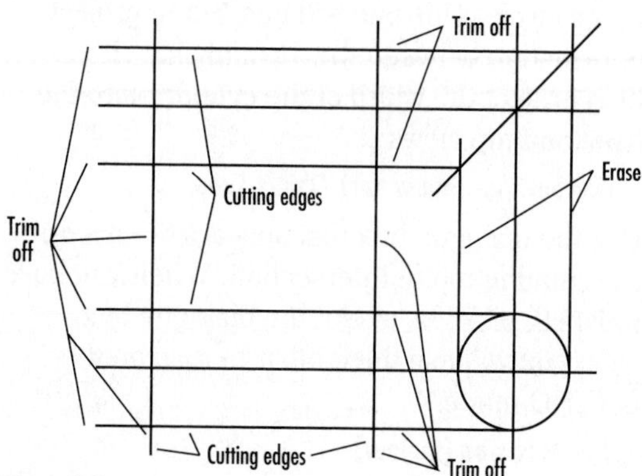

Figure 5.5

Now turn off the running mode OSNAP, Intersection and then remove all excess lines. Use the LINETYPE command to load the linetypes into your AutoCAD drawing, as you learned in Tutorial 2. Create a layer called CENTERLN, making the linetype CENTER and the color green. Change the center lines to their correct layer, using the menu bar to select Modify, Change, Properties and then using the Layer. . . option from the dialogue box that appears. Choose CENTERLN as the new layer for the lines you selected. Break the center lines on the front and top views .5 inch from the right edge of each view, so that your screen looks similar to Figure 5.6. (Refer to Tutorial 4 if you need to review LAYER and Tutorial 2 if you need to review CHANGE, Properties.) Leave the miter and projection lines as shown. Layer 0 remains current. When you have completed these steps, save your drawing under the file name CYL1ORTH.

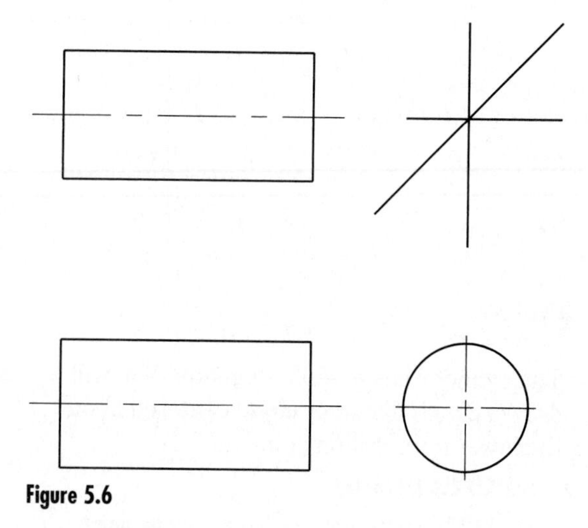

Figure 5.6

Using Your Drawing as a Prototype

In past tutorials you have started new drawings from the default prototype named ACAD.DWG that is provided with the AutoCAD software. Any saved drawing can be used as a prototype from which to start a new drawing. The advantage to this is that your new drawing will be started with all of the entities, layers, and other basic settings that were in the prototype drawing. In Tutorial 6 you will create a drawing containing many basic settings to use as a prototype.

You have completed CYL1ORTH, the first cylinder drawing, and will be starting a second cylinder drawing. You will use CYL1ORTH as an existing prototype drawing, but name your new drawing CYL2ORTH to continue with this tutorial. This will keep CYL1ORTH unchanged on your disk and allow you to continue with CYL2ORTH.

> ■ ***TIP*** You could also open file CYL1ORTH and then use SAVEAS to save the drawing to the new file name CYL2ORTH. However, it is easy to forget to use SAVEAS and save to a new name. If you use SAVE or QSAVE, you will modify the original file that you did not intend to change. For this reason it is generally better to use the existing file as a prototype. ■

Adapting for Architecture

If a drawing that you created earlier has many useful symbols and shapes, use the SAVEAS command to save that drawing with a new name. This sets your default drawing name to the new name. You can then make changes to this new drawing and retain the information that is useful. Use the SAVEAS command to make a new drawing for your elevation or floor plan, and then draw over the top of the old plan. Erase all of the unwanted entities when you are done. ■

On your own, select File, New from the menu bar. You will see the New File dialogue box appear on your screen. Type in "CYL1ORTH" for the prototype drawing name in place of ACAD. For the new file name, enter "CYL2ORTH". Remember to enter the drive and directory with the file name, or use the dialogue boxes to select them.

Flat Surfaces on Cylinders

Figure 5.7 shows a cylinder with two flat surfaces.

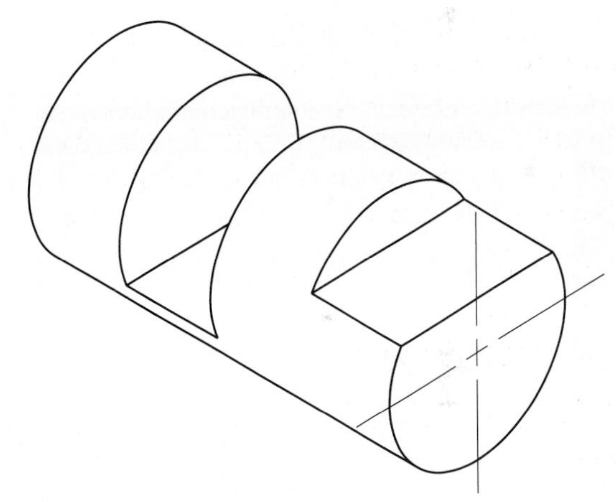

Figure 5.7

The shallow surface is located .5 above the center line. The deep surface is located .38 below the center line. To draw the orthographic views of these surfaces, you will start with the side view and draw two horizontal lines, one .5 above the horizontal center line and one .38 below the center line.

Pick: **LINE *(toolbox)***

For the first line, the coordinates are

From point: **10.75,3** ↵

To point: **5,3** ↵

To point: ↵

You will use the OFFSET command to create a parallel line .88 inches below the line you just drew.

Pick: **Construct *(menu bar)*, Offset**

Offset distance or through <Through>: **.88** ↵

Select object to offset: ***(pick the line you just created)***

Side to offset? ***(pick below the line)***

Select object to offset: ↵

Pick: ***(the toolbox icon from the toolbar)***

The toolbox changes to a list along the left-hand side of the screen.

Your screen should look like Figure 5.8.

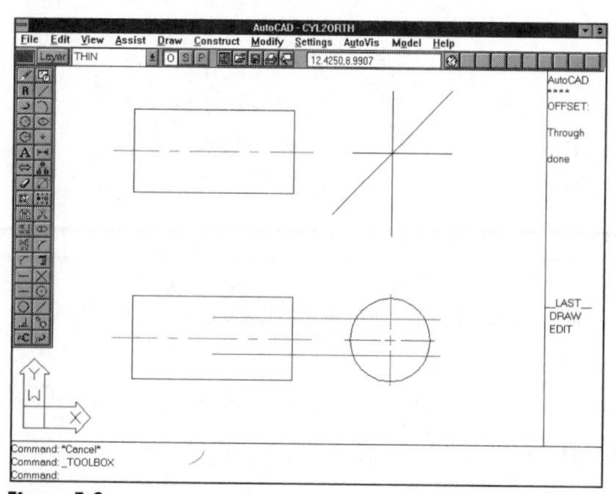

Figure 5.8

Now project the points of intersection with the circle into the top view.

On your own, turn the running mode Object Snap, Intersection on and check to see that ORTHO is still turned on.

Pick: **LINE *(toolbox)***

Use ORTHO and OSNAP, Intersection to draw vertical lines from points 1, 2, 3, and 4 in the side view, as specified in Figure 5.9, so that they intersect the miter line on your own.

■ ***TIP*** Be careful to miss any previously drawn intersections when targeting the line, or OSNAP may jump to the intersection. Using Zoom or projecting points 2 and 3 first will help. ■

Continue to use Intersection and draw horizontal projection lines across the top view, as shown. Your drawing should look similar to Figure 5.9.

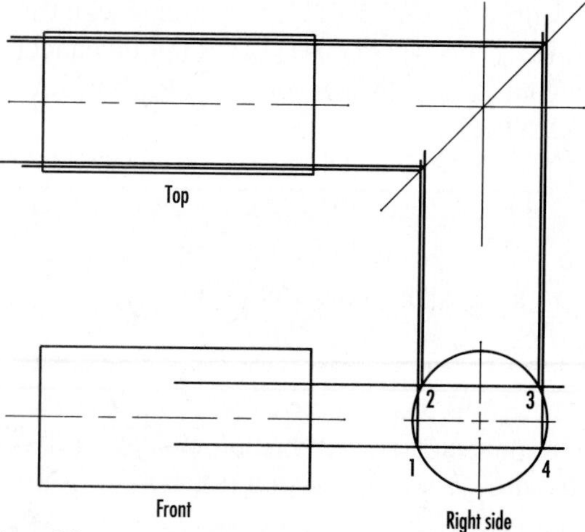

Figure 5.9

Next you will use the OFFSET command to create lines defining the width of the shallow surface.

Pick: **Construct *(menu bar)*, Offset**

Offset distance or Through<0.8800>: **1** ↵

Select object to offset: ***(pick the right-hand line of the front view)***

Side to offset? ***(pick any point to the left of the line)***

Select object to offset: ***(pick the right-hand line of the top view)***

Side to offset? ***(pick any point to the left of the line)***

Select object to offset: (↵)

When you have finished this step, your drawing should look like Figure 5.10.

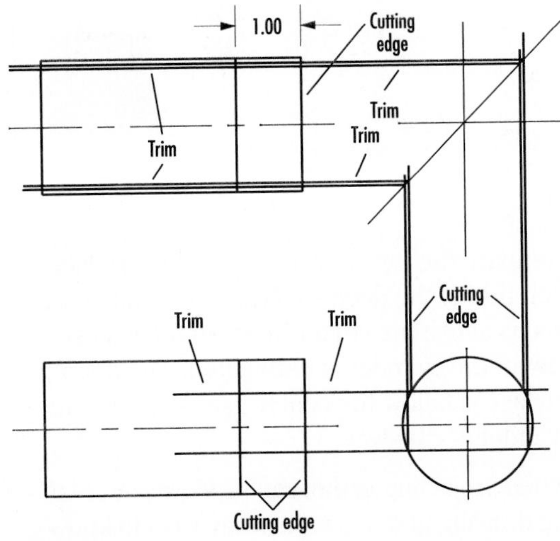

Figure 5.10

Use the TRIM and ERASE commands to remove some of the excess lines, as shown in Figure 5.10 and Figure 5.11.

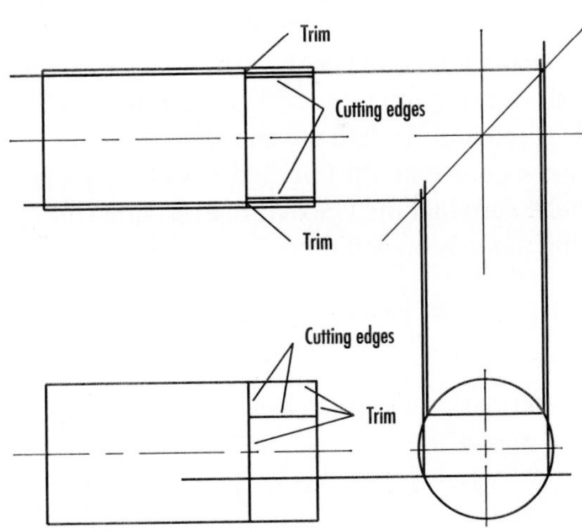

Figure 5.11

Your screen should look similar to Figure 5.12 when done.

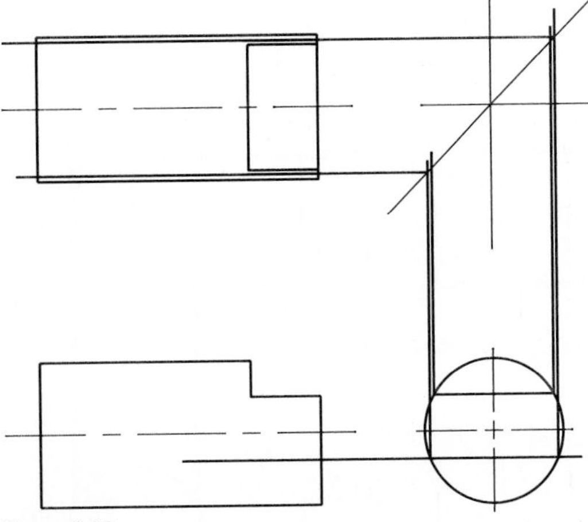

Figure 5.12

Note that the shallow surface appears as a rectangle in the top view.

Next you will use OFFSET once again to create vertical lines 1 and 2 to the right of the left side of the front and top views, defining the width of the deep cut. Refer to Figure 5.13.

Pick: **Construct *(menu bar)*, Offset**

Offset distance or Through <1.0000>: (↵) ***(to accept the default)***

Select object to offset: ***(pick the left edge of the front view)***

Side to offset? ***(pick any point to the right of the line)***

Select object to offset: ***(pick the line that was just created by the offset)***

Side to offset? ***(pick any point to the right of the line)***

Select object to offset: ***(pick the left-most line in the top view)***

Side to offset? ***(pick any point to the right of the line)***

Select object to offset: ***(pick the line that was just created by the offset)***

Side to offset? ***(pick any point to the right of the line)***

Select object to offset: (↵)

If necessary extend the projection line you drew from the side view into the front view on your own. Use line 1 as the boundary edge for the EXTEND command. Your screen should look similar to Figure 5.13.

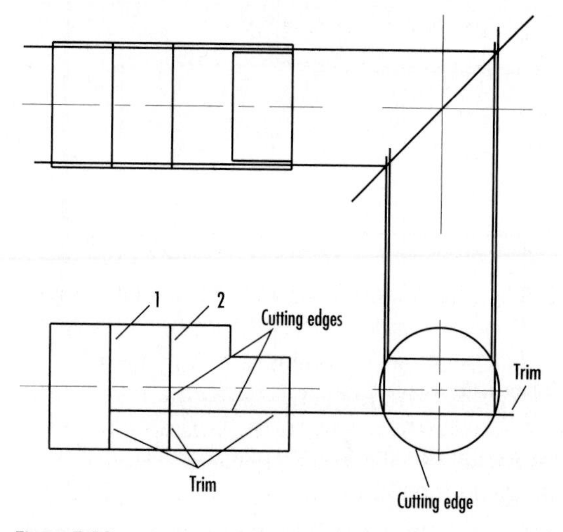

Figure 5.13

On your own, remove all excess lines, using TRIM. Refer to Figure 5.13.

Now use LAYER to create a new layer for the hidden line (call it HIDDEN, with color blue and linetype HIDDEN). Use CHPROP to change the hidden line in the side view to the correct layer, HIDDEN. Your screen should look similar to Figure 5.14.

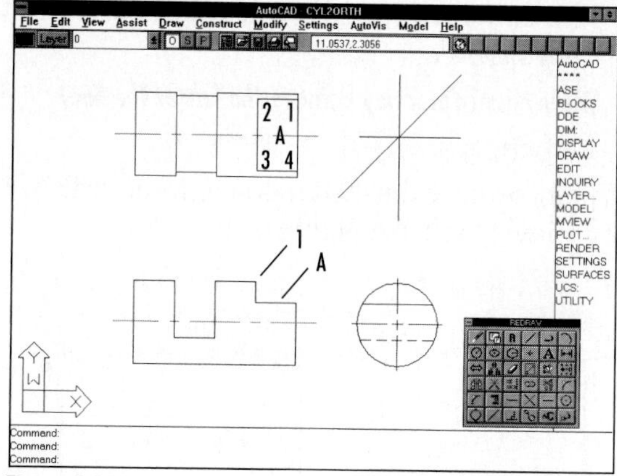

Figure 5.14

Compare the top view of the shallow surface with that of the deep surface. The shallow surface is above the center lines, so the widest part of the cylinder is untouched. The deep surface is below the center line, so part of the cylinder is cut away.

When projecting orthographic views, or creating drawing geometry, you may wish to know the exact coordinates of a point in your drawing. AutoCAD provides inquiry commands that you can use to get information from your drawing.

Using ID

You can find out the coordinates of any point in your drawing or on the screen with AutoCAD's ID command. To find the coordinates of the intersection marked 1 in Figure 5.14, check to make sure that the OSNAP, Intersection running mode is on and then,

Pick: **Assist *(menu bar)*, Inquiry, ID Point**

Point: ***(target intersection 1)***

X=6.000 Y=3.500 Z=0.000

Your coordinates may appear different, depending on the placement of your original vertical lines of 4-inch spacing.

You can use the ID command to find out the coordinates of a point you want to type in. ID is also useful for checking your drawing to make sure it is accurate. It is often necessary to use one of the Object Snap modes if you want to select a point on the existing drawing geometry. Without Object Snap, you will find the location of the closest position of the crosshairs on the screen, not the location of the intersection or endpoint that you want to identify.

Using AREA

Another useful command is AutoCAD's AREA command. It gives you the area and perimeter of a closed plane surface. When you want to find the area of a surface in a 2D engineering drawing, make sure that the surface is shown true size in the view before you use the AREA command. (If the surface is not true size, the AREA command still gives an area, but it is the area of the apparent size of the surface in that view.) A surface is true size in any view where the adjacent view shows that surface as an edge, or straight line. The surface in Figure 5.14 marked A is shown true size in the top view. In Tutorial 12 you will learn to create auxiliary views showing the true size of a surface, using 2D and solid modeling techniques.

Pick: **Assist *(menu bar)*, Inquiry, Area**

<First point>/Entity/Add/Subtract: ***(pick the point marked 1 in Figure 5.14)***

Next point: ***(pick the point marked 2)***

Next point: ***(pick the point marked 3)***

Next point: ***(pick the point marked 4)***

Next point: ↵

Area = 1.7321

Perimeter = 5.4641

Adapting for Architecture

The AREA command is useful if invoked immediately after the perimeter of your building is done. Use the Entity option to select the line around your building, and the area will be given. After you add the wall openings, you can add a guideline to use as the entity for area selection. Put the guideline on a layer that you will turn off or freeze before plotting. ■

Now turn the running mode OSNAP, Intersection off by picking Settings, Object Snap, and using the dialogue box to turn off Intersection.

You have completed this drawing. Save your drawing as CYL2ORTH. You will use the cylinders you just drew to learn about projecting curved lines later in this tutorial.

To restore the toolbox to its square floating shape, you will pick the toolbox icon from the toolbar twice.

Pick: **Toolbox *(three times from the toolbar)***

The toolbox should return to a square shape that you can position anywhere on your screen.

Oblique Lines

Figure 5.15 shows an object that contains an *oblique line* 1-2. An oblique line is neither parallel nor perpendicular to any of the three principal views. It appears angled in the top, front, and right-side views. The foreshortened shape of an oblique surface is shown in all three principal orthographic views.

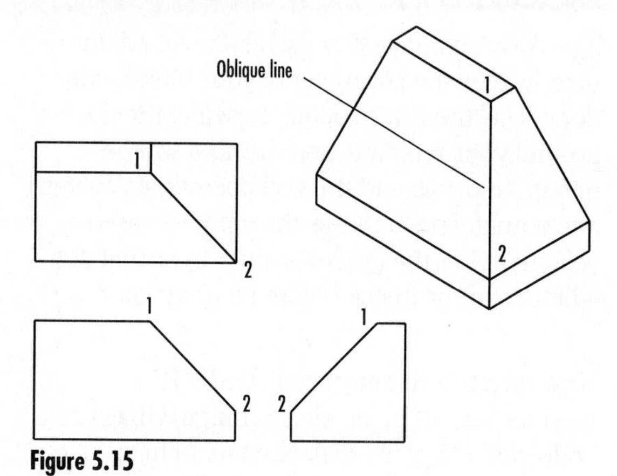

Figure 5.15

Oblique Surfaces

Figure 5.16 shows an object that contains an *oblique surface* 1-2-3-4. Oblique surfaces are surfaces that are neither parallel nor perpendicular to any of the three principal views. Oblique surfaces do not appear on edge in any principal view.

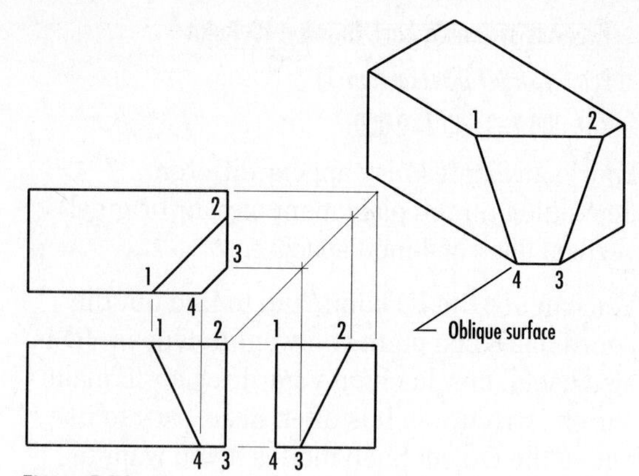

Figure 5.16

To project this oblique surface between orthographic views, you will project the four corner points and then connect the points. If the surface has curved edge lines, you will learn how to define additional points within the curved line and then project the added points. You then connect these added points with a smooth line to create a projected view of the curved line edge. Continue with the drawing of the adapter, using the drawing ADAPT1 from the data files that came with your software.

Pick: **File, New**

You will start your drawing from the file provided with the data files named ADAPT1. Type "ADAPT1" in the area provided for the prototype drawing, or pick Prototype and pick ADAPT1 from the listed files. Name your new drawing ADAPT1-O. The drawing of the orthographic views for the adapter should appear on your screen, as shown in Figure 5.17.

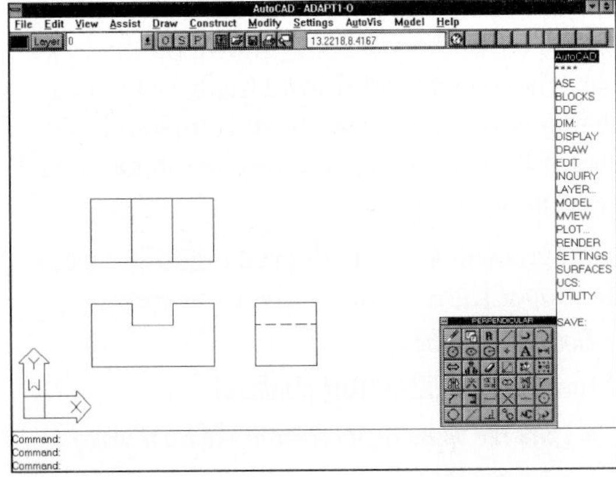

Figure 5.17

Figure 5.18 shows the object originally used to create the orthographic views on your screen, but with the addition of an oblique surface 1-2-3-4.

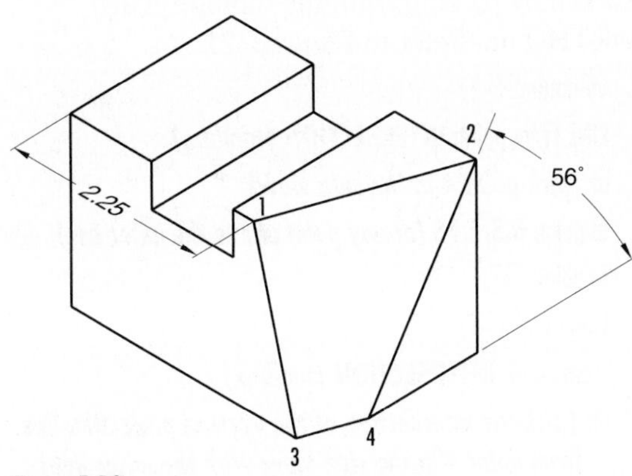

Figure 5.18

The location and size of the oblique plane are defined using only two dimensions and a statement that lines 1-2 and 3-4 are parallel. This means that only the side view of the oblique surface and part of the top view can be drawn directly. Projection must be used to complete the top and front views.

Drawing Oblique Surfaces

You will add the oblique surface to the orthographic drawing. The first step is to study the drawing for overall shape and dimensions. Point 2 of the oblique surface is known to be directly on the top back corner of the object.

Pick: **LINE *(toolbox)***

From point: ***(pick INTERSECTION from the toolbox, then point 2 in the side view in Figure 5.19)***

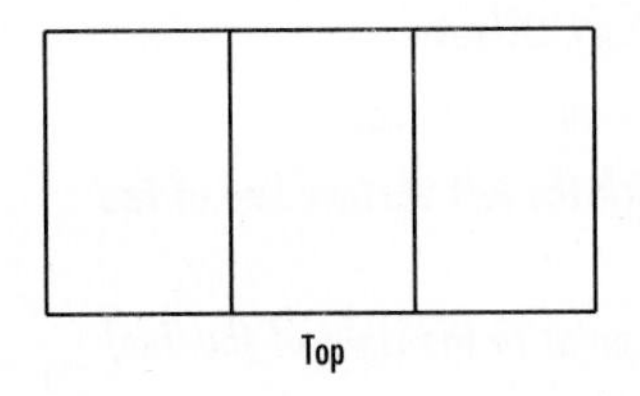

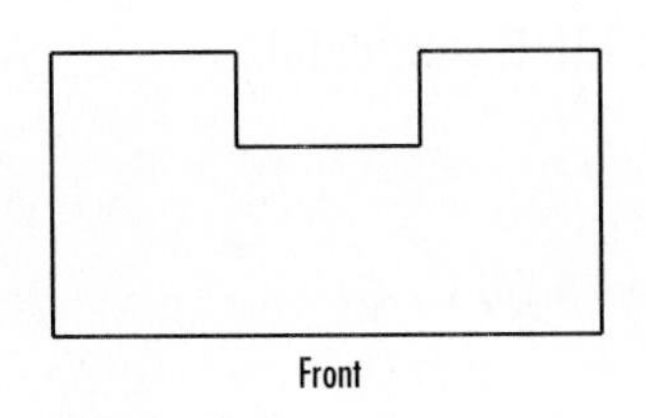

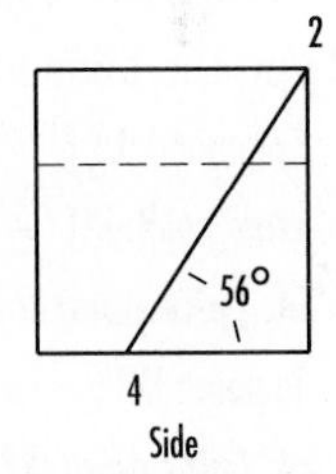

Figure 5.19

Point 2 is 56 degrees to the horizontal and ends at the bottom surface. Since 180 + 56 = 236, use 236 degrees as the angle to draw downward from point 2; 56 degrees would draw upwards along the angled line. Use relative coordinate values to locate the second point. (You could also give a negative distance angled at 56 degrees, but this may be confusing, as distances are not usually negative.)

To point: **@2<236** ↵

To point: ↵

Now use the TRIM command on your own to remove the excess line.

Next you will draw line 1-2 in the top view by starting in the back right corner of the object. You will offset the left vertical line of the top view to the right by a distance of 2.25. Then use Object Snap, Intersection by typing "INT" and select point 2 in the upper right corner of the top view. To draw the line to point 1, the intersection of the offset line with the lower horizontal line, you will use Intersection.

Pick: **Construct *(menu bar)*, Offset**

Offset distance or Through<Through>: **2.25** ↵

Select object to offset: ***(pick the left vertical line of the top view)***

Side to offset: ***(pick any point to the right of the line)***

Select object to offset: ↵

Type the alias for the LINE command.

Command: **L** ↵

From point: INT ↵

of: ***(pick point 2 in Figure 5.20)***

To point: INT ↵

of: ***(pick point 1)***

To point: ↵

Your drawing should look similar to Figure 5.20.

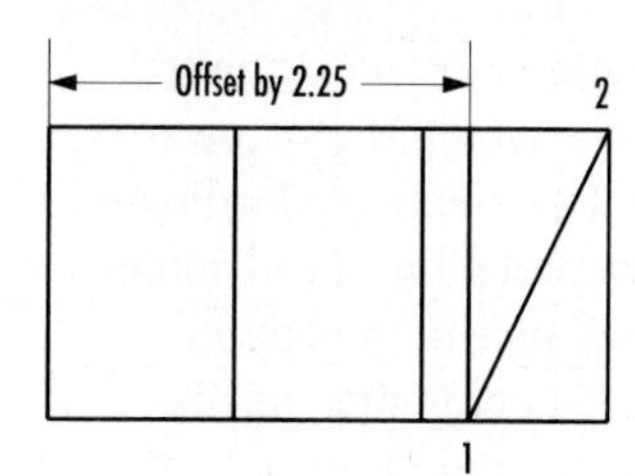

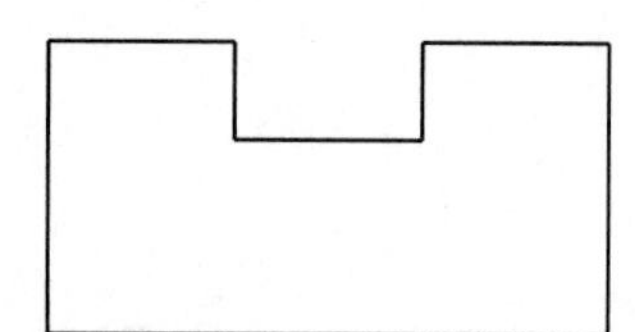

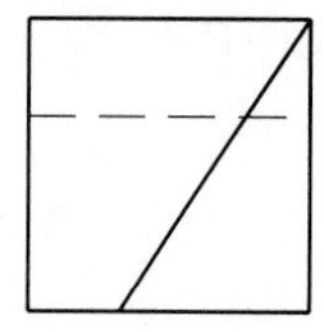

Figure 5.20

Set layer PROJ as the current layer by picking on the current layer name shown on the toolbar. Then select PROJ from the list of names that appears. When you have completed this step, PROJ should appear on the toolbar as the current layer name.

Next you will add a 45-degree miter line from the upper right corner of the front view.

Pick: **LINE *(toolbox)***

From point: **INTERSECTION *(toolbox)***

of ***(pick the upper right corner of the front view)***

To point: **@4<45** ↵

To point: ↵

You can now project point 4 from the side view to the top view. Point 4 is on the right edge of the top view at a location defined by the projection line from the side view. Use OSNAPs as shown by picking from the toolbox. Turn ORTHO on. Refer to Figure 5.21.

Command: ↵

LINE From point: **INTERSECTION *(toolbox)***

of ***(pick point 4 in the side view)***

To point: **6.5,4.75 *(or any point above the miter line)*** ↵

To point: ↵

Command: ↵

From point: **INTERSECTION *(toolbox)***

of: ***(pick the intersection of the vertical projection line from point 4 in the side view with the miter line)***

To point: ***(pick a point beyond the right edge line of the top view)*** ↵

To point: ↵

To complete the projection, use the OFFSET command to draw line 3-4 parallel to line 1-2 in the top view.

Pick: **Construct *(menu bar)*, Offset**

Offset distance or Through <2.2500>: **T** ↵

Select object to offset: ***(pick line 1-2 in the top view)***

Through point: **INTERSECTION** ***'(toolbox)***

of ***(pick point 4 in the top view)***

Select object to offset: ↵

Now use TRIM to remove excess lines on your own. When you have completed trimming the lines, your screen should look similar to Figure 5.21.

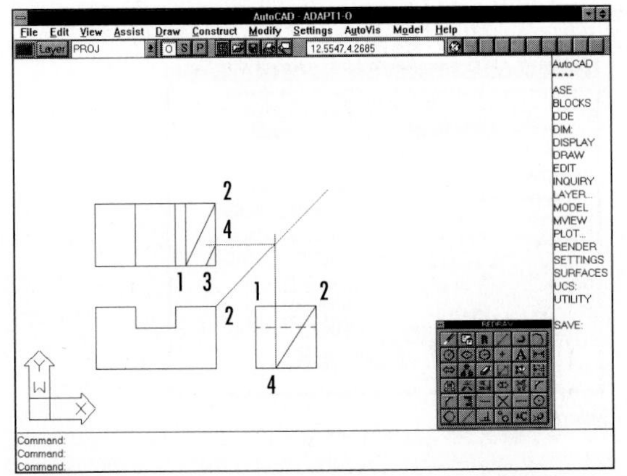

Figure 5.21

Next you will project points 1 and 3 into the front view. ORTHO should still be on.

Use Settings (menu bar), Object Snap to turn on the running mode Intersection to aid you in projecting the points.

For point 1,

Command: **L** ↵

From point: ***(target the intersection at point 1 in the top view)***

To point: ***(pick a point beyond the top line of the front view)***

To point: ↵

> ■ ***TIP*** Make sure that no intersection is inside the aperture box for the second point picked; otherwise AutoCAD will snap to the intersection. ■

For point 3,

Command: ↵

From point: ***(target the intersection at point 3 in the top view)***

To point: ***(pick a point beyond the bottom line of the front view)***

To point: ↵

On your own erase the line you created with OFFSET to define point 1. Your screen should look similar to Figure 5.22.

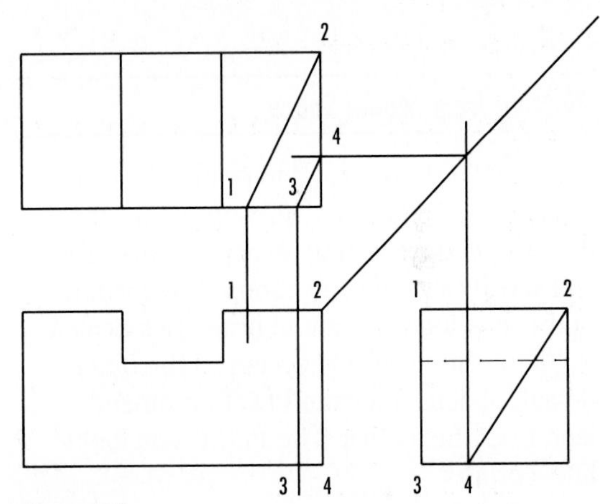

Figure 5.22

To finish the drawing, turn ORTHO off. Set Layer 0 as the current layer and draw line 1-3 in the front view. Trim the corner of the object in the top view, where it extends past line 3-4. Remove all excess lines. Freeze layer PROJ. Do these steps on your own. When you have finished, your drawing should look similar to Figure 5.23. Save your drawing at this point.

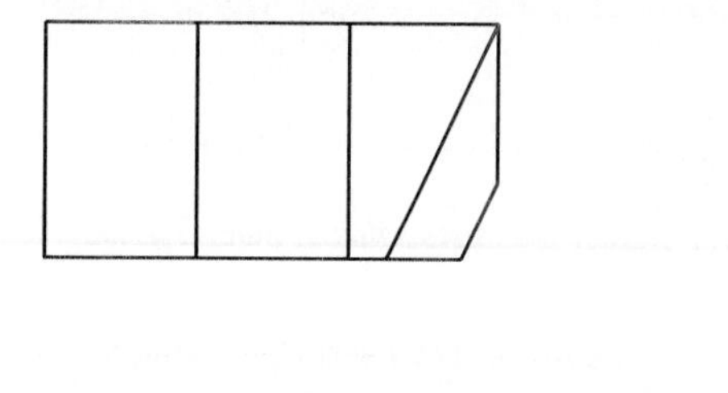

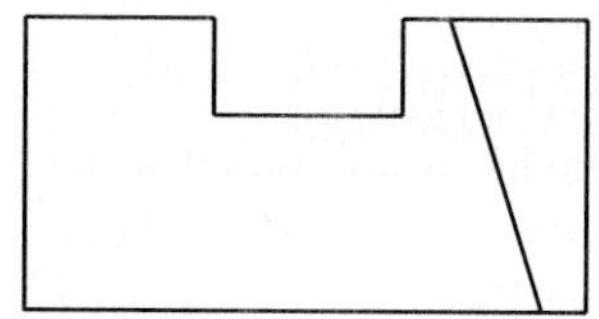

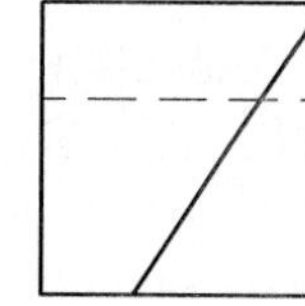

Figure 5.23

Plotting from Model Space

Use the PLOT command to print a copy of the drawing. This time you will print your model directly, without setting up paper space. You will specify a window to choose the portion of the drawing you want to print, pick Scaled to Fit for the scale, and accept all the other default options. Pick the PLOT command icon from the toolbar. The PLOT icon looks like a printer.

Pick: **PLOT *(toolbar)***

The Plot Configuration dialogue box appears on your screen, as shown in Figure 5.24. You will use it to select the options for plotting your drawing. Your dialogue box may have different default options displayed, depending on the printer or plotter you are using. To specify the area of the drawing you want to print, you will pick on the rectangular Window. . . button just above OK in the dialogue box.

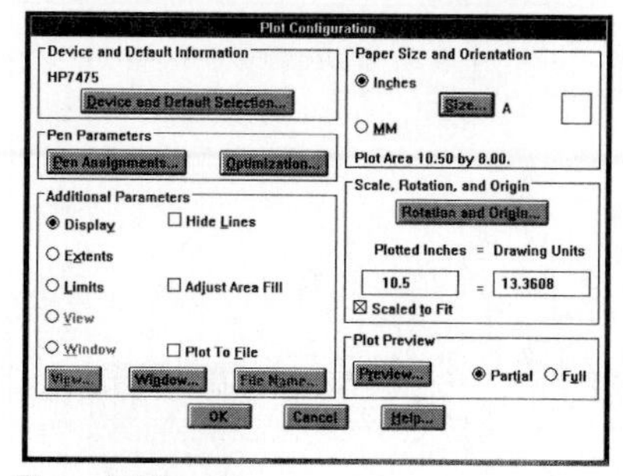

Figure 5.24

Pick: **Window. . .**

The Window Selection dialogue appears on your screen, as shown in Figure 5.25. Using it, you can enter the X and Y coordinates to specify the corners of the window, or you can select Pick and pick the corners to specify the window from the drawing screen. Notice that the selection Pick has the < character after it. This indicates that you will be returned to your drawing to make the selection and then back to the dialogue box.

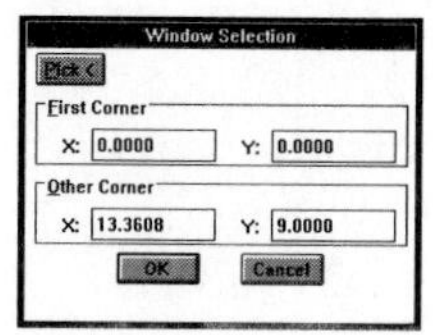

Figure 5.25

Pick: **Pick<**

The "First corner" prompt appears at the command line. You will select a point from your screen as the corner for the window. Refer to Figure 5.26.

First corner: ***(pick a point above and to the left of your drawing)***

Other corner: ***(pick a point below and to the right of your drawing)***

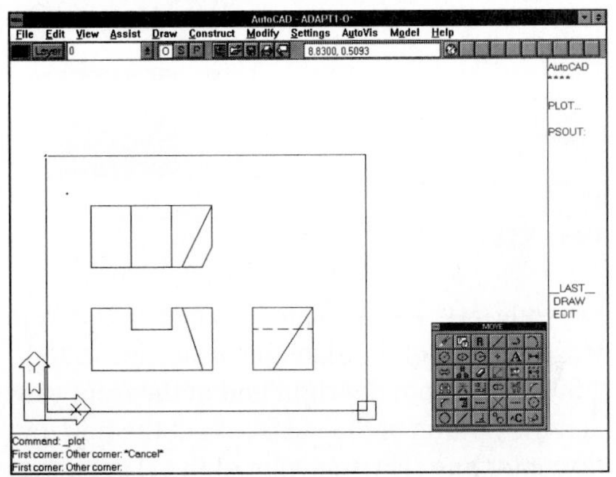

Figure 5.26

After you specify the window, you return to the Window Selection dialogue box. Pick OK to return to the Plot Configuration dialogue box. Notice that the radio button for Window is now filled in. Check to see that the paper size, rotation, origin, and other settings are set the way you want them. Refer to Tutorial 3 if you need help with the plot dialogue, or use AutoCAD's help command. Select Scaled to Fit for the scale. Pick the button for Full next to Preview and then Preview your drawing. It should appear similar to Figure 5.27, depending on your printer or plotter and the other selections you have made.

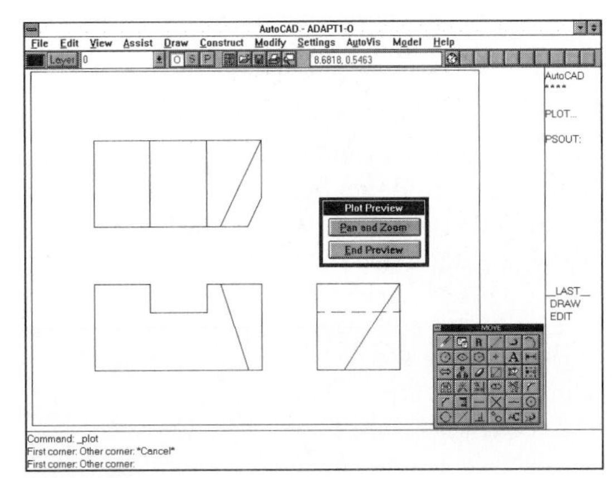

Figure 5.27

■ ***TIP*** You can drag the Plot Preview box to move it if it covers information in your drawing that you want to see. ■

■ ***TIP*** If you have difficulty getting a drawing to print so that lines are not clipped off, it may be due to your plotter's or printer's limits, as discussed in Tutorial 3. Sometimes an easy way to get the drawing to fit on the paper is to select Extents as the area to print, specify your printer's limits as the paper size, and then pick Scaled to Fit for the scale. ■

Try to visualize the orthographic views of your final drawing in relation to the pictorial view shown in Figure 5.18. You have completed this drawing.

Projecting Slanted Surfaces on Cylinders

You will continue to work with the orthographic views of cylinders you created earlier in this tutorial. Begin by opening the existing drawing CYL1 from the data files that came with your software.

> ■ ***TIP*** Your data files should be installed on the hard drive. Do not open files directly from your floppy disk. Doing so can cause you to encounter several problems, such as running out of disk space, or AutoCAD temporary files being left on your disk if you do not exit properly or the program crashes. If you must open a file from a floppy, it is a good practice to pick File, New and then use the file you wish to open as a prototype. The new drawing file name should be specified so that it is created on the hard drive. This will prevent many problems and the likelihood of corrupted drawing files. ■

Adapting for Architecture

When using the computer to work on multiple projects, try to develop a DOS directory system that reflects the projects you are working on. Place each project in a different subdirectory of your major drawing or projects directory so that a file does not get inadvertently overwritten. Also, this will help you when you need to find all of the drawings for a particular project. In addition, having all of your projects in subdirectories of a main projects directory will make backing up your files easier, because usually you will have to back up only the projects directory on a daily basis and not the software itself. ■

From the File menu, select Open. Select drawing CYL1. Your screen should look similar to Figure 5.28.

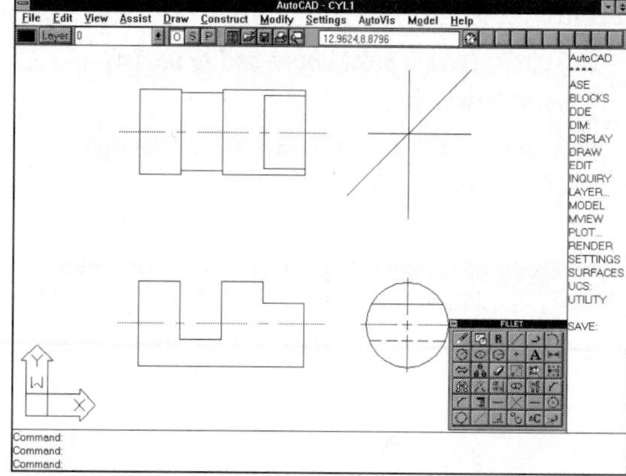

Figure 5.28

On your own, add a slanted surface to the front view. The top of the slanted surface is located 1.50 inches from the right end of the front view and the bottom of the surface is at the horizontal center line. The top point of the slanted surface, the intersection of the vertical center line and the edge of the cylinder in the side view, is labeled 1 in Figure 5.29. The bottom edge of the slanted surface is labeled 2-3 and is located directly on the horizontal center line in the side view.

Next, remove all lines created for the shallow surface in the front view above and to the right of the slanted surface. Remove the shallow surface from the top and side views. Your screen should look similar to Figure 5.29.

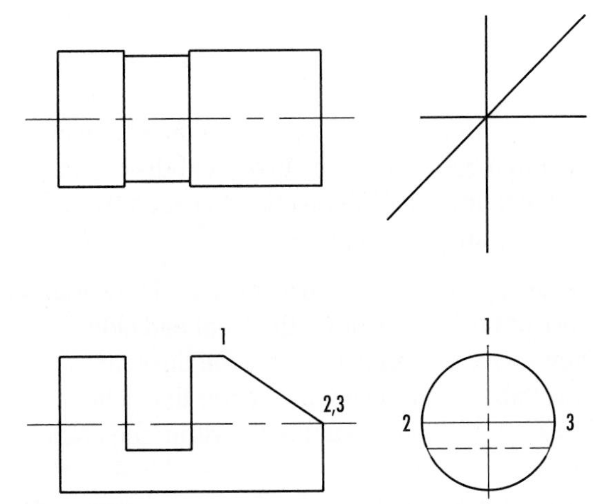

Figure 5.29

What is the shape of the slanted surface in the top view? The front view of the surface appears as a straight slanted line. The side view is a semicircle, but in the top view the shape is an ellipse. Refer to Figure 5.30. A circular shape seen from an angle other than straight on is an ellipse. Since the locations of points 1, 2, and 3 on the ellipse are known, you can use the ELLIPSE command you learned in Tutorial 3 to draw the shape in the top view.

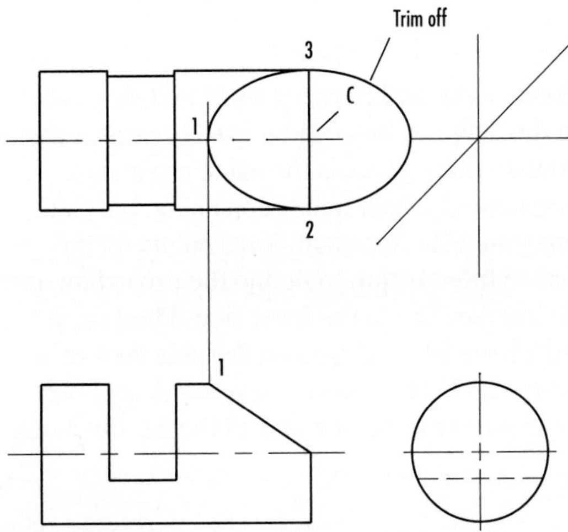

Figure 5.30

On your own, project point 1 into the top view. To do this, change to layer PROJ. The running mode Object Snap, Intersection should still be on. Use it and the LINE command to draw a vertical line from point 1 in the front view extending up into the top view past the center. When you are finished, change the current layer back to Layer 0.

> *Pick:* **Draw *(menu bar)*, Ellipse, Center, Axis, Axis**
>
> Center point: ***(pick the point marked C in Figure 5.30)***
>
> Axis endpoint 1: ***(pick point 1 in the top view, where your projection line crosses the top line)***
>
> Axis endpoint 2: ***(pick point 2 in the top view)***

Your drawing should now look like Figure 5.30.

Use the TRIM command to remove the unnecessary portion of the ellipse. The remaining curve represents the top view of the slanted surface. Remove the projection line from the screen by freezing layer PROJ. Your drawing should appear similar to Figure 5.31.

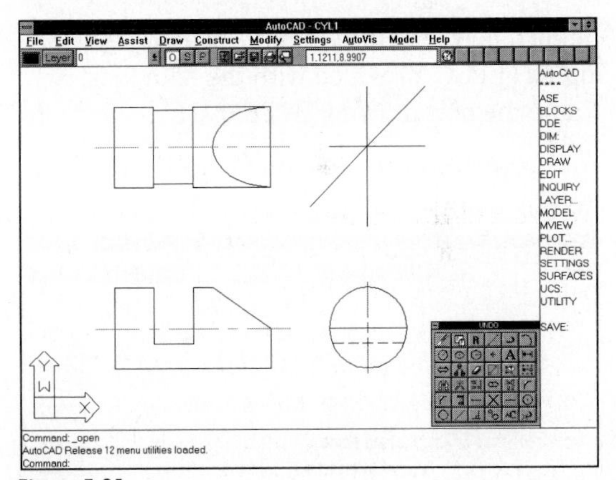

Figure 5.31

Use the SAVEAS command to save the drawing as CYL3ORTH on your disk. Print the drawing from model space, as you did previously in this tutorial.

Going Further

Circular shapes appear as ellipses when tipped away from the direction of sight, as you saw in the drawing you just finished. Not all surfaces are uniform shapes like circles and ellipses; some are irregular. Irregularly curved surfaces can be created using the PLINE command and the Spline option that you learned in Tutorial 3. To project an irregularly curved surface to the adjacent view, identify a number of points along the curve and project each point. Use the PLINE command to connect the points. Then use the PEDIT, Spline option to create a smooth curve through the points.

Intersections

Begin a new drawing from the prototype drawing INTERSC, provided with the data files. Name the new drawing INTERSC1.

Your screen should look similar to Figure 5.32.

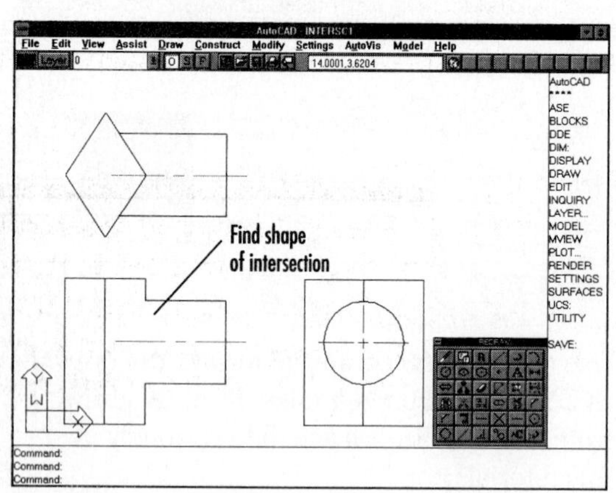

Figure 5.32

The views on your screen show the incomplete orthographic views of a cylinder that intersects a prism. The top and side views are complete, but the front view does not show the shape of the edge between the cylinder and the prism. You will draw the intersection between the cylinder and the prism.

Set layer PROJ as the current layer. Draw four horizontal lines through the front and side views. Use OFFSET to locate the lines .38 apart above and below the center line. The lines can be located randomly within the circle in the side view. Your screen should look similar to Figure 5.33.

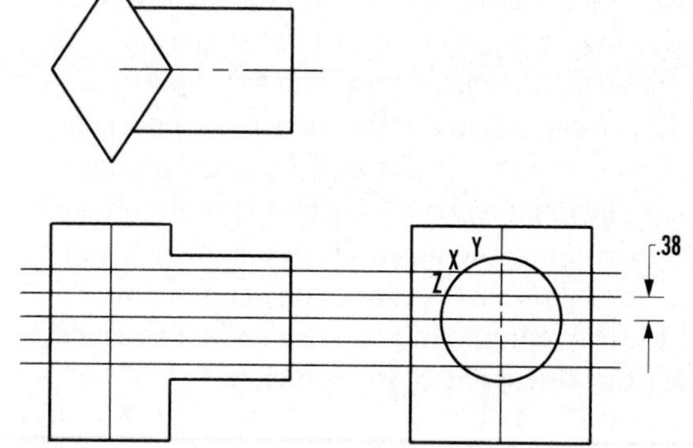

Figure 5.33

These horizontal lines are used to define points on the cylinder that can be used to project the circular shape. This is the same projection technique that you have been using, but this time you will create additional points on the curved intersection to define the projection of the intersection in the front view. Points x, y, and z have been labeled on the side view of Figure 5.33. The object is symmetrical about the center line. Point y and all the intersections on the right side of the center line do not need to be projected, because their projections lie directly behind the intersection from the left side of the center line. The points below the horizontal center line do not need to be projected because the object is symmetrical and one half of the line can be mirrored to form the entire intersection.

Draw a miter line and (with ORTHO on) project points x and z, shown in the side view of Figure 5.34, into the top view. Your screen should look similar to Figure 5.34.

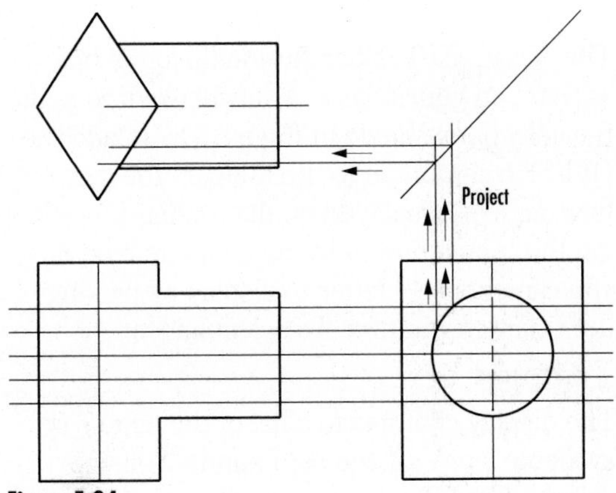

Figure 5.34

Now, project the points from the top view into the front view, using vertical lines. You will project points x, z, and w. Refer to Figure 5.35. Set Layer 0 as the current layer; turn ORTHO off. Use the PLINE command to draw a polyline connecting points w, z, x, and y. Your drawing should look like Figure 5.35.

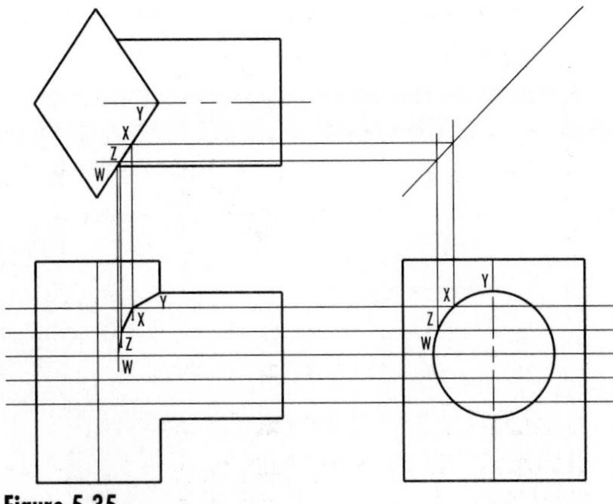

Figure 5.35

Mirror the polyline about point w and the horizontal line formed to the right of point w. Next use PEDIT, Join to join the two halves of the mirrored polyline. While still in the PEDIT command, use Fit curve to connect the intersection points created by the intersection of the projection lines with a smooth curve. Refer to Tutorial 3 if you need to review these commands. Freeze layer PROJ.

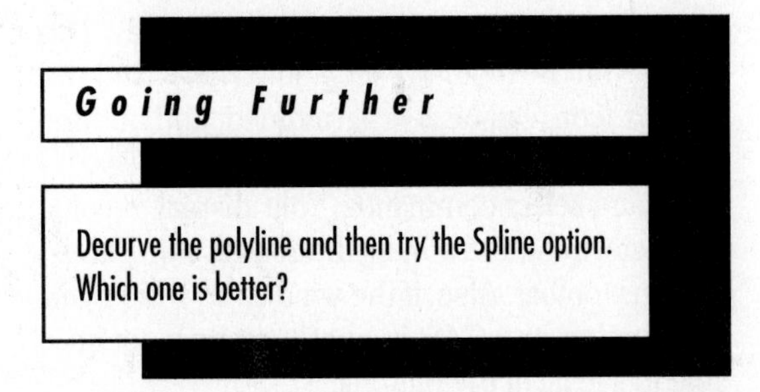

Going Further
Decurve the polyline and then try the Spline option. Which one is better?

Your screen should look similar to Figure 5.36.

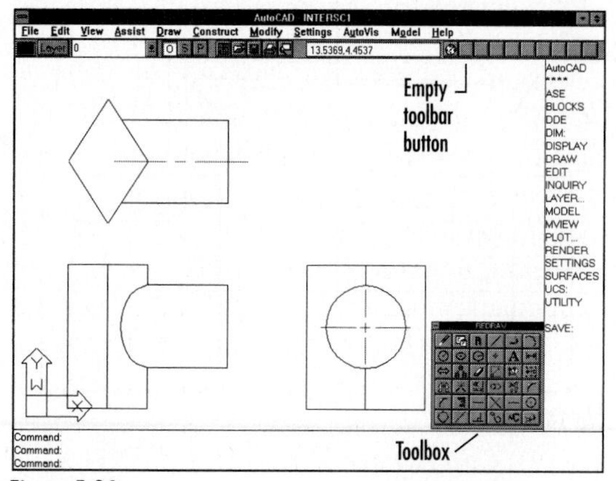

Figure 5.36

Save the drawing INTERSC1 on your disk. Print the drawing using model space.

Programming the Toolbox and Toolbar

One of the ways you can *customize* your AutoCAD software is by programming the buttons on the toolbox and toolbar so that they contain the commands you use most frequently. The buttons on the toolbar, except for O, S, P, and the toolbox icon, can be reprogrammed, and buttons that are blank can be programmed to display icons and select commands. Your display resolution determines how many buttons are displayed on your toolbar. Also, if the window in which you are running AutoCAD is small, you may not be able to see all of the buttons.

Any of the 36 standard buttons on the toolbox can be reprogrammed. You can also add additional buttons for a total of 40 buttons. To program the buttons, press the right mouse button when the cursor is positioned over the button you would like to change.

First you will add the OFFSET command to an empty button on the toolbar.

Pick: ***(on an empty button on the toolbar; use the right mouse button and refer to Figure 5.36)***

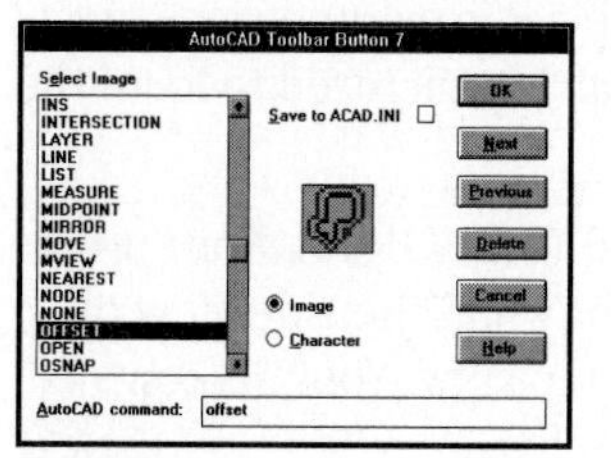

Figure 5.37

The AutoCAD Toolbar Button dialogue box appears on your screen. You will use it to make the selections shown in Figure 5.37 to add the OFFSET command to the toolbar. You can have an icon displayed on the toolbar by picking the Image button in the dialogue box, or you can choose a letter to display by picking the Character button. To select an icon,

Pick: **Image**

The display changes to a list of the names of available icons for the commands. You will select OFFSET.

Pick: **OFFSET**

You will see the OFFSET icon displayed in the space near the center of the dialogue box. Next you will turn off the selection Save to ACAD.INI. Saving your changes to ACAD.INI will change the toolbar section of the Windows ACAD.INI file, thus saving the changes that you have made to the toolbar so that they are available the next time you start AutoCAD. For this tutorial you do not need to save these changes. When Save to ACAD.INI is not selected, the changes you make are for the current drawing session only.

Pick: ***(to turn off Save to ACAD.INI; no X should appear in the box to its right)***

At the bottom of the dialogue box is an area where you add the AutoCAD command that you want the toolbar button to use when it is picked. Pick inside the empty box to the right of AutoCAD command: and press the pick button so that you can enter text.

Type: **OFFSET**

Now you are ready to exit the dialogue box and try the command that you added to the toolbar.

Pick: **OK**

You should notice the icon added to the toolbar, as shown in Figure 5.38.

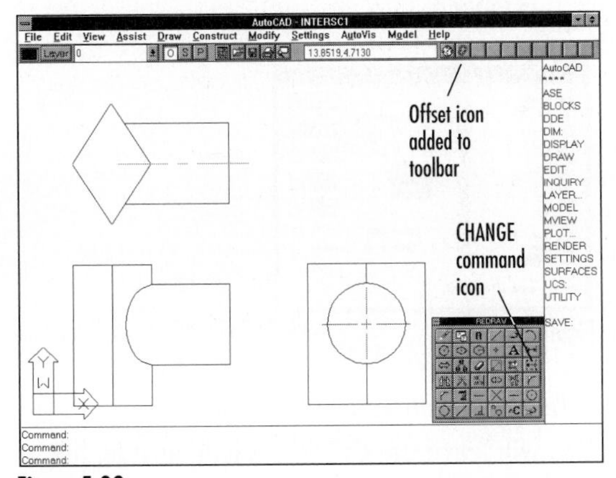

Figure 5.38

Pick: **OFFSET *(toolbar)***

Try offsetting some of the lines of your INTERSC1 drawing to see that it works. Try adding some other commands to the toolbar.

Using Special Characters in Programmed Commands

There are some special characters that you can use in programming the toolbox and toolbar. One of these is \3, which has the same effect as pressing Ctrl-C from the keyboard to cancel. If you put \3 in front of the command name you are programming, it will cancel any unfinished command when you select its button from the toolbox or toolbar. Putting cancel before the command is useful because the DDCHPROP commands you will program cannot be selected during another command. Do not add cancel before the toggle modes or before transparent commands (they must be preceded by ' [apostrophe]) because if you cancel before them they cannot be used during another command. In programming the menus and buttons, cancel often appears twice before a command in case a subprompt has been left active, where it would take two cancels to return to the Command prompt.

A space or ↵ is automatically added to the end of every command you program for the buttons. This way the command is entered when the button is selected. You can enter a string of commands, or a command and its options, by separating them with a space to act as ↵. Below is a list of special characters that can be used to program the toolbox and toolbar buttons.

Special Characters

Character	Meaning
space	↵
;	Suppresses the addition of space to the end of a command string
\\	The \ character (used in path names)
\n	New line
\2	Ctrl-B Snap mode toggle
\3	Ctrl-C Cancel
\4	Ctrl-D Coordinates toggle
\5	Ctrl-E Isoplane toggle
\7	Ctrl-G Grid mode toggle

Next you will add a toggle mode for the grid to the toolbar in place of the OPEN command, which has an opening folder for its icon.

Pick: ***(on the OPEN icon from the toolbar; use the right mouse button)***

Use the dialogue box that appears to select the character G to appear on the button, and do **not** select to save your changes to ACAD.INI. For the command entry, type "\7" in place of the text in the AutoCAD Command box. (Do not include the quotation marks.) When you have finished, pick OK.

The button is changed so that the letter G appears on it instead of the OPEN icon. Pick the GRID button that you added. The grid should toggle off. Pick the button again; the grid should reappear.

Next you will reprogram the CHANGE command from the toolbox so that it uses the command DDCHPROP instead of the CHANGE command. DDCHPROP is the command that you have used by selecting Modify, Change, Properties from the menu bar. As you did to program the toolbar, you will right-click on the toolbox icon you want to change. The CHANGE command icon is in the third row and sixth column.

Pick: ***(the CHANGE icon from the toolbox; use the right mouse button)***

The dialogue box shown in Figure 5.39 appears on your screen. You will use it to change the toolbox button so that it uses the DDCHPROP command.

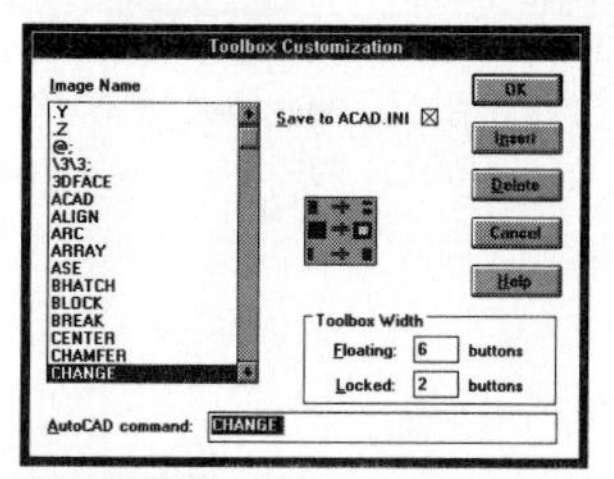

Figure 5.39

Pick: ***(to turn off Save to ACAD.INI)***

You will leave the CHANGE icon as it is, but change the AutoCAD command to read "\3\3DDCHPROP".

Because of the programmed cancels (\3), your DDCHPROP command can be selected even if another command is still active at the command prompt. It automatically cancels the other command and then starts the DDCHPROP command.

In the AutoCAD command area, highlight CHANGE and then,

Type: **\3\3DDCHPROP** ***(do not use a space between \3\3 and DDCHPROP)***

Pick: **OK**

The CHANGE icon still appears in the same position on the toolbox, but now it will activate the DDCHPROP command instead of the CHANGE command.

Pick: **CHANGE icon** ***(toolbox)***

Select objects: ***(pick a line from your drawing)*** ↵

The Change Properties dialogue box should appear on your screen. Now that you have seen how this works,

Pick: **Cancel**

This time, you will select another command and leave it active at the command prompt. Then you will pick the CHANGE icon from the toolbox and notice how it cancels the command. Start the LINE command by typing the alias at the command prompt.

Type: **L** ↵

From point: ***(pick the CHANGE icon from the toolbox)***

Notice that the LINE command is cancelled and the DDCHPROP command is started. To cancel the DDCHPROP command,

Press: **Ctrl-C**

Reshaping the Toolbox

You can change the shape of the toolbox by picking on any one of its buttons with the right mouse button and then changing the number of rows in the toolbox width portion of the dialogue box. Changing the width by giving a new number of floating buttons changes the appearance of the floating toolbox. Changing the width for the number of locked buttons changes how the toolbox appears when it is locked to the left or right side of the drawing area, as you saw in Tutorial 1.

Right pick on any button from the toolbox. Make sure that Save to ACAD.INI is not selected and then use the dialogue box to change the floating width to 8 buttons and the locked width to 3 buttons. When you have finished, pick OK. The toolbox changes so that it is 8 buttons wide. Some space in the bottom row is not used.

Pick: **Toolbox icon** ***(toolbar)***

Notice that the toolbox changes to a 3-button-wide array of buttons locked to the left side of the drawing area. Pick the toolbox icon again; the toolbox is turned off. Pick it a third time; the toolbox is 3 buttons wide and is locked to the right side of the drawing area. Pick it again and the 8-button-wide floating toolbox returns.

You have completed this tutorial. Because you have chosen not to save the changes to the toolbox, next time you start AutoCAD the toolbox and toolbar will be restored to their original appearance.

KEY TERMS

customize
oblique line
oblique surface

KEY COMMANDS

Area
Toolbox

EXERCISES

Draw front, top, and right-side orthographic views of the following objects. The letter M after an exercise number means that the given dimensions are in millimeters (metric units).

5.1M Compound Block

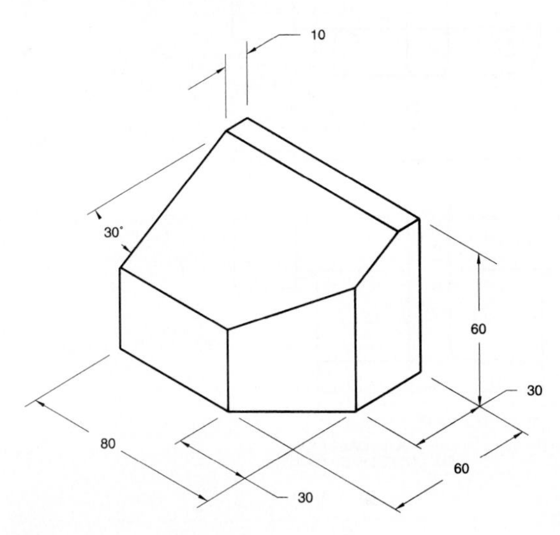

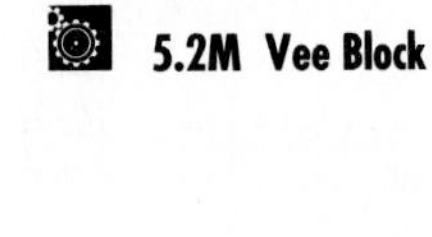

5.2M Vee Block

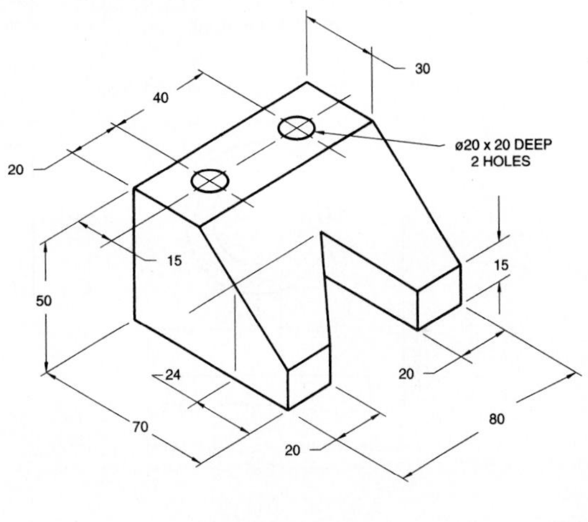

5.3 Corner Guide

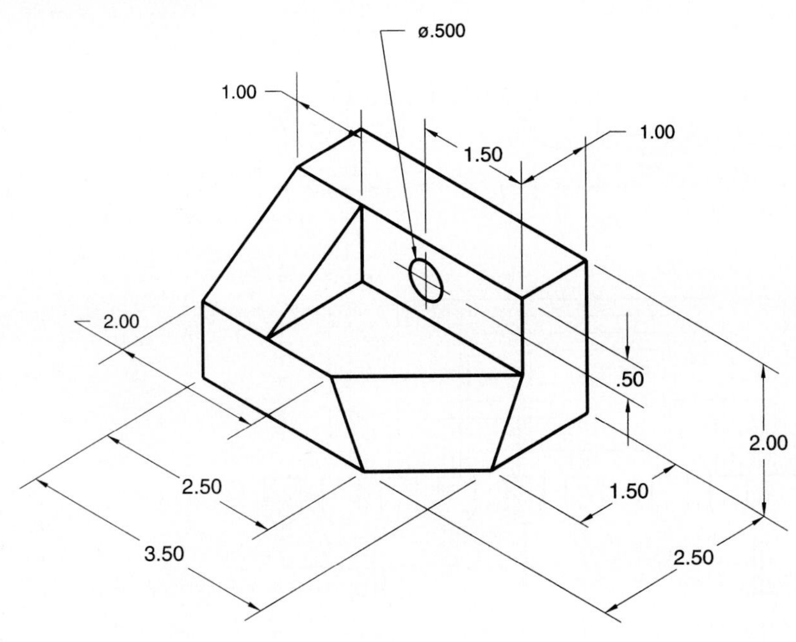

5.4 Shaft Hanger

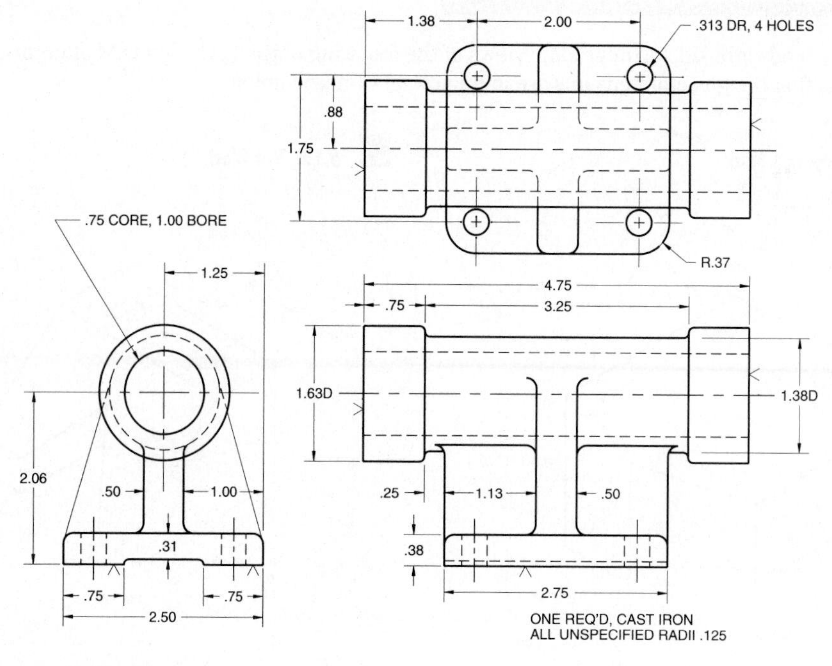

5.5M Arithmetic Logic Unit

Draw the circuit shown. Create the components according to the metric sizes shown.

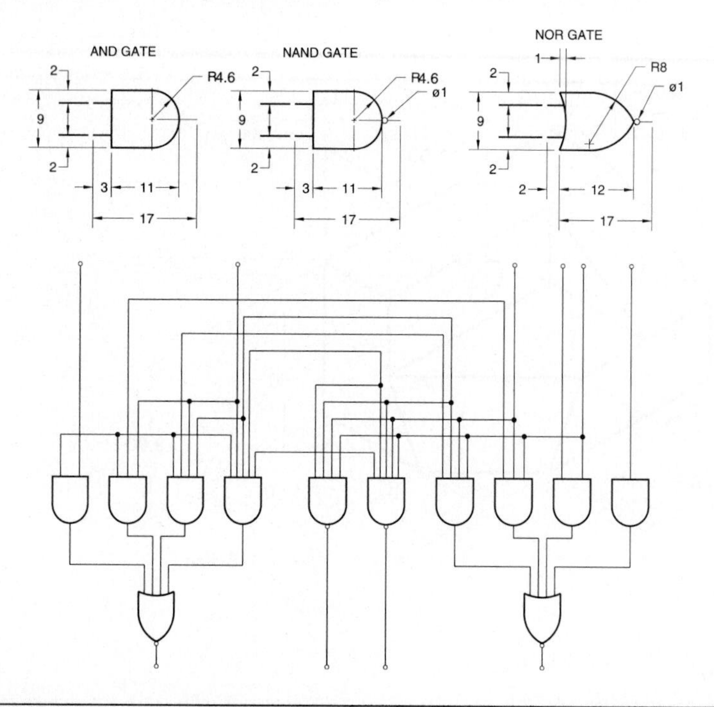

Draw front, top, and right-side orthographic views of the following objects.

5.6 Geneva Wheel

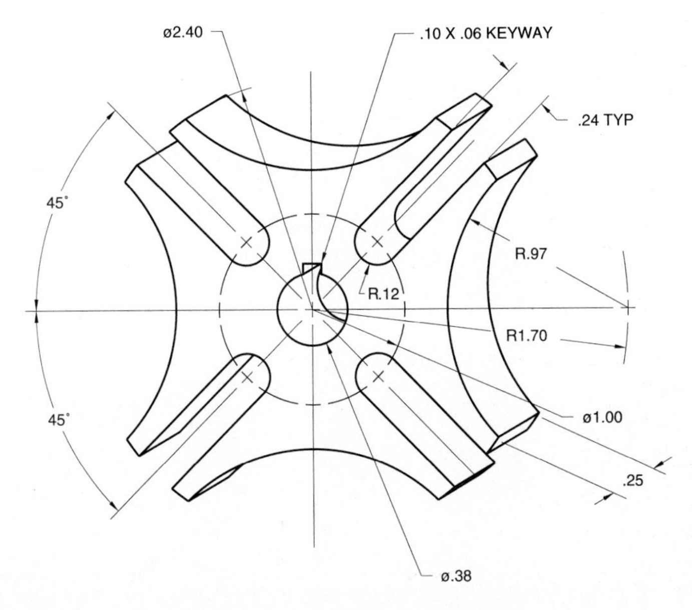

5.7 Slide Support

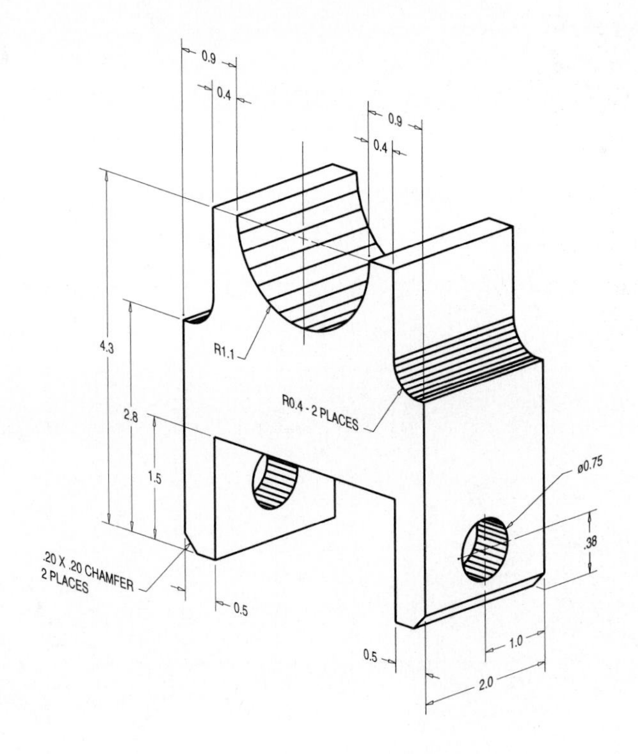

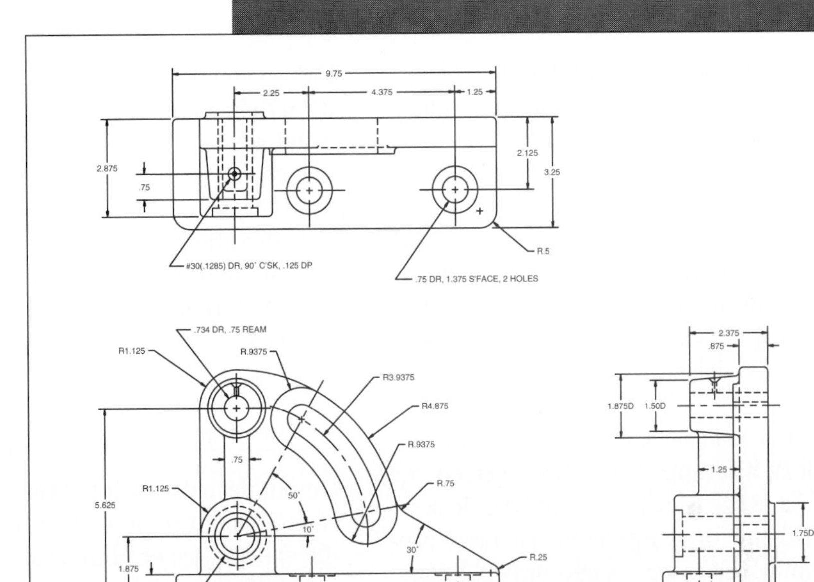

TUTORIAL 6

Prototype Drawings and More Orthographic Views

Objectives

When you have completed this tutorial, you will be able to

1. Establish a system of layers for basic drawings.
2. Preset VIEWRES, DIMCEN, LIMITS and other defaults in a prototype drawing.
3. Set up paper space and model space in a prototype drawing.
4. Create drawings of castings and sheet-metal objects.

Introduction

One of the advantages of using AutoCAD is that you can easily rescale, change, copy, and reuse drawings. Up to this point, most of the drawings you have created began from a drawing called ACAD.DWG, which is part of the AutoCAD program. In ACAD.DWG many variables are preset to help you begin drawing. In this tutorial you will learn how to make a drawing containing default settings of your own from which you will start drawings in succeeding tutorials, as you did with CYL1ORTH and ADAPT1-O in Tutorial 5. A drawing in which specific default settings have been selected and saved for later use is called a prototype drawing. Any existing drawing can be used as a prototype from which to start a new drawing. You may need to establish more than one prototype drawing to be used for different scales and types of drawings. You will use the prototype drawing you establish in this tutorial for many of the drawing exercises in this book that are based on inch units.

Setting up prototype drawings can eliminate repetitive steps and make your work with AutoCAD more efficient. The amount of time you spend creating one prototype is roughly the amount of time you will save on each subsequent drawing that you start from the prototype drawing. Your prototype drawing will contain your custom defaults for layers, limits, grid, snap, and text size and font for use in future drawings. You will also enable paper space and set up a viewport where you can view model space.

Starting

Before you begin, launch AutoCAD. If you need help, please review the AutoCAD for Windows section of Chapter 3, AutoCAD Basics, in Part 1, Getting Started. You should be at the AutoCAD drawing editor. Make sure that the toolbox and screen menu are turned on. If they are not, use the selection File, Preferences from the menu bar to turn them on.

Determining the Limits of Your Output Device

Output devices, such as printers and plotters, cannot plot or print all the way to the edge of the sheet of paper. Here is a simple test you can perform to determine the limitations of your output device.

Begin a new drawing and call it PTEST.

Next you will draw a horizontal line from point 0,0 to point 11,0 and then a vertical line from 0,0 to 0,8.5. These two lines show the width and height of an 8.5" × 11" sheet of paper.

Pick: **LINE *(toolbox)***

From point: **0,0** ↵

To point: **11,0** ↵

To point: ↵

Command: ↵ ***(to restart the LINE command)***

From point: **0,0** ↵

To point: **0,8.5** ↵

To point: ↵

Command: **SAVE** ↵

Pick: **OK**

Use the command PLOT and plot or print the drawing limits on 8.5" × 11" paper (size A). You will see the defaults you selected when you configured your output device in the plot dialogue box. Select Limits as the drawing area to plot. Be sure that the drawing origin is set to 0,0, and the scale of plotted inches to drawing units is 1=1, not Scaled to Fit. If either is not set correctly, make corrections in the dialogue box, as you learned to do in Tutorial 3. When the settings are correct, pick OK to plot your drawing.

Your output shows as much of the two lines you have drawn as will fit on the paper at full scale. Measure the actual length of the lines that were plotted to determine the limits of your output device. Where the two lines intersect at point 0,0 in your drawing is the origin for the paper; in other words it is the spot closest to the lower left corner of the paper that the printer can reach. Knowing this location will help you in figuring out how to correctly center drawings on the sheet of paper for your printer. (If you have difficulty determining the limits and origin of your output device, ask your technical support person for help.)

For the purposes of the tutorials, we will use the values 10.25" × 7.75" as the limits of the output device. You should substitute the correct limits for your output device. If your output device uses more than one paper size, determine the limits for each paper size.

Making a Prototype Drawing

> *Pick:* **File *(menu bar)*, New**

to begin a new drawing. Check to make sure that the box No Prototype is **not** selected (no X should appear in the box to its left). Make sure that ACAD is the prototype drawing from which your new drawing will be started. Type the name "C:\DRAWINGS\MYPROTO" in the empty box next to New Drawing Name. . . .

> *Pick:* **OK *(to exit the dialogue box)***

The main AutoCAD drawing editor should appear on your display screen. You will set the limits, grid, snap, layers, text size, and text style in this drawing, as well as set up the paper space limits, viewport, and linetype scale. This will save time, make plotting and printing easier, and keep future drawings neatly organized into layers.

Effective Use of Layers

To use layers effectively, choose layer names that make sense and separate the entities you draw into logical groups.

Pen selection on plotters is controlled by the color of the entity. This is also true for the line thickness on printers that are capable of printing different line weights. As discussed in Tutorial 4, the default in AutoCAD is to set color by using different layers. You should use different layers in order to use more than one color or line thickness effectively.

Using a prototype drawing helps to maintain a consistent standard for layer names. Using consistent and descriptive layer names makes it possible for more than one person to work on the same drawing without puzzling over the purpose of various layers. On networked computer systems, many different people can use or work on a single drawing. A prototype drawing is an easy way to standardize layer names and other basic settings, such as linetype.

Loading the Linetypes

Before you can select a linetype in the Layer Control dialogue box, it must be loaded into AutoCAD. This only needs to be done one time in the drawing. In Tutorial 4 you learned to use the LAYER, LType command to load a selected linetype automatically. In Tutorials 2 and 5 you loaded all the linetypes before using them. Now you will load all the linetypes into your prototype drawing, so that they will be available from the Modify Layer dialogue box in any drawing you start from your MYPROTO prototype.

■ ***TIP*** You do not always need all of the linetypes loaded. To keep your prototype drawing size smaller and see a shorter list of linetypes when you use the Set Ltype option in the Layer Control dialogue, you can load only the linetypes that you use frequently into your prototype drawing. Other linetypes can always be loaded as needed during the drawing process. ■

The LINETYPE command is located under SETTINGS on the screen menu. LINETYPE, like other commands, can also be typed in from the keyboard.

Command: **LINETYPE** ↵

■ ***TIP*** If you are not sure of the name of the linetype you wish to load, type "?" at the prompt and press ↵. Press ↵ when the Select Linetype File dialogue box appears to accept the default file, ACAD.LIN, where the line patterns are stored, and to list the available linetypes and a brief description of each. You will see a list on your screen similar to Figure 6.1. Continue to press ↵ until the complete list has been shown and you return to the "?/Create/Load/Set" prompt. Double-click the close box in the upper left corner of the text window to close it and return to the drawing screen. ■

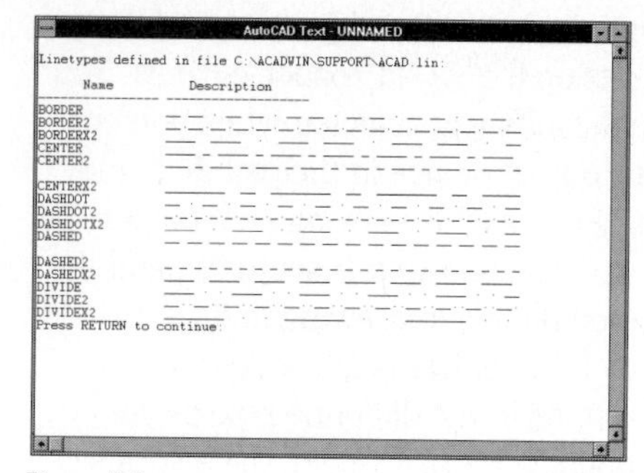

Figure 6.1

?/Create/Load/Set: **L** ↵ ***(to select the Load option)***

Linetype(s) to load: * ↵

■ ***TIP*** The * (asterisk) acts as a wildcard to match to any name. It is very useful with the LAYER command for turning on and off all layers. It can also be used in combination with characters. Typing "C*" selects all of the linetypes that begin with the letter C, for instance. ■

The Select Linetype File dialogue box appears on your screen again. The standard AutoCAD line patterns are stored in the file ACAD.LIN; since it is the default in the file selection dialogue box,

Pick: **OK *(or press* ↵ *to accept the default)***

You will see the messages scroll by on your screen telling you that Linetype BORDER has loaded, Linetype BORDER2 has loaded, etc. You are returned to the drawing screen with the LINETYPE prompt still displayed. To end the command,

?/Create/Load/Set: ↵

Now the linetypes are loaded and will be available in the Modify Layer dialogue box.

Viewing the Text Window

When you were loading the linetypes, the names of the linetypes scrolled by at the command prompt very quickly. If you wish to review text that appeared at the command line, you can select Edit, Text Window from the menu bar, or you can press (F2). This opens a text window on your screen and you can scroll through the text that previously appeared at the command prompt. The number of lines of text that are saved in the text window is set in the File, Preferences dialogue box.

Pick: **Edit *(menu bar)*, Text Window**

The text window appears on your screen, as shown in Figure 6.2. When you are finished reviewing the list of linetypes that were loaded in the previous command step, double-click the close box to remove the window from your screen.

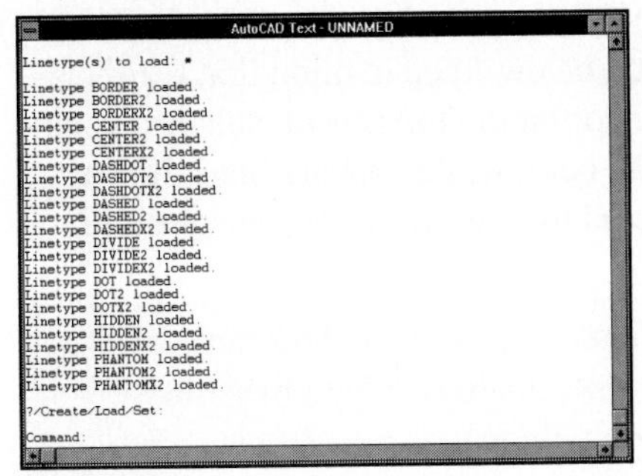

Figure 6.2

Defining the Layers

Use the Modify Layer dialogue box to create a set of layers for your prototype drawing.

Pick: **Layer *(toolbar)***

The Layer Control dialogue box appears on your screen. The typing cursor is positioned in the empty box directly below the list of layer names. From the keyboard, type in the new layer names listed below one at a time. Pick the New box after each name.

Type: **VISIBLE**

Pick: **New**

Type: **THIN**

Pick: **New**

Type: **HIDDEN**

Pick: **New**

Type: **CENTERLN**

Pick: **New**

Type: **PROJ**

Pick: **New**

Type: **HATCH**

Pick: **New**

Type: **TEXT**

Pick: **New**

Type: **DIM**

Pick: **New**

Type: **BORDER**

Pick: **New**

Each time you pick New, the new name pops up onto the list of layer names. If the list of layer names is long, sometimes you may need to scroll up and down the list, using the boxes that are located near the right-hand side of the dialogue box.

> ■ ***TIP*** To type in the list of layers quickly, you can also use the LAYER command from the "Command:" prompt. If you wish to do this, type "LA" (the alias for the LAYER command) at the "Command:" prompt and press (↵). Select the option Make from the screen menu, or type "M" at the LAYER command prompt. Type the list of layer names you wish to create, separated by commas (,) and no spaces. Press (↵) twice when you are done. ■

Setting the Color and Linetype

Now you will set the colors and linetypes for the layers you have created. On the right of the dialogue box are buttons for On, Off, Thaw, Freeze, Unlock, Lock, Cur VP:Thw and Frz (Current Viewport Thaw and Freeze), New VP: Thw and Frz (New Viewport Thaw and Freeze), Set Color and Set Ltype. Notice that the layers you have created are turned on. The color for all the layers is white. Keep in mind that the color named white appears black on your screen if you are using the dark vectors on a light background setting in the display configuration.

Move the arrow cursor to the name THIN and press the pick button. The selected layer name becomes highlighted. Use the same method to select layer HATCH and layer TEXT from the list of layers. You should now have three layers selected.

Pick: **Set Color. . .**

The Select Color dialogue box, which you used in Tutorial 4, pops up on the screen. Use the standard colors from the top row. Change the color to red.

Pick: ***(the red box in the very top row of colored boxes under the heading Standard Colors)***

The word red appears in the box near the bottom of the dialogue box, indicating that it is the color choice for the layers that you selected.

Pick: **OK**

Pick: **Clear All *(to unselect the layers)***

Next you will set the linetype for layer HIDDEN. The Set Ltype. . . box is below the Set Color box. First you will select the layer HIDDEN from the list of layers, and then you will pick to set the linetype.

Pick: **HIDDEN *(to highlight the layer name)***

Pick: **Set Ltype. . .**

The Select Linetype dialogue box appears on your screen. You will see the linetype CONTINUOUS listed. To select linetype HIDDEN, pick on the button for NEXT that you see near the bottom of the dialogue box and you will see more linetypes appear. HIDDEN is displayed near the bottom of the box. Pick the dashed line to the left of the name HIDDEN. Notice that the word HIDDEN appears next to Linetype: at the bottom of your dialogue box. Pick OK to close the Select Linetype dialogue box. This changes the linetype for the layer named HIDDEN to linetype HIDDEN.

To unselect layer HIDDEN before you continue, pick once on the layer name to unselect it.

Repeat these steps to set the following colors and linetypes for the other layers you have created. When you are setting the colors for the layers listed below, keep in mind that CYAN is the aqua color on the top row of standard colors and that the color white appears black if you have selected to draw on a light background.

■ ***TIP*** When you are selecting the color and linetype, make sure you have highlighted only the name(s) of the layer(s) you wish to set. If other layer name(s) are already highlighted, pick on their name(s) again to turn the highlighting off. ■

Layer	Color	Linetype
VISIBLE	WHITE (appears black on a white background)	CONTINUOUS
THIN	RED	CONTINUOUS
HIDDEN	BLUE	HIDDEN
CENTERLN	GREEN	CENTER
PROJ	MAGENTA	CONTINUOUS
HATCH	RED	CONTINUOUS
TEXT	RED	CONTINUOUS
DIM	CYAN	CONTINUOUS
BORDER	WHITE	CONTINUOUS

Before you exit the dialogue box, set the current layer to BORDER. Highlight layer name BORDER and

Pick: ***(on the Current box)***

When you are finished creating the layers and setting the colors and linetypes, the dialogue box on your screen should appear similar to Figure 6.3.

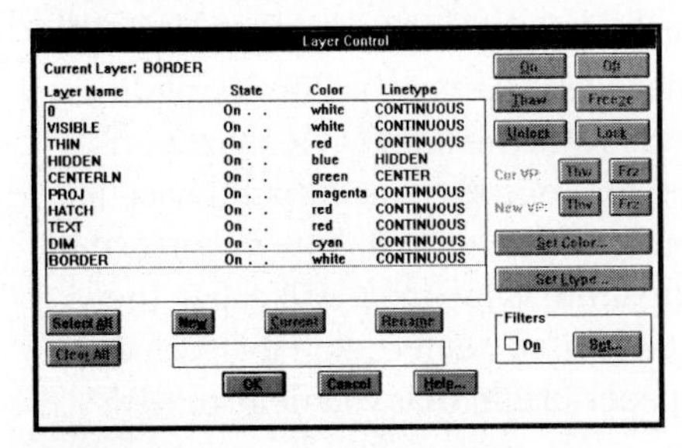

Figure 6.3

Pick: **OK**

You have now created a basic set of layers that will be used in future drawings. When you return to the Layer Control dialogue in the future, you will notice that the list of layer names has become alphabetized.

Save your drawing before continuing.

Adapting for Architecture

Layering in architectural drawings is the most effective way to develop efficient AutoCAD drawing techniques. The American Institute of Architects publishes a set of layer guidelines for CAD, but they are not readily available to students. Instead, students should use layers that are set up methodically, using colors to augment recognition of the layer scheme. Setting up layers to describe different types of walls, i.e., foundation, brick, gypsum, CMU, or others, and using similar colors for each type allows you to effectively manage drawings with many different layers. An easy way to use these layers that you set up as the standard for all new drawings you create, including plans, sections, and elevations, is to start from a prototype drawing or a series of prototypes. (Use a prototype and create other prototypes from it.) If you do these things, it will be easy to plot your drawings so that all line-weight information will remain consistent through an entire set of drawings. ■

Setting Drawing Aids

Use the Drawing Aids dialogue box to set SNAP, GRID, and ORTHO.

Pick: **Settings *(menu bar),* Drawing Aids. . .**

You will set the X spacing for the snap to .25.

Pick: ***(highlight the input box next to X Spacing under Snap)***

Type: **.25** ↵

> ■ ***TIP*** A fast way to replace the entry in the input box with a new value is to hold the pick button down and drag the cursor across the text to be selected (the value 1.0000). It becomes highlighted and then you can type ".25", which replaces the selected text. ■

At the left of the dialogue box are five boxes for Ortho, Solid Fill, Quick Text, Blips, and Highlight. An X appearing in the box to the left of the name indicates that the setting is active.

> ■ ***TIP*** Blips are the little crosses that appear on the screen when you select a point. Sometimes these are useful. If you find them annoying, you can turn them off here. Otherwise, REDRAW always removes them from the screen. ■

Move the arrow cursor over the button to the left of Ortho and pick it to turn ORTHO on. Move to the On buttons below Snap and Grid and turn these on. Leave the values for Grid set to 0.0000. This way the grid will automatically be set to whatever value you set for the snap.

Once you have finished making these selections, the Drawing Aids dialogue box should look like Figure 6.4.

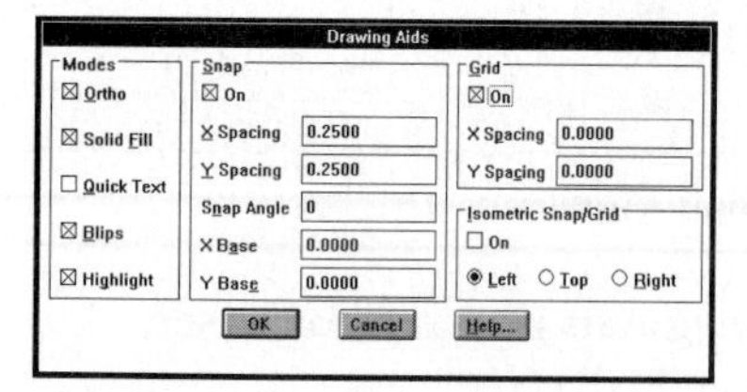

Figure 6.4

Pick: **OK *(to exit from the dialogue box)***

You should see a grid of dots on your screen. You will use ZOOM, All if the dots do not fill the entire screen area. Do not be concerned if the grid does not fill entirely to the right edge of the screen. Currently your drawing limits are set to 12 × 9; if your drawing area on the screen does not have the same aspect ratio (the ratio of the height to the width), only one dimension will be filled completely. If you wish, you can figure out the aspect ratio of your drawing area and always set your drawing limits so that the grid fills the entire screen, but this is unnecessary. When you start a drawing from your prototype, you will set the drawing limits at that time to a value that is large enough for the particular part you will draw. Then you can use the ZOOM command to view the new drawing limits. For now,

Pick: **View *(menu bar)*, Zoom, All**

Creating a Paper Space Viewport

You will use the method you learned in Tutorial 3 to create a paper space viewport that can be used for easily fitting views on the sheet of paper and plotting your drawing to a specified scale. Size the viewport so that it will fit inside the limits that you determined for your output device when paper space is plotted full size. The values used in this tutorial are general and may work for your printer or plotter. You can substitute the limit values that you determined for your specific output device in the beginning of the tutorial. You will probably want to substitute values that will cause the border to be plotted centered on the sheet, using the paper origin that you determined.

Figure 6.5 shows an example of how to determine the drawing coordinates for the viewport you will create.

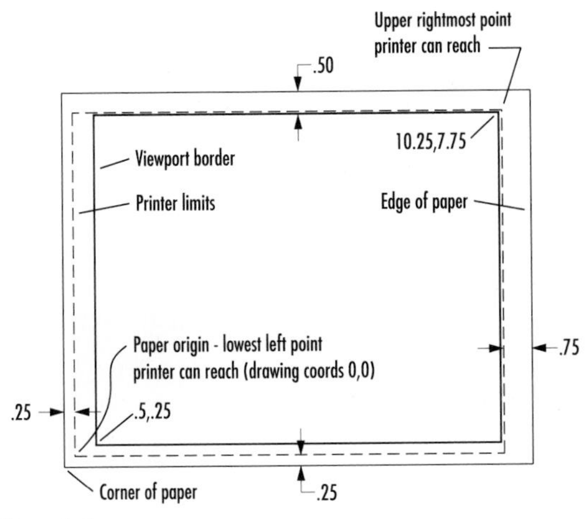

Figure 6.5

The outer line in Figure 6.5 represents the edge of the paper. Printers cannot print all the way to the edge. The distance from the edge that a printer can reach is different for each printer. It is also not necessarily the same distance from the left edge as it is from the right edge or the top and bottom edges. The limits of the printer may also be different for each sheet size that you are printing on.

The dashed line represents the limits of a particular printer. At the beginning of this tutorial you determined the limits for the printer you are using.

The thick line represents the viewport border you will create. In this example, the printer places the lowest corner of the drawing at a location .25" above the bottom of the paper and .25" in from the left edge of the paper, when you select to plot the origin at 0,0 (in the Configuration Plot dialogue). The printer can only reach to within .5 of the top border and .75 of the right edge of the sheet. In order to create a viewport that is centered on the paper, specify .5,.25 for the lower left corner of the viewport (this will move the left edge of the viewport in so that it is .75 from the left edge of the paper and .5 from the bottom). Specify 10.25,7.75 for the upper right corner of the viewport (that is as far as the printer will reach and is .75 from the right edge and .5 from the top of the paper). This will produce a viewport that is centered on your sheet when you print the drawing from paper space so that the area from 0,0 to 10.25,7.75 is full size on a sheet of 8.5 × 11 paper.

When you are doing the steps listed below, use your printer limits in place of the suggested values. Decide what values you will need to use in order to get your drawing centered on the paper. Remember, each style of printer will have its own limits. Take the time to set your prototype drawing up correctly so that when you print your drawings they will look their best.

> ■ ***TIP*** If you have access to several different printers or work with several different sheet sizes, it is very useful to have several different prototype drawings. ■

Your current layer should now be BORDER (see the toolbar). If it is not, set the layer to BORDER before continuing.

Pick: **View *(menu bar)*, Tilemode**

Picking View, Tilemode toggles the variable TILEMODE to the opposite of its previous value. It was previously set to one (1). Picking Tilemode has set it to zero (0). You are now in paper space. Notice that the P button on the toolbar is highlighted, telling you you are in paper space. Your screen will appear similar to Figure 6.6.

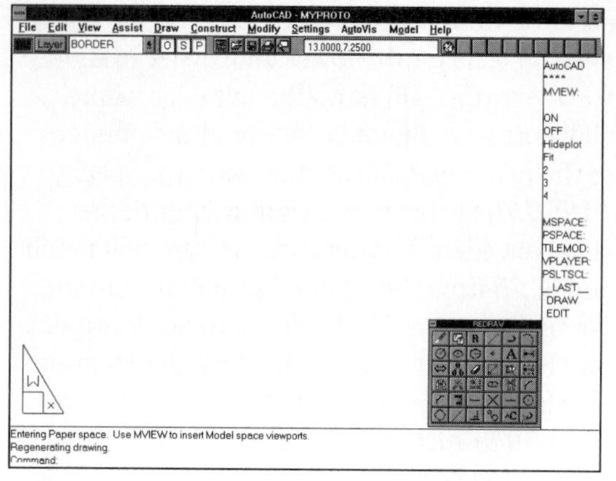

Figure 6.6

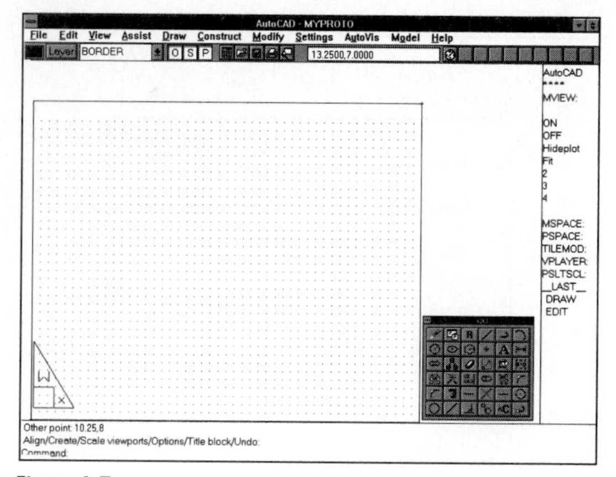

Figure 6.7

Pick: **View *(menu bar)*, Layout, MV Setup**

MVSetup, Version 1.15, (c) 1990-1993 by Autodesk, Inc.

Align/Create/Scale viewports/Options/Title block/Undo: **C** (↵)

Delete objects/Undo/<Create viewports>: (↵)

Pressing (↵) takes you to a text screen where you will see the choices for common arrangements of viewports, as you saw in Tutorial 3. You will make selection 1 for a single viewport.

Redisplay/<Number of entry to load>: **1** (↵)

You are returned to the AutoCAD drawing editor screen for the remaining selections.

Bounding area for viewports. First point: **.5,.25** (↵)

Other point: **10.25,7.75** (↵)

Align/Create/Scale viewports/Options/Title block/Undo: (↵)

The size of the viewport has been selected to correspond exactly to the output device limitations that you tested at the beginning of this tutorial. The values .5,.25 and 10.25,7.75 may work for you, but if you have determined the exact size that your output device can print, substitute these values when specifying the viewport boundary.

You will see the black lines of the viewport boundary drawn on the screen with the grid contained inside them, similar to Figure 6.7.

Using Limits

The LIMITS command lets you predefine a boundary in your drawing. When the limits are turned on, you cannot draw outside the area that is specified. You can turn the limits off at any time if you wish to draw outside this area. The LIMITS command can be useful in producing plots located exactly where you want them on the sheet. You can define separate limits in the drawing when you are in paper space getting ready to plot and when you are in model space creating your drawing geometry.

Setting the Paper Space Limits

The LIMITS command is found under SETTINGS on the screen menu. Use limits in your prototype drawing to represent the edge of the printer limits in paper space. (The viewport represents the area inside the printer limits where you wish to center your drawing.) Setting the upper right corner of the limits slightly beyond the viewport is useful because then when you use Zoom, All in paper space, the viewport border will be slightly in from the edge of the AutoCAD drawing screen, which can make it easier to select.

Pick: **SETTINGS** ***(screen),*** **LIMITS**

Reset Paper Space limits: ON/OFF/<Lower left corner> <0.0000,0.0000>: **0,0** ↵

Upper right corner <12.0000,9.0000>: **10.5,8** ↵

Restart the LIMITS command and turn the limits on.

Command: ↵

ON/OFF/<Lower left corner> <0.0000,0.0000>: **ON** ↵

Pick: **View** ***(menu bar),*** **Zoom, All**

to show the entire limits area on the screen. Next switch back to model space by picking the Paper space/Model space toggle from the toolbar.

Pick: **P button** ***(toolbar)***

to return to model space where you can create your drawing geometry. Notice that the UCS icon has returned to your screen.

Now you have a viewport border in your prototype drawing. It is on a separate layer so that it can be frozen when you do not want it to print. The next step will be to establish a relationship between the number of units in model space and the number of units in paper space. For now you will set up the drawing so that one unit on the object in model space will equal one unit in paper space. To establish this relationship, you will use the ZOOM command to specify the XP (meaning times paper space) scale factor. The XP scale factor is a ratio. It is the number of units for the object in paper space divided by the number of units in model space. For example, if you wish the model space object to appear twice its size on the paper, specify 2XP as the scale factor (2 paper space units / 1 model space unit). In Tutorial 3 you saw how you could use the LISP program MVSETUP to set up the ZOOM Scale factor for you. You specified the number of paper space units and the number of model space units. The MV Setup routine actually uses the ZOOM command, Scale XP option to set up the relationship between paper space and model space units. The value you specify for ZOOM XP scale factor is just the number of units for paper space divided by the number of units for model space. This time you will learn to set the ZOOM, Scale XP factor directly, without using the MVSETUP program. (If you liked using MV Setup, you can use that method for your future drawings.)

Command: **Z** ↵

All/Center/Dynamic/Extents/Left/Previous/VMax/Window/ Scale (X/XP): **1XP** ↵

Your screen should appear similar to Figure 6.8. The ZOOM XP scale factor has been set up so that if you plot paper space at a scale of 1=1, the object you create in model space in your drawing will be full size on the paper. If you use ZOOM, Window to enlarge your drawing, be sure to use ZOOM, Previous, not ZOOM All, to return to the original size before you plot. Additionally, you can always use ZOOM and specify a different XP scale factor at a later time if you wish.

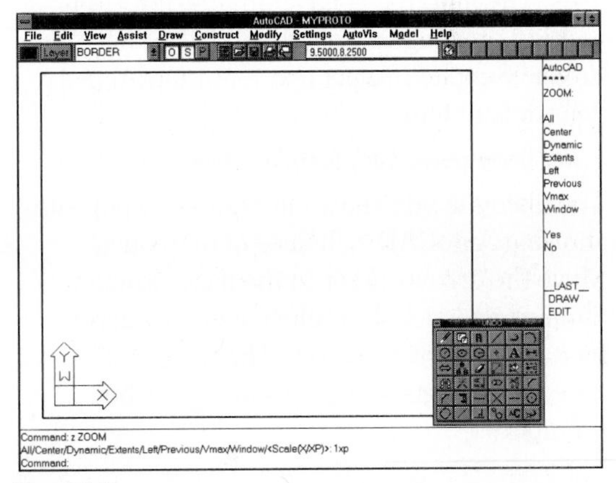

Figure 6.8

Setting Other Defaults

Default values for many other variables and settings for other aids can be customized to suit your drawing needs. You will set three more defaults for your prototype drawing before continuing with a new drawing.

The DIMCEN Default

As you learned in Tutorial 2, DIMCEN is the dimensioning variable that controls the style of center line that is drawn when you are using Draw, Dimensions, Radial, Center Mark to add the center marks to your drawing. You have to set DIMCEN to a negative value to get center lines with a tick at the center that extend slightly past the edge of the circle. (A positive value just places a tick at the center.) You will set a negative value for DIMCEN for your prototype.

Command: **DIMCEN** ↵

New value for **DIMCEN** <0.0900>: **–.125** ↵

Selecting the Default Text Font

AutoCAD offers a number of fonts for different uses. The font that is best for lettering engineering drawings is called ROMANS, for Roman Simplex. Select text font ROMANS as your default font.

Pick: **Draw *(menu bar),* Text, Set Style. . .**

The dialogue box shown in Figure 6.9 pops up, showing AutoCAD's choices of text fonts. Move the arrow cursor to the name Roman Simplex and pick it to select it as the current font. Pick OK or press ↵. Then you will accept the defaults by pressing ↵ at the prompts.

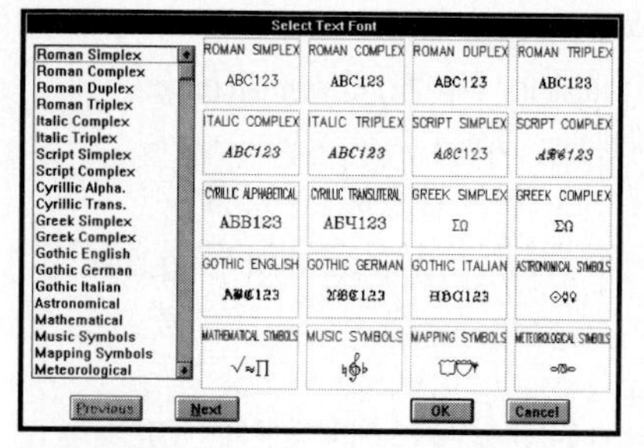

Figure 6.9

Text style name (or ?)<STANDARD>:romans

New style.

Font file <rtxt>: romans

Height <0.0000>: ↵

Width factor <1.0000>: ↵

Obliquing angle <0>: ↵

Backwards? <N>: ↵

Upside down? <N>: ↵

Vertical? <N>: ↵

ROMANS is now the current text style

The VIEWRES Default

VIEWRES controls how many line segments are used to draw a circle on your monitor. This does not affect the way that circles are plotted, just how they appear on the screen. Have you noticed that when you use Zoom Window to enlarge a portion of the drawing, circles may appear as octagons? This is because VIEWRES is set to a low number. The default setting is low to save time when circles are drawn on the screen. With faster processors and high-resolution graphics, you can use a larger value. The VIEWRES command is located on the screen menu under DISPLAY, VIEWRES. You will type the command name at the command prompt.

Command: **VIEWRES** ↵

Do you want fast zooms? <Y>: ↵

Enter circle zoom percent (1-20000) <100>: **5000** ↵

■ ***TIP*** If you are using a slower computer system, you may notice that performance on your computer slows down. It may be because of this setting. If you need to, you can reset the VIEWRES variable to a lower number. Type "REGEN" at the "Command:" prompt to regenerate circles that do not appear round. ■

Adding a Title Block

You can easily add a title block to your drawing, using lines and text in paper space. It is easy to edit the text with the DDEDIT command to make changes to the standard information you provide in the title block. (In Tutorial 14 you will learn the BLOCK command and how to use attributes to have AutoCAD prompt you for the information to enter into the title block.) Now you will add the lines and text for your title block.

Return to paper space before adding the lines and text to make up the title block.

Pick: **P *(toolbar)***

You will see the paper space icon return to your screen. Check the toolbar to see that BORDER is the current layer.

On your own, draw the lines for the title block you see in Figure 6.10. (Refer to Tutorial 3 if you need to review the steps you used before.) Then set the current layer to TEXT and add text specifying the drawing title, date, scale, and drafter's name, as shown.

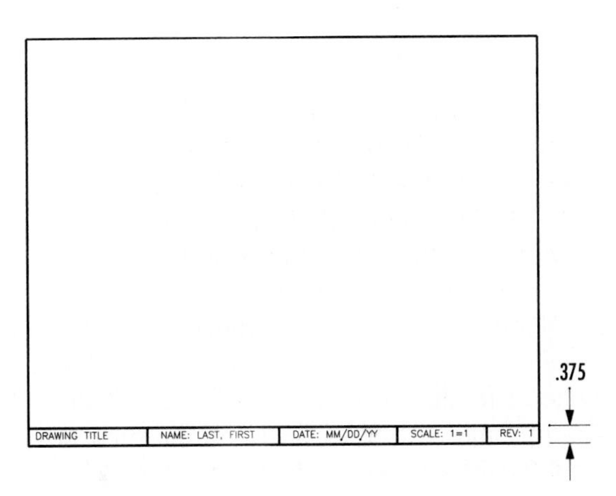

Figure 6.10

When you have completed these steps, return to model space by picking P from the toolbar. Set the current layer to VISIBLE by picking on the current layer name shown on the toolbar (BORDER). Use the list of names that pulls down to select VISIBLE as the current layer.

You will save this drawing with VISIBLE set as the current layer. This way, when you begin a new drawing from this prototype, you will be ready to start drawing in the layer for VISIBLE lines.

Now you have completed the drawing MYPROTO. Save this drawing.Use the toolbar to pick the QSAVE command to save the file to the default name. The icon for QSAVE looks like a 3.5" disk.

Pick: QSAVE icon *(toolbar)*

Be sure that you keep a copy of the drawing on your own floppy disk.

You also should make a second copy of your drawings on a separate floppy as a backup disk, in case the first disk becomes damaged.

Adapting for Architecture

It is very useful to create a separate prototype drawing for each of the standard sheet sizes: A (8.5 × 11), B (11 × 17), C (18 × 24), and D (24 × 36). When setting up the prototype drawing, use the plotter limits as the limits you set in paper space. Figure out where to locate the corners of the viewport so that it is centered on the sheet. Set up a systematic scheme for the layer names and colors. Name your prototype drawing based on the sheet size and ZOOM XP scale factor set. Keep in mind when setting the ZOOM XP scale factor that the base measurement for architectural units is the inch. For a drawing scale of 1/8" = 1', the Zoom XP scale factor would be 1/8" divided by 1', or 1/96, which is .0104167XP. (Or use the MV Setup, Scale viewport option and specify 1 for the number of paper space units and 96 for the number of model space units.) ■

Beginning a New Drawing from a Prototype Drawing

Any AutoCAD drawing can be used as a starting point for a new drawing. The settings that you have made in drawing MYPROTO will be used to start future drawings. An identical prototype drawing, called PROTO, is provided with your data files. If you wish to use the prototype you just created, substitute MYPROTO whenever you are asked to use PROTO. To start a drawing from a prototype,

Pick: **File *(menu bar)*, New. . .**

Pick: **Prototype. . .**

Use the dialogue box that appears to select the drive and directory where you have stored your drawings. Pick the drawing PROTO, which is like drawing MYPROTO you created, from the list that appears. When you are finished making this selection, pick OK to return to the Create New Drawing dialogue box, shown in Figure 6.11, where you will provide a name for the new drawing that you will start from the prototype.

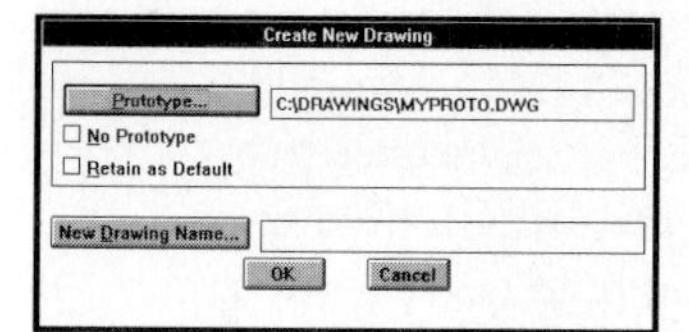

Figure 6.11

> ■ ***TIP*** You can select the box Retain as Default in the Create New Drawing dialogue box if you want your prototype drawing name to always appear in the box instead of the default drawing, ACAD. ■

Type: **C:\DRAWINGS\SHMETAL *(for the New Drawing Name)***

Pick: **OK**

This starts a new drawing (called SHMETAL) from a copy of the drawing called PROTO. The drawing PROTO will remain unchanged, so that it can be used to start other drawings. Your current drawing name is now SHMETAL. You will create an orthographic drawing of a clip made from sheet metal. For future drawings in this book, use PROTO as a prototype drawing unless you are directed otherwise.

Changing the Title Block Text

The border, text, and lines of the title block were created in paper space. To make a change to them, you must first return to paper space. Then you will use the DDEDIT command to change the title block text so that it is correct for the new drawing you are starting.

Command: **PS** (↵)

Command: **DDEDIT** (↵)

<Select a text or ATTDEF object>/Undo: ***(select the text DRAWING TITLE)***

The DDEDIT box appears on your screen, as shown in Figure 6.12, containing the text you selected. Click and drag to highlight the words DRAWING TITLE and type the name SHEET METAL CLIP. When you are finished editing the text,

Pick: **OK *(to exit the dialogue box)***

<Select a text or ATTDEF object>/Undo: (↵) ***(to end the command)***

Figure 6.12

Remember to return to model space before starting your drawing.

Pick: **P *(toolbar) (to return to model space)***

You are now ready to use your drawing, created from the prototype, to create an orthographic drawing of a sheet metal clip.

Sheet-Metal Objects

The orthographic views for sheet-metal objects follow the same drawing rules and conventions as all other objects. Figure 6.13 shows an object made from sheet metal.

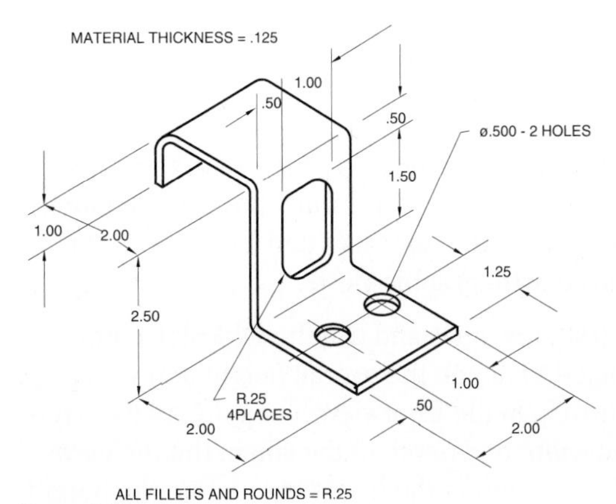

Figure 6.13

Sheet-metal objects have very thin walls. Sheet-metal thickness is specified either by using a numerical value or by specifying a gauge. The lower the gauge number, the thicker the sheet metal. For example, 10-gauge material has a thickness of 0.1019 and 6-gauge material has a thickness of 0.1620.

Edges for sheet-metal objects are created by bending the corners so that they are rounded. Rounded edges are defined by the inside bend radius and the outside bend radius. The outside bend radius is equal to the inside bend radius plus the material thickness. See Figure 6.14.

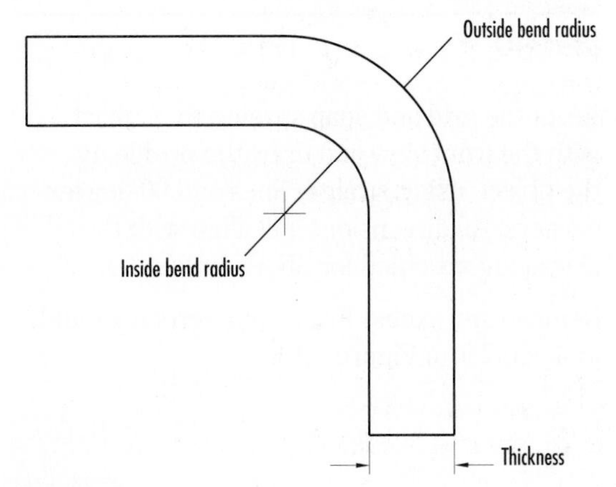

Figure 6.14

When drawing a sheet-metal object, be sure to distinguish between the inside and outside bend radii.

To draw the orthographic views of the object shown in Figure 6.14, study the overall dimensions to define the sizes and locations of the three orthographic views.

First draw lines and use the OFFSET command to define the overall height and width of the clip in the front view. Then define the overall width and depth of the clip in the top view. To the right of the front view, define the height and depth of the clip in the right-side view. When you are finished, your screen should look similar to Figure 6.15.

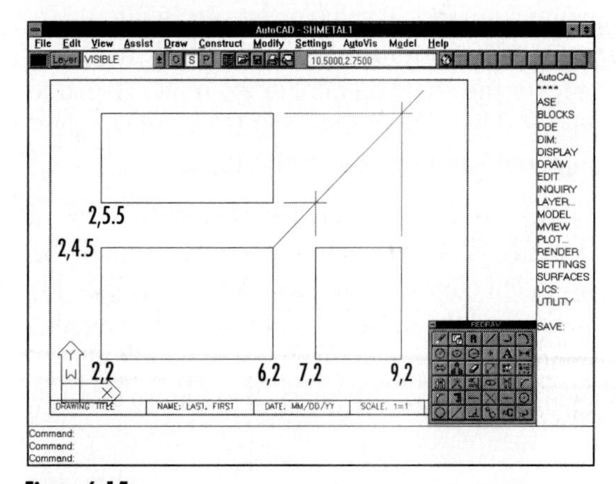

Figure 6.15

Reset the grid and snap spacing to .5. Start with the front view and draw the profile of the object, using straight lines and 90-degree corners. All dimensions will align with the .5 spacing specified for SNAP and GRID.

Remove any excess lines. Your screen should look similar to Figure 6.16.

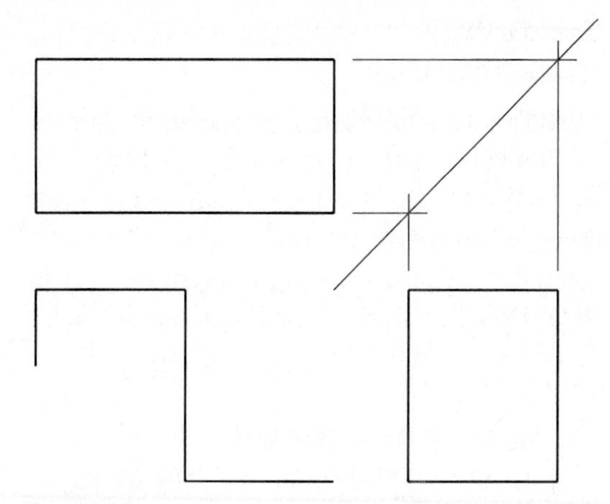

Figure 6.16

Use the OFFSET command to add the .125 material thickness to the front view. Be careful which side you select for the offset.

Use the FILLET command to add the rounded corners. The drawing note specifies an inside bend radius of .125. Set the fillet for a radius of .125. (Refer to Tutorial 2 if you need to review FILLET.) Draw all the inside bend radii.

Set the fillet radius for .25 (.125 Inside Bend Radius + .125 material thickness) and draw the outside bend radii. Your screen should look similar to Figure 6.17.

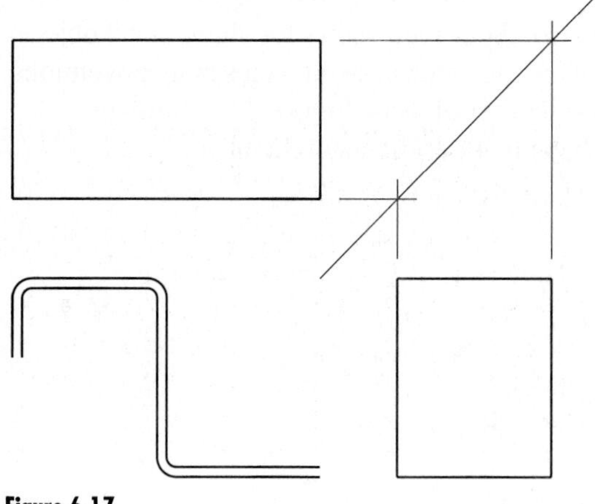

Figure 6.17

Use ZOOM, Window to enlarge the area that you are working in.

Use OSNAP, Endpoint to help you connect the thickness lines at both ends of the object. Remember to use ZOOM, Previous to restore your original workspace.

Add the rectangular slot to the side view. Use FILLET to draw the rounded internal corners.

Use the given dimensions to add the two holes in the top view.

Project the material thickness, hole, and slot into the other views. Change appropriate lines to hidden lines. Your screen should look similar to Figure 6.18.

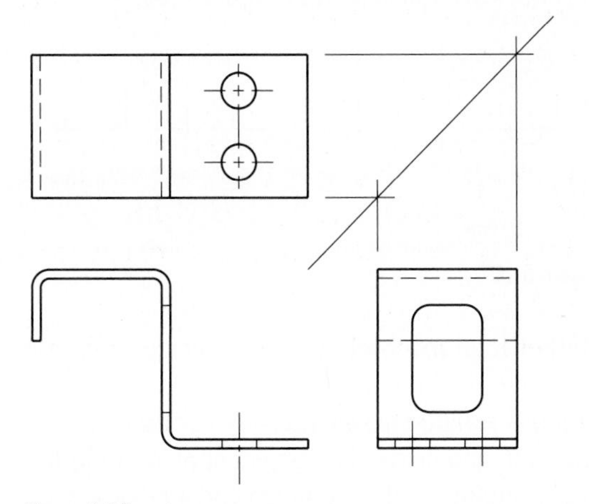

Figure 6.18

■ ***TIP*** Because the material is so thin, it is difficult to clearly show the slot and holes penetrating the material thickness. Drawings of holes should always include center lines, but it may not be possible to actually show the dash in the center line or draw a hidden line pattern between the two surface lines. ■

Because the layers are assigned different colors, the hidden lines and center lines are color coded, reducing the importance of the line pattern for visual clarity. Also, the lines can be plotted with different line thicknesses to differentiate them. It is also possible to create an enlarged detail of the vague area, as has been done in Figure 6.19. The vague area is circled and marked with a letter that refers to an enlarged detail on the drawing. The enlarged detail is marked with the same letter, and an enlargement scale is specified. In Figure 6.19, a scale of 4:1 was used. This means that the detail is drawn four times larger than the actual size.

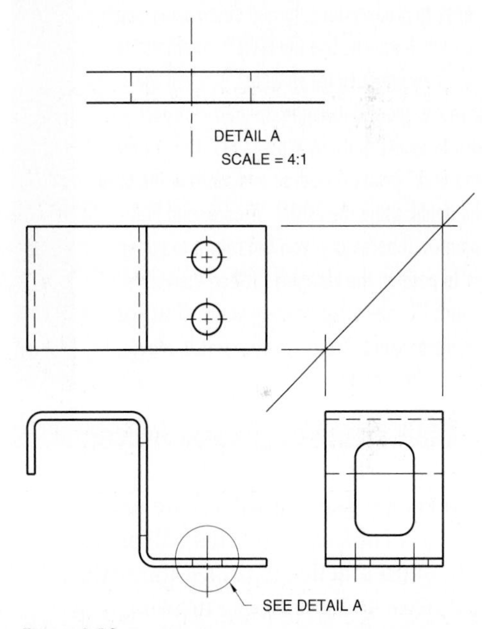

Figure 6.19

It is acceptable to have unbroken line segments rather than hidden line patterns represent hidden lines in thin-material objects. However, when possible, a hidden line pattern should be shown. Sometimes adjusting LTSCALE will make the lines appear dashed.

Remove any excess lines and save your drawing.

Plot your drawing by first switching to paper space and then using the PLOT command.

Pick: **P button *(toolbar)***

Pick: **PLOT *(toolbar)***

Print the drawing, using limits and a scale of 1=1.

Going Further

It is easy to produce an enlarged detail using paper space and viewports. Use the MVIEW command to make a new paper space viewport. You will see your model space drawing in the new viewport. Return to model space by typing "MS" (↵) at the "Command:" prompt. Enlarge and position the area of the detail, using the ZOOM, Window and PAN commands. If necessary, you can return to paper space to position the viewport further. Viewports are much like any other drawing entity when you are in paper space. You can scale, stretch, move, and erase them as desired.

In the next exercise you will create orthographic views of a casting. This will provide you with extra practice in projecting orthographic views and practice in drawing countersunk and counterbored holes. This exercise is optional.

Castings

Casting is one of the oldest known manufacturing processes. Metal is heated to liquid form and then poured into a mold and allowed to cool. The metal solidifies into the shape designated by the mold. Castings usually have rough surfaces; that is, the surface of a casting is not as smooth as a surface that has been machined. Rough surfaces do not bear loads as well as smoother surfaces. For example, a bolt pulling against a rough surface actually sits on the high points of the surface. A bolt sitting on a smoother surface has better surface contact and distributes the load more evenly. These differences are illustrated in Figure 6.20.

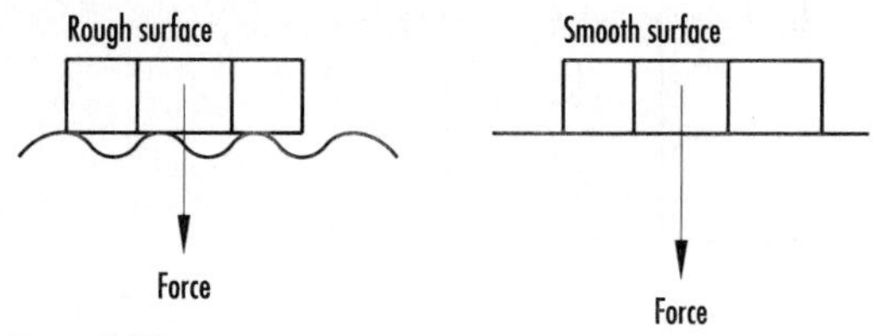

Figure 6.20

Rather than machining entire surfaces of a casting, manufacturers use bosses and spotfaces to smooth isolated areas, thereby saving machining time and costs. The object shown in Figure 6.21 contains both a spotface and a boss.

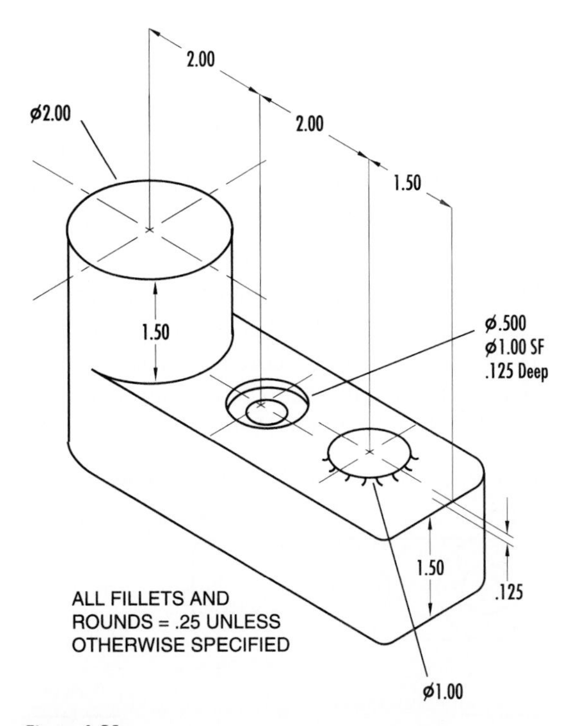

Figure 6.21

A *boss* is a turret-like shape that is raised slightly above the cast surface. The size of a boss is specified by a diameter and a height. A boss can be easily machined without machining the entire surface. The radius of the side arc of a boss is equal to the specified height of the boss above the surface. A *spotface* is a circular shallow hole cut into the surface of a casting just deep enough to create a smooth surface. Often no depth specification is given for a spotface. The diameter and depth (if any) of a spotface are given in a drawing note (callout), as shown in Figure 6.21. Spotfaces usually surround a hole whose diameter is specified as part of the spotface drawing note.

Figure 6.22 shows a runout.

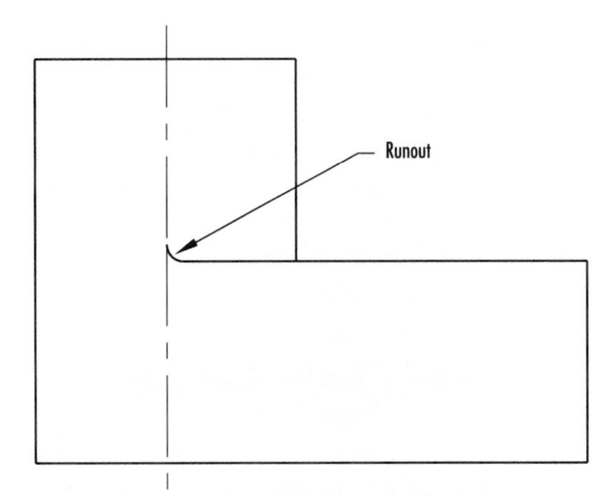

Figure 6.22

A *runout* occurs where two rounded edges blend into (become tangent to) the surface of the object. Runouts are shown on drawings by a small arc drawn at the approximate location of the blending.

Cast edges are not square (90 degrees). The size of the edge round of a casting's edges is usually specified with a drawing note, e.g., ALL FILLETS AND ROUNDS = .25 UNLESS OTHERWISE SPECIFIED. A fillet is a concave arc; a *round* is a convex arc. See Figure 6.23.

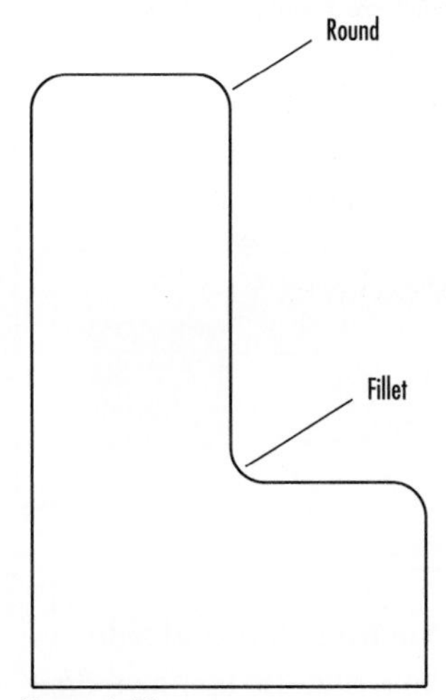

Figure 6.23

■ *TIP* Both fillets and rounds are drawn using the FILLET command. ■

You will draw the orthographic views of the casting shown in Figure 6.21. You will retrieve the drawing HOLDER that was provided with the data files that came with your software as the prototype to begin a new drawing.

Pick: **File *(menu bar)*, New...**

Pick: **Prototype... *(from the left side of the Create New Drawing dialogue box)***

Pick: **HOLDER *(from the list of files, changing the drive and directory if necessary)***

Pick: **OK *(to exit the Prototype Drawing File dialogue box and return to the Create New Drawing dialogue box)***

Type: **C:\DRAWINGS\CASTORT *(in the New Drawing Name box)***

Pick: **OK**

A new drawing is created from the drawing HOLDER. The new drawing is called CASTORT and drawing HOLDER is unchanged. Your screen should look similar to Figure 6.24.

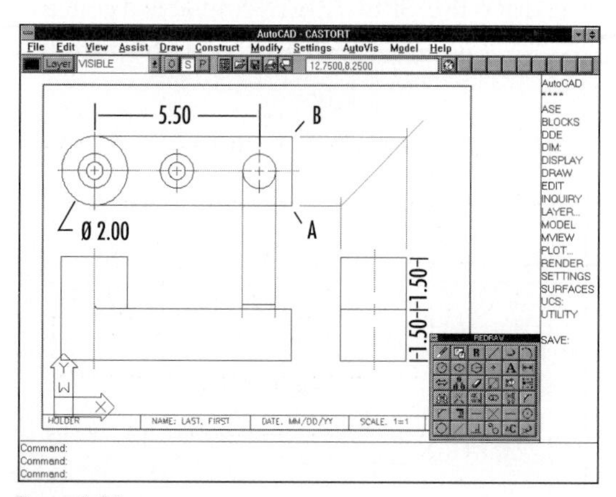

Figure 6.24

The drawing shows the front, top, and side views; however, the boss and the spotface do not appear in the front and side views.

Note that GRID and SNAP are on.

The front view shows a runout created with the FILLET command. The runout is where the two rounded edges blend together. You will add fillets and rounds to the drawing.

Use the FILLET command to draw the rounds. Pick the FILLET icon from the toolbox. The first time you invoke the command, use the Radius option to set the FILLET radius to .25. Then start the FILLET command again and pick the lines that create the rounds at points A and B, as indicated in Figure 6.24.

Your screen should look similar to Figure 6.25.

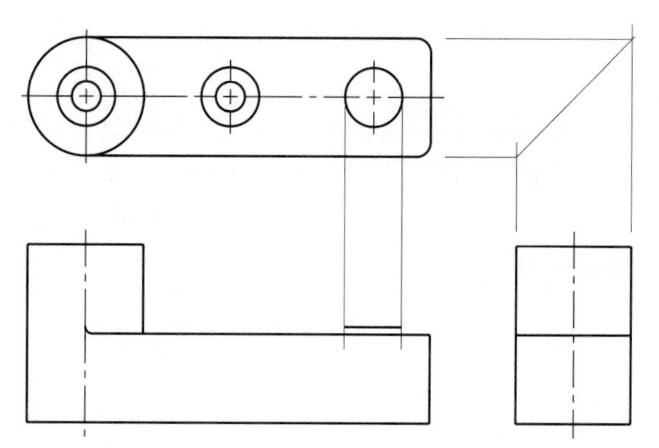

Figure 6.25

Next you will draw the boss in the front view. The boss looks like a circle 1 inch in diameter in the top view. Some projection lines extend from it to help you get started. You will add the boss to the front and side views. The height of the boss is .125 inches. A line has been offset and trimmed to act as the top of the boss in the front view. You will add the fillets for the boss.

On your own, ZOOM the boss area in the front view.

Notice that the VISIBLE layer is current so that you can draw the fillets for the boss and have them in the correct layer for visible lines.

In order to keep the FILLET command from erasing a large portion of the line, use the BREAK command with the @ option and Object Snap, Intersection to break the bottom line of the boss at both intersections where it intersects the two projection lines. Refer to Tutorial 4 if you need to review the BREAK command. Do this now on your own.

You will use the FILLET command with a radius of .125 to create the fillets for the boss.

> Command: **FILLET *(toolbox)***
>
> Polyline/Radius/<Select first object>: **R** ↵
>
> Enter Fillet Radius <0.2500>: **.125** ↵
>
> Command: ↵ ***(to restart the FILLET command)***
>
> Polyline/Radius/<Select first object>: ***(pick line 1, shown in Figure 6.26)***
>
> Select second object: ***(pick line 2)***

On your own, repeat these steps for lines 3 and 4. Then use EXTEND to extend the bottom line of the boss so that it intersects the arcs created with the FILLET command. Your screen should look like Figure 6.26. When you are finished with this step, use ZOOM, Previous to restore the drawing to its original size. Copy the boss to the side view.

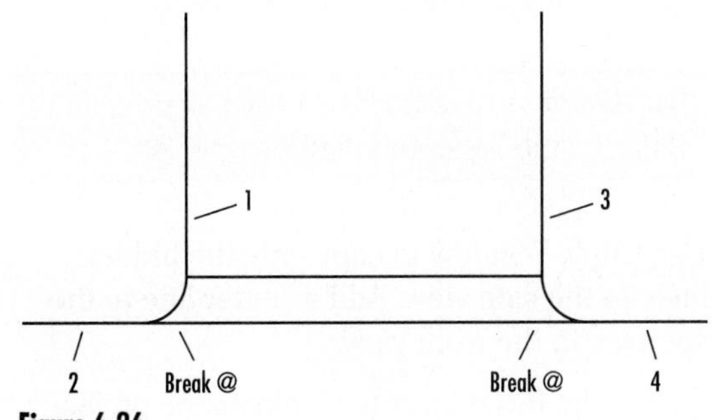

Figure 6.26

Projecting the Spotface

The middle set of two concentric circles in the top view, 1 and .5 inches in diameter, represents a spotface. Figure 6.27 shows counterbored, countersunk, and spotfaced holes. Spotfacing is used to give a flat bearing surface for a bolt head, nut, washer, or similar item. Use the depth of .125 for the spotface in your drawing. The .5-diameter hole goes all the way through, so you will draw your projection lines all the way to the base of the front view.

On your own, project the spotface center line and diameter into the front view on layer PROJ. On your own, draw the horizontal line that represents the depth of the spotface in the front view, using OFFSET at .125 inches. Refer to Figure 6.27 for an example of a spotfaced hole to draw in the front view.

Counterbored and Countersunk Holes

Counterbored holes and *countersunk* holes are also very common on drawings. Figure 6.27 shows examples of the orthographic views of counterbored and countersunk holes, along with a spotfaced hole.

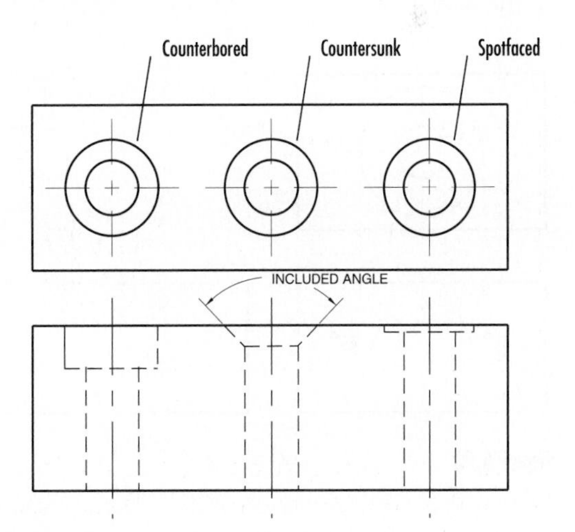

Figure 6.27

Similar to a spotface, a counterbore is like a second, larger hole drilled around the first hole. The first line of the drawing callout for a counterbore specifies the hole diameter and, if necessary, the hole depth. The second line of the callout gives the diameter of the counterbore. The third line gives the depth of the counterbore. Counterbored holes are most often used in designs to recess bolt heads below the surface of the object.

Countersunk holes have tapered edges cut to match the shape of flat-head screws and bolts. The first line of the drawing callout for a countersunk hole specifies the hole diameter and, if necessary, the hole depth. The second line gives the diameter and included angle of the counterbore. The included angle of most flat-head screws is 82 degrees, but is usually drawn as 45 degrees on technical drawings. This is a carry-over from the pencil drawing days, when it was very easy to draw a 45-degree line using a 45-degree triangle. Figure 6.28 shows how to draw a countersunk hole.

In your drawing, the counterbored hole appears as two concentric circles of diameter .50 and 1.00 at the left side of the top view. You will project it to the front view and then copy it to the side view.

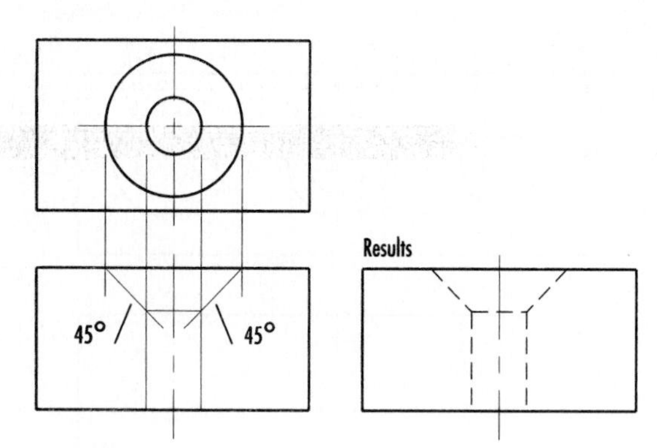

Figure 6.28

On your own, project the widths of the .5-diameter hole and the 1-diameter counterbore from the left of the top view into the front view. Use the OSNAP, Intersection command in running mode. Use OFFSET once again to offset the .25 line representing the depth of the counterbore and the .75 line representing the depth of the hole. Your drawing should look like Figure 6.29.

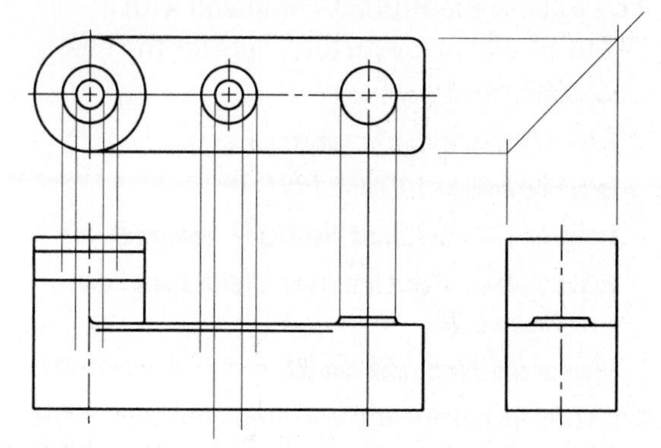

Figure 6.29

Draw the 30 degree drill point for the counterbored hole. TRIM the excess from the offset lines. Use the CHPROP command to change all of the lines for the holes in the front view to hidden lines. The projection lines will be frozen later, so they do not need to be erased.

■ ***TIP*** Be sure to use the LAyer option and change the layer, not the linetype. ■

Use Copy, Window to copy only the hidden lines to the side view. Add a center line to the spotface in the front view.

Freeze the PROJ layer to eliminate the projection lines from the display. Use LTSCALE if necessary to make your center lines look better. Your screen should look similar to Figure 6.30.

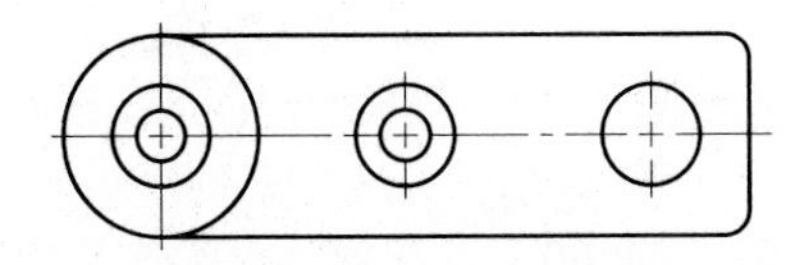

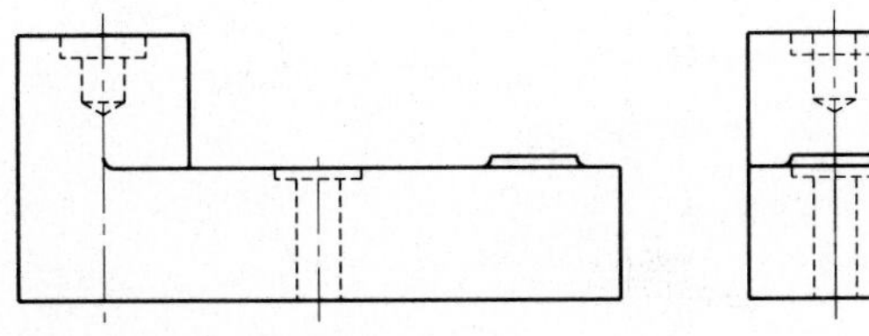

Figure 6.30

Command: **SAVE** (↵)

The file name CASTORT should appear in the File name box.

Pick: **OK *(to accept this and save your drawing)***

The drawing is saved as CASTORT.DWG on your disk. The original drawing, HOLDER, is not altered.

Exit AutoCAD. You have completed this tutorial.

KEY TERMS

boss
counterbored
countersunk
runout
round
spotface

KEY COMMANDS

View Resolution

EXERCISES

Draw front, top, and right-side orthographic views of the following objects. The letter M after an exercise number means that the given dimensions are in millimeters (metric units).

6.1M Cover Fitting

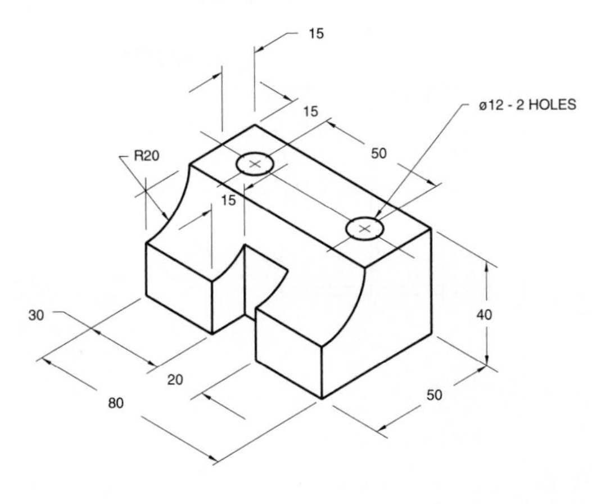

6.2 Lathe Stop

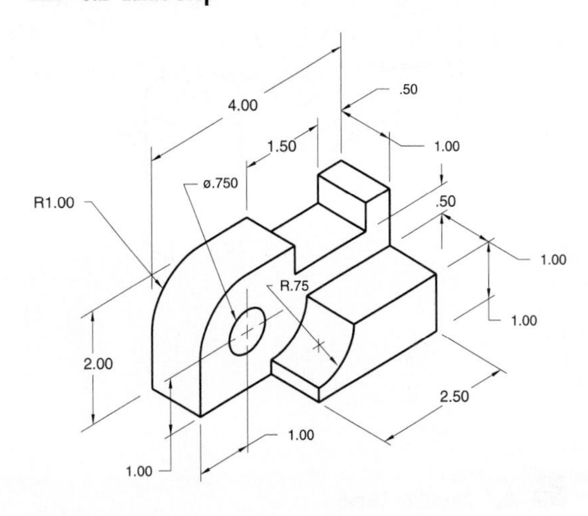

6.3 Side Clip

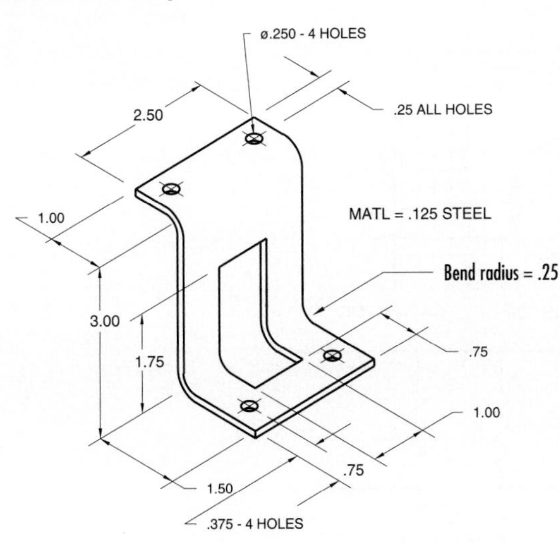

6.4 Crank Bearing

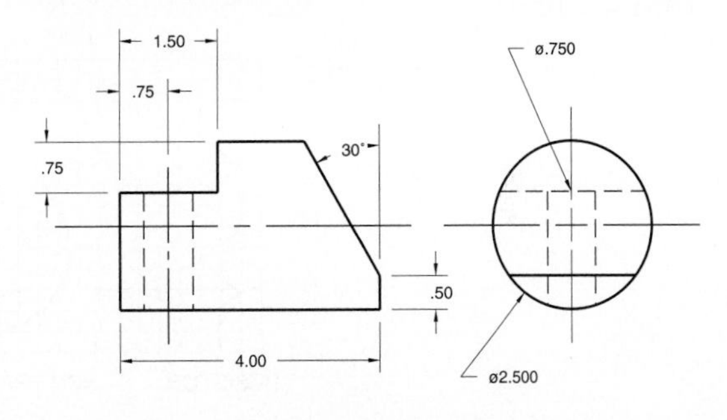

6.5M Alignment Casting

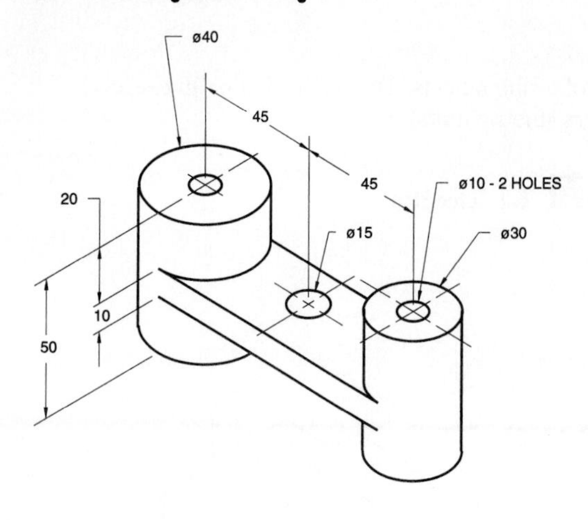

6.6 Rod Holder

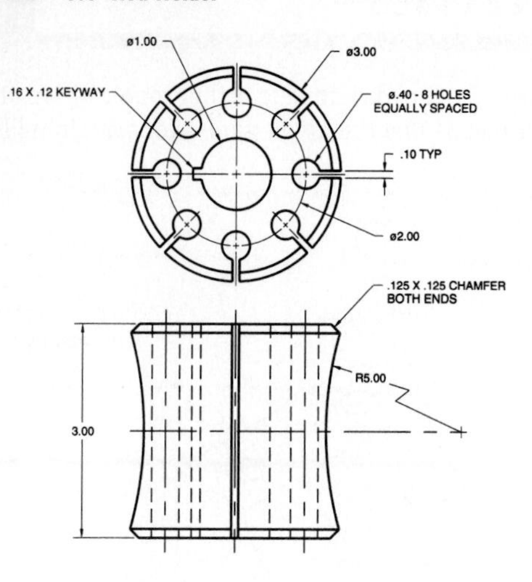

6.7 Amplifier Circuit

Draw the amplifier circuit. Use the grid at the top to determine the sizes of the components. Each square=0.0625.

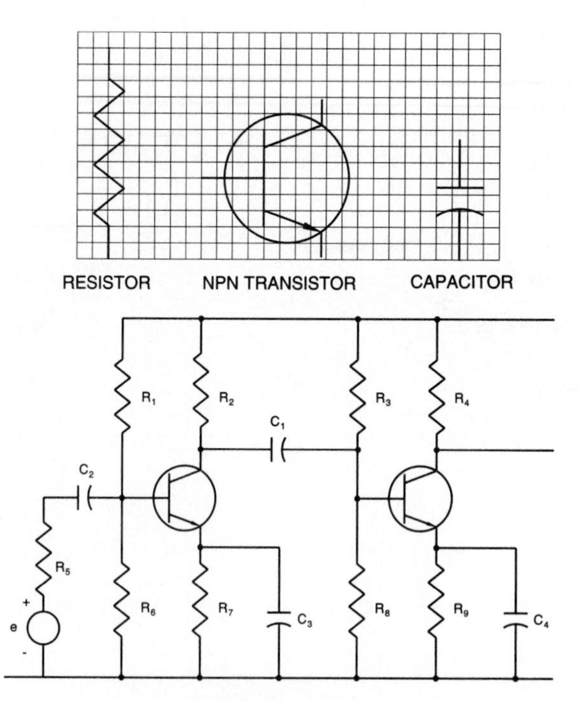

6.8 Idler Pulley Bracket

Create the top, front, and right side views for the object shown.

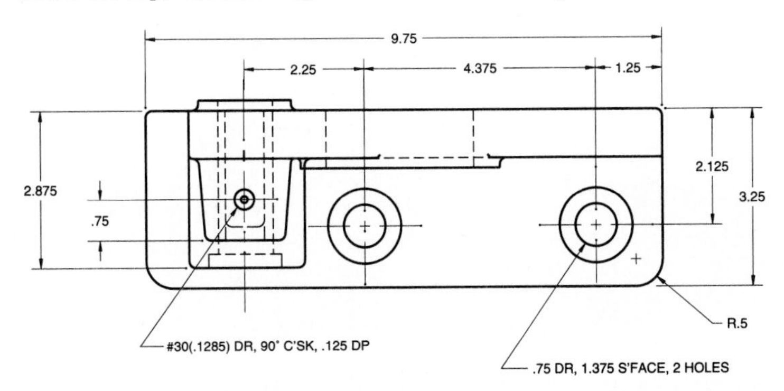

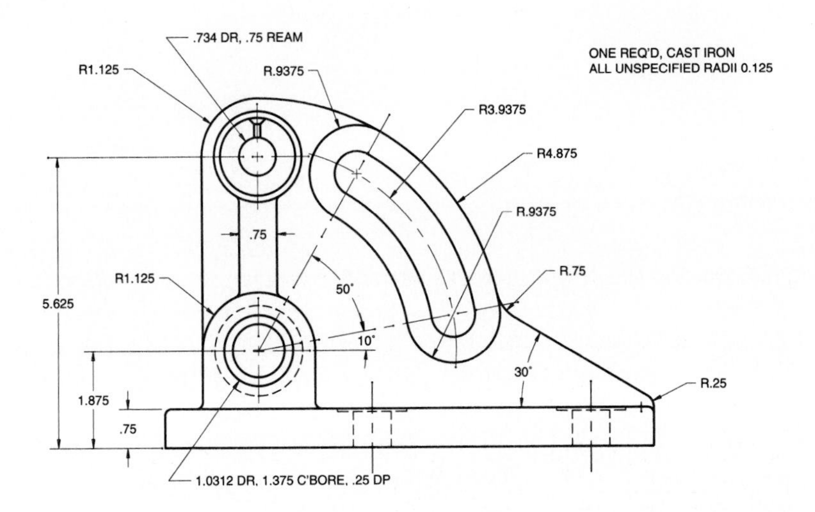

ONE REQ'D, CAST IRON
ALL UNSPECIFIED RADII 0.125

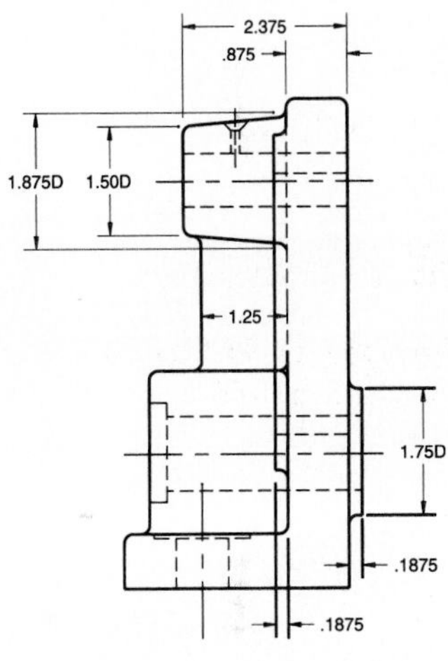

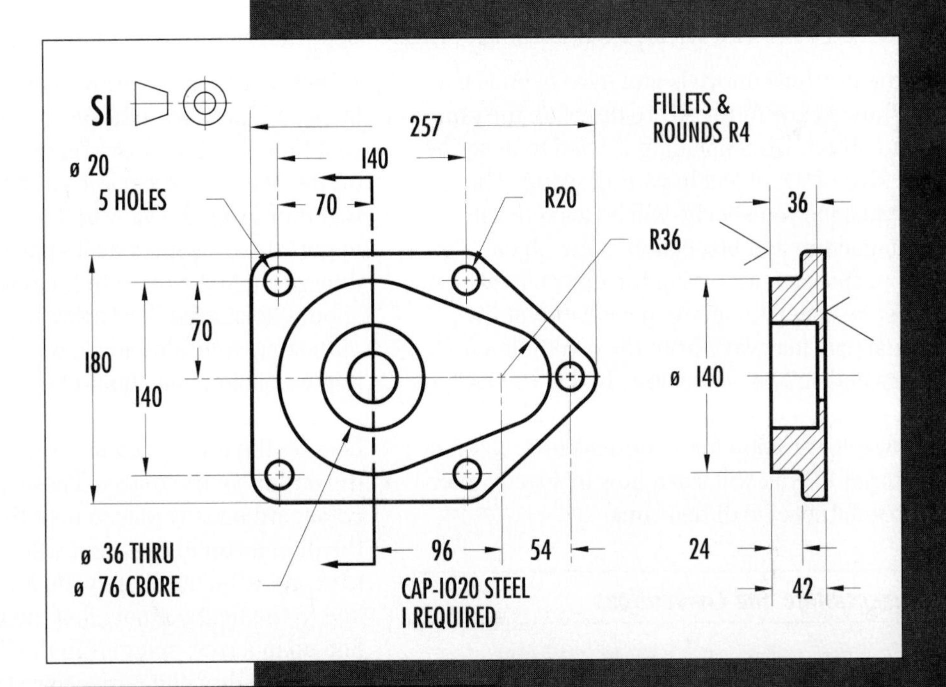

TUTORIAL 7

Basic Dimensioning

Objectives

When you have completed this tutorial, you will be able to

1. Understand dimensioning nomenclature and conventions.
2. Control the appearance of dimensions, using DIMVARS.
3. Set the dimension scaling factor with DIMSCALE.
4. Locate dimensions on drawings.
5. Use the UNITS command to set precision.
6. Dimension a shape.
7. Save a dimension style and add it to the prototype drawing.
8. Use associative dimensioning (DIMASO) to create dimensions that can update.
9. Check the dimension variable settings with STATUS.

Introduction

In the previous tutorials you have been learning how to use AutoCAD to describe the **shape** of an object. Dimensioning is used to describe the **size** of the object in your drawing. The dimensions you specify will be used in the manufacture and inspection of the object. For the purpose of inspecting the object, a *tolerance* must be stated to define to what extent the actual part may vary from the given dimensions and still be acceptable. In this tutorial you will use a general tolerance note to give the allowable variation for all dimensions. Later, in Tutorial 13, you will learn how to specify tolerances for specific dimensions.

Nomenclature and Conventions

Figure 7.1 shows a dimensioned drawing.

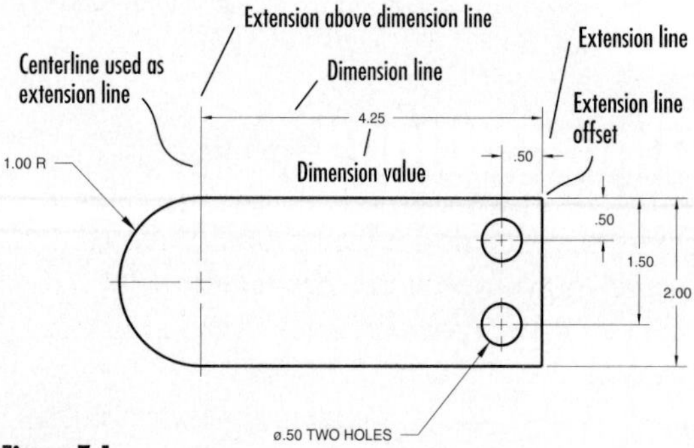

Figure 7.1

Dimensions are used to accurately describe the details of a part or object so that it can be manufactured. In the drawing, dimensions are always placed outside of the object outline. *Extension lines* are used to relate the dimension to the feature on the part. There should always be a gap of 1/16" on the plotted drawing between the edge of the part and the beginning of the extension line. Center lines, however, can be extended across the object outline when used as extension lines, without leaving a gap where they cross object lines.

Dimension lines are drawn between extension lines and have arrowheads at each end to indicate how the dimension relates to the feature on the object. Dimensions should be grouped together around a view and be evenly spaced to give the drawing a neat appearance. The dimension line closest to the object outline should be at least 3/8" away from the object outline on your plotted drawing. Each succeeding dimension line should be at least 1/4" away from the previous dimension line. The numbers on the dimension line should never touch the outline of the object. These *dimension values* are usually placed near the midpoint of the dimension line, except when it is necessary to stagger the numbers from one dimension line to the next so that all of the values do not line up in a row; staggering the numbers makes the drawing easier to read.

Since dimension lines should not cross extension lines or other dimension lines, begin by placing the shortest dimensions closest to the object outline. Place the longest dimensions farthest out. It is perfectly acceptable for extension lines to cross other extension lines.

When you are selecting and placing dimensions, think about the operations used to manufacture the part. When possible, provide *overall dimensions* that give the greatest measurements that exist for each dimension of the object, because this tells the manufacturer the starting size of the material used to make the part. The manufacturer should never have to add shorter dimensions or make calculations to arrive at the sizes needed for anything in the drawing. All necessary dimensions should be specified in your drawing, but no dimensions should be duplicated, as this may lead to confusion, especially when determining whether a part meets the specified tolerance.

Starting

Before you begin, launch AutoCAD. If you need help, please review the AutoCAD for Windows section of Chapter 3, AutoCAD Basics, in Part 1, Getting Started. The AutoCAD drawing editor should appear on your display screen. You will begin this tutorial by drawing an object and dimensioning it. To begin a new drawing,

Pick: **File *(menu bar)*, New. . .**

Name your drawing OBJ-DIM in the C:\DRAWINGS directory. Start the drawing from the prototype drawing you created, MYPROTO, or the one provided in the data files, PROTO. In the prototype area of the Create New Drawing dialogue box, replace the word ACAD with PROTO. (You may need to specify the drive and directory name for the prototype drawing.)

Pick: **OK *(to exit the Create New Drawing dialogue box)***

You return to the drawing editor with the border and settings you created in the prototype drawing on your screen.

Dimensioning a Shape

Review the object in Figure 7.1. You will redraw the shape and then dimension it.

Layer VISIBLE should be the current layer in the drawing. If it is not, set it as the current layer.

If SNAP and GRID are not already set, set the grid for .5 spacing and the snap for .25 spacing. Make sure that SNAP is turned on. Look at the toolbar; if you do not see the letter S highlighted, pick it to turn the SNAP function on.

Use the commands you learned in the previous tutorials to draw the object shown in Figure 7.1, according to the specified dimensions, before continuing. It is not necessary to draw the center lines at this time. Keep in mind that many of CAD's benefits, such as semi-automatic dimensioning, result from its accurate database. It is important to create the drawing geometry exactly if you are going to derive the most benefit from AutoCAD's semi-automatic dimensioning capabilities.

Using the DIM Layer

In order to produce a clear drawing of a subject, the outline and visible lines of the object are drawn with a thick width when printing or plotting. The dimension, hidden, center, and hatch lines are plotted or printed with a thin width. This way your eye is drawn first to the bold shape of the object and then to the details of its size and other features.

As you recall from previous tutorials, in AutoCAD pen width is chosen by the color of the entity on your drawing screen. In order for you to be able to select a thin pen width for the dimension lines, they must be a different color than the thick lines of the object. Frequently, you will want to turn off all of the dimensions in the drawing. Having dimensions on a separate layer makes this an easy task.

Pick: ***(the layer name VISIBLE on the toolbar)***

Use the list of layers that pulls down to set DIM as the current layer.

Adapting for Architecture

It is useful to set up several different layers for dimensions in a drawing. Use one layer for base dimensioning, including overall widths and heights, and a second layer for more detailed dimensions. Think of each layer in terms of what you want to plot. If not all the dimensions are needed at one time, do not put them all on one layer. Electrical and plumbing dimensions are two examples of dimensions that should go on their own layers. ■

Drawing Scale and Dimensions

There are standards and rules of good practice that specify how the dimension lines, extension lines, arrowheads, text size, and various aspects of dimensioning should appear in the finished drawing. For example, the extension lines should start 1/16" away from the feature they are extended from. Arrowheads and text should be approximately 1/8" tall on 8.5" × 11" drawings. When you are adding dimensions to your drawing, it is important to have determined the scale to which you will plot your drawing on the sheet of paper so that you will know how to set up the dimension features to give the correct appearance on the final plot. If you are going to plot from paper space, you should set the ZOOM XP scaling factor before you dimension your drawing. You have already set this to 1XP in your MYPROTO drawing, from which you started the current drawing. It is a good idea to check this by repeating the ZOOM, XP scale command option or by using MVSETUP and selecting Scale viewports. Make sure your drawing is zoomed to 1XP before continuing.

■ **TIP** Dimensions take quite a bit of drawing space, especially between the views of a multi-view drawing. Often you may need to zoom your drawing to half size (.5XP) or some other scale in order to have room to add dimensions. It is best to do this before you start dimensioning. ■

Using Settings, Dimension Style

Many features controlling the appearance of the dimensions are set by *dimension variables* (*dim vars*), which you can set using the Settings, Dimension Style selection from the menu bar. The same dialogue box can be called with the DDIM icon in the toolbox (second row, far right column). Dimension variables all have names and can be set by typing the dimvar name at the command prompt. In addition, you can pick DIM from the screen menu and select DIMVARS and set the dimension variables by selecting from the screen menu. The dialogue box allows you to set many variables easily, so you will select it from the menu bar.

Pick: **Settings *(menu bar)*, Dimension Style**

The Dimension Styles and Variables dialogue box should appear on your screen, as shown in Figure 7.2.

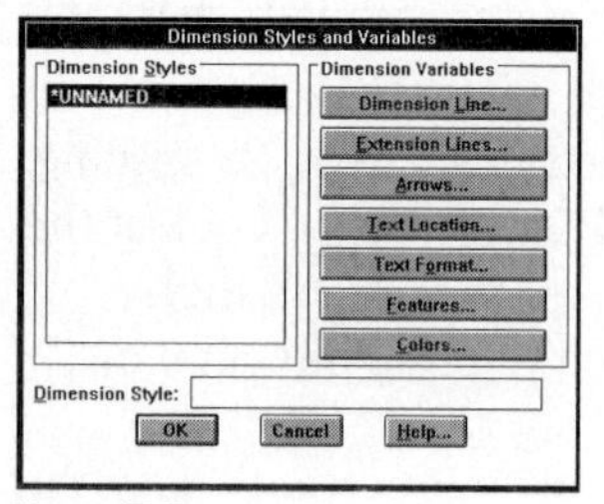

Figure 7.2

Creating a Named Dimension Style (DDIM)

The Dimension Styles and Variables dialogue allows you to easily change the dimension variables that control the appearance of the dimensions. Notice that the current style name being used is *UNNAMED. This basic set of features is provided as the default.

You can create your own *dimension style* with a name that you specify. This way you can save different sets of dimension features that will be useful for different purposes. Create a style name called RADIAL by typing it in the empty box next to Dimension Style:.

Type: **RADIAL** ↵

Notice that RADIAL now appears highlighted in the list near the top of the dialogue box, replacing *UNNAMED. Near the bottom of the dialogue box you will see the message "New style RADIAL created from *UNNAMED." RADIAL is now the current style and will be affected by changes that you make to the dimension variable settings.

To set the dimension variables, use the Dimension Variables boxes on the right-hand side of the dialogue box. The Features box that appears near the bottom of the column allows you to control many of the dimension variable settings in one place.

Pick: **Features**

A new dialogue box appears on your screen on top of the previous one. It should look like Figure 7.3.

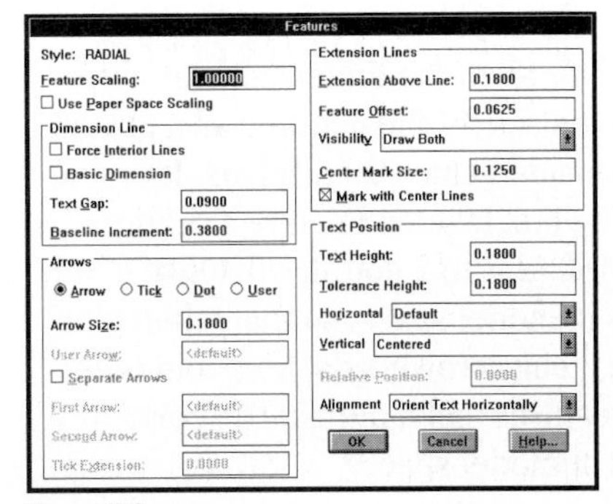

Figure 7.3

Setting the Features

In this dialogue box you can change many features of the dimensions. An important dimensioning variable is the scaling factor.

The Dimension Scaling Factor (DIMSCALE)

There are essentially two ways to scale the dimension features: in model space or in paper space. Think about a drawing that is to be plotted at a scale of 1 plotted inch equals 2 model units. If you want your arrowheads and text to be 1/8" on the plotted sheet, then at this scale they need to be 1/4" tall in the drawing, so that when they are reduced by half they will still appear 1/8". To do this you could double all of the feature settings that control sizes in the dimensions, but there are many of them, and it would be time-consuming. Instead, AutoCAD provides you with the ability to automatically scale all of the size features at once.

The variable DIMSCALE provides a scaling factor to use for all of the dimension variables that control the size of the features as a group, not the dimension values themselves. Its value appears in the box labeled Feature Scaling:. Setting DIMSCALE to 2 doubles the size of all the features in model space, so that when plotted half size, your arrowheads, text, and other dimension features will maintain the correct proportions in model space.

Picking Use Paper Space Scaling, so that an X appears in the box to its left, is equivalent to setting the dimensioning variable DIMSCALE to zero. The effect of doing this is that all of the dimension size features are multiplied by the current paper space zoom ratio.

> ■ ***TIP*** Using paper space scaling for dimensions can be tricky, because if you have zoomed in on the view when you add a dimension, the dimension features will be a different size (smaller) than the dimension you add when you are not zoomed in. You will see how to use the DIM: UPDATE command to update these dimensions to the correct scale once you have returned to the original zoom factor. It is harder to control the placement of dimensions when you use UPDATE. ■

For this tutorial, you will use paper space scaling for the dimensions. This means that when paper space is plotted full size, the dimension features will be shown the same size you set them in the dialogue box.

Pick: **Use Paper Space Scaling**

Adapting for Architecture

Keep a list of commonly used scales near your computer for quick reference. This will allow you to quickly calculate the DIMSCALE and LTSCALE factors. To calculate the DIMSCALE, multiply the denominator of your scale by 12, e.g. 1/8" = 1' is equivalent to a scale factor of 96. ■

Next you will use the Features dialogue to set the standard sizes for dimension features used in engineering drawings. The settings that you will make are based on an 8.5" × 11" sheet size. Larger drawing sheets use larger sizes.

Arrow Size (DIMASZ)

Arrow size is controlled by the variable DIMASZ. To set the arrow size, change the value in the box to the right of the words Arrow Size:. You will replace the default value, 0.1800, with .125, the decimal equivalent of 1/8". Refer to Figure 7.4.

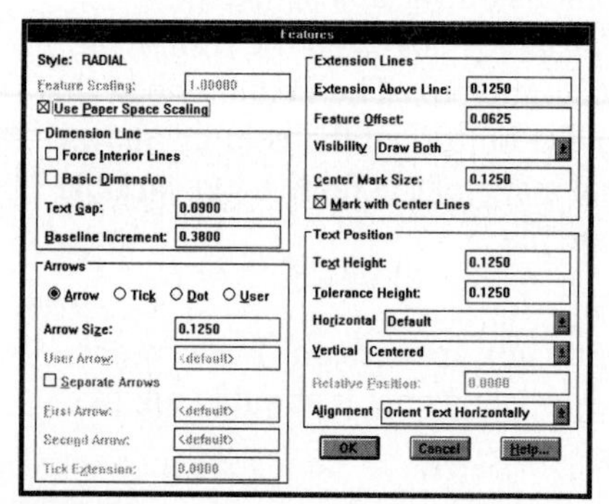

Figure 7.4

(highlight the text to the right of Arrow Size)

Type: **.125**

Continue to refer to Figure 7.4 for the remaining selections in the Features dialogue.

Extension Above Line (DIMEXE)

To change the length that the extension line extends beyond the dimension line, change the value of the DIMEXE variable shown in the box to the right of Extension Above Line:.

(highlight the text to the right of Extension Above Line:)

Type: **.125**

Extension Line Visibility (DIMSE1, DIMSE2)

In the Extension Lines area of the dialogue box, the visibility for extension lines is set to Draw Both. You can change this to suppress the first or last extension line, or both, while you are dimensioning if it is necessary. Move the arrow cursor to the box with the words Draw Both and press the pick button. You will see the available options pull down. Pick outside the options box to remove the options from the screen and leave this setting unchanged.

Center Mark Size (DIMCEN)

In the prototype drawing you started from, the value for DIMCEN was set to –.125, so the Center Mark Size is already set to .1250. Notice that the box for Mark with Center Lines already contains an X, indicating that DIMCEN is negative and therefore full center marks will be drawn. You will type the value .1 in the box for Center Mark Size to create smaller center marks. You will need smaller center marks because the holes that you will dimension are small and a .125 center mark would be too large. If the center mark value is too large, full center marks will not be drawn; just the center tick mark will be drawn. Leave the box Mark with Center Lines selected so that full center marks are drawn. These changes are equivalent to setting DIMCEN to –.1.

(highlight the text to the right of Center Mark Size:)

Type: **.1**

Text and Tolerance Height (DIMTXT, DIMTFAC)

The text height and tolerance text height (which you will learn about in Tutorial 13) can be changed in a similar manner. You will set them to .125, the standard height for 8.5" × 11" drawings.

(highlight the text to the right of Text Height:)

Type: **.125**

(highlight the text to the right of Tolerance Height:)

Type: **.125**

> ■ ***TIP*** Be sure that the default text height in your drawing, which you set using Draw, Text, Set Style, is set to zero (0) (as it was in MYPROTO) before you dimension. If the text height in the drawing is anything other than 0, the drawing text height will override the text height setting in the dimension style, causing DIMSCALE to have no effect on your dimension text height. If you are adding dimensions and cannot seem to get the text height to change, check Draw, Text, Set Style. ■

Text Placement (DIMTIX, DIMTAD, DIMTVP)

Under the Text Position area, you can control the placement of the text with respect to the dimension line by selecting the box to the right of Horizontal. A list showing the available options, similar to the one you see in Figure 7.5, appears. To select an option, position the arrow cursor over the item and press the pick button. The choice Force Text Inside (DIMTIX) puts the text inside the extension lines even if the dimension line and arrows do not fit. This is equivalent to setting DIMTIX to on. On many drawings there is not enough room for all of the dimensions if they are written outside the dimension lines, so this setting can help with fitting crowded dimensions on the drawing. Do not change this option at this time; return the selection to Default. The Vertical placement of the text can also be changed to be positioned above the dimension line (DIMTAD), or adjusted relative to the text height (DIMTVP). Leave the vertical setting at Centered.

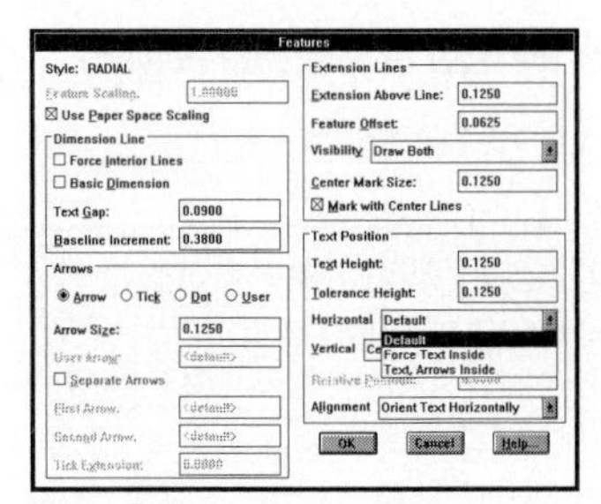

Figure 7.5

> ■ ***TIP*** When you are adding diameter and radius dimensions, use the Features dialogue to set Text Position, Horizontal to Default (setting DIMTIX to off), as you just did with the dimension style RADIAL. This causes the diameter and radius dimensions in your drawing to be drawn using a *leader line* that you can position. Otherwise, the dimension value is placed inside the circle or arc you are dimensioning. Remember that the standard practice is to place dimensions outside the object outline unless dimensioning inside the object outline would add to the clarity of the drawing. Refer to Figure 7.6. ■

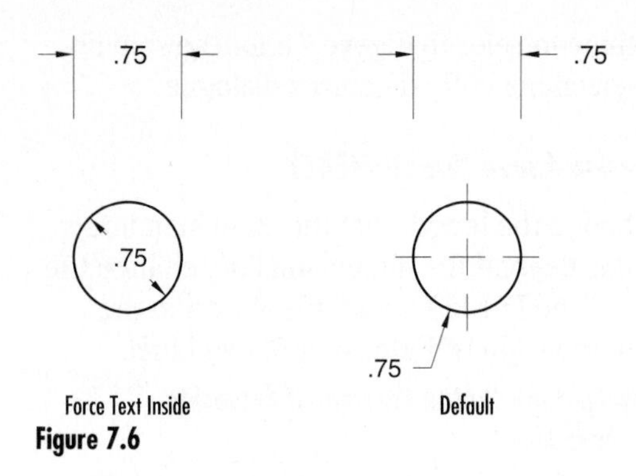

Figure 7.6

Text Alignment (DIMTIH, DIMTOH)

Under the Alignment option, the current default alignment for text is Orient Text Horizontally. This is called *unidirectional dimensioning* and is a common standard. The *aligned* method requires the dimension value to be placed in the drawing with the same orientation as the dimension line. The aligned method may allow you to space successive dimensions more closely because the text for vertical dimensions is aligned with the dimension line, taking less space in the horizontal direction. To change from the default horizontal orientation, pick on the box below Alignment to pull down the list of available options. The options that pull down set combinations of the variables controlling both text inside dimensions (DIMTIH) and text outside dimensions (DIMTOH) to achieve the desired effect. Do not change this setting at this time; return the selection to Orient Text Horizontally.

Pick: **OK *(to exit the Features dialogue box)***

Adapting for Architecture

Aligned dimensioning with the dimension value on top of the dimension line is the standard in architectural drawings. Architectural dimensions should read from top to bottom and from left to right. The arrow style name TICK is frequently preferred. ■

You return to the Dimension Styles and Variables dialogue box.

Setting the Colors

Next you will set the colors for the extension lines, and dimension lines and arrowheads, as well as the text in the dimensions. The dimension variables that control dimension colors are DIMCLRD (dimension line and arrowhead color), DIMCLRE (extension line color), and DIMCLRT (dimension text color). To set the colors, move the arrow cursor to the word Colors. . . and press the pick button to select.

Pick: **Colors**

The Colors dialogue box appears on the screen on top of the previous dialogue box. It should appear similar to Figure 7.7.

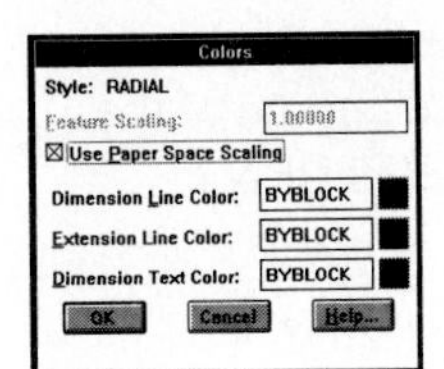

Figure 7.7

Pick in the box to the extreme right of the words Dimension Line Color: (to the right of BYBLOCK). The Select Color dialogue box you see in Figure 7.8 appears on your screen, on top of the previous dialogue box. Make the selection BYLAYER, so that the dimension lines take on the color of the current layer.

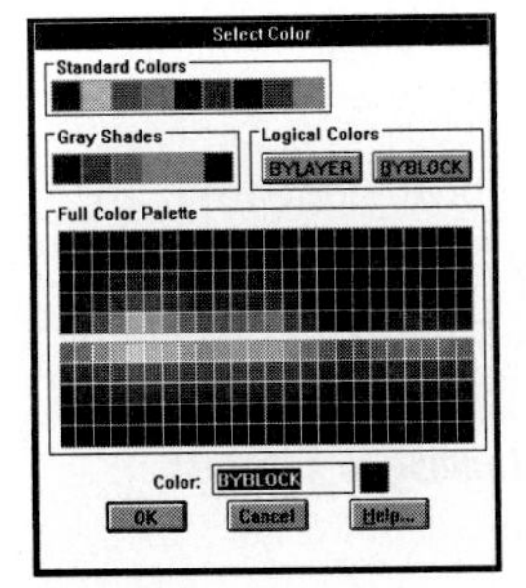

Figure 7.8

Pick: **BYLAYER**

Pick: **OK *(to exit this dialogue box)***

You return to the Colors dialogue.

Set Extension Line Color: and Dimension Text Color: to BYLAYER, using the same method you used for Dimension Line Color:.

Pick: **OK *(to exit this dialogue box)***

You will return to the Dimension Styles and Variables dialogue.

Using Text Format

Move the arrow cursor to the words Text Format and press the pick button. The Text Format dialogue box, shown in Figure 7.9, appears on your screen. Use this dialogue box to set the text format so that leading zeros are not included in the dimension values when you show decimals smaller than 1. This is the standard practice when using decimal inch measurements.

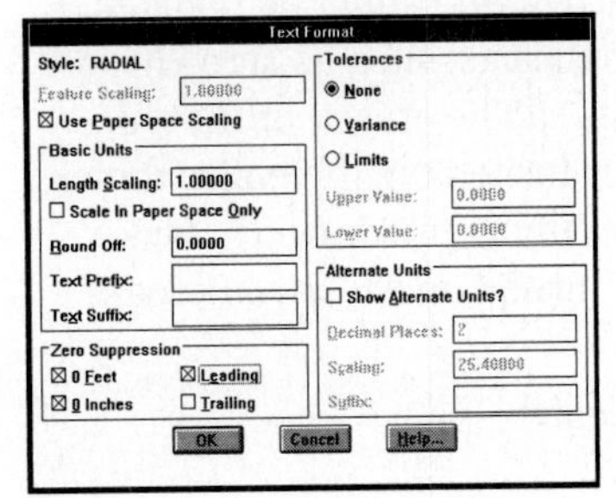

Figure 7.9

Suppressing Leading Zeros (DIMZIN)

Find the words Zero Suppression in the lower left corner of the dialogue box. Beneath it are four boxes. Picking in the box to the left of the word Leading suppresses leading zeros. An X appears in the box when it is selected.

Pick: ***(the box to the left of Leading to suppress leading zeros)***

Pick: **OK *(to exit the Text Format dialogue box)***

Pick: **OK *(to exit the Dimension Styles and Variables dialogue box)***

Now you have set up your basic sizes for the dimensions. The selections you have made apply to dimension style RADIAL only. As you dimension your drawing, you can return to this dialogue box and create a new style if you need to create dimensions with a different appearance.

Associative Dimensioning (DIMASO)

The DIMASO variable controls whether *associative dimensioning* is turned on or off. Associative dimensioning means that each dimension is inserted as a group of drawing entities relative to the points selected in the drawing. If the drawing is scaled or stretched, the dimension values automatically update. This can be a very useful feature. Also, dimensions created with DIMASO turned on are automatically updated if you make a change to their dimension styles. Dimensions created with DIMASO turned off cannot be updated, but their individual parts, such as arrowheads or extension lines, can be erased or moved. When DIMASO is turned on, the entire dimension acts as one entity in the drawing. Make sure DIMASO is turned on when you create your dimensions.

Pick: **DIM *(screen menu)***

Pick: **DIM VARS**

Pick: **DIMASO**

Current value <On> New value: ***(if the current value is not ON, pick ON; otherwise press ↵)***

DIM: **EXIT ↵**

Using DIM, STATUS

As you have seen, there are many variables that you can change to affect the appearance of the dimensions you add to your drawings. You can set these variables either through the Settings, Dimension Style dialogue box on the menu bar, or by selecting DIM, Dim Vars from the screen menu. You can also type in the name of the variable you want to change at the command prompt. To get a listing of the variable names, brief descriptions, and their current settings, you can use the DIM, STATUS command. Select it from the screen menu or type "STATUS" after the "DIM:" prompt.

Pick: **DIM *(screen menu)*, next, STATUS**

A text window listing of all the variable names appears on your screen. At the bottom of the screen are the words, "Press RETURN to continue."

Press ↵ to see the rest of the listing. Depending on your equipment, you may need to press ↵ again to get the final page of the list.

When you are done looking at the list, close the text box by double-clicking the close box to remove it from your screen. You will still be in the DIM command; type "exit" to return to the "Command:" prompt.

Setting the Unit Precision

When you are dimensioning a drawing, it is important to consider the precision of the values used in the dimensions. Specifying a dimension to four decimal places, which is AutoCAD's default, implies that accuracies of

1/10,000th of an inch are appropriate tolerances for this part. The standard is to specify decimal inch dimensions to two decimal places (accuracies of 1/100th of an inch) unless the function of the part makes a tighter tolerance desirable. Before you begin dimensioning, use the UNITS command to set the unit precision.

Pick: **Settings *(menu bar)*, Units Control. . .**

A dialogue box appears on your screen. In the lower left corner of the dialogue box, below the word Precision:, you will see the number 0.0000, representing the current precision value. Move the arrow cursor to the downward-pointing arrow and press the pick button to cause the precision choices to appear in the dialogue box. Position the cursor over the selection 0.00 and press the pick button.

Pick: **OK *(to exit the dialogue box)***

Look at the toolbar, near the top of your drawing screen. You will notice that the coordinates now display the cursor position with only two decimal places. AutoCAD continues to keep track of your drawing and the previous settings you have made in the drawing database to a precision of at least 14 decimal places.

Now you are ready to create the diameter and radius dimensions in your drawing. AutoCAD automatically adds the center marks when the dimensions are created.

Radial Dimensioning

AutoCAD has dimensioning subcommands for radius and diameter dimensions. Typing "DIM" at the command prompt or selecting the dimension commands from the screen menu invokes the DIM command. The DIM command has its own special prompt of "Dim:" to replace the "Command:" prompt. This is useful because you can stay in the dimensioning submenu and place several dimensions. To repeat a dimension when at the DIM prompt, press the ⏎ key or spacebar, just as you do at the "Command:" prompt. Remember, to exit the DIM command you need to type "exit" or select EXIT from the screen menu.

When you select dimension commands from Draw on the menu bar, the DIM1 command is used. DIM1 executes a single dimension command and then automatically exits from the special "DIM:" prompt. To place another dimension of the same type, you must select the command again. Pressing ⏎ only restarts the DIM1 command; it does not repeat your particular dimensioning selection, such as Horizontal or Vertical.

> ■ ***TIP*** When dimensioning a full circle of 360 degrees (as opposed to an arc), always specify the diameter command, rather than the radius. This is important because equipment used to manufacture and inspect holes and cylinders is designed to measure diameter, not radius. The machinist who is making the part should never have to calculate any of the dimensions. This includes not having to double the radius to arrive at the diameter. It is very difficult to measure the radius of a hole, because its center has already been drilled out. ■

Adding Special Text-Formatting Characters

Special characters can be typed in during any text command and when entering the dimension text.

You can add special text characters to the dimensioning text by preceding the text with the code %% (double percent signs). The most common special characters have been given letters so that they are easier to remember. Otherwise, you can use any special character in a text font by typing its ASCII number. (Most word processor documentation includes a list of ASCII values for symbols in an appendix.)

The most common special characters and their codes are listed in the table below:

Code	Character	Symbol
%%c	diameter symbol	∅
%%d	degrees symbol	°
%%p	plus/minus sign	±
%%o	toggles on and off the overscore mode	Example
%%u	toggles on and off the underscore mode	Example
%%%	draws a single percent sign	%
%%n	draws special character number	*n*

You will use the special character %%c to draw the diameter symbol in the dimension.

On your own, turn SNAP off, if it is on, to make it easier to select the circles. Turn ORTHO off, if it is on, to make it possible to draw angled leader lines.

Now you are ready to add the diameter dimension for the two small holes. The DIM: DIAMETER command adds the center marks and draws a leader line from the point you select on the circle to the location you select for the dimension value. The leader line produced is a radial line. This means that if extended, it would pass through the center of the circle. A line extended from the center through the point on the circle that you selected will give you the direction of the leader line that will be drawn. Keep this in mind when you are selecting the point on the circle. Remember that this only happens when the dimension variable DIMTIX is off, causing the text to be placed outside the extension lines, as you selected when setting up style RADIAL.

Pick: **Draw *(menu bar)*, Dimensions, Radial, Diameter**

Select arc or circle: ***(pick on the lower of the two small circles, at about 7 o'clock)***

Dimension text <.50>:2 X **%%c .50** ↵

Enter leader length for text: ***(pick a point below and to the left of the circle, outside the object outline)***

Refer to Figure 7.10 for placement of the dimension.

Now use DIM: RADIUS to create the radius dimension and center marks for the rounded end.

Pick: **Draw *(menu bar)*, Dimensions, Radial, Radius**

Select circle or arc: ***(pick on the rounded end, at about 10 o'clock)***

Dimension text <1.00>: ↵

Enter leader length for text: ***(pick a point above and to the left of the circle, outside the object outline)***

Add the center marks for the upper of the two small holes at the right of the object.

Pick: **Draw *(menu bar)*, Dimensions, Radial, Center Mark**

Select arc or circle: ***(pick on the upper small circle)***

The center marks for the circle are added. Your drawing should look like Figure 7.10.

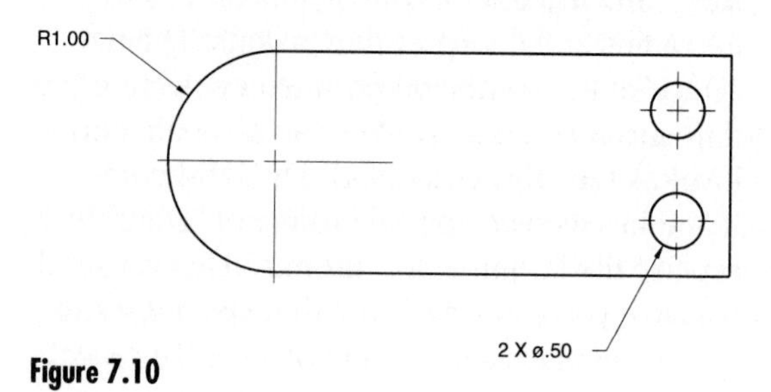

Figure 7.10

Creating Dimension Style Standard

Now create a new dimension style that you will use for linear dimensions. The only difference between this style and the radial style will be that the text will be forced inside the extension lines. You will set DIMTIX to on, using the Settings (menu bar), Dimension Style dialogue.

Pick: **DDIM *(toolbox)***

The Dimension Styles dialogue box appears on your screen. Use it to create a new style with the setting for Text Placement set to Force Text Inside. By creating a new style based on RADIAL, you ensure that the new style will start out with all of the changes you made in setting up RADIAL.

Type: **STANDARD ↵ *(in the box provided for Dimension Styles)***

Pick: **Features...**

Pick: ***(the box below Text Position, Horizontal on the word Default)***

Pick: **Force Text Inside *(from the list of available options that appears)***

Pick: **OK *(to exit the Features dialogue)***

Pick: **OK *(to exit the Dimension Styles and Variables dialogue)***

The current dimension style is now set to STANDARD and dimension text will be forced inside the extension lines. Next you will add the linear dimensions.

Using DIM, LINEAR, Horizontal

The horizontal dimensioning command measures and annotates an object within a drawing with a horizontal dimension line. The value inserted in the dimension line is the perpendicular distance between the extension lines. If you use the horizontal dimension command and dimension a line drawn at an angle on the screen, the value AutoCAD returns is just the X axis component of the length.

Turn SNAP on, so that when placing dimensions in your drawing you can use it as a reference to locate the dimensions .5 units away from the object outline (thus meeting the criterion that a dimension must be at least 3/8", or .375, away from the object outline).

Use the Settings (menu bar), Object Snap menu selection to turn the Intersection running mode on. You will use this to select the exact intersections in the drawing for the extension lines so that the dimensions are accurate.

To dimension the location of the center point of the upper of the two small holes, refer to Figure 7.11:

Pick: **Draw *(menu bar)*, Dimensions, Linear, Horizontal**

First extension line origin or RETURN to select: ***(target the top right-hand corner of the object and press the pick button)***

Second extension line origin: ***(target point A, the intersection between the small circle and its center line)***

Dimension line location (Text/Angle): ***(pick a point two snap units above the top line of the object)***

Dimension text <.50>: ↵

The dimension should appear in your drawing, as shown in Figure 7.11.

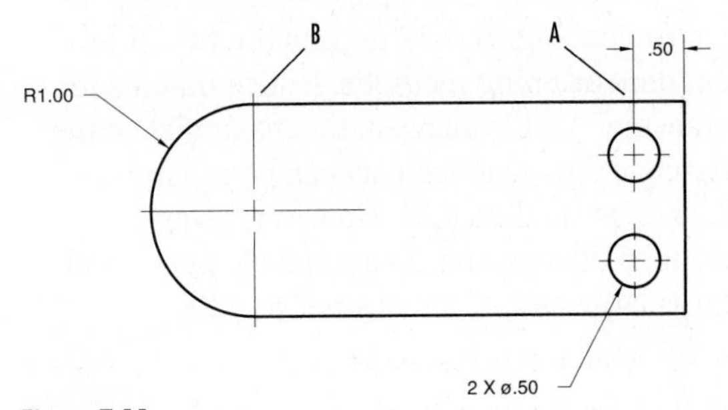

Figure 7.11

> ■ ***TIP*** When using AutoCAD's dimensioning features, you must sometimes draw a short line between the center line and the extension line to eliminate the gap that is created by AutoCAD's dimensioning feature; or you can create a dimension style that has the feature offset value set to 0. ■

Next you will use baseline dimensioning to add the 4.25 dimension showing the major size of the part.

Baseline Dimensioning

Baseline and chained dimensions are two different methods of relating one dimension to the next. In *baseline dimensioning*, as the name suggests, each succeeding dimension is measured from one extension line or baseline. In *chained* or *continued dimensioning*, each succeeding dimension is measured from the last extension line of the previous dimension. Baseline dimensioning can be more accurate, because the tolerance allowance is not added to the tolerance allowance of the previous dimension, as it is in chained dimensions. However, chained dimensioning may often be preferred because the greater the tolerances allowed, the cheaper the part should be to manufacture. The more difficult the tolerance is to achieve, the more parts that will not pass inspection. Figure 7.12 depicts the two different dimensioning methods. Notice that if a tolerance of ±.01 is allowed, the major size of the baseline dimensioned part can be as large as 4.26 or as small as 4.24. However, using chained dimensions, an acceptable part could be as large as 4.27, or as small as 4.23.

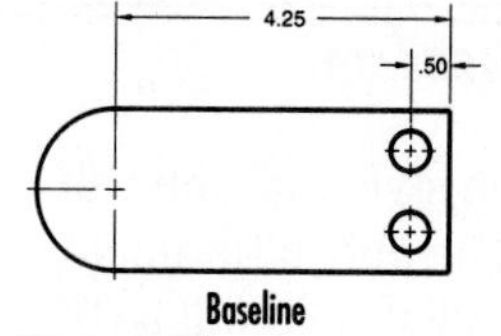

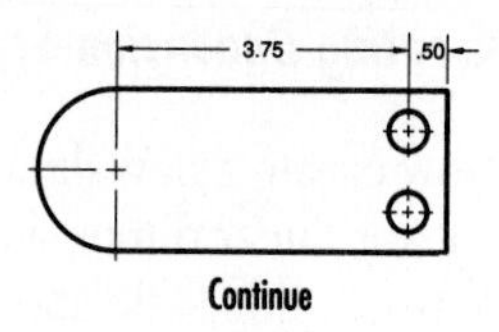

Figure 7.12

AutoCAD provides options in the linear dimensioning commands to make baseline and chained dimensioning easy. Use the Baseline option to create the next dimension. It is preferable to add dimensions with Baseline or Continue, because adding a second dimension using only the Horizontal option will draw the extension line a second time, which will give a poor appearance to your drawing when it is plotted.

Pick: **Draw *(menu bar)*, Dimensions, Linear, Baseline**

Second extension line origin or RETURN to select: ***(pick the point labeled B on Figure 7.11)***

Dimension value <4.25>: ↵

The new dimension in your drawing should appear, as shown in Figure 7.13. Notice that AutoCAD automatically selected the location for the dimension based on the placement of the .50 dimension.

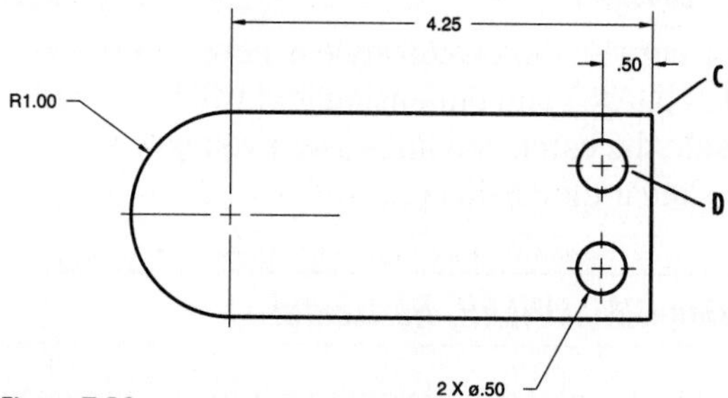

Figure 7.13

Now you will place the vertical dimension in your drawing for the location of the small hole in the upper right corner of the part. The command to place vertical dimensions works like the command for horizontal dimensions, except that only the vertical component of the distance is used. In other words, it measures the perpendicular distance between the two horizontal extension lines.

Pick: **Draw *(menu bar)*, Dimensions, Linear, Vertical**

First extension line origin or RETURN to select: ***(target the intersection labeled C in Figure 7.13)***

Second extension line origin: ***(target the point labeled D)***

Dimension line location (Text/Angle): ***(pick a point two snap units to the right of the object outline)***

Dimension text <.50>: ↵

The dimension should appear in your drawing, as shown in Figure 7.14.

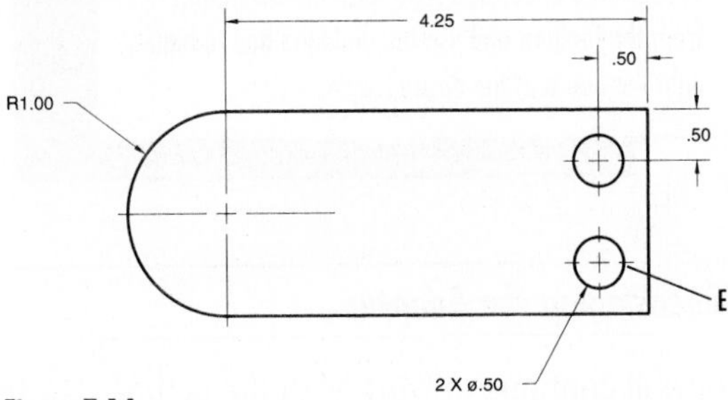

Figure 7.14

Now use baseline dimensioning again to give the distance to the second vertical hole. Refer to Figure 7.14.

Pick: **Draw *(menu bar)*, Dimensions, Linear, Baseline**

Second extension line origin or RETURN to select: ***(pick point E, where the center line crosses the small circle)***

Dimension text <1.50>: ↵

The baseline dimension from the top edge of the part to the center of the second hole should appear on your screen.

Give the overall vertical size of the part from the baseline.

Pick: **Draw *(menu bar)*, Dimensions, Linear, Baseline**

Second extension line origin or RETURN to select: ***(pick the bottom corner on the right-hand side)***

Dimension value <2.00>: ↵

Now you have completed giving the overall sizes and the locations of the holes and rounded end. Your completed drawing with the dimensions should resemble Figure 7.15.

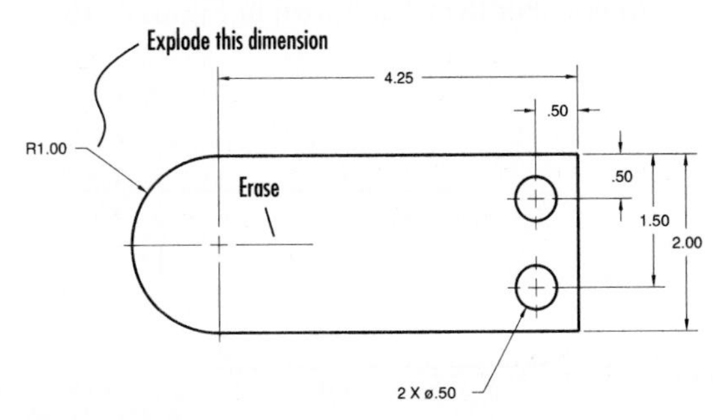

Figure 7.15

Exploding Dimensions

To complete the drawing, you must erase the right horizontal center line from the rounded end, because the rounded end is only a portion of a circle and should not have full center marks. Dimensions created with the variable DIMASO turned on are created as a block, or group, of drawing entities. You will learn more about the BLOCK command in Tutorial 14. You will use the EXPLODE command to modify the radial dimension so that it is no longer a block. Then you will be able to erase a single line from the center mark without erasing the entire dimension.

Pick: **Modify *(menu bar)*, Explode**

Select objects: ***(pick on the radial dimension for the left-hand rounded end)***

Select objects: ↵

You will see the lines of the dimension and the center mark change to color white, which appears black on a light screen background, indicating that the dimension has been exploded and its color has been returned to the setting BYBLOCK.

Use the CHPROP command to set the color for the entities back to BYLAYER, and the layer to DIM. Then use the ERASE command to remove the right-hand horizontal center line, as indicated in Figure 7.15.

The finished drawing is shown in Figure 7.16.

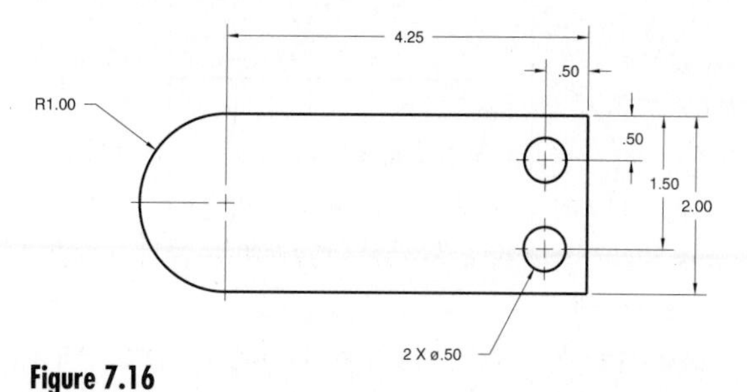

Figure 7.16

Adapting for Architecture

After the drawing is completely dimensioned and ready for output, you may need to explode some dimensions to clean up overlapping lines. Only do this when you are ready to create presentation drawings after all of the changes have been made, because once a dimension is exploded, it will not update if you make a change to the dimension style. ■

Going Further

Add a note similar to ALL TOLERANCES ± .01 UNLESS OTHERWISE NOTED. Use the %%p special character to make the ± sign. Below the tolerance note add a second note indicating the material from which the part is to be made, such as MATERIAL: SAE 1020. Use DDEDIT to change the text in your title block, noting the name of the part, revision number, drafter's name, scale, and date, to complete the drawing.

Save your drawing, using the QSAVE command. Pick the icon from the toolbar (it looks like a 3.5" floppy disk).

Going Further

Call up the prototype drawing MYPROTO you created in Tutorial 6 and create the dimension styles RADIAL and STANDARD. Set the UNITS command precision to two decimal places. Save the prototype drawing back to your disk. After you have done this, drawings started from your prototype drawing will already have these dimension styles available. To select the dimension style, pick the DDIM icon from the toolbox and use the dialogue box to highlight the name of the desired style.

Dimensioning the Adapter

You will continue to work with the orthographic views of the adapter from Tutorial 4 by adding dimensions to the drawing. Use the file ADAPT4 that was provided with the data files that came with your software.

Use File, New to start a new drawing. In the dialogue box, use the file ADAPT4 from the data files as the prototype drawing. In the drawing name box, type the name "C:\DRAWINGS\ADAPT_DM".

Your screen should look like Figure 7.17. This is the same drawing you did in Tutorial 4, except that the views have been moved farther apart to make room for dimensions. Also, the layers, dimension styles, and other settings from the prototype have been added.

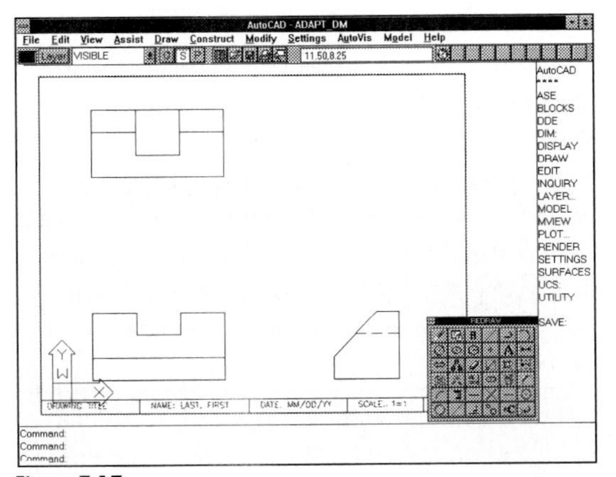

Figure 7.17

Dimensions are usually placed between views when possible, except for the overall dimensions, which are often placed around the outside to make it easier to determine the size of the block of material needed to manufacture the part.

Pick: **DDIM icon *(toolbox)***

Check to see that dimension style STANDARD is highlighted, indicating that it is the current style. If it is not the current style, pick it before selecting OK.

Pick: **OK *(to exit the dialogue box)***

Pick: **Settings *(menu bar)*, Units Control...**

Set the precision to two decimal places after the zero. When you are done,

Pick: **OK *(to exit the dialogue box)***

Check to see that associative dimensioning is turned on. Later in the tutorial, you will use the dimensioning command UPDATE to automatically update dimensions. They cannot be updated unless they were created with DIMASO turned on.

Type: **DIMASO** (↵)

New value for DIMASO <1>: (↵) ***(if the default value is 0, type "1" and press (↵))***

Use Settings, Object Snaps to turn on the running mode Intersection. Check the toolbar to see that you are in layer DIM. If not, make it the current layer.

Add the horizontal dimension that shows the width of the left-hand portion of the block. The shape of this feature shows clearly in the front view, so add the dimension to the front view. You will use the RETURN to select option, which allows you to pick an entity from the screen instead of specifying the two extension line locations. AutoCAD will automatically locate the extension lines at the extreme ends of the entity you select.

Pick: **Draw *(menu bar)*, Dimensions, Linear, Horizontal**

First extension line origin or RETURN to select: (↵)

Select line, arc, or circle: ***(pick the top left-hand line in the front view)***

Dimension line location <Text/Angle>: ***(pick two snap units above the object outline)***

Dimension text <1.00>: (↵)

Your drawing should appear similar to Figure 7.18.

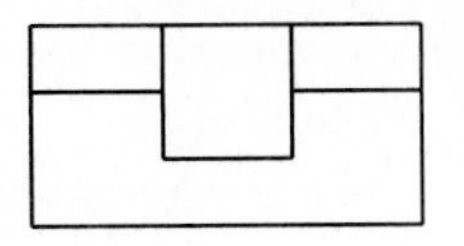

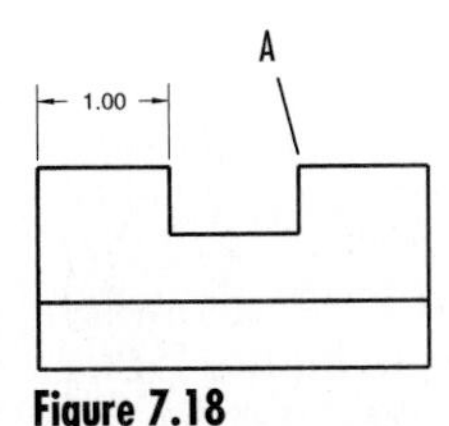

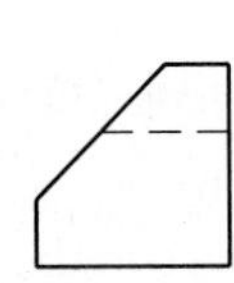

Figure 7.18

Using CONTINUE

Now use AutoCAD's dimension command CONTINUE to add a chained dimension for the size of the slot. Refer to Figure 7.18. This time you will use the RETURN to select option to tell AutoCAD which dimension is to be continued. The BASELINE dimensioning command has a similar option so that if you have added other dimensions, you can go back and select a different dimension as the base dimension. When using this feature, pick near the extension line you want to have continued (or to be the baseline).

Pick: **Draw *(menu bar)*, Dimensions, Linear, Continue**

Second extension line origin or RETURN to select: ↵

Select continued dimension: ***(pick the right-hand extension line of the existing dimension)***

Second extension line origin or RETURN to select: ***(pick point A)***

Dimension text <1.00>: ↵

The chained dimension should appear in your drawing, as shown in Figure 7.19.

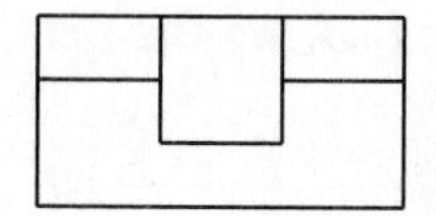

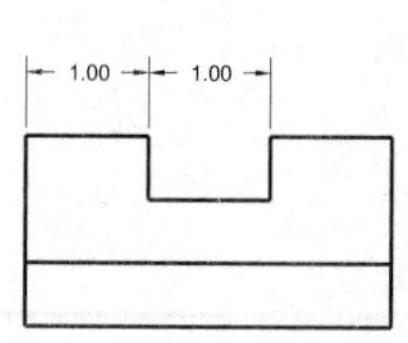

Figure 7.19

Adding the Angular Dimension

Add the angular dimension for the angled surface in the side view, referring to Figure 7.19.

Pick: **Draw *(menu bar)*, Dimensions, Angular**

Select arc, circle, line (or RETURN): ↵

Angle vertex: ***(pick the point labeled Origin)***

First angle endpoint: ***(pick on the snap increment in line with the top line of the side view, labeled 1)***

Second angle endpoint: ***(pick on the angled line near the point labeled 2)***

Dimension arc line location (Text/Angle): ***(pick a point between the points you selected)***

Dimension text <45>: ↵

Enter text location or RETURN: ↵

Pressing ↵ at the "Enter text location" prompt places the text at the center of the dimension arc. You can pick the location from the screen instead if you wish. The angular dimension is added to the side view, as shown in Figure 7.20. You do not have to use the %%d special character to make the degree sign; AutoCAD inserts it automatically unless you override the default text.

> ■ ***TIP*** You may want to explode the angular dimension and erase the extension line that is drawn over the top of the object line. Also, you can then extend the upper extension line so that it is closer to the angle origin. ■

Add the dimension for the depth of the top surface in the side view.

Pick: **Draw *(menu bar)*, Dimensions, Linear, Horizontal**

First extension line origin or RETURN to select: ↵

Select line, arc, or circle: ***(pick the short horizontal line labeled A in Figure 7.19)***

Dimension line location (Text/Angle): ***(pick two snap units above the top line of the side view)***

Dimension text<.50>: ↵

Your screen should look like Figure 7.20.

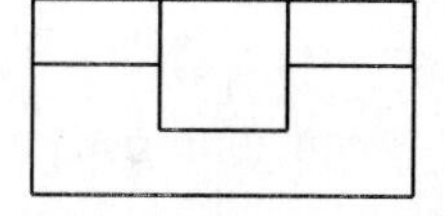

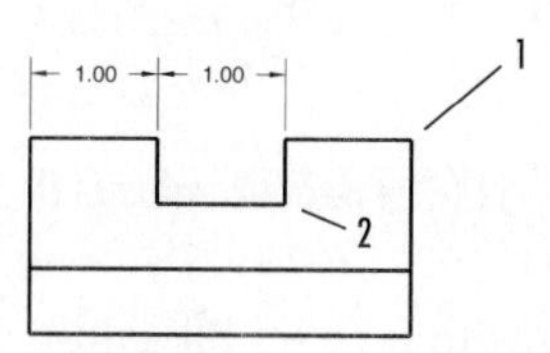

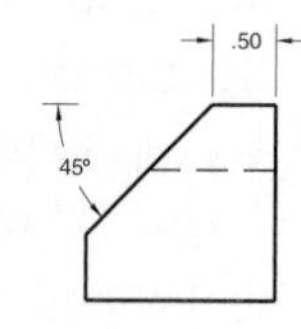

Figure 7.20

Now add the dimension for the height of the slot in the front view. Refer to Figure 7.20.

Pick: **Draw (menu bar), Dimensions, Linear, Vertical**

First extension line origin or RETURN to select: ***(pick the intersection labeled 1)***

Second extension line: ***(pick the right-hand bottom corner of the slot, labeled 2)***

Dimension line location(Text/Angle): ***(pick two snap units away from the right-hand side of the front view)***

Dimension text <.50>: ↵

The dimension for the slot should appear in your drawing, as shown in Figure 7.21.

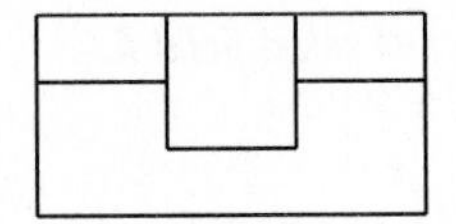

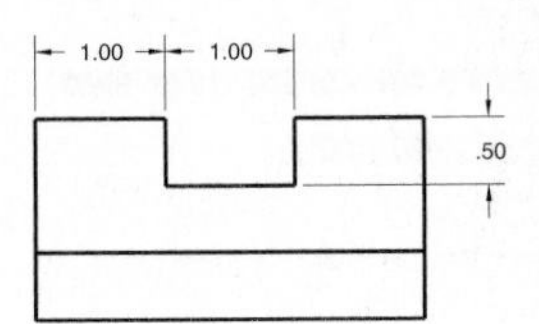

Figure 7.21

On your own, add the overall dimensions to the outsides of the views, so that your drawing looks like Figure 7.22.

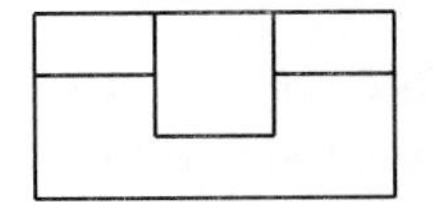

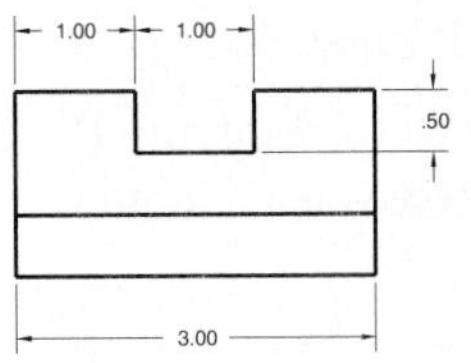

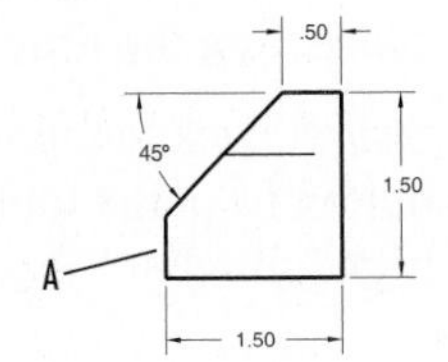

Figure 7.22

■ ***TIP*** Notice that you do not need dimensions for the short vertical line in the side view, labeled A. This is because its length is already defined by the overall dimension for the height of the part, the .50 distance across the top surface, and the 45-degree angle. To include this dimension would be an example of over-dimensioning. You will learn more in the advanced dimensioning tutorial about why over-dimensioning must be avoided. If you want to give this dimension, include the value in brackets, or followed by the word REF, to indicate it is a reference dimension only. ■

Adding the Tolerance Note

Switch to paper space by picking on the P button shown on the toolbar so that it becomes highlighted. Use the toolbar to make layer TEXT current.

Now use the text command to add .125" text stating: ALL TOLERANCES ARE ± .01 UNLESS OTHERWISE NOTED. Use the %%p special text character to create the symbol. Add a second note below the first stating, MATERIAL: SAE 1020.

If you wish, plot your drawing while in paper space. Plot the drawing limits at scale 1=1.

Switch back to model space by picking the P button from the toolbar so that it is no longer highlighted.

Save your drawing as ADAPT_DM before you continue.

Your finished drawing should appear similar to Figure 7.23.

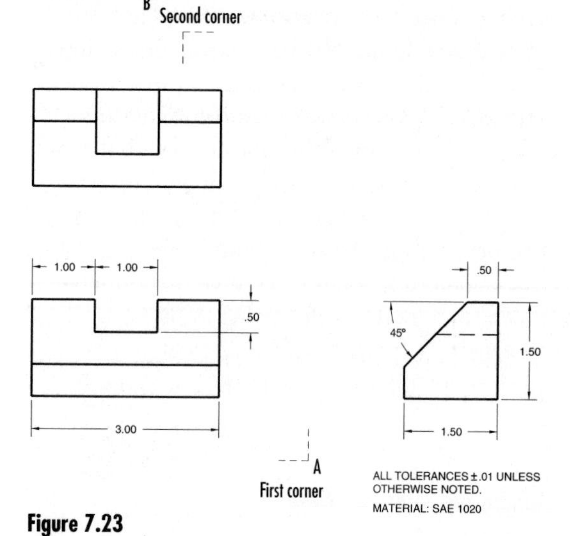

Figure 7.23

Automatically Updating Dimension Values Created with DIMASO

Dimensions created with DIMASO turned on are an AutoCAD block entity. Blocks are a group of entities that behave as one item. If you try to erase a dimension that was created with DIMASO on, the entire dimension is erased, including the extension lines and arrowheads. Because these dimensions have the special properties of a block, they also can be updated automatically.

You will use the STRETCH command to make the adapter wider. When you do this, the appropriate dimensions automatically update to the new size. Notice that the overall width of the front view is currently 3.00.

Pick: **EDIT *(screen menu)*, next, STRETCH**

Select objects to stretch by window or polygon.

Select objects: C

First corner: ***(use implied crossing and select point A on Figure 7.23)***

Other corner: ***(select point B)***

10 found

Select objects: ↵

Base point or Displacement: ***(target the bottom right-hand corner of the front view)***

Second point of displacement: ***(move the cursor over two snap increments to the right and pick)***

> ■ ***TIP*** If you have trouble stretching, double-check to make sure that you are not still in paper space. Also, the STRETCH command only works when the Crossing option is used. If you type the command, you must make sure to select Crossing or type "C" and press ↵ afterwards, or use implied crossing as you did in the previous step. ■

Notice that the overall dimension now reads 3.50. It has updated automatically. The result is shown in Figure 7.24.

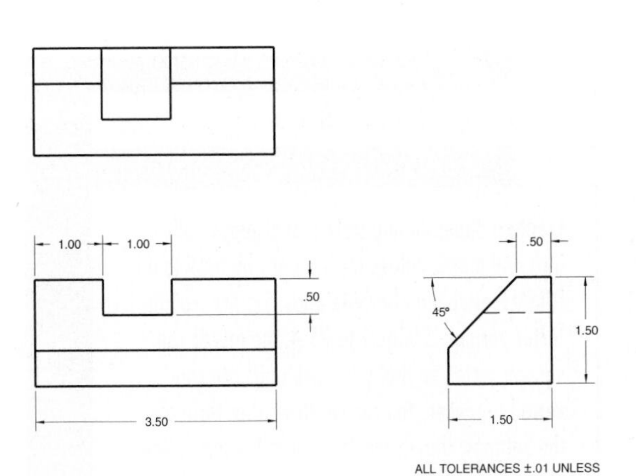

Figure 7.24

Updating Dimensions

When you change a dimension style, all of the dimensions that were created using that style automatically change to take on the new appearance. (This only works for dimensions created with DIMASO on.) You will change the vertical dimensions so that the text aligns with the dimension line. First set the dimension variable. Use the Settings, Dimension Style dialogue box to change the variable for text alignment.

Pick: **DDIM *(toolbox)***

The Dimension Styles and Variables dialogue box appears on your screen with STANDARD highlighted. You will use the Features. . . option.

Pick: **Features. . .**

Pick: ***(on the words Orient Text Horizontally under the Alignment option)***

The choices for alignment pull down on the screen, as shown in Figure 7.25.

Pick: **Align With Dimension Line**

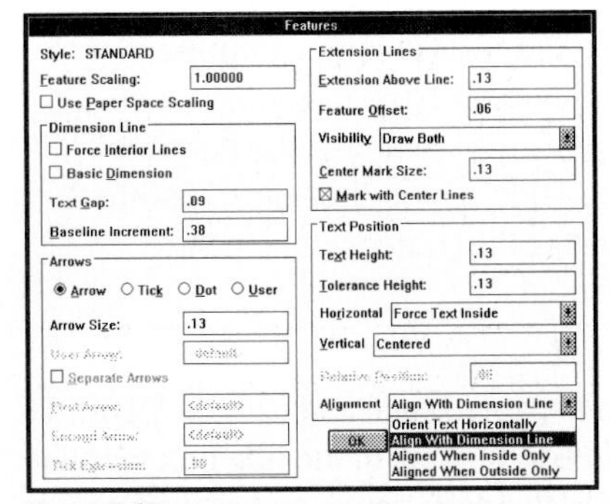

Figure 7.25

Pick: **OK *(to exit the Features dialogue)***

Pick: **OK *(to exit the Dimension Styles dialogue)***

The dimensions in the drawing update automatically to reflect this change. The vertical dimensions now have text that aligns with the dimension line. Your drawing should appear similar to Figure 7.26.

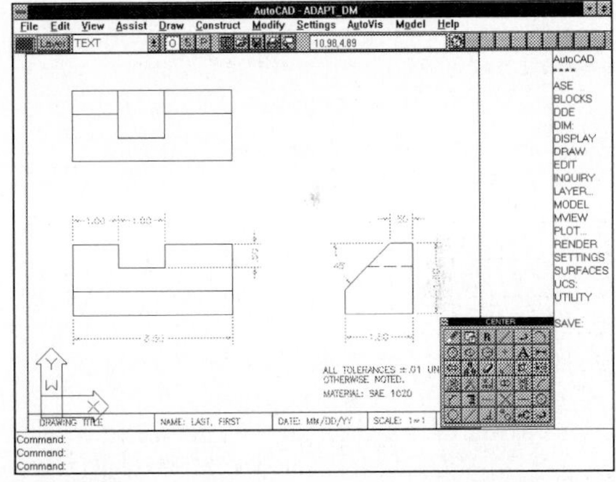

Figure 7.26

■ ***TIP*** Use the dimensioning command UPDATE to update dimensions created with a different style to use the current dimension style. To do this, pick Modify (menu bar), Edit Dimension, Update Dimension. ■

Now switch to paper space and use the DDEDIT command to edit the text in the title box to make corrections to the date, name, and scale if necessary. Title your drawing ADAPTER.

Going Further

Create a dimensioning style that displays both inch and metric values for the units by turning on DIMALT, enabling alternate units. Set the scaling factor variable DIMALTF to 25.4, the metric conversion factor, so that your inch units are converted to metric. You can set this either through the Settings, Dimension Style, Text Format option picked from the menu bars or by typing in the variable names at the "Command:" prompt. Update the dimensions in your drawing to show both units.

You have completed this tutorial on adding dimensions. Now practice adding dimensions to the drawings you create. Strive for organized dimensions that clearly show the size of the object. Do not double dimension. That is, do not dimension the same distance twice within the same drawing. Check to see that the same dimension is not shown in another view. Use the dimensioning variables to help change dimensions so they follow correct drawing standards.

KEY TERMS

aligned dimensioning
associative dimensioning
baseline dimensioning
chained (continued) dimensioning
dimension line
dimension style
dimension value
dimension variables (dim vars)
dimensions
extension line
leader line
overall dimensions
tolerance
unidirectional dimensioning

KEY COMMANDS

Angular
Baseline
Continue
Diameter
Dimension Style
Dynamic Dialogue Dimension Style
Explode
Horizontal
Radius
Status
Units
Update
Vertical

EXERCISES

Draw and dimension the following shapes. The letter M after an exercise number means that the units are in millimeters. Add a note to the drawing stating "METRIC: All dimensions are in millimeters" for metric drawings. Specify a general tolerance for the drawing.

7.1M Stop Plate

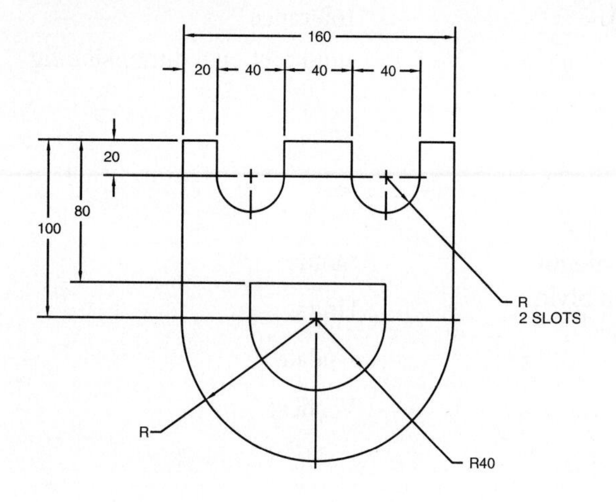

7.2M Hub

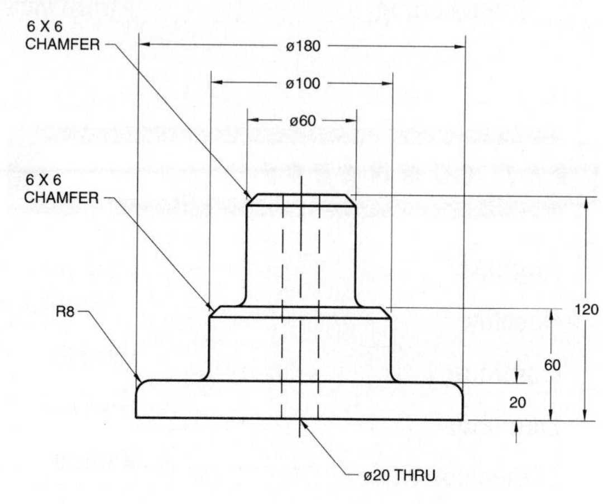

7.3 Guide Block

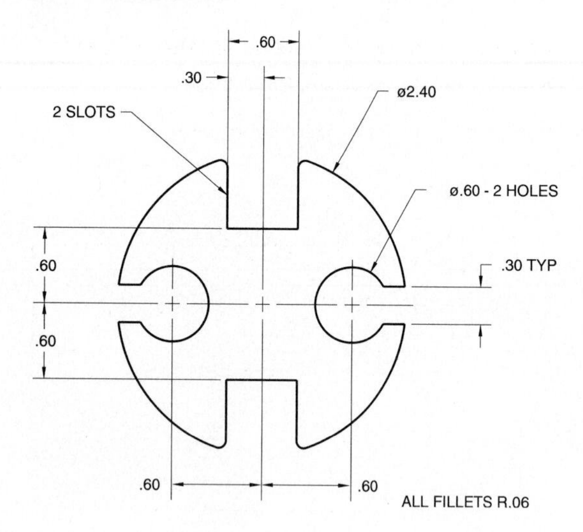

7.4 Angle Bracket

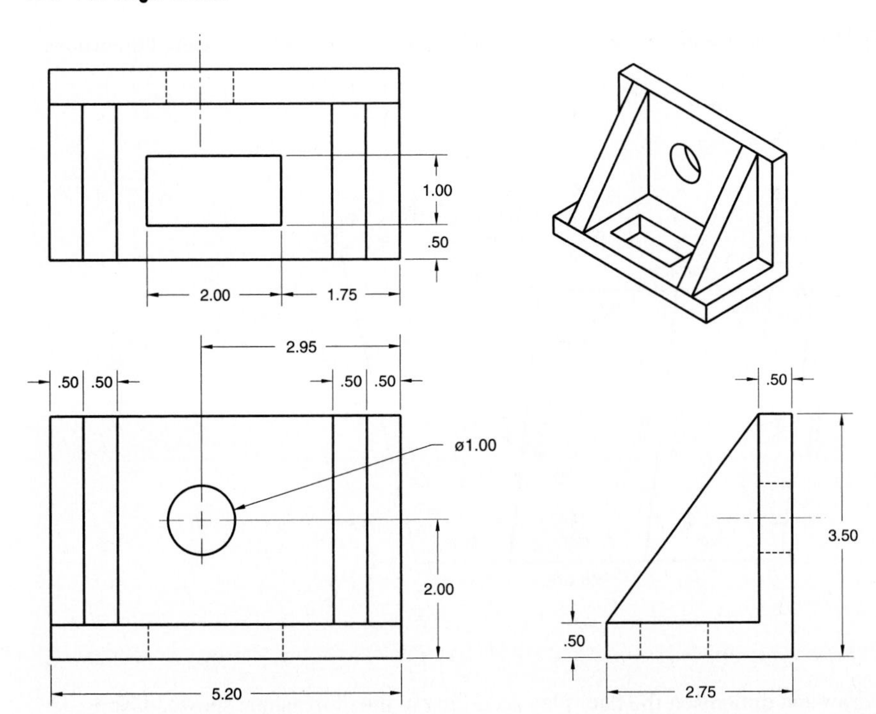

7.5 Interchange

Draw and dimension this intersection, then mirror the circular interchange for all lanes.

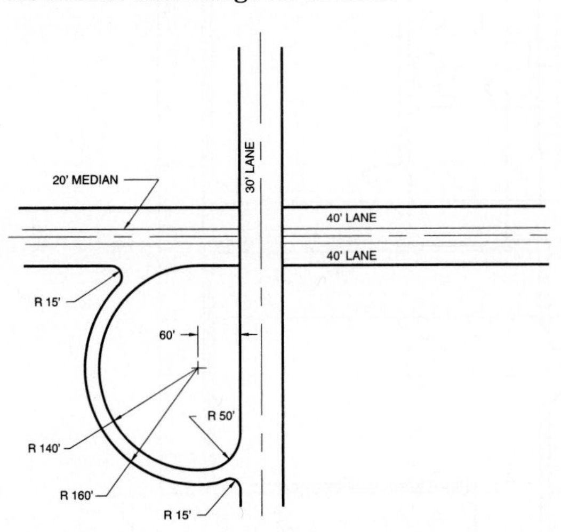

7.6 Bearing Box

Draw and dimension the following shape. Specify a general tolerance for the drawing.

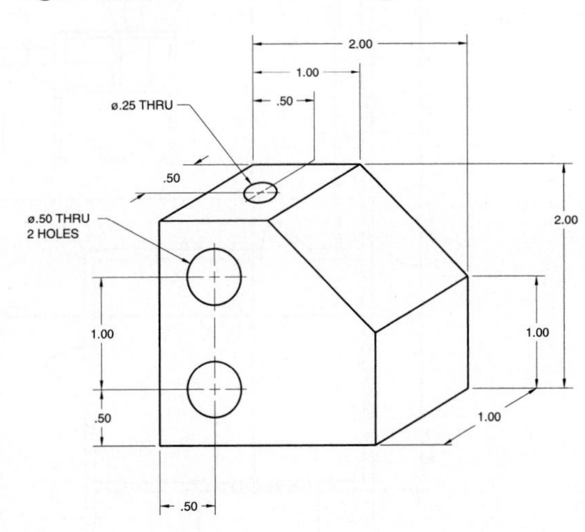

7.7 Plot Plan

Draw and dimension using the civil engineering dimensioning style shown, and find the missing dimensions.

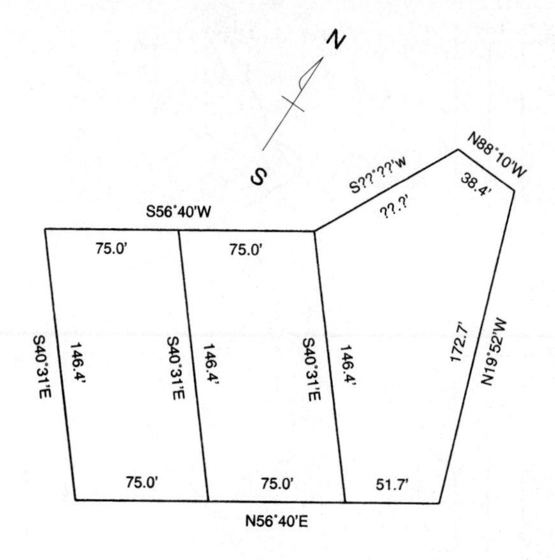

7.8 Floor Plan

Use architectural units to draw and dimension the floor plan according to the dimensions shown, making good use of layers.

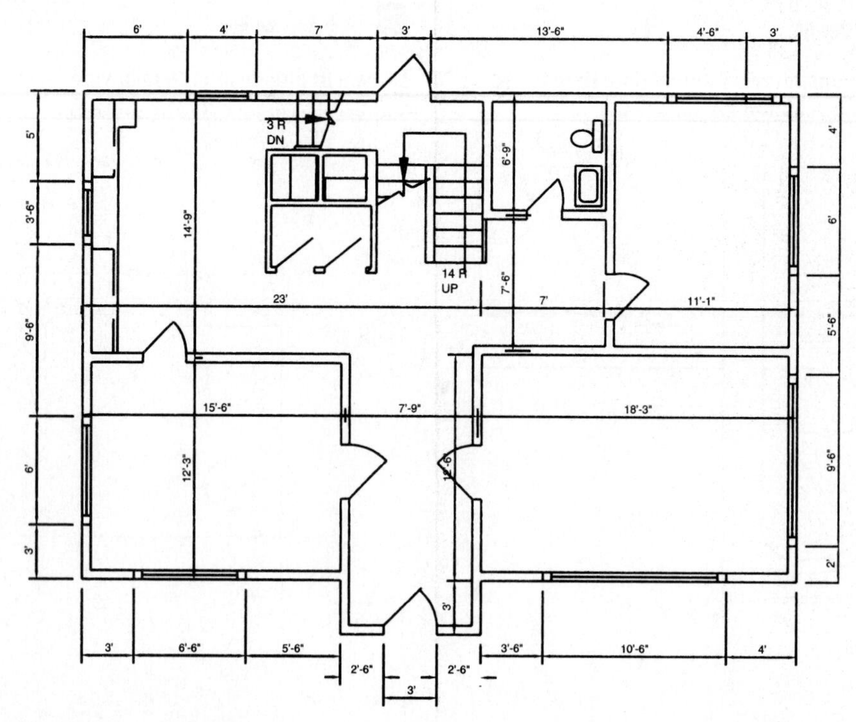

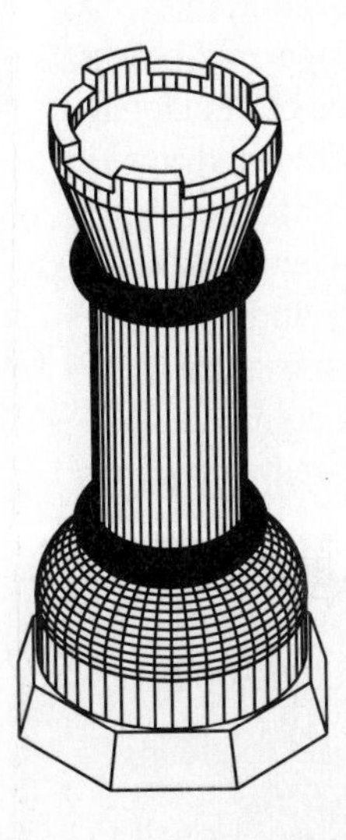

TUTORIAL 8

Introduction to Solid Modeling

Objectives

When you have completed this tutorial, you will be able to

1. Change the 3D viewpoint.
2. Split the screen into multiple viewports.
3. Set individual limits, grid, and snap for each viewport.
4. Create and save User Coordinate Systems.
5. Use layers to organize your solid model drawings.
6. Create model geometry, using primitives, extrusion, and revolution.
7. Use Boolean operators to add, subtract, and intersect parts of your model.
8. Save settings as a solid modeling prototype drawing.
9. Use region modeling.
10. Set the SOLWDENS variable.
11. MESH and SHADE your model.

Introduction

Though you may not have realized it, in Tutorials 1 through 7 you have learned how to use AutoCAD to represent three-dimensional objects. When you create a multiview drawing, it is a model of the object that contains enough information within the various views to give the person interpreting it an understanding of the complete three-dimensional shape represented. Your models have been composed of multiple two-dimensional views, which are used to convey the information. Now you will learn to use AutoCAD's AME (Advanced Modeling Extension) feature to create a three-dimensional solid model of the object.

AutoCAD allows three types of 3D modeling: *wireframe*, *surface*, and *solid modeling*. Wireframe modeling uses 3D lines, arcs, circles, and other entities to represent the edges and other features of the object. It is called wireframe because it looks like a sculpture made from wires. Surface modeling takes 3D modeling one step further to add surfaces to the wireframe so that the model can be shaded and hidden lines removed. A surface model is like an empty shell. There is nothing to tell how the inside behaves. Solid modeling represents a volume, just like the actual object. A solid model represents not just the lines and surfaces, but the volumes that are contained within.

Using the computer, it is possible to represent three dimensions in the drawing database; that is, drawings are created using x, y, and z coordinates. Solid modeling is the term for creating an accurate 3D model of the drawing that goes beyond representing just the lines that form the edges of the surfaces, to describing a volume that is contained by the surfaces making up the object. Some of the benefits of solid models are: they are easier to interpret; they can be rendered (shaded) so that someone unfamiliar with engineering drawing can visualize the object easily; two-dimensional views can be generated directly from the model; materials can be assigned to the object; and the mass properties can be analyzed. The need to create a physical prototype of the object may even be eliminated.

Creating a solid model is in some ways like sculpting the part out of clay. You can add and subtract material with *Boolean operators* and create parts by *revolution* and *extrusion*. You can tell the computer from what material parts are made and then analyze their mass properties. At first, AutoCAD's solid modeling looks much like wireframe or surface modeling. This is because wireframe representation is usually used in AutoCAD's AME to make many operations quicker. Then surfaces are applied and the object can be shaded or lines hidden.

Adapting for Architecture

Wireframe, surface, and solid modeling all play important roles in the creation of three-dimensional architectural drawings. Wireframe models make it easy to create simple perspective views that can later be added to by hand to create presentation drawings. Wireframes can be used to look at simple spaces in three dimensions. AutoCAD's surface modeling is effective for creating drawings to be shaded or exported for rendering, but it is difficult to make changes later, and therefore it is not a good design tool. Solid modeling is the most flexible modeling method for both design and presentation. Wireframes, shaded drawings, and renderings may all be created using solid modeling, and in addition it is easy to make design changes. ■

Starting

Before you begin, launch AutoCAD. If you need help, please review the AutoCAD for Windows section of Chapter 3, AutoCAD Basics, in Part 1, Getting Started. The AutoCAD drawing editor should be on your display screen. To start this tutorial you will simply begin drawing, rather than creating a new file. Later you will name and save your file.

The grid is very useful when you are working in 3D. It can help you relate visually to the current viewing direction and coordinate system. To turn on the grid,

Press: F7

You should see the regularly spaced grid dots appear at a spacing of 1 unit.

3D Coordinate Systems

AutoCAD defines the model geometry using precise x, y, z coordinates in space called the *World Coordinate System*, or *WCS*. This WCS is fixed and drawing geometry in both 2D and 3D is stored in the database using the WCS coordinate system. Its default orientation is a horizontal X axis, with positive values to the right, and a vertical Y axis, with positive values above the X axis. The Z axis is perpendicular to the computer screen, with positive values in front of the screen. The default orientations of the axes are shown in Figure 8.1.

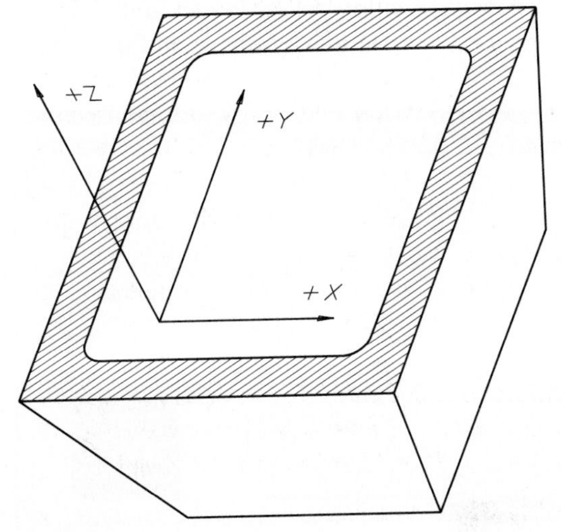

Figure 8.1

While you have been creating 2D geometry, you have been using this default WCS. You have been looking straight down the Z axis, so that a line in the Z direction appears as a point. This made it easy for you to create and save 2D drawings.

Setting the Viewpoint

When you are creating 3D geometry, it is useful to establish a different direction, or several directions, from which to view the XY plane, so that you can see the object's height along the Z axis. You can do this with the VPOINT command. You will use the pull-down View menu to set the viewpoint.

Pick: **View *(menu bar)*, Set view, Viewpoint, Axes**

Rotate/<View point> <0.0000,0.0000,1.0000>:

An x, y, z *coordinate system locator* and *globe* appear on your screen, as shown in Figure 8.2.

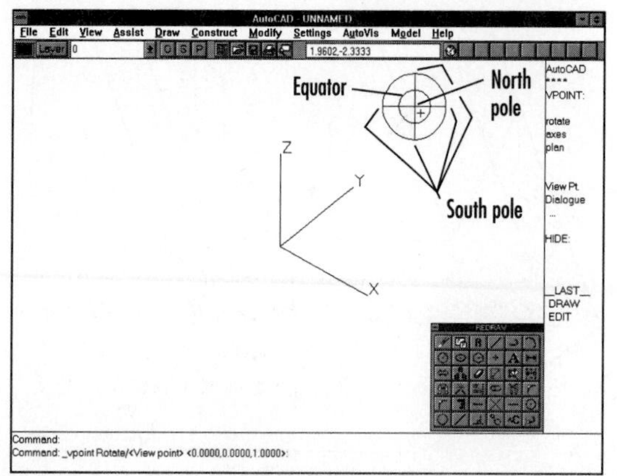

Figure 8.2

You will use the globe to select the viewing direction. You can think of the center point of the globe as the view looking straight down on the top of the XY plane. The center circle is like the equator. Any point inside the inner circle shows the view looking down on the object from the top. Points selected outside the inner circle show the view looking up at the object from below. A horizontal line divides the globe into front and back. If you pick a point below the line, you are viewing the object from the front; pick a point above the line and you are viewing the object from the back.

Move your pointing device so that the crosshairs are inside the inner circle in the lower right-hand quadrant. When you have them positioned where the cross is shown in Figure 8.2, press the pick button to select the viewing direction.

Your screen should appear similar to Figure 8.3, depending on the exact point you selected. Notice that your view has changed. You are no longer looking straight down on the XY plane represented by the grid area. Your view is from an angled direction.

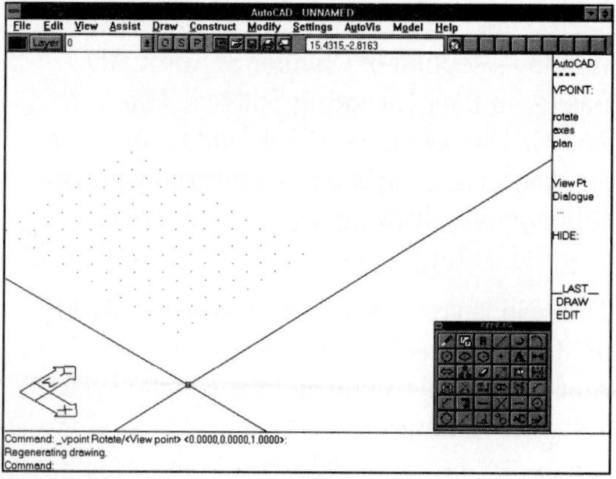

Figure 8.3

User Coordinate Systems

A *User Coordinate System* or *UCS* is a set of x, y, z coordinates that you can define to help make it easy to create models of any shape you want. You can define your own User Coordinate System, which may have a different origin and rotation from, and can be tilted at any angle with respect to, the World Coordinate System. UCSs are helpful since your mouse only moves in two dimensions, and UCSs let you orient the basic drawing coordinate system at any angle, so that you can still draw using your mouse or other pointing device. You can define any number of UCSs, give them names, and save them in a drawing; however, only one can be active at a time.

The UCS Icon

The User Coordinate System (UCS) icon appears in the lower left corner of the grid area on the screen. It will help you orient yourself when looking at 2D views of the object. Since the monitor screen is essentially flat, even if the object is a 3D solid in the database, only 2D views of it can be represented on the monitor. Because wireframe models look the same from front and back, or from any two opposing viewpoints, it is especially important to keep track of what view you are seeing on the screen.

The UCS icon is always drawn in the XY plane of the current UCS. The arrows at the X and Y ends always point in the positive direction of the X and Y axes of the current UCS. A "W" appearing in the UCS icon tells you that the UCS is currently lined up with the World Coordinate System. The box in the lower corner of the icon indicates that you are viewing the UCS from above. A plus sign in the lower left corner of the icon indicates that the icon is positioned at the origin of the current UCS. The UCSICON command can be used to reposition the icon so that it is not at the origin of the x, y, z coordinate system. When you do this, no plus sign appears in the icon.

A special symbol may appear instead of the UCS icon to indicate that the current viewing direction is viewing the UCS edgewise. (Think of the x, y coordinate system of the UCS as a flat plane like a piece of paper; the viewing direction is set so that you are looking directly onto the edge of the paper.) When this happens you cannot use most of the drawing tools, so the icon appears as a box containing a broken pencil. Take special notice of this icon.

The perspective icon replaces the UCS icon when perspective viewing is in effect. It appears as a cube drawn in perspective. Many commands are also limited when perspective viewing is in effect. You will learn to create perspective views in Tutorial 11.

Figure 8.4 shows the different icons.

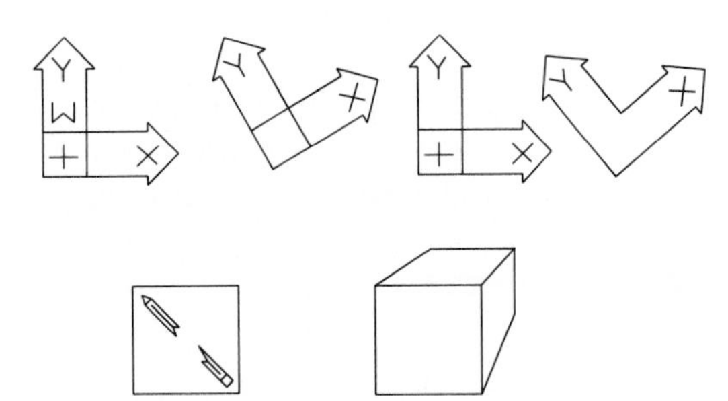

Figure 8.4

On your own, create two new layers. One layer will contain the solid model and the other will contain viewports. Use the Settings (menu bar), Layer Control dialogue box to create the following layers:

MODEL	On	Magenta	Continuous
VPORTS	On	White	Continuous

Set layer MODEL as the current layer.

Creating an Object

AutoCAD has three methods you can use to create model geometry: extrusion, revolution, and primitives. Primitives are basic shapes that can be joined together to form more complex shapes. You will create a solid three-dimensional box. Later in this tutorial you will learn how to join the shapes together with Boolean operators and how to create other shapes with extrusion and revolution.

Pick: **Model *(menu bar)*, Primitives...**

A dialogue box appears on your screen, as shown in Figure 8.5, showing the solid primitives. Many complex shapes can be created by joining these few basic primitives together with the Boolean commands you will learn later. For now you will insert a box into your drawing.

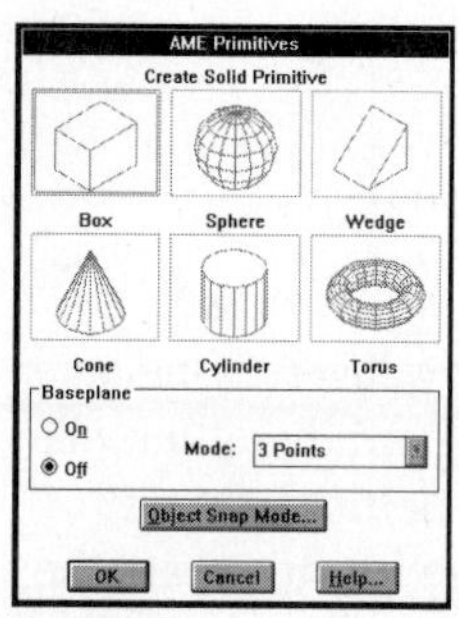

Figure 8.5

Pick: ***(select the picture of the box primitive)***

Pick: **OK**

> ■ ***TIP*** Before you can use AME for the first time in a drawing session, the AME module must be loaded for use in AutoCAD. If you haven't loaded AME yet when you select a command, you are prompted, "No modeler is loaded yet. Both AME and Region modeler are available. Autoload Region/<AME>:." Press ↵ to load the AME module if you see this message. If you have trouble, check with your technical support person. ■

The prompt for the box primitive appears. The default method of defining a box is to specify two corners across the diagonal in the XY plane and the height in the Z direction. By selecting Center, you can give the center of the base and the length, width and height, instead of the corners of the diagonal and the height. The Cube option specifies that all dimensions are equal, so you are only prompted for one length. You will draw a box using the default method and type in the coordinates.

Baseplane/Center/<Corner of box> <0,0,0>: **2,2,0** ↵

Cube/Length/<Other corner>: **8,6,0** ↵

Height: **3** ↵

Phase I - Boundary evaluation begins.

Phase II - Tessellation computation begins.

Updating the Advanced Modeling Extension database.

Your drawing should appear similar to Figure 8.6.

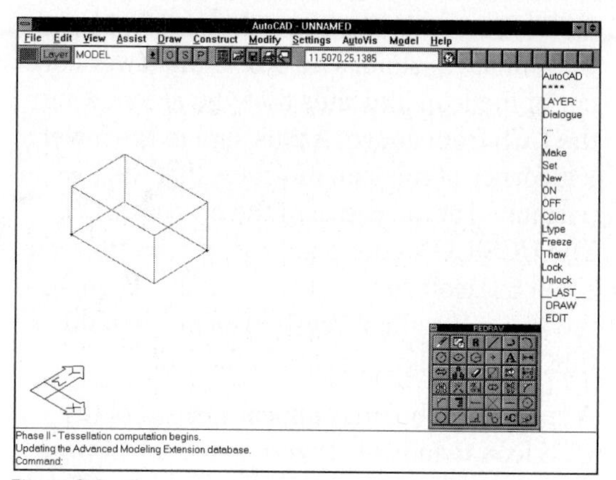

Figure 8.6

Creating Multiple Viewports

Now you have a 3D solid object on your screen. You will next create viewports to show several views of the object on your screen at the same time. This way you can create just one solid model and produce a drawing with the necessary two-dimensional orthographic views directly from the 3D model. You have already used a single paper space viewport for printing and plotting in Tutorials 3 and 6. Now you will create four viewports and then change them so that they contain four different views of the model.

On your own, set layer VPORTS as the current layer before you continue.

Pick: **View *(menu bar)*, Tilemode**

You are automatically switched from model space into paper space. Notice the triangular paper space icon in the lower left corner of your screen. As you remember from Tutorial 3, paper space allows you to arrange views of your model, text, and other entities as you would on a sheet of paper. You cannot see through the paper to your model until you create "holes" called viewports in the paper space. This is done with the MVIEW command. You will pick it from View on the menu bar.

Pick: **View *(menu bar)*, Mview, 4 Viewports**

The MVIEW command is echoed in the command prompt area. Then its prompt appears in the command prompt area, allowing you to size the viewports. Fit the viewports inside the area that you want to plot full size and centered on your page, as you did in Tutorial 3. You may find the values used below work for your printer. If you determined a different setting in Tutorial 6, use the one that works for your printer.

Fit/<First Point>: **.25,.25** ↵

Second point: **10.25,7.75** ↵

Four viewports appear on your screen, each one containing an identical view of the object. Now set the paper space limits to the size of the sheet of paper you will use when plotting, so that it will look like 8.5 × 11" paper on the screen. Each viewport (and also paper space) can have its own limits, grid, and snap setting.

The default limits in AutoCAD are set to 12, 9. Because the paper size that you will print on is only 11 × 8.5, the default limits are too large. It is a good practice to set the limits in paper space close to the paper size, because that way you see how much area you actually have to draw on the sheet. Starting the limits at 0,0 usually makes it easier to position your plots on the page where you want them when you are printing. Also, this way if you ZOOM, All, the drawing area fills your screen and not a larger area (which would make your viewports smaller on the screen and harder to work in). While still in paper space,

Pick: **Settings *(menu bar)*, Drawing limits**

Reset Paper space limits:

ON/OFF/<Lower left corner> <0.0000,0.0000>: ↵

Upper right corner <12.0000,9.0000>: **10.5,8** ↵

To fill the screen area with the new drawing limits,

Pick: **View *(menu bar)*, Zoom, All**

Your drawing should appear similar to Figure 8.7.

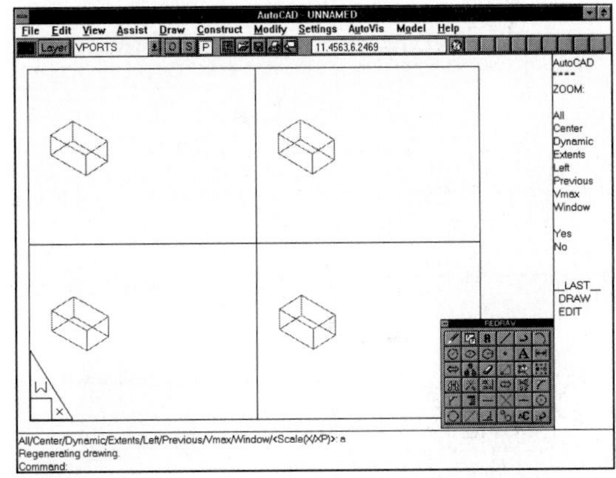

Figure 8.7

Now you will change the viewpoint for each viewport so that together they show a top, front, right-side, and oblique view of the model.

When you are in paper space, you cannot change things that are in model space. The original box was created in model space, where you create and make changes to your model. You will pick the highlighted button P from the toolbar to toggle from paper space to model space.

Pick: **P button *(toolbar, to switch to model space)***

You can tell that you are in model space when you see that the UCS icon has reappeared and is now displayed in each of the viewports.

Now you will make the top left-hand viewport active and change it to show the view of the model looking down from the top.

Selecting the Active Viewport

To make the upper left viewport active, you will move the arrow cursor until it is positioned in the top left-hand viewport and then press the pick button.

Pick: ***(anywhere in the upper left viewport)***

You will see the crosshairs appear in the view-port as shown in Figure 8.8, indicating that this is now the active viewport.

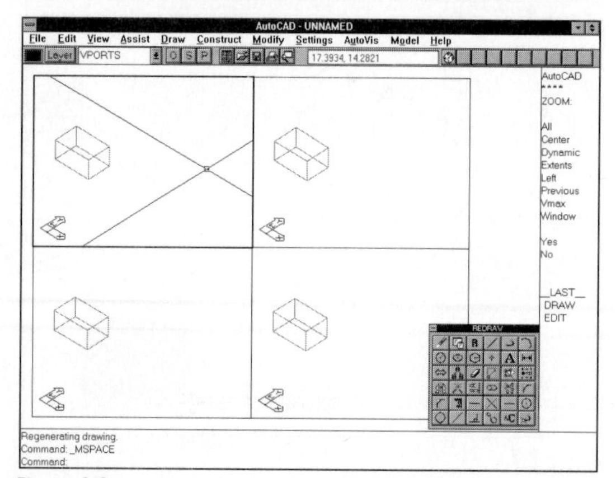

Figure 8.8

■ ***TIP*** You can also toggle the active viewport to each succeeding viewport by pressing Ctrl-V. This is useful because it can be done during a command, where sometimes picking does not work. ■

Only when a viewport is active can you draw in it and pick points from it. After you create something, whatever you create is visible in all other viewports showing the same area of the WCS, unless the layer that the object is in is frozen. A useful feature of the viewports is that you can start drawing something in one view-port and finish drawing it in another viewport.

Next you will set up the viewing direction for the top view.

Using PLAN

The PLAN command produces a view where you are looking straight down along the Z axis to see the XY coordinates of the specified coor-dinate system, as you have in your previous drawings.

Command: **PLAN** ↵

<Current UCS>/Ucs/World: ↵

The view in the upper left viewport changes. Now you are looking straight down on top of the box.

■ ***TIP*** If you get lost in a drawing (by zooming too far, in using VPOINT, or by panning in the wrong direction), use the PLAN command to get back to a World Coordinate view. At that point, you can restore whatever view you were using and get back to where you can understand your model. ■

The top view of the box is too large to fit entirely within the view. You will use the ZOOM command with the Scale XP (meaning relative to paper space) option to move the viewing distance farther away so that the object appears smaller and fits into the view-port. Type "Z" ↵ at the command prompt. The Left option of the ZOOM command allows you to specify the coordinates of the point that will be placed in the lower left-hand corner of the viewport when the zoom is performed. Use the Left option with the ZOOM command so that the views align between viewports.

Command: **Z** ↵

All/Center/Dynamic/Extents/Left/Previous/Vmax/Window/
<Scale(X/XP)>: **L** ↵

Lower left corner point: **0,0,0** ↵

Magnification or Height <4.5000>: **.5XP** ↵

The top view of the box should fit into the viewport at half paper space scale. Your drawing should appear similar to Figure 8.9.

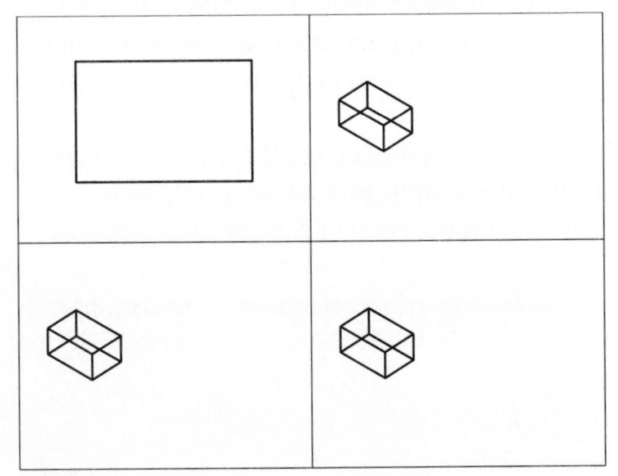

Figure 8.9

Each viewport can contain its own setting for GRID, SNAP, and ZOOM. Now you will set the grid to .5 in the upper left viewport.

Command: **GRID** ↵

Grid spacing (x) or ON/OFF/Snap/Aspect <0.0000>: **.5** ↵

The grid in the top viewport now has a spacing of .5 units.

On your own, make the lower left viewport active by moving the arrow cursor into that viewport and pressing the pick button. The crosshairs appear in the lower left viewport.

Changing the Viewpoint

Now change the *viewpoint* for the lower left-hand viewport so that it shows the front view of the object. The numbers you enter in the VPOINT command are the x, y, and z coordinates of a point that defines a *vector*, or directional line. The other point defining the vector is the origin point, 0,0,0. Your line of sight, or viewpoint, is defined by this vector, or imaginary line, toward the origin from the coordinates of the point you enter. The actual **size** of the number you enter does not matter, only the **direction** it establishes. Thus entering "2,2,0" is the same as entering "1,1,0", because only the direction of sight is determined by this number. See Figure 8.10.

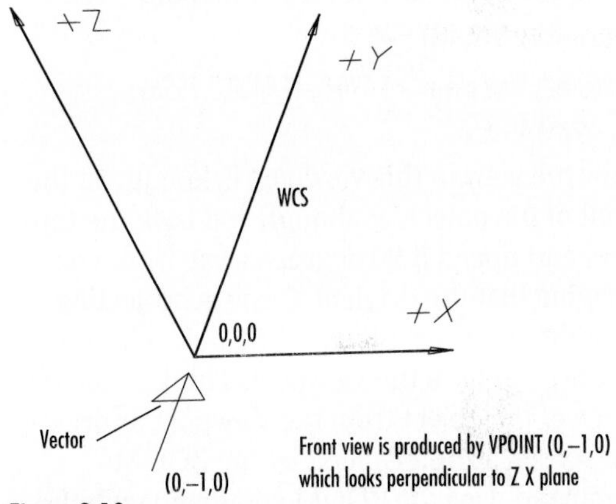

Figure 8.10

You can also select the Rotate option and establish the viewing direction by specifying the rotation angle in the XY plane from the X axis, and then the rotation above the XY plane for the viewpoint. See Figure 8.11.

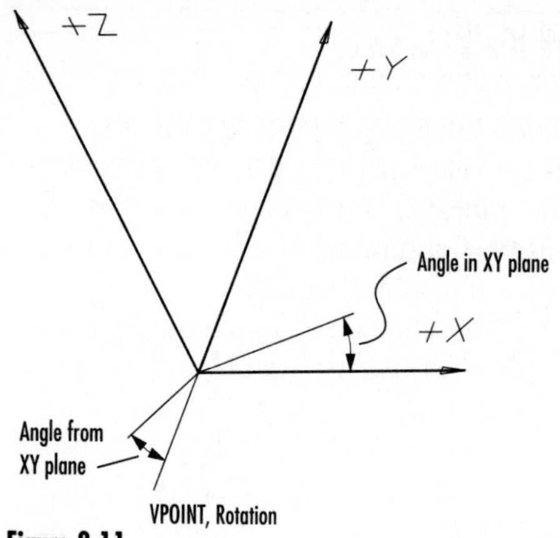

Figure 8.11

The prompt you see for the VPOINT command may vary from what is listed below, depending on the point you originally selected when using the globe to set the viewing direction.

Command: **VPOINT** ↵

Rotate/<View point> <1.5904, –2.9420,2.2556>:
0,–1,0 ↵

Now the view in this viewport is looking at the front of the object, as though you took the top view and tipped it 90 degrees away from you. Imagine that the original Y axis is projecting straight into your monitor. The object is again too large to fit in the viewport. Think of the distance of the object from the viewport or drawing screen as determined by the ZOOM command. Use the ZOOM command with the Left option and Scale XP to zoom out so that the entire view fits in the viewport.

Command: **Z** ↵

All/Center/Dynamic/Extents/Left/Previous/Vmax/Window/
<Scale(X/XP)>: **L** ↵

Lower left corner point: **0,0,–1** ↵

Magnification or Height <4.5000>: **.5XP** ↵

Now you see the entire front view of the object in the viewport. Your drawing should appear similar to Figure 8.12.

Notice the broken pencil icon in the lower left corner. This icon tells you that your current XY drawing plane or UCS is parallel to the viewing direction. If you were to try to draw, you couldn't keep track of what was being created. Every shape you drew would appear as a straight line because you are viewing your XY drawing surface edgewise. Think about the results you would get if you looked edgewise at a piece of paper at eye level and then tried to draw on it. You may also have seen the message "Grid too dense to display," when you originally changed your viewpoint. If the coordinate system is viewed edge on, the grid is, of course, a solid line of dots, making it too dense to appear on the screen in a meaningful fashion.

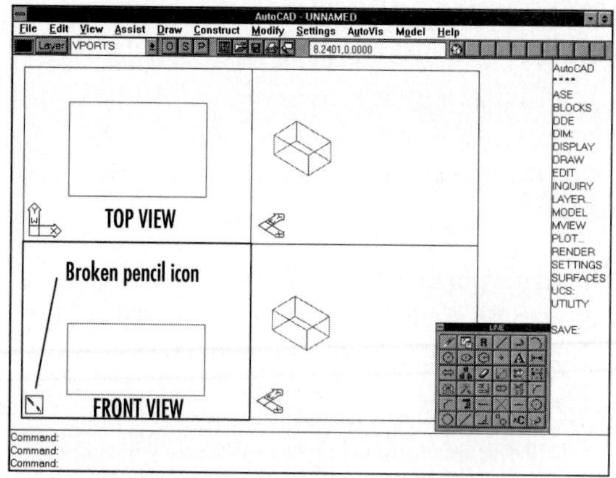

Figure 8.12

Creating Named User Coordinate Systems

You will use the UCS command to create a User Coordinate System, so you can draw in the front view. The UCS command allows you to position a User Coordinate System anywhere with respect to the World Coordinate System. You can also use it to change the origin point for the coordinate system and save and restore named coordinate systems. You will rotate the coordinate system around the X axis 90 degrees to create a UCS where the XY plane is parallel to the front viewing plane.

Command: **UCS** ↵

Origin/ZAxis/3point/Entity/View/X/Y/Z/Prev/Restore/Save/Del/?/<World>: **X** ↵

Rotation angle about X axis <0>: **90** ↵

The grid in your drawing now appears in the front view (lower left viewport). The broken pencil appears in the top view (upper left viewport). Now you are able to draw in the front view, but not the top view. Save this UCS so you can return to it later when you want to draw in the front view. You will press the ↵ key or right mouse button to repeat the UCS command, pick the Save option, and name the UCS FRONT because you see it in the front view.

Command: ↵ ***(to restart the UCS command)***

UCS Origin/ZAxis/3 point/Entity/View/X/Y/Z/Prev/Restore/Save/Del/?/<World>: **S** ↵

?/Desired UCS name: **FRONT** ↵

Adapting for Architecture

The UCS command and the VIEW command work well in conjunction. After you have established a User Coordinate System, set up a view that aligns with it by using the PLAN command and selecting the UCS option. This allows you to easily define a view that corresponds to any defined UCS. Use the VIEW command to save the view with the same name as the UCS with which it is aligned. Possible combinations of view and coordinate systems include: plans at any height, multiple sections, and elevations. Save views of any important spaces in your model. ■

Set the grid spacing for this viewport to .5 units.

Command: **GRID** ↵

Grid spacing (X) or ON/OFF/Snap/Aspect <0.0000>: **.5** ↵

Having completed setting the viewing direction and UCS for the front view, you will now select the lower right viewport to be active so you can create a side view.

Position the arrow cursor in the lower right viewport and press the pick button. The crosshairs should appear in this viewport to indicate that it is active. Use the VPOINT command to select the viewing direction for this view.

Command: **VPOINT** ↵

Rotate/<View point> <1.5904,–2.9420,2.2556>: **1,0,0** ↵

The view changes to show a right-side view of the object. Again, the entire object does not fit in the viewport at the present zoom factor. Use the ZOOM command with the XP option to zoom the view relative to paper space.

Command: **Z** ↵

All/Center/Dynamic/Extents/Left/Previous/Vmax/Window/<Scale(X/XP)>: **L** ↵

Lower left corner point: **0,–1,0** ↵

Magnification or Height <4.5000>: **.5XP** ↵

Now the right-side view fits in the lower right viewport, but this viewport has the broken pencil icon.

To create a UCS that is parallel to the viewing plane, where the direction of sight for the view is perpendicular to the UCS, use the View option.

Command: **UCS** ↵

Origin/ZAxis/3point/Entity/View/X/Y/Z/Prev/Restore/Save/Del/?/<World>: **V** ↵

The grid appears in the lower right-hand viewport and the broken pencil icon appears in the top and front views. Save this User Coordinate System so you can return to it when you want to draw in the right-side view. Press the ↵ key to repeat the previous command.

Command: ↵

Origin/ZAxis/3 point/Entity/View/X/Y/Z/Prev/Restore/ Save/Del/?/<World>: S ↵

?/Desired UCS name: SIDE ↵

> ■ ***TIP*** If you have trouble lining up the views, select the MVSETUP LISP program and use the Align option. Select whether you want to use Horizontal or Vertical alignment. Then pick a point in one viewport (using OSNAP, Endpoint or some other mode) and then a point that should align in the other viewport (again using OSNAP). The view in the second viewport is shifted to line up with the first point selected. ■

Set the grid for this viewport to .5 units. When you are finished, your drawing should look like Figure 8.13.

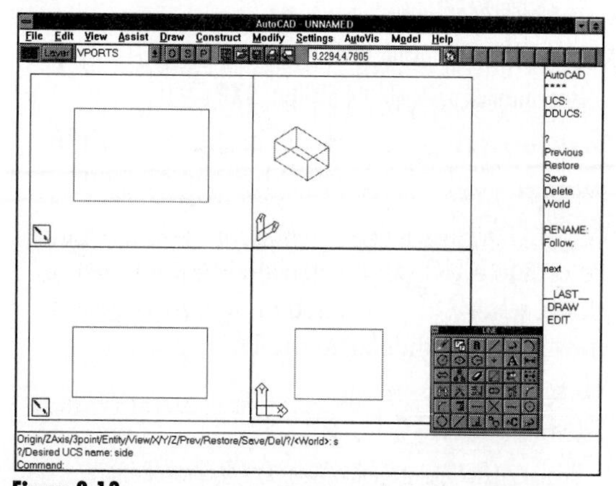

Figure 8.13

In the next portion of the tutorial, you will familiarize yourself with the basic solid modeling primitives that can be used to create drawing geometry. You will add and subtract them with Boolean commands to create more complicated shapes.

To restore the coordinates in the top left viewport,

Command: UCS ↵

Origin/ZAxis/3 point/Entity/View/X/Y/Z/Prev/Restore/ Save/Del/?/<World>: ↵ ***(to accept the default of World)***

This returns the drawing to the original World Coordinate System. In AutoCAD the default XY plane is thought of as the *plan view* of the WCS. A plan view is basically a top view. It may sound familiar if you have worked with architectural drawings. Any time you want to restore the original coordinate system, set the UCS equal to World Coordinates with the command you used above.

On your own, set layer MODEL as the current layer. Make the upper right-hand viewport, in which the box appears as its 3D shape, active by moving the arrow cursor to this viewport and pressing the pick button. You will see the crosshairs appear in the viewport when it is selected. Use ZOOM, Window to enlarge the object so that it fills the upper right viewport.

Setting SOLWDENS

Before you create any cylindrical, spherical, or toroidal solids, you will need to set the solid wire-density variable called SOLWDENS. This variable controls the appearance and accuracy of cylinders, spheres, and tori. The higher the value for SOLWDENS, the better the appearance of these shapes and the more accurate the surface area calculations will be. You can select a value between 1 and 12. 1 is the default setting, which looks very poor, but saves time in the calculations that are used to create the planes approximating the shape of the circular feature. The highest setting looks the best, but takes more time for the calculations, especially when processing a complex drawing. AME uses a formula to calculate the number of *tessellation* lines, or edges, that curved surfaces will have. Tessellation lines are lines displayed on a curved surface that help you better visualize the surface. The number of tessellation lines also determines the accuracy of surface area calculations. The formula for tessellation varies as follows for the different types of entities:

Cylindrical and Conical surfaces	Tessellations= SOLWDENS × 4
Toroidal surfaces	Tessellations= SOLWDENS × 8
Spherical surfaces	Tessellations= SOLWDENS × 4–1

As a compromise, you will set a value somewhere in the middle. You can pick the solid wire-density variable from the Model menu bar, as you see in Figure 8.14.

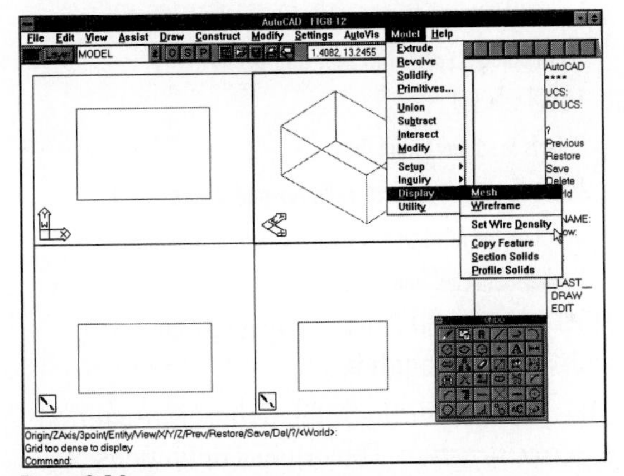

Figure 8.14

Pick: **Model *(menu bar)*, Display, Set Wire Density**

Wireframe mesh density (1 to 12) <1>: 4 ↵

You will not see the effect of this variable until you create a cylinder, sphere, or torus.

Now add a cylinder to the drawing. Later, you will turn it into a hole by using the Subtract command. Cylinders are created by specifying the center of the circular shape and the radius or diameter in the XY plane, then specifying the height in the Z direction of the current UCS. You can use the Baseplane option to change the height above the XY plane that the circular shape is drawn in. The Elliptical option allows you to specify an elliptical shape instead of a circular one, and then go on to specify the height. The Center of other end option allows you to specify the center of the other end by picking or typing coordinates, instead of specifying the height.

Pick: **Model *(menu bar)*, Primitives. . .**

Select the cylinder from the dialogue box, either by double-clicking on its picture or by picking it once to highlight it and then picking OK.

Baseplane/Elliptical/<Center point> <0,0,0>: 4,4 ↵

(Notice that if you do not specify a z coordinate, it is assumed to be your current elevation, which is presently 0.)

Diameter/<Radius>: .375 ↵

Center of other end/<Height>: 3 ↵

Now you will change the color of the cylinder:

Pick: **Modify *(menu bar)*, Entity**

Select object to modify: *(pick the cylinder)*

The Modify Block Insertion dialogue box appears on the screen. You will use the Color option to set the color for the cylinder to blue while leaving it in layer MODEL (which will still remain magenta).

Pick on the word Color. . . that currently has the word BYLAYER next to it.

From the color chart that appears on your screen, select the color blue from the band of standard colors across the very top of the box. It is color number 5, the fifth color from the left.

Pick: **OK *(to accept the color selection)***

Pick: **OK *(to exit the dialogue box)***

The cylinder should be changed to the new color, making your drawing look like Figure 8.15.

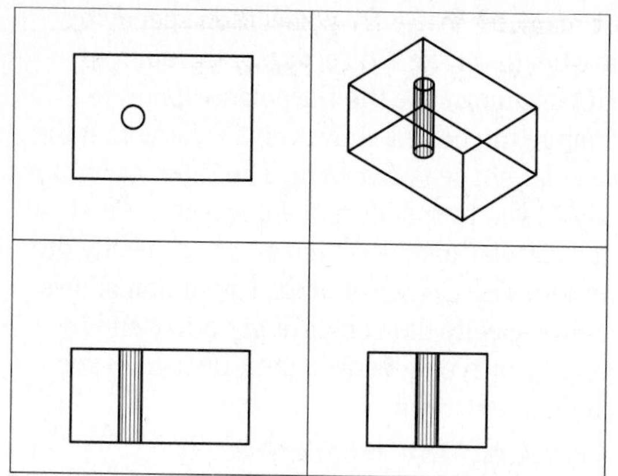

Figure 8.15

Now you have a box and a cylinder, each occupying the same space. This could not be done in the real world, but in the drawing database, these two objects are both occupying the volume inside the cylinder. Now it is time to use the Boolean operator Subtract to remove the cylinder from the box so that it forms a hole.

Using Booleans

Boolean operators find the *union* (addition), *difference* (subtraction), and *intersection* (common area) of two or more sets. In AutoCAD the sets can be 2D areas called regions, or they can be 3D solids. Often Venn diagrams are used to represent sets and Boolean operations. Figure 8.16, shown below, will help you understand how union, subtract, and intersect work. The order in which the objects are selected is only important when subtracting (i.e., A subtract B is different than B subtract A).

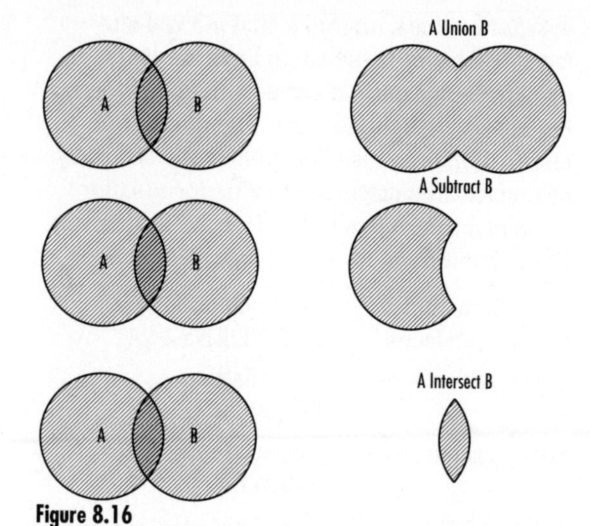

Figure 8.16

Subtract the volume of the cylinder from the box to form a new solid with a hole in it.

Pick: **Model *(menu bar)*, Subtract**

Source objects...

Select objects: ***(pick the box and press ↵)***

1 solid selected

Objects to subtract from them...

Select objects: ***(pick the cylinder and press ↵)***

Updating the Advanced Modeling Extension database.

1 solid subtracted from 1 solid.

Now a new solid exists, a rectangular prism with a hole through it.

The database for the solid models is organized as a *tree structure*. The original definitions of the primitives are not eliminated from the database, but rather stored, along with the subtract operations, to form the definition of the new object. This is called the Constructive Solid Geometry, or CSG, method of solid modeling. This method takes less storage space in the computer. It also makes it easy to change one of the parts even after it has been joined to another part, as you will see in Tutorial 9.

The CSG tree is more efficient if it is balanced; that is, the same number of items are subtracted in balanced groups. If you have several objects you want to subtract, doing it all at once and letting AutoCAD take care of balancing the tree is usually more effective than subtracting one thing at a time. Figure 8.17 shows two CSG trees. In the figure, each dot represents the AutoCAD handle number assigned to an object in the drawing. At the lowest level are primitives. The top level represents the final object. The levels in between represent a subtraction, difference, or union of the parts below. The tree on the left is balanced; it has the same number of nodes joining at each level. The structure on the right is unbalanced. It represents the results if you create one part and then join it to the next, then create another, and so forth.

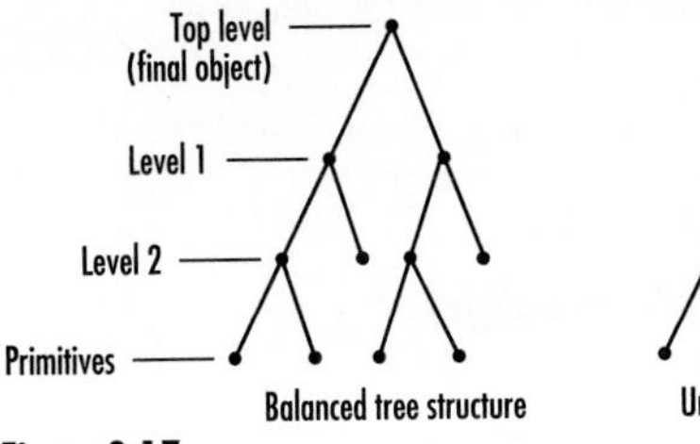

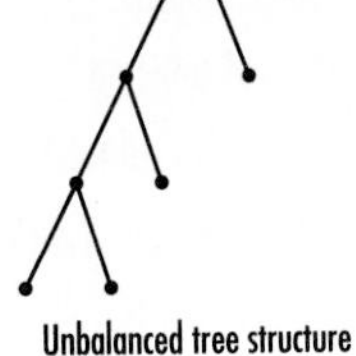

Figure 8.17

A disadvantage of the CSG method is that the surfaces that define the boundaries of the object are not fully defined in the drawing database at all times. Before you can use many of the surface commands, such as HIDE and SHADE, you must tell AutoCAD to calculate the surface boundaries.

You will use the MESH command selected from the Model, Display menu bar selection to calculate the surfaces of the object.

Pick: **Model *(menu bar)*, Display, Mesh**

Select object: ***(pick the object in the top right-hand viewport)***

1 found

Select objects: ↵

1 solid selected.

Surface meshing of solid is completed.

Creating block for mesh representation...

Done.

Now you can shade your model in the top right-hand viewport. You should have the AutoVis selection available near the right end of the menu bar. If you have not loaded AutoVision, you will see the selection Render on the menu bar; you can use it with the Render option instead.

Pick: **AutoVis *(menu bar)*, Render**

The AutoVision Render dialogue box appears on your screen, as shown in Figure 8.18.

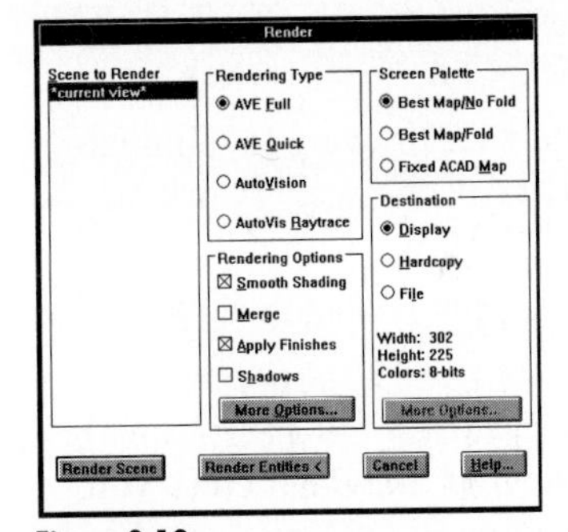

Figure 8.18

Select AVE Full as the type of rendering to perform. This will shade the objects on your screen, using the same rendering method that is available in the AME package. You will learn more about using AutoVision in Tutorial 16.

Pick: Render Scene

The model in the active viewport becomes shaded. Notice that you can now tell that the cylinder has formed a hole in the block. The color inside the hole is blue and the rest of the block is magenta.

Your drawing should appear similar to Figure 8.19.

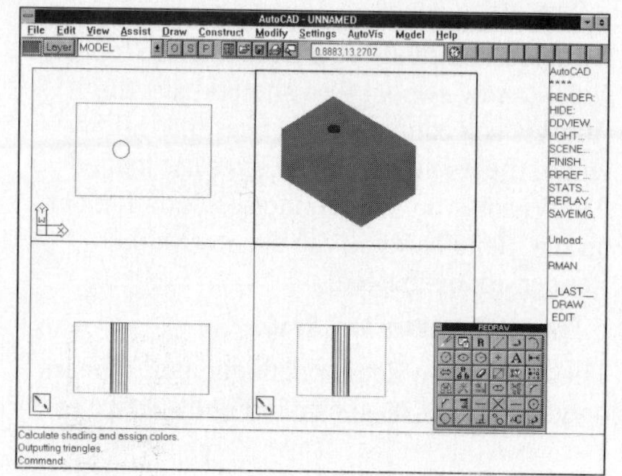

Figure 8.19

You will regenerate your drawing to eliminate the shading so you can continue to work on it by typing "REGEN" at the "Command:" prompt. (You cannot select objects when they are shaded.)

Command: **REGEN** ↵

Use SAVE and save your drawing before you continue. Use the name BLOCK to describe this drawing. Saving periodically will prevent you from losing your drawing in the event of a power failure or other hardware problem. Also, it is useful to save after you complete a major step in your work before you go on to the next thing. That way, if you want to return to the previous step, you can open the previous version of the drawing, discarding the changes you have made to the current drawing.

Now use the wedge primitive to create a wedge and subtract it from the block.

Pick: **Model *(menu bar)*, Primitives. . .**

The AME Primitives dialogue box appears on the screen.

Pick: ***(the box containing the wedge)***

Pick: **OK**

Baseplane/<Corner of Wedge> <0,0,0>: **8,6** ↵

Length/<Other corner>: **6,2** ↵

Height: **3** ↵

The wedge primitive starts by drawing the rectangular shape from the first point you select to the second point you select as the diagonal of the rectangular base. The height given starts at the first point you select and gets smaller in the X direction toward the second point.

Subtract the wedge from the object.

Pick: **Model *(menu bar)*, Subtract**

Source objects. . .

Select objects: ***(pick the box with the hole in it)***

Select objects: ↵

1 solid selected

Objects to subtract from them. . .

Select objects: ***(pick the wedge)***

Select objects: ↵

With the wedge subtracted, your drawing should look similar to Figure 8.20.

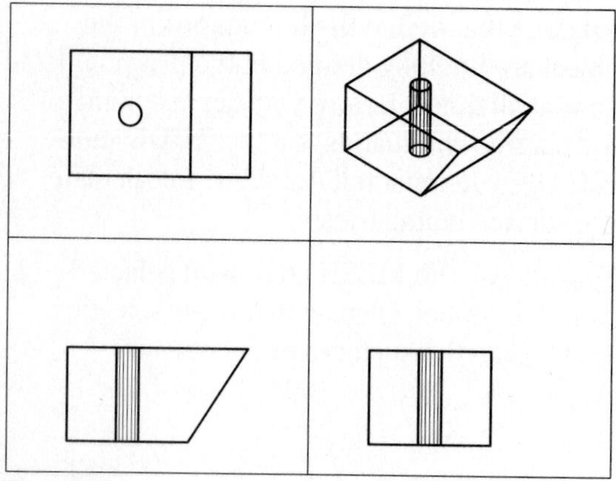

Figure 8.20

You will use MESH to calculate the surfaces for the object once again, since it has been changed, and then use HIDE to remove hidden lines from the upper right-hand view.

Command: **MESH** ↵

Select objects: ***(pick the rectangular block in the upper right-hand viewport)***

Select objects: ↵

Command: **HIDE** ↵

You will see the object on your screen with the hidden lines removed. It should look similar to Figure 8.21.

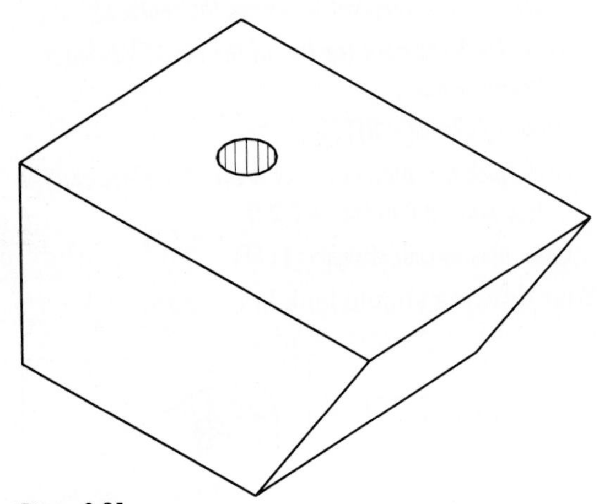

Figure 8.21

You will regenerate your drawing display from the drawing database, so that you can continue to work using wireframe.

Command: **REGEN** ↵

Next you will create a cone, using the cone primitive.

Pick: **Model *(menu bar)*, Primitives. . .**

Pick: ***(the cone)***

Pick: **OK**

Baseplane/Elliptical/<Center point> <0,0,0>: **4,4,3** ↵

Diameter/<Radius>: **.625** ↵

Apex/<Height>: **–.75** ↵

You will use the Boolean operator to subtract the cone from the block to make a countersink for the hole.

Pick: **Model *(menu bar)*, Subtract**

Source objects. . .

Select objects: ***(pick the rectangular block)***

1 found

Select objects: ↵

1 solid selected

Objects to subtract from them. . .

Select objects: ***(pick the cone)***

1 found

Select objects: ↵

1 solid selected. . .

Updating the Advanced Modeling Extension database

1 solid subtracted from 1 solid

Now you will mesh the new object in order to define its surfaces so you can use the Hide command to display it with the back (or hidden) lines removed.

Pick: **Model *(menu bar)*, Display, Mesh**

Select objects: ***(pick the object in the top right-hand viewport)***

1 found

Select objects: ↵

1 solid selected

Surface meshing of current solid is completed.

Creating block for mesh representation. . .

Done.

Now the object can be displayed with the back lines that wouldn't be visible in the view removed. Type the Hide command at the command prompt.

Command: **HIDE**

The upper right viewport now displays a view of the object with the hidden lines removed. Your drawing should look like Figure 8.22.

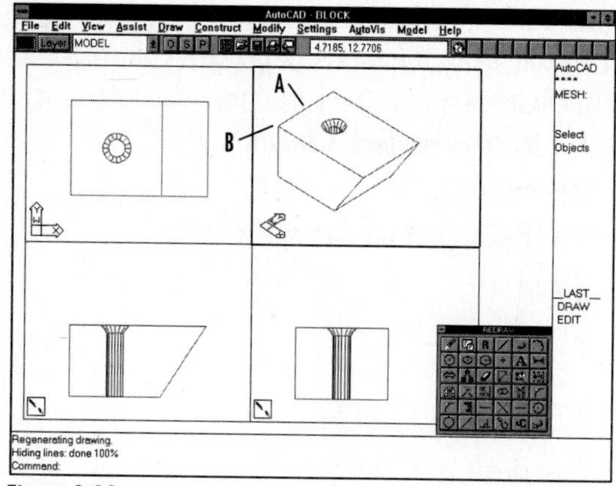

Figure 8.22

Now use the cylinder primitive to add a rounded surface to the top of the block.

Adapting for Architecture

The addition and subtraction techniques in solid modeling are very effective in creating architectural models. You can add walls to one another to create whole forms. You can subtract windows and doors from walls to create openings. Even the site plan can be added to and subtracted from to conform to the shape of your building model. ■

You will use the UCS command to restore the User Coordinate System that you earlier saved for drawing in the side view. This will make it easier for you to create entities that are parallel to the side view.

Command: **UCS** ↵

Origin/ZAxis/3point/Entity/View/X/Y/Z/Prev/Restore/Save/Del/?/<World>: **R** ↵

?\Name of UCS to restore: **SIDE** ↵

The grid appears in the side view. The broken pencil icon appears in the top and front views. In the oblique view in the upper right viewport, the grid changes to a different angle, since it now lines up with the side and not the top of the object.

Select the upper right viewport to make sure it is active.

Pick: ***Model (menu bar),*** **Primitives. . .**

Pick: ***(the cylinder)***

Pick: **OK**

Baseplane/Elliptical/<Center point> <0,0,0>: **MID** ↵ ***(or pick the Midpoint icon from the toolbox)***

mid of ***(pick the back top line of the block, labeled A in Figure 8.22)***

Diameter/<Radius>: **INT** ↵

int of ***(pick the intersection of the back surface and the top, labeled B in Figure 8.22)***

Center of other end/<Height>: **1** ↵

Your drawing should look like Figure 8.23.

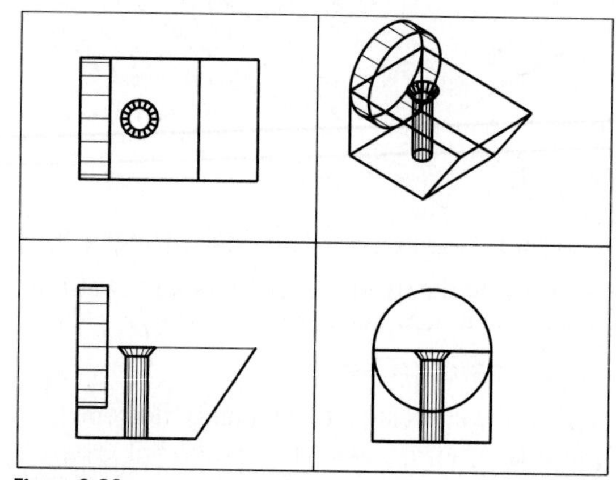

Figure 8.23

On your own, use the Boolean operator Union to join the cylinder to the block. When you have finished, your drawing should appear similar to Figure 8.24.

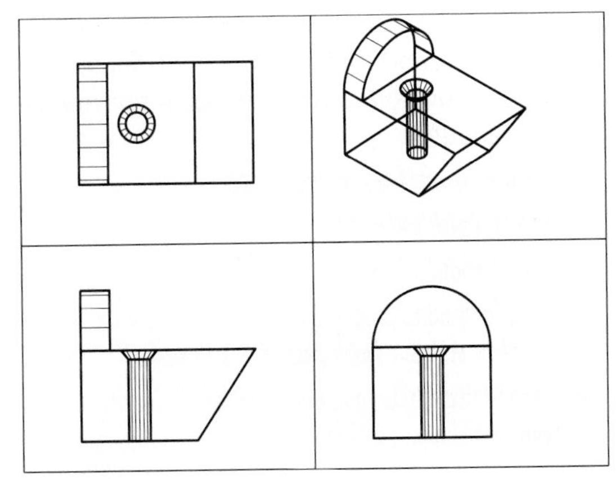

Figure 8.24

Save your completed drawing to your disk with the default file name BLOCK.

Plot your multiview drawing of the block. First change to paper space by picking the paper space button from the toolbar.

Pick: **P button *(toolbar)***

The paper space icon replaces the UCS icons. You may want to freeze layer VPORTS if you do not want to have the viewport lines plot out on your drawing. You can use the LINE command to draw a border around all of the viewports while you are in paper space. Add a title strip and notes if you wish.

Plot the drawing limits at a scale of 1=1. The views you have drawn should be exactly half size on the finished plot, because the ZOOM XP scale factor was set to .5.

Saving Your Multiview Setup as a Prototype

Switch your drawing back to model space by picking the P toggle button from the toolbar.

Pick: **P button *(toolbar)***

The UCS icons are restored to the viewports.

On your own, thaw layer VPORTS if you have frozen it while plotting your drawing.

Now you will erase the object and save the basic settings to use as a prototype drawing when creating new 3D drawings. You will type the alias for the ERASE command at the prompt.

Command: **E** ↵

Select objects: ***(pick the solid block object you have drawn)***

Select objects: ↵

It is erased from all viewports.

Next you will restore the World Coordinate System.

Command: **UCS** ↵

Origin/ZAxis/3 point/Entity/View/X/Y/Z/Prev/Restore/Save/Del/?/<World>: ↵

Next you will save this drawing with a new name, using the Save As option of the File menu:

Pick: **File *(menu bar)*, Save As. . .**

Type "C:\DRAWINGS\SOLPROTO" for the file name and pick OK. You will see the message "Current drawing name set to C:\DRAWINGS\SOLPROTO." You may see a different directory name, depending on your system.

Adapting for Architecture

Architectural modeling does not have to start out very detailed to be useful. It is best done from simple to complex, without getting caught up in the details early on. Three-dimensional models can become complex and difficult to manage, especially because the larger the file, the longer it takes to perform commands such as SUBTRACT or MESH. Start simple. Openings can be modeled without doors and windows, then those elements can be added later as needed. Rooms that are not used for rendering do not need to have elements like windows and furniture added. A simpler model is often as effective as a complex one and it is always quicker and easier to change. ■

Creating Solids with EXTRUDE and REVOLVE

Start a new drawing, using File, New. In this drawing you will learn how to create new solid objects, using the extrusion and revolution methods. Use the prototype drawing SOLPROTO that you just created, or the one provided with your data files, SOLPRO_D. Call the new drawing EXTRUSN. When you have named the drawing,

Pick: **OK *(to exit the dialogue box)***

Your screen should appear similar to Figure 8.25.

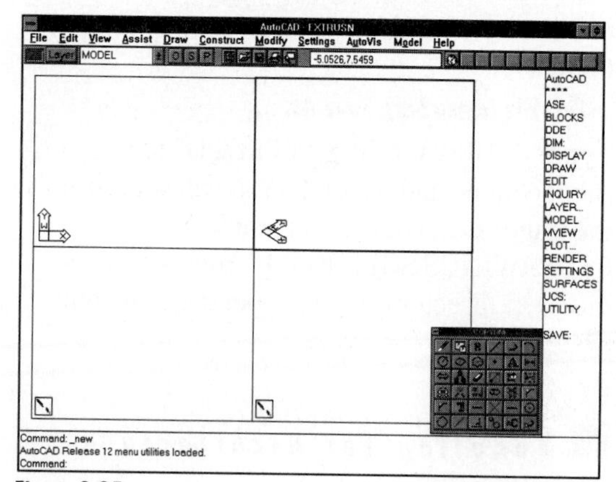

Figure 8.25

Since you started your new drawing from the solid modeling prototype, the viewports are already created. The UCSs called FRONT and SIDE that you saved previously are still available to use with the UCS, Restore option. Layer MODEL should be the current layer.

On your own, pick in the upper left viewport to make it active. Check to see that GRID and SNAP are turned on. If they are not, turn them on.

Draw the shape from Figure 8.26, using the 2D Polyline command. Some of the coordinates have been provided to make it easier for you to select the points.

Pick: **Draw *(menu bar)*, Polyline, 2D**

From point: *(pick point A)*

Current line-width is 0.0000

Arc/Close/Halfwidth/Length/Undo/Width/
<Endpoint of line>: *(pick points B-L in order)*

Arc/Close/Halfwidth/Length/Undo/Width/
<Endpoint of line>: C ↵

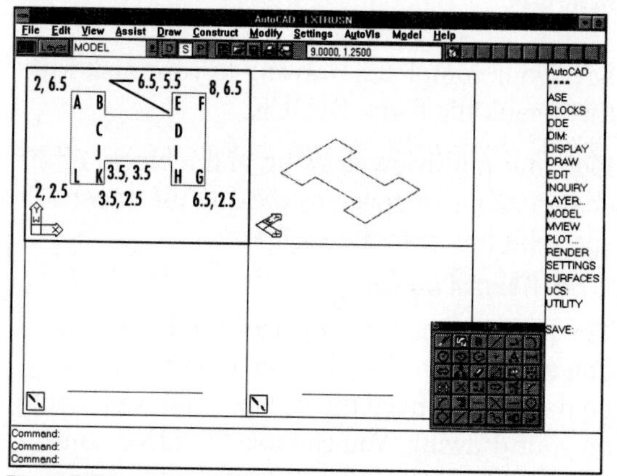

Figure 8.26

You will use the FILLET command with a radius of .25 units to round all the corners of the polyline.

Command: FILLET ↵

Polyline/Radius/<Select first object>: R ↵

Enter fillet radius <0.0000>: .25 ↵

Command: ↵

FILLET Polyline/Radius/<Select first object>: P ↵

Select 2D polyline: *(pick the polyline you just created)*

12 lines were filleted

> ■ ***TIP*** If you did not close your object with C, you will get the message "11 lines were filleted." ■

On your own, use SNAP to draw the two circles shown in Figure 8.27.

Region Modeling

The Boolean operators can also be used with the closed 2D shapes made by circles, ellipses, and closed polylines. Closed 2D shapes are called regions; they are essentially 2D solids, or areas. When you use Boolean commands on 2D closed shapes, they automatically become regions. Regions are hatched so that you can identify them. Region modeling and extrusion can be combined very effectively to create complex shapes. Turn SNAP off to make it easier to select.

Pick: **Model *(menu bar),* Subtract**

Source objects. . .

Select objects: ***(pick the polyline)***

1 found

Select objects: ↵

1 region selected.

Objects to subtract from them. . .

Select objects: ***(pick on one circle)***

1 found

Select objects: ***(pick on the other circle)***

1 found

Select objects: ↵

2 regions selected

2 regions subtracted from one region

The result should appear similar to Figure 8.27.

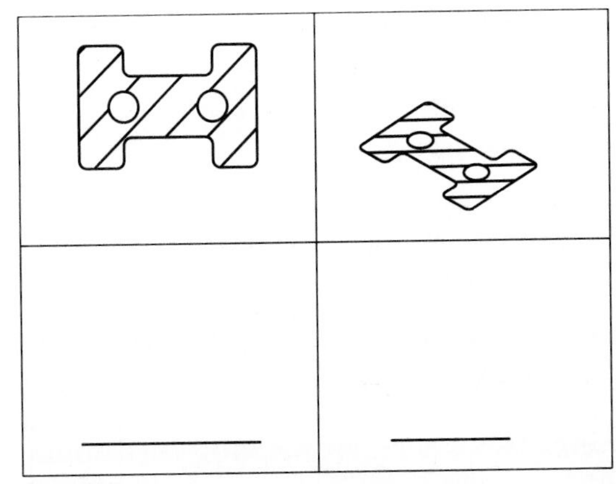

Figure 8.27

Now you can extrude this shape to create a three-dimensional object. Extrusion is the process of forcing material through a shaped opening to create a long strip with the shape of the opening. AutoCAD's extrusion command works in a similar way to form the shape. Any closed 2D shape can be given a height, or extruded. You can specify a taper angle if you want the top of the extrusion to be a different size than the bottom.

Pick: **Model *(menu bar),* Extrude**

Select regions, polylines and circles for extrusion. . .

Select objects: ***(pick the polyline)***

1 found

Select objects: ↵

Height of extrusion: **2** ↵

Extrusion taper angle <0>: ↵

Extrude loops to different heights? <N>: ↵

. . .Updating the Advanced Modeling Extension database

Next you will MESH and SHADE the object in the upper right viewport.

On your own, make the upper right viewport active.

Command: MESH ↵

Select objects: *(pick the shape)*

Select objects: ↵

. . .Done.

Command: SHADE ↵

You should now see a solid object, as shown in Figure 8.28.

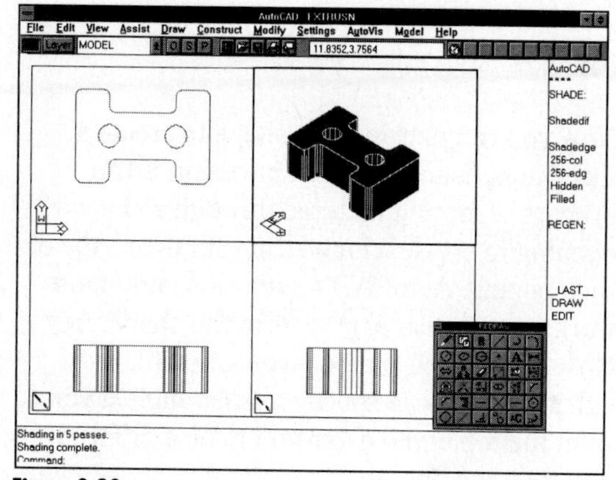

Figure 8.28

On your own, save your drawing EXTRUSN and start a new drawing. Start the new drawing from the solid modeling prototype. Use SOLPROTO, or SOLPRO_D that came with the data files. Call your new drawing REVOLUTN.

Creating a Solid by Revolution

Creating a solid by revolution is similar in some ways to creating an extrusion. It can be used to sweep a 2D polyline, circle, or region about a circular path to create a symmetrical solid that is basically circular in cross section.

Use the 2D Polyline command on your own to draw the line you see in Figure 8.29.

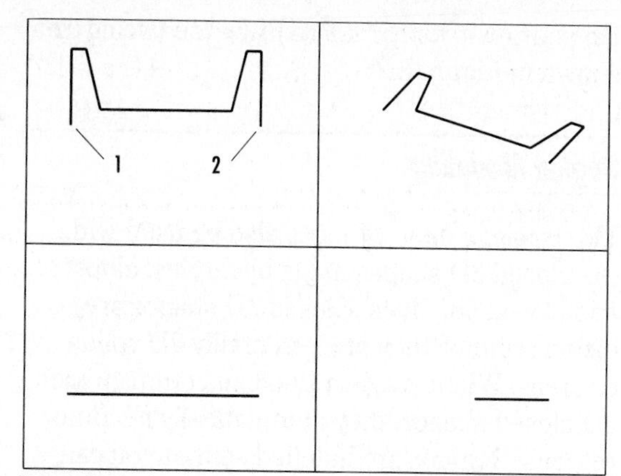

Figure 8.29

Now you will revolve the polyline about an axis to create a solid. The axis line need not be drawn but can be specified by two points.

Pick: **Model *(menu bar)*, Revolve**

Select region, polyline or circle for revolution. . .

Select objects: *(pick the polyline)*

Select objects: ↵

Axis of revolution - Entity/X/Y/<Startpoint of axis>:
(pick endpoint 1)

End point of axis: *(pick endpoint 2)*

Angle of revolution <full circle>: ↵

You should see a shape similar to Figure 8.30.

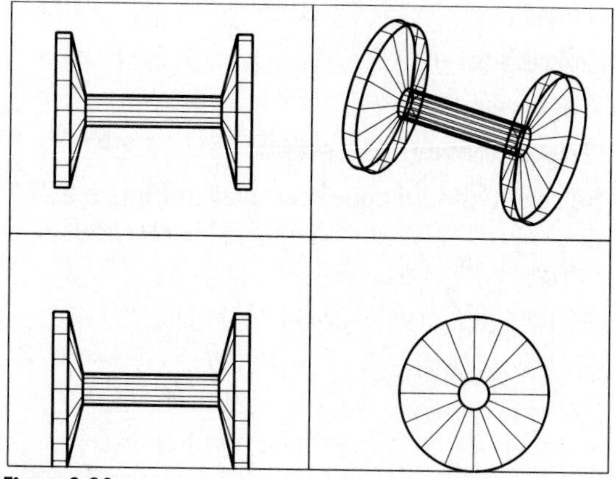

Figure 8.30

Save your drawing and start a new drawing on your own. Start the new drawing from the solid modeling prototype. Call your new drawing INTSCT.

Using the Boolean Operator INTERSECT

Like the UNION and SUBTRACT Boolean operators you learned to use earlier in the tutorial, INTERSECT lets you create complex shapes from simpler shapes. INTERSECT returns only the area that is common to the two or more solids or regions you have selected. Next you will create the shape you see in Figure 8.31 by creating two solids and finding their intersection.

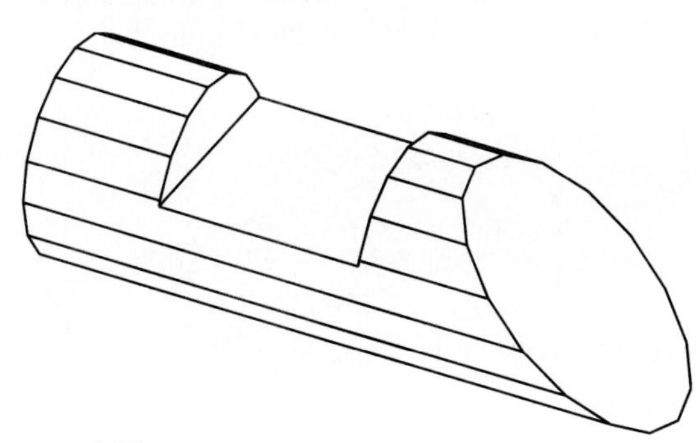

Figure 8.31

First create in the front view the shape of a surface that you will extrude to create the angled face and notch.

Pick: ***(in the lower left viewport to make it active)***

Command: **UCS** ↵

Origin/ZAxis/3point/Entity/View/X/Y/Z/Prev/Restore/
Save/Del/?/<World>: **R** ↵

?\Name of UCS to restore: **FRONT** ↵

The grid appears in the lower left viewport, parallel to the front view. Use the PLINE command to create a polyline that defines the shape of the object in the front view.

Pick: **PLINE icon *(toolbox)***

From point: **2.5,0** ↵

Current line-width is 0.0000

Arc/Close/Halfwidth/Length/Undo/Width/
<Endpoint of line>:**2.5,1.5** ↵

Arc/Close/Halfwidth/Length/Undo/Width/
<Endpoint of line>: **3.5,1.5** ↵

Arc/Close/Halfwidth/Length/Undo/Width/
<Endpoint of line>: **3.5,1** ↵

Arc/Close/Halfwidth/Length/Undo/Width/
<Endpoint of line>: **5,1** ↵

Arc/Close/Halfwidth/Length/Undo/Width/
<Endpoint of line>: **5,1.5** ↵

Arc/Close/Halfwidth/Length/Undo/Width/
<Endpoint of line>: **5.5,1.5** ↵

Arc/Close/Halfwidth/Length/Undo/Width/
<Endpoint of line>: **7,0** ↵

Arc/Close/Halfwidth/Length/Undo/Width/
<Endpoint of line>: **C** ↵

Once you have drawn the shape of the object in the front view, your drawing will look like Figure 8.32.

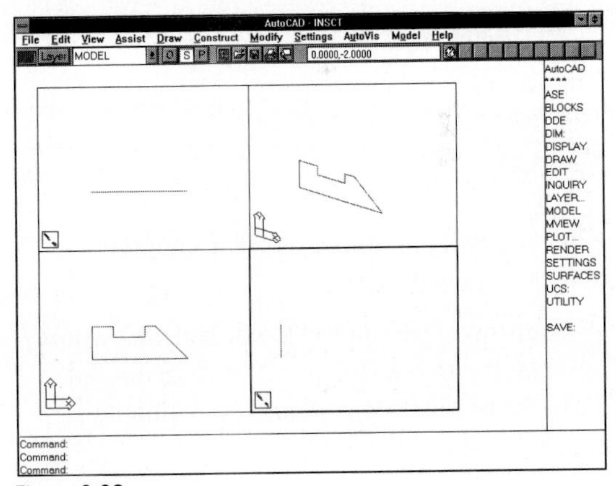

Figure 8.32

■ ***TIP*** You may not be able to see the top and side views if the object is drawn so that they are near the boundaries of the viewports. You can use the PAN command to pan the object inside the viewports to bring them into range. ■

Now extrude this shape to form a solid.

Pick: **Model *(menu bar)*, Extrude**

Select regions, polylines and circles for extrusion. . .

Select objects: ***(pick the polyline)*** ⏎

Height of extrusion: **–3** ⏎

Extrusion taper angle <0>: ⏎

The solid that you see in Figure 8.33 is created.

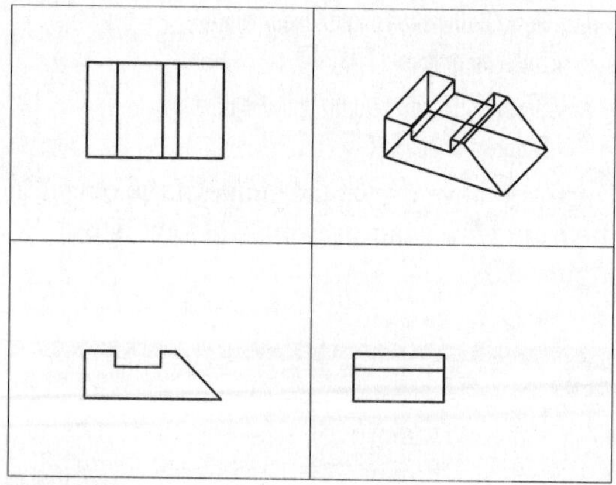

Figure 8.33

Next you will create the circular shape of the object in the side view.

On your own, pick in the lower right viewport to make it current. Restore the UCS named SIDE to activate the grid and coordinates parallel to the side view.

Pick: **CIRCLE *(toolbox)***

CIRCLE 3P/2P/TTR/<Center point>: **2P** ⏎

First point on diameter: **1.5,0** ⏎

Second point on diameter: **1.5,1.5** ⏎

In the top view, front view, and right-side view of your entire object, the circle is drawn a distance away from the previously drawn solid. You will use the EXTRUDE command to elongate the circle into a cylinder.

Pick: **Model *(menu bar)*, Extrude**

Select regions, polylines and circles for extrusion. . .

Select objects: ***(pick the circle)*** ⏎

Height of extrusion: **10** ⏎

Extrusion taper angle <0>: ⏎

The oblique view of your drawing in the upper right viewport should look like Figure 8.34.

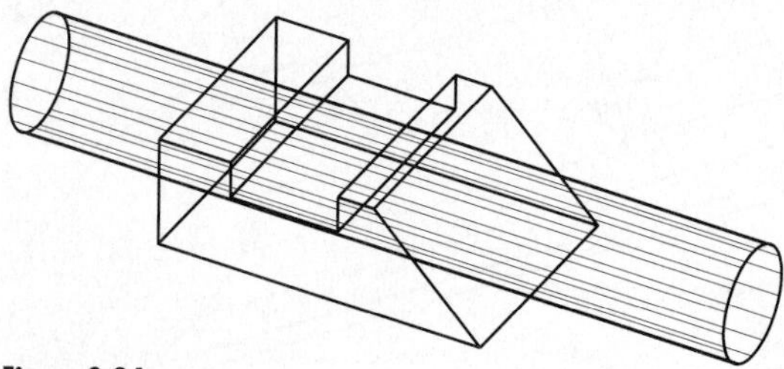

Figure 8.34

Now you are ready to use the INTERSECT command to create a new solid from the overlapping portions of the two solids you have drawn.

Pick: **Model *(menu bar)*, Intersect**

Select objects: ***(pick the extruded circle and the extruded polyline)*** ⏎

The solid modeling database is updated. The oblique view of your resulting drawing will look like Figure 8.35.

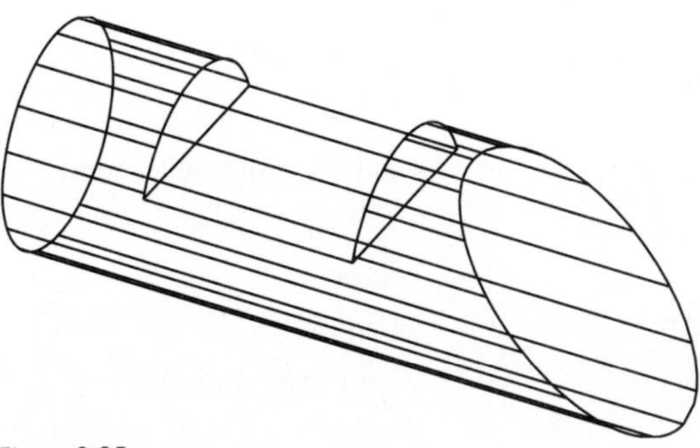

Figure 8.35

Save your drawing.

■ ***Warning:*** Because the solid modeling database is stored using *handles*, blocks, and layer AME_FRZ, you must not use commands that will destroy or change these items in the drawing. Therefore, do not thaw layer AME_FRZ. Do not use the EXPLODE command on the model, because it destroys block information. Do not use the PURGE command, because it can destroy handles. Also, do not turn handles off with the HANDLES, Off option. ■

Going Further

The SOLDELENT variable controls whether the 2D object is automatically deleted after being extruded, revolved, or solidified. A value of 1 means never delete the 2D entity, 2 means ask during the command whether to delete, and a value of 3 means always delete the 2D entity. The default setting in AutoCAD is 3 (always). You can use the AME System Variables dialogue box, or you can type "SOLDELENT" at the "Command:" prompt, to change the setting. To select the dialogue box from the menu bar, pick Model, Setup, Variables. In the lower left corner of the dialogue box, under the heading Entities, you will see that Deletion is set to Always. Pick on Always and reset the selection to Never. Now you can create a polyline and extrude it in one direction using a taper angle. The original polyline will remain. Select it again and extrude it in the other direction, using the same taper angle. This way you can create a surface that tapers in both directions. Experiment with this on your own. When you are done, use the dialogue box again to reset entity deletion to Always. If you have difficulty selecting an entity that coincides with a solid or other entity, try using crossing to select both entities and then use Remove and remove the entity you do not wish to select from the selection set. When you are finished building the selection set, be sure to press enter to signal AutoCAD that the selection set is complete.

You have completed this tutorial. Now you know how to establish viewports and viewing directions and create the basic shapes used in solid modeling. With these tools you can create a wide variety of complicated shapes. In the next tutorials, you will learn how to apply more of the power of solid modeling to change the solids, analyze the mass properties, create sectional and auxiliary views from the solid model, and add dimensions and notes to the views. Practice creating shapes and working with the User Coordinate Systems on your own. You are now ready to begin the next tutorial.

KEY TERMS

Boolean operators
coordinate system locator
difference
extrusion
globe
handles
intersection
plan view
revolution
solid modeling
surface modeling
tessellation
tree structure
union
User Coordinate System (UCS)
vector
viewpoint
wireframe modeling
World Coordinate System (WCS)

KEY COMMANDS

Extrude
Hide
Intersect
Mesh
Mview
Plan
Primitives
Render
Revolve
Shade
Solid Delete Entity
Solid Wire Density
Subtract
Union
User Coordinate System
User Coordinate System Icon
Viewpoint

EXERCISES

Use solid modeling to create the parts shown according to the specified dimensions.

8.1 Connector

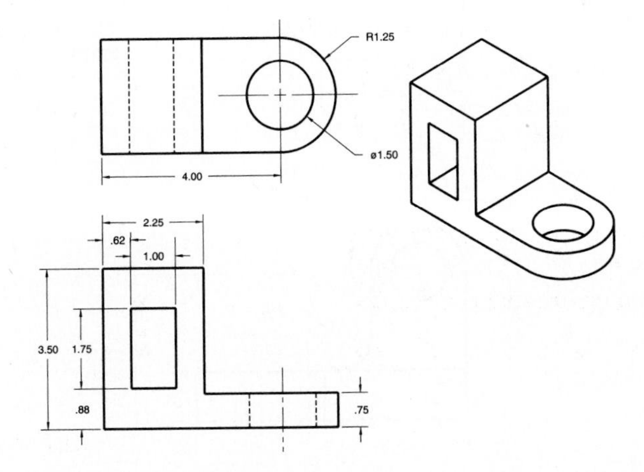

8.2 Angle Link

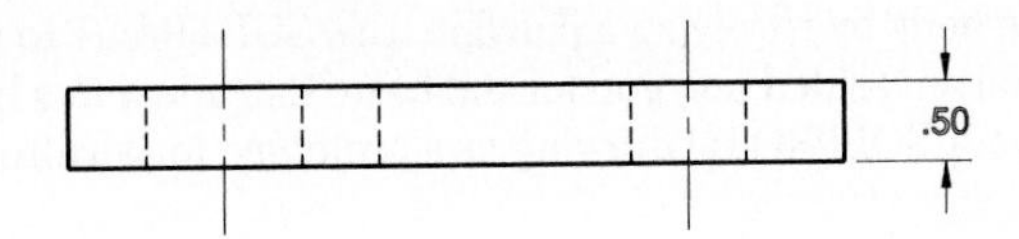

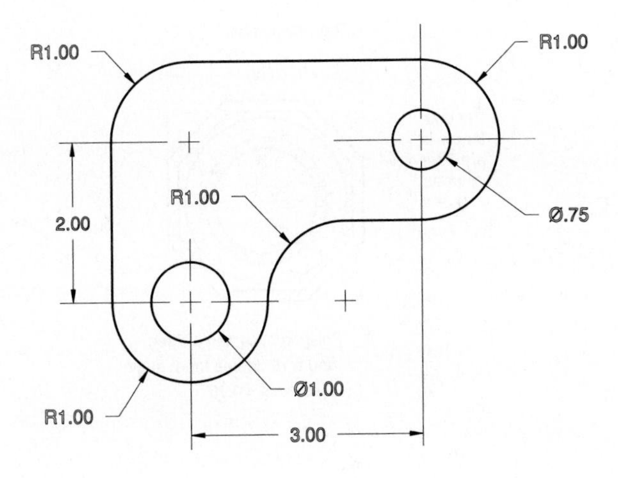

8.3 Support Base

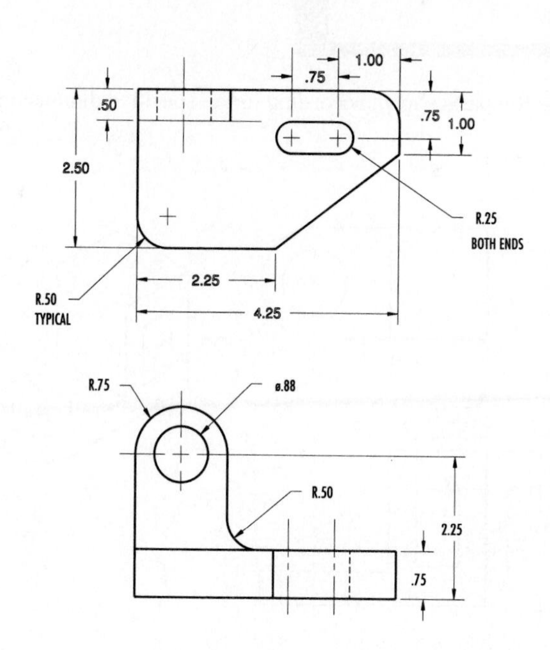

8.4 Chess Piece

Create the rook chess piece body by revolving a polyline. Use SUBTRACT to remove box primitives to form the cutouts in the tower. Add an 8-sided polygon for the base. Extrude it to a height of .15 and use a taper angle of 15 degrees. (Use your SOLPROTO drawing as a prototype to start from.)

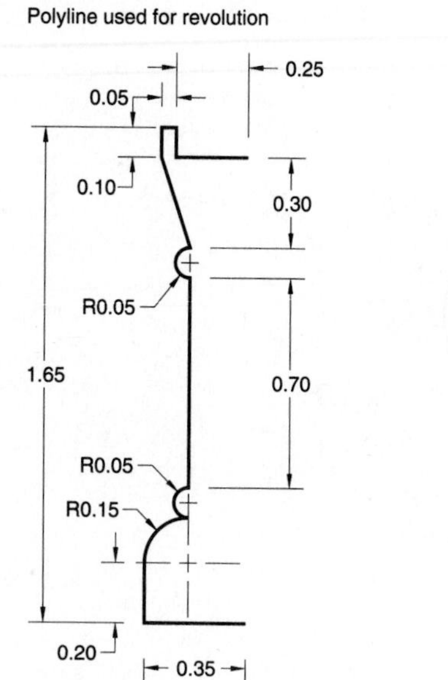

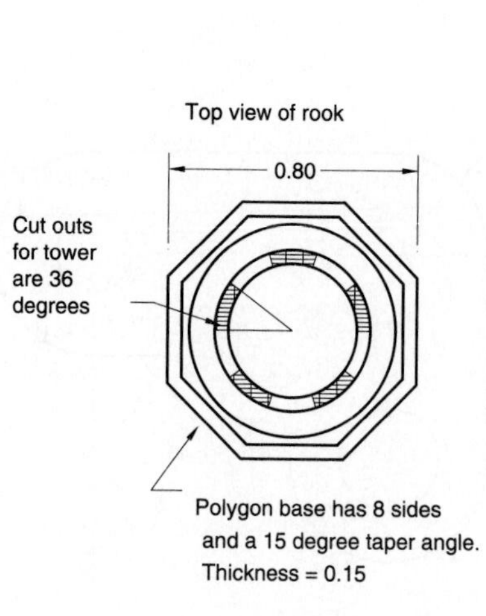

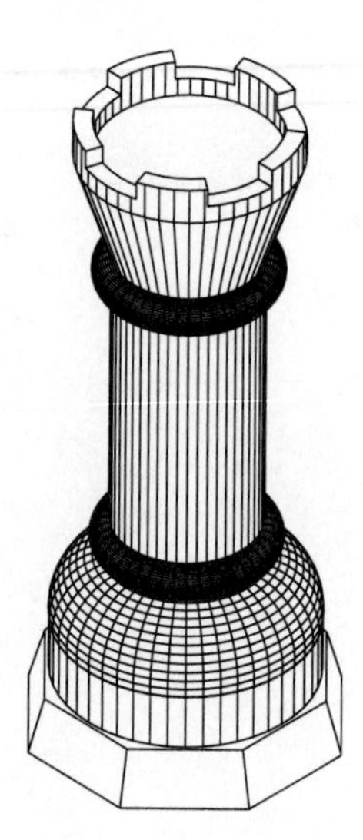

Draw the following shapes using solid modeling techniques. The letter M after an exercise number means that the units are millimeters.

8.5M Bushing Holder

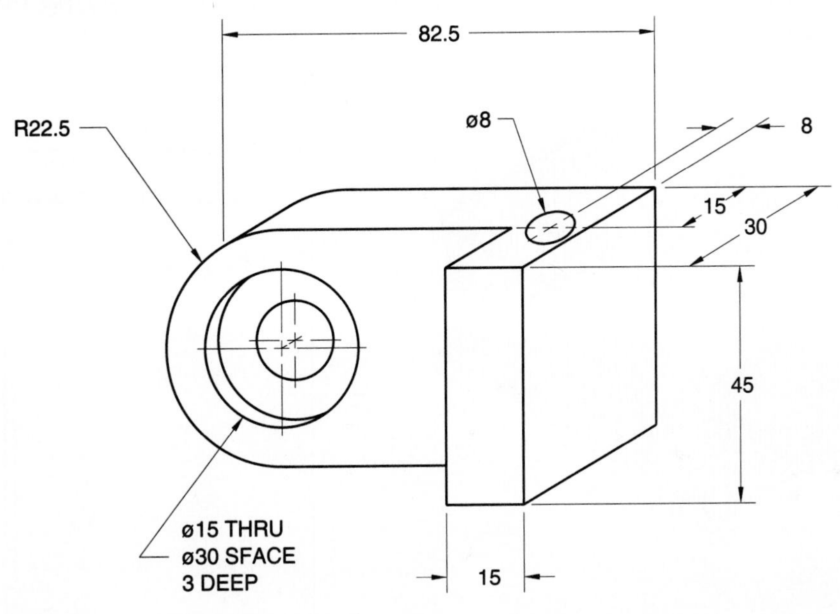

8.6 Shaft Support

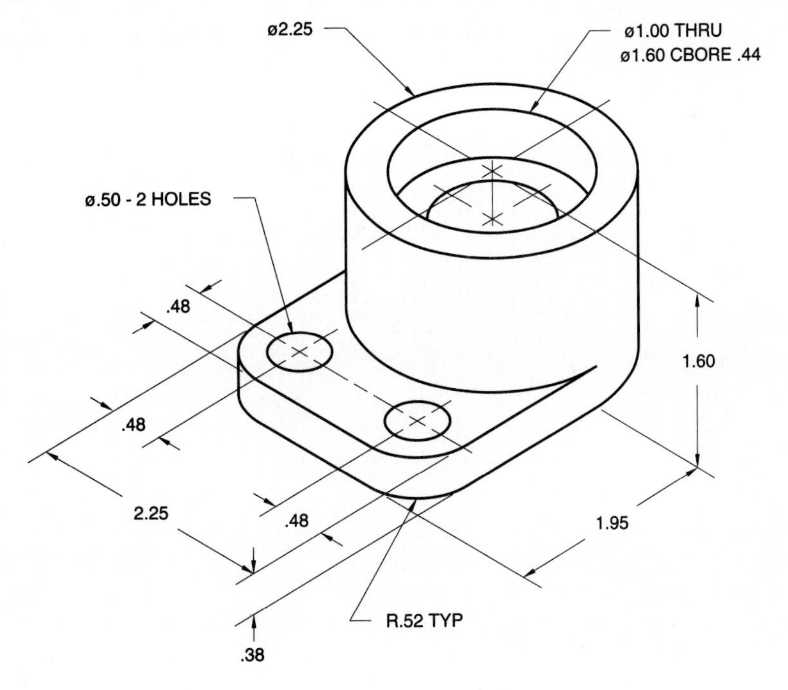

8.7 Balcony

Design a balcony like the one shown here, or a more complex one, using the solid modeling techniques you have learned. Use "two-by-fours" (which actually measure 1.5" × 3.5") for vertical pieces. Use DIVIDE to insure equal spacing.

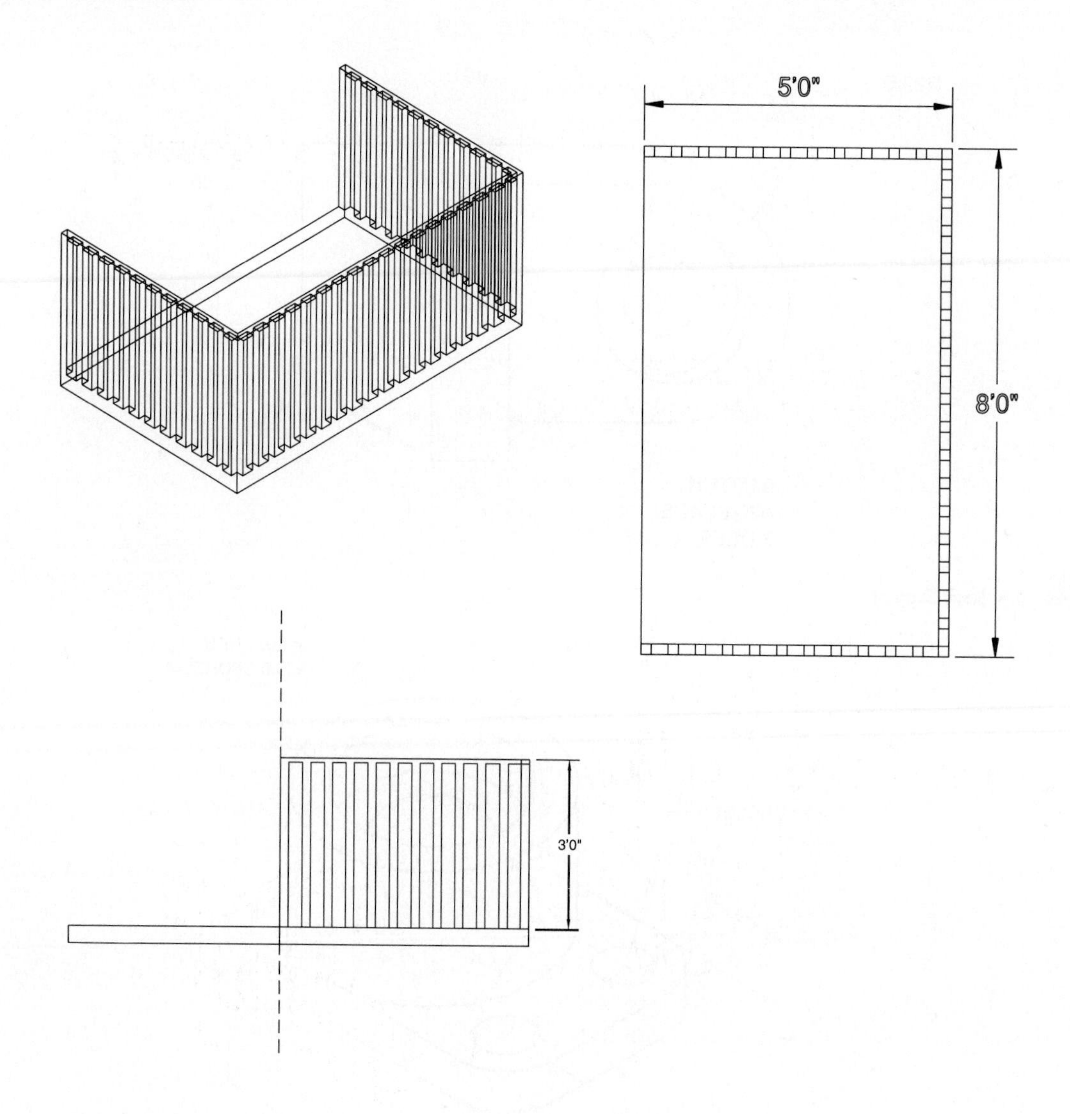

8.8 Bridge

Create a bridge as shown below. First determine the size of the bridge that you want and the area that you would like left open with the arc. Use SOLEXT to create the arc. Add the structure of the bridge, making sure that the supports are evenly spaced and of sufficient height. (You can enter one half of the supports and then use MIRROR.)

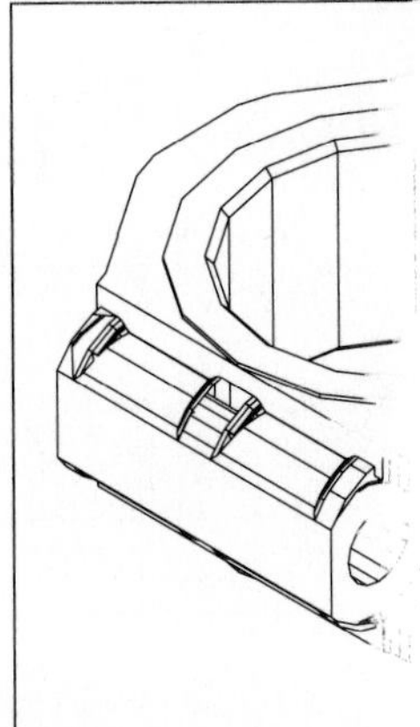

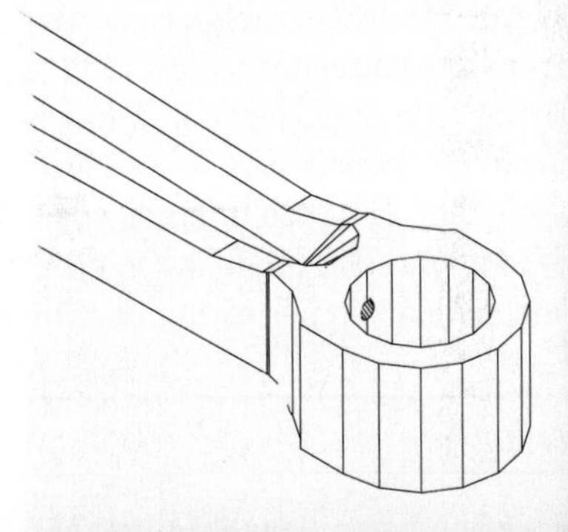

TUTORIAL 9

Changing and Plotting Solid Models

Objectives

When you have finished this tutorial, you will be able to

1. Add a rounded fillet between two surfaces, using SOLFILL.
2. Add an angled surface or chamfer to your model, using SOLCHAM.
3. Change properties, such as the color and size of primitives, using SOLCHP.
4. Separate parts joined with Boolean operators, using SOLSEP.
5. Remove a portion from a solid, using SOLCUT.
6. List the solid information and tree structure with SOLLIST.
7. Plot 2D views of the model with hidden lines shown correctly, using SOLPROF.
8. Control visibility of layers within each viewport with VPLAYER.

Introduction

You have learned how to create solid models and use multiple viewports. In this tutorial, you will learn to use the solid modeling editing commands to make changes and create a larger variety of shapes. Using AME, you can create solid models for many engineering drawing needs. From the solid models, you can directly generate 2D orthographic views that use the correct line patterns to show hidden lines. In Tutorial 13 you will learn how to add dimensions to the views that you generate from the solid model. In future tutorials you will learn how to apply solid modeling to create many different standard types of engineering drawings.

Starting

Before you begin, launch AutoCAD. If you need help, please review the AutoCAD for Windows section of Chapter 3, AutoCAD Basics, in Part 1, Getting Started. Your computer display shows AutoCAD's drawing editor. You will open an existing drawing file by using the OPEN command icon from the toolbar.

Pick: ***Open (toolbar)***

Open the drawing file called BLOCK that you created in Tutorial 8, or use the drawing SOLBLOCK from the data files provided with your software.

The block you created in Tutorial 8 should appear on your screen, as shown in Figure 9.1.

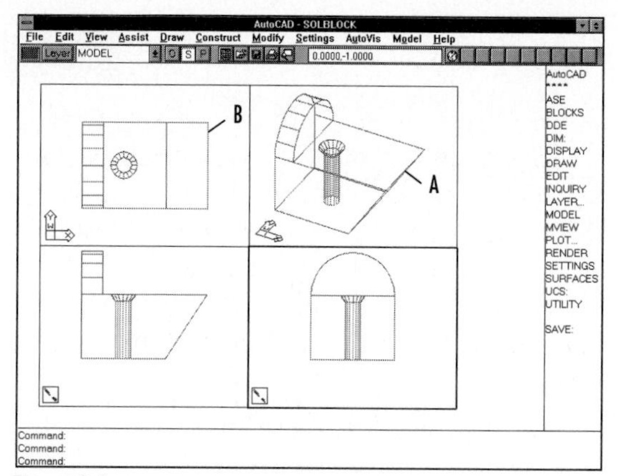

Figure 9.1

Use the REGENALL command to return your model to wireframe representation and regenerate the display, if it has been shaded.

Command: **REGENALL** (↵)

■ ***TIP*** As you are working through the tutorial, you may need to redraw or regenerate the drawing to eliminate partially shown lines or shading. Use REDRAW to eliminate partially shown lines in a single viewport. Use REDRAWALL to redraw all of the viewports at once. The REDRAW commands refresh the screen from the current display file. The REGEN commands recalculate the display file from the drawing database and refresh the screen. Use REGEN to regenerate the current viewport or REGENALL to regenerate all of the viewports at once.

To make selecting easier, remember the 'ZOOM, Window command. Transparent zooming allows you to zoom a view during another command. You can use it to enlarge an area to make selecting easier. To return the area to the original size, always use 'ZOOM, Previous, not 'ZOOM, All. When using transparent ZOOM, don't forget to add the apostrophe in front of the command, select it from the toolbar, or select it from View on the menu bar. ■

Using SOLFILL

AutoCAD's solid fillet command lets you add concave or convex rounded surfaces between plane or cylindrical surfaces on an existing solid. You will use the SOLFILL command to create a rounded edge for the front, angled surface of the object. You will select SOLFILL from the menu bar by picking Model, Modify, Fillets Solids.

Pick: **Model *(menu bar)*, Modify, Fillet Solids**

Pick edges of solids to be filleted (press Enter when done):
(pick the top edge of the angled surface marked A in Figure 9.1) ↵

1 edges selected.

Diameter/<Radius> of fillet <0.00>: **.5** ↵

Phase I - Boundary evaluation begins.

Phase II - Tessellation computation begins.

Updating the Advanced Modeling Extension database.

Your drawing with the rounded corner added should look like Figure 9.2.

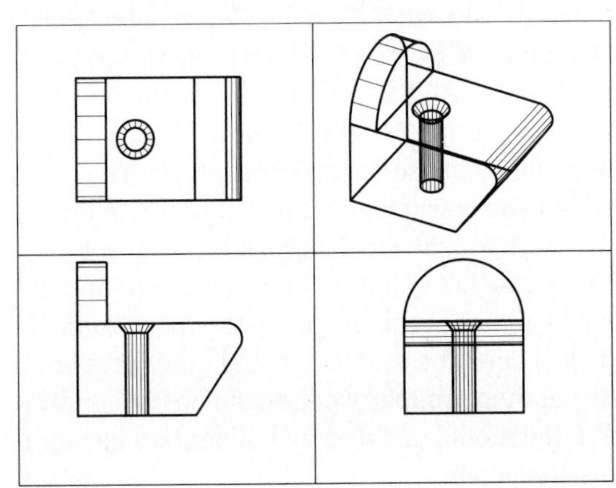

Figure 9.2

Adapting for Architecture

The SOLFILL command can be used to create curved soffits or rounded walls. Experiment with different radii and try using the DVIEW command to view the spaces to see if you like the appearance of the rounded surfaces you have made. ■

You will use the UNDO command to remove the fillet and then use the SOLCHAM command to add an angled surface in its place.

Command: **U** ↵

The fillet that you added to your drawing is eliminated.

Using SOLCHAM

The solid chamfer command is like the solid fillet command, except that it adds an angled surface instead of a rounded one. You will select SOLCHAM from the menu bar by picking Model, Modify, Chamfer Solids. When using the SOLCHAM command, you are prompted to select a base surface and then the edge or edges you want the chamfer between. Selection of the correct surface will be easier if you make the upper left-hand viewport active.

On your own, make the upper left viewport active and return the UCS to the World Coordinates.

Pick: **Model *(menu bar)*, Modify, Chamfer Solids**

Pick base surface: ***(pick the top horizontal surface labeled B in Figure 9.1)***

Next/<OK>: ***(If the correct surface is highlighted, press*** ↵***. If the wrong surface is highlighted, type "N" to select the next surface.)***

> ■ ***TIP*** When you are picking on the solid model, it is often difficult to tell at first which surface you want to select because each line of the wireframe represents not one surface, but the intersection between two surfaces. Many commands have the Next option to allow you to move surface by surface until the one you want to select is highlighted. If the surface you want to select is not highlighted, use the Next option until it is. When the surface you want to select is highlighted, press ↵. ■

Pick edges of this face to be chamfered (press Enter when done): ***(pick the front edge, where you had the fillet)*** ↵

1 edges selected.

Enter distance along base surface <0.00>: **.75** ↵

Enter distance along adjacent surface <0.75>: ↵

Phase I. . . Updating the Advanced Modeling Extension database

On your own, use the MESH command to mesh the solid so that it can be shaded. Once you have the object meshed, shade it in the upper right viewport. Your drawing with the chamfer should look like Figure 9.3.

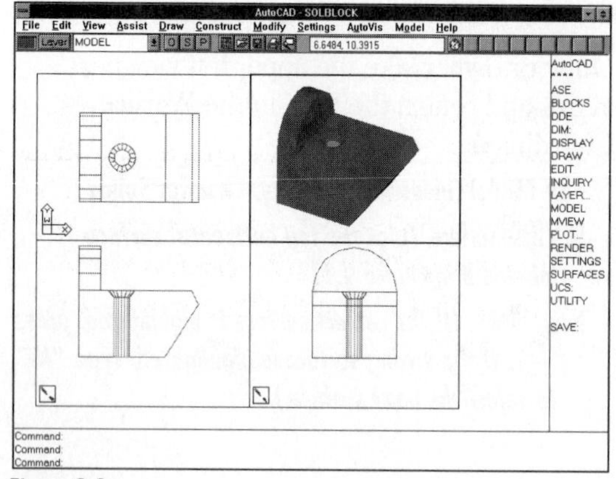

Figure 9.3

Adapting for Architecture

The SOLCHAM command is useful for creating shed roofs or gables. Experiment with multiple chamfers in different directions to create roof planes of any configuration. ■

Making Changes with SOLCHP

The SOLCHP command, which stands for Solid Change Primitives, is very useful. With it you can change the size and color of a primitive, delete a primitive, move primitives, and replace one primitive with another. You can try things to see how they will look without exiting the command, using the Evaluate option. Additionally, you can create an identical primitive in the same place as one you have already joined or subtracted from the model, using the Instance option. The instanced primitive can then be moved or used in place.

AutoCAD can make changes to the model in this way because it uses the Constructive Solid Geometry (CSG) method to create the complex model. All the information for the primitives and simpler shapes is stored in the drawing database, using a tree structure, which you learned about in Tutorial 8. When you want to make a change, it is possible to step back through the tree structure to find the simpler shapes that make up the more complex shape. The size, color, and other properties of these simpler shapes can be changed and the model updated by building up through the tree again.

Use the solid change primitives command to delete the chamfer and the undercut surface and change the color of the through hole. When you are deleting a primitive, AutoCAD asks whether you want to retain the detached primitive, which you can then use during later commands. If retained, the primitive becomes a separate drawing entity from the major solid in the drawing.

Command: **REGEN** ↵

Pick: **Model *(menu bar)*, Modify, Change Primitives**

Select a solid or region: ***(pick the object in the upper right viewport)***

Phase I. . .

Select primitive: ***(pick the chamfer)***

Color/Delete/Evaluate/Instance/Move/Next/Pick/Replace/Size/eXit <N>: **D** ↵

Retain detached primitive? <N>: ↵

Once the chamfer is deleted, the upper right hand view of your drawing should look like Figure 9.4.

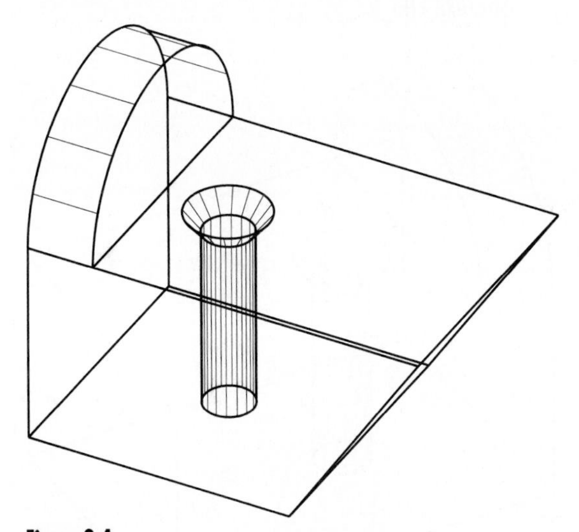

Figure 9.4

You should still see the SOLCHP prompt on your screen. To select and delete the wedge, press the ↵ key to use the Next option to cycle through the primitives on the screen until the wedge primitive is highlighted, as shown in Figure 9.5. When the correct primitive is highlighted, type "D" and press ↵ to use the Delete option of the SOLCHP command and delete the wedge on your own. You will remain in the SOLCHP command, where you will make other selections. The drawing on your screen will not necessarily be updated until you exit the command or pick Evaluate. After you delete the wedge you will go on to select the box and change its size.

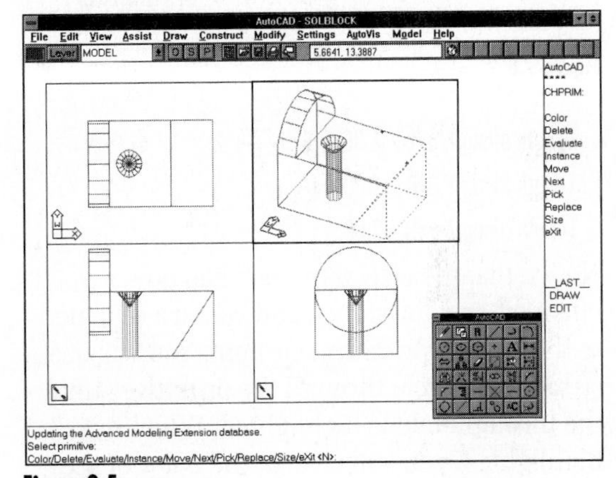

Figure 9.5

Color/Delete/Evaluate/Instance/Move/Next/Pick/Replace/Size/eXit <N>: ***(press ↵ until the box primitive is highlighted)***

Color/Delete/Evaluate/Instance/Move/Next/Pick/Replace/Size/eXit <N>: **S** ↵

The *Motion Coordinate System (MCS)* icon is displayed at the corner of the box, as shown in Figure 9.6. This icon enables you to locate the x, y, z coordinate system of the box. The line with one arrow shows the X axis, two arrows show the Y directions, and three arrows show the Z direction.

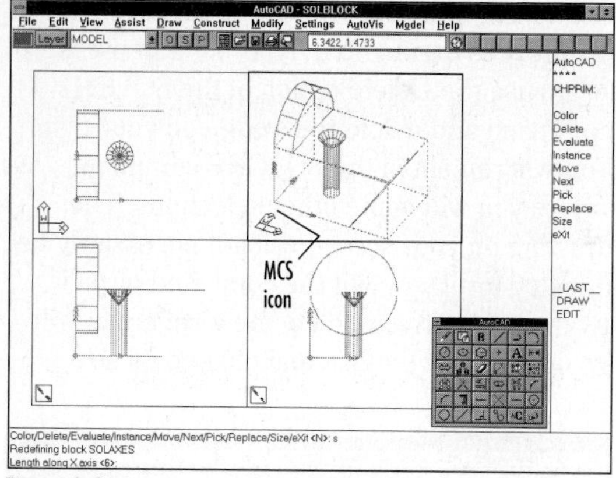

Figure 9.6

> **Length along X axis <6.00>: 5.5** ↵
> **Length along Y axis <4.00>:** ↵
> **Length along Z axis <3.00>:** ↵

Notice that the size of the box has now changed on your screen and you are returned to the change primitives prompt. You will use ↵ again to cycle through the primitives until the through hole is highlighted. When it is highlighted, you will change the color of the primitive to red.

> **Color/Delete/Evaluate/Instance/Move/Next/Pick/Replace/ Size/eXit <N>: *(highlight the hole)***
> **Color/Delete/Evaluate/Instance/Move/Next/Pick/Replace/ Size/eXit <N>: C** ↵
> **New color for primitive <5 (blue)>: 1** ↵

The color of the hole changes to color 1 (red) and the same prompt reappears.

> **Color/Delete/Evaluate/Instance/Move/Next/Pick/Replace/ Size/eXit <N>: *(Now the cone that you made for the countersink should be highlighted. If it is not, press ↵ until it is and then type "C" and press ↵ to change its color.)***
> **New color <6 (magenta)>: 3** ↵

The countersink changes to the color green.

Often, while you are changing many primitives, it becomes unclear what the model will look like when you finally exit the command. To see how the object will look once it is recreated, you can use the Evaluate option. This way you can see the results of the changes you have been making before you exit the command, and you will not have to start the entire command process again if there is something that you have missed. You should still be inside the prompt for the change primitive command.

> **Color/Delete/Evaluate/Instance/Move/Next/Pick/Replace/ Size/eXit <N>: E** ↵

Your drawing should look like Figure 9.7. The hole should be red and the countersink area green. Now that you are done changing primitives, exit the command to cause the changes you have been making to take effect.

> **Color/Delete/Evaluate/Instance/Move/Next/Pick/Replace/ Size/eXit <N>: X** ↵

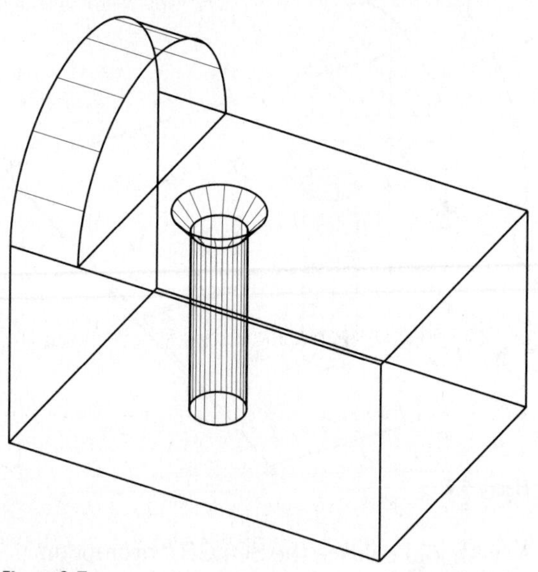

Figure 9.7

Using SOLSEP

You will use the solid separate command to take the block apart so that the large cylinder forming the rounded top surface is again a separate primitive and not part of the block. You will then add a rectangular box solid and rejoin the cylinder so that it sits higher up on the block. SOLSEP undoes the most recent Boolean operation. You can continue using SOLSEP to step back and undo each Boolean operation in your drawing. You will select SOLSEP from the menu bar by picking Model, Modify, Separate.

Pick: **Model *(menu bar)*, Modify, Separate**

Select objects: ***(pick the object)***

Select objects: ⏎

The entire original cylinder should reappear. It is no longer joined to the block. Your drawing should look like Figure 9.8.

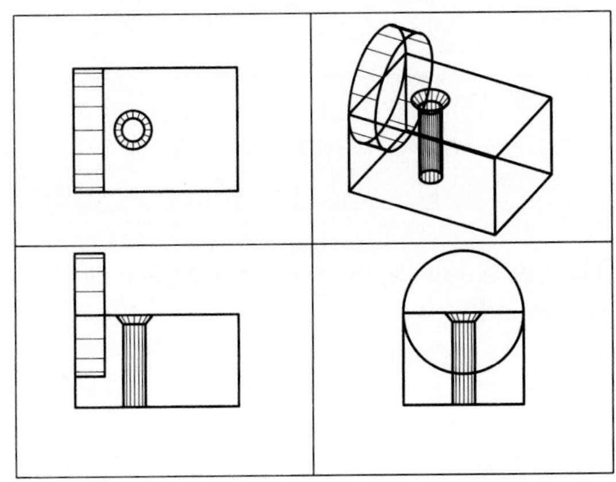

Figure 9.8

Using SOLLIST

The SOLLIST command lists solid database information about the object you select. Use the SOLLIST command to inquire about the block. You will select the SOLLIST command from the menu bar by picking Model, Inquiry, List Objects.

Pick: **Model *(menu bar)*, Inquiry, List Objects**

Edge/Face/Tree/<Object>: ⏎

Select objects: ***(pick the rectangular block)***

Select objects: ⏎

AutoCAD automatically switches to the text screen, where a listing of information about the solid block appears, similar to the list shown in Figure 9.9. The list shows the object type, the handle number, type of representation, and rigid motion for the object.

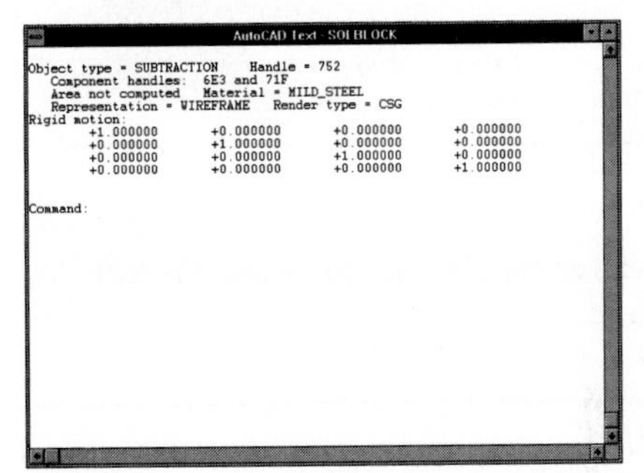

```
AutoCAD Text - SOLBLOCK
Object type = SUBTRACTION    Handle = 752
   Component handles:  6E3 and 71F
   Area not computed   Material = MILD_STEEL
   Representation = WIREFRAME   Render type = CSG
Rigid motion:
        +1.000000    +0.000000    +0.000000    +0.000000
        +0.000000    +1.000000    +0.000000    +0.000000
        +0.000000    +0.000000    +1.000000    +0.000000
        +0.000000    +0.000000    +0.000000    +1.000000

Command:
```

Figure 9.9

Press: F2 ***(to return to the graphics screen)***

Next you will repeat the SOLLIST command; this time, list the tree structure of the solid modeling database for the rectangular block. You will see that the object is a subtraction made from three primitives: a box, a cylinder, and a cone.

Command: ⏎ ***(to restart the SOLLIST command)***

Edge/Face/Tree/<Object>: **T** ⏎

Select objects: ***(pick the rectangular block)***

Select objects: ⏎

The tree structure of the solid modeling database is listed on your screen, as shown in Figure 9.10. When you are finished reading the information, press ⏎ to see the next page if necessary.

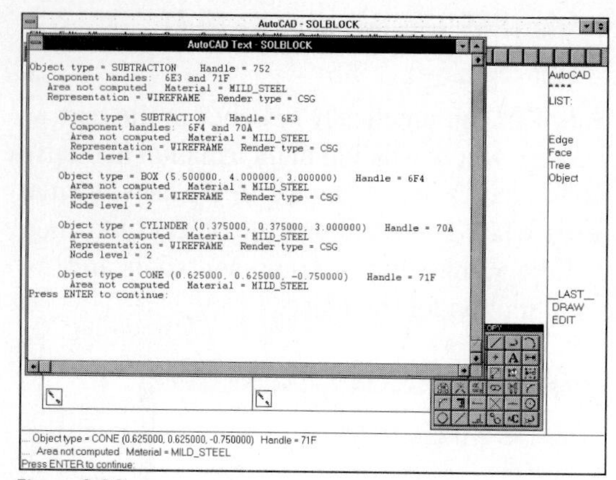

Figure 9.10

Pick: ***(twice on the Close box to remove the text window)***

Using MOVE

Many of the editing commands that you have learned in the 2D tutorials are still effective with solid modeling. Don't be afraid to try them when they would be useful. You will use the MOVE command to move the cylinder upward 1 unit in the Z direction and then create a new rectangular piece beneath it.

You have used MOVE by specifying a base point and a displacement. You can also specify just the displacement, as you will in this sequence. Pressing (↵) tells AutoCAD the first entry is not a point, but the distance you want to move along each axis.

Pick: **MOVE *(toolbox)***

Select objects: ***(pick the large cylinder that you separated from the block)***

Select objects: (↵)

Base point or displacement: **0,0,1** (↵)

Second point of displacement: (↵)

The cylinder is moved upward 1 unit.

Now create the rectangular box within the cylinder, as shown in Figure 9.11. The WCS should still be active. Type "SOLBOX" to begin drawing the box solid primitive:

Command: **SOLBOX** (↵)

Baseplane/Center/<corner of box:<0,0,0>: **INT** (↵)

of: ***(pick corner A in Figure 9.11)***

Cube/Length/<other corner>: **L** (↵)

Length: **1** (↵)

Width: **4** (↵)

Height: **1** (↵)

> ■ ***TIP*** Don't forget that you can quickly pick the OSNAP overrides from the tool box. ■

The box should appear on your screen as shown in Figure 9.11.

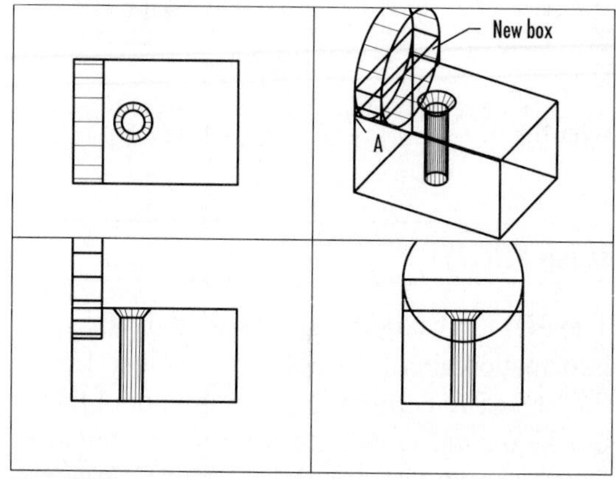

Figure 9.11

Using SOLCUT

Using the SOLCUT command, you can cut a solid off beyond a specified *cutting plane*. The cutting plane does not have to be an existing drawing entity. You can specify the cutting plane several ways:

Option	**Function**
3points	choose three points to define a plane
XY, YZ, ZX	choose a plane parallel to the XY, YZ, or ZX coordinate planes and through a point
Entity	select an existing planar entity
Zaxis	specify a point for the origin and a point that gives the direction of the Z axis of the cutting plane
View	align a plane parallel to the current view and through a point
Last	align a plane with the last cutting plane or construction plane used

The options for the cutting plane are the same options used whenever the CP, or *construction plane*, prompt appears. When you have specified the cutting plane, you are prompted to pick a point on the desired side of the plane, where you want the object to remain. The portion on the other side is then deleted. You can choose the Both sides option so that the object is cut into two pieces and neither side is deleted.

In this example, you will use the 3points option to specify three points defining the cutting plane. Often you have existing geometry drawn, so by using the Object Snap override modes, you can easily specify the points for the cutting plane. Refer to Figure 9.12.

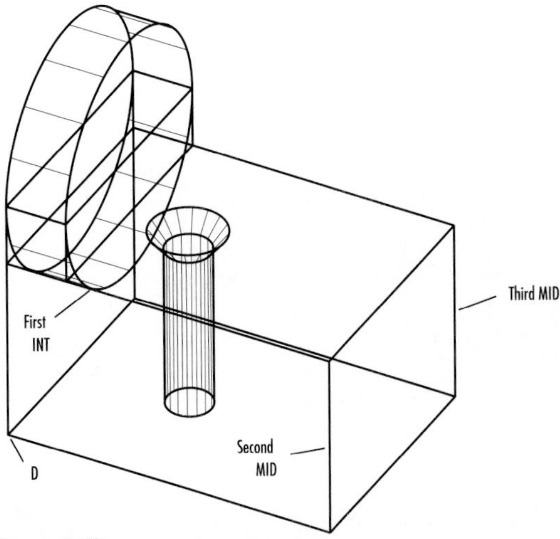

Figure 9.12

Pick: **Model *(menu bar)*, Modify, Cut Solids**

Select objects: ***(pick the rectangular block with the countersunk hole)***

1 found

Select objects: ↵

1 solid selected

Cutting plane by Entity/Last/Zaxis/View/XY/YZ/ZX/<3points>: ↵

1st point on plane: **INT** ↵

of ***(target the intersection labeled First INT)***

2nd point on plane: **MID** ↵

of ***(target the front vertical edge, labeled Second MID)***

3rd point on plane: **MID** ↵

of ***(target the rightmost vertical edge, labeled Third MID)***

Both sides/<Point on desired side of the plane>: ***(pick the bottom left corner, labeled D)***

The upper portion of the block is cut off, leaving an angled surface, as shown in Figure 9.13.

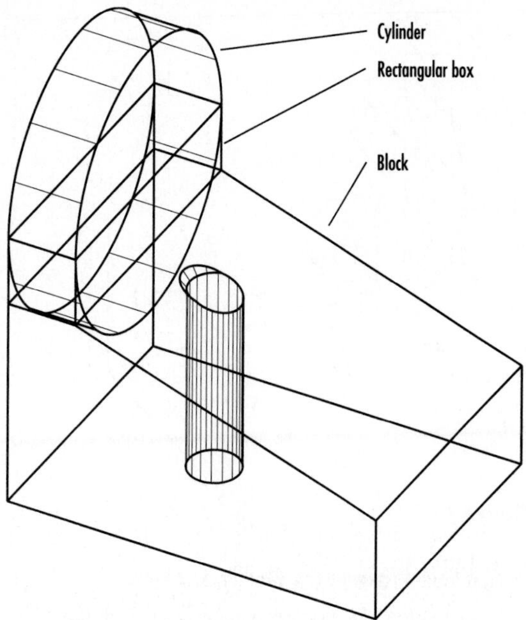

Figure 9.13

Adapting for Architecture

Use the View option to create a section along the lines of a view you have previously defined for your section cut. You can add text to these views to create a presentation drawing, as well as removing the hidden lines for clarity. ■

Now use the SOLUNION command to join all three parts together.

Pick: **Model *(menu bar)*, Union**
Select objects: ***(pick the large cylinder)***
1 found
Select objects: ***(pick the large rectangular block)***
1 found
Select objects: ***(pick the small box)***
1 found
Select objects: ↵
3 solids selected
Phase I - Boundary evaluation begins.
Phase II - Tessellation computation begins.
Updating the Advanced Modeling Extension database.
3 solids unioned.

Your drawing looks similar to Figure 9.14.

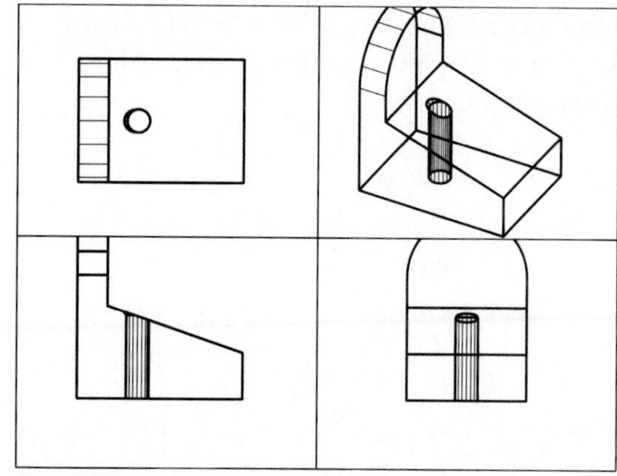
Figure 9.14

Centering the Views

Since you changed the height of the solid, it is not centered well in the viewports. You will use the ZOOM command with the Center option to view the object from farther away. The Center option of the ZOOM command locates the coordinates you specify in the center of the viewport. Then you can use the Scale XP option to specify a relative paper space scaling factor for the object. (This method works to line up views only if the viewports are the same size, because the center of the model is placed at the center of the viewport.) This method is similar to using the Left option, which you learned in Tutorial 8. The XP option is useful because if you use paper space to plot your views, the size is to a known scale. You will use .4XP for the isometric view. You can also zoom the isometric view with ZOOM, Dynamic or ZOOM, Window until it has the right appearance. To fit the front and side views into the viewports, you will use the PAN command and specify a displacement.

Make the upper right viewport active before you use the ZOOM command.

Command: Z ↵

All/Center/Dynamic/Extents/Left/Previous/Vmax/Window/ <Scale(X/XP)>: C ↵

Center point: 4.5,4,2.5 ↵

Magnification or Height <7.5000>: .4XP ↵

Next you will use the PAN command and pan the two lower viewports down so that the model fits inside the window. Move each one the same distance so that they will still align. You will specify a displacement of 0 for X, 0 for Y, and –1 for Z, to move the view down one unit in the Z direction; then, as you did for the MOVE command, press ↵ to specify that the value is a displacement and not a point. (Do not use the MOVE command to reposition the views, because this moves the object on the coordinate system and will have the effect of moving it in every viewport.)

Pick in the lower right viewport, where the side view of the object is shown, to make this viewport active.

Command: P ↵ ***(the alias for the PAN command)***

PAN Displacement: 0,0,–1 ↵

Second point: ↵

Repeat this process on your own for the lower left viewport, which shows the front view. First, pick the lower left viewport to make it active, then use the PAN command as you did above.

The views should fit into the viewports now and the drawing should appear similar to Figure 9.15.

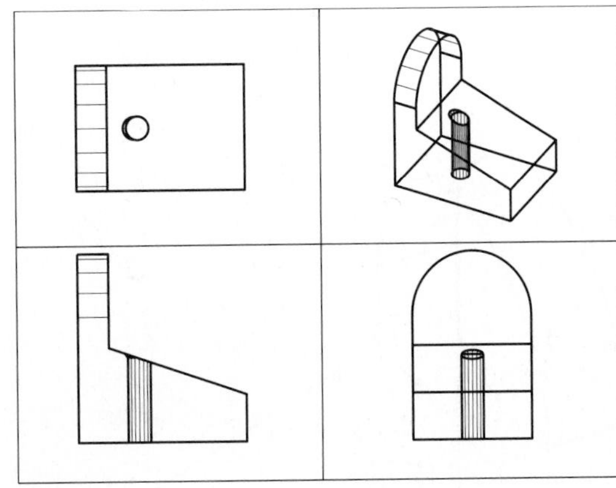

Figure 9.15

> ■ ***TIP*** Sometimes you can use ZOOM, Extents so that the drawing extents fill the viewport, but this will not align the views as exactly as ZOOM Center. ■

Now you will add a .375 deep hole of diameter .5, perpendicular to the angled surface.

To create a hole perpendicular to the angled surface, you will create a User Coordinate System that is aligned with the angled surface. For this you will use the UCS command with the 3point option to locate the origin and X and Y axes.

The upper right viewport should already be active. On your own, turn on the running mode OSNAP, Intersection so that it will be available to select intersections during the next commands. Refer to Figure 9.16 as you pick points.

Command: UCS ↵

Origin/Zaxis/3points/Entity/View/X/Y/Z/Prev/Restore/Save/ Del/?/<World>: 3 ↵

Origin point <0,0,0>: *(target the lower left corner of the angled surface, point 1 in Figure 9.16)*

Point on positive portion of the X-axis <8.5,2,1.5>: *(target the lower right corner of the angled surface, point 2)*

Point on positive-Y portion of the UCS XY plane <6.5,2,1.5>:
(target the upper left corner of the angled surface, point 3)

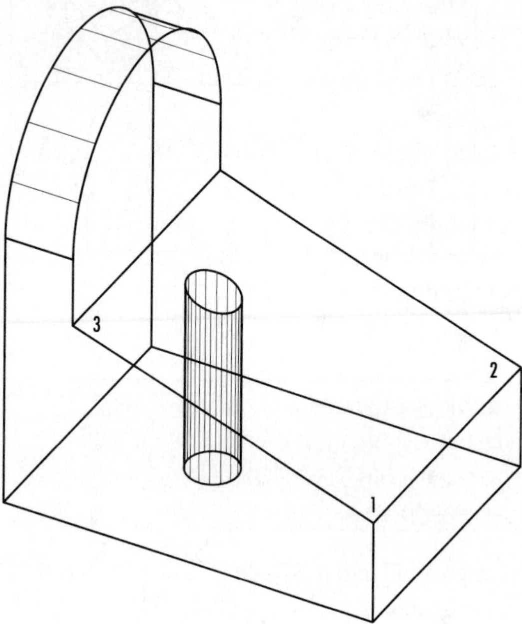

Figure 9.16

The grid in all the views changes so that it is now aligned with the angled surface.

> ■ ***TIP*** You can also use the SOLUCS command to align a User Coordinate System with the edge or face of a solid. Pick Model, Utility, SolUCS and at the prompt "Edge/<Face>:", choose Face if you want to align the UCS by picking a surface and Edge if you want to pick just an edge. At the next prompt, select the item with which to align the UCS. You will see the coordinate system align with the edge or surface you selected. ■

> ■ ***TIP*** It is useful to always keep the grid turned on so that you can see how the UCS is aligned. You can also look at the UCS icon, but often the grid is more noticeable. ■

Now use the PLAN command to align your view so that you are looking straight down the Z axis. The resulting view shows the XY plane of the new UCS that you created in the previous step. The PLAN command fits the drawing extents inside the viewport, so after using PLAN you will need to zoom the view to enlarge it.

Command: **PLAN** ↵

<Current UCS>/UCS/World: ↵

The view in the upper right viewport should now be aligned so that you are looking directly perpendicular to the angled surface on the object. On your own, use ZOOM, Window to enlarge the plan view so that it fills the viewport, as you see in Figure 9.17.

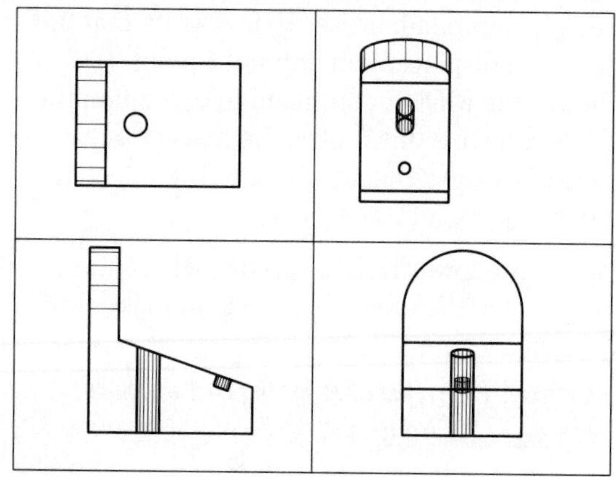

Figure 9.17

Save the view and the UCS so that you can restore them later if you wish.

Command: **UCS** ↵

Origin/Zaxis/3points/Entity/View/X/Y/Z/Prev/Restore/Save/Del/?/<World>: **S** ↵

?/Desired UCS name: **ANGLE** ↵

Command: **VIEW** ↵

?/Delete/Restore/Save/Window: **S** ↵

View name to save: **ANGLE** ↵

> ■ ***TIP*** AutoCAD has a built-in geometry calculator that lets you specify points that would be impossible by other drawing means. Whenever you are at a prompt requesting input of a point, real number, integer, or vector, you can use the transparent command 'CAL. 'CAL lets you write an expression in infix notation, such as 1+2*sin(30), at the prompt and the resultant value is used. You can also use osnap functions in combination with the geometry calculator. The geometry calculator is useful in creating complex models. ■

Creating the Hole

You will use the cylinder primitive and then subtract it to create the hole.

Pick: **Model *(menu bar)*, Primitives**

Pick: ***(the cylinder icon)*** ↵

Baseplane/Elliptical/<Center point> <0,0,0>: **2,1** ↵

Diameter/<Radius>: **D** ↵

Diameter: **.5** ↵

Center of other end/<Height>: **–.375** ↵

Subtract the cylinder to form a hole in the object.

Pick: **Model *(menu bar)*, Subtract**

Source objects...

Select objects: ***(pick the large rectangular block)***

Select objects: ↵

1 selected

Objects to subtract from them...

Select objects: ***(pick the short cylinder you just created)***

Select objects: ↵

1 solid subtracted from 1 solid

Restoring the World Coordinates

Now you will use the UCS command to change back to the World Coordinates.

Command: **UCS** ↵

Origin/Zaxis/3points/Entity/View/X/Y/Z/Prev/Restore/Save/Del/?/<World>: ↵

Reset the viewpoint for the upper right viewport with the VPOINT command.

Pick: **View *(menu bar)*, Set View, Viewpoint, Set Vpoint**

Rotate/<View point> <0.3162,0000,0.9487>: **1.5,–3,2.4** ↵

A view similar to the original view should be restored. Name this view 3D, using the VIEW command.

Command: **VIEW** ↵

?/Delete/Restore/Save/Window: **S** ↵

View name to save: **3D** ↵

On your own, use ZOOM, Window to enlarge the isometric view. Your drawing should now look like Figure 9.18.

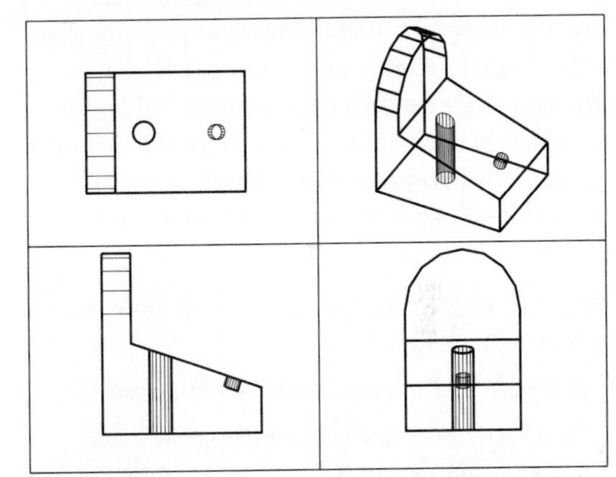

Figure 9.18

Use the Save As selection from the File menu to save the drawing. Name your drawing ANGLBLOK.

AME_FRZ Layer

Pick the Layer button to the left of the current layer name shown on the toolbar. Look at the list of layers. You will notice that besides

MODEL and VPORTS, the two layers you created in Tutorial 8, there is also a layer called AME_FRZ. AME_FRZ is where AutoCAD stores the solid model database information containing the block commands and handle numbers. This layer is frozen and you should not thaw it, **ever**. If you do, you may damage the solid model database and then you will not be able to change and update your model. If layer AME_FRZ is thawed, you will see a copy of your model with white lines. Changes to these entities corrupt your solid modeling database.

Pick: ***OK (to leave the Layer Control dialogue box without making any changes)***

Plotting Your Solid Model Drawing

To generate views that plot correctly, using hidden lines, you can use the SOLPROF command to create a 2D projection of each view into the viewport. AutoCAD automatically generates separate layers for hidden and visible lines for each viewport. The tangential edges, or multiple lines, that make up circular features can also be automatically deleted. You will need to *profile* the object in each viewport, creating a flat 2D view in the viewport.

On your own, make the upper right viewport active.

Command: ↵ ***(to restart the SOLPROF command)***

Select objects: ***(pick on an edge of the object in the upper right viewport)***

1 found

Select objects: ↵

1 solid selected

Display hidden profile lines on separate layer? <Y>: ↵

Project profile lines onto a plane?: <Y>: ↵

Delete tangential edges? <Y>: ↵

Phase I of hidden line removal computation has started.

Phase II of hidden line removal computation of current solid has started.

Phase III of hidden line removal computation of current solid has started.

Hidden line removal computation of current solid is completed.

You will see lines drawn over the original colored lines that designate the edges of your model in the current viewport. The default color for the profile lines is white (which appears black on a light background).

Next, pick the upper left viewport to make it active.

Then repeat the process to create a 2D profile of the object in the upper left viewport.

Pick: **Model *(menu bar)*, Display, Profile Solids**

Select objects: ***(pick on an edge of the object in the upper left viewport)***

1 found

Select objects: ↵

1 solid selected

Display hidden profile lines on separate layer? <Y>: ↵

Project profile lines onto a plane?: <Y>: ↵

Delete tangential edges? <Y>: ↵

Phase I of hidden line removal computation has started.

Phase II of hidden line removal computation of current solid has started.

Phase III of hidden line removal computation of current solid has started.

Hidden line removal computation of current solid is completed.

You will see lines appear over the colored edge lines in this viewport.

On your own, repeat this process for the two remaining viewports.

When you have completed profiling the object in each viewport, you will see only white lines (which appear black on a light-colored background) and colored tessellation lines on the screen. The SOLPROF command creates new layers for the lines of the profile, and the default color setting is white. Because you responded "Yes" to the prompt for displaying hidden profile lines on a new layer, there are two kinds of new layers in the drawing, one for visible profile lines and one for hidden profile lines.

AutoCAD automatically names the layers for visible profile lines. The layer names for profiled visible lines start with the letters PV-. The layer names for profiled hidden lines start with the letters PH-. The remaining portion of the layer name is based on the handle number of the viewport that the object was profiled in. To find out the handle number for each viewport, switch to paper space and use the LIST command. Later you will use this information to selectively freeze and thaw the profiled lines for the desired layers.

Command: PS (↵)

Notice that the paper space icon is now displayed in the lower left-hand corner of your screen. You will list the information for the viewports. To select a viewport, you must pick on its border and not just somewhere inside the viewport.

Command: LIST (↵)

Select objects: ***(pick the border of the upper right viewport)***

Select objects: (↵)

You will see a list displayed on your screen containing the information shown in Figure 9.19.

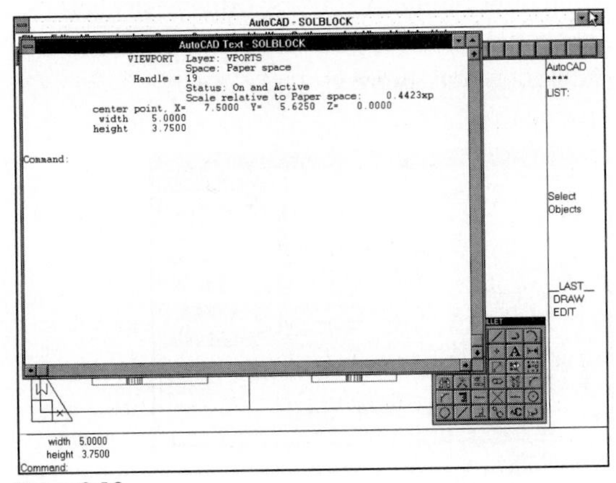

Figure 9.19

Write down the handle number for the upper right-hand viewport in the space provided below. The handle numbers begin numbering with hexadecimal number 1, which is assigned to the very first thing you create in your drawing, and then proceed with hexadecimal numbers for each entity. (Hexadecimal representation for decimal number 10 is A; 11 is B; and so forth.) The handle number that you see in your drawing may be different from that listed in Figure 9.19, depending on how you created each item in the drawing.

Pick: ***(twice on the close box to remove the text window)***

Command: (↵) ***(to restart the LIST command)***

Select objects: ***(pick the border of the upper left viewport)***

Select objects: (↵)

The information and handle number for the upper left viewport are listed on the text screen. Write down the handle number for the upper left viewport in the space provided below.

Upper Right Viewport Handle Number:

Upper Left Viewport Handle Number:

Lower Left Viewport Handle Number:

Lower Right Viewport Handle Number:

On your own, repeat this process and list the handles for the lower left and lower right viewports. Write them down in the space provided. You will need to keep track of these numbers in order to freeze and thaw profile layers in any particular viewport.

Loading the Linetypes

Because this drawing was not started from your MYPROTO prototype, which has all the linetypes loaded, you must load the linetypes before they can be used.

On your own, return to model space and use the LINETYPE command to load all the line-types into the drawing on your own. If you need help, refer to Tutorial 2 for details of the LINETYPE, Load command.

Setting the Linetypes and Colors for Generated Layers

Now you will use the Layer Control dialogue box to set the color and linetype for the new layers.

Pick: **Layer *(toolbar)***

The Layer Control dialogue box should appear on your screen. Notice that there are eight more layers listed in the dialogue box than were there previously. These are the generated layers for the profiles that AutoCAD created when you used the SOLPROF command. You will use the dialogue box to set the color and linetype of the *generated hidden line* layers, type. . . to select hidden lines for the PH- layers:

Pick: **(each of the layer names that start with PH-)**

Pick: **Set Ltype. . .**

Pick: **Next *(to see the rest of the linetypes)***

Pick: ***(the dashed line appearing next to the name HIDDEN)***

Pick: **Set Color**

Pick: **(Color 5 blue)**

Pick: **OK**

You have finished setting the color (blue) and the linetype (HIDDEN) for the generated profile hidden line layers. Now you will freeze the *generated visible line* layers. Each of these layer names starts with the letters PV- and ends with the hexadecimal number for the viewport in which the profile was created. Use the selection Clear All, which appears near the bottom of the Layer Control dialogue.

Pick: **Clear All**

Pick: ***(each of the layer names that start with PV-)***

The layer names that start with PV- appear highlighted on the list of layer names.

Pick: **Freeze**

The linetype and color for these layers are already set to CONTINUOUS and white, so you do not need to change them. You have now frozen them, so that when you exit the Layer Control dialogue box, you will not see the visible lines. Next, clear all the highlighted layers:

Pick: **Clear All**

Next you will set Layer 0 as the current layer:

Pick: ***(Layer 0 from the list of layers)***

Pick: **Current**

You will continue to use the dialogue box to freeze layer MODEL, so that you will not see the original solid model you created underneath the hidden lines. This will make it easier to select specific lines as you continue to work on your drawing.

Pick: ***(layer MODEL from the list of layers)***

Pick: **Freeze**

An F appears adjacent to layer MODEL on the list of layers.

When you have finished making all of the selections, the list of layers should look like the one in Figure 9.20. If you need to, go back and make changes on your own until your list matches the one in the figure. The letter C you see next to the PH- and PV- layers indicates that they are frozen in the current viewport. AutoCAD does this automatically for you when generating the layers; otherwise each 2D profile would appear in every viewport, creating a real mess.

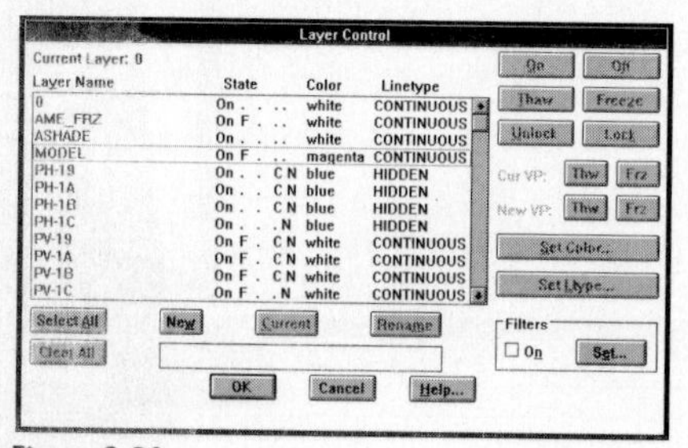

Figure 9.20

Pick: ***OK (to exit the Layer Control dialogue)***

When you return to your drawing, you should have only blue hidden lines on the screen (besides the viewport borders), as you see in Figure 9.21.

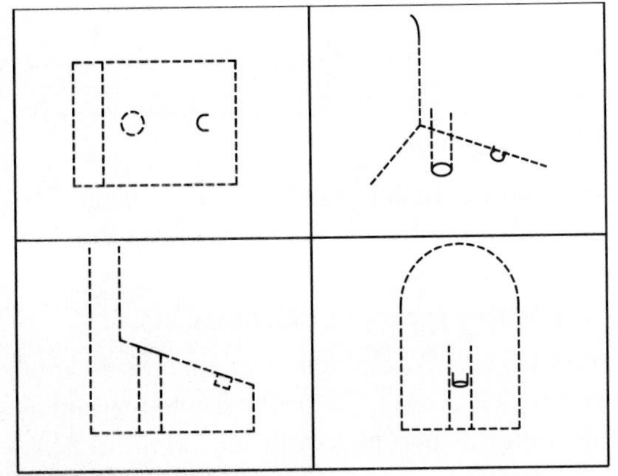

Figure 9.21

Eliminating Duplicate Hidden Lines

When you are printing or plotting your drawing, it is usually not good practice to double-plot lines. You do not want to plot hidden lines in the drawing that will be plotted over with visible lines. This would cause these lines to appear darker than normal. To eliminate the unwanted hidden lines, you will explode the blocks in which they were created and then erase the unwanted lines. You will learn more about using blocks and the EXPLODE command in Tutorial 13. You have read important warnings in Tutorial 8 telling you not to explode the model because the AME database is stored in as a block in a frozen layer named AME_FRZ. If you use the EXPLODE command to explode the actual model, you will destroy the solid modeling database. To make sure this does not happen, you have frozen layer MODEL, where you created the actual model. The lines remaining on your screen are the profile lines.

Before you can erase the unwanted hidden lines, you must use the EXPLODE command to turn the block of hidden lines back into single entities. The EXPLODE command changes a block, which is a collection of entities made into a single group, back into individual items. Make the upper right viewport active and explode the hidden line block:

Pick: **Modify *(menu bar),* Explode**

Select objects: ***(pick on the hidden lines in the upper right viewport)*** ↵

The lines turn white (appears black) when the hidden line block is exploded.

On your own, explode the block of the hidden lines in each of the other viewports. All the lines should turn to white, showing that this has been done. To keep track of the layers visually, return these items to their layer color (blue).

You will use CHPROP from the screen menu to change the color properties of the lines back so that the color is set to BYLAYER.

Activate the upper right viewport on your own. You will know it is active if the crosshairs appear in the viewport.

Pick: **EDIT *(screen menu),* CHPROP**

Select objects: ***(use the implied crossing window to select all the hidden lines in the upper right viewport)***

Select objects: ↵

Change what property (Color/LAyer/LType/Thickness)?: **C** ↵

New color <varies>: **BYLAYER** ↵

Change what property (Color/LAyer/LType/Thickness)?: ↵

■ ***TIP*** You can either type in the responses to the prompts or pick the appropriate selections, COLOR and BYLAYER, from the screen menu. ■

After you end the command, the lines in the upper right viewport should turn blue, the appropriate color for the hidden line layer.

Use the CHPROP command on your own to return all the hidden lines in each viewport so that their color is set to BYLAYER.

Then use the ERASE command to remove the outer hidden lines and any others that have visible lines over the top. Erase all of the lines, except those showing the depth of the blind hole, in the isometric view, because hidden lines are not usually shown in isometrics unless they are needed to show the depth of a hole or some other feature that cannot be inferred without them. In an isometric view, holes are assumed to be through holes unless you can see the depth indicated in the drawing by hidden lines, a visible back surface showing the depth, or a note.

Use REDRAWALL to redraw your views before you continue.

When you are done, your drawing should look like Figure 9.22.

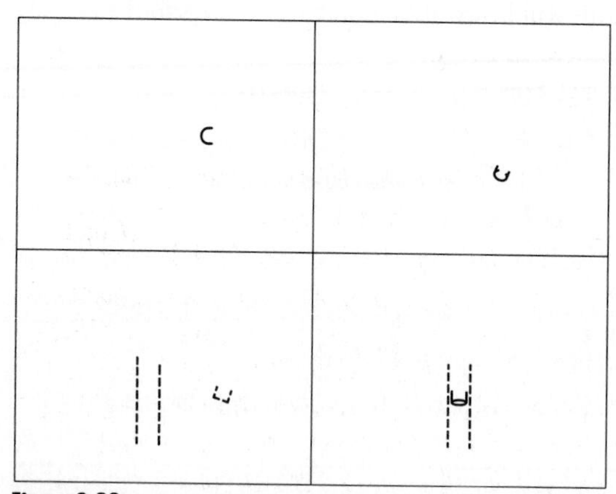

Figure 9.22

Now thaw the profile visible layers. This time you will type the LAYER command alias and use the wildcard (*) to match to the viewport handle number portion of the name.

Command: **LA** ↵

LAYER ?/Make/Set/New/ON/OFF/Color/Ltype/Freeze/Thaw/LOck/Unlock: **T** ↵

Layer name(s) to Thaw: **PV*** ↵

?/Make/Set/New/ON/OFF/Color/Ltype/Freeze/Thaw/LOck/Unlock: ↵

Now the visible lines should reappear.

Pick in the lower left viewport to make it active before continuing.

Next you will restore the UCS for the front view, using the UCS dialogue box from the Settings menu bar.

Pick: **Settings *(menu bar)*, UCS, Named UCS...**

The UCS Control dialogue box appears on your screen. Select the UCS for the front view and then make it current, as you see in Figure 9.23.

Pick: **FRONT**

Pick: **Current**

Pick: **OK *(to exit the dialogue box)***

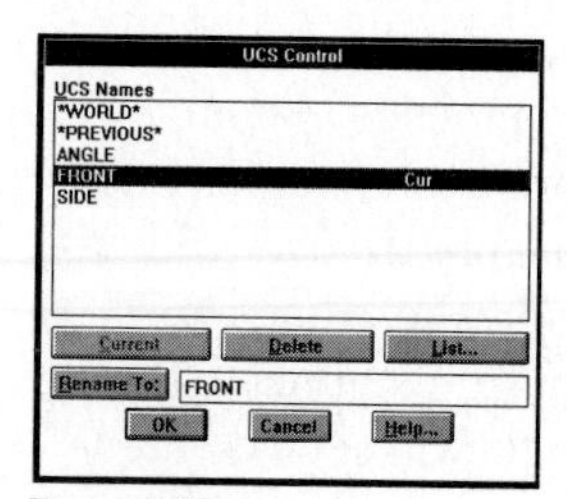

Figure 9.23

When you have restored the UCS for the front view, you will notice that the grid now appears in the lower left-hand viewport. Now you are ready to draw the center line for the front view. Your screen should look like Figure 9.24.

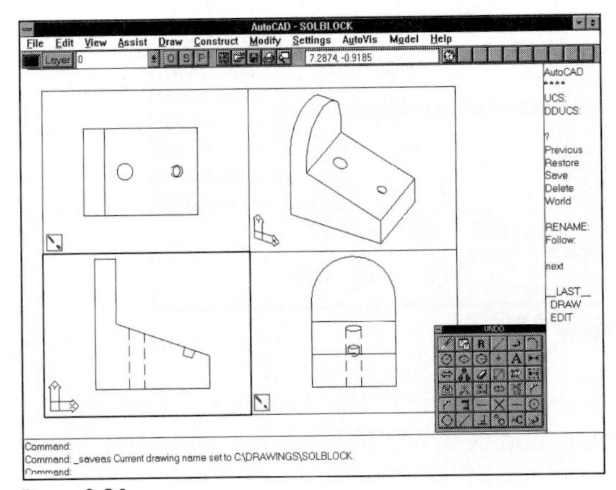

Figure 9.24

Adding the Center Lines

Next you will draw the center lines for the front view. First you will create a new layer named CL-FRONT for the front view center lines, using the alias for the LAYER command.

Command: **LA** ↵

LAYER ?/Make/Set/New/ON/OFF/Color/Ltype/Freeze/Thaw/LOck/Unlock: **M** ↵

New current layer <0>: **CL-FRONT** ↵

?/Make/Set/New/ON/OFF/Color/Ltype/Freeze/Thaw/LOck/Unlock: **C** ↵

Color: **3** ↵

Layer name(s) for color 3 (green) <CL-FRONT>: ↵

?/Make/Set/New/ON/OFF/Color/Ltype/Freeze/Thaw/LOck/Unlock: **LT** ↵

Linetype (or ?) <Continuous>: **CENTER** ↵

Layer name(s) for linetype CENTER <CL-FRONT>: ↵

?/Make/Set/New/ON/OFF/Color/Ltype/Freeze/Thaw/LOck/Unlock: **S** ↵

New current layer <CL-FRONT>: ↵

?/Make/Set/New/ON/OFF/Color/Ltype/Freeze/Thaw/LOck/Unlock: ↵

On your own, make sure SNAP is turned on and use SNAP and the LINE command to draw a center line for the through hole in the front view. When you are finished, your drawing should appear similar to Figure 9.25.

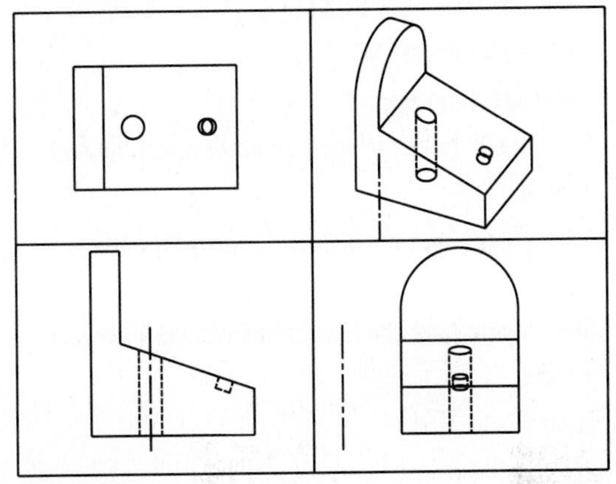

Figure 9.25

What happened? Notice that the line you drew showed up in the other viewports. Anything you add in model space will be visible in all the views unless you tell AutoCAD otherwise. You can use the command VPLAYER to turn off layers in specific viewports.

Using VPLAYER

The VPLAYER command controls the visibility of layers within specific viewports. When you add lines such as center lines and dimensions to 3D drawings, it is usually necessary to create layers for each viewport. Using VPLAYER, you can turn off the visibility of the layers in the viewports where you do not want the lines to show. AutoCAD did this for you with the generated layers for profile visible and profile hidden. You must control the visibility for layers that you create unless you want them to show in every viewport. Imagine putting dimensions in the front view and having them show up edgewise in the top and side views.

Enter the VPLAYER command at the command prompt to set the visibility for the CL-FRONT layer that you created in the previous step:

Command: **VPLAYER** ↵

?/Freeze/Thaw/Reset/Newfrz/Vpvisdflt: **F** ↵

Layer(s) to Freeze: **CL-FRONT** ↵

All/Select/<Current>: **S** ↵

Switching to Paper space.

Select objects: ***(pick the upper right viewport border)***

1 found

Select objects: ***(pick the upper left viewport border)***

1 found

Select objects: ***(pick the lower right viewport border)***

1 found

Select objects: ↵

?/Freeze/Thaw/Reset/Newfrz/Vpvisdflt: ↵

Regenerating drawing.

Now the center line you drew should only be visible in the front view. You can also use the Layer Control dialogue box to set the visibility for layers within each viewport. You will use it to create layers for the top and side view center lines, and then set their visibility and draw the appropriate center lines. Draw the center line for the smaller hole before continuing.

On your own, pick the upper left viewport, which contains the top view, to make it active.

Pick: ***Layer (toolbar)***

The Layer Control dialogue appears on your screen. Use the techniques you have learned to create two new layers: CL-SIDE and CL-TOP. Set their linetypes to CENTER and colors to green. When you have finished creating the layers, you are ready to control their visibility. Refer to Figure 9.26.

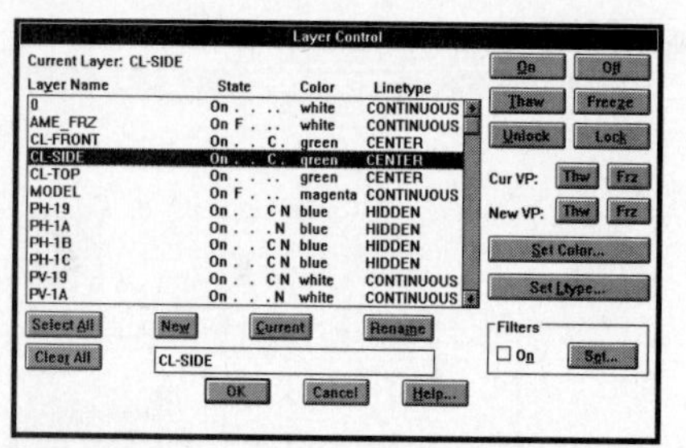

Figure 9.26

At the right side of the dialogue box are the selections Cur VP (for current viewport), Thw (thaw), and Frz (freeze). These selections allow you to pick a layer and freeze it only in the current viewport. You have already made the top view the active, or current, viewport. In Figure 9.26 you will notice the letter C across from the layer names CL-FRONT and CL-SIDE as well as some of the generated profile layers (generated layers also have an N next to their names). The letter C tells you that the layer is frozen in the current viewport. You use the current viewport freeze and thaw selections to do this. You will freeze the layers you created so that your list looks like the one shown. Layer CL-FRONT should already have a C next to its name because you froze it with the VPLAYER command in the previous step. You will freeze CL-SIDE in the current viewport.

Pick: ***(to select CL-SIDE; it becomes highlighted)***

Pick: **Frz** ***(to the right of Cur VP)***

Pick: **Current** ***(to make CL-SIDE the current layer so that you can draw in it)***

The letter C appears across from layer CL-SIDE, indicating that it is frozen in the upper left viewport (which is the current viewport). CL-SIDE should also be listed as the current layer.

Pick: **OK** ***(to exit the dialogue box)***

On your own, restore the UCS for the side view. Make the lower right viewport current. Draw the side view center lines. The lines will not appear in the top view because it is frozen in that viewport.

On your own, make the lower left viewport containing the top view current and then return to the Layer Control dialogue box. This time, use the dialogue box to freeze layers CL-SIDE and CL-TOP in the lower left viewport. Make layer CL-TOP current. When you have finished, pick OK to exit the dialogue box.

Then use the UCS command to restore the WCS. Draw the top view center lines.

Make the lower right viewport active and use the Layer Control dialogue box to freeze all of the center line layers in that viewport except CL-SIDE. Then make the isometric viewport active and freeze all of the center line layers in that viewport.

Your drawing should appear similar to Figure 9.27.

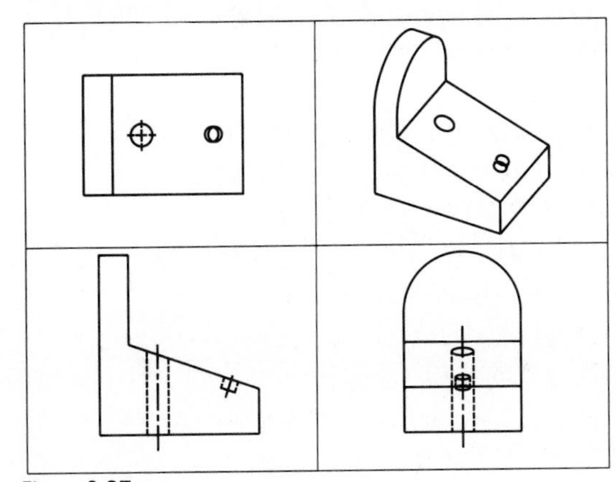

Figure 9.27

Plotting

Now you are ready to plot your drawing. Switch to paper space for plotting. Use the P button on the toolbar.

Pick: **P button *(toolbar)*** ↵

The paper space icon appears in the lower left of the screen, replacing the UCS icon.

Next adjust LTSCALE so that the center lines and hidden lines in the drawing appear at an appropriate scale.

Command: **LTSCALE** ↵

New scale factor <1.00>: **.5** ↵

■ ***TIP*** Try various values until you are pleased with the results. ■

Usually, multiview engineering drawings do not have border lines drawn between the views. This is why you created the layer VPORTS when you created the viewport boundaries. Now you will freeze this layer so that the views of your drawing plot in the correct fashion, with no lines dividing the views.

Command: **LA** ↵

?/Make/Set/New/ON/OFF/Color/Ltype/Freeze/Thaw/LOck/Unlock: **F** ↵

Layer name(s) to Freeze: **VPORTS** ↵

?/Make/Set/New/ON/OFF/Color/Ltype/Freeze/Thaw/LOck/Unlock: ↵

The border lines disappear from the screen.

On your own, use Save As to save your drawing to the file name ANGL_PLT before you plot.

Use the PLOT command to plot your drawing. If you need help, refer to Tutorial 3.

Going Further

You can use the ADS application named SOLVIEW.exe to generate views of your model. When doing this, it is not necessary to have multiple viewports on the screen and create profiles in them. Simply create your model in a single viewport and then load the ADS application by picking File, Applications from the menu bar. Pick File when the dialogue box appears on your screen; use the new dialogue box that appears to change the directory to C:\ACADWIN\SAMPLES and select SOLVIEW.exe from the list. When you have it selected, pick OK. The previous dialogue box will be restored to your screen. Make sure that SOLVIEW.exe is highlighted and then pick LOAD. The ADS application is now loaded. To activate the SOLVIEW program, type "SOLVIEW" and press ↵ at the command prompt. You will be prompted to generate UCS, Ortho, Auxiliary, or Section views or exit the command. To create orthographic views, type "O" and press ↵. At the prompt, "Pick side of viewport to project:" Pick on the viewport border in the direction you want to view the model. Then at the next prompt pick a location for the view center. The next prompt allows you to specify the layer for the generated lines. When you have answered all of the prompts, the view will be generated.

You have completed this tutorial.

KEY TERMS

block
construction plane
cutting plane
generated hidden lines
generated visible lines
Motion Coordinate System (MCS)
profile

KEY COMMANDS

Application Load
Calculator
Handles
Purge
Redraw All
Regenerate All
Solid Chamfer
Solid Change Primitive
Solid Cut
Solid Fillet
Solid List
Solid Profile
Solid Separate
Solid User Coordinate System
Solid View
Viewport Layer

EXERCISES

9.1 Angled Support

Create this figure as a three-dimensional solid model. Create necessary views and plot with correct hidden lines and center lines.

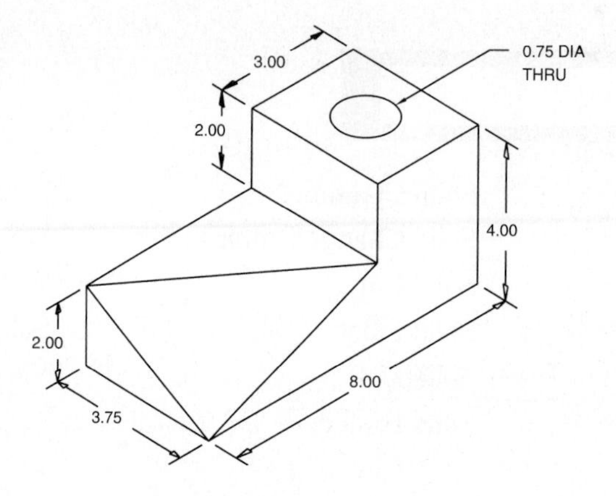

9.2 Step Model

Construct a solid model of this object. Grid spacing is at 0.25 inches. Use vpoint of (3,–3,1) in the upper right viewport.

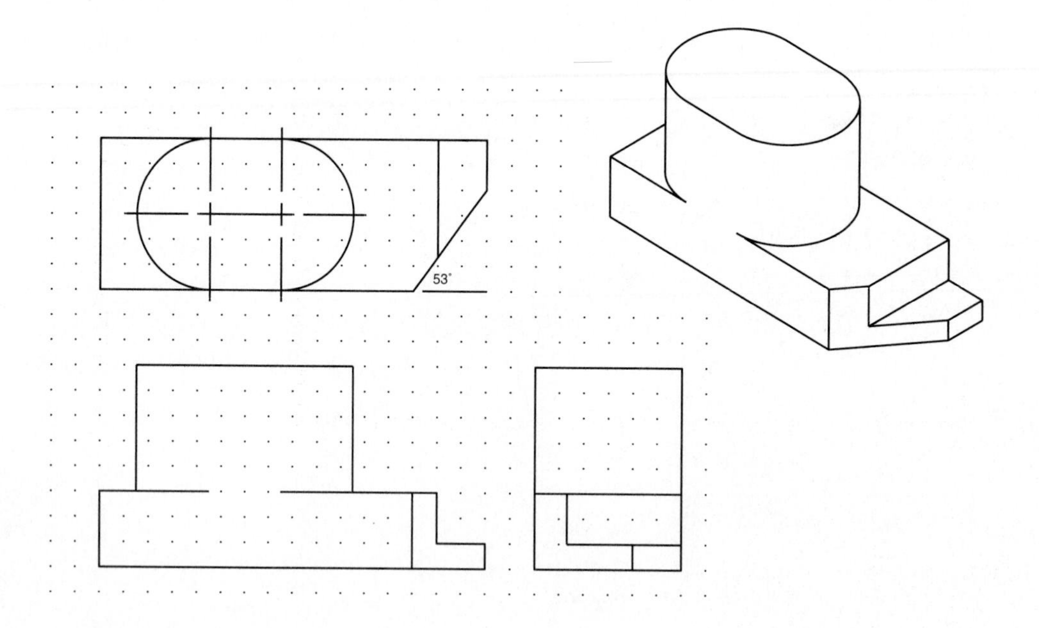

9.3 Office Plan

Use this floor plan as a basis to create a model of a similar office using the solids modeling techniques you have learned. Make the outside walls 8 feet high, and subtract solid boxes to make room for the windows. The desks are 2 1/2 feet high; design your own dimensions for the chairs and windows.

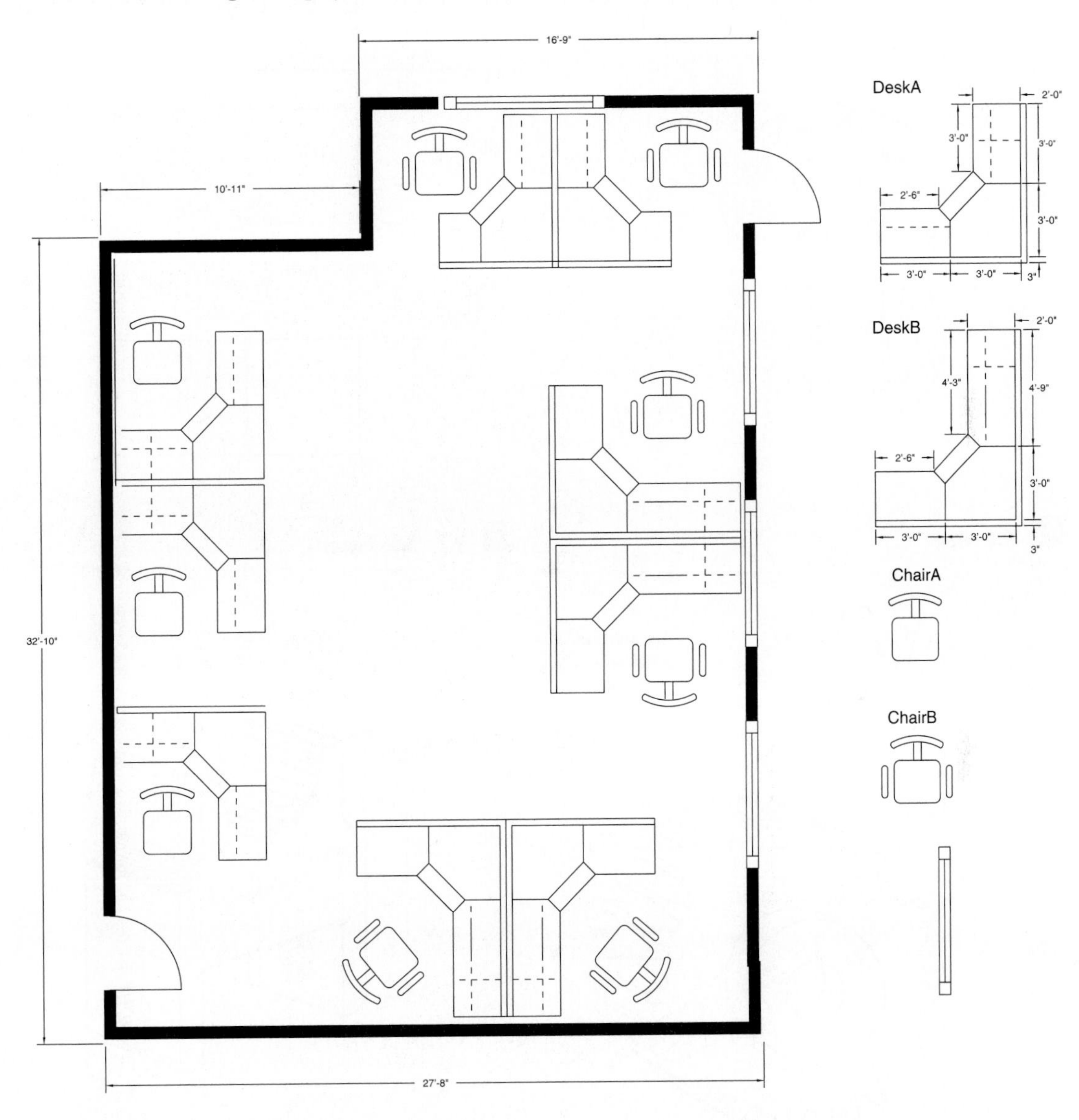

Create solid models for the objects shown. Show the necessary orthographic views in the correct viewports. Use SOLPROF to generate correct hidden lines.

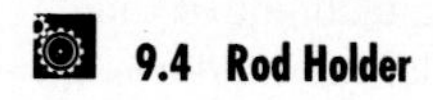

9.4 Rod Holder

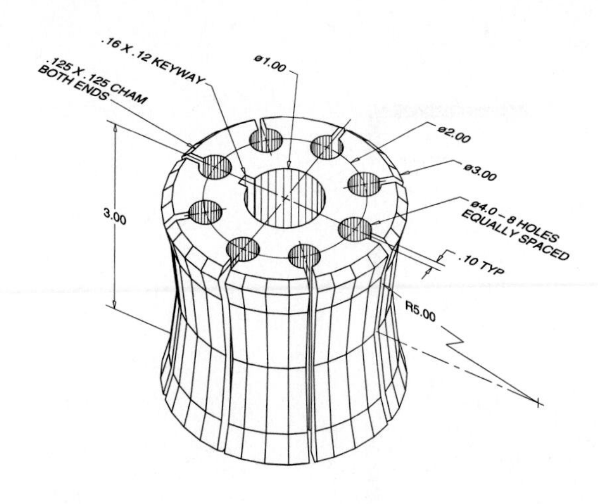

9.5M Router Guide

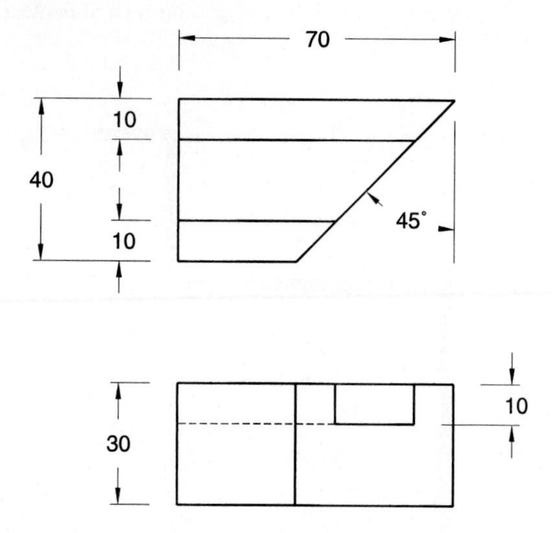

9.6 Gear

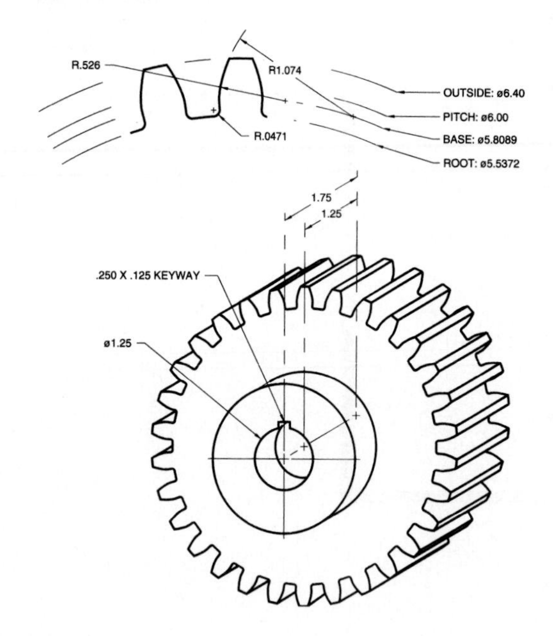

9.7 Slide Support

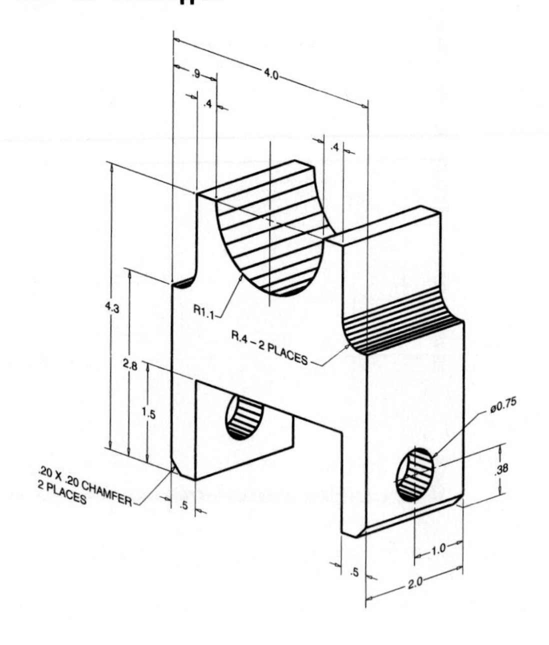

9.8M Spacer

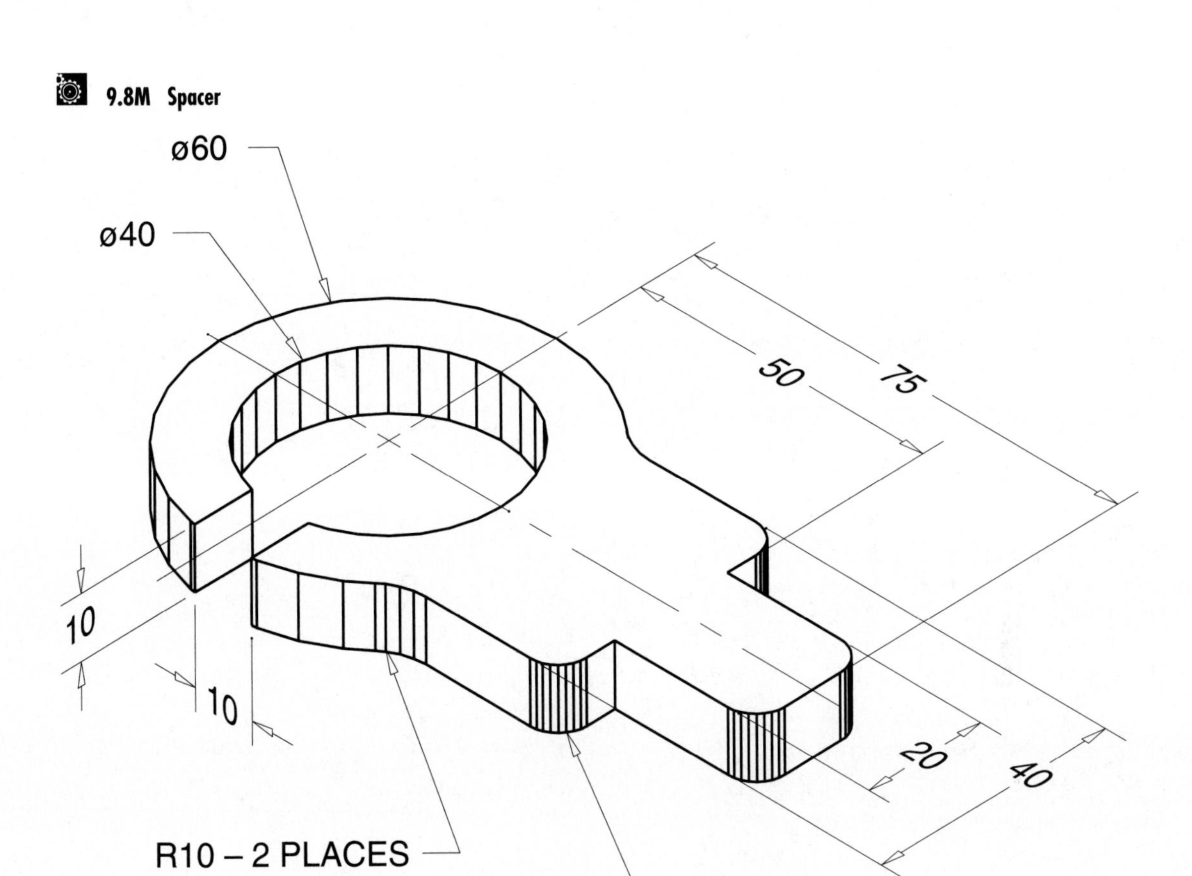

ø60
ø40
50
75
10
10
20
40
R10 – 2 PLACES
R5 TYP

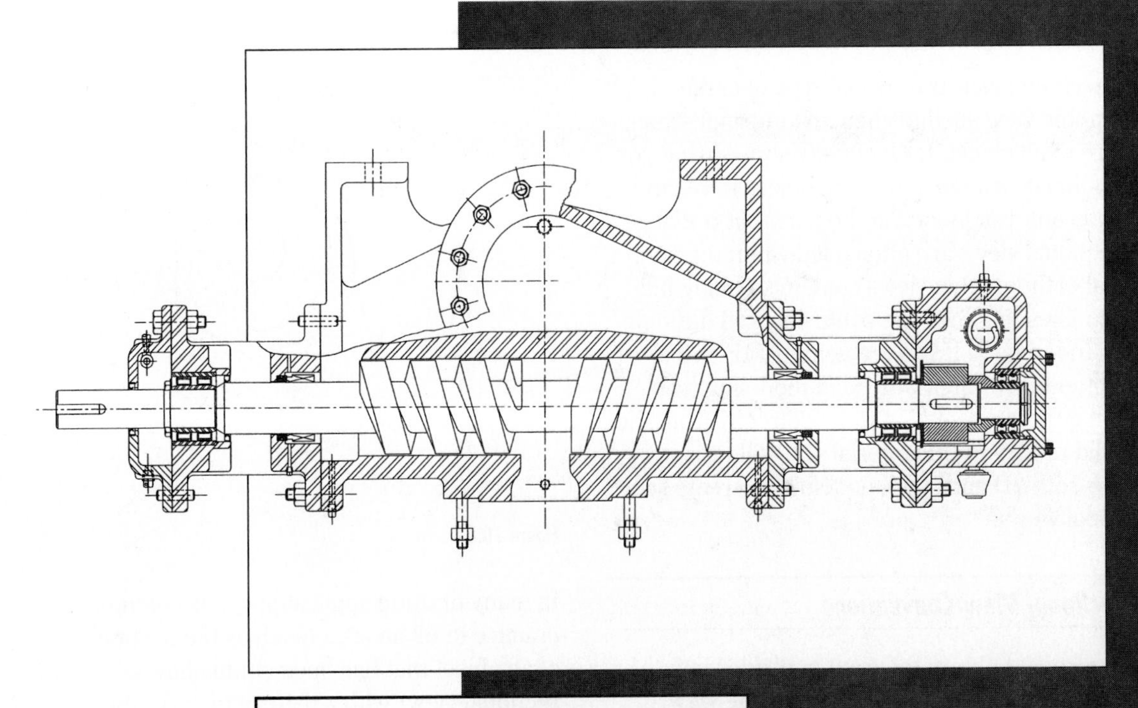

TUTORIAL 10

Creating Section Views Using 2D and Solid Modeling

Objectives

When you have completed this tutorial, you will be able to

1. Show the internal surfaces of an object, using 2D sectional views.
2. Locate and draw cutting plane lines and section lines on appropriate layers.
3. Use the BHATCH command to fill areas with a pattern.
4. Use leaders to identify lines and planes.
5. Generate a section of a solid model, using the SOLSECT command.
6. Change the default hatching used by SOLSECT.

Introduction

A *sectional view* is a special type of orthographic view used to show the internal structure of an object. It essentially shows what you would see if a portion of the object were cut away and you looked at the part that remains. Sectional views are often used when the normal orthographic views contain so many hidden lines that they are confusing and difficult to understand. If you are using AME and creating your drawings with solid modeling, you can generate a sectional view directly from the solid model. In this tutorial you will learn to use both 2D and solid modeling to create sectional views.

Sectional View Conventions

Figure 10.1 shows the front and side views of a circular object. Notice that the side view contains many hidden lines and is somewhat difficult to interpret.

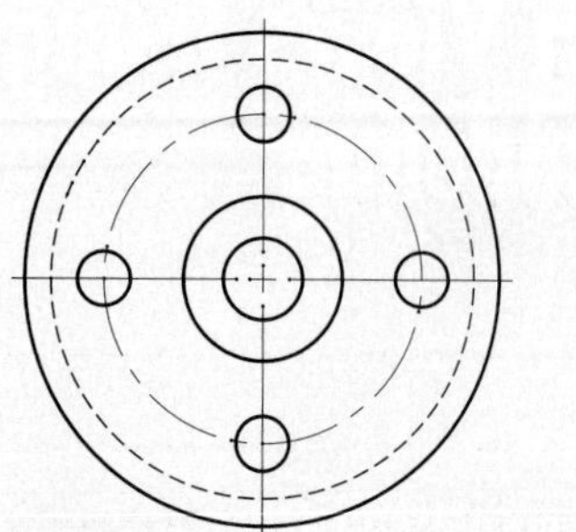

Figure 10.1

Figure 10.2 shows a pictorial drawing of the same object cut in half along its vertical center line. This is called a *full section*.

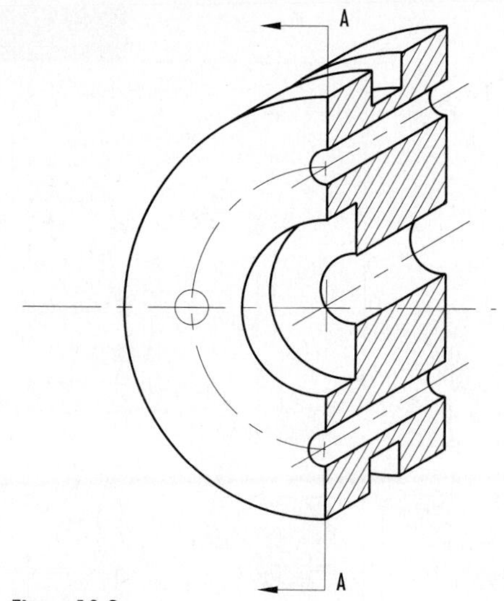

Figure 10.2

In many drafting applications, it is common practice to fill an area (such as the portion of an object that has been cut to show a sectional view) with a pattern to make the drawing easier to interpret. The pattern can help differentiate components of a three-dimensional object, or it can indicate the material composing the object. This process, called *crosshatching* or "pattern filling," can be accomplished using AutoCAD's BHATCH (boundary hatch) command.

In Figure 10.2, crosshatching is used to show the solid portions of the object, where material was cut to make the section view.

Figure 10.3 shows a front and a sectional view of the same circular object. A *cutting plane line*, line A-A, is used to define where the sectional cut is to be taken on the object and to indicate the direction in which the object is to be viewed.

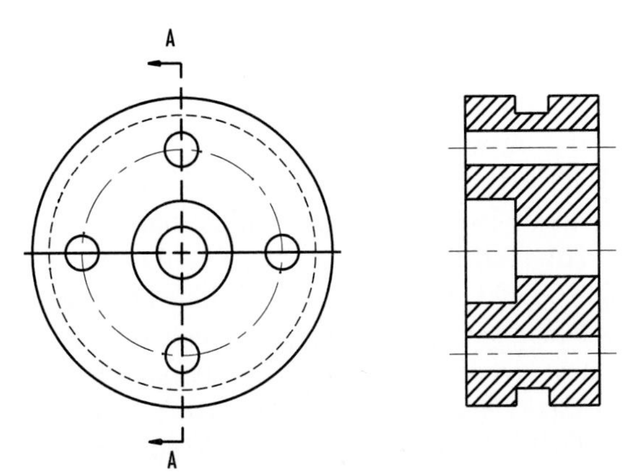

Figure 10.3

Compare the side view in Figure 10.1 with the sectional view in Figure 10.3 and the three-dimensional section view shown in Figure 10.2. Figures 10.2 and 10.3 are easier to interpret than the front and side views shown in Figure 10.1.

Figure 10.4 shows a different object with a cutting plane line and the appropriate sectional view.

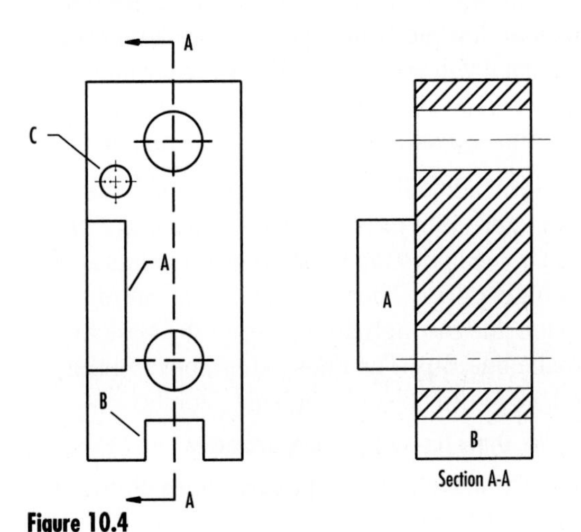

Figure 10.4

Sectional Lines

Sectional lines are used to show where material has been cut. Note in Figure 10.4 that the surfaces labeled A and B are not crosshatched. Only material that has been cut by the cutting plane is crosshatched. A and B are shown because they are visible surfaces once the object is cut, but they are not hatched because they were not cut by the cutting plane.

A sectional view shows what would be seen if you looked at the object in the direction the arrows on the cutting plane line point, with all of the material in back of the arrows removed. When you are creating a sectional view, ignore the portion of the object that will be cut off. Draw the remaining portion, to which the arrows on the cutting plane line point. Remember that once the object is cut, some features that were previously hidden will become visible and should be shown. The hole labeled C in Figure 10.4 is in the remaining portion of the object, but is not directly visible, so it is not shown in the section view. The purpose of a section view is to show the internal structure without the confusion of hidden lines. Hidden lines should only be used if the object would be misunderstood if they were not included.

Starting

Before you begin, launch AutoCAD. If you need help, please review the AutoCAD for Windows section of Chapter 3, AutoCAD Basics, in Part 1, Getting Started. Your computer display shows AutoCAD's drawing editor. To begin this tutorial, you will use the data file CAST2 that came with your software as a prototype file. Select the File menu option to begin a new drawing:

Pick: **File *(menu bar)*, New**

When the Create New Drawing dialogue box appears on your screen, use the drawing CAST2 from the data files as a prototype. If necessary, use the dialogue to select the directory where your data file drawings are stored.

Pick: **CAST2 *(as the prototype)***

Type: **BOSSECT *(for the new file name)***

Pick: **OK *(to exit the dialogue box)***

Creating 2D Sectional Views

The top, front, and side orthographic views of the casting drawing you created for Tutorial 6 are displayed on your screen. A countersunk hole has been added to the boss on the drawing and the horizontal center lines have been erased in the top view. Your screen should look like Figure 10.5.

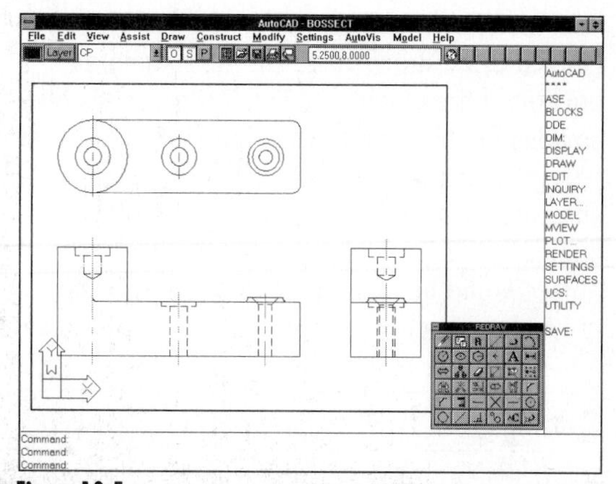

Figure 10.5

Often one or more of the orthographic views are replaced with section views. You will use the front orthographic view to draw a front sectional view, and the side view to draw a side sectional view through the boss. This will give you practice in drawing sections and you will see how to create them in more than one direction.

Cutting Plane Lines

A cutting plane line can be one of two different line patterns, either a line made up of long dashes (DASHED) or a long line with two short dashes followed by another long line (PHANTOM). Only one type of cutting plane line should be used in any one drawing. You will make dashed cutting plane lines by making a new layer with the DASHED linetype. The DASHED linetype has longer dashes than the HIDDEN linetype, but you should still use a different color for the cutting plane layer to help distinguish it from the HIDDEN layer. Also, cutting plane lines are drawn with a thick pen when drawings are plotted. Since layer color determines pen selection when plotting, you must use a different color for thick cutting plane lines than for thin hidden lines.

Creating Dashed Lines

Create a new layer for the cutting plane lines on your own. Name the new layer CP. Assign it color 7, white (which appears black on your screen if you are using a white background) and the linetype DASHED. Set layer CP as the current layer. Make sure that SNAP is turned on.

You will add a horizontal cutting plane line in the figure that passes through the center of the holes in the top view, between points A-A in Figure 10.6. Then, add a vertical cutting plane line through the center of the boss to make line B-B. The lines extend beyond the edges of the object by at least .5 units.

Pick: **Draw *(menu bar)*, Line, Segments**

Draw the dashed cutting plane lines shown in Figure 10.6 on your own.

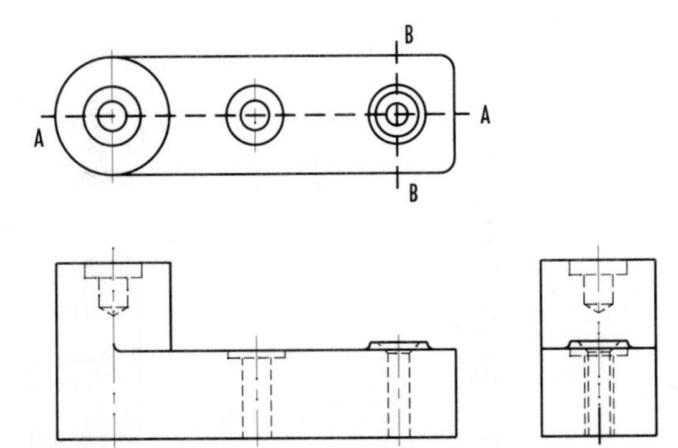

Figure 10.6

The cutting plane lines as shown in Figure 10.6 should now appear in the layer CP.

Drawing Leader Lines

Leaders are often drawn from dimension text to objects being dimensioned to allow placement of the dimension some distance away from the object. You can also use leader lines to identify lines in the object. Leaders must sometimes be routed around other objects in the drawing. The DIM, LEADER command is provided to let you construct complex leaders.

You will use the DIM, LEADER command to add the arrowed line segments and the identifying letters for the cutting plane lines. Because these are part of the cutting plane lines, they can be drawn in layer CP.

The DIM, LEADER command prompts for a "Leader start:" point, followed by any number of "To point" prompts, similar to the LINE command prompts. AutoCAD places an arrow at the start point of the leader line. You will start the leader .5 units to the left of the top end of the cutting plane line B-B.

■ ***TIP*** The DIM, LEADER command will not draw the arrows if the first line segment of the leader is too short. In order to have AutoCAD draw an arrow, the first line segment must be longer than the current arrowhead size (DIMASZ). You can set the arrowhead size using the dimensioning variables or the Dimension Style selection under Settings on the menu bar. ■

On your own, make sure that SNAP is set to .25 before you draw the leader line. Use ORTHO to assist you in drawing straight lines; turn it on by picking the O button on the toolbar.

Pick: **Draw *(menu bar)*, Dimensions, Leader**

Leader start: ***(select a point .5 units left of and even with the top end of line B-B)***

To point: ***(pick Endpoint from the toolbox)***

endp of ***(target the top end of the cutting plane line; press the pick button)***

To point: ↵

Dimension text <>: **B** ↵

Repeat these steps for the bottom of line B-B. Note that the dimension command, when picked from the menu bar, uses DIM1, which only stays active for one dimension command. To restart the LEADER command, you will need to pick Draw, Dimensions, Leader again. (When the command is picked from the screen menu, the "Dim:" prompt stays active.)

■ ***TIP*** You can type "U" at the "To point:" prompt to remove the last leader segment drawn if you make an error. ■

Text notes and dimensions require a short horizontal line segment before the text; this is drawn with the LEADER command. For line A-A, you will cancel the command after the first segment of the line is drawn and use the DTEXT command to place the text labeling line A-A. You will use the menu bar to pick the LEADER command. Because the cutting plane lines were drawn on the snap, you don't need to use OSNAP, Endpoint this time.

Pick: **Draw *(menu bar)*, Dimensions, Leader**

Leader start: ***(select a point .5 units above and even with the left endpoint of line A-A)***

To point: ***(pick the left endpoint of line A-A)***

To point: Ctrl-**C**

Pick: **Draw *(menu bar)*, Dimensions, Leader**

Leader start: ***(pick a point .5 units above the right end-point of line A-A)***

To point: ***(pick the right endpoint of line A-A)***

To point: Ctrl-**C**

Pick: **DTEXT icon *(toolbox; the icon looks like the letter A)***

Justify/Style/<Start point>: ***(pick a point below the end of the left leader for line A-A)***

Height: <0.20000>: ↵

Rotation angle <0>: ↵

Text: **A** ↵

Text: ***(pick a point below the end of the right leader for line A-A)***

Text: **A** ↵

Text: ↵

When completed, your leader lines should look similar to the ones shown in Figure 10.7.

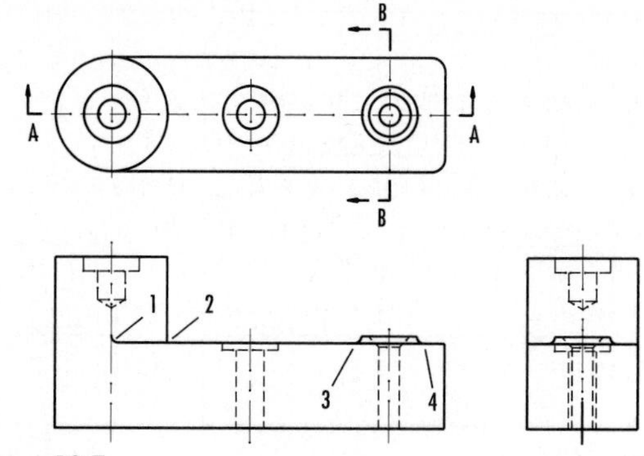

Figure 10.7

Adjusting Drawing Lines

As you have seen in previous tutorials, you can change the scale factor for a line to improve the overall appearance of the cutting plane lines, using the LTSCALE command located on the SETTINGS screen menu.

Pick: **SETTINGS *(screen menu)*, next, LTSCALE**

The prompt asks for a scale factor:

New scale factor <0.7000>: **.5** ↵

Observe how the overall lines are affected.

Command: ↵ ***(to restart the LTSCALE command)***

New scale factor <0.5000>: **.75** ↵

You can continue to try different values until the lines suit your particular needs.

Next, you must remove the unnecessary lines from the front view. When you draw a section view, you will not see the lines that represent intersections and surfaces that are on the outside of the object.

On your own, use the TRIM and ERASE commands to remove the line segment from point 1 to point 2 and the runout. Use the ERASE command to remove the solid line from point 3 to point 4 that defines the surface in front of the boss, as shown in Figure 10.7. Use ZOOM, Window to help identify the points. Your drawing should look similar to Figure 10.8 when you are finished.

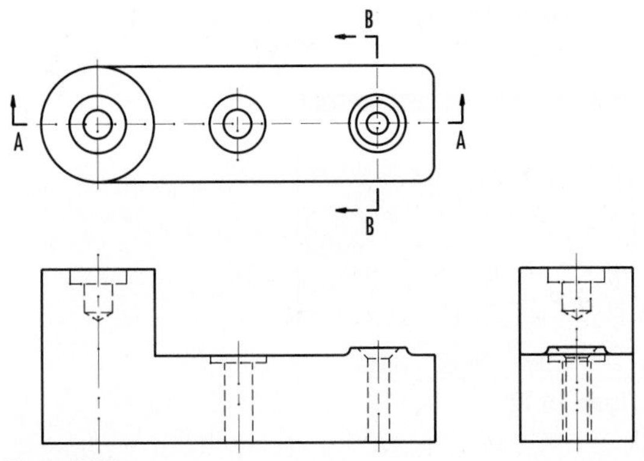

Figure 10.8

Using CHANGE

When you section the drawing, the interior details become visible. You will use the CHANGE command to change the layer property of the hidden lines to the VISIBLE layer. You will pick the CHANGE icon from the toolbox (third row, far right column).

Pick: **CHANGE icon *(toolbox)***

Select objects: ***(pick all the hidden lines in the front view)***

Select objects: ↵

Properties/<Change point>: **P** ↵

Change what property? Color/LAyer/Elev/Ltype/Thickness: **LA** ↵

New layer <HIDDEN>: **VISIBLE** ↵

Change what property?: Color/LAyer/Elev/Ltype/Thickness: ↵

Now the layer of all the hidden lines in the front view should be changed to layer VISIBLE. Your drawing should look similar to Figure 10.9.

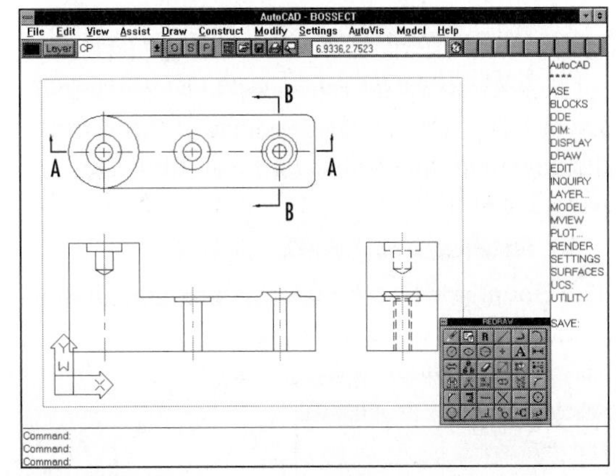

Figure 10.9

If you have zoomed your drawing, pick ZOOM, Previous to return to the original size.

Using the BHATCH Command

Your sectional view needs to include cross-hatching. Hatches can be composed of a series of lines, dashes, or dots that form a pattern. Sectional lines are created in AutoCAD using the BHATCH command. BHATCH is located under DRAW on the screen menu and as Draw, Hatch. . . on the menu bar. The BHATCH command helps automatically select the boundary to fill with the pattern. To activate the BHATCH command, select Hatch. . . from the Draw menu bar. The BHATCH command displays a dialogue box that lets you select the area you want to hatch by two different methods. You can pick inside an area to be hatched, or you can select the object lines that form a boundary for the hatching.

Hatching should be on its own layer and should be plotted with a thin pen. Having the hatch on its own layer is useful because frequently you will want to freeze it so that it is not displayed while you are working on the drawing. In your prototype drawing, you have already created a separate layer for the hatching.

To set HATCH as the current layer,

Pick: ***(on the current layer name, CP, in the toolbar)***

Pick: **HATCH *(from the list of names that pulls down)***

Layer HATCH is set as the current layer and displayed on the toolbar to the right of the word Layer.

Pick: **Draw *(menu bar)*, Hatch...**

The Boundary Hatch dialogue box appears on your screen, as shown in Figure 10.10.

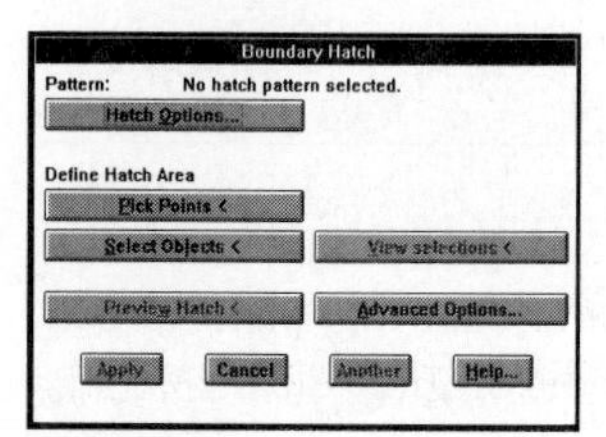

Figure 10.10

First you must select the hatch pattern and other options that you will use when cross-hatching your sectional view. To do this,

Pick: **Hatch Options...**

A second dialogue box, the Hatch Options dialogue, appears on top of the previous one. Here you can select the hatch pattern, the scale for the hatch pattern, and whether only the outer areas or both the outer areas and islands are filled. The dialogue box looks like Figure 10.11.

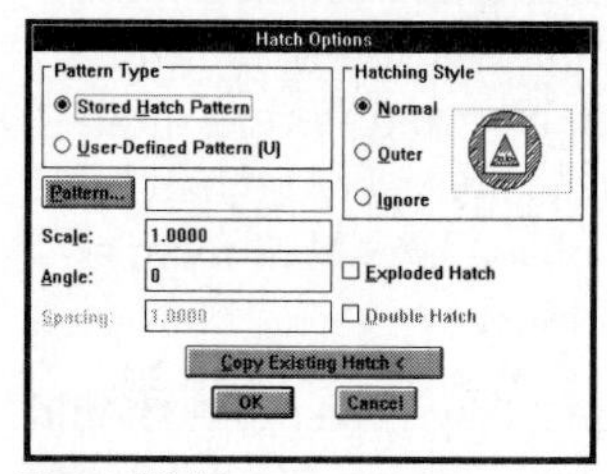

Figure 10.11

To select the hatch pattern,

Pick: **Pattern...**

Another dialogue box appears on the screen on top of the previous one, as shown in Figure 10.12. This dialogue box contains icons of the existing hatch patterns. You will select the standard straight-line 45-degree hatching pattern called ANSI31. To select it,

Pick: ***(the box containing the angled lines above the name ANSI31)***

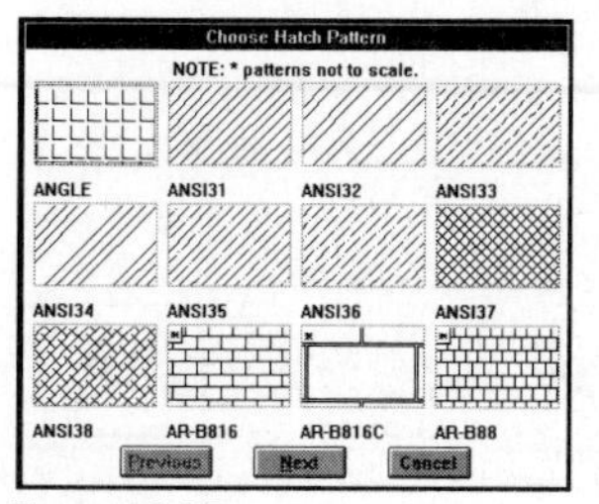

Figure 10.12

After you have made a selection from the Choose Hatch Pattern dialogue box, you automatically return to the Hatch Options dialogue box.

Adapting for Architecture

The ANSI31 hatch pattern works well for denoting masonry or CMU in sections. The SAND texture can be altered to work well as a semi-black hatch for walls. Set the hatch pattern scale to a small number and then hatch the object with SAND. This will give it a fine grayscale appearance on the final plot. This also works well for casting shadows on plans, sections, and elevations, much like hand-drawn stippling. ■

Setting the Scale for the Hatch Pattern

You can set the scale for the hatch pattern using the Hatch Options dialogue box. This determines how far apart the hatched lines are in your drawing. The default scale of 1.0000 is the correct size for full-scale drawings, resulting in hatched lines that are about 1/16" apart. If the views will be plotted at a smaller scale, half-size for instance, you will need to increase the spacing for the hatch by setting the scale to a **larger** value, so that the lines of the hatch are not close together. Be cautious when specifying a smaller size, because if the hatch lines are very close together, AutoCAD will take a long time to calculate all of them and may even run out of space on your hard disk. For this drawing, you will not need to change the scale of the hatch pattern.

Setting the Angle for the Hatch Pattern

In the hatch pattern you selected, ANSI31, the lines are drawn at an angle of 45 degrees. Because the angled edge of the countersunk hole is drawn at 45 degrees, you will change the angle of the hatch pattern so that the hatch is not parallel to features in the drawing. Highlight the 0 value for Angle in the edit box and type “15” as the new value. The 45-degree hatch is rotated an additional 15 degrees.

Setting the Style for the Hatch Pattern

Look at the upper right-hand area of the Hatch Options dialogue. The Hatching Style is set to Normal. You can use this area of the dialogue to change to Outer, so only the outer area is hatched and any islands inside are left unhatched. You can also choose Ignore, so all of the inside is hatched, regardless of the structure. Try these options on your own. When you are finished observing the effect of these selections on the sample picture, leave this area of the dialogue set to Normal.

Pick: **OK *(to exit the Hatch Options dialogue)***

Now you are ready to specify which areas of your drawing you want to have filled with the hatch pattern. The two methods of selecting, Pick Points and Select Objects, appear in the middle of the Boundary Hatch dialogue box. When using the Pick Points method, you will return to your drawing to select points **inside** of the areas that you want to have hatched. AutoCAD determines the boundary around the areas you picked. If there are islands inside the area you do not want hatched, pick them after you pick the area to be hatched. When you are finished selecting, press ↵ to tell AutoCAD you are finished selecting and want to continue with the command. To use the Select Objects method, you will return to your drawing and pick **on the entities** that form the boundary. You can use any standard selection method to select the entities. You will use the Pick Points method to select the areas you want to hatch. Refer to Figure 10.13.

Pick: **Pick Points**

You are returned to your drawing screen and the following command prompt appears:

Select internal point: ***(pick a point inside the area labeled C)***

The perimeter of the area you have selected is highlighted, and you again see the prompt:

Select internal point: ***(pick inside the area labeled D)***

Select internal point: ***(pick inside the area labeled E)***

Select internal point: ***(pick inside the area labeled F)***

Select internal point: ↵

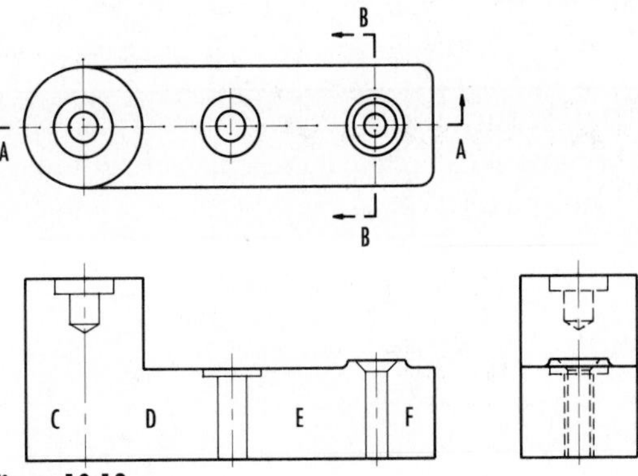

Figure 10.13

Now you are returned to the Boundary Hatch dialogue box. The choices that were previously grayed out (so you couldn't select them) are now available.

Pick: **Preview Hatch**

You are returned to your drawing screen with the hatch showing so that you can confirm that the areas you selected are correct. If the area was not hatched correctly, make the necessary changes and then preview the hatch again. When what you see is correct, pick Apply to apply the hatch:

Press: ⏎ ***(to return to the Boundary Hatch dialogue box)***

Pick: **Apply *(from the lower left of the dialogue box)***

The area that you selected becomes hatched in your drawing.

Your drawing should now look like Figure 10.14.

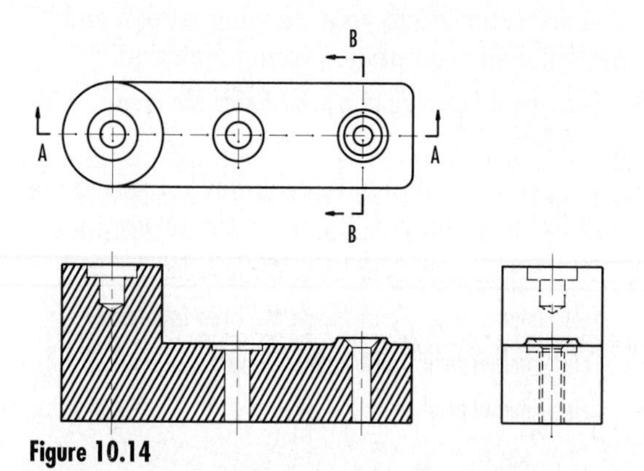

Figure 10.14

> ■ ***TIP*** Turn GRID off before previewing, because it can make it difficult to read the hatch pattern. ■

Adapting for Architecture

Typically, in architectural sections or plans (plans are a section cut on a horizontal plane), walls are not hatched, but poched in black. (Poched means the walls are filled in with black.) AutoCAD provides no easy way to do this, but it can be accomplished by manipulating several techniques. One technique is to poche the walls with a hatch pattern set to a small scale, so that when it is plotted it appears dense and black. This technique is cumbersome and does not facilitate easy design changes in the future. Wide polylines can also be used to fill walls for poche. This technique involves drawing the walls from the center with an approximate line thickness of 6" or 1'. Neither of these techniques is perfect and often black poche walls are added by hand after the drawing is printed. To facilitate this, plot all the walls that will be poched by hand with a thick pen; this will make filling in by hand easier. ■

Adjusting Your Drawing Area

To draw section B-B, you will need to increase the size of your drawing area in the view. You will use Zoom to create a view in which more drawing area is shown in the viewport.

Command: **Z** ⏎

All/Center/Dynamic/Extents/Left/Previous/Vmax/Window/<Scale(x/XP)>: **.75XP** ⏎

Your drawing appears smaller, so more of it fits into the viewport.

You can use the PAN command if you need to move the view around in the viewport so that all three views can be seen.

Command: **P** (↵)

Displacement: ***(pick a point to the left of the front view)***

Second point: ***(pick a point inside the border, left of the first point)***

Now you have space to create section B-B to the right of the top view.

You will use the Rotate command to re-orient the side view so that it can be aligned with the top view, as you see in Figure 10.15.

Pick: **ROTATE icon *(toolbox)***

Select objects: ***(select all the entities in the side view with implied crossing)***

Select objects: (↵)

Base point: ***(with SNAP on, pick the top left corner of the side view)***

<Rotation angle>/Reference: **90** (↵)

> ■ ***TIP*** You can also use the hot grips to rotate. Use the implied crossing mode to select all of the objects you want to rotate. Once they are selected and you see all of the blue hot grips, pick a base grip to be the base point in the Rotate command. Once you have selected the base grip, you will see the Stretch command in the command prompt area. Press the (↵) key twice to pass Stretch and Move; the next command is Rotate. Follow the prompts that appear on your screen to rotate the objects in the side view. ■

Now you will use the MOVE command to align the rotated side view with the top view.

Pick: **MOVE *(toolbox)***

Select objects: **P** (↵) ***(for previous selection set)***

Select objects: (↵)

Base point or displacement: ***(pick the upper left corner of the rotated object)***

Second point of displacement: ***(pick a point on the snap that lines up with the top line in the top view)***

Your drawing should now look like Figure 10.15.

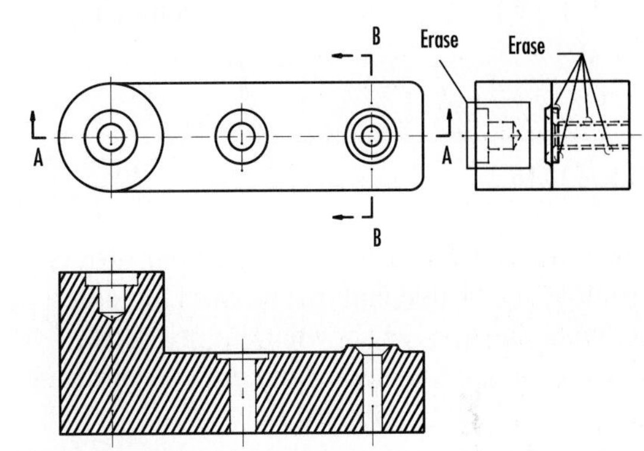

Figure 10.15

On your own, use the ERASE command to remove the unnecessary hidden lines from the rotated object. See Figure 10.15. Then change the hidden lines for the countersunk hole in the rotated side view to layer VISIBLE, because this hole is the only one that will show in the sectional view.

> ■ ***TIP*** You may need to use ZOOM, Window to enlarge the area on the screen. When you are finished erasing and changing the lines, use ZOOM, Previous to return the area to its original size. ■

Your screen should look similar to Figure 10.16 when you are finished.

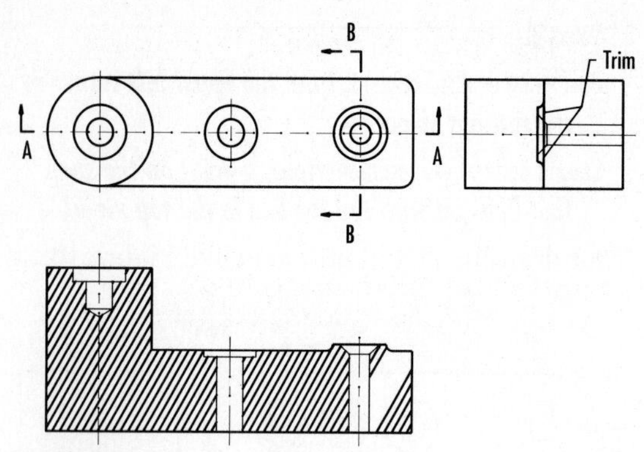

Figure 10.16

Next use the TRIM command on your own to remove the visible line that crosses the outer edge of the boss, as shown in Figure 10.16. When you are finished trimming, your drawing should look like Figure 10.17.

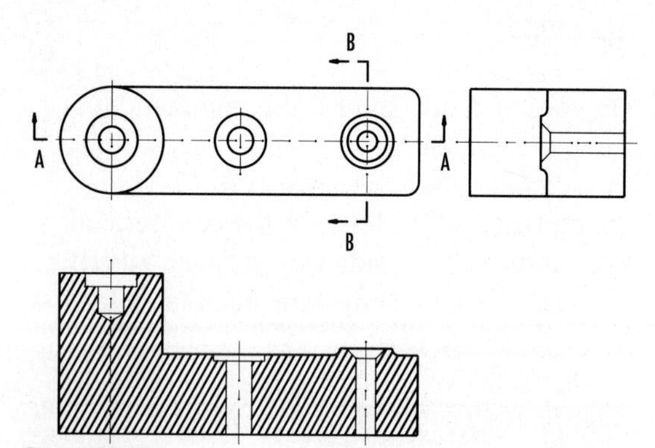

Figure 10.17

Now you are ready to add the hatching.

Pick: **Draw *(menu bar)*, Hatch. . .**

In the Boundary Hatch dialogue box, the hatch pattern ANSI31 should already be selected and shown at the top as the current pattern.

Pick: **Pick Points**

Select inside the areas you want to have hatched and press ⏎ when you have finished to return to the Boundary Hatch dialogue box. Refer to Figure 10.18.

Pick: **Preview Hatch *(to make sure the hatching shows correctly)***

Press: ⏎ ***(to return to the dialogue box)***

If the hatching appears the way you want,

Pick: **Apply**

When you are done, your drawing should appear similar to Figure 10.18.

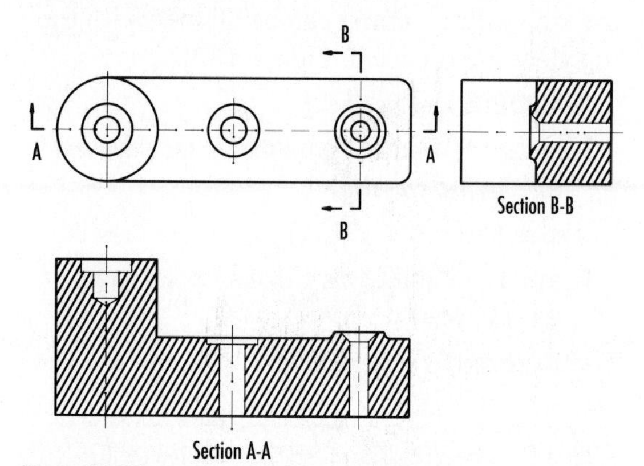

Figure 10.18

On your own, make layer TEXT current and use DTEXT to label the sectional views SECTION A-A and SECTION B-B. Place the text directly below the sectional views, as shown in Figure 10.18. Save your drawing as BOSSECT.

Adapting for Architecture

When creating section drawings that have details that extend beyond what you are showing in your drawing, create a partial hatch by setting up a guide layer and drawing the boundary. After you add the hatch, you can freeze the guide layer so that it will not print. If you use HATCH to denote shadows on a drawing, use the same technique to create the hatch boundary on a separate layer, and then make sure to freeze the boundary layer before you print. ■

■ ***TIP*** Remember to save frequently while creating drawings. AutoCAD has an autosave feature that saves automatically for you to a file named AUTO.SV$. The time interval for the autosave feature is set with the system variable SAVETIME. The default is to save every 120 minutes. You would not want to lose two hours' worth of work, so save frequently on your own. To set AutoCAD to automatically save at shorter intervals, type "SAVETIME" at the "Command:" prompt and enter the new number in minutes. However, do not rely on automatic saves. Save your file whenever you have made a major change that you want to keep or about every 10 minutes. ■

Plot your drawing on your own. Before you plot, be sure to switch to paper space. If you need help plotting, refer to Tutorial 3.

You have completed the 2D portion of this tutorial. Now you will learn how to automatically create section views from a solid model, using the SOLSECT command.

Creating Sections from a Solid Model

This time you will start your drawing from a solid model prototype provided with the data files. It is similar to the one that you created in Tutorial 9.

Pick: **File *(menu bar)*, New**

In the Create New Drawing dialogue box, use SOLBLK2 as the prototype for your new drawing. For the new file name, type "BLKSECT" in the empty box at the bottom of the dialogue box. Pick OK when you are done.

A drawing similar to the one you created in Tutorial 9 appears on your screen. A hole has been added to the rounded portion at the top. Your screen should appear similar to Figure 10.19.

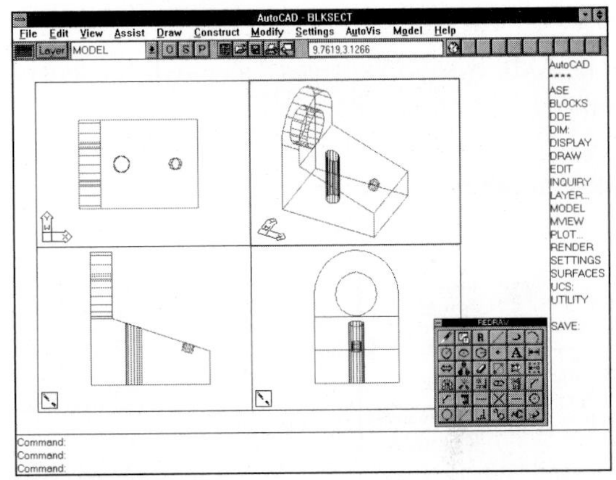

Figure 10.19

Create layer HATCH on your own in order to place the hatching that AutoCAD will generate on a separate layer. Assign color 1 (red) and linetype CONTINUOUS to layer HATCH. Make it the current layer.

You will first restore the UCS for the front view to the lower left viewport:

Pick: ***(the lower left viewport to make it active)***

Command: **UCS** ↵

Origin/ZAxis/3point/Entity/View/X/Y/Z/Prev/Restore/Save/Del/?/<World>: **R** ↵

?/Name of UCS to restore: **FRONT** ↵

The UCS for the front view should be restored. You can tell this has happened because the grid is now displayed normal to the front view.

Before using the SOLSECT command, familiarize yourself with the system variables that determine what type and size of hatch pattern and what type of entity are created when you use SOLSECT.

Pick: **Model *(menu bar)*, Setup, Variables**

If your system does not preload AME and you have not used it yet during this drawing session, you will see the prompt "No modeler loaded yet. Both AME and Region Modeler are available. Autoload Region/<AME>:". Press ↵ to load AME if necessary.

The AME System Variables dialogue box appears on your screen, as shown in Figure 10.20.

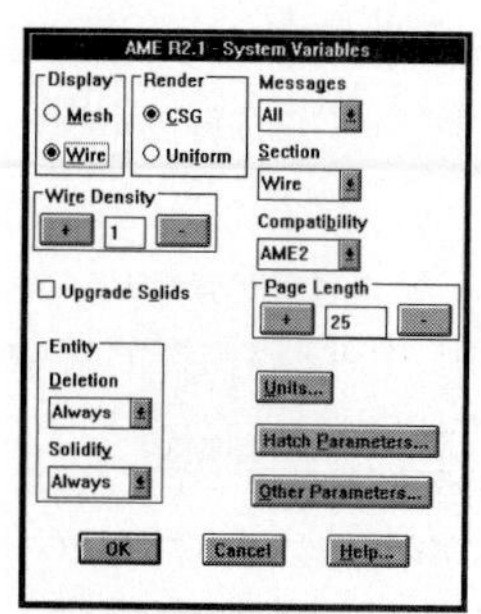

Figure 10.20

Pick: **Hatch Parameters**

You will use the Hatch Parameters dialogue box to set the hatch pattern, angle, and spacing for the *generated hatch*. The Hatch Parameters dialogue box appears on your screen, as shown in Figure 10.21.

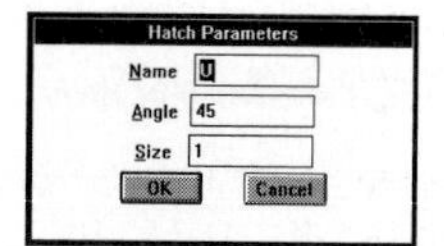

Figure 10.21

In the edit box to the right of Name,

Type: **ANSI31**

Next, set the angle to 0 because hatch pattern ANSI31 is already angled at 45 degrees. In the edit box to the right of Angle,

Type: **0**

Leave the size set at 1. This drawing is set up to be plotted full scale on 8.5" × 11" paper, so the scale of 1 should produce hatching lines the correct distance apart.

Pick: **OK *(to accept the hatch parameters)***

You can also use the AME System Variables dialogue box to select the type of entity you want the SOLSECT command to create. To change the type of entity created by the command,

Pick: **Wire *(under the heading Section)***

You will see the selections Wire, Polyline, and Region pull down. The Wire choice creates the hatching in your drawing as lines, circles, and arcs. The Polyline selection creates a polyline entity for the generated hatch boundary. Selecting Region creates a 2D region entity, which you learned about in Tutorial 8, for the generated hatching. Do not change the selection; leave it set to Wire.

Pick: **OK *(to exit the dialogue box)***

Turn on the Object Snap, Midpoint running mode on your own so that it is available for the next command. Make the upper right viewport active.

Command: **SOLSECT** ↵

Select objects: ***(pick the object displayed in the upper right viewport)***

Select objects: ↵

1 solid selected

Sectioning plane by Entity/Last/Zaxis/View/XY/YZ/ZX/<3points>: ↵

The methods by which you can select the cutting plane for the section are very similar to the methods you learned in the last tutorial for using SOLCUT. You will specify three points to define the cutting plane, which will pass through the middle of the object. OSNAP, Midpoint will select the midpoint of the lines you pick. Refer to Figure 10.22.

1st point on plane: ***(pick line A)***

2nd point on plane: ***(pick line B)***

3rd point on plane: ***(pick line C)***

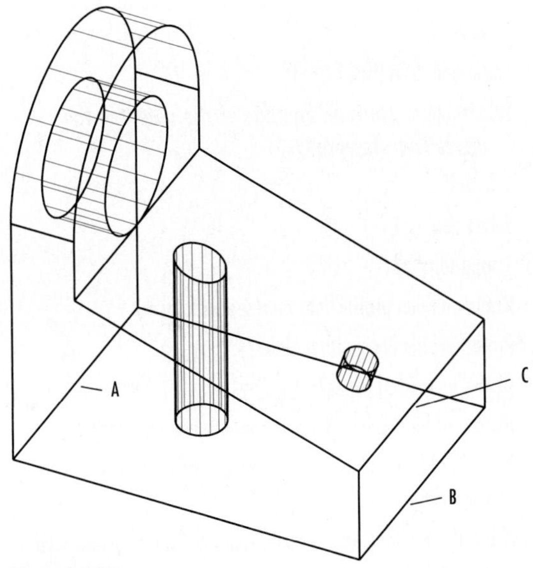

Figure 10.22

> ■ ***TIP*** If you want to select in a viewport that is not active, press Ctrl-V to toggle the active viewport during commands. ■

The SOLSECT command creates two new blocks in your drawing. One block contains the hatch lines and the other contains the boundary of the hatching. You should see them appear in your drawing, as shown in Figure 10.23.

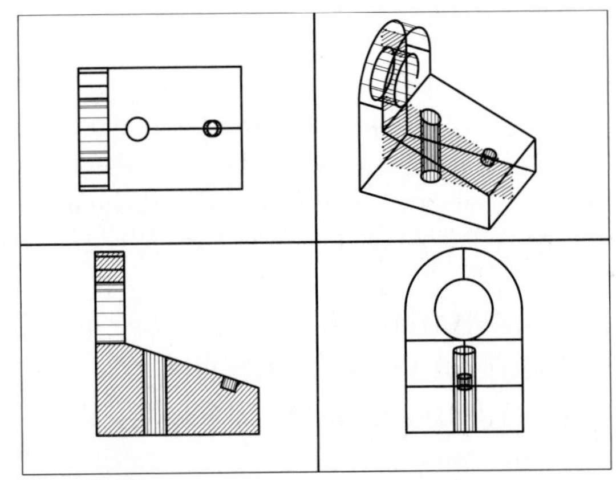

Figure 10.23

Turn off the running mode object snap for Midpoint on your own. Remember that many commands do not work correctly with a running mode OSNAP on. In addition, selecting entities can be difficult with an object snap on.

On your own, use ERASE to remove the hatch boundary created by the SOLSECT command, leaving only the hatching. (Or you can change the hatch boundary to a separate layer and freeze that layer.) Use ZOOM, Window to enlarge an area near the edge of the hatching so that you can see the hatch boundary clearly to erase it. Erasing it eliminates the double line in your drawing that would be produced by the boundary and the edge of the object coinciding. Use ZOOM, Previous to return to the original view.

The hatching should only appear in the sectional view, but at this point it is still visible in every view on the drawing. You will change the visibility for the HATCH layer, using the VPLAYER command, so that the hatching only shows in the front view.

Controlling Layer Visibility

Use the VPLAYER command to freeze the hatching in all of the viewports except the lower left one. If you have difficulty, refer to Tutorial 9, where you used VPLAYER to control the visibility for the center lines in your drawing.

Command: **VPLAYER** ↵

?/Freeze/Thaw/Reset/Newfrz/Vpvisdflt: **F** ↵

Layer name(s) to Freeze: **HATCH** ↵

All/Select/<Current>: **S** ↵

Switching to Paper space.

Select objects: ***(pick the upper right viewport border)***

1 found

Select objects: ***(pick the lower right viewport border)***

1 found

Select objects: ***(pick the upper left viewport border)***

1 found

Select objects: ↵

Switching to Model space

?/Freeze/Thaw/Reset/Newfrz/Vpvisdflt: ↵

Regenerating drawing

Your drawing should look like Figure 10.24. Save your drawing.

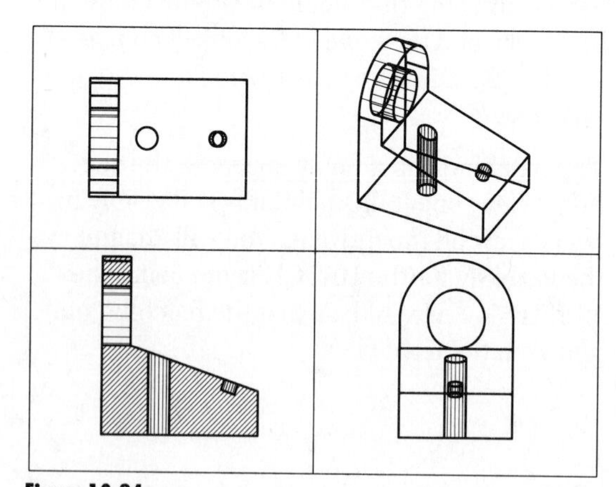

Figure 10.24

Going Further

Use the directions below to profile the object into the viewports in order to produce a standard orthographic drawing with correct hidden lines, etc. Use the methods you learned in Tutorial 9 to profile each view into its viewport.

Pick: ***(in the upper left-hand viewport to make it active)***

Command: **SOLPROF** ↵

Select objects: ***(pick on an edge of the object in the upper left viewport)***

1 found

Select objects: ↵

1 solid selected

Display hidden profile lines on a separate layer? <Y>: ↵

Project profile lines onto a plane? <Y>: ↵

Delete tangential edges? <Y>: ↵

Phase I of hidden line removal computation has started.

Phase II of hidden line removal computation of current solid has started.

Phase III of hidden line removal computation of current solid has started.

Hidden line removal computation of current solid completed.

The lines of the projected block are drawn over the object lines in your drawing.

Repeat this process on your own for each of the other viewports.

Use the Settings, Layer Control dialogue box to freeze the PV- layers and then make the PH- layers blue. Set the current layer to 0. Freeze layers MODEL and HATCH. Pick OK when you are done to exit the dialogue.

Explode the hidden line blocks. You will see their color change. Use the CHPROP command and the Previous selection set option to change the hidden lines so that their color is set to BYLAYER.

Erase the extra hidden lines from the outer edge of the object.

Use CHPROP again to change the hidden lines in the front view (lower left viewport) to layer PV-1B (the handle number for the lower left viewport).

Use the LAYER command to thaw all the layers that start with PV- and layer HATCH.

> ■ ***TIP*** If you use the LAYER command, you can then use the Thaw option and type in "PV*" for the layer names to thaw. The * is a wildcard that matches any characters. ■

Create a layer for the cutting plane that is visible only in the top view. Add a cutting plane line and leaders to the top view. (To do this you will have to restore the World Coordinates.) Then create new layers for the center lines so that each center line layer is visible only in its own viewport. Restore the appropriate UCSs and add the center lines to your drawing. Freeze the hidden line layer for the upper right viewport where the isometric view shows.

Your drawing should now look like Figure 10.25.

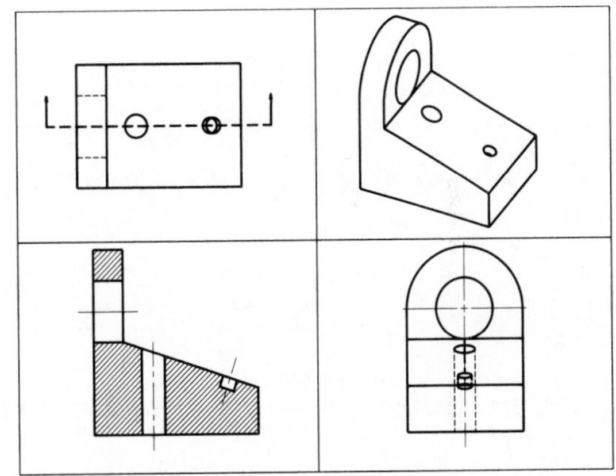

Figure 10.25

You have completed Tutorial 10. Now you know how to create both 2D and 3D section views.

KEY TERMS

crosshatching
cutting plane line
full section
generated hatch
sectional lines
sectional view

KEY COMMANDS

Boundary Hatch
Hatch
Leader
Solid Section
Save Time

EXERCISES

Redraw the given front view and replace the given right side view with a sectional view. Use 2D methods or solid modeling. Assume that the vertical centerline of the front view is the cutting plane line for the sectional view. The letter M after an exercise means that the given dimensions are in millimeters.

10.1 High Pressure Seal

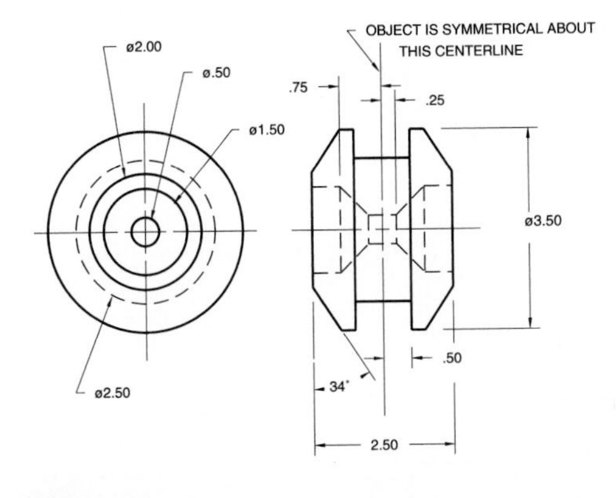

10.2M Pulley

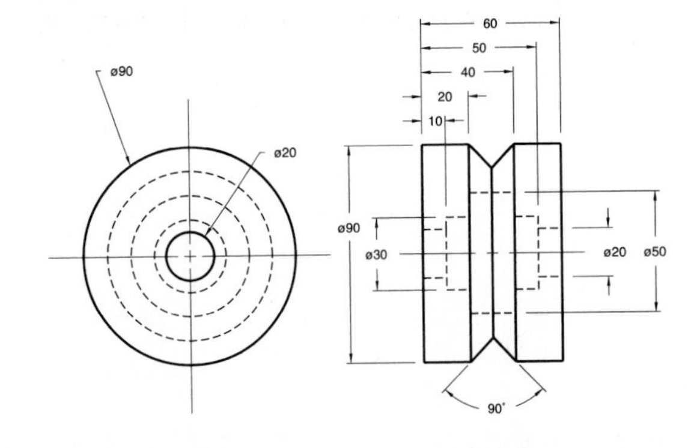

10.3 Valve Cover

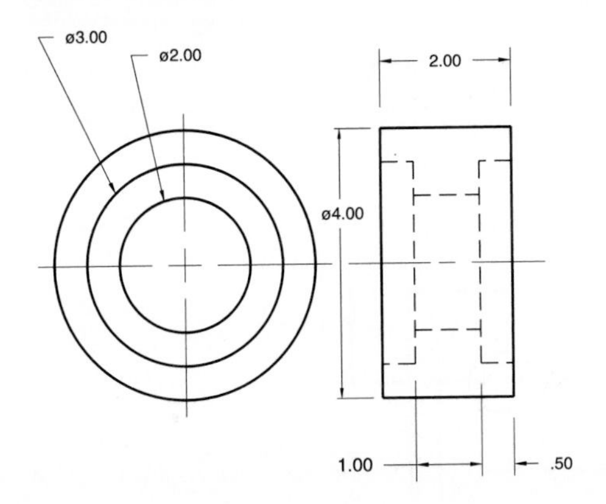

10.4 Double Cylinder

Use 2D techniques to draw this object; the grid shown is 0.25". Show the front view as a half section and show the corresponding cutting plane in the top view. On the same views, completely dimension the object to the nearest 0.01 inches. Include any notes that are necessary.

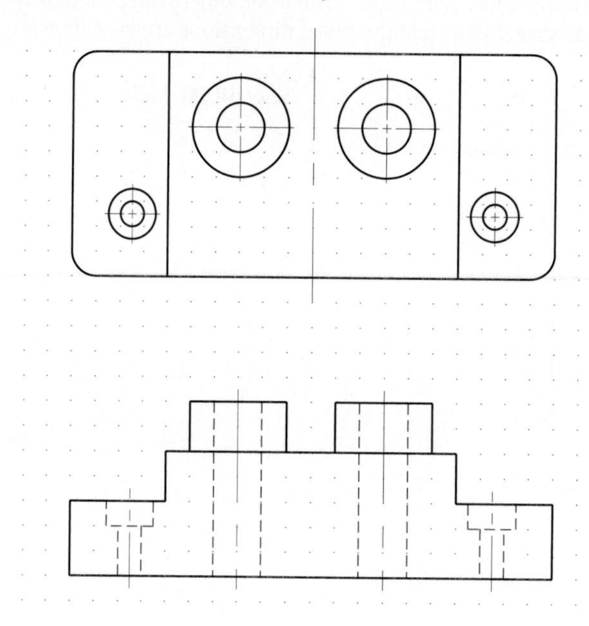

10.5 Plate

Use 2D to construct the top view with the cutting plane shown and the sectioned front view.

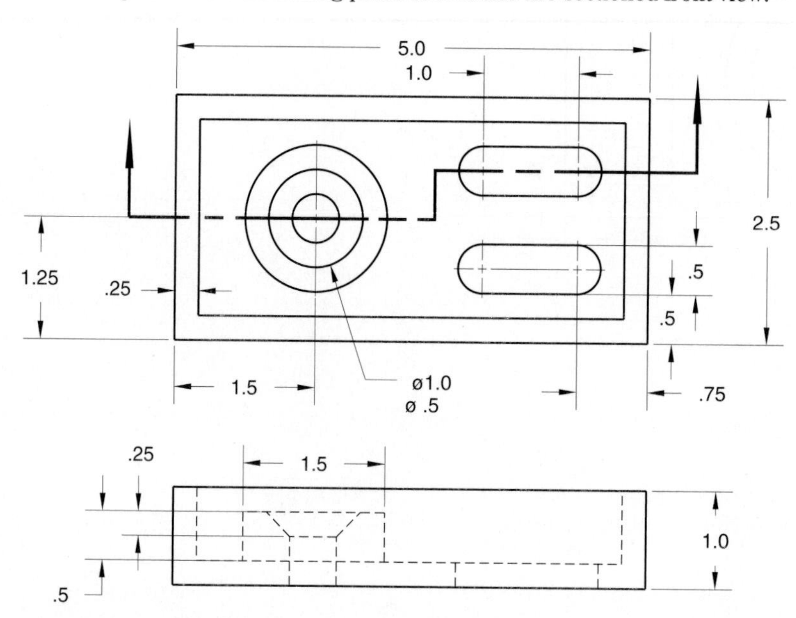

10.6 Wedge

Make a solid model based on the given views, then produce a plan view and a full-sectioned front view. Make sure the sectioned front view is aligned with the plan view. Hidden lines and/or cutting planes are not needed in the plan view.

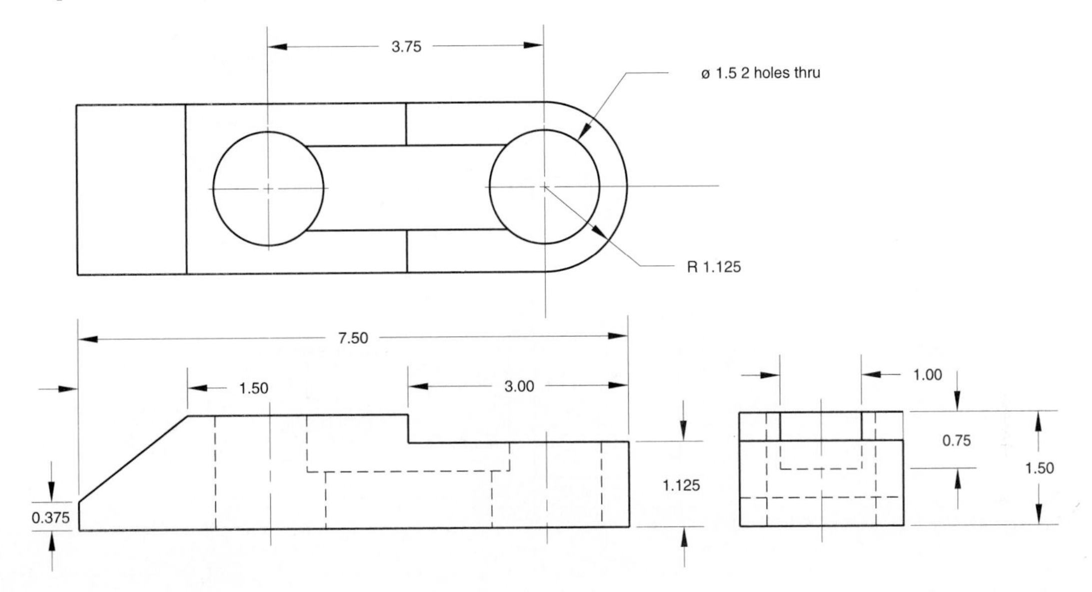

10.7 Support Bracket

The figure uses the DIMALT dimension variable to show both inches and millimeters (in brackets). Redraw the figure in either inches or millimeters. Try using DIMALT to list both dimensions. Use DIMALTD to set the number of decimal places showing in the alternate units, and DIMALTF to set the conversion scale (use 2.54 to convert from inches to millimeters).

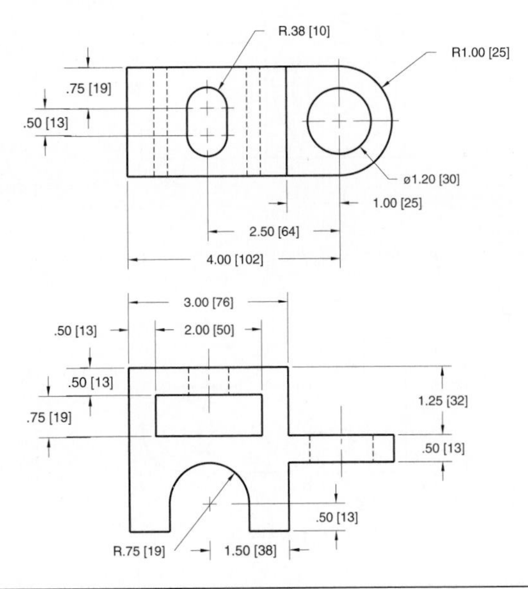

10.8 Turned Down Slab Detail

Use 2D methods to create the drawings shown. Use the BHATCH command to fill the areas with the appropriate patterns for concrete, sand, and earth.

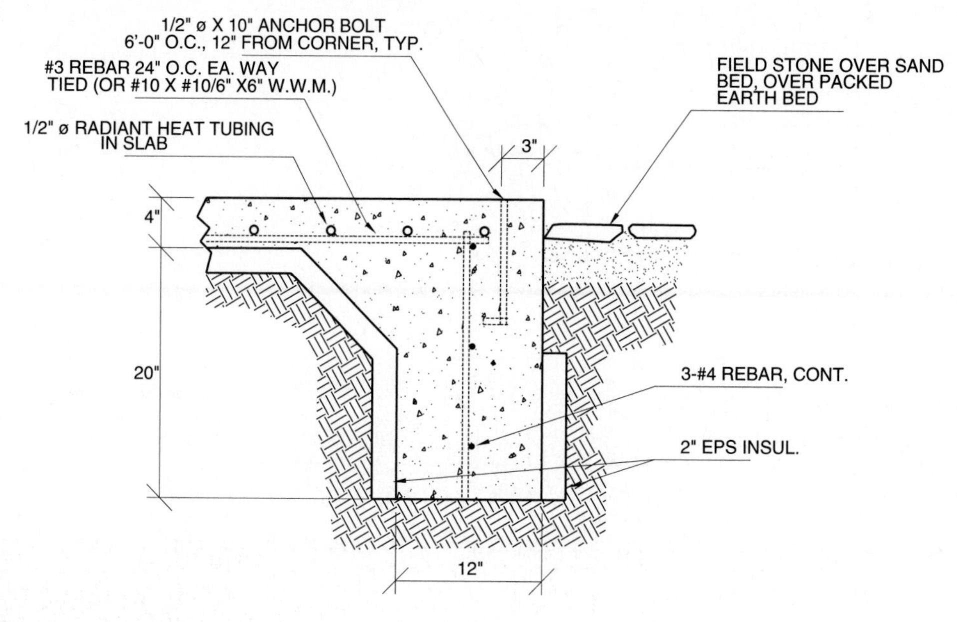

10.9 Shaft Support

Redraw the given front view and create a sectional view. Assume that the vertical centerline of the shaft in the front view is the cutting plane line for the sectional view.

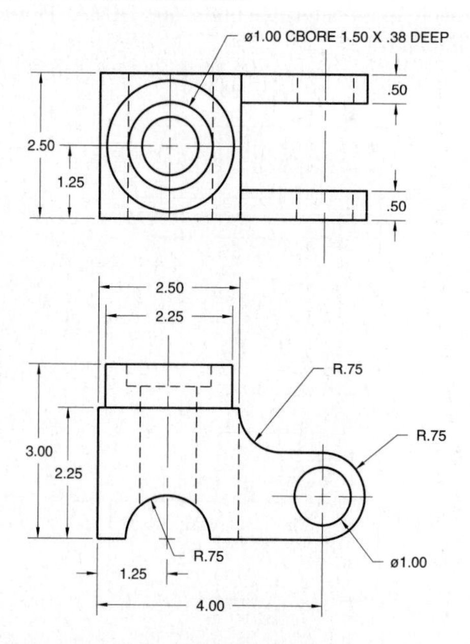

TUTORIAL 11

Pictorial Drawings Using 2D and 3D Methods

Objectives

When you have completed this tutorial, you will be able to

1. Create 2D isometric drawings.
2. Use AutoCAD's 2D isometric commands.
3. Transfer angular and circular dimensions from orthographic views to isometric views.
4. Create isometric and perspective drawings from drawings from solid models.

Introduction

2D isometric drawings are standard orthographic projection drawings that give the appearance of being three-dimensional drawings. Because they are drawn on your computer screen in the same way you would draw on a piece of paper, they are not truly three-dimensional drawings. The drawings appear to have three dimensions because the object is shown tipped toward the viewing plane. The result is that the top, front, and side surfaces are all visible at once in the view. For instance, if the object being drawn were a cube, it would be tilted so that you would be looking onto the diagonal through the cube. You may find it useful to think of a 2D isometric drawing as a photograph, and a true three-dimensional drawing as a hologram, as you work through the tutorial to prepare the 2D isometric drawing.

You will create pictorials from 3D solid model drawings later in the tutorial. You have already seen how the 3D solid model drawings can be used to create 2D views, using the SOLPROF command. You can also choose to view your 3D models in perspective; i.e., the farther away a surface is, the smaller it appears. This is not the case in an isometric drawing; the surfaces at the back of the object appear as large as if they were at the front.

The Isometric Axis

An *isometric axis* is defined by three lines 120 degrees apart. Figure 11.1 shows an isometric axis and angles measured between the axis lines.

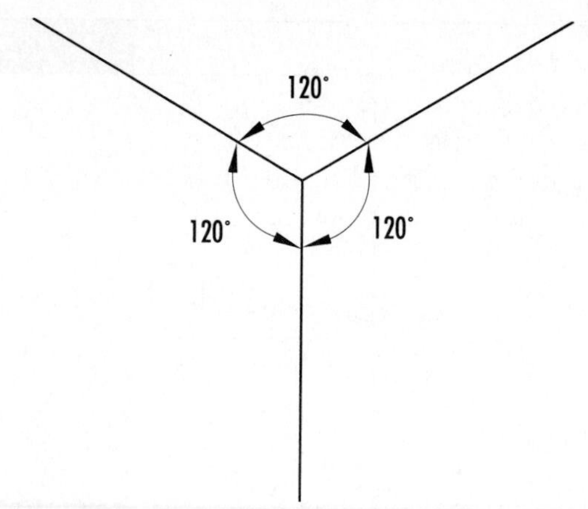

Figure 11.1

Figure 11.2 shows a rectangular prism drawn on an isometric axis.

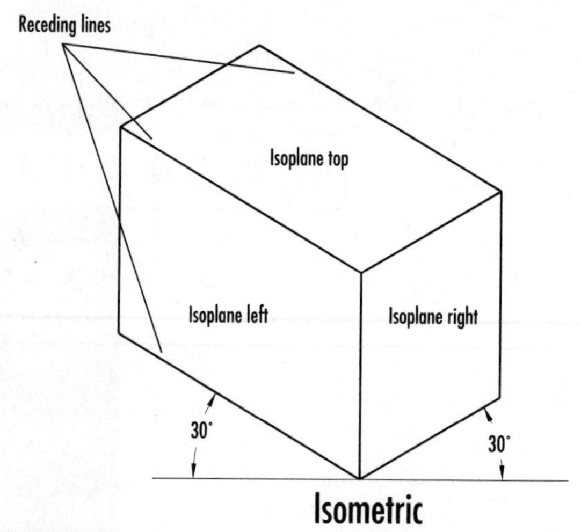

Figure 11.2

Note that the lines that would appear to recede in a photograph, or if you were looking at the actual object, are drawn parallel to each other at 30 degrees to the horizontal. Because the lines are parallel and do not converge, isometric drawings sometimes have a distorted visual appearance. The top corner may look as if it is slightly higher than it should be. Correct visual appearances are created using perspective drawings. Perspective drawings have receding lines that converge at a vanishing point. Figure 11.3 shows the same rectangular prism in perspective. Notice that the back surface of the object appears smaller than in the isometric drawing.

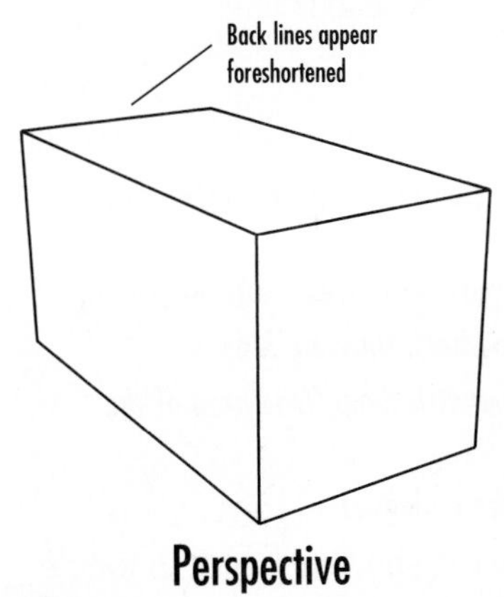

Figure 11.3

Starting

Start AutoCAD from the Autodesk Collection interface as instructed in Chapter 3. AutoCAD's drawing editor should be on your display screen.

Pick: **File *(menu bar)*, New**

Use the prototype drawing named PROTO provided with the data files to begin a new drawing on your own. Name your drawing FLANGE in the DRAWINGS directory. When you have finished,

Pick: **OK *(to exit the dialogue box)***

The lines of the border appear on your screen and layer VISIBLE should be current.

Preparing to Draw in Isometric

Figure 11.4 shows an isometric drawing of the flange.

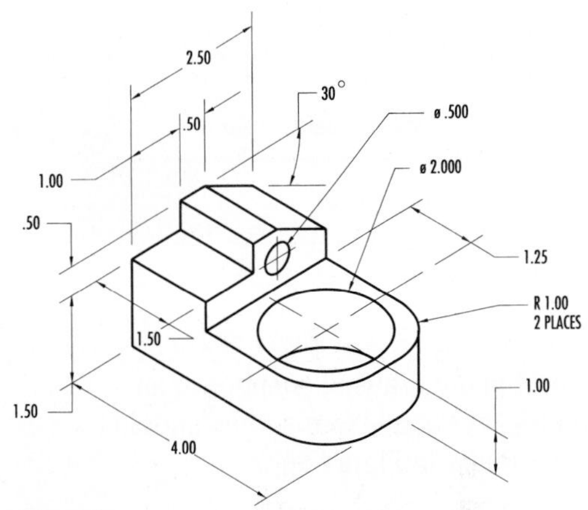

Figure 11.4

Working through this tutorial, you will complete the steps needed to draw this isometric drawing, excluding the dimensions. You will use the Drawing Aids dialogue box to set up an isometric grid to use in creating 2D isometric drawings.

Pick: **Settings *(menu bar)*, Drawing Aids**

Leave the grid spacing set to 0. Use the appropriate areas of the dialogue box to set the snap to .25 and turn on the isometric snap/grid. Pick in the box adjacent to On in the Isometric Snap/Grid area of the dialogue box to turn on the isometric style grid and snap. Notice that the current isoplane is set to Left. The dialogue box should appear similar to Figure 11.5 before you exit it by picking OK.

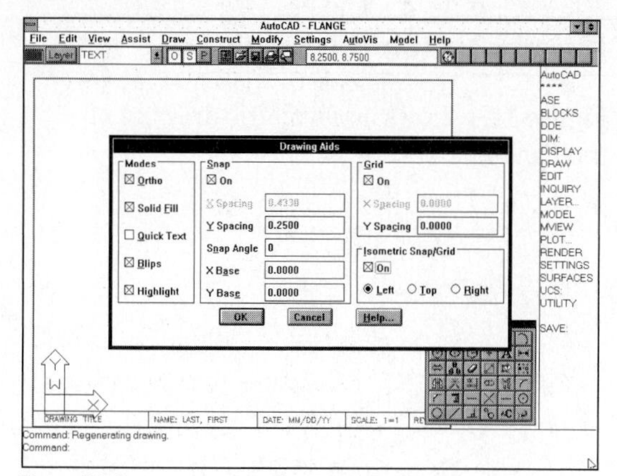

Figure 11.5

The grid in the drawing changes to an isometric-style grid. Your screen should appear similar to Figure 11.6.

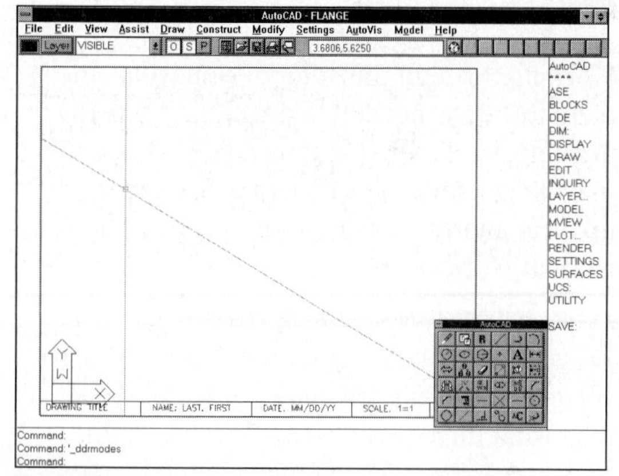

Figure 11.6

Isoplane Left

Move the cursor around on the screen. Note that instead of a horizontal and vertical line for the crosshairs, there is now a vertical line and a 30-degree slanted line. This is one of three crosshair patterns used in isometric drawings. The one you are looking at is for the left isoplane. Use it when you are drawing parallel to the left isoplane, as shown in Figure 11.2.

The Left isoplane option of the dialogue box selects the left-handed plane, defined by the 90-degree and 150-degree axis pair. When SNAP mode is on, the ↑ and ↓ cursor keys move along the 90-degree axis, and the ← and → cursor keys move along the 150-degree axis. Using ORTHO also constrains movement and drawing to only these axis lines.

Isoplane Top

The top isometric drawing plane is the top face of the cube; it uses the 30-degree and 150-degree axis pair. Select the top isoplane.

Pick: ***Settings (menu bar),*** **Drawing Aids**

Pick: **Top** ***(in the Isometric Snap/Grid area of the dialogue box)***

Pick: **OK** ***(to exit the dialogue)***

Next, you will use the shortcut Ctrl-E to toggle the isoplane to the right isoplane.

Press: **Ctrl-E**

"<Isoplane Right>" appears at the command line.

Isoplane Right

Move the crosshairs around on the screen. You will see that they have changed to display the right isometric plane, which is the right-hand plane, defined by the 90-degree and the 30-degree axis pair.

Toggling the Isoplane

You can toggle to the next isoplane, even in the middle of a command, by pressing Ctrl-E.

Press: **Ctrl-E**

The prompt says "<Isoplane Left>" and the isoplane left crosshairs are active.

Press: **Ctrl-E**

and the isoplane top crosshairs appear, as well as "<Isoplane Top>" in the prompt area.

It is critical to be in the correct isoplane when drawing isometric ellipses and tangent lines. It is not necessary for drawing lines unless you want to use the snap, although it is useful to be in the correct isoplane to help you visualize the drawing plane.

Working with Isometric Views

You will start the drawing by creating a rectangular prism, 2.00 × 2.50 × 4.00. These are the overall dimensions of the object shown in Figure 11.4. You will start by drawing the left surface of the rectangular prism.

You will use AutoCAD's relative coordinate entry to specify the lengths and angles of the lines. As you remember from Tutorial 1, AutoCAD measures angles from 0 degrees towards the East, going in a counter-clockwise direction for positive angles. A line drawn at –30 degrees from one endpoint of a line is the same as a line drawn from the other endpoint at an angle of 150 degrees. The general form for relative coordinate entry is @*L*<*A* (replace the L and A with the length and angle you want to specify).

> ■ ***TIP*** When you are working on an isometric drawing and you are not sure of the angle to specify for relative coordinate entry, turn ORTHO on and stretch the line in the direction in which it should go. Read the coordinates at the top of the toolbar; the correct angle is displayed there. If the coordinates do not display that angle, you may need to toggle the coordinate display mode by picking on the coordinates displayed on the toolbar. ■

Press: Ctrl-**E** Ctrl-**E** ***(to toggle to the left isoplane)***

Pick: **LINE icon *(toolbox)***

From point: ***(Use SNAP and look at the coordinates to pick the point 6.0622,1.5000 from the lower center area of the screen)***

To point: **@4<150** ↵

To point: **@2<90** ↵

To point: **@4<330** ↵

To point: **C** ↵

Now you will add the front right-hand surface.

Press: Ctrl-**E** Ctrl-**E** ***(to toggle to the right isoplane)***

Command: ↵ ***(to restart the LINE command)***

From point: ***(pick INTERSECTION from the toolbox)***

int of ***(pick the intersection of the top line with the right-side line)***

To point: **@2.5<30** ↵

To point: **@2<–90** ↵

To point: **@2.5<210** ↵

To point: ↵

> ■ ***TIP*** Notice that you can't use Close here because you started at the top point and are ending at the bottom point of the vertical line from the previous parallelogram. ■

The two surfaces you have drawn should look like Figure 11.7.

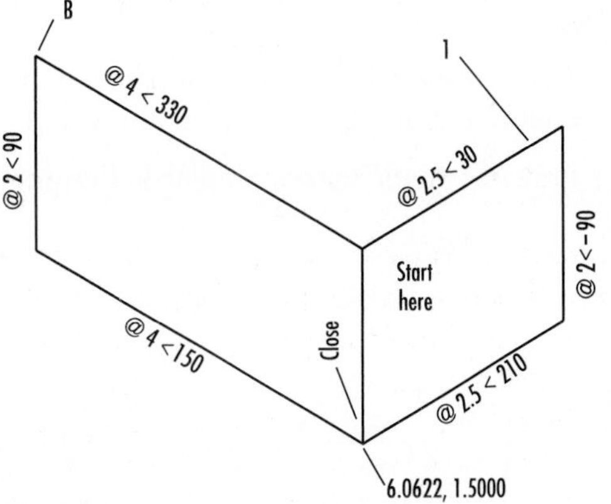

Figure 11.7

You will copy the top line of each surface to create the top plane of the object. You will use the hot grips and the Move, Copy option to perform the copy. To use hot grips, make sure your command prompt is cleared; it should read "Command:", with **no** AutoCAD command active after the prompt. Refer to Figure 11.7 as you pick points.

Pick: ***(line 1)***

Hot grips boxes appear on the line's endpoints and midpoints.

Pick: ***(the grip box at the left endpoint)***

The box becomes highlighted to indicate that it is the base grip for the command. The command prompt area displays the options for the STRETCH command:

STRETCH

<Stretch to point>/Base point/Copy/Undo/eXit: ↵

MOVE

<Move to point>/Base point/Copy/Undo/eXit: **C** ↵

MOVE (multiple)

<Move to point>/Base point/Copy/Undo/eXit: ***(use OSNAP, Endpoint to pick endpoint B in Figure 11.7; make sure that ORTHO is turned off)***

MOVE (multiple)

<Move to point>/Base point/Copy/Undo/eXit: ↵

Press: Ctrl-**C** Ctrl-**C** ***(to de-activate the hot grips for line 1)***

Repeat this process for the other top line of the object, labeled 2 in Figure 11.7, on your own.

Your drawing should appear similar to Figure 11.8.

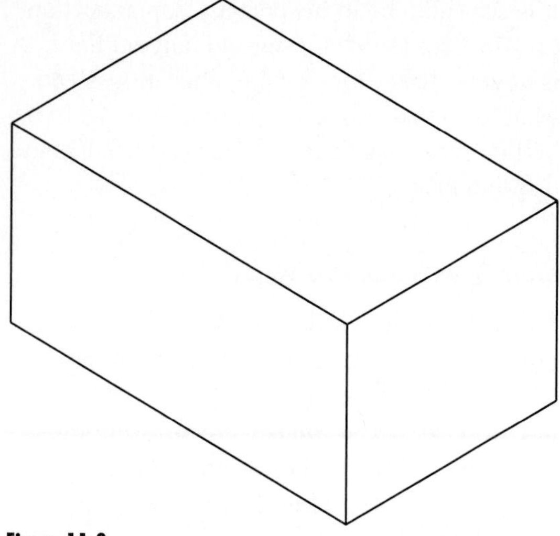

Figure 11.8

You will create the L shape of the object by removing the top right section. You will create parallel lines by using the COPY command with a specified displacement. Then you will use the lines you copied to trim off the removed portion.

■ ***Warning:*** You cannot use the OFFSET command to create a parallel line a specified distance away in the isometric drawing mode. The OFFSET command measures distances perpendicular to the entity, not the isometric axes. ■

Pick: **COPY *(toolbox)***

Select objects: ***(pick line A in Figure 11.9)*** ↵

<Base point or displacement>/Multiple: **1.5<330** ↵

Second point of displacement: ↵

Your drawing should appear similar to Figure 11.9.

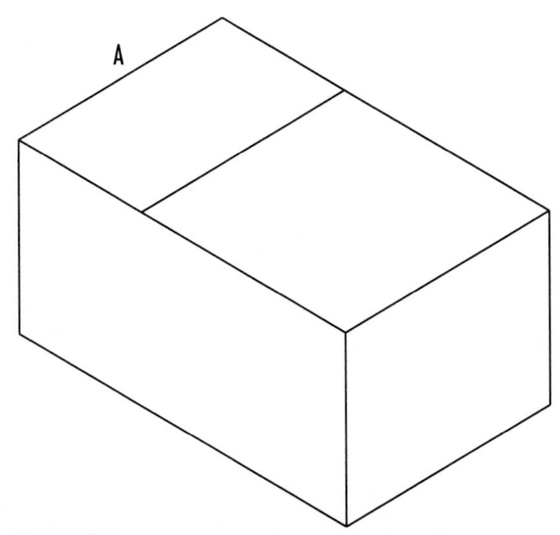

Figure 11.9

Now you will copy the top surface straight down. Refer to Figure 11.10 as you pick points.

> Command: ↵ ***(to restart the COPY command)***
>
> Select objects: ***(pick lines C, D, E, and F)*** ↵
>
> <Base point or displacement>/Multiple: **1<270** ↵
>
> Second point of displacement: ↵

Your drawing should now look like Figure 11.10.

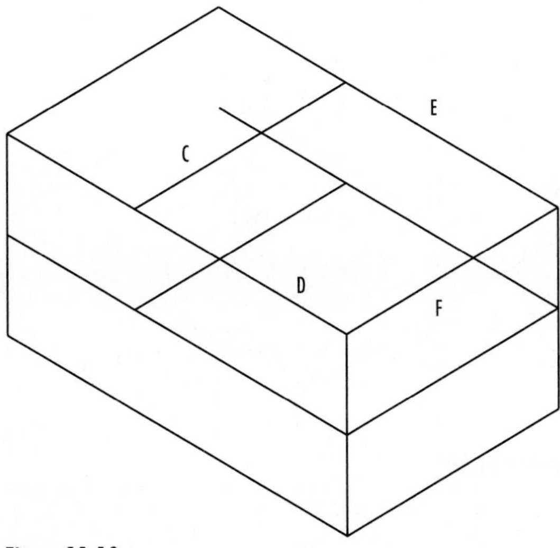

Figure 11.10

Draw lines to connect the endpoints of the middle line in the top surface to the middle line in the lower surface. Refer to Figure 11.11 when selecting the points.

> *Pick:* **LINE *(toolbox)***
>
> From point: ***(use Endpoint and pick point A)***
>
> To point: ***(use Endpoint and pick point B)***
>
> To point: ↵

Use the same procedure to create the line in the back surface on your own.

Your drawing should look like Figure 11.11.

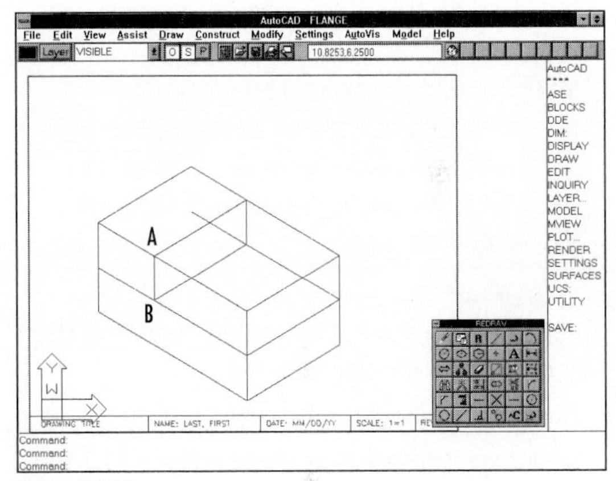

Figure 11.11

Use the Trim and Erase commands to remove the excess lines on your own, so that your drawing looks similar to Figure 11.12.

> ■ ***TIP*** Sometimes it is easier to select lines with SNAP turned off. Press F9 or pick S from the toolbar to turn off the snap, and then turn it on again when you have finished trimming and erasing. ■

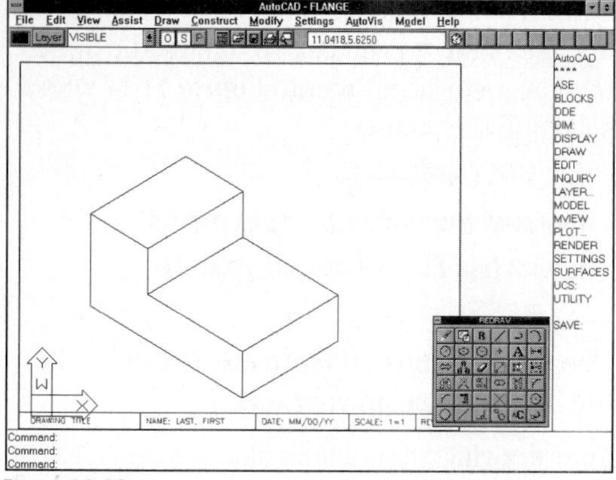
Figure 11.12

■ ***TIP*** Redrawing your screen can be accomplished quickly by pressing the (F7) key two times. This turns the grid off and back on again. In the process, it redraws the screen. ■

You will now remove the top left corner of the object, using a similar method.

Pick: **COPY** ***(toolbox)***

Select objects: ***(pick line A, as shown in Figure 11.13)*** ↵

<Base point or displacement>/Multiple: **1.5<210** ↵

Second point of displacement: ↵

Command: ↵ ***(to restart the COPY command)***

Select objects: ***(pick lines B, C, D, and E, as shown in Figure 11.13)*** ↵

<Base point or displacement>/Multiple: **.5<270** ↵

Second point of displacement: ↵

Your drawing should look similar to Figure 11.13.

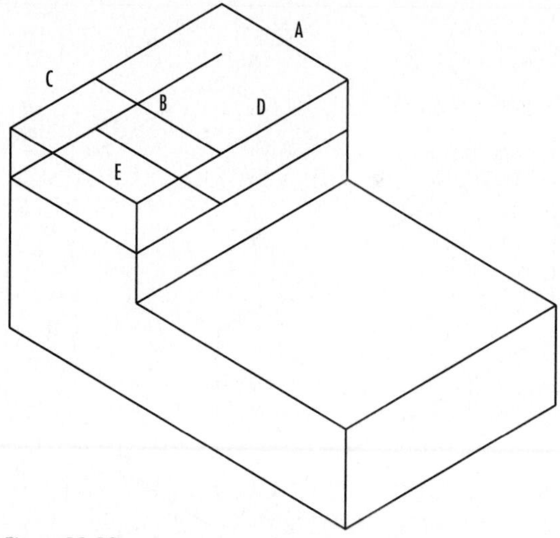

Figure 11.13

Draw a line to connect the endpoints of the middle line in the top surface to the endpoints of the middle line in the lower surface on your own.

Your drawing should look similar to Figure 11.14.

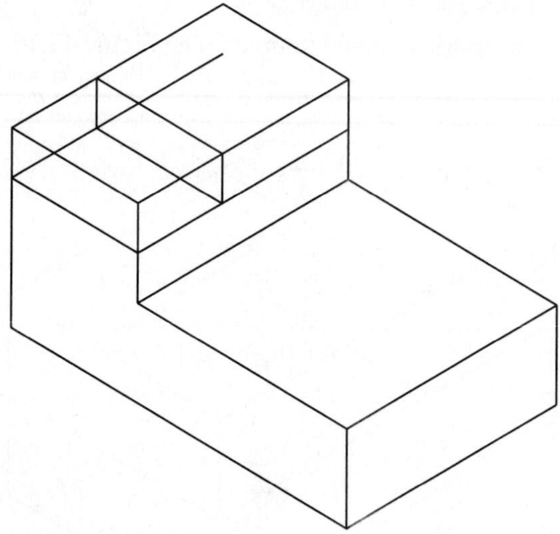
Figure 11.14

On your own, use the ERASE and TRIM commands to remove the excess lines.

Your screen should look similar to Figure 11.15.

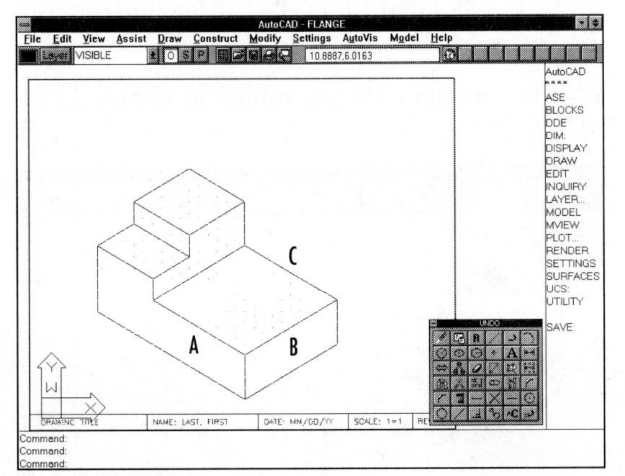

Figure 11.15

Pick: **REDRAW *(toolbox)***

Drawing an Isocircle

You will add the two rounded corners to the front view of the object. Circles (shapes of constant radius) cannot be used on an isometric axis to represent circular isometric shapes. You must draw an isometric ellipse, called an *isocircle* by AutoCAD. Isocircles look like circles in isometric drawings. AutoCAD makes ellipses by drawing four connecting polyline arcs. This method of constructing ellipses, called the four center method, is approximate. Because the ellipse is actually drawn with four arcs with their centers at different locations, some of the commands you have been using, such as OSNAP, Center and DIM: CEN, will not work to find the center of an ellipse. Usually, when you are drawing isometric ellipses, it is easiest to make construction lines for the center lines. Then when you are ready, you can draw center lines over them or use the CHPROP command to change them to another layer. These construction lines are usually necessary to help construct the isometric drawing, so you would draw them anyway.

You will use the COPY command to create a construction line for the center of the front and back arcs.

Pick: **COPY *(toolbox)***

Select objects: ***(pick line A, as shown in Figure 11.15)*** ↵

<Base point or displacement>/Multiple: **1<30** ↵

Second point of displacement: ↵

Command: ↵ ***(to restart the COPY command)***

Select objects: ***(pick line B, as shown in Figure 11.15)*** ↵

<Base point or displacement>/Multiple: **1<150** ↵

Second point of displacement: ↵

Command: ↵ ***(to restart the COPY command)***

Select objects: ***(pick line C, as shown in Figure 11.15)*** ↵

<Base point or displacement>/Multiple: **1<210** ↵

Second point of displacement: ↵

Next you will change the lines that you have just drawn so that they are on layer PROJ, which you created in the prototype drawing for construction lines.

Pick: **CHANGE *(toolbox)***

Select objects: ***(pick the three lines that you just created with the COPY command)***

Select objects: ↵

Properties/<Change Point>: **P** ↵

Change what property (Color/LAyer/LType/Thickness)?: **LA** ↵

New layer <VISIBLE>: **PROJ** ↵

Change what property (Color/LAyer/LType/Thickness)?: ↵

The lines change to layer PROJ and appear magenta on your color monitor. You will use these construction lines to draw the ellipse. Be sure that SNAP is on. Your screen should look similar to Figure 11.16.

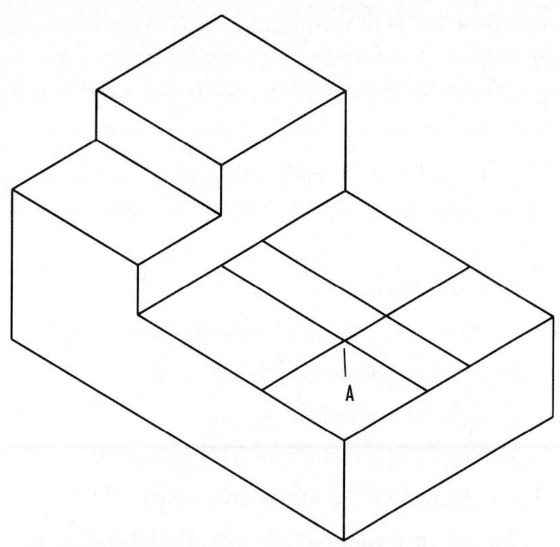

Figure 11.16

Press: **Ctrl-E Ctrl-E** ***(to toggle to the top isoplane)***

Pick: **ELLIPSE** ***(toolbox)***

<Axis endpoint 1>/Center/Isocircle: **I** ↵

Center of circle: ***(use Intersection and pick intersection A in Figure 1.16)***

<Circle radius>/Diameter: **1** ↵

Your screen should look similar to Figure 11.17.

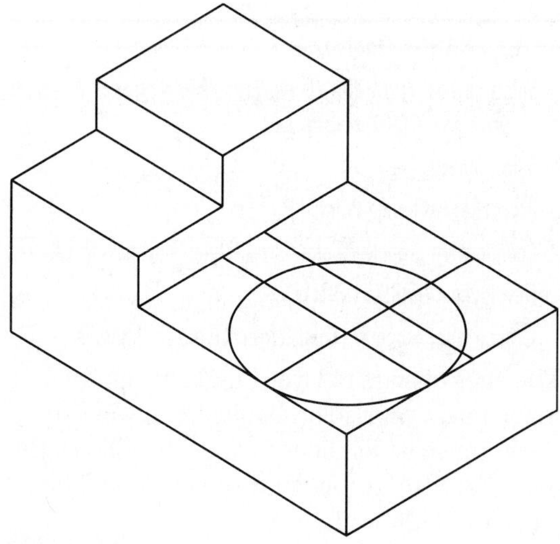

Figure 11.17

On your own, copy the ellipse you just drew over to the other side to form the other arc. Use the intersection of the construction center lines as the base point and pick the back set of construction center lines as the second point of displacement.

Your screen should look similar to Figure 11.18.

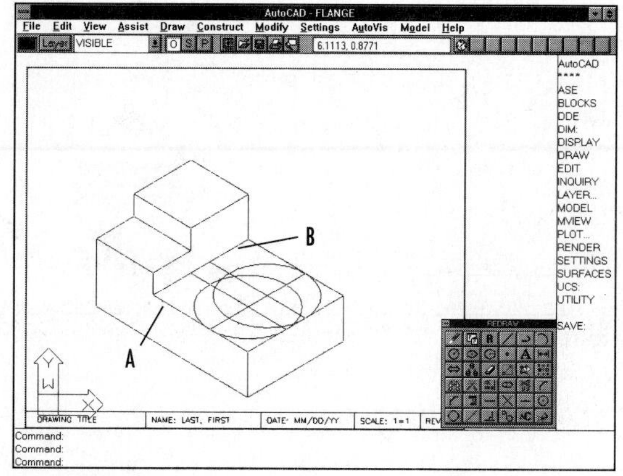

Figure 11.18

Adding the Large Hole

Next, you will locate the center lines for the 2-diameter hole through the front surface. You will use the COPY command to copy the lines that form the edges of the large horizontal surface into the center for this purpose.

Pick: **COPY** ***(toolbox)***

Select objects: ***(pick line A, as shown in Figure 11.18)*** ↵

<Base point or displacement>/Multiple: **1.25<30** ↵

Second point of displacement: ↵

Command: ↵ ***(to restart the COPY command)***

Select objects: ***(pick line B, as shown in Figure 11.18)*** ↵

<Base point or displacement>/Multiple: **1.25<–30** ↵

Second point of displacement: ↵

Next you will change the lines you just created using the COPY command to layer PROJ. This way, they can be used to locate the center of the hole and then they can be frozen so that they will not appear when the drawing is completed.

Pick: **Modify *(menu bar)*, Change, Properties**

Select objects: ***(pick the copied lines)***

Select objects: ↵

Use the dialogue box to change the lines to layer PROJ. Pick OK when you are finished.

Next you will use the ELLIPSE command with the Isocircle option to create the large center hole.

Pick: **ELLIPSE *(toolbox)***

<Axis endpoint 1>/Center/Isocircle: **I** ↵

Center of circle: ***(use Intersection to pick intersection 1 in Figure 11.19)***

<Circle radius>/Diameter: **1** ↵

On your own, use the center lines as the cutting edges for the TRIM command and remove the square corners and excess portions of the ellipses.

Your drawing should look similar to Figure 11.19.

> ■ ***TIP*** If you have trouble using TRIM, try using the BREAK command with the OSNAP, Intersection mode and selecting the intersection of the lines. ■

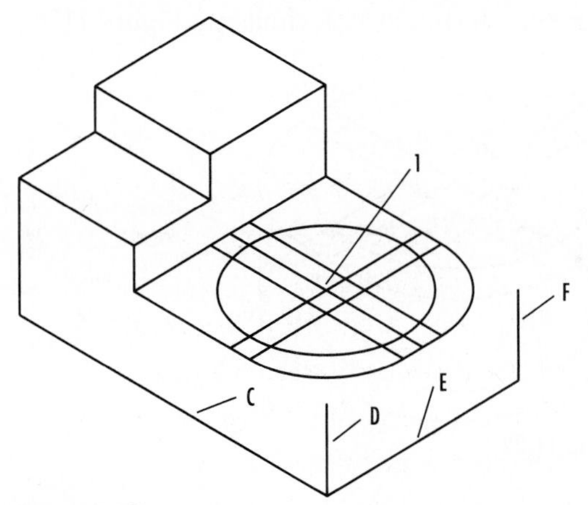

Figure 11.19

Erase lines D, E, and F on your own so that your drawing looks like Figure 11.20. Do not erase line C; you will trim off the unnecessary portion later.

When you have finished erasing the lines, your drawing should look like Figure 11.20.

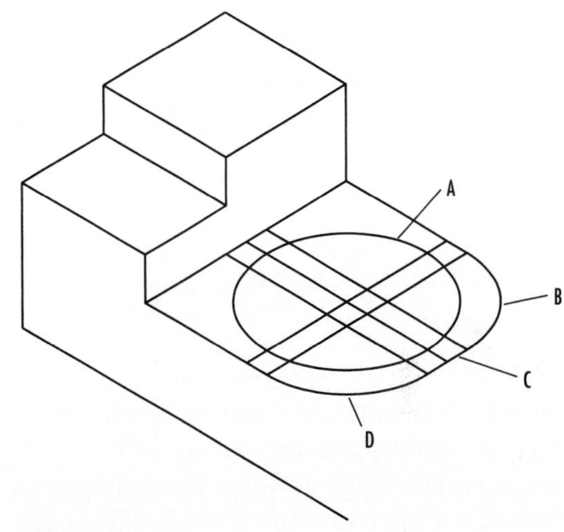

Figure 11.20

Next, you will copy the center hole, the corner arcs, and the short line between them to the bottom surface of the part.

Pick: **COPY *(toolbox)***

Select objects: ***(pick ellipse A, line C, and arcs B and D, as shown in Figure 11.20)*** ↵

<Base point or displacement>/Multiple: **1<270** ↵

Second point of displacement: ↵

On your own, use TRIM and remove the excess portion of the bottom line where it extends past the arc. Select the arc as the cutting edge.

Your drawing should look like Figure 11.21.

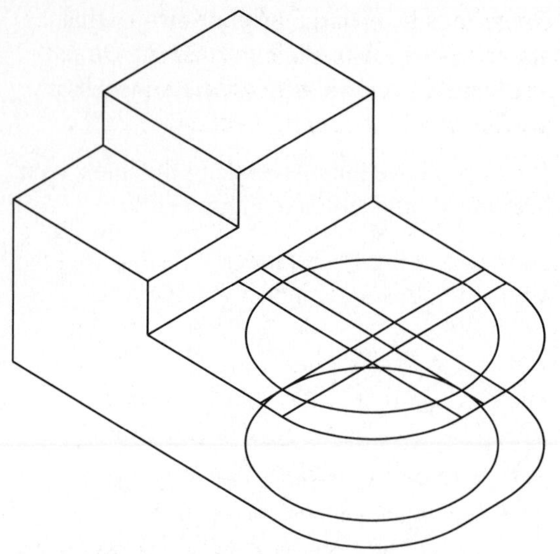

Figure 11.21

You will use the OSNAP, Tangent running mode to draw the limiting element of the curved surface in the drawing. The limiting element is a line representing the farthest edge of the curve from the direction of sight. It is a line that is tangent to the arcs in the top and bottom surfaces.

Pick: **Settings *(menu bar)*, Object Snap. . .**

The Running Object Snap dialogue box appears on your screen. You will select in the box to the left of the Tangent mode to turn it on.

Pick: **Tangent**

This turns on the running mode OSNAP for Tangent. Remember, the running mode OSNAPs stay turned on until you turn them back off. If you forget to turn them off when you are done, you may have difficulty with other commands.

Pick: **OK *(to exit the dialogue box)***

Next, enlarge your view with ZOOM, Window to make it easier to select.

Pick: **ZOOM *(toolbar)***

First corner: ***(pick a point above and to the left of the upper arcs)***

Other corner: ***(pick a point below and to the right of the lower arcs)***

The area you selected fills the screen.

Pick: **LINE *(toolbox)***

From point: ***(target the upper arc on the right-hand side of the object)***

To point: ***(target the lower arc on the right-hand side of the object)*** ↵

■ ***TIP*** When you are constructing a line tangent to two circles or arcs, you do not see the line rubberbanding from the first point you selected. This is because the tangent line cannot be determined until after the second circle or arc is selected. Because AutoCAD uses the four center approximations to draw the ellipse, you must pick as close to the actual tangent point as you can. If you select too far from the actual point, you may be on a different arc and will get the response "No Tangent Found." If this happens, restart the LINE command and try again. Zooming the drawing and toggling to the correct isoplane will also help you to draw the tangent line. ■

Your screen should look similar to Figure 11.22.

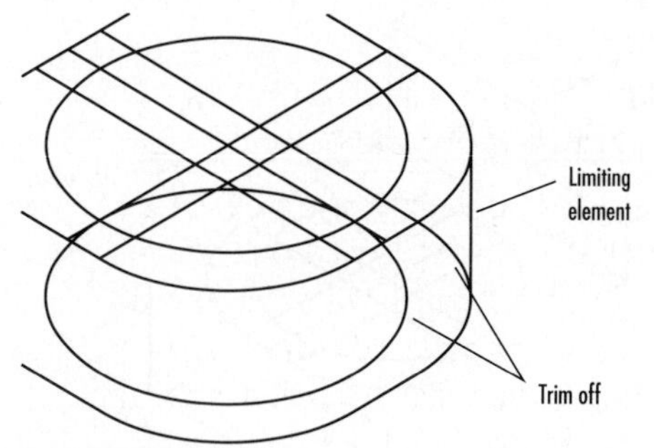

Figure 11.22

On your own, use the TRIM command to trim the bottom arc where it crosses behind the limiting element (the tangent line you just drew) and would no longer be visible from the front. Remove the portion of the lower ellipse where it crosses the top ellipse and is no longer visible as well. Refer to Figure 11.22.

When you have finished the trim, you will restore the original zoom factor and turn the OSNAP, Tangent running mode off.

> Command: **Z** ↵
>
> All/Center/Dynamic/Extents/Left/Previous/Vmax/Window/ <Scale (X/XP)>: **P** ↵
>
> *Pick:* **Settings *(menu bar)*, Object Snaps. . .**
>
> *Pick:* ***(in the box to the left of Tangent to de-select it)***
>
> *Pick:* **OK *(to exit the dialogue)***

Your screen should look like Figure 11.23.

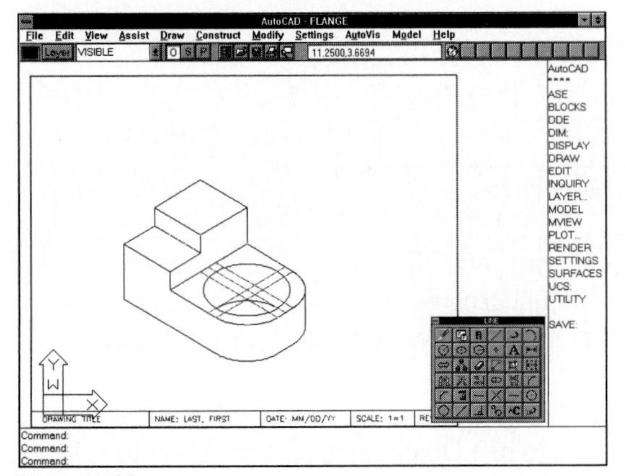

Figure 11.23

Transferring Angular Dimensions

You will add the 30-degree slanted surface to the top back corner of the object. Angular dimensional values cannot be transferred directly to the isometric axis. They must be adjusted to accommodate the different axis angular values.

For example, the given 30-degree dimensional value is measured from a horizontal line in the orthographic view. Lines in an isometric drawing are foreshortened equally if they are drawn along the axis lines in the isometric drawing. In fact, this is what isometric means: equal measure. Lines that are at some other angle are foreshortened differently, depending on the angle at which they are drawn. Angles do not show their true measure in this case. For this reason, when constructing a line from an angular measurement, you must first determine the locations of the endpoints of the line with respect to the isometric axis line. To do this, you have to turn the isometric grid off and return to a normal grid. You will use the menu bar to select the Drawing Aids dialogue box.

> *Pick:* **Settings *(menu bar)*, Drawing Aids**
>
> *Pick:* ***(the checked box to the left of On in the Isometric Snap/Grid area to turn off the isometric snap mode)***
>
> *Pick:* **OK *(to exit the dialogue box)***

Pick on the layer name shown on the toolbar and set the current drawing layer to PROJ on your own.

> *Pick:* **LINE *(toolbox)***

On your own, draw the front orthographic view of the surface, where you are able to see the angled line, using the dimensions in Figure 11.24. Draw this figure in the lower left portion of your screen now. Your screen should look like Figure 11.24 when you are finished.

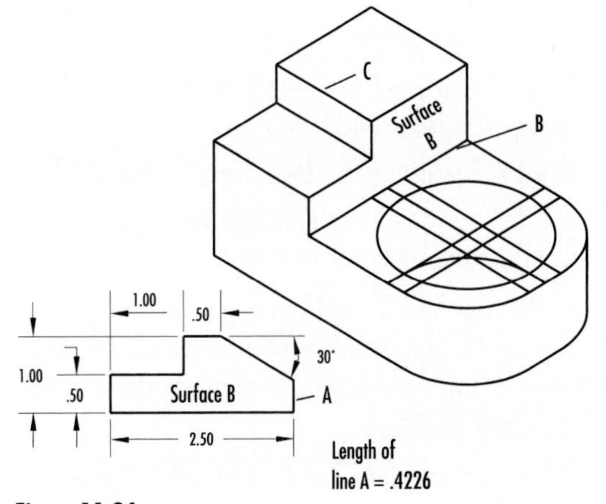

Figure 11.24

Now determine the actual length of the short vertical line A, which connects to the endpoint of the vertical line.

Pick: **Assist *(menu bar)*, Inquiry, List**

Select objects: ***(pick line A)*** ↵

The listing includes the length of the line, which should be 0.4226. This is the measurement you need to complete the isometric drawing.

> ■ ***TIP*** You can also determine the length of a line by dimensioning it or by using the DIST command, which displays the distance between two points. ■

On your own, use the Drawing Aids dialogue box to turn the isometric grid back on. Set layer VISIBLE as the current drawing layer.

You will use the COPY command to copy line B in Figure 11.24 by a distance of .4226 to create a construction line.

Pick: **COPY *(toolbox)***

Select objects: ***(pick line B, as shown in Figure 11.24)*** ↵

<Base point or displacement>/Multiple: **.4226<90** ↵

Second point of displacement: ↵

Pick: **CHANGE *(toolbox)***

Select objects: **L** ↵ ***(to select the last item you created)***

Select objects: ↵

Properties/<Change Point>: **P** ↵

Change what property (Color/LAyer/LType/Thickness)?: **LA** ↵

New layer <VISIBLE>: **PROJ** ↵

Change what property (Color/LAyer/LType/Thickness)?: ↵

The line changes to layer PROJ and appears magenta on your color monitor.

You will copy line C of the topmost surface in Figure 11.24 a distance of .5 to create the line where the top surface starts to angle downward.

Pick: **COPY *(toolbox)***

COPY Select objects: ***(pick line C, as shown in Figure 11.24)*** ↵

Select objects: ↵

<Base point or displacement>/Multiple: **.5<30** ↵

Second point of displacement: ↵

When you have finished copying the lines, your drawing should appear similar to Figure 11.25.

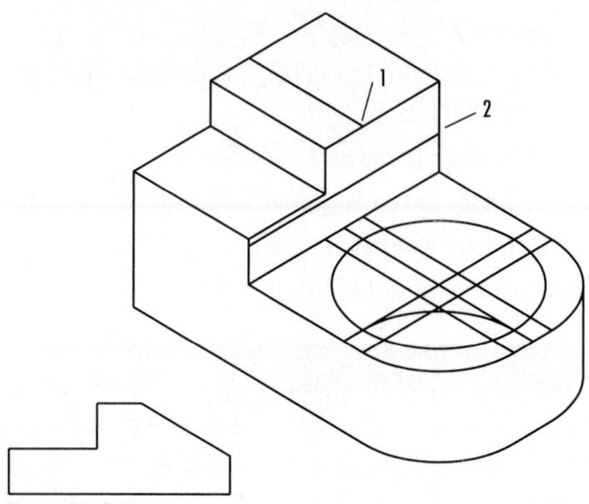

Figure 11.25

On your own, draw a line from where the line you just created intersects the front edge of the surface, identified as point 1 in Figure 11.25, to where the construction line intersects the side of the object, identified as point 2. Be sure to use Object Snap, Intersection to select the two points.

Next, copy the line you just drew to the back of the object to form the back line of the surface.

Pick: **COPY *(toolbox)***

Select objects: **L** ↵ ***(to copy the last entity created, the new line you drew)***

Select objects: ↵

<Base point or displacement>/Multiple: **ENDP** ↵

of ***(target endpoint 1 of the line identified in Figure 11.26)***

Second point of displacement: **ENDP** ↵

of ***(target endpoint 2 of the line identified in Figure 11.26)***

On your own, use the TRIM and ERASE commands to remove the upper lines and vertical edge where they cross the angled lines, using the angled lines as cutting edges. Erase the upper rightmost line.

When you are finished erasing and trimming, your drawing should appear similar to Figure 11.26.

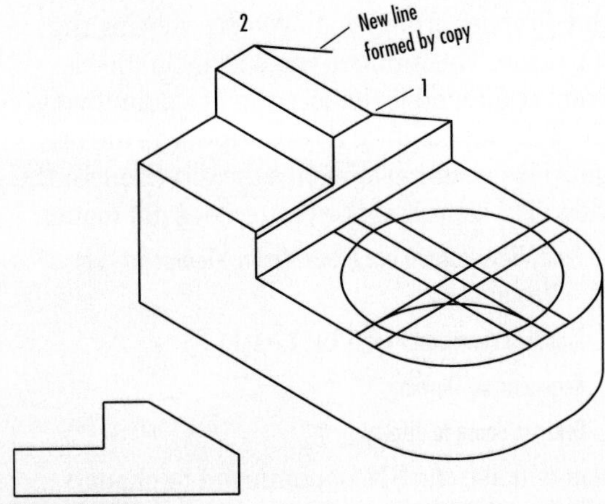

Figure 11.26

Draw the line between the endpoints of the two angled lines (using Object Snap, Endpoint) on your own.

When you are finished, your drawing should look like Figure 11.27.

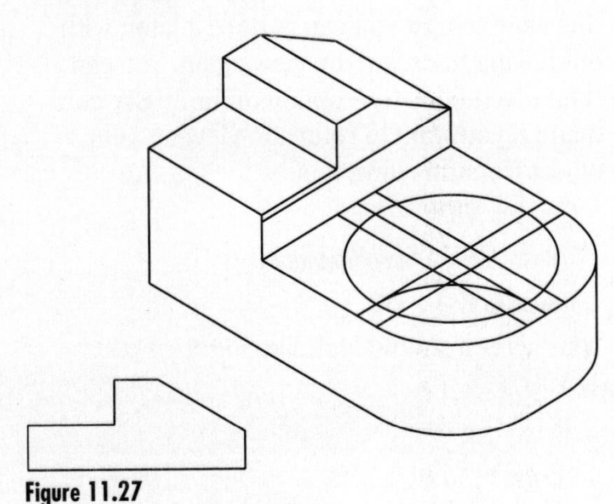

Figure 11.27

Now you are ready to add the final lines to the drawing, to make the small hole in the upper portion.

Adding the Small Hole

Press: **Ctrl-E** ***(to toggle the cursor to the Isoplane Right mode)***

Pick: **ELLIPSE** ***(toolbox)***

<Axis endpoint 1>/Center/Isocircle: **I** ↵

Center of circle: **5.1962,5** ↵ ***(you can pick this with the cursor because it is on the snap increment)***

<Circle radius>/Diameter: **.25** ↵

The ellipse should appear on your drawing screen in the position shown in Figure 11.28.

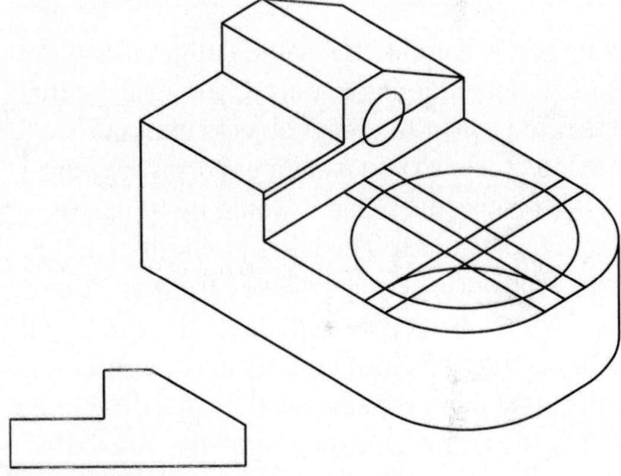

Figure 11.28

On your own, make layer THIN current and freeze layer PROJ. Set the snap to .0625 and draw the center lines for the major ellipses in the top and front surfaces. You cannot use the DIM: CEN command to add center lines to ellipses. This is because the ellipse is drawn using four polyline arcs and the four center approximation method. To add the center lines, use the LINE command. When you are finished, save your drawing.

Your finished drawing should appear similar to Figure 11.29.

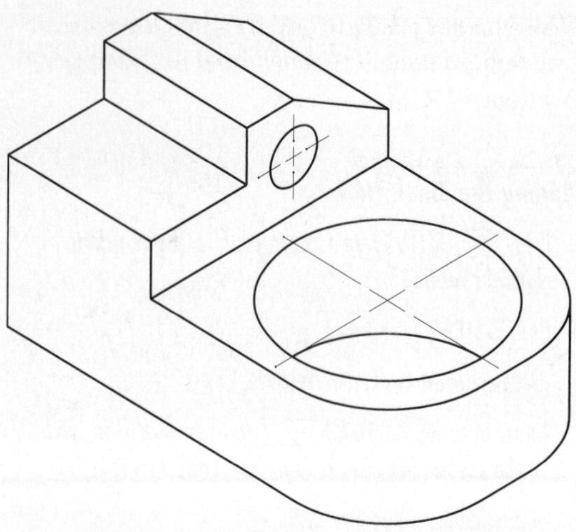

Figure 11.29

Creating the Flange, Using AME

Now you will create the same flange, using the AME solid modeling features. You will see that it is often easier to create objects using the AME features, if you want a pictorial drawing or 3D perspective, than it would be to use the isometric features. The added benefit is that a true 3D drawing can be viewed from any direction, which is not true with an isometric. If you change your 3D viewpoint on an isometric view, you will see that viewed from a direction 90 degrees different, your isometric drawing appears as a straight line.

You will create a new drawing from your prototype drawing.

Pick: **File *(menu bar)*, New...**

Use the dialogue box to create a new drawing from the prototype drawing PROTO provided with the data files. Call the new drawing FLANG-3D. (Remember to select the DRAWINGS directory) When you are done naming the file, pick OK to exit the dialogue box.

You are returned to the AutoCAD drawing editor. The border, grid, and snap settings from the prototype drawing should appear on your screen. Layer VISIBLE should be the current layer.

Setting and Saving the Isometric Viewpoint

You will use the VPOINT command to change the direction from which you are viewing the XY plane. The number you specify in the viewpoint command is the location of a point that is the starting point for a vector towards the origin. This vector establishes the direction for the view. The length of the vector does not matter.

Pick: **View *(menu bar)*, Set View, Viewpoint, Set Vpoint**

Rotate/<Viewpoint> <0,0,1>: **1,–1,1** ↵

Regenerating Drawing.

Grid too dense to display

You will use the SNAP command to change the snap spacing to .5 so that the grid appears. Remember that since GRID is set to 0, it will follow the spacing set for the snap.

Command: **SNAP** ↵

Snap spacing or ON/OFF/Aspect/Rotate/Style <0.2500>: **.5** ↵

Next, you will use the VIEW command to save this view so that you can restore it later, without having to create the view again. You can then use the Restore option of the VIEW command if you want to return to viewing your object from this direction.

Command: **VIEW** ↵

?/Delete/Restore/Save/Window: **S** ↵

View name to save: **ISO** ↵

Your screen should look like Figure 11.30.

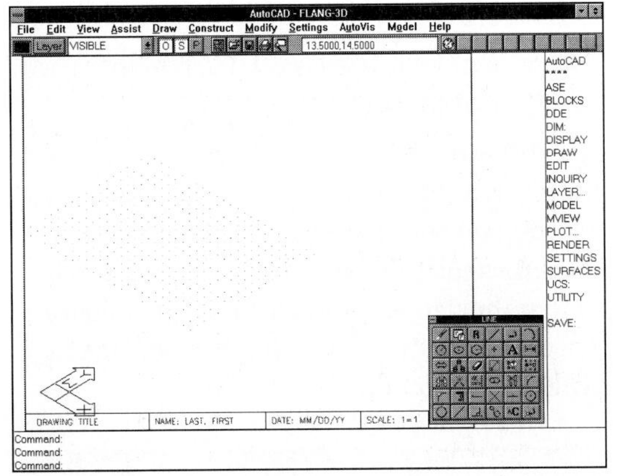

Figure 11.30

Next, you will create a cube to help you visualize the solid model as it will be shown from an isometric viewpoint. Later you will erase it and draw the flange in its place.

Pick: **Model *(menu bar)*, Primitives. . .**

Use the dialogue box to select the box primitive by picking it once to highlight it and then selecting OK. You return to the following command prompt:

Baseplane/Center/<Corner of box> <0,0,0>: ↵

Cube/ Length/<Other corner>: **C** ↵ ***(to select the cube option)***

Length: **1** ↵

Phase I - Boundary Evaluation begins.

Phase II - Tessellation computation begins.

Updating the Advanced Modeling Extension database.

A 1-unit cube appears on the grid in the lower left portion of your drawing.

Pick: **ZOOM *(toolbar)***

First corner: ***(pick a point on the screen at the lower left of the cube)***

Other corner: ***(pick a point on the screen above and to the right of the grid area, so that the entire grid is zoomed to fill the screen)***

■ ***TIP*** You may need to use the PAN command to bring the cube into the center of the screen. ■

Your view of the cube is enlarged and your drawing appears similar to Figure 11.31.

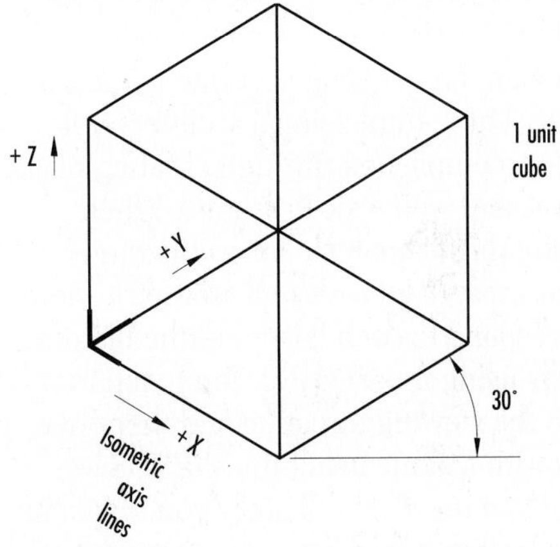

Figure 11.31

Your 3D viewpoint for the drawing is set so that you are looking directly onto the diagonal of the cube. As you can see, the bottom lines are angled at 30 degrees from horizontal on the screen, just like the lines of the isometric grid. The UCS icon helps you to remember the directions for the positive X and positive Y axis. The model that you create using AME will appear as an isometric drawing in this view.

Erase the cube you have created, as it is not needed to create the drawing of the flange.

Pick: **ERASE *(toolbox)***

Select objects: ***(pick the cube)***

Select objects: ↵

The cube is erased from your drawing.

Adapting for Architecture

Generally, two-dimensional isometric drawings take too long to draw to be a useful tool in architecture. However, isometric views are important for creating accurate models in AutoCAD. Three-dimensional architectural design is accomplished through creating plans, elevations, and isometric drawings. When developing three-dimensional architectural drawings, create and save four isometric views that correspond to each corner of the building. Do this by using the VPOINT command to establish the viewing direction and then save the view with a name using the VIEW, Save command option. This will allow you to quickly call up those views and look at your model to aid in making design decisions. ■

Creating the Flange

Next, you will create a new User Coordinate System that aligns with the front plane of the object. You will leave the viewpoint the same; this way you will continue viewing the object as an isometric, but will be able to draw in the front 2D plane. This will make it easy for you to create the front L-shaped surface and extrude it into a 3D solid entity. You will use the X axis rotation option of the UCS command to create a UCS parallel to the front plane of the object.

Command: **UCS** ↵

Origin/ZAxis/3point/Entity/View/X/Y/Z/Prev/Restore/Save/Del/?/<World>: **X** ↵

Rotation angle about X axis <0>: **90** ↵

Notice that the UCS icon has changed so that it is aligned with the new coordinate system. The crosshairs line up with the X and Y axis so that they appear similar to the crosshairs when you are drawing in the left isoplane in 2D isometric mode.

> ■ ***TIP*** Use the UCS command with the Save option to save this UCS with the name FRONT so that you can restore it later if you need to. Saving useful settings of the UCS with recognizable names makes it easier for you to switch the UCS. You do not have to create a new one each time; you can use the Restore option to return to a named UCS you have created. ■

Use the PLINE command to draw the front view of the L-shaped surface. Circles, ellipses, and joined 2D polylines are the only entities that you can select to extrude with the AME EXTRUDE command. Either use the relative polar coordinates you see below, or use SNAP and GRID to draw the polyline on your own according to the dimensions given in Figure 11.4.

Pick: **PLINE *(toolbox)***

From point: **0,0** ↵

Current line-width is 0.0000

Arc/Close/Halfwidth/Length/Undo/Width/<Endpoint of line>: **@1.5<90** ↵

Arc/Close/Halfwidth/Length/Undo/Width/<Endpoint of line>: **@1.5<0** ↵

Arc/Close/Halfwidth/Length/Undo/Width/<Endpoint of line>: **@.5<−90** ↵

Arc/Close/Halfwidth/Length/Undo/Width/<Endpoint of line>: **@2.5<0** ↵

Arc/Close/Halfwidth/Length/Undo/Width/<Endpoint of line>: **@1<-90** ↵

Arc/Close/Halfwidth/Length/Undo/Width/<Endpoint of line>: **C** ↵

The polyline for the front surface of the flange appears in your drawing, as shown in Figure 11.32.

> ■ ***TIP*** If the entire polyline does not show in your view, you can use ZOOM, Extents to fit what is drawn into the viewport. If the result of ZOOM, Extents is too large, use the ZOOM command with the .75X option to make the shape appear smaller on the screen. ■

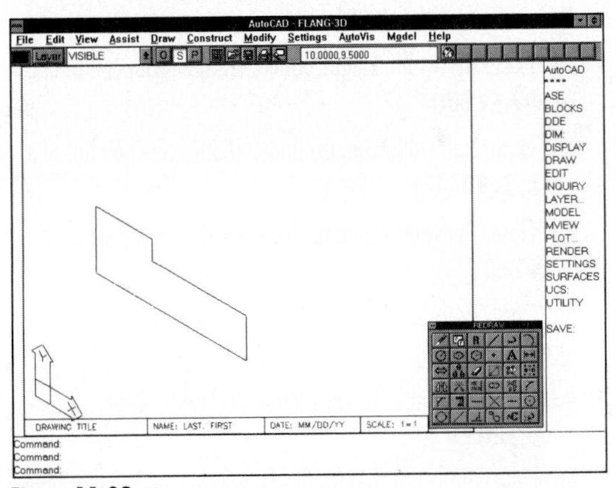

Figure 11.32

Now you will use the EXTRUDE command from the AME module to make the object into a solid of thickness 2.5". The extrusion height will be 2.5, the thickness (or depth) of the object. The taper angle will be 0, as the object is the same size at front and back.

Pick: **Model *(menu bar)*, Extrude**

If you have not used the AME module or preloaded it, you will get a message asking whether to load the AME module. If you see the message, press the ↵ key to respond yes, you do want to load the module. The prompt continues:

Select objects: ***(pick the polyline you just created)***

1 found

Select objects: ↵

Height of extrusion: **2.5** ↵

Extrusion taper angle <0>: ↵

Pick: **View *(menu bar)*, Zoom, Extents**

Command: ↵ ***(to restart the ZOOM command)***

All/Center/Dynamic/Extents/Left/Previous/Vmax/Window/<Scale (X/XP)>: ***.75X*** ↵

The basic L shape of the flange should appear in your drawing, as shown in Figure 11.33.

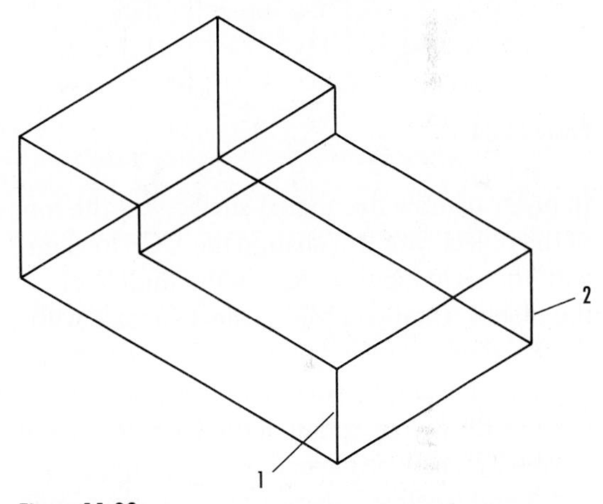

Figure 11.33

You will set the solid wire density variable so that rounded surfaces are created using more tessellation lines.

Command: **SOLWDENS** ↵

Wireframe mesh density (1 to 12)<1>: **4** ↵

Next, you will use the SOLFILL command to add the rounded corners to the front of the object.

Pick: **Model *(menu bar)*, Modify, Fillet Solids**

Pick edges of solids to be filleted (press ENTER when done): ***(pick the lines labeled 1 and 2 in Figure 11.33)*** ↵

Diameter/<Radius> of fillet <0.00>: **1** ↵

Phase I. . .

Phase II. . .

Updating. . .

Your drawing with the fillets added should appear similar to Figure 11.34.

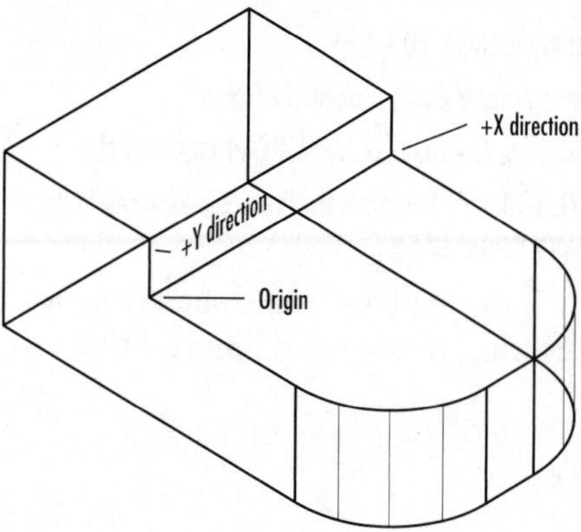

Figure 11.34

In order to draw the angled surfaces at the top of the object, you will change the UCS to align with the right-hand surface in the middle of the object. Then you will create a surface with the Polyline command that you can extrude to form the top angled portion of the object. You will use the 3point option of the UCS command to specify a new origin and points on the positive X and positive Y axes. Use the Object Snap overrides to select the exact points. You may need to turn SNAP off to make selecting easier.

Command: **UCS** ↵

Origin/ZAxis/3point/Entity/View/X/Y/Z/Prev/Restore/Save/Del/?/<World>: **3** ↵

Origin point <0,0,0>: **END** ↵

of ***(pick the point labeled Origin in Figure 11.34)***

Point on positive portion of the X-axis <2.500,1.000,2.500>: **END** ↵

of ***(pick the point labeled +X direction in Figure 11.34)***

Point on positive-Y portion of the UCS XY plane <1.500,2.000,2.500>: **NEA** ↵

to ***(pick the point labeled +Y direction in Figure 11.34)***

You will notice that the grid and crosshairs change to line up with this surface. The crosshairs appear similar to the right isoplane crosshairs used in the 2D isometric drawing mode.

On your own, use the Layer Control dialogue box to change the current layer to PROJ. This way you are able to see the lines you draw better, because they are a different color.

You will create most segments of the polyline at one time and then use the Join option of the PEDIT command to join the final segments to it.

Pick: ***PLINE (toolbox)***

From point: **END** ↵

of ***(point labeled A in Figure 11.35)***

Current line-width is 0.0000

Arc/Close/Halfwidth/Length/Undo/Width/<Endpoint of line>: **@2.5<180** ↵

Arc/Close/Halfwidth/Length/Undo/Width/<Endpoint of line>: **@.5<90** ↵

Arc/Close/Halfwidth/Length/Undo/Width/<Endpoint of line>: **@1<0** ↵

Arc/Close/Halfwidth/Length/Undo/Width/<Endpoint of line>: **@.5<90** ↵

Arc/Close/Halfwidth/Length/Undo/Width/<Endpoint of line>: **@.5<0** ↵

Arc/Close/Halfwidth/Length/Undo/Width/<Endpoint of line>: **@2<–30** ↵

Arc/Close/Halfwidth/Length/Undo/Width/<Endpoint of line>: ↵

Use ↵ to restart the Polyline command and draw the vertical line from point A up to where it crosses the angled line of the polyline on your own. Be sure that ORTHO is turned on.

Your drawing should appear similar to Figure 11.35.

Use the TRIM command and trim the polylines where they cross each other on your own.

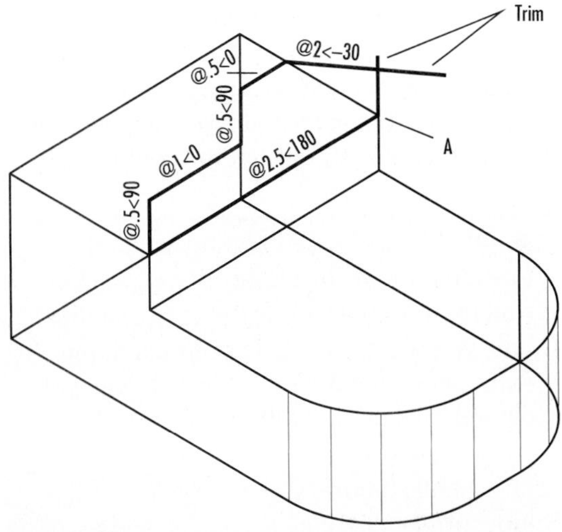

Figure 11.35

Now you will use the PEDIT command to join the two polylines to form one line so that it can be extruded.

Pick: **PEDIT *(toolbox)***

Select objects: ***(pick the first magenta polyline you drew)*** ↵

Close/Join/Width/Edit vertex/Fit/Spline/Decurve/Ltype gen/Undo/eXit <X>: **J** ↵

Select objects: ***(pick the second vertical polyline)*** ↵

1 segments added to polyline

Close/Join/Width/Edit vertex/Fit/Spline/Decurve/Ltype gen/Undo/eXit <X>: ↵

> ■ ***TIP*** If it is difficult to select the polylines, use the implied crossing box and cross each polyline where it extends above the object. ■

Set layer VISIBLE as the current layer on your own.

You will use the EXTRUDE command to make the surface into a solid. This time, give a negative height for the extrusion. This will cause the solid to extend in the negative Z direction. Otherwise, the new solid will be extruded to the front of the polyline you created.

Pick: **Model *(menu bar)*, Extrude**

Select objects: ***(pick the polyline you just created)***

1 found

Select objects: ↵

Height of extrusion: **−1.5** ↵

Extrusion taper angle <0>: ↵

If necessary, use ZOOM, Extents to fit the object on the screen on your own. Your drawing should appear similar to Figure 11.36.

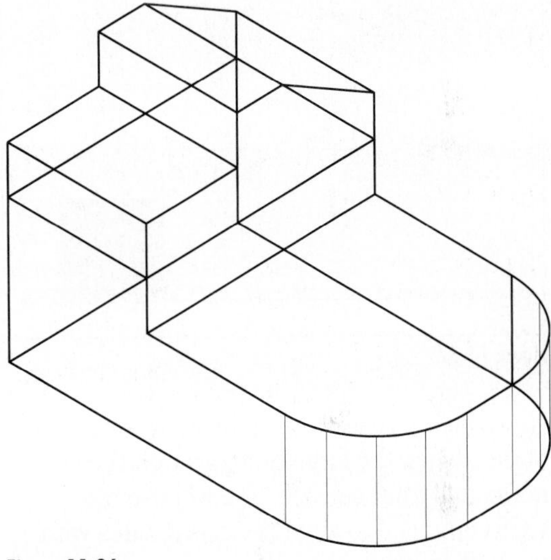

Figure 11.36

Next, you will create the cylinder that will be subtracted to create the small hole through the top portion of the objects.

Pick: **Model *(menu bar)*, Primitives. . .**

The AME Primitives dialogue box appears on your screen. Use the dialogue box to select the cylinder primitive. To do this, pick it once to highlight it and select OK. You return to the following command prompt:

Baseplane/Elliptical/<Center point> <0,0,0>: **1.5,1,0** ↵

Diameter/<Radius>: **D** ↵

Diameter: **.5** ↵

Center of other end/<Height>: **−1.5** ↵

Phase I - Boundary Evaluation begins.

Phase II - Tessellation computation begins.

Updating the Advanced Modeling Extension database.

With the cylinder added, your screen should look like Figure 11.37.

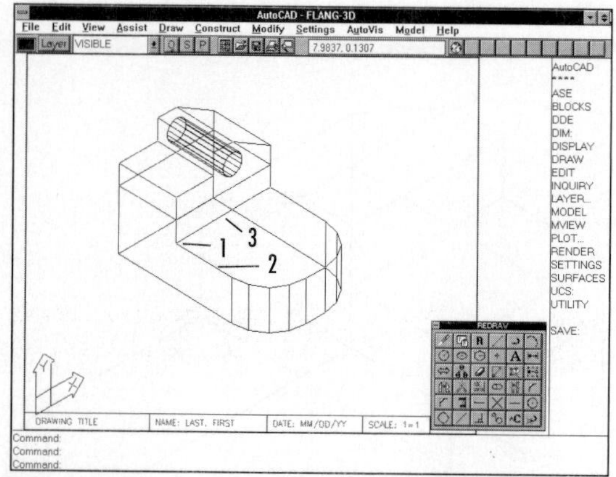

Figure 11.37

Now you are ready to add the final feature of the object, the large hole through the horizontal front surface. You will use the UCS command to align the coordinates with the bottom surface.

Command: **UCS** ↵

Origin/ZAxis/3point/Entity/View/X/Y/Z/Prev/Restore/Save/Del/?/<World>: ↵

The World coordinates are restored. The grid, UCS icon, and crosshairs appear in the drawing lined up with the bottom surface. The general appearance of the crosshairs is similar to the top isoplane crosshairs in 2D isometric mode.

You will use the cylinder primitive again to create a cylinder for the hole. You will select the Baseplane option and create a temporary base plane to specify the locations for the cylinder you will create in the rest of the command.

■ ***TIP*** When you are creating a cylinder to subtract to form a hole, it often works well to make the cylinder longer than the hole you want. Once it is subtracted, the extra portion of the cylinder that does not extend through the object is eliminated. If you create a cylinder that is too short, even by a small amount, you may be left with a thin surface covering the top or bottom of the hole, where the cylinder did not extend through the other solid. ■

Pick: **Model *(menu bar),* Primitives**

Use the AME Primitives dialogue box to select the cylinder primitive and pick OK. At the command prompt, type the following responses:

Baseplane/Elliptical/<Center point> <0,0,0>: **B** ↵

Baseplane by Entity/Last/Zaxis/View/XY/YZ/ZX/<3points>: ↵

1st point on plane: **INT** ↵

of ***(target the intersection labeled 1 in Figure 11.37)***

2nd point on plane: **NEA** ↵

to ***(target the line near the point marked 2 in Figure 11.37)***

3rd point on plane: **NEA** ↵

to ***(target the point marked 3)***

Baseplane/Elliptical/<Center point> <0,0,0>: **1.25,1.25** ↵

Diameter/<Radius>: **D** ↵

Diameter: **2** ↵

Center of other end/<Height>: **−1.5** ↵

Phase I - Boundary Evaluation begins.

Phase II - Tessellation computation begins.

Updating the Advanced Modeling Extension database.

Your drawing should appear similar to Figure 11.39. Notice that the large cylinder is longer than the hole you will create.

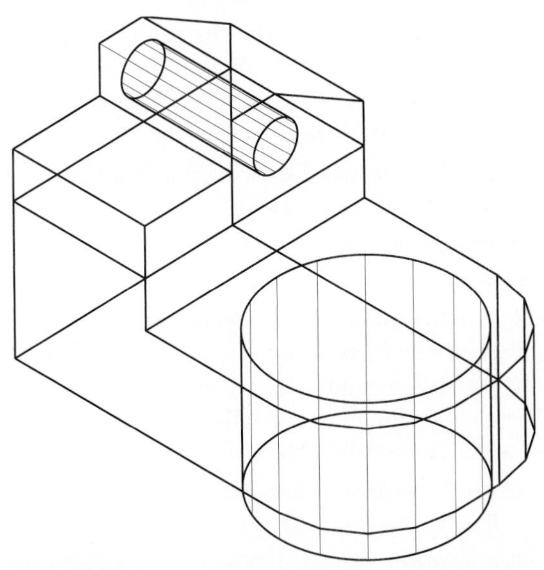

Figure 11.38

First you will use the UNION command to join the two blocks you created by extruding the polylines. Then you will use the SUBTRACT command to remove the cylinders to form holes in the unioned part.

Pick: **Model *(menu bar)*, Union**

Select solids to union: ***(pick the L-shaped block and the angled block)*** ↵

2 solids unioned.

The two solids become joined and the lines where they used to touch one another are eliminated.

Pick: **Model *(menu bar)*, Subtract**

Source objects. . .

Select objects: ***(pick the block that was created by unioning)*** ↵

Objects to subtract from them. . .

Select objects: ***(pick the two cylinders)*** ↵

2 solids subtracted from 1 solid.

The two cylinders form holes in the solid. You will notice that the larger hole now only extends through the object and not beyond.

Next, you will establish the surfaces, using the MESH command, for the resulting solid so that it can be shaded.

Pick: **Model *(menu bar)*, Display, Mesh**

Select objects: ***(pick the solid)*** ↵

Surface meshing of current solid is completed.

Creating block for mesh representation. . .

Done.

Command: **SHADE** ↵

Your drawing screen should appear similar to Figure 11.40.

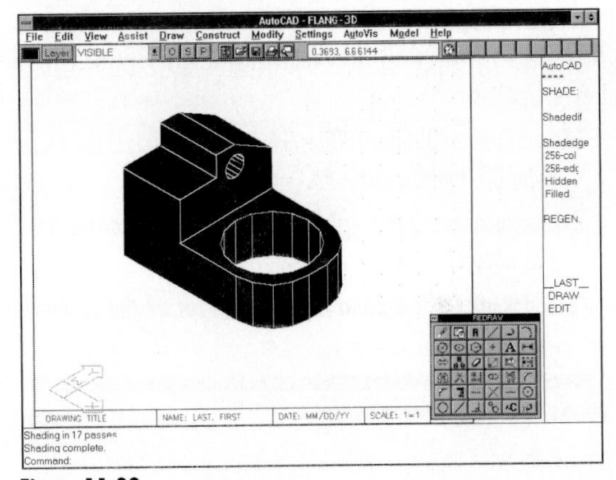

Figure 11.39

Viewing Your Model with DVIEW

You will return your drawing to wireframe display by using the REGEN command to recalculate the display from the drawing database.

Command: **REGEN** ↵

Now you will use the DVIEW command for dynamic viewing of your drawing. This way you can see the appearance on the screen and select a view that shows the object well.

Pick: **View *(menu bar)*, Set View, Dview**

Select objects: ***(pick the solid)***

1 found

Select objects: ↵

CAmera/TArget/Distance/POints/PAn/Zoom/TWist/CLip/
Hide/Off/Undo/<eXit>: **CA** ↵

Toggle angle in/Enter angle from XY plane <35.26>: ↵

Move the crosshairs around on your screen. You will see that as you move the crosshairs left to right, you are moving the camera around the object. As you move up and down, you are moving the camera above and below the object. Position the crosshairs so that a view similar to what you see in Figure 11.41 appears on your screen, and press the pick button. You remain in the DVIEW command; now pick the PAN option.

CAmera/TArget/Distance/POints/PAn/Zoom/TWist/CLip/
Hide/Off/Undo/<eXit>: **PA** ↵

Displacement base point: ***(pick a point near the center of the object)***

Second point: ***(pick a point near the center of the screen)***

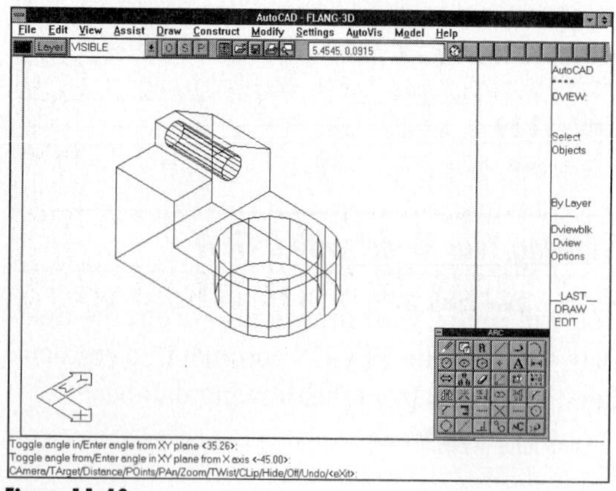

Figure 11.40

As you move the crosshairs this time, you will see the object move around on the screen, while keeping the same viewpoint. This is handy for positioning the object at the center of the view. Move the crosshairs until the object is centered in the view, and press the pick button. You are returned to the DVIEW prompt. This time, pick the Zoom option.

CAmera/TArget/Distance/POints/PAn/Zoom/TWist/CLip/
Hide/Off/Undo/<eXit>: **Z** ↵

Adjust zoom scale factor <1>:

Move the crosshairs around and notice the effect of the Zoom option. Do not pick a zoom enlargement; instead press Ctrl-C to return to the DVIEW prompt, where you will use the Distance option to change the display to a perspective view of the object.

CAmera/TArget/Distance/POints/PAn/Zoom/TWist/CLip/
Hide/Off/Undo/<eXit>: **D** ↵

New camera/target distance<1.7300>:

Move the crosshairs around the screen and notice how it affects the perspective view of the object. Use the slider bar, as you see in Figure 11.42, to select a point between 4x and 9x. Press the pick button.

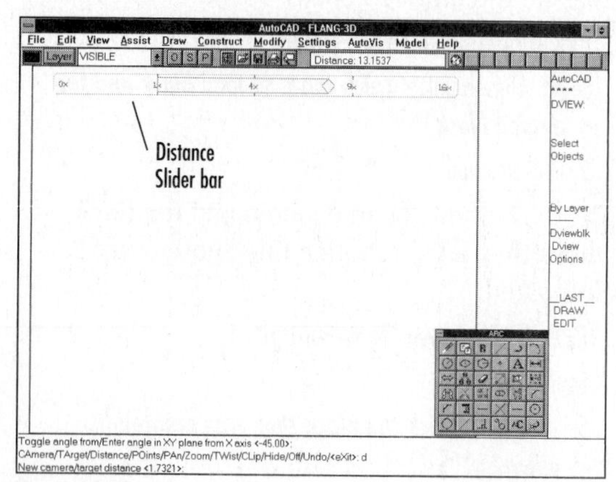

Figure 11.41

Exit the command by pressing ↵ at the prompt.

CAmera/TArget/Distance/POints/PAn/Zoom/TWist/CLip/
Hide/Off/Undo/<eXit>: ↵

Your drawing should appear similar to Figure 11.42. As you may have picked somewhat different points, your screen may not appear exactly the same. Notice the perspective icon displayed in the lower left of the screen. As you can see, the lines at the back of the object are foreshortened in the perspective view. When you are viewing the drawing in perspective, many of the commands and tools do not work. Usually, you would create your drawing in the standard parallel viewing mode, and then when finished, use the DVIEW command and perspective view to produce a clear view of the object that is easy to interpret.

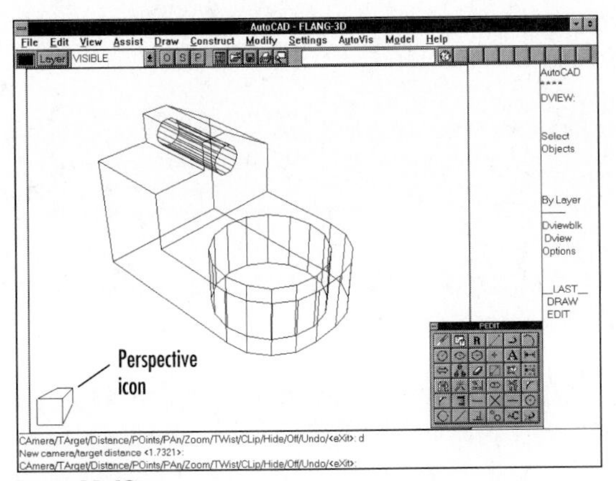

Figure 11.42

> ■ ***TIP*** If you want to continue to work with this drawing, use the DVIEW command with the Off option to turn perspective viewing off. ■

Adapting for Architecture

The DVIEW command is useful for looking at your design from all sides and angles, and also for creating perspectives to be used for presentation drawings. Typically, architectural perspectives are created by viewing from a standard height of 5'6". By moving this point of view up or down, extreme, dynamic views can be created that exploit the potential of your design. However, remember not to make these so extreme that information is lost because of the viewing angle.

One way to create architectural presentation drawings from your perspective views is to plot them to a file, using Hewlett-Packard® plotting language, or to export the drawing in standard drawing exchange format by picking File, Import/Export, DXF Out. Many paint-type programs allow you to import these types of drawings, so that you may use solid fill to shade the drawing yourself, or import a background and set your perspective against it. ■

Going Further

Use the SHADE command to render the object to the screen. The rendered object should appear on your screen. When you are finished, type "REGEN" and press ↵ at the command prompt to return to the original appearance. Objects must be meshed before they can be rendered correctly. You used the MESH command earlier in the tutorial and have not changed the model since; therefore you did not need to re-mesh this object. Do not forget to mesh other objects before you render them.

Save your drawing and exit AutoCAD. You have finished Tutorial 11.

KEY TERMS

isocircle
isometric axis

KEY COMMANDS

Drawing Exchange File Out
Dynamic View
Isometric Plane
List

EXERCISES

Create isometric drawings of the following using either 2D or 3D methods. The letter M after an exercise number means that the given dimensions are in millimeters.

11.1 Gasket

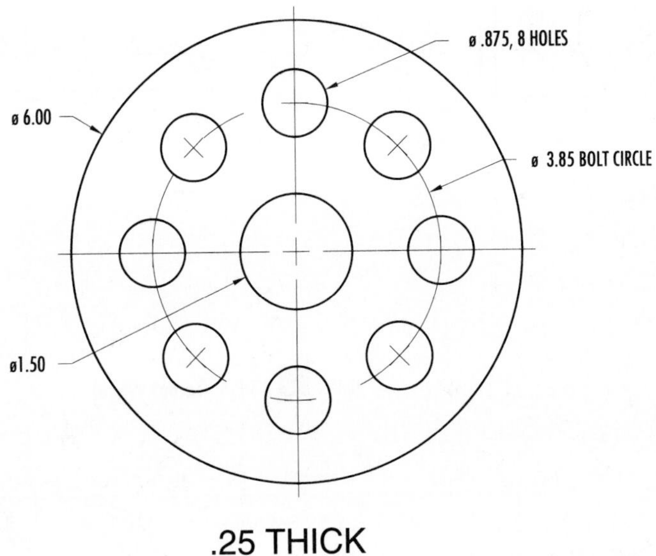

11.2 Locator Block

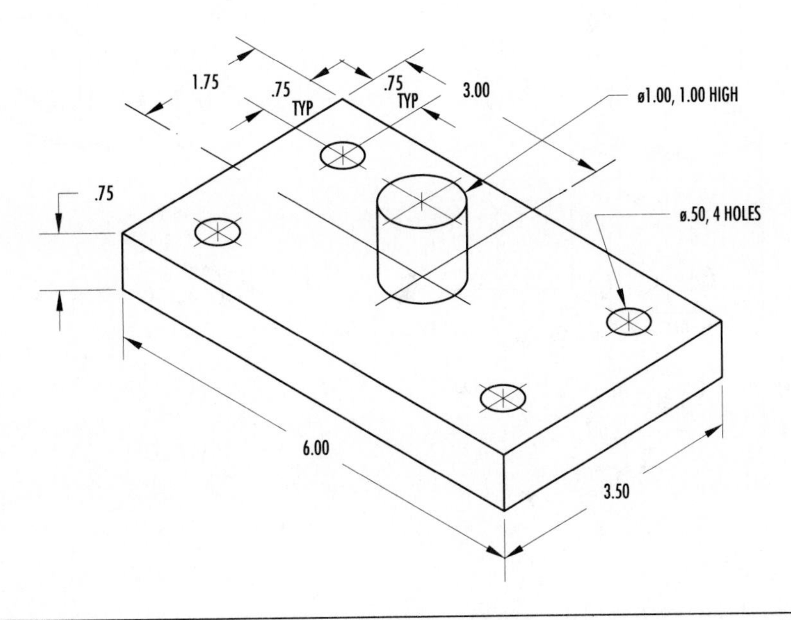

11.3M Brace Guide

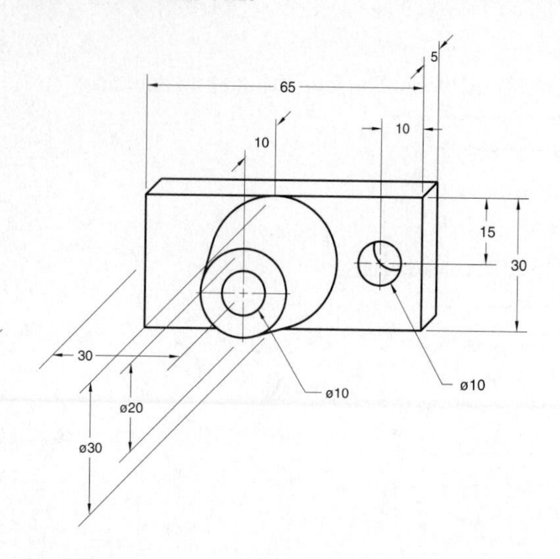

11.4M Slider Block

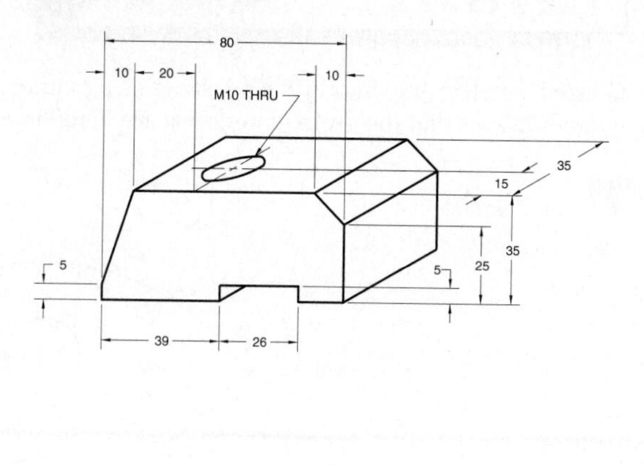

11.5M Shaft

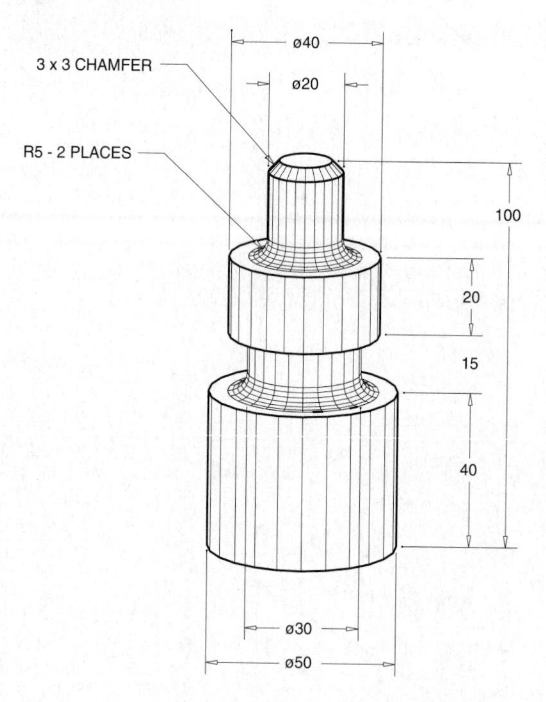

11.6 Rachet Wheel

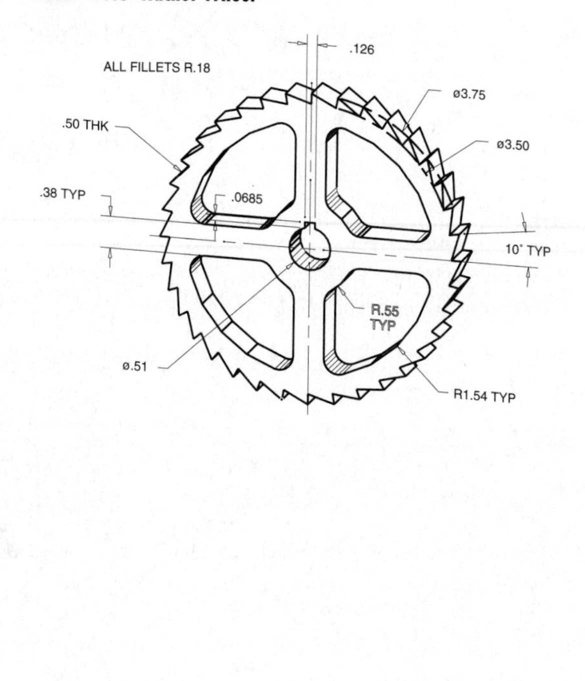

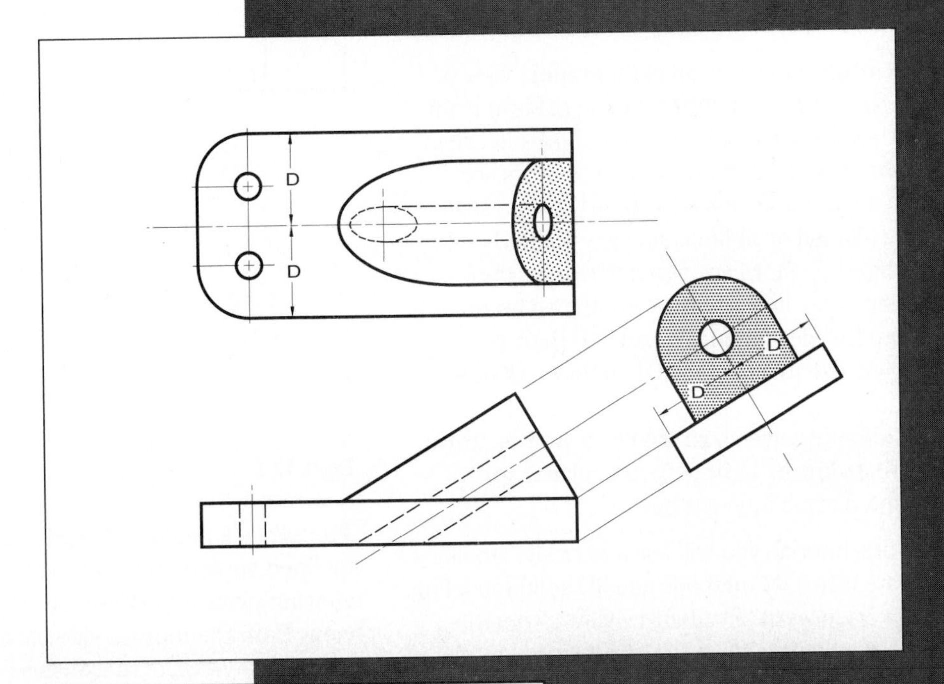

TUTORIAL 12

Creating Auxiliary Views with 2D and AME Methods

Objectives

When you have completed this tutorial, you will be able to

1. Draw auxiliary views, using 2D projection.
2. Set up a UCS to help create a 2D auxiliary view.
3. Use SNAP, Rotate to help create a 2D auxiliary view.
4. Draw auxiliary views of rounded surfaces.
5. Create auxiliary views from 3D solid models.

Introduction

An *auxiliary view* is an orthographic view of the object using a different line of sight from the six *basic views* (front, top, right-side, rear, bottom, and left-side). Auxiliary views are most commonly used to show the true size of a slanted or oblique surface. Slanted and oblique surfaces are *foreshortened* in the basic views because they are tipped away from the viewing plane, causing their projected size to be smaller than their actual size. To show the true size and shape of a slanted or oblique surface, an auxiliary view is drawn, with its line of sight perpendicular to the slanted or oblique surface.

In this tutorial, you will learn to create auxiliary views using 2D methods and 3D solid modeling. You can project 2D auxiliary views from the basic orthographic views by rotating the snap or by aligning a new User Coordinate System (UCS). Auxiliary views can be generated directly from the solid model, either by changing the viewpoint to show the true size of the surface or by extracting the true-size feature with the SOLFEAT (solid features) command.

Auxiliary Views

Figure 12.1 shows three views of an object and an auxiliary view of the object.

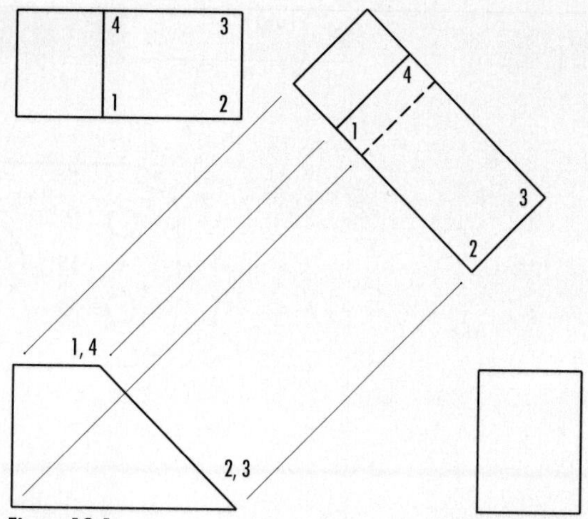

Figure 12.1

The surface defined by vertices 1-2-3-4 is an inclined surface. It is perpendicular to the front viewing plane and shows on edge in the front view. Both the top and side views show foreshortened views of the surface; that is, neither shows the true shape and size of that surface of the object.

To project an auxiliary view showing the true size of surface 1-2-3-4, create a new view by drawing projection lines perpendicular to the edge view of the surface, in this case the angled line in the front view. Transfer the width of the surface, measured from a *reference surface,* to the auxiliary view to complete the projection. Note that as with the front, top, and side views, the auxiliary view shows the entire object with all of its surfaces as viewed with the line of sight perpendicular to the surface that is to be shown true-size, causing the base of the object to show as a hidden line.

Starting

Start AutoCAD from the Autodesk Collection interface as you were instructed in Chapter 3.

On your own, select the menu bar option File, New to start a new drawing from the prototype drawing, ADAPT4, provided with the data files. Name your drawing AUXIL1.

AutoCAD's drawing editor appears on your display screen. Figure 12.2, the drawing of the orthographic views for the adapter with the oblique surface, should be on your screen.

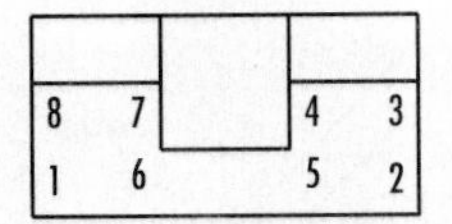

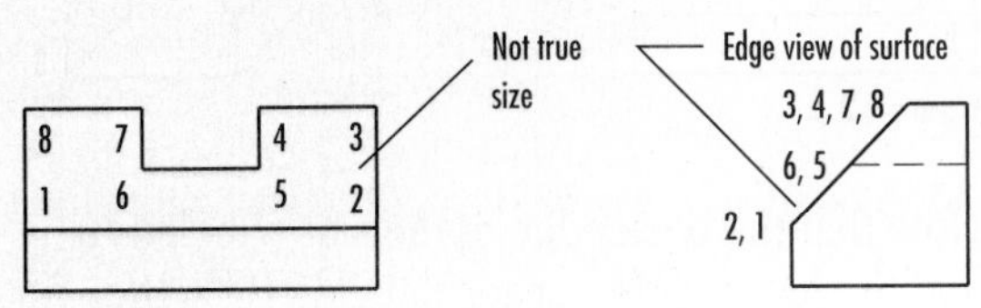

Figure 12.2

An auxiliary view is needed in this drawing, since the given views do not show the true shape of the inclined surface. The object is shown in Figure 12.2 with surface 1-2-3-4-5-6-7-8 labeled.

Drawing Auxiliary Views Using 2D

You can create the auxiliary view using information from any two views, since any two views with a 90-degree relationship provide all of the principal dimensions. For this tutorial, you will erase the top view and use the front and side views to project the auxiliary view.

Pick: ERASE ***(toolbox)***

Select objects: ***(window the top view)***

Select objects: ↵

Your drawing will look like Figure 12.3 once the top view has been erased.

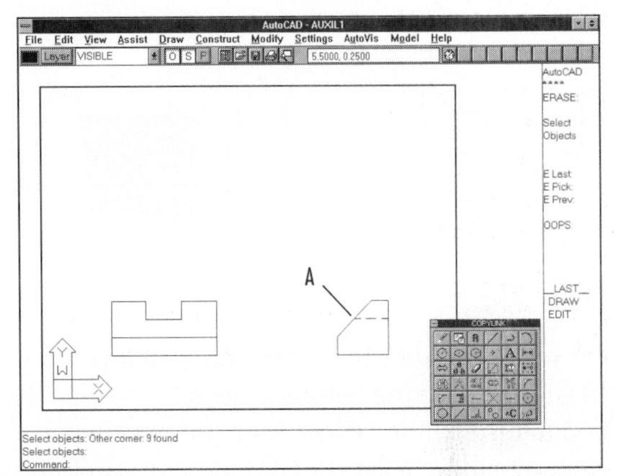

Figure 12.3

Next you will draw projection lines perpendicular to surface 1-2-3-4-5-6-7-8 in the side view. You will create a new UCS that is aligned with the edge view to help you project these lines easily.

Aligning the UCS with the Angled Surface

Set the UCS so that it is aligned with the angled surface. You will use the Entity option to align the new coordinate system. The Entity option prompts for the existing drawing entity with which you want to align the UCS. You will align the UCS with the angled line in the side view.

Command: **UCS** ↵

Origin/ZAxis/3point/Entity/View/X/Y/Z/Prev/Restore/Save/Del/?/<World>: **E** ↵

Select object to align UCS: ***(pick the angled line in the side view, identified as A in Figure 12.3)***

When you have finished aligning the UCS, your screen should look like Figure 12.4. Notice that the crosshairs and grid, as well as the UCS icon, now line up with the angled surface.

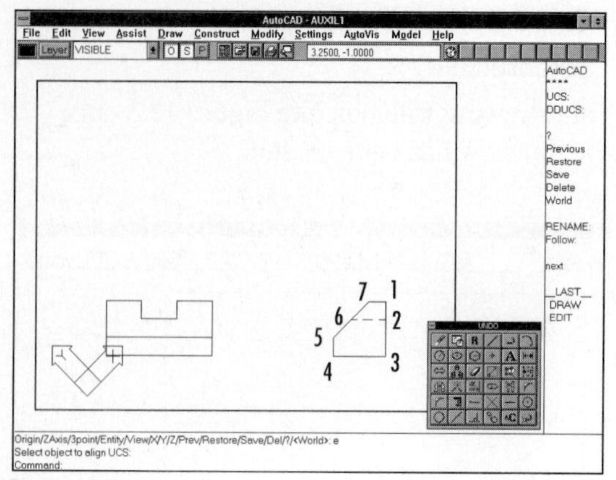

Figure 12.4

On your own, set PROJ as the current layer. In addition, use the Settings menu bar selection to turn on the Object Snap, Intersection running mode. Turn ORTHO on (if it is not already on) by pressing (F8) or picking O from the toolbar. Turn SNAP off, if necessary, by pressing (F9) or picking S from the toolbar.

> ■ ***TIP*** It is easy to confuse Intersection with Insertion, so doublecheck. Be sure to turn the running mode Object Snap back off when you are done using it, or you may have difficulty when using other commands. You will notice the aperture box whenever an Object Snap mode is active. ■

Now you will draw lines from each intersection of the object in the side view into the open area of the drawing above the front view.

Pick: **LINE icon *(toolbox)***

From point: ***(target intersection 1 in Figure 12.4)***

To point: ***(with ORTHO turned on, pick a point above and to the left of the side view, about 4 inches away)***

To point: (↵)

On your own, restart the LINE command and draw projection lines from points 2-5 in the side view. Then draw a reference line perpendicular to the projection lines. The location of this line can be anywhere along the projection lines but it should extend about .5 inch beyond the top and bottom projection lines.

Your screen should look similar to Figure 12.5.

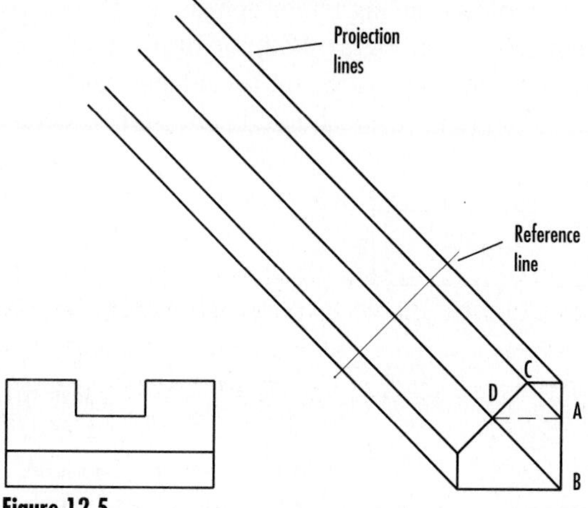

Figure 12.5

Note that the back edge of the slot (labeled A) and the lower right corner (labeled B) in the side view align with the projection lines through the corners of the angled surface (labeled C-D) to produce a single projection line. If points C and D did not line up on the projection lines you created, you would need to project them.

Next you will use the OFFSET command to draw a line 3 units away from and parallel to the reference line. The length of the object is known to be three inches.

> ■ ***TIP*** If you did not know the dimensions, you could use the DISTANCE command with Object Snap, Intersection in the front view to determine the distance. ■

Pick: ***Construct (menu bar), Offset***

Offset distance or Through <Through>: **3** ↵

Select object to offset: ***(pick the reference line)***

Side to offset? ***(pick a point anywhere to the left of the reference line)***

Select object to offset: ↵

Your screen should look similar to Figure 12.6.

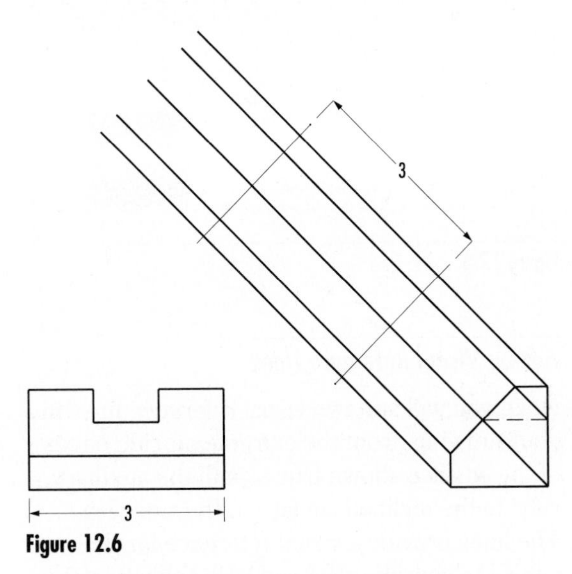

Figure 12.6

> ■ ***TIP*** If the lines are not long enough, you can use the STRETCH command to lengthen them. ■

Add the width of the slot on your own by using OFFSET to draw two more parallel lines 1 inch apart. Your screen should look similar to Figure 12.7.

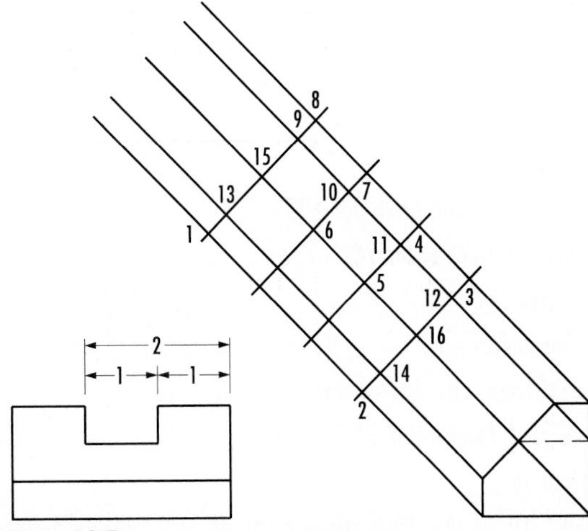

Figure 12.7

Set layer VISIBLE as the current layer and turn on the Object Snap, Intersection running mode, if it is not already on, before you continue.

Next, you will draw the visible lines designated in Figure 12.7 on top of the projection lines. Be sure you draw the correct shape of the object as it will appear in the auxiliary view.

Pick: **LINE *(toolbox)***

From point: ***(pick the intersection of the projection lines at point 1, shown in Figure 12.7)***

To point: ***(pick point 2)***

To point: ***(pick point 3)***

To point: ***(pick point 4)***

To point: ***(pick point 5)***

To point: ***(pick point 6)***

To point: ***(pick point 7)***

To point: ***(pick point 8)***

To point: **C** ↵

Restart the LINE command and draw the short line segments where the two short top surfaces of the object intersect the slanted front surface:

Command: ↵

LINE From point: ***(pick point 9)***

To point: ***(pick point 10)***

To point: ↵

Command: ↵

LINE From point: ***(pick point 11)***

To point: ***(pick point 12)***

To point: ↵

Next, draw the line representing the back edge of the slot in the auxiliary view.

Command: ↵

LINE From point: ***(pick point 10)***

To point: ***(pick point 11)***

To point: ↵

Now add the line showing the intersection of the vertical front surface with the angled surface.

Command: ↵

LINE From point: ***(pick point 13)***

To point: ***(pick point 14)***

To point: ↵

On your own, set layer HIDDEN as the current layer.

Next, draw the line showing the intersection of the bottom surface and the back surface. It will be hidden from the line of sight.

Command: LINE ↵

From point: ***(pick point 15)***

To point: ***(pick point 16)***

To point: ↵

Use the TRIM command on your own to remove the portion of the hidden line that coincides with the visible line from point 5 to point 6. Freeze layer PROJ.

When you are finished, your screen should look like Figure 12.8.

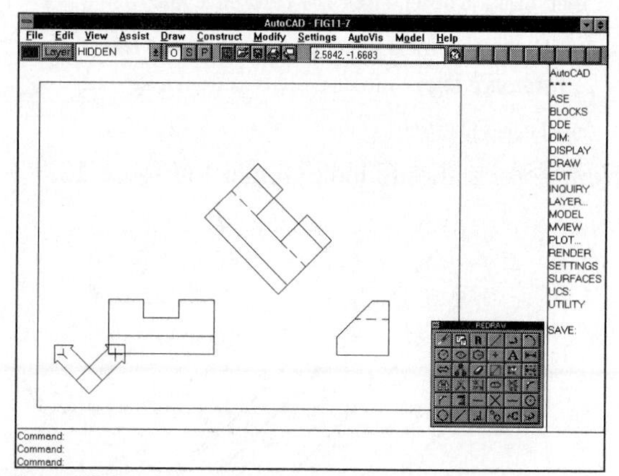

Figure 12.8

Adding Visual Reference Lines

Next, you will add two visual reference lines to your drawing, from the extreme outside edges of the surface shown true size in the auxiliary view to the inclined surface in the side view. The lines provide a visual reference for the angles in your drawing and help show how the auxiliary view aligns with the standard views. A center line can be extended from the primary view to the auxiliary view, or one or two projection lines can be used for the reference lines. In this case, since there are no center lines, you will create two reference lines.

On your own, thaw layer PROJ. Then pick the CHANGE icon from the toolbox and select the two lines you want to use as visual reference lines from the projection layer and change them to layer THIN. You can verify that the lines have changed to layer THIN visually because the lines will turn red (the color for that layer).

On your own, freeze layer PROJ. Then use the BREAK command to create a gap of about 1/16th of an inch between the views and the reference lines. Remember to turn off the OSNAP, Intersection running mode before using the BREAK command. (You could also offset the edge of the object by 1/16" in each view and then use TRIM to create the gap.) Create a similar gap where the hidden lines extend from the visible line, forming the front of the slot in the auxiliary view.

■ ***TIP*** A hidden line should not extend to a visible object line in the same direction; the hidden line should start with a small gap (about 1/16" on the plotted drawing). To do this, you can use the BREAK command. A more sophisticated method, because it leaves the line the correct length, is to create a linetype that starts with a gap, instead of a dash, and draw the hidden line with this linetype. Use the LINETYPE, Create option to create and save your own custom linetypes. Refer to the Going Further in Tutorial 4. Use the online help facility if you need assistance. ■

Your drawing should look like Figure 12.9.

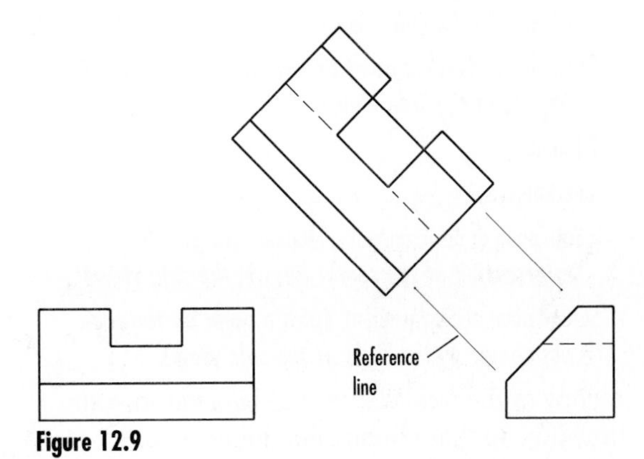

Figure 12.9

On your own, save your drawing, using the File, Save menu selection from the menu bar.

Curved Surfaces

Now you will create an auxiliary view of the slanted surface in a cylinder drawing, like the one you created at the end of Tutorial 5. The drawing has been provided for you as CYL3 on the data files that came with your software.

On your own, use the File, New selection from the menu bar to begin a new drawing. Use CYL3 as a prototype. Name your new drawing AUXIL3.

You return to AutoCAD's drawing editor. Figure 12.10 shows the orthographic views of the cylinder with the slanted surface that should be on your screen.

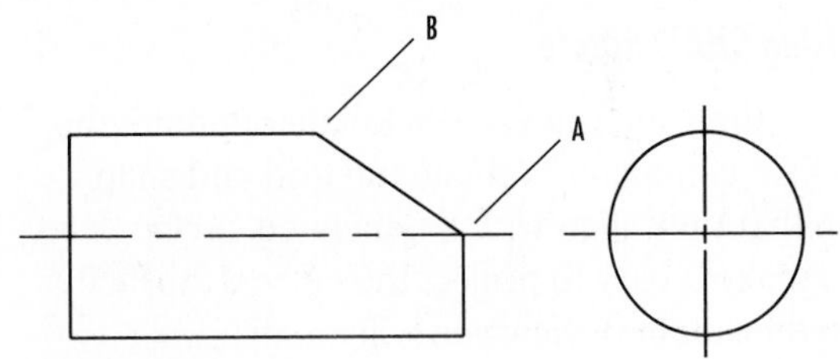

Figure 12.10

The drawing shows the front and side view of the slanted surface, but not the true shape of the surface. You will draw a *partial auxiliary view* to show the true shape of the surface. Partial auxiliary views are often used because in the auxiliary view, the inclined or oblique surface chosen is shown true size and shape, but the other surfaces are all foreshortened. Since these other surfaces have already been defined in the basic orthographic views, there is really no need to show them in the auxiliary view. A partial auxiliary view shows only the inclined surfaces (leaving out the normal surfaces), thus saving time in projecting the view and giving a clearer appearance to your drawing.

Figure 12.11 shows a front view of an object, plus two partial auxiliary views.

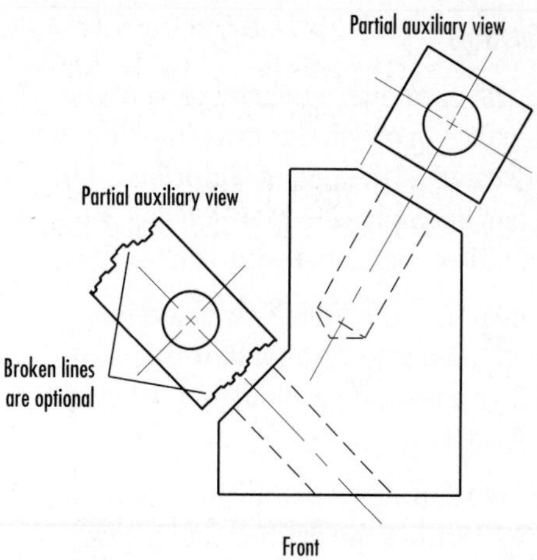

Figure 12.11

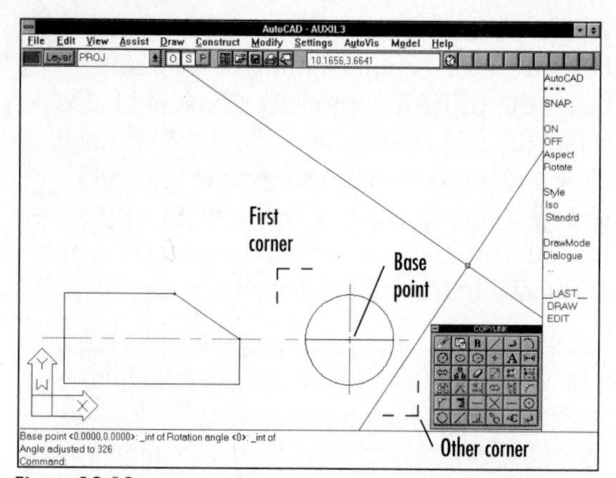

Figure 12.12

Using SNAP, Rotate

This time you will use the Rotate option of the SNAP command to rotate the grid and snap so that they align with the inclined surface, to make it easy to project the curved surface to the auxiliary view you will create.

On your own, turn on the running mode Object Snap, Intersection, using the Settings, Object Snap selection from the menu bar. Turn on GRID (if needed) by pressing (F7). PROJ should be the current layer.

Now, you will rotate the snap angle using the SNAP command. You will pick two points (identified in Figure 12.10) to define the angle.

> Command: **SNAP** (↵)
>
> Snap spacing or ON/OFF/Aspect/Rotate/Style <0.1250>: **R** (↵)
>
> Base point <0.0000,0.0000>: ***(target the intersection labeled A)***
>
> Rotation angle: ***(target the intersection labeled B)***
>
> Angle adjusted to 326

Your screen should look similar to Figure 12.12. Notice that the crosshairs and grid have aligned with the inclined surface.

Next, you will copy the object in the side view and rotate it so that it aligns with the rotated grid and snap. This makes it easy to project the depth of the object from the side view into the auxiliary view, so that you do not have to use a reference surface to make depth measurements, as you did in the previous drawing.

Make sure that ORTHO and SNAP are turned on. Refer to Figure 12.12.

> Pick: **COPY *(toolbox)***
>
> Select objects: ***(pick a point above and to the left of the objects in the side view)***
>
> Other corner: ***(pick a point below and to the right of the objects in the side view)***
>
> 7 found
>
> Select objects: (↵)
>
> <Base point or displacement>/Multiple: ***(target the intersection of the center lines in the side view)***
>
> Second point of displacement: ***(pick a point on the snap above and to the right of the side view)***

A copy of the side view should appear in your drawing, so that it looks like Figure 12.13.

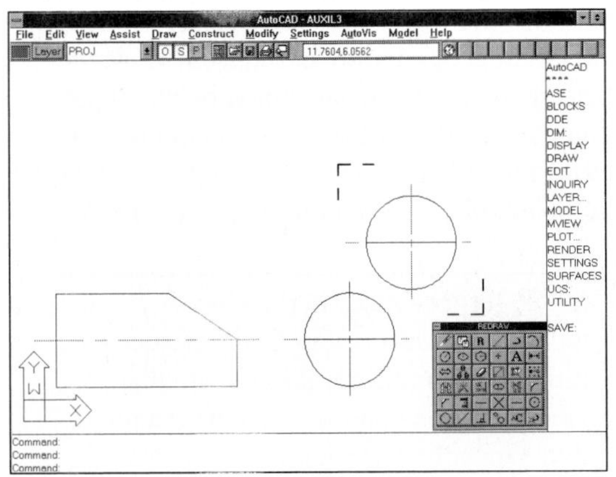

Figure 12.13

Now you will change the copy onto layer PROJ, as it is part of the construction of the drawing, not something you will leave in once you are finished. Layer PROJ will be frozen when you have finished the drawing.

Pick: **Modify *(menu bar)*, Change, Properties. . .**

Select objects: ***(window the copy you created, as shown in Figure 12.13)***

7 found

Select objects: ↵

Use the dialogue box to change the layer to PROJ. When you are finished changing the layer,

Pick: **OK**

The objects you selected are changed onto layer PROJ. You will notice that their color is now magenta, which is the color for layer PROJ.

Now you are ready to rotate the copied objects so that they align with the snap and can be used to project the auxiliary view. Use the ROTATE command to accomplish this.

Pick: **ROTATE *(toolbox)***

Select objects: **P** ↵

7 found

Select objects: ↵

Base point: ***(target the intersection of the center lines of the copied objects)***

<Rotation angle>/Reference: ***(with ORTHO turned on, select a point above and to the right of the base point you picked, as shown in Figure 12.14)***

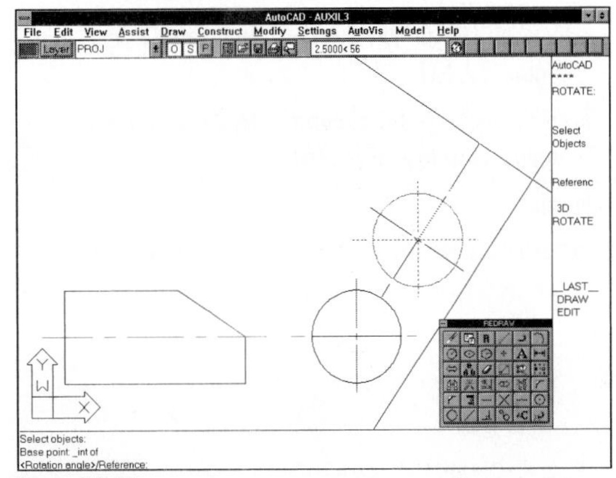

Figure 12.14

The objects you copied previously should now be rotated into position so that they align with the snap and grid. Your drawing should look like Figure 12.15.

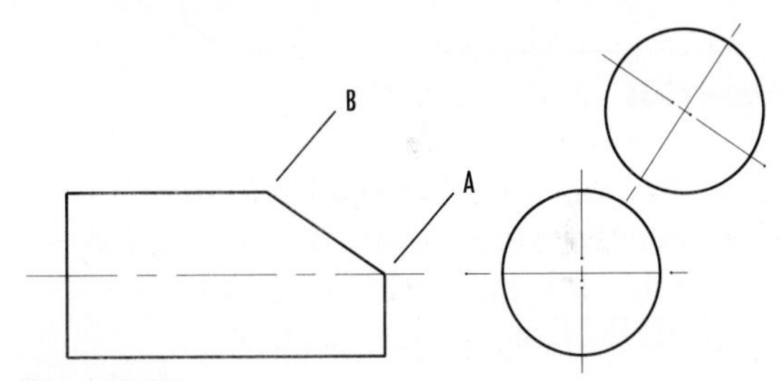

Figure 12.15

Next you will draw projection lines from the front view out into the empty area where the auxiliary view will be located. You will use the alias L for the LINE command by typing it in (ORTHO and the Osnap, Intersection running mode should be active). Refer to Figures 12.15 and 12.16.

Command: **L** ↵

From point: ***(target the intersection labeled A in Figure 12.15)***

To point: ***(pick a point above the copied side view, as in Figure 12.16)***

To point: ↵

Command: ↵ ***(to restart the LINE command)***

From point: ***(target the intersection labeled B in Figure 12.15)***

To point: ***(pick a point above the copied side view again, as in Figure 12.16)***

To point: ↵

Your screen should look like Figure 12.16.

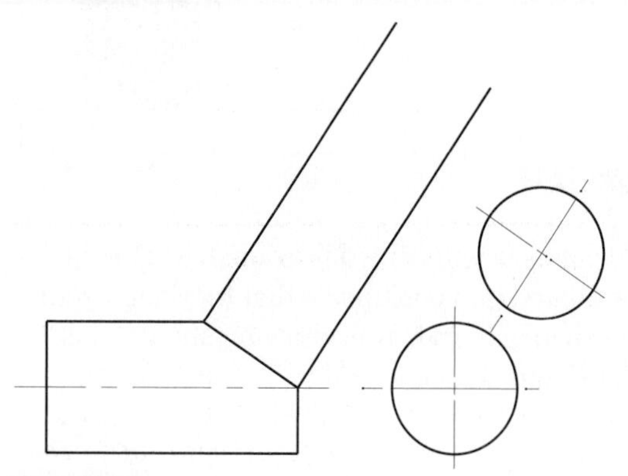

Figure 12.16

On your own, draw projection lines from the intersections in the copied side view, so that your drawing looks like Figure 12.17. Then set layer VISIBLE as the current layer.

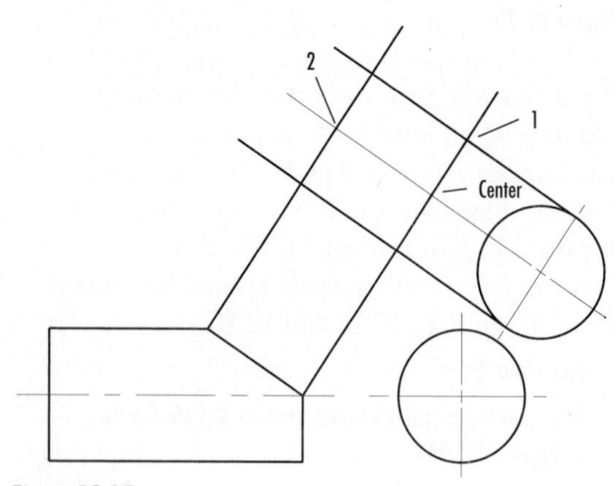

Figure 12.17

Because the object appears circular in the side view, and is tilted away in the front view, the true shape of the surface must be an ellipse. You will use the ELLIPSE command from the Draw menu bar to create the elliptical surface in the auxiliary view. Refer to Figure 12.17.

> ■ ***TIP*** If the surface in the side view was an irregular curve, you could project a number of points out into the auxiliary view and then connect them with a polyline. Once they are connected, you could connect them in a smooth curve, using the Fit Curve or Spline option of the PEDIT command. This also works to draw an ellipse; however, the Ellipse command is quicker. ■

Pick: **ELLIPSE *(toolbox)***

<Axis endpoint 1>/Center: **C** ↵

Center of ellipse: ***(target the intersection where the center projects into the auxiliary view)***

Axis endpoint: ***(target the point identified as 1)***

<Other axis distance>/Rotation: ***(target the point identified as 2)***

The ellipse in your drawing should appear as shown in Figure 12.18. The lower portion of it will need to be trimmed off to create the final surface.

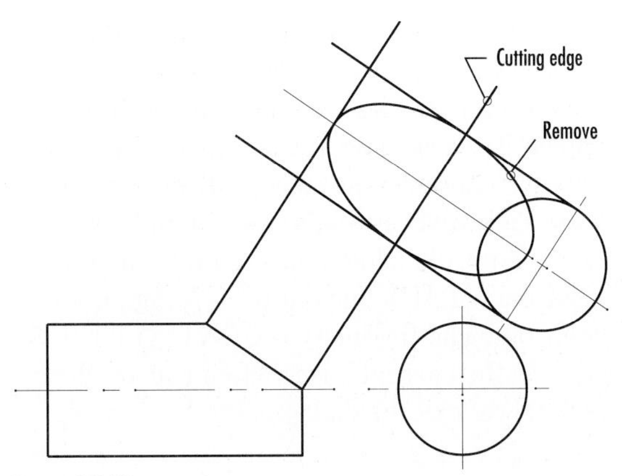

Figure 12.18

You will use the TRIM command to eliminate the unnecessary portion of the ellipse in the auxiliary view:

Pick: **TRIM *(toolbox)***

Select cutting edge(s)...

Select objects: ***(pick the cutting edge in Figure 12.18)***

Select objects: ↵

<Select object to trim>/Undo: ***(pick on the ellipse to the right of the cutting edge)***

<Select object to trim>/Undo: ↵

The lower portion of the ellipse is now trimmed off.

Change the two projection lines from the front view onto layer THIN on your own. Use the BREAK command to break them so that they do not touch the views. Draw in the final line across the bottom of the remaining portion of the ellipse in layer VISIBLE. Freeze the PROJ layer to remove the construction and projection lines from your display. Save your drawing before continuing.

When you are finished, your drawing should look like Figure 12.19.

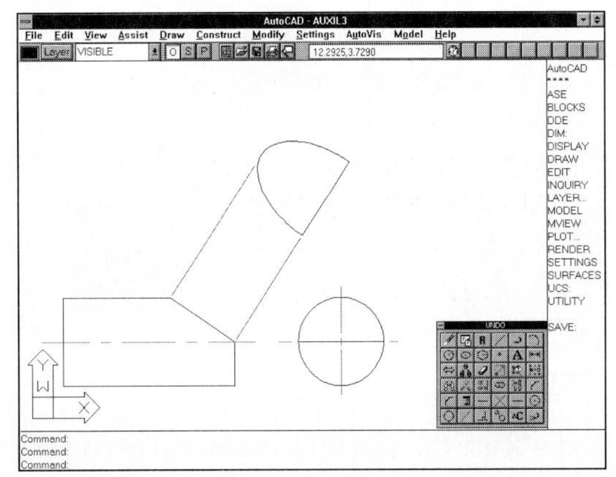

Figure 12.19

Creating an Auxiliary View from a 3D Solid Model

On your own, use the File, New selection to create a new drawing called AUX3D. Use the drawing ANGLBLK that is provided with the data files as the prototype.

A drawing similar to the solid model you created in Tutorial 9 should appear on the screen, as shown in Figure 12.20. You will continue working with this drawing, adding fillets to the corners of the angled end and creating a partial auxiliary view showing the true size of the inclined surface, using AutoCAD's SOLFEAT command.

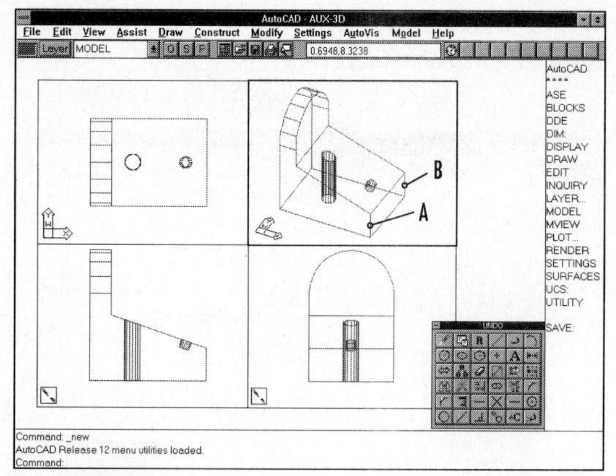

Figure 12.20

You will use the SOLFILL command to create a rounded corner of radius 1.00 on the front edges of the object.

Pick: **Model *(menu bar)*, Modify, Fillet Solids**

Pick edges of solids to be filleted (press ENTER when done): ***(pick the vertical lines labeled A and B in Figure 12.20)*** ↵

Updating object...

Done.

2 edges selected

Diameter/<Radius> of fillet <0.00>: **1** ↵

Phase I...

Updating the Advanced Modeling Extension database

When you have completed this step, your drawing should look like Figure 12.21.

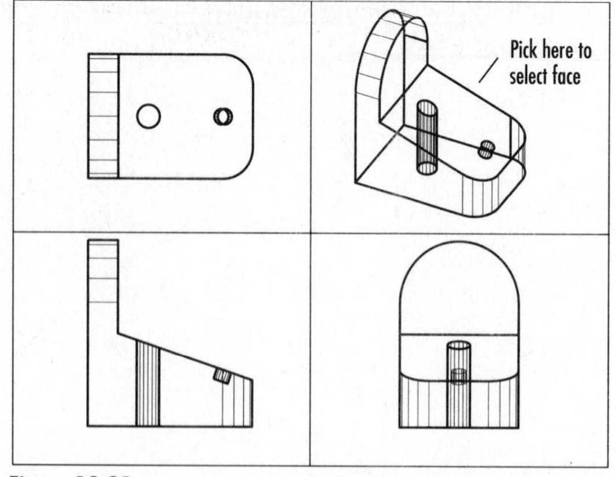

Figure 12.21

When you are using solid modeling, you can freeze layers in specific viewports so that the 3D object in the drawing database does not appear in every view. You will make this possible by creating a new layer for the auxiliary view. Pick Layer from the toolbar and use the Layer Control dialogue box to create a new layer named AUX on your own. Assign it the color blue and the linetype CONTINUOUS. Set AUX as the current layer. When you are done, pick OK to exit the dialogue box.

Copying a Solid Feature

The SOLFEAT command creates a copy of any face or edge of the solid object that you select. You can use this command to copy the inclined face to produce an auxiliary view. The copy is created on the current layer and is positioned exactly aligned with the face on the solid model. You can rotate the copied feature so that it appears true size in the viewport in order to create a partial auxiliary view. This command is also very useful for development drawings, which are often used in creating pattern layouts for sheet-metal or duct work.

Pick: **Model *(menu bar)*, Display, Copy Feature**

solfeat Edge/<Face>: ↵

All/<Select>: ↵

Pick a face: ***(select the edge of the face, as indicated in Figure 12.21)***

Next/<OK>: ***(If the top inclined face is highlighted, press ↵ for OK; if not, type "N" and press ↵ to highlight the next face. Continue this process until the correct face is highlighted and then press ↵.)***

Pick a face: ↵

A copy of the face is created on top of the existing lines in each viewport. Because it is in layer AUX, its color is blue, so it can be distinguished from the lines of the model. Your screen should look like Figure 12.22.

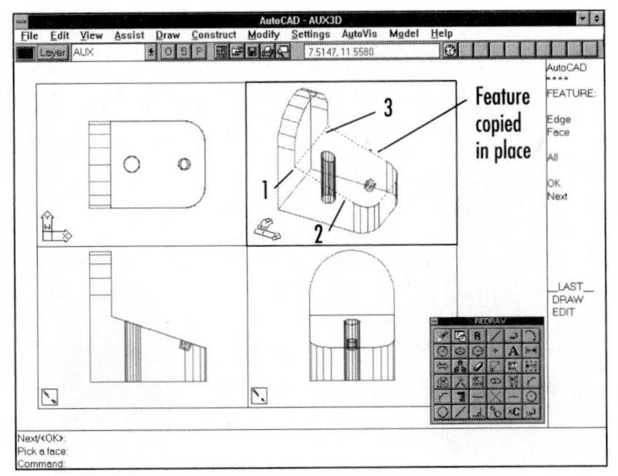

Figure 12.22

Next you will align the UCS with the inclined face so that it is easy to specify the angle to rotate the copied feature so that it projects from the front view. You may need to use ZOOM, Window accurately choose your points. Remember to use ZOOM, Previous to restore your original view.

■ ***TIP*** In the following steps remember that you can pick the OSNAP overrides from the toolbox instead of typing "INT" and pressing ↵. ■

Command: **UCS** ↵

Origin/ZAxis/3point/Entity/View/X/Y/Z/Prev/Restore/Save/Del/?/<World>: **3** ↵

Origin <0,0,0>: **INT** ↵

of ***(target the intersection shown in Figure 12.22 as point 1)***

Point on positive portion of the X-axis <4.0000,2.0000,3.0000>: **END** ↵

of ***(target a point past the midpoint of the lower line, identified as point 2)***

Point on positive-Y portion of the UCS XY plane <3.0000,3.0000,3.0000>: **END** ↵

of ***(target a point past the midpoint of the line, identified as point 3)***

The UCS icon should change so that it is oriented with the inclined surface.

■ ***TIP*** You could also use the SOLUCS command with the Face option to align the UCS. ■

Now you will use the Rotate 3D command to rotate the copied feature so that it is shown true size in the front view.

Pick: **Modify *(menu bar)*, Rotate 3D**

rotate3d

Initializing. . .

Select objects: ***(pick the copied feature by selecting the blue lines)***

1 found

Select objects: ↵

Axis by Entity/Last/View/Xaxis/Yaxis/Zaxis/<2points>: ↵

1st point on axis: **END** ↵

of ***(target the endpoint of the front edge of the copied feature, identified as point 1 in Figure 12.22)***

2nd point on axis: **END** ↵

of ***(target the other endpoint of the same line, identified as point 2)***

<Rotation angle>/Reference: **R** ↵

Reference angle <0>: ↵

New angle: **90** ↵

The feature you copied is now rotated 90 degrees so that it appears true size in the front view. Your drawing should appear similar to Figure 12.23.

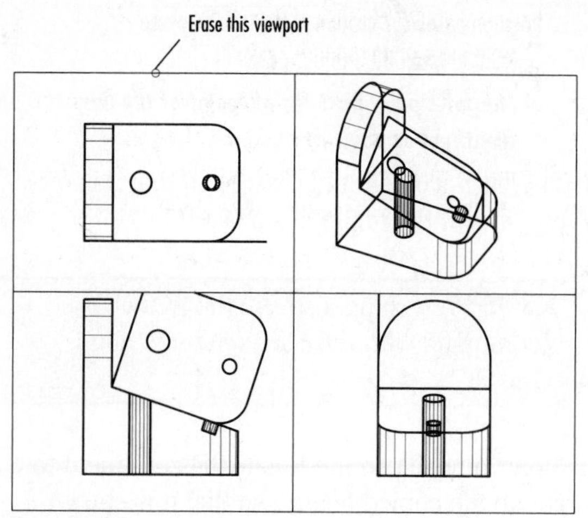

Figure 12.23

Now you will create room for the auxiliary view by erasing the upper left viewport that contains the top view. You will pick the P button from the toolbar to switch to paper space. When you are in paper space, the viewports can be erased, stretched, scaled, and changed like any other drawing entity.

Pick: **P button *(toolbar)*** ↵

The paper space icon is displayed in the lower left corner of your screen.

Now that you are in paper space, you will erase the upper left viewport and stretch the lower left viewport up to make room for the partial auxiliary view.

Command: **E** ↵

ERASE Select objects: ***(pick on the upper border of the upper left viewport, as indicated in Figure 12.23)***

Select objects: ↵

The upper left viewport and its contents disappear from your drawing. Type "R" to redraw the screen.

Command: **R** ↵

Your screen should look similar to Figure 12.24.

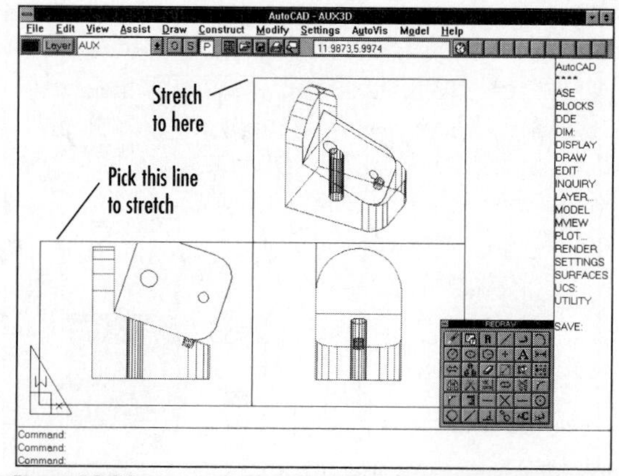

Figure 12.24

On your own, use the hot grips to stretch the lower left viewport so that it is twice as tall as before. Pick on the line indicated in Figure 12.24 to turn on the grips. Make the grip at the right end of the line the hot, or active, grip by picking on it. You will see the STRETCH command in the command line area of the screen. Pick the upper left intersection of the upper right-hand viewport as the point to which you want to stretch. Make sure ORTHO is turned on!

Your drawing should now look like Figure 12.25.

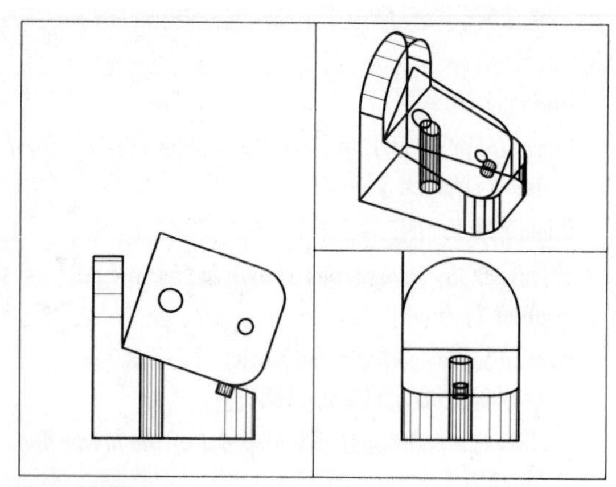

Figure 12.25

Notice that you can still see this copied and rotated feature in every viewport. Use the VPLAYER command to freeze the layer in selected viewports so that it is only visible in the left-hand viewport. Your change will not be visible on the screen until you exit the VPLAYER command.

Command: **VPLAYER** ↵

?/Freeze/Thaw/Reset/NewFrz/Vpvisdflt: **F** ↵

Layer(s) to Freeze: **AUX** ↵

All/Select/<Current>: **S** ↵

Select objects: ***(select the upper right and lower right viewports)***

Select objects: ↵

?/Freeze/Thaw/Reset/NewFrz/Vpvisdflt: ↵

When you have completed this, be sure to switch back to model space by picking the P button from the toolbar.

Pick: **P button *(toolbar)***

Next you will align a UCS with the auxiliary view to make it easier to position the partial auxiliary feature.

Command: **UCS** ↵

Origin/ZAxis/3point/Entity/View/X/Y/Z/Prev/Restore/Save/Del/?/<World>: **E** ↵

Select object to align UCS: ***(pick a blue line of the auxiliary view in the left viewport)***

You will see the UCS icon align with the auxiliary view.

After making sure that ORTHO is turned on (pick O from the toolbar), you will use the MOVE command to move the partial auxiliary view away from the front view to create a clearer drawing.

Pick: **Modify *(menu bar)*, Move**

Select objects: ***(pick on one of the blue lines that form the auxiliary view surface)***

1 found

Select objects: ↵

Base point or displacement: ***(pick the lower left intersection of the surface)***

Second point of displacement: ***(pick a point on the snap above the angled line in the front view, so that the auxiliary view is moved away from the front view, but is still shown in the viewport)***

Your drawing should appear similar to Figure 12.26.

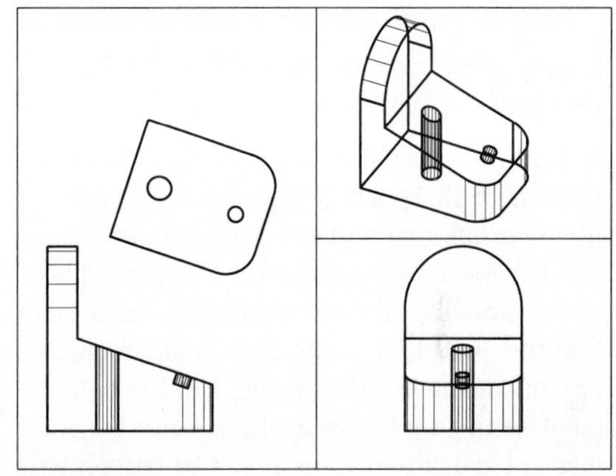

Figure 12.26

On your own, create a new layer named THIN, which is color red and linetype CONTINUOUS. Then draw two reference lines for the partial auxiliary view, as you see in Figure 12.27. Use the Change, Properties selection to change the layer of the two reference lines you created to THIN, since reference lines should be thin lines when plotted; they should not be the same color that you use for object lines. Freeze layer THIN in the two right-hand viewports with VPLAYER.

Next, use the SOLPROF command that you learned in Tutorial 9 to create 2D profiles in the viewports to display the correct hidden and visible lines.

Pick: **Model *(menu bar)*, Display Profile Solids**

Select objects: ***(pick on an edge of the object, not the auxiliary, in the leftmost viewport)***

1 found

Select objects: ↵

Display hidden profile lines on separate layer? <Y>: ↵

Project profile lines onto a plane? <Y>: ↵

Delete tangential edges? <Y>: ↵

Phase I of hidden line removal computation has started.

Phase II of hidden line removal computation of current solid has started.

Phase III of hidden line removal computation of current solid has started.

Hidden line removal computation of current solids completed.

Lines appear over the colored lines in the viewport.

Repeat this process on your own for the two remaining viewports. When you have completed profiling the object in each viewport, you will see lines on the screen over the lines of the model in all three viewports. Remember that the SOLPROF command creates new layers for the lines of the profile, and the default color setting for these layers is white. As you learned in Tutorial 9, because you responded Yes to the prompt for displaying hidden profile lines on a separate layer, there are two new kinds of layers in the drawing: profile visible lines with names starting with PV- and ending with the viewport handle number, and profile hidden lines starting with PH- and ending with the handle number of the viewport where the profile was created.

Use the Settings, Layer Control selection to change the color and linetype of the hidden layers (PH-. . .) to color blue (they should already be linetype HIDDEN). Use color 7 (white) and linetype CONTINUOUS for the profile visible lines (PV-. . .). Freeze all the layers starting with PV- and also layer MODEL.

You will use the EXPLODE command on the blocks containing the hidden lines so unnecessary lines can be erased.

Pick: **Modify *(menu bar)*, Explode**

Select objects: ***(pick on the hidden line block in the left viewport)***

Notice that the lines have changed color. Next you will use the CHPROP command to change their color back to the layer color. You will select the EDIT, CHPROP command from the screen menu and use the option Previous to select the previously selected hidden lines.

Pick: **EDIT *(screen)*, CHPROP**

Select objects: **P** ↵ ↵

Change what property (Color/LAyer/LType/Thickness)? **C** ↵

New color <varies>: **BYLAYER** ↵

Change what property (Color/LAyer/LType/Thickness)? ↵

The lines change back to blue on your screen.

On your own, repeat the entire process of exploding and changing the hidden line blocks in each viewport. When you are finished, use the ERASE command to erase the outer hidden lines on the object, where a visible line would be drawn on top of the hidden line. When you are finished, your drawing should look like Figure 12.27.

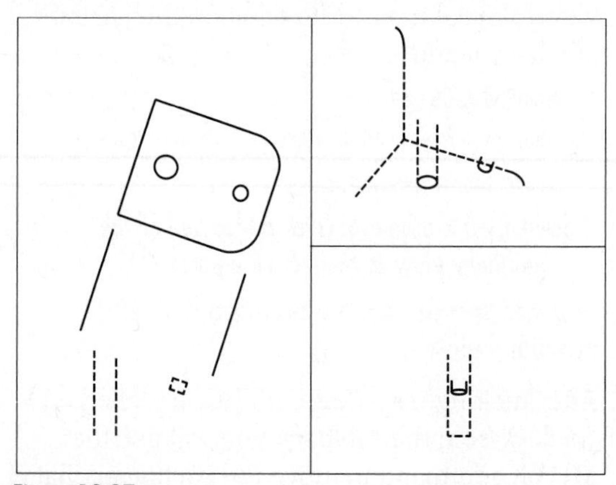

Figure 12.27

Next, you will use the LAYER command to thaw all of the layers that begin with the letters PV-. Once you have completed this, the profiled visible lines show up on your display screen.

Command: **LA** ↵

?/Make/Set/New/ON/OFF/Color/Ltype/Freeze/Thaw/LOck/
Unlock: **T** ⏎

Layer name(s) to thaw: **PV*** ⏎

?/Make/Set/New/ON/OFF/Color/Ltype/Freeze/Thaw/LOck/
Unlock: ⏎

You will use the LTSCALE command to adjust the linetype scale factor so that the hidden lines in the drawing look as good as possible.

Command: **LTSCALE** ⏎

New Scale factor <1.0000>: **.7** ⏎

Try other settings until you are pleased with the results.

On your own, save your drawing with the procedures you have learned. You have now completed this tutorial, and your drawing should look like Figure 12.28.

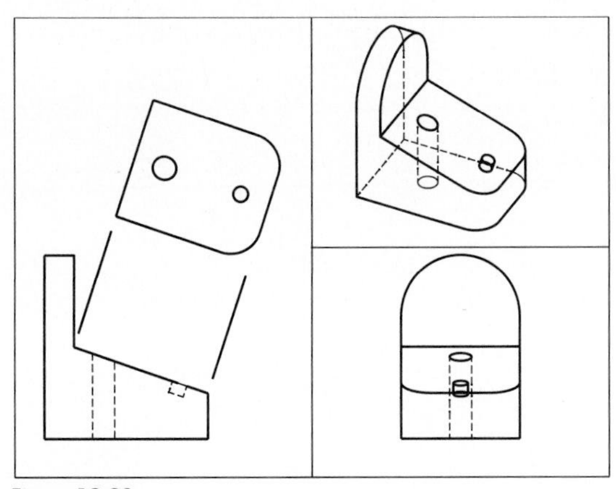

Figure 12.28

Going Further

The AutoCAD variable PSLTSCALE causes the paper space LTSCALE factor to be used for every viewport when it is set to the default value of 1 (one). This way, when viewports are zoomed to different scales, you do not have to adjust LTSCALE in each viewport separately so that they appear the same on the paper. Using PSLTSCALE set to 0 causes the model space LTSCALE factors to be used to generate the linetype scales individually for each viewport.

Another useful variable is UCSFOLLOW. Pick in a viewport to make it active, then set UCSFOLLOW to 1 (one). AutoCAD automatically generates a plan view of the current UCS in that viewport whenever you change the UCS.

KEY TERMS

auxiliary view
basic view
foreshortened
partial auxiliary view
reference surface

KEY COMMANDS

Paper Space Linetype Scale
Rotate 3D
Solid Features
User Coordinate System Follow

EXERCISES

Use the 2D or solid modeling techniques you have learned in the tutorial to create an auxiliary view of the slanted surfaces for the objects below. The letter M after an exercise number means that the given dimensions are in millimeters.

12.1 Stop Block

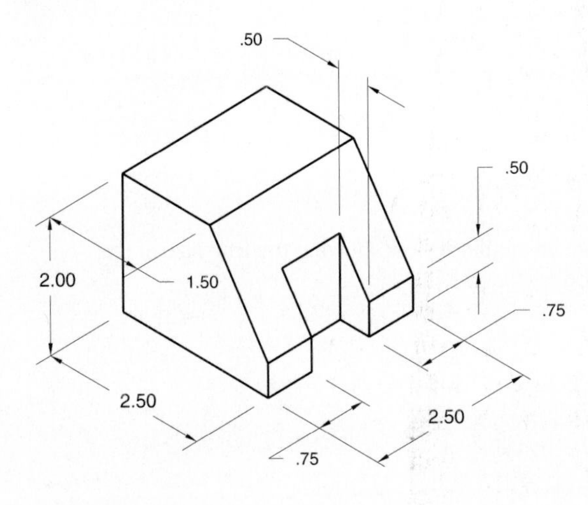

12.2M Lever

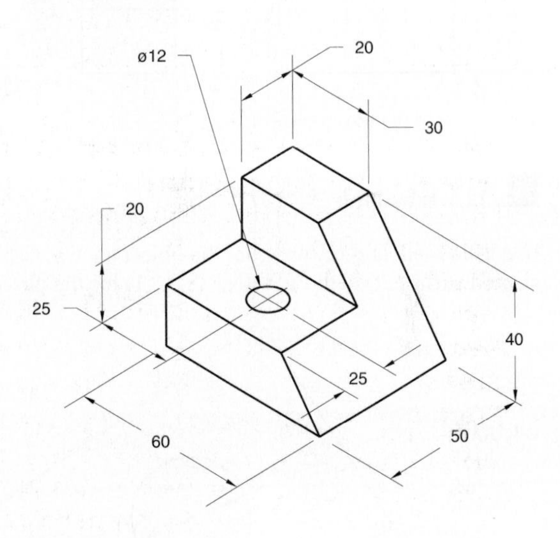

12.3 Bearing

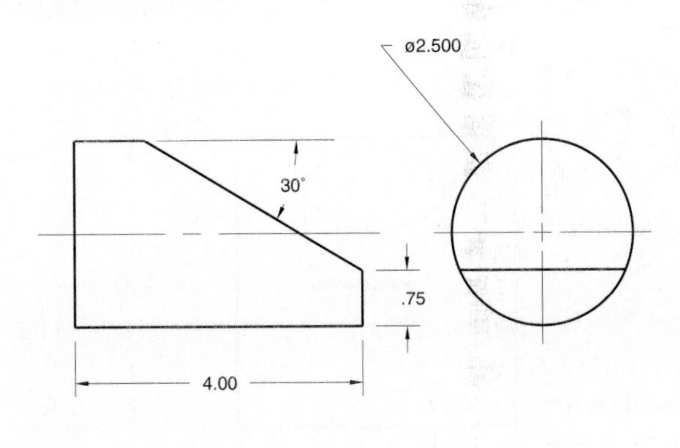

12.4M Router Guide

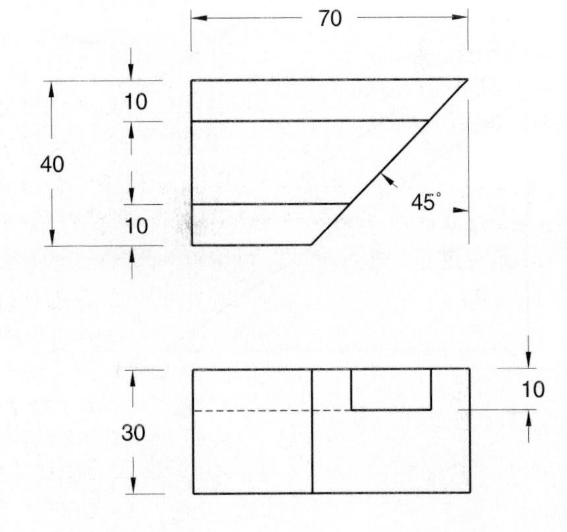

12.5 Tooling Support

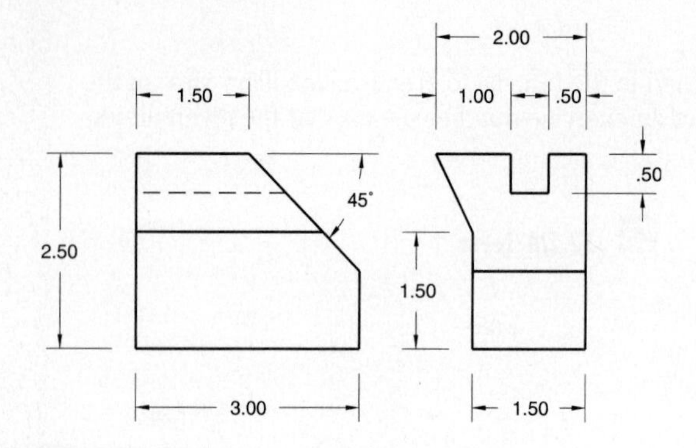

12.6 Incline Block

Use solid modeling to construct the object shown. Create an auxiliary view showing the true size of the slanted surface. Use the VPOINT (3, –3,1) for the pictorial view.

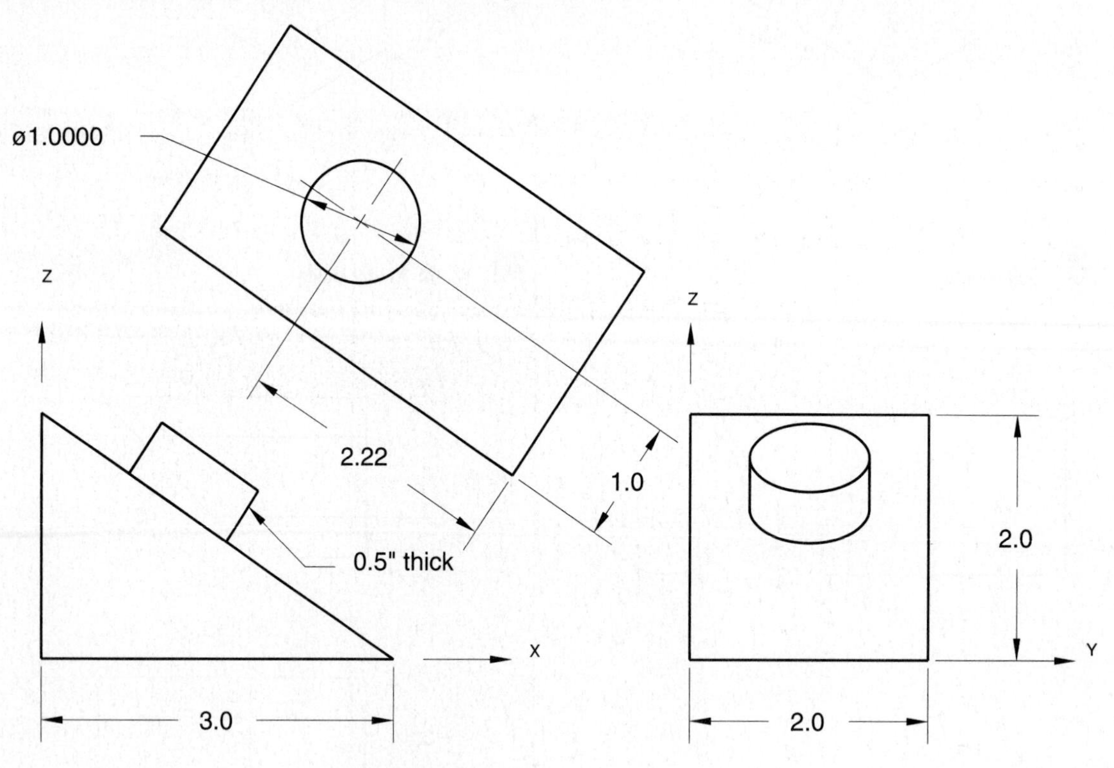

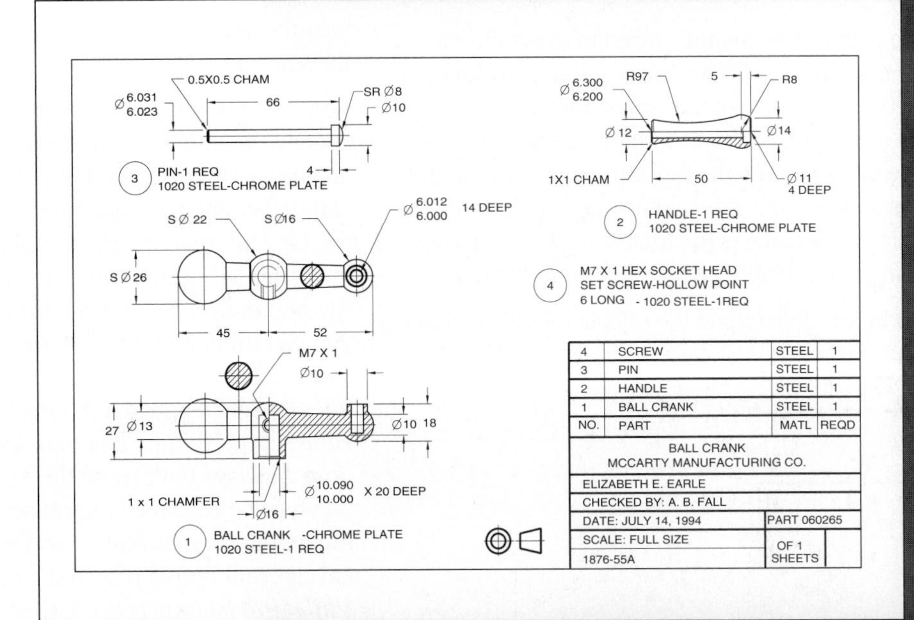

TUTORIAL 13

Advanced Dimensioning

Objectives

When you have completed this tutorial, you will be able to

1. Use tolerances in a drawing.
2. Set up the dimension variables to use variance (plus/minus) tolerances.
3. Set up the dimension variables to use limit tolerances.
4. Edit dimensions with the DIM: UPDATE and NEWTEXT commands.
5. Add dimensions in viewport-specific layers in your solid model drawings.

Tolerance

No part can be manufactured to exact dimensions. There is always some amount of variation between the size of the actual object when it is measured and an exact dimension specified in the drawing. To take this into consideration, tolerances are specified along with the dimensions. Tolerance is the total amount of variation that an acceptable part is allowed to have.

To better understand the effects tolerances have on a part's dimensions, refer to Figure 13.1.

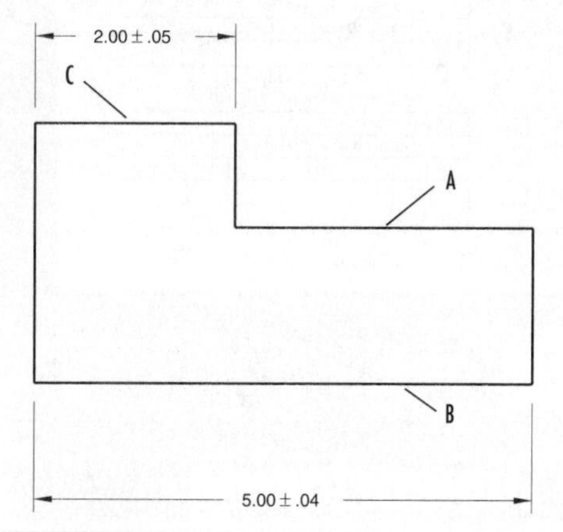

Figure 13.1

The dimensions given in the drawing are used to make and inspect the part. Included with the dimension is the allowable amount of variation (tolerance) that a part can have and still be acceptable. In order to determine whether a part is acceptable, you compare the measurements of the actual part to the toleranced dimensions specified in the drawing. If the part falls within the tolerance range specified, it is an acceptable part.

In Tutorial 7, you saw how you can add a general tolerance note to your drawing to specify this allowable variation. AutoCAD provides two kinds of tolerances to specify with the dimension for the part: variance tolerances and limit tolerances.

Limit tolerances specify the upper and lower allowable measurements for the part. An actual part measuring anywhere between the two limits is acceptable.

Variance tolerances or *plus/minus tolerances* specify the nominal dimension and the allowable range that is added to it. From this you can determine the upper and lower limits. Add the plus tolerance to the nominal size to get the upper limit. Subtract the minus tolerance from the nominal size to get the lower limit. (Or you can think about it like this: you always add the tolerance, but when the sign of the tolerance is negative, the effect is that you subtract the value.) The plus and minus values do not always have to be the same. There are two types of variance tolerances: bilateral and unilateral. *Bilateral tolerances* specify a nominal size and both a plus and a minus tolerance. *Unilateral tolerances* are a special case where either the plus or minus value specified for the tolerance is zero. You can create both bilateral and unilateral tolerances using AutoCAD.

Consider surface A in Figure 13.1. Surface A is longest when the 5.00 overall dimension, surface B, is at its longest and when the 2.00 dimension, surface C, is at its shortest.

$$A_{max} = 5.04 - 1.95 = 3.09$$

Surface A is shortest when the 5.00 overall dimension, surface B, is at its shortest and when the 2.00 dimension, surface C, is at its longest.

$$A_{min} = 4.96 - 2.05 = 2.91$$

In other words, the given dimensions with the added tolerances permit surface A to vary between 3.09 and 2.91 units.

Figure 13.2 shows the drawing you dimensioned in Tutorial 7 with tolerances added to the dimensions. Tolerances A, B, F, and G are examples of bilateral tolerances. Tolerances C, D, and E are limit tolerances.

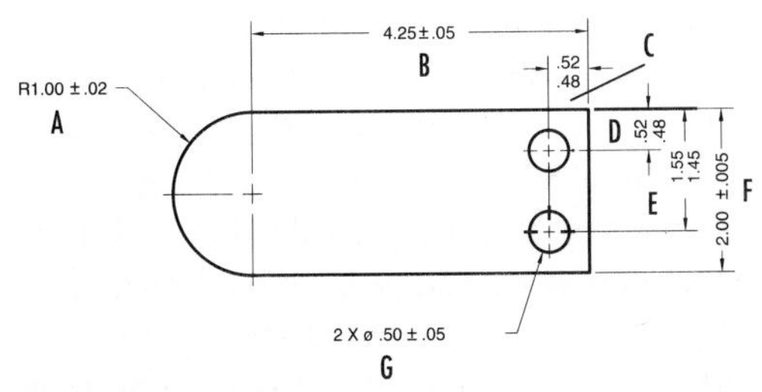

Figure 13.2

Next you will change the dimensions for the drawing you created in Tutorial 7 to add tolerances. You will use the file OBJ_DIM provided with the data files or use the drawing you created to start your new drawing.

Start AutoCAD from the Autodesk Collection Interface as instructed in Chapter 3. The drawing editor appears on your screen. From the AutoCAD drawing editor,

Pick: **File *(menu bar)*, New. . .**

As you have learned to do in previous tutorials, select the drawing OBJ_DIM as the prototype for your new drawing. Name your new drawing TOLERNC. Pick OK when you are finished.

Your screen should appear similar to Figure 13.3. Be sure that layer DIM is set as the current layer. If it is not, pick on the current layer name shown on the toolbar and then pick DIM from the list of layer names that pulls down.

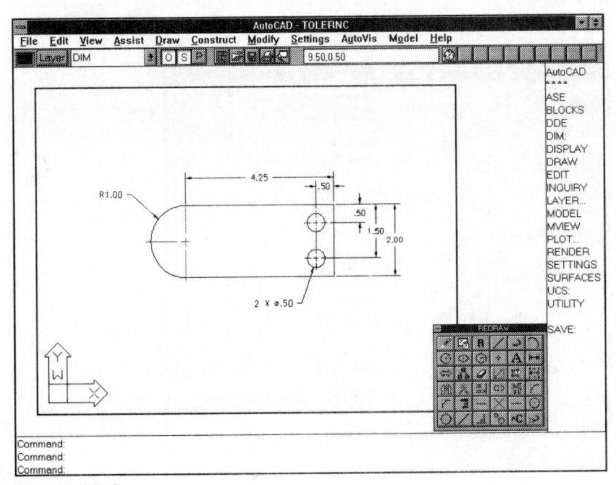

Figure 13.3

In the next steps, you will use the dimensioning command UPDATE to update the dimensions. First you will set up the dimension variables to use tolerances.

■ ***TIP*** Much of the power of CAD is the ability to quickly make changes to your drawing. You will save time if you do not erase and redraw parts of your drawing but instead use the special features of AutoCAD to edit and change your drawing. In this tutorial you will learn to use one such feature, DIM: UPDATE. Try not to draw anything over; think of ways to copy, rotate, resize, and change, or update, what you have already drawn. ■

Automatic Bilateral Tolerances

You can have AutoCAD automatically add bilateral tolerances by setting the dimensioning variables. To set dimension variables, you can either type the exact name of the variable at the command prompt, or select it from the standard screen DIM menu selection under DIMVARS. As you learned in Tutorial 7, the Dimension Styles dialogue box also aids you in setting the dimension variables. This is probably the easiest method because you do not need to remember the cryptic names of the dimension variables. You will pick DDIM from the toolbox and use the Dimension Styles dialogue box to set the variables.

Pick: **DDIM *(toolbox)***

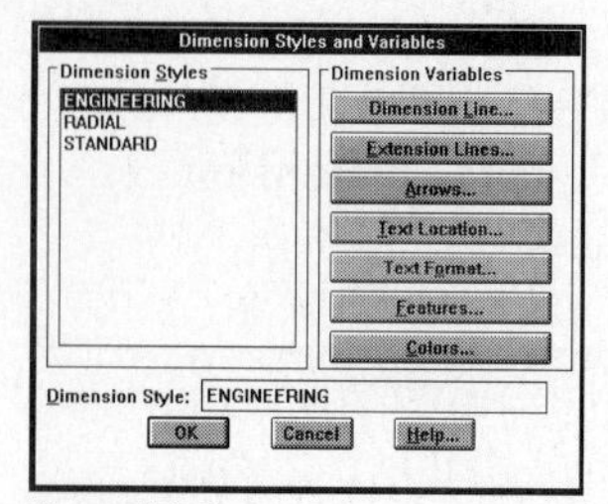

Figure 13.4

The Dimension Styles dialogue box appears on your display screen, as shown in Figure 13.4. The text cursor is displayed in the box to the right of the words Dimension Style:. Use this box to enter the name of the new dimension style you are creating. Call the new style VARTOLERNC. Press the ↵ key when you are done typing in the name. "New Style VARTOLERNC created from ENGINEERING" appears at the bottom of the dialogue box. You will see the name appear in the dimension styles name list. It is already highlighted. Changes that you make to the dimension style now affect only the dimensions that are created while this style is current, or dimensions on which you use the DIM: UPDATE command.

Next you will make some changes to the new dimension style, VARTOLERNC. The dimension variable names listed in parentheses are the variable names that you could type at the command prompt.

Pick: **Text Format**

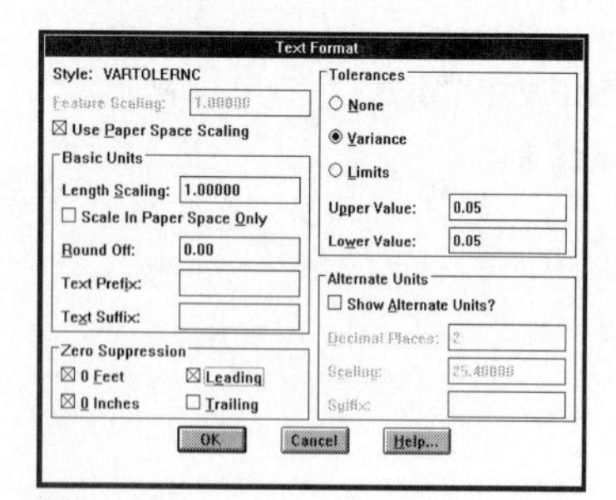

Figure 13.5

The Text Format dialogue box appears, as shown in Figure 13.5. Select the radio button to the left of the word Variance in the Tolerances area to turn on bilateral tolerances (DIMTOL). Use the same area of the dialogue box to set the upper and lower values for the tolerance. Although the upper and lower values do not have to be the same, for this tutorial set both the upper and the lower values to .05 on your own. When you have finished this step, you will return to the Dimension Styles dialogue.

Pick: **OK**

Pick: **Features**

In the Text Position area on the bottom right of the Features dialogue box, you will see the default setting of .13 (the same size as the dimension text) for the tolerance height (DIMTFAC). This will make limit tolerances and unequal bilateral tolerances the same height as the dimension text height. If you want to use the tolerances with smaller text, you can change this setting. For this tutorial, leave it set to .13.

Use the Text Position area again on your own to set the alignment for the text to Align With Dimension Line. This way, the dimensions with tolerances will fit in the available space. Change the Center Mark size to .06 on your own. Refer to Figure 13.6 for the dialogue settings.

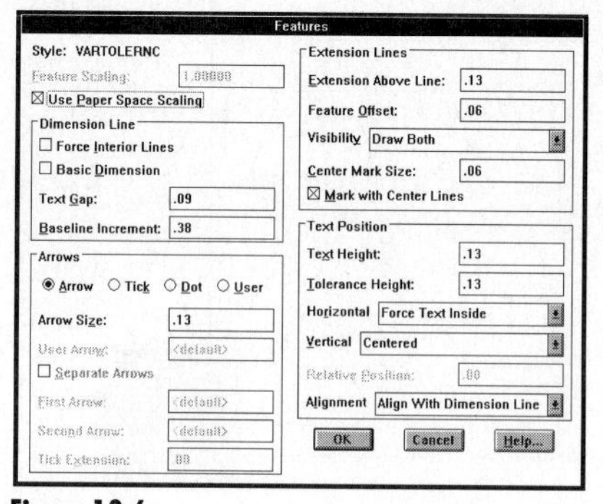

Figure 13.6

Pick: **OK** ***(to exit the Features dialogue box)***

Pick: **OK** ***(again to exit the Dimension Styles and Variables dialogue box)***

Updating the Dimensions

Now you are ready to update the dimensions to use variance or bilateral tolerances. You will use the Modify menu bar selection to pick the UPDATE command.

Pick: **Modify** ***(menu bar)*****, Edit Dimensions, Update dimension**

Select objects: ***(pick the 4.25 horizontal dimension and the 2.00 vertical dimension)*** ↵

The dimensions you have selected will be updated to include the bilateral tolerance. Refer to Figure 13.7.

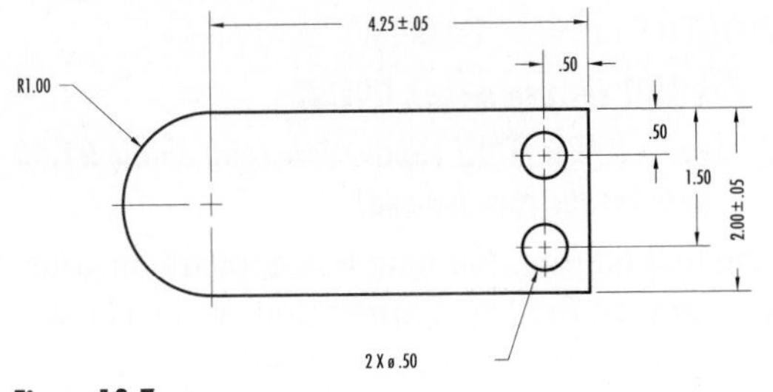

Figure 13.7

> ■ ***TIP*** When you have paper space scaling for the dimensions turned on and you use ZOOM to enlarge the area before adding a dimension, the sizes of the dimension text, arrows, and other default settings change to the specified sizes, relative to the zoomed view. You can use the Update command to change these dimensions back to their normal appearance after you zoom back to the previous enlargement. ■

Next, you will change the dimension variables in order to use limit tolerances for the remaining dimensions. Since you have already updated some of the dimensions to use the new style, VARTOLERNC, changing the dimension variables of the style would cause those updated dimensions to change to reflect the new settings. Likewise, any dimension created using that style would also update automatically to reflect any change made to that style. To prevent this, you will create a new dimension style for limit tolerances.

Pick: **DDIM** ***(toolbox)***

Type "LIMTOLERNC" in the box to the right of Dimension Style:. When you press the ↵ key, this name appears in the list of dimension styles at the left of the dialogue box. "New style LIMTOLERNC created from VARTOLERNC" appears at the bottom of the dialogue box. The new style is already highlighted. Select Text Format. . . and change the setting of the radio buttons in the Tolerances area of the Text Format dialogue box to the Limits setting.

Pick: **OK** ***(to exit the Text Format dialogue box)***

Pick: **OK** ***(to exit the Dimension Styles and Variables dialogue)***

On your own, use DIM: UPDATE and select the remaining two vertical dimensions and the .50 horizontal dimension. When you are done, your drawing will appear similar to Figure 13.8.

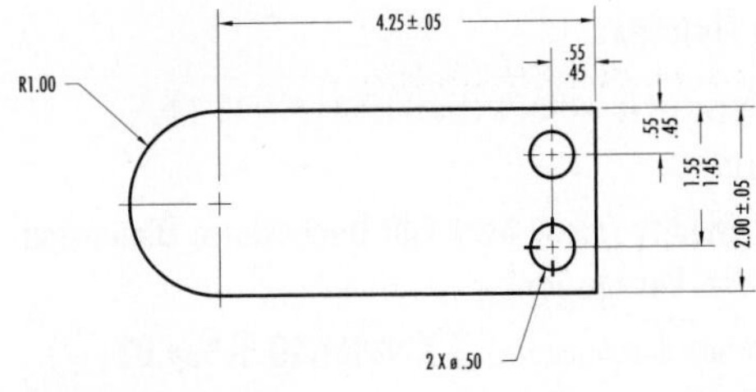

Figure 13.8

Updating Dimension Text

Text you type into a dimension cannot be updated with DDEDIT, the way you edited text in Tutorial 1. To change dimension text, you will use the DIM: NEWTEXT command.

Before you can successfully change the text for the diameter dimensions for the two holes, you must restore the dimension style that you used when you added them. Before you change the text, you will restore the dimension style RADIAL that was used when creating the dimension.

Pick: **DDIM *(toolbox)***

The Dimension Styles dialogue box appears on your screen. Highlight the dimension style named RADIAL in the list at the left side of the dialogue box. Refer to Figure 13.9. When you are done,

Pick: **OK *(to exit the dialogue)***

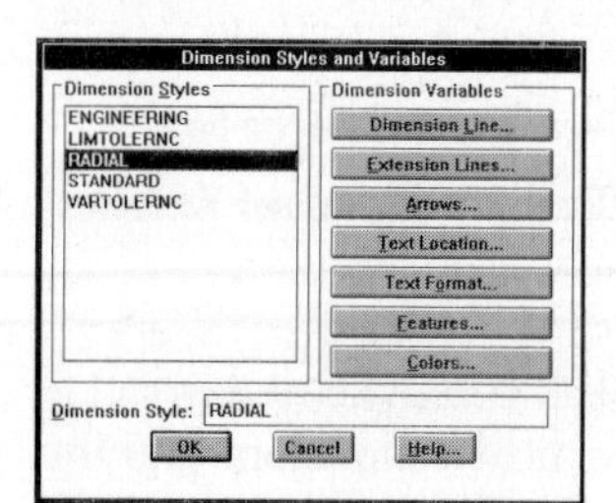

Figure 13.9

Using Newtext

Next you will select the DIM: NEWTEXT command.

Pick: **Modify *(menu bar)*, Edit Dimensions, Dimension Text, Change Text**

Enter new dimension text: **2 X %%c.50 %%p.02** ↵

Select objects: ***(pick the dimension for the size of the two holes)***

Select objects: ↵

Notice that the dimension text has been replaced with the new text that you typed. The special characters for diameter and plus/minus have replaced the %%c and %%p text you typed.

> ■ ***TIP*** You can also activate Newtext from the standard screen menu by selecting DIM: EDIT, Newtext. When you select DIM: in this manner, it stays active until you exit. ■

Using DDEDIT

Text created when using the LEADER command is entered by AutoCAD through use of the DTEXT command so, unlike dimension text, it can be changed with the DDEDIT command. Use the standard EDIT screen menu to select DDEDIT or type "DDEDIT" and press ↵.

Pick: **EDIT *(screen menu)*, DDEDIT**

<Select a TEXT or ATTDEF object>/Undo: ***(pick on the R1.00 note for the rounded end)***

The text editing dialogue box appears on your screen with the text highlighted. You will use the special text characters to add the {plus/minus} symbol for the tolerance.

Type: **R1.00 %%p.02**

Pick: **OK *(to exit the Edit Text dialogue box)***

<Select a TEXT or ATTDEF object>/Undo: ↵ ***(to exit the DDEDIT command)***

> ■ ***TIP*** You can also use the text portion of the Modify, Entity command from the menu bar to change text. ■

All the text in your drawing should be updated now. Refer to Figure 13.10.

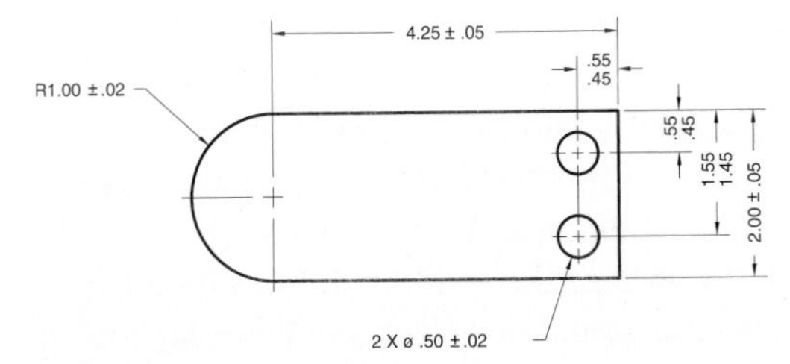

Figure 13.10

You have completed adding tolerances to your dimensions for this drawing. Save your drawing. If you wish, plot your drawing from paper space as you learned in Tutorial 3. If you plot from paper space, be sure to return to model space before continuing the tutorial. Now you are ready to continue and add dimensions to your solid model drawings.

Adapting for Architecture

Exploding dimensions and editing their text with DDEDIT is a useful technique for adding specific notes to the dimensions. This should only be done at the end of the drawing phase. By exploding dimensions, you lose the ability of associative dimensions to automatically update; therefore design changes are not reflected in your dimensions unless you make them manually. It is a good idea to clarify dimensions by adding text similar to X' On Center (O.C.) to make drawings read clearly. ■

Going Further

Limit and plus/minus dimensioning is not usually mixed within the same drawing. Use the DIM: UPDATE command to change the style of the plus/minus dimensions to limit dimensions on your own. Use the Dimension Styles dialogue box to set LIMTOLERNC as the current dimension style. Then pick Modify, Edit Dimensions, Update Dimension and pick all of the plus/minus dimensions. Remember to press ↵ when you are finished selecting the dimensions. When you are finished, all the dimension text will use the LIMTOLERNC dimension style. Remember to save your drawing.

Next you will learn how to add dimensions to a 3D solid modeled drawing.

Adding Viewport-Specific Dimensions

When adding dimensions to a 3D drawing, you can add dimensions either in paper space or in model space. Each behaves differently. Paper space is two dimensional. Dimensions added in paper space do not scale, move, or stretch with the model space object. The Length Scaling area of the Text Format dialogue (DIMLFAC) can be set to automatically adjust the dimension length values so that they are corrected for the paper space scaling factor.

Normally, dimensions are added in model space in the drawing. When dimensions are added in model space, they can be changed when changes are made to the model. Unlike in paper space, entities in model space, including dimensions, show in every viewport. Dimensions added for the top view of an object in a general layer show up as lines in the front and side views because they appear on edge in those views. Similarly, dimensions added to the side and front views show up in the other viewports. In Tutorial 9 you learned to set the visibility for layers in certain viewports, using the VPLAYER command. To make dimensions that are visible only in the desired viewport, you will create three new layers and control their visibility so that each is visible in only one viewport. Dimensions added to these layers will appear correctly in your solid model drawings.

Pick: **File *(menu bar),* New**

Start your new drawing using SOL-ADPT, a solid model drawing that was provided with your data files, as a prototype. Call the new drawing SOL_DIM. When you are finished naming your drawing,

Pick: **OK**

You are returned to the AutoCAD drawing editor screen with a 3D drawing. Refer to Figure 13.11.

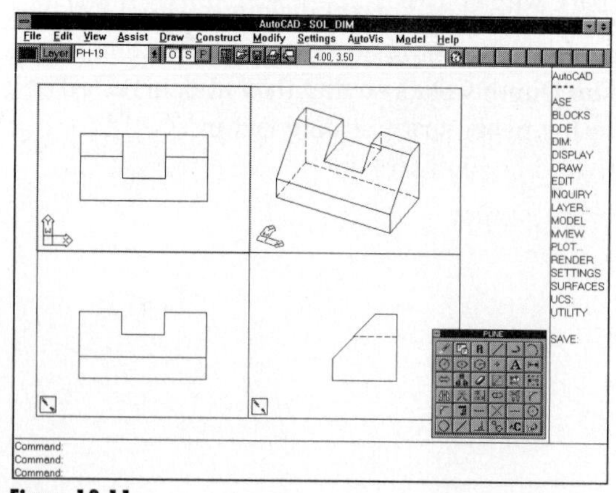

Figure 13.11

The prototype drawing you started from, SOL-ADPT, was created using AutoCAD's AME module. The views have already been profiled with the SOLPROF command to produce their hidden and visible lines. The layer MODEL, where the solid model was created, has been frozen. You will create three layers for dimensioning and set their visibility with the VPLAYER command. Then you will add dimensions with limit tolerances to the drawing.

On your own, use the Layer Control dialogue box to create three new layers: DIM_TOP, DIM_FRONT, and DIM_SIDE. Set the color for each of these layers to cyan and leave the linetypes set to the default, CONTINUOUS. Set layer DIM_FRONT as the current layer.

Using VPLAYER

You will use the VPLAYER command to set the visibility for the dimension layers you just created. You will use the same procedure you used in Tutorial 9 when you created layers to add center lines to your solid model drawing.

Command: **VPLAYER** ↵

?/Freeze/Thaw/Reset/Newfrz/Vpvisdflt: **F** ↵

Layer(s) to Freeze: **DIM_FRONT** ↵

All/Select/<Current>: **S** ↵

Switching to Paper space.

Select objects: ***(select on the border line of the upper left viewport)***

Select objects: ***(select on the border of the upper right viewport)***

Select objects: ***(select on the border of the lower right viewport)***

Select objects: ↵

Switching to Model space

You will not see anything in particular happen in the drawing because you have not yet created any dimensions in the layer DIM_FRONT. If you had, you would see that they no longer show up in the viewports that you selected to freeze. The general LAYER Freeze/Thaw and On/Off commands take precedence over the VPLAYER visibility, so if you want to freeze a layer altogether, you can still use the regular LAYER command. If a layer is frozen with the LAYER command or Layer Control dialogue box, it is not visible in any viewports even if the VPLAYER visibility is on for that viewport. You are still in the VPLAYER command prompt and you will now continue the command to set the visibility for layer DIM_SIDE:

?/Freeze/Thaw/Reset/Newfrz/Vpvisdflt: **F** ↵

Layer(s) to Freeze: **DIM_SIDE** ↵

All/Select/<Current>: **S** ↵

Switching to Paper space.

Select objects: ***(select on the border line of the upper left viewport)***

Select objects: ***(select on the border of the upper right viewport)***

Select objects: ***(select on the border of the lower left viewport)***

Select objects: ↵

Switching to Model space

Finally, you will set the viewport visibility for layer DIM_TOP.

?/Freeze/Thaw/Reset/Newfrz/Vpvisdflt: **F** ↵

Layer(s) to Freeze: **DIM_TOP** ↵

All/Select/<Current>: **S** ↵

Switching to Paper space.

Select objects: ***(select on the border line of the lower left viewport)***

Select objects: ***(select on the border of the upper right viewport)***

Select objects: ***(select on the border of the lower right viewport)***

Select objects: ↵

Switching to Model space

?/Freeze/Thaw/Reset/Newfrz/Vpvisdflt: ↵

Pressing ↵ at the VPLAYER command prompt ends the command. You return to the "Command:" prompt.

Using a Dimension Style

You will set the previously created dimension style STANDARD as the current style and set the dimension variables for it so that your dimensions appear correctly in the drawing. STANDARD is set so that the dimension variables are automatically scaled by AutoCAD to adjust for the ZOOM scaling factor for paper space. This way, the dimensions will be sized correctly on your plotted drawing. (Example: to produce an arrowhead of 1/8" on the plot in a drawing where the object is scaled to half size relative to paper space in the viewport, the actual arrowhead needs to be twice the size, or 1/4" in model space.) AutoCAD adjusts the sizes of dimension features so that the size you specify in the dialogue box is what you get in paper space when paper space scaling is selected.

Pick: **DDIM *(toolbox)***

The Dimension Styles dialogue box appears on your screen. The style name STANDARD should be highlighted in the list of styles.

Pick: **Features**

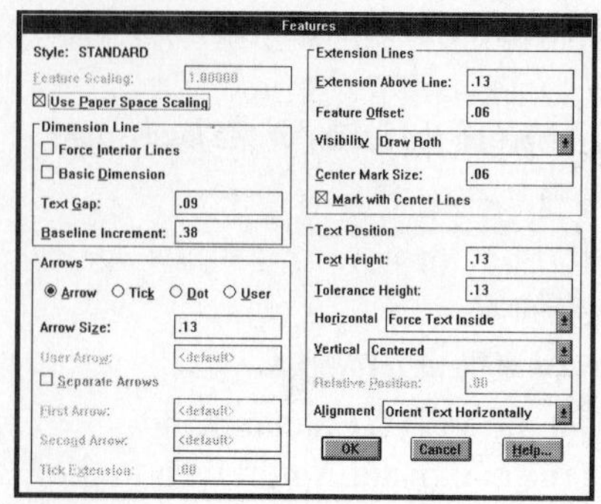

Figure 13.12

You will use the Features dialogue box to check the settings controlling the appearance of the dimensions. Refer to Figure 13.12 for the settings you will make in the Features dialogue box. Settings in the dialogue boxes are affected by the number of decimal places you select using the UNITS command. The size of the arrowhead has been rounded by AutoCAD to .13 because the units are set to two decimal places. The accuracy for coordinate values that you type in using more decimal places is maintained within the drawing database, but this is not true for the dimension styles. These values are rounded up. The Text Height and Extension Above Line settings are also .13. Under the heading Text Position, check to see that Force Text Inside is selected and make sure that Alignment is set to Orient Text Horizontally.

Pick: ***OK (to exit the Features dialogue box)***

You return to the Dimension Styles dialogue box.

> ■ ***TIP*** The amount of variation in the text and arrow sizes caused by rounding is usually not significant, but you may encounter problems if you set the decimal places to zero, as is common when working with metric drawings. Text sizes that were smaller than .5 will become zero. Selecting Use Paper Space Scaling will not adjust these zero values. ■

Pick: **Text Format**

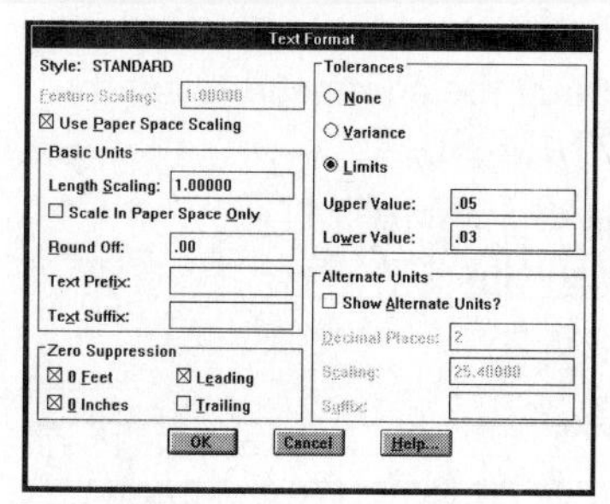

Figure 13.13

You will use the Text Format dialogue box to set up limit tolerances for the dimensions. In the Tolerances area of the dialogue box,

Pick: ***(the radio button to the left of Limits)***

When you have made this selection, the Upper and Lower Value selections turn from gray to black, indicating that they are available for you to enter the upper and lower tolerance values.

Pick: ***(highlight the text for Upper Value)***

Type: **.05**

Pick: ***(highlight the text for Lower Value)***

Type: **.03**

Continue to set the Text Format for the dimension style STANDARD. Refer to Figure 13.13 for the appropriate settings. When you are finished setting the tolerance limits,

Pick: ***OK (to exit the Text Format dialogue box)***

Pick: ***OK (to exit the Dimension Styles dialogue box)***

Before you can add dimensions to the front view, you must restore the coordinates that are parallel to the front view with the UCS, Restore command. You will pick the named UCS that was previously created for the front view by using the Settings, UCS, Named UCS. . . selection from the menu bar:

Pick: **Settings *(menu bar)*, UCS, Named UCS**

The UCS Control dialogue box appears on your screen, as shown in Figure 13.14. The User Coordinate Systems that were previously created for this drawing (from the prototype) appear in the list.

Pick: **FRONT**

Pick: **Current**

Pick: ***OK (to exit the dialogue box)***

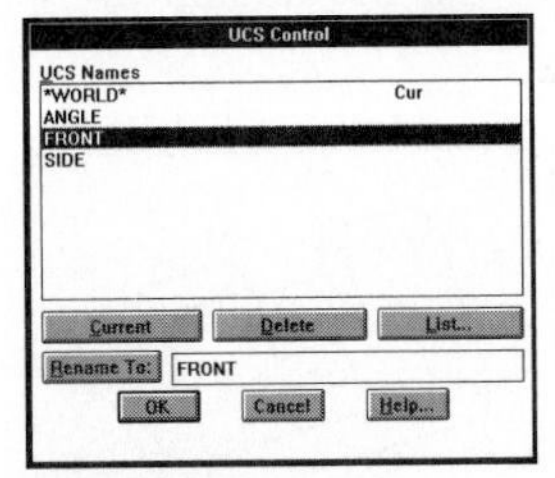

Figure 13.14

Now you are ready to add the dimensions for the front view.

On your own, be sure that DIM_FRONT is the current layer. Activate SNAP if the word Snap is not currently displayed on the toolbar.

Pick: **Draw *(menu bar)*, Dimensions, Linear, Horizontal**

First extension line origin or RETURN to select: (↵)

Select line, arc or circle: ***(pick the bottom line of the front view of the object in the lower left viewport)***

Dimension line location (Text/Angle): ***(pick a point one snap unit (.5) below the bottom line of the front view)***

Dimension text <3.00>: (↵)

The dimension for the overall width of the object should appear in your drawing, with the limit tolerances. Refer to Figure 13.15.

> ■ ***TIP*** You may have to toggle SNAP off in order to accurately pick the line. Toggle it back on when you are finished. ■

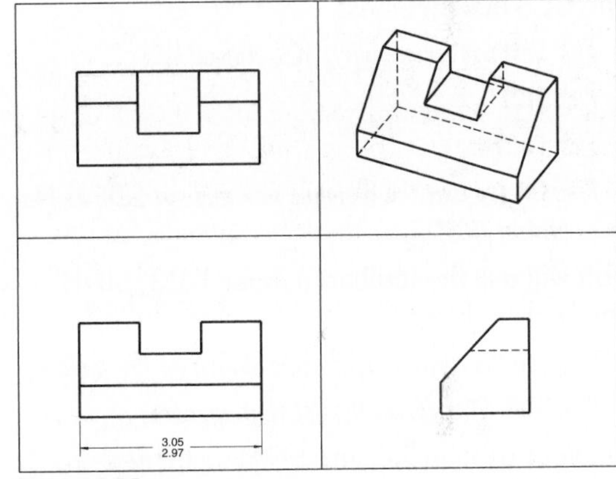

Figure 13.15

On your own, add the dimensions to the front view for the distance from the left edge of the object to the left edge of the slot and then from the same edge of the object to the right edge of the slot. Also, add the height of the slot to the front view. Refer to Figure 13.16.

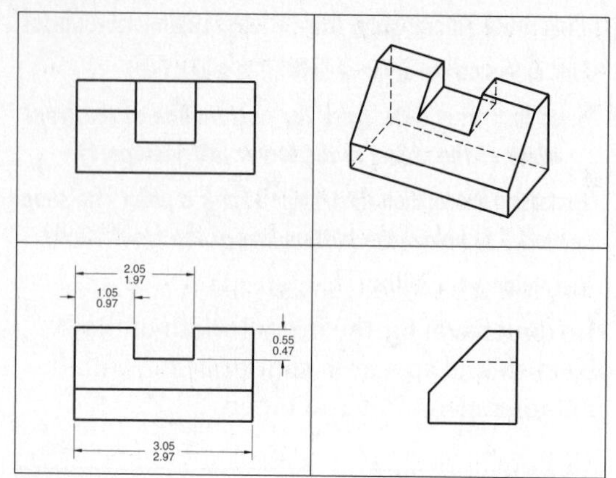

Figure 13.16

Before you add dimensions to the side view, you need to restore the UCS for the side view and make layer DIM_SIDE current. First use the UCS dialogue box,

Pick: **Settings *(menu bar)*, UCS, Named UCS. . .**

Pick: **SIDE**

Pick: **Current**

Pick: **OK *(to exit the dialogue box and set SIDE as the current UCS)***

You will use the toolbar to make DIM_SIDE the current layer.

Pick: ***(on the current layer name shown on the toolbar)***

Pick: **DIM_SIDE *(from the list that appears)***

On your own, make sure SNAP is turned on for this viewport by pressing (F9) or picking the letter S from the toolbar if it is not selected. Pick in the lower right-hand viewport to make it current.

Now you are ready to add dimensions to the side view.

Pick: **Draw *(menu bar)*, Dimensions, Linear, Vertical**

First extension line origin or RETURN to select: (↵)

Select line, arc or circle: ***(pick the right-hand vertical line in the side view of the object in the bottom right-hand viewport)***

Dimension line location (Text/Angle): ***(pick a point one snap unit (.5) to the right of the right-most vertical line of the side view)***

Dimension text <1.50>: (↵)

The dimension should appear in your drawing, as shown in Figure 13.17.

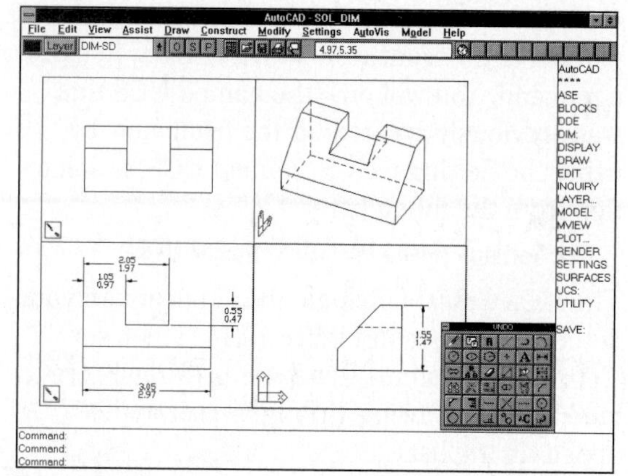

Figure 13.17

On your own, add the remaining linear dimensions for the side view. When you have completed this step, your drawing should appear similar to Figure 13.18.

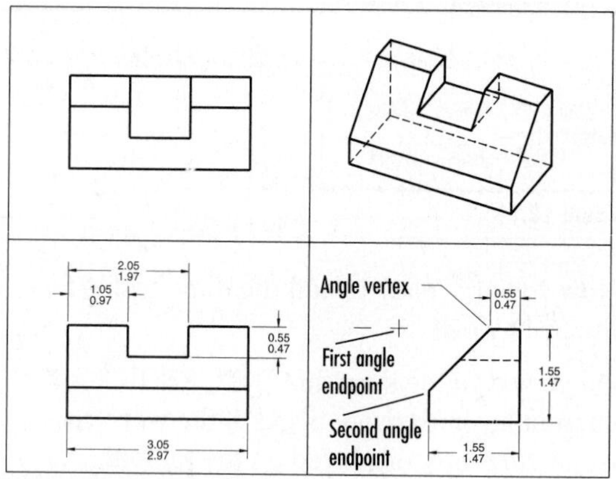

Figure 13.18

Adapting for Architecture

Many different layers can be used for dimensioning. By freezing certain dimension layers, you can create plots using the same drawing information and showing only the appropriate dimensions. Framing plans, roof plans, foundation plans, plumbing plans, and electrical plans all share the same basic outlines and information, but each needs to show the dimensions unique to its purpose. ■

Adding the Angular Dimension

For the angled dimension, you need to create a new dimension style. The current dimension style, STANDARD, has limit dimensioning set. This causes the upper and lower values to be printed for the angle, which is not what you want.

Pick: **DDIM *(toolbox)***

In the box for naming new dimension styles, type "ANGULAR" and press the ↵ key. ANGULAR appears highlighted in the list of dimension styles.

Pick: **Text Format...**

You will turn off limit tolerancing by selecting the radio button for None that appears in the Tolerances area of the Text Format dialogue.

Pick: ***(on the radio button for None)***

Pick: **OK *(to exit the Text Format dialogue box)***

Pick: **OK *(to exit the Dimension Styles and Variables dialogue box)***

Be sure that Ortho mode is not active. Now you are ready to add the angular dimension to the drawing.

Pick: **Draw *(menu bar)*, Dimensions, Angular**

Select arc, circle, line or RETURN: ↵

Angle vertex: ***(pick the indicated point in Figure 13.18)***

First angle endpoint: ***(pick the indicated point in Figure 13.18)***

Second angle endpoint: ***(pick the indicated point in Figure 13.18)***

Dimension arc line location (Text/Angle): ***(pick a point one snap unit to the left of the object in the side view)***

Dimension text <45>: **45%%d%%p1%%d** ↵

Enter text location (or RETURN): ***(press F9 to turn SNAP off and pick a point midway along the dimension line arc)***

Your finished drawing should appear similar to Figure 13.19.

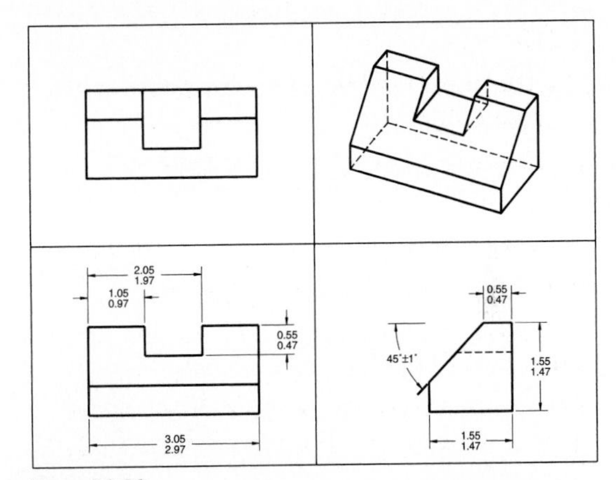

Figure 13.19

On your own, save and plot your drawing, using paper space and a scale of 1 to 1. Exit AutoCAD. You have completed this tutorial.

KEY TERMS

bilateral tolerances
limit tolerances
plus/minus tolerances
unilateral tolerances
variance tolerances

KEY COMMANDS

New Text

EXERCISES

Directions: Draw the necessary views and dimension the following shapes. Include tolerances if indicated. Use either solid modeling techniques or 2D orthographic views.

13.1 Stop Base

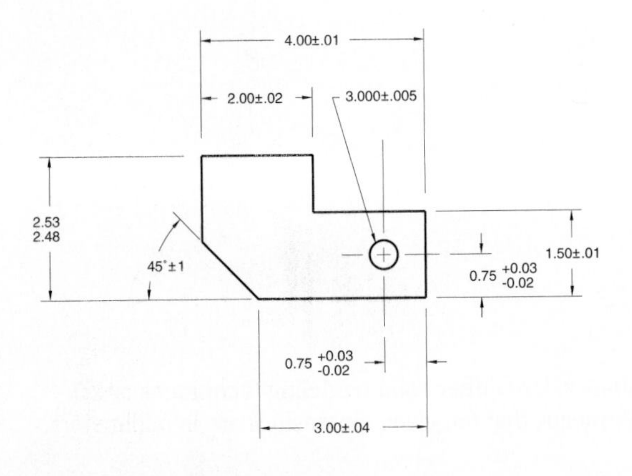

13.2 Lathe Stop

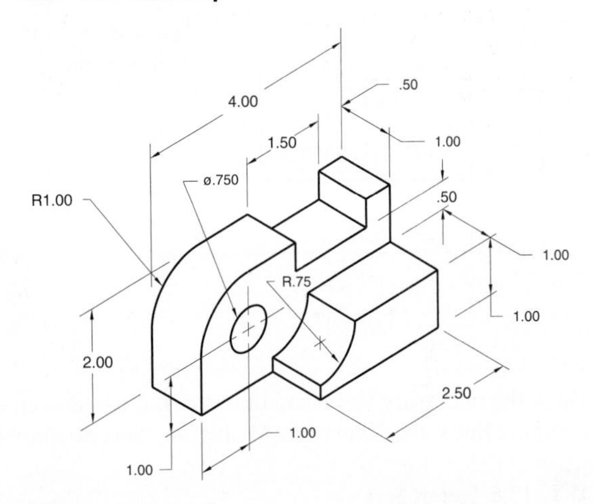

13.3M Vee Block

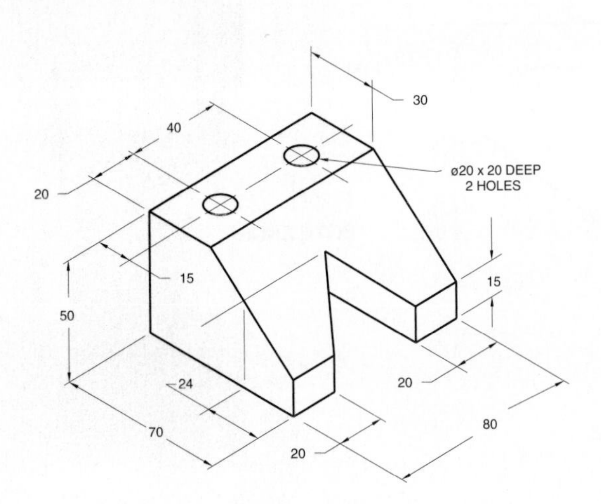

13.4M Mill Tool

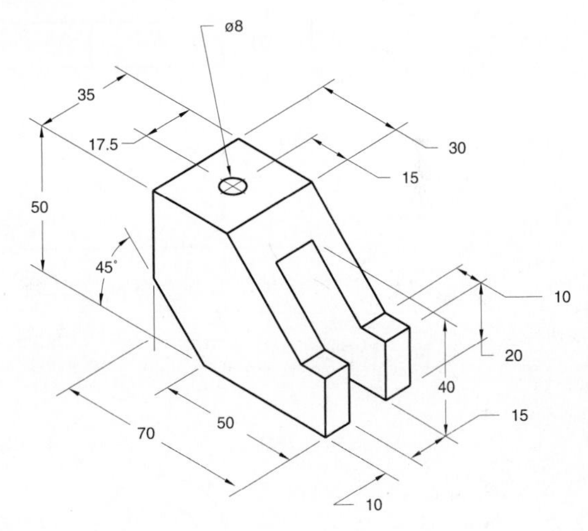

13.5 Tolerance Problem

Calculate the maximum and minimum clearance between parts A and B and Part C as shown.

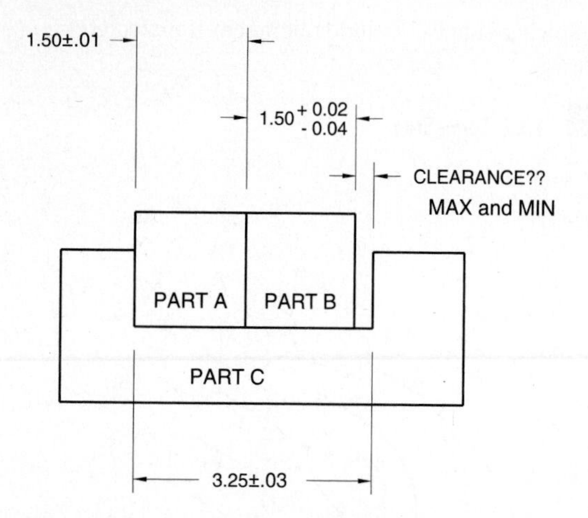

Draw the necessary views and dimension the following shapes. Use either solid modeling techniques or 2D orthographic views. The letter M after an exercise number means that the given dimensions are in millimeters.

13.6 Support Base

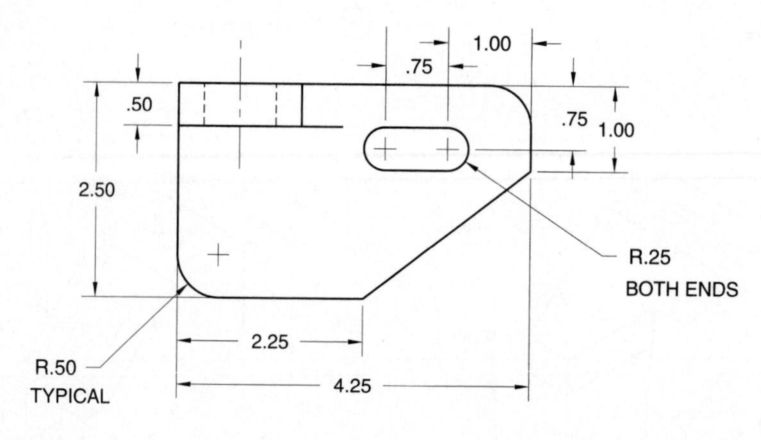

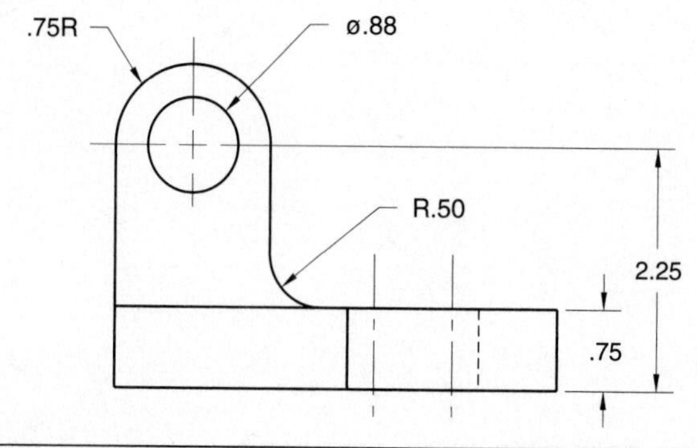

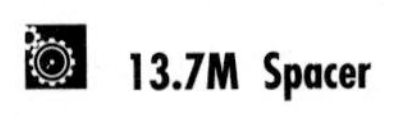

13.7M Spacer

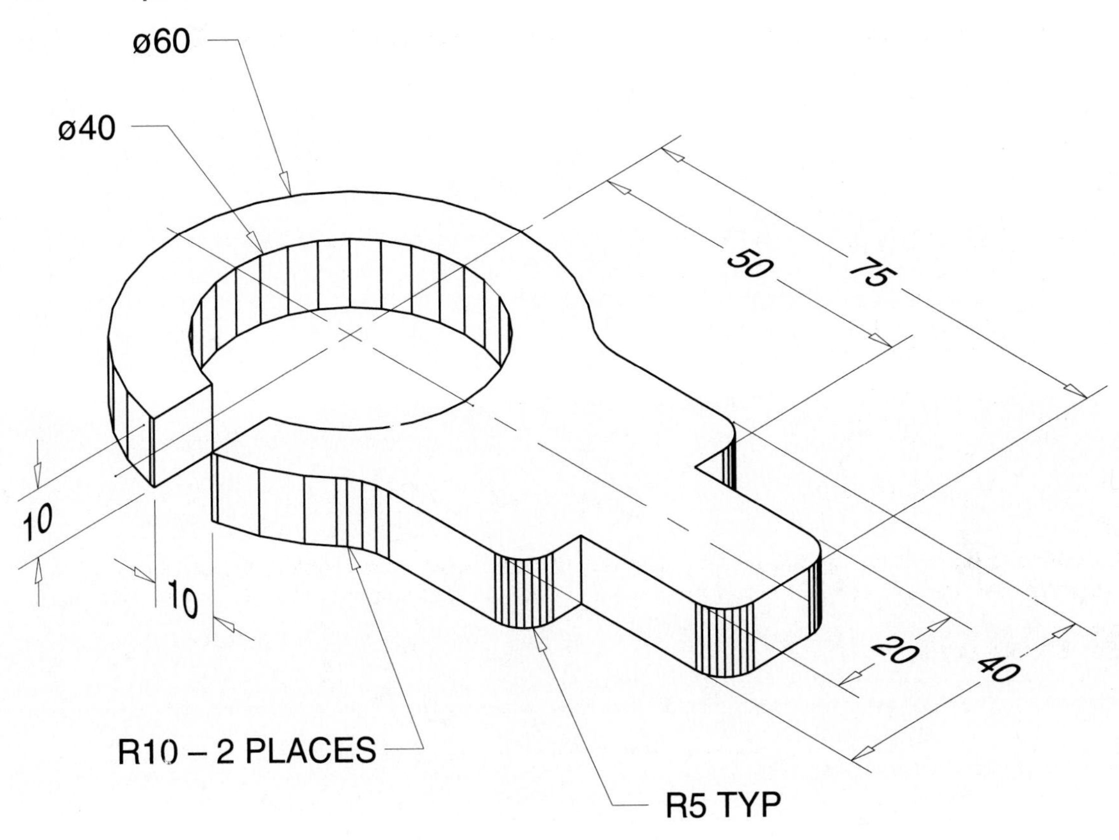
ø60
ø40
50
75
10
10
20
40
R10 – 2 PLACES
R5 TYP

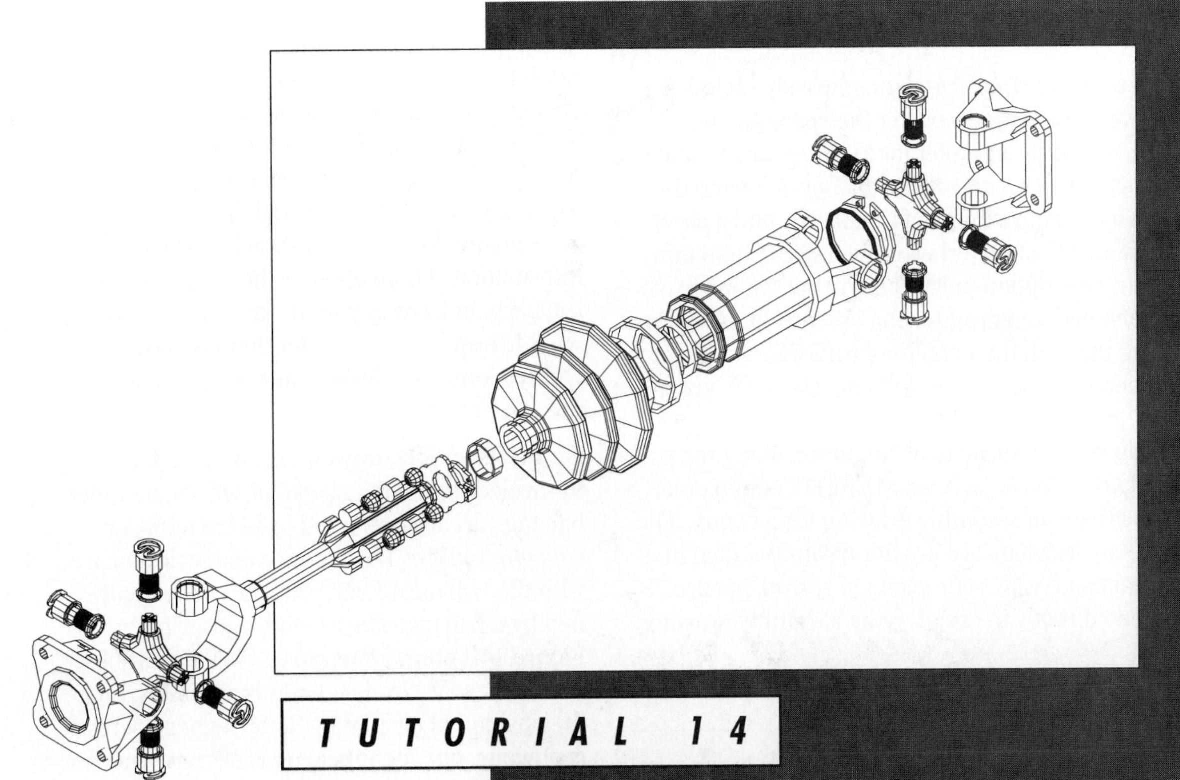

TUTORIAL 14

Working Drawings

Objectives

When you have finished this tutorial, you will be able to

1. Create 2D assembly drawings from a set of detail drawings.
2. Cut and paste between multiple AutoCAD sessions.
3. Use the BLOCK, WBLOCK, and INSERT commands.
4. Make blocks with attributes.
5. Use DDATTE to change attribute values.
6. Use Dynamic Data Exchange to export attributes to a spreadsheet program.
7. Paste text from a spreadsheet into an AutoCAD drawing.

Introduction

A set of *working drawings* generally includes *detail drawings* (showing the shape, material, dimensions, and tolerances necessary to make each part), an *assembly drawing* (showing the assembled positions of the parts), and a *parts list*, or bill of materials (showing the item number, description, material, and part number of each part required for the assembly). In working through the preceding tutorials, you have been developing the skills necessary to create detail and assembly drawings. In this tutorial you will use these skills together, using the BLOCK, WBLOCK, and INSERT commands, to create an assembly drawing for a clamp. The detail drawings are provided with the data files that came with your package so you can proceed directly to creating the assembly drawing.

Assembly Drawings

Figure 14.1 shows an assembly drawing for a clamp.

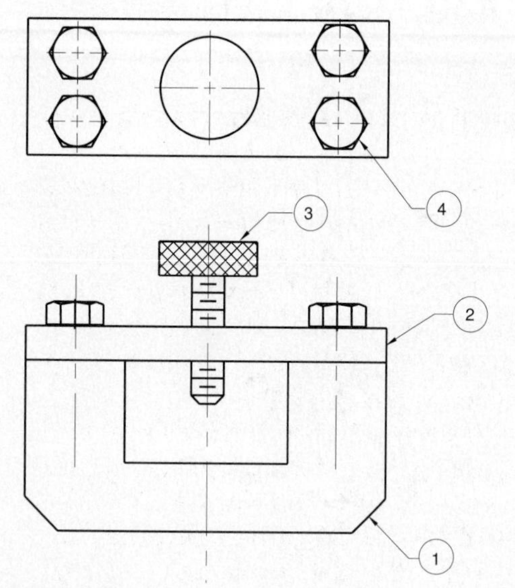

Figure 14.1

Assembly drawings usually show parts in their assembled positions. Note that there are no hidden lines. Hidden lines do not need to be shown unless they add to the clarity of the assembly drawing. It is not necessary to completely describe the shape of each part in the assembly drawing. The detail drawings that accompany the assembly drawing provide that information. Think about it this way: if you had the parts in front of you, the assembly drawing would show you how to put them together. Dimensions and hidden lines are not usually necessary for this purpose.

On the assembly drawing, parts are identified by circled numbers called *ball tags*. Sometimes ball tags are also referred to as balloons, or *balloon numbers*. Leader lines connect the parts with the ball tags. Each part should be identified by a ball tag. The assembly drawing in Figure 14.1 shows four parts. Part 4 identifies the hexhead screw used in this assembly. Since the position of each of the four hexhead screws is obvious, one identification is all that is necessary. If the drawing showed more than one type of screw, each would have to be identified.

The knurled adjusting screw, Part 3, is shown inserted halfway into the object. In general, parts are shown in neutral positions and not in extreme closed or open positions. Bolts and nuts are usually shown fully inserted. The assembly drawing should make the relationships among the parts clear, and try to suggest the function of the part, not necessarily show the entire shape of the part. A single view is often all that is necessary. Sectioning, including *partial* or *broken-out* sections, is also often used, as it can show very effectively how the parts fit together, where hidden lines would be confusing.

Figure 14.2 shows an *exploded view* of the clamp assembly that you will work with in this tutorial. An exploded view is usually an isometric drawing that shows an assembly taken apart, but with each part still in line with its assembled position.

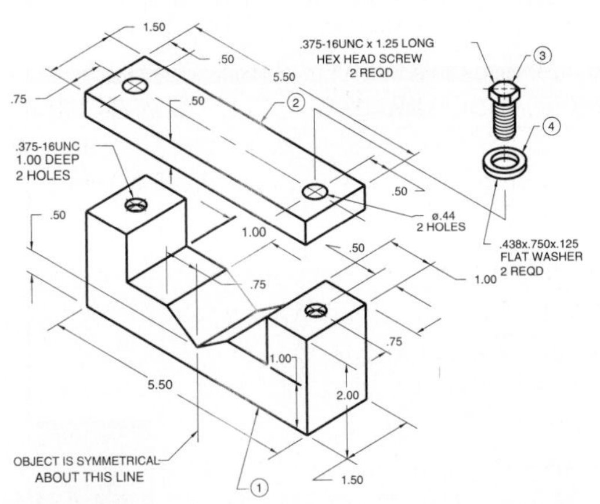

Figure 14.2

For your set of working drawings, you will create the assembly drawing first and then the parts list.

Adapting for Architecture

Architectural working drawings differ from their engineering counterparts in many ways. Architectural drawings are generally broken into four categories: architectural, structural, mechanical, and electrical. Within these categories are plans, sections, elevations, details, and schedules for doors, windows, lights, and other components of a building system. Architectural working drawings begin by showing the overall building in plan, section, and elevation, and then develop specific construction methods through details. Architectural specifications, which are generally created on a word processor, are used to generate the final appearance of a building, including paints, brick types, appliances, and all of the other finish elements of a building. ■

Using the Windows Clipboard to Create an Assembly Drawing

In preparing a set of working drawings, you could create the part drawings first and then make the assembly drawing. You can use AutoCAD for Windows to *paste* the part drawings into the assembly drawing. Or, if you are designing an assembly, you might want to work on sizing the part drawings in the assembly so that you can see how the parts fit together with mating parts. You could then export the parts into separate drawings to which you would add the necessary dimensions and tolerances. In Tutorials 1–13 you learned the commands necessary to describe the size and shape of the part for a detail drawing. For this assembly drawing, two part drawings have been provided. They are CLMPBASE and CLMP-TOP. You will use the Windows clipboard to copy the part from the part drawing and paste it into the assembly drawing.

■ ***Warning:*** To cut and paste between drawings you will need to open multiple sessions of AutoCAD running under Windows. It is recommended that you have at least 8 MB of memory to run one AutoCAD session and 4.5 MB for each additional session, for up to three sessions. You may notice that your computer takes more time to perform operations when you have more than one AutoCAD session running. If you cannot open a second AutoCAD session to do the next part of the tutorial, you can still use AutoCAD's BLOCK, WBLOCK, and INSERT commands to insert the part drawing into the assembly, as explained later in this tutorial. ■

Starting

Start AutoCAD from the Autodesk Collection Interface as instructed in Chapter 3. AutoCAD's drawing editor should be on your display screen. You will use the File selection from the toolbar to open the existing drawing called CLMPBASE.

Pick: **Folder icon *(toolbar)***

In the Open File dialogue box, select the file CLMPBASE, which is provided with the data files. If necessary, select the drive and directory from the dialogue box.

Pick: **CLMPBASE**

Pick: **OK *(to exit the dialogue box)***

The AutoCAD drawing editor should return to your screen. The dimensioned detail drawing of the clamp base should be displayed in the drawing area. Your screen should look similar to Figure 14.3.

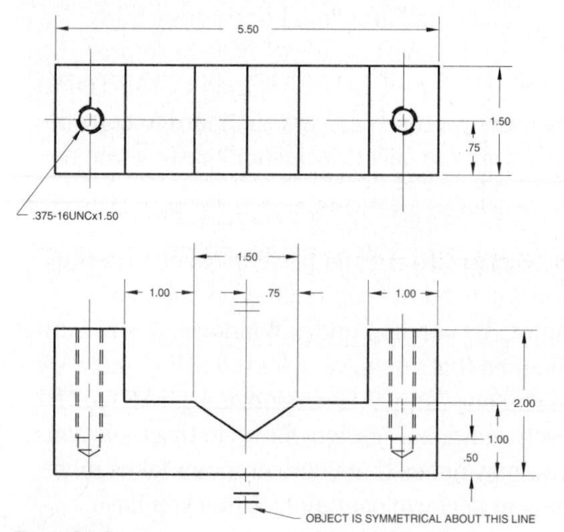

Figure 14.3

On your own, use the commands you have learned to freeze layer DIM so that the dimensions do not appear on the screen. Erase the top view of the clamp base. Use SAVEAS to save your drawing in the DRAWINGS directory with the name ASSEMBLY. When you have finished, your drawing will look like Figure 14.4.

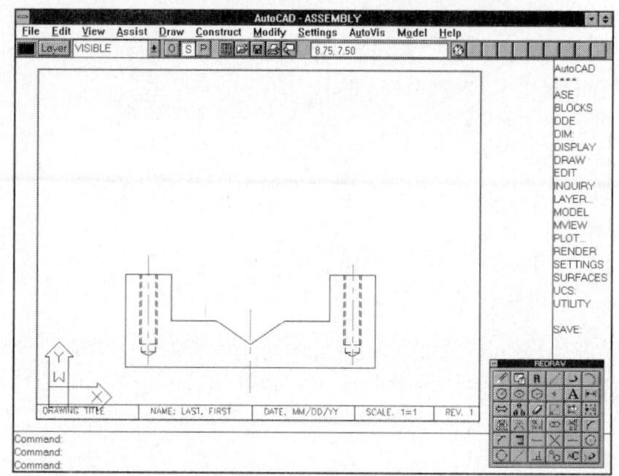

Figure 14.4

Next you will start a second session of AutoCAD and open the drawing CLMP-TOP. Then you will copy the front view of the clamp top to the Windows clipboard so that it can be pasted into the assembly drawing. Before you start another AutoCAD session, you will make the current session smaller so that there is room on your screen.

Resizing the Current Window

To resize the current session, move the cursor near one of the corners of the window that is running AutoCAD until you see a double arrow replacing the regular cursor. Press the pick button and drag the window to the new size. Make your new window fill about half of the screen.

Starting a Second AutoCAD Session

To bring the Program Manager to the front,

Pick: ***(outside the AutoCAD window or press ALT and ESC at the same time until you see the Program Manager or its icon)***

To start a new session of AutoCAD, double-click on the Program Manager icon and open the AutoCAD program group if necessary. Then,

Pick: ***(double-click on the AutoCAD program icon)***

A new AutoCAD session opens. The number 2 appears in the title bar, so that you can tell it from the previous session. Some commands, such as Dynamic Data Exchange, can only be used in the session that was opened first.

On your own, use the techniques you have learned to resize both windows running AutoCAD so that each fills about half of the screen. Open the drawing CLMP-TOP in the second session. Freeze the DIM layer. With this layer frozen, it will be easier to select the objects you want to copy. When you are finished, your screen should look like Figure 14.5.

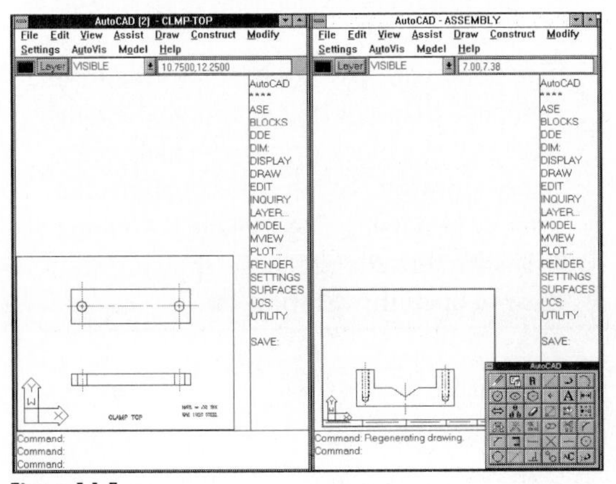

Figure 14.5

Copying to the Windows Clipboard

Using the Windows clipboard, you can copy *images* (bitmaps) or vectors (which are used in AutoCAD and other engineering drawing and graphing programs). You can also use Windows embedding and linking to place AutoCAD graphics in other programs.

■ **TIP** AutoCAD acts as a *server* program for linking and embedding. You may want to try embedding AutoCAD drawings in your Windows word processing programs to create engineering reports or other desktop-published documents. In Windows programs that provide support for *object linking and embedding* as a *client* application, double-clicking on the AutoCAD drawing embedded or linked inside the other application automatically starts AutoCAD and opens that drawing for editing. Unfortunately, AutoCAD does not act as a client application for programs such as Windows spreadsheets and word processors. However, you can still paste images from other applications into AutoCAD. Later in the tutorial, you will learn how you can use Dynamic Data Exchange to access spreadsheet information in AutoCAD, if DDE is supported by your spreadsheet. ■

Using the Copy Vectors option from the Edit menu bar selection to copy the front view of the clamp top to the Windows clipboard allows you to paste the selected items into your other AutoCAD drawing, so that the lines, arc, and other entities are still defined as such. Using the Copy Image selection results in a bitmap, which cannot be edited using AutoCAD.

Pick: **Edit** ***(menu bar),*** **Copy Vectors**

Select objects: ***(use implied windowing to select the front view of the clamp top)***

Select objects: ↵

The entities that you selected are now contained in the Windows clipboard. Now they can be pasted into the assembly drawing.

Pasting from the Clipboard

To make the first AutoCAD session active,

Pick: ***(inside the window running the original AutoCAD session showing drawing ASSEMBLY)***

Pick: **Edit** ***(menu bar),*** **Paste**

The entities that you copied to the clipboard appear grouped together and attached to the crosshairs. You can move them around the screen as you move the crosshairs. Move the crosshairs so that the clamp top is above the clamp base; then,

Block name (or ?): ACADDE66

Insertion point: ***(pick a location for the clamp top above the clamp base)***

X scale factor <1>/Corner/XYZ: ↵

Y scale factor (default = X): ↵

Rotation angle <0>: ↵

The copied entities appear in the assembly drawing.

On your own, use the MOVE command with the INTERSECTION Osnap override picked from the toolbox to move the clamp top into position, as shown in Figure 14.6.

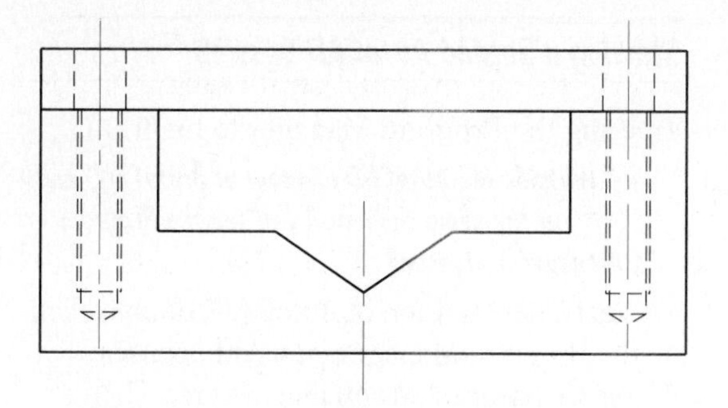

Figure 14.6

■ ***TIP*** You can use the BASE command to change the point that will be selected as the base point when pasting vectors into another AutoCAD drawing. The coordinates 0,0 are used as the base point if no others are specified. This is why the clamp top was attached to the crosshairs at its lower left-hand corner when you pasted it into the assembly drawing. To use BASE, type it at the command prompt as follows:

Command: **BASE** ↵

Base point <0.0000,0.0000,0.0000>: ***(from the drawing, pick the new point that you want to act as the base point)***

The point you selected becomes the insertion base point for that drawing when it is inserted as a block or an externally referenced drawing. To have this change take effect when using Copy Vectors, you must first save this change to the drawing and then re-open the drawing. ■

Next you will minimize session 2 of AutoCAD and enlarge the original session so that it once again fills your screen.

Pick: ***(anywhere on AutoCAD session 2 to make it active)***

Pick: ***(the minimize icon [down arrow] on the title bar of AutoCAD session 2)***

Pick: ***(the up arrow in the upper right corner of the original session to maximize it)***

On your own, use ZOOM, Window to enlarge the drawing so that it fills the screen. Refer to Figure 14.2, the exploded assembly view of the clamp. The next items that you need to create for the assembly drawing are the washer and the .375 hexhead screw. These are stock parts that would usually be purchased, rather than manufactured specifically for the particular assembly. You might want to build a block library of these standard parts; however, they can often be ordered from third-party sources. There are many third-party vendors that offer disks of standard shapes saved in block form. A library of blocks can be created and used for all the standard parts needed for any application. In this tutorial, you will use blocks for the washer and the hexhead screw.

Using BLOCK

A block is a set of entities grouped together into a compound object or symbol. You define a block from a set of objects in your current drawing. You specify the block name and then select the entities you want to be part of the block. The *block name* is used whenever you insert the group of entities into the drawing. Each insertion of the block into the drawing, the *block reference*, can have different scale factors and rotation. A block is treated as a single object by AutoCAD; you select the block for use with commands like MOVE or ERASE simply by pointing to any entity within the block. Entities that are copied to the Windows clipboard as vectors are inserted as blocks when pasted into the new drawing.

There are many advantages to using blocks. A drawing can be constructed by assembling blocks that consist of small details. Drawing entities that appear often can be drawn once and then inserted, rather than being drawn in repeatedly. Inserting blocks rather than copying basic entities results in smaller drawing files, saving time in loading and regenerating drawings.

A block can be composed of entities that were drawn on several layers, with several colors and linetypes. The layer, color, and linetype information of these entities is preserved in the block. Upon insertion, each entity is drawn on its original layer, with its original color and linetype, no matter what the current drawing layer, entity color, and entity linetype happen to be. There are three exceptions to this rule:

1. Entities that were drawn on Layer 0 are generated on the current layer when the block is inserted and take on the characteristics of that layer.
2. Entities that were drawn with color BYBLOCK inherit the color of the block (either a specified color or BYLAYER).
3. Entities that were drawn with linetype BYBLOCK inherit the linetype of the block (either a specified linetype or BYLAYER).

■ ***TIP*** Block names used in a drawing can be up to 31 characters long and can contain letters, digits, and the special characters $ (dollar sign), - (hyphen), and _ (underscore). AutoCAD converts any letters to uppercase. If a block with the name already exists, AutoCAD prompts you that the name already exists. In this case, you can either exit without changing so that you do not lose the original block, or you can choose to redefine the block. ■

■ ***Warning:*** Blocks defined using the BLOCK command are stored only in the current drawing and can be inserted only into the drawing in which they were created. To save a block so that it can be transferred to another drawing, use the WBLOCK command after you have created the block or use the Windows clipboard with Copy Vector, as you have seen in the previous example. The WBLOCK command writes the block definition to a disk file as a separate drawing file with the extension .DWG. ■

In the assembly drawing, you will create a block to use for the washer.

Drawing the Washer

If needed, pick inside the AutoCAD session where drawing ASSEMBLY is loaded to make it active. Be sure that layer VISIBLE is the current drawing layer. If it is not, set it as the current layer.

You will draw the washer in the front view, where the washer will appear rectangular. You need only draw one. Then you can use the BLOCK command to make a block that you can insert as many times as necessary.

Pick: **LINE *(toolbox)***

LINE From point: ***(pick any point 1" or more to the left of the assembly)***

To point: **@.75<0** (↵)

To point: **@.125<90** (↵)

To point: **@.75<180** (↵)

To point: **C** (↵)

Figure 14.7 shows the completed washer.

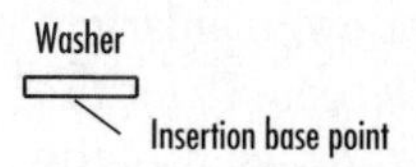

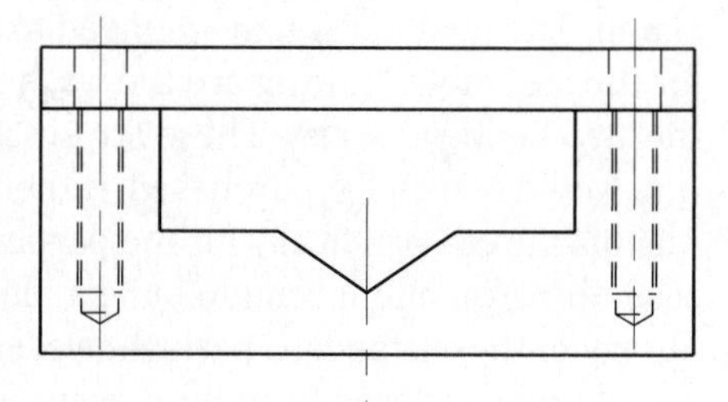

Figure 14.7

Pick: **BLOCKS *(screen menu)*, BLOCK**

Block name (or ?): **WASHER** (↵)

Insertion base point: **MID** (↵)

of ***(target the bottom line of the washer to select its midpoint)***

Select objects: ***(select the lines that make up the washer)***

Select objects: (↵)

The washer you drew disappears from the drawing. Because entities selected with the BLOCK command are removed from the screen automatically with AutoCAD's ERASE command, they can be brought back by using the OOPS command. However, you will not use OOPS to bring the washer back, because you drew it off to the side and do not want it located there.

Using INSERT

The INSERT command is used to insert blocks or other drawings into your drawing. Using the INSERT command, you specify the insertion point (the location for the base point you picked when you created the block), the scale, and the rotation for the block. A selection of 1 for the scale causes the block to remain the original size. The scale factors for the X, Y, and Z directions do not have to be the same. Using the same size, however, ensures that the inserted block has the same proportions, or aspect ratio, as the original. A rotation of 0 degrees ensures the same orientation as the original. The DDINSERT command, which displays a dialogue box, can be started from the menu bar by picking Draw, Insert. You can also use the INSERT command without a dialogue box by picking BLOCKS, INSERT from the screen menu.

You will select Draw, Insert from the menu bar to use the dialogue box to insert the washer into the assembly.

Pick: **Draw *(menu bar)*, Insert. . .**

The Insert dialogue box appears on your screen, as shown in Figure 14.8.

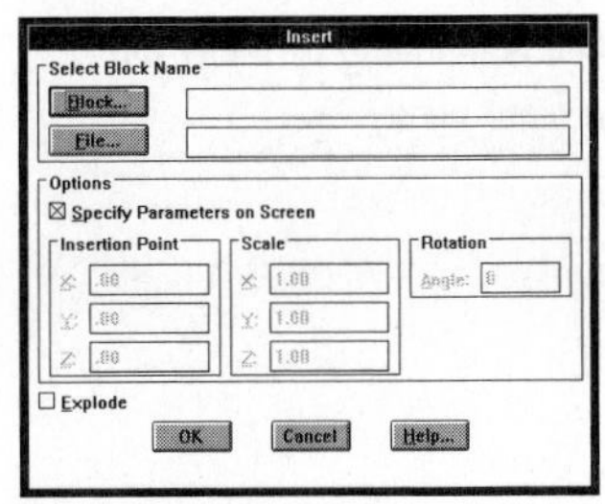

Figure 14.8

Select the Block. . . button from the dialogue box to bring up another dialogue box, which lets you select from the blocks that are defined in your drawing. The Blocks Defined in this Drawing dialogue box looks like Figure 14.9.

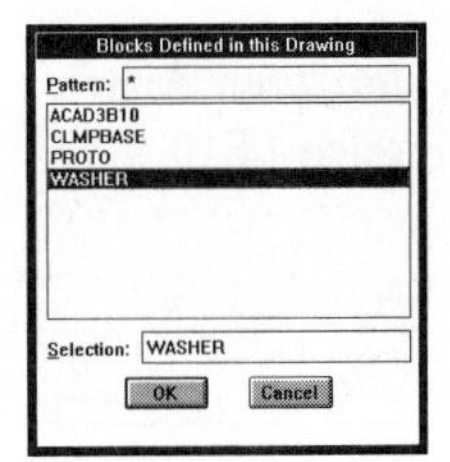

Figure 14.9

Pick: **WASHER *(the block you created in the previous step)***

Pick: **OK**

You return to the Insert dialogue box. Make sure that the box to the left of Specify Parameters on Screen has an X in it. To exit the dialogue box and begin specifying the insertion parameters on screen,

Pick: **OK**

The washer appears, attached to the crosshairs by its bottom midpoint, the insertion point you specified. Continuing with the Insert command,

Insertion point: **INT** ↵

of ***(target the intersection of the left center line with the top line of the clamp top)***

X scale factor <1>/Corner/XYZ: ↵

Y scale factor (default = X): ↵

Rotation angle <0>: ↵

> ■ ***TIP*** You can use ZOOM, Window in order to pick points more easily. ■

The washer should appear on the left side of the assembly.

On your own, use Insert to repeat this process, selecting the insertion point on the right side; or mirror the washer to the right side of the assembly.

When you are done with this step, your drawing should appear similar to Figure 14.10.

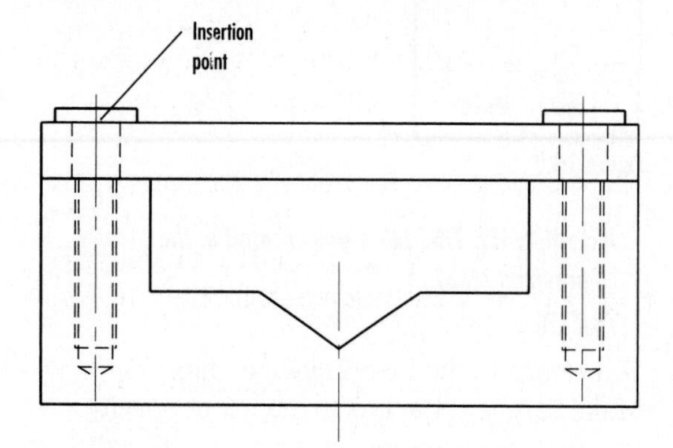

Figure 14.10

Adapting for Architecture

Use of blocks is the single most important feature in AutoCAD for automating drawing tasks. Any common feature of a building should be made a block for repeat insertion. Common blocks are door and window symbols, trees, typical wall sections, common fixtures and appliances, and there are many others. Develop an extensive block list of every symbol you make for a drawing, and soon you will find that creating a set of working drawings is as easy as cutting and pasting the various elements together. ■

Next you will maximize the second session of AutoCAD, and open the drawing HEXHEAD (provided with the data files) and create a block from the front view of the hexhead screw.

Press: (ALT)-(ESC) ***(until you see the minimized AutoCAD session 2 icon)***

Pick: ***(double-click on the minimized AutoCAD session 2 icon)***

Pick: ***(the up arrow on the title bar, so that session 2 fills the entire screen)***

Now that you have maximized session 2, you will use it to open the file HEXHEAD and make a block from the front view of the hexhead bolt.

Pick: **File *(menu bar)*, Open**

Pick: **HEXHEAD**

Pick: **OK**

Drawing HEXHEAD, showing a top and front view of a hexhead screw, should appear on the screen, as shown in Figure 14.11. Next, create the block for the front view of the hexhead screws. You do not need the top view because the assembly drawing will be a single view.

Pick: **Construct *(screen menu)*, Block**

Block name (or ?): **HEXFRNT** (↵)

Insertion base point: **INT** (↵)

of ***(pick the intersection shown as Base point in Figure 14.11)***

Select objects: ***(use implied windowing to select all of the objects in the front view)***

Select objects: (↵)

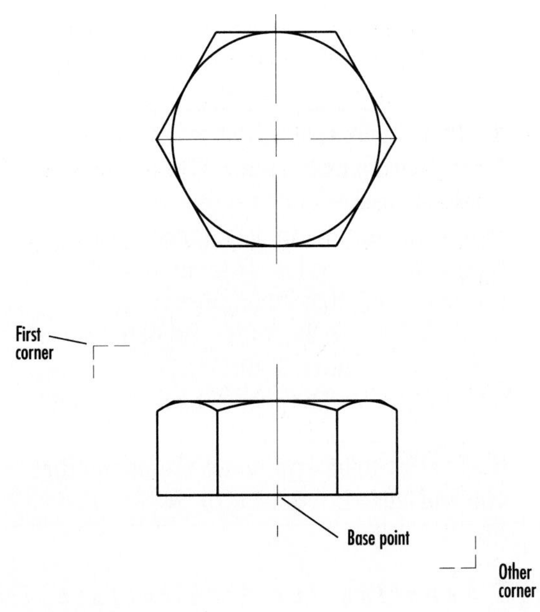

Figure 14.11

The entities that were selected as part of the block are erased from the screen. In order to have these entities remain in the detail drawing, select the OOPS command from the standard screen menu to restore the entities.

Pick: **OOPS *(screen)***

The entities from the block are restored in your drawing.

> ■ ***TIP*** Remember, OOPS can be used to restore only the last entities that were erased in your drawing. ■

Using WBLOCK

The block you just created is defined only in the current drawing. You must use the WBLOCK command to make this block into a separate drawing so that it is available for use in other drawings. The WBLOCK command creates a separate AutoCAD drawing file of the block.

The drawing file made with the WBLOCK command is the same as any other drawing file. It can be called up and edited like any other drawing you have created. Because any drawing can be used as a block and inserted into any other drawing, this is a very powerful feature in creating assembly and other drawings.

When using WBLOCK you are first prompted for the name to which the file will be written. The second prompt asks for the name of the block. The WBLOCK command allows you to specify the name of the block for use in other drawings four ways:

1. Type the name of a block you have previously created in the current drawing and press the ↵ key. The entities composing the specified block are written to the file name you specified.
2. Type the equal sign (=) and press the ↵ key. This is a shortcut you can use when the block you previously created has the same name as the wblock file you specified.
3. Type an asterisk (*) and press the ↵ key. This saves the entire drawing to the name specified as the file name (as does the Save command), except that unused entities are eliminated.
4. Press the ↵ key. This null response is followed by prompts that allow you to specify the objects and the insertion base point, as in the BLOCK command prompts. The selected objects are written to the file name you specified and are deleted from the current drawing. You can use the OOPS command to retrieve them, if necessary.

You will use the WBLOCK command to write the block you created to a new file called HEX-FR.

Pick: **BLOCKS *(screen)*, WBLOCK**

If you have AutoCAD configured to use dialogue boxes for file operations (the default), the Create Drawing File dialogue box shown in Figure 14.12 appears on the screen.

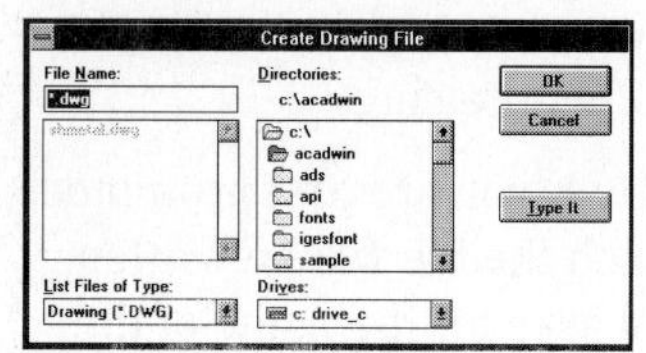

Figure 14.12

You will type the name for the file that will be created on the disk in the box to the right of File:. You do not need to include the file extension; the .DWG extension is automatically added. The name must have only eight characters to be a legal DOS file name. (You may want to select a directory for the new file to keep your hard drive organized.)

Type: **HEX-FR**

When you have finished,

Pick: **OK**

■ ***Warning:*** Do not give the wblock the same name as an existing drawing. If you do this, you will see the AutoCAD message, "The specified file already exists. Do you want to replace it?" Select No unless you are certain that you no longer want the old drawing file. ■

The next prompt is for the block name. Type in the name of the block you created previously that contained the front view of the clamp base.

Block name: **HEXFRNT** (↵)

The block you created, named HEXFRNT, is saved to the new file called HEX-FR.

■ ***TIP*** WBLOCK does not save views, User Coordinate Systems, viewport configurations, unreferenced symbols (including block definitions), unused layers, linetypes, and text styles. This can have the positive effect that it compresses your drawing file size by getting rid of unwanted overhead. Do not use the WBLOCK command with solid models, because the solid database may be destroyed; instead use the special solid write block command that you will learn in Tutorial 15. ■

Adapting for Architecture

Remember to use WBLOCK for all of the blocks that you develop that you want to share across many drawings. It is a good practice to put all of your block files in a separate directory, and to occasionally create and plot a drawing to refer to that includes all of a certain type of block symbols, along with their file names, so that you do not have to search for a certain block. You can insert this entire drawing, which can function as a block library, into the desired drawing, and then cancel the insertion after you pick the insertion point. This will insert all of the blocks into the block library drawing, so that they are available locally as blocks in the current drawing. ■

Next you will insert the front view of the hex-head screw into the assembly drawing. To activate the original AutoCAD session, use (ALT)-(ESC) on your own until you see the original session restored to your screen. Then,

Pick: ***(inside the original AutoCAD session window, where drawing ASSEMBLY is loaded)***

Inserting the Hexhead

■ ***TIP*** Frequently used symbols are often made based on a 1-unit dimension, because this makes it easy to calculate the scale factor at which to insert the block to produce a different size in the new drawing. An example is a standard hex head for a bolt. If you base the block on a nominal diameter of 1 unit, then you insert the block at a scale factor of .75 (or 3/4") to produce a 3/4" bolt. Drawing HEXHEAD showed two views of a hexhead screw, based on a nominal diameter of 1". Knowing the diameter of the original is 1" makes it easy to calculate the scale factor needed when inserting the hexhead screw. Of course, all parts may not be suitable for use with unit scaling. ■

Pick: **BLOCKS *(screen)*, INSERT**

INSERT Block name (or ?)<WASHER>: **HEX-FR** ↵

Block HEX-FR should appear attached to the crosshairs so that you can drag it into position.

Insertion point: ***(using OSNAP, Intersection, pick the point where the center line for the hole crosses the top line of the washer on the left)***

Insertion point: X scale factor <1>/Corner/XYZ: **.375** ↵

Y scale factor (default = X): ↵

Rotation angle <0>: ↵

Block HEX-FR should appear in your drawing. Refer to Figure 14.13. The center lines may not appear dashed. If necessary, you will use the LTSCALE command to scale the linetypes so that the lines appear correctly.

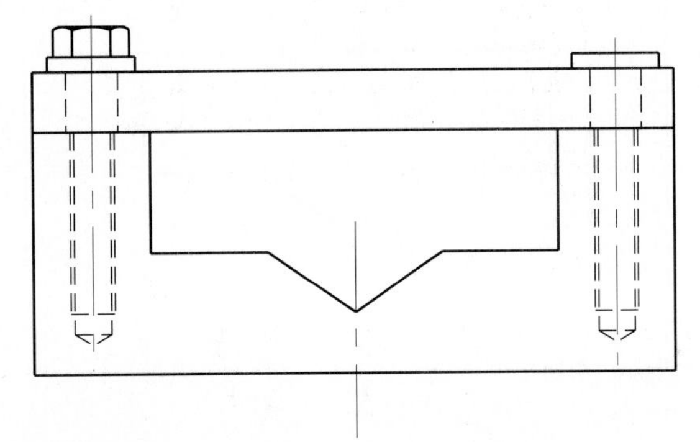

Figure 14.13

Pick: **SETTINGS *(screen)*, next, LTSCALE**

LTSCALE New scale factor <1.0000>: **.7** ↵

The center and hidden lines now have shorter dashes on your screen.

Use the COPY command to copy the hexhead to the other side of the assembly.

Pick: **EDIT *(screen)*, COPY**

Select objects: ***(pick on the hexhead block)***

Select objects: ↵

<Base point of displacement>/ Multiple: **INT** ↵

of ***(target the intersection of the center line with the top line of the washer on the left)***

Second point: **INT** ↵

of ***(target the same point on the right washer)***

You have completed the assembly drawing. Refer to Figure 14.14.

Save your drawing on your own at this point.

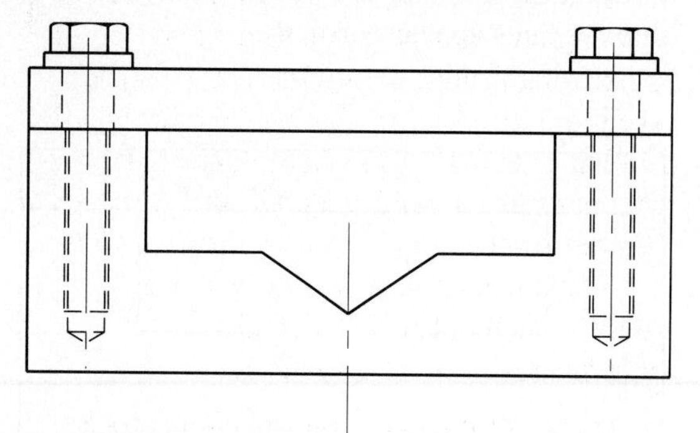

Figure 14.14

Freezing the Hidden Line Layers

You will use the Layer Control dialogue to freeze the layers that use hidden lines.

Pick: **Layer *(toolbar)***

Use the Layer Control dialogue box that appears on your screen to select layer HIDDEN and Freeze it. When you are done, pick OK to exit the dialogue box.

Now remove the center line from the base of the clamp on your own. It shows the symmetry of the object for dimensioning, but is not necessary for the assembly drawing.

Next you will use the EXPLODE command to change the block for the clamp top back into individual entities in the drawing.

Using EXPLODE

AutoCAD treats blocks as single entities. A block cannot be edited without first being broken into its component entities. The EXPLODE command replaces a block reference with copies of the simple entities composing the block. EXPLODE also turns 2D (and 3D) polylines, associative dimensions, and 3D mesh back into individual entities. When a block is exploded, the resulting image on the screen is identical, except that the colors and linetypes of the entities may change. This occurs because properties such as the color and linetype of the block return to the settings determined by their original method of creation, either BYLAYER or the set color and linetype. There will be no difference unless the entities were created in Layer 0 or with the color and linetype set to BYBLOCK.

You will use the EXPLODE command to break the CLMP-TOP block for the top of the clamp into individual entities for editing. (You might try adding a chamfer without doing this, so that you can see clearly that the entire block is selected.)

Pick: **Modify *(menu bar)*, Explode**

Select objects: ***(pick a line on the clamp top block)*** ↵

The block is now broken into its component entities.

Chamfer the upper corners of the clamp top:

Pick: **Construct *(menu bar)*, Chamfer**

Polyline/Distances/<Select first line>: **d** ↵

Enter first chamfer distance <0.00>: **.125** ↵

Enter second chamfer distance <0.13>: ↵

Command: ↵ ***(to restart the CHAMFER command)***

Polyline/Distances/<Select first line>: ***(pick on the left end of the top line of the clamp top)***

Select second line: ***(pick on the leftmost vertical line of the clamp top)***

Repeat this last step on your own to add the chamfer for the right side of the clamp top.

When you are finished, your drawing should look like Figure 14.15.

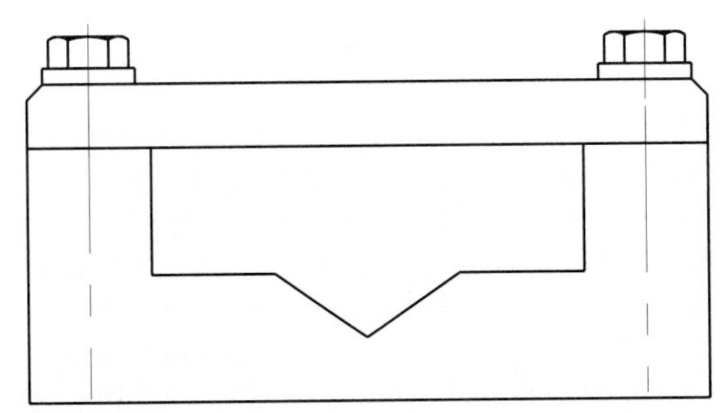

Figure 14.15

Adapting for Architecture

The EXPLODE command is an extremely useful companion for use with blocks. If you have a detail that varies only slightly from an existing block design, like a footing detail at 32" instead of 48", insert the wrong block, explode and edit it, and then resave it as a new block in case you ever need it again. ■

■ **TIP** Title blocks or drawing headings can be quickly added by using blocks and then exploding and editing with DDEDIT to change the information to match the drawing. This is a lot faster than placing new text in the drawing with DTEXT. ■

Save your drawing on your own before continuing.

Creating a Block for the Ball Tags

To make it easy to add the assembly drawing part numbers to the drawing, you will make a simple block with one *visible attribute* and several *invisible attributes*. An *attribute* is basically text information that can be associated with a block. It can be used very effectively for adding information to the drawing. Attribute information can also be extracted from the drawing and imported into a database or word processing program for other uses. You will use the AutoCAD for Windows Dynamic Data Exchange (DDE) capability to export the attributes to a spreadsheet. (If you do not use a Windows spreadsheet, such as Excel or Lotus 1-2-3, that has DDE capability, you can still use AutoCAD's ATTEXT command to extract attribute data from a drawing.)

Ball tags like the ones you will create are shown in Figure 14.16.

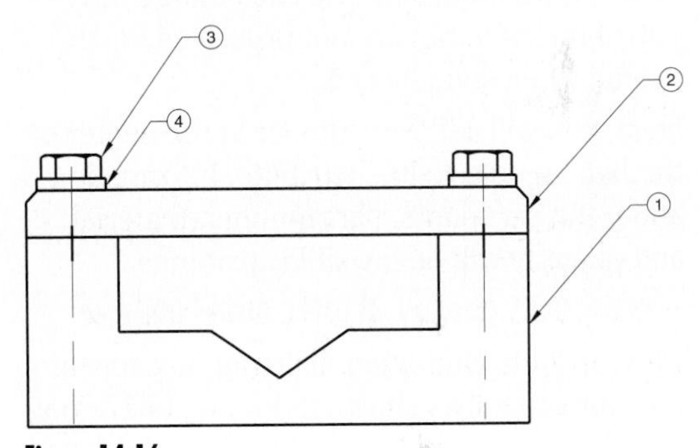

Figure 14.16

On your own, set layer TEXT as the current drawing layer.

The numbers are called ball tags because they are enclosed inside a circle. Draw the circle first. Then you will add the attributes and make the circle and attribute entities into a block.

Pick: **CIRCLE *(toolbox)***

On your own, draw a circle of diameter .25 above and to the right of the assembly drawing.

Defining Attributes

The ATTDEF command and DDATTDEF dialogue box let you create the special attribute text entities. Attributes can have the special properties listed below. They can be:

Invisible, which means they do not appear in the drawing but can still be used for purposes like extracting to a database.

Constant, which means the value is set at the beginning instead of being prompted for on insertion of the block.

Verified, which means the value is checked after it is typed in.

Preset, which means you can change the attribute later, but are not prompted for the value when you insert it.

Next, you will add the number in the center of the ball tag as a visible attribute. Information about the part name, part number, material, and quantity will be invisible attributes.

Pick: **BLOCKS *(screen)*, ATTDEF:, AttDef Dialogue**

The Attribute Definition dialogue box appears on your screen, as shown in Figure 14.17. You will use the information that you see displayed in Figure 14.17 to make changes in the dialogue box.

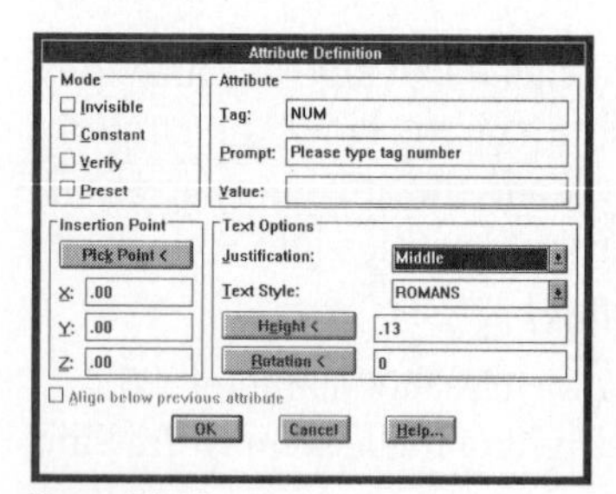

Figure 14.17

Attribute Modes

The options for modes, Invisible, Constant, Verify, and Preset, are available in the Mode area of the dialogue. Leave each of the boxes to the left of these options empty to indicate that you do not want Invisible, Constant, Verified, or Preset attributes. You want the attribute you create for the ball tag to be visible, variable, not verified, and typed in.

Attribute Tag

The attribute tag name is like a variable name that is replaced with the value that you type when you insert the block containing the attribute. The tag name appears when the block is exploded or before the attribute is made into a block. You will use NUM for the attribute tag. Position the arrow cursor over the empty box to the right of Tag: and press the pick button to select the box to type in the tag name.

Type: **NUM**

Attribute Prompt

The attribute prompt is the prompt that appears in the command area when you insert the block into a drawing.

■ ***TIP*** Make your prompt descriptive, so that it is clear what information needs to be typed in. For instance, "Enter the date (dd/mm/yy)" is a prompt that specifies not only what to enter (the date), but also the format (numeric two-digit format, with day first, then month, then year). ■

Position the arrow cursor in the empty box to the right of Prompt: and press the pick button. The typing cursor appears in the box.

Type: **Please type tag number**

When you insert the block, this prompt will be displayed on the command line. Since it will appear with a colon (:) after it to make it clear that some entry is expected, you do not need to include a colon when you type the prompt.

Default Attribute Value

Leaving the box to the right of Value: empty results in no default value for the tag. Since every tag number should be different, there is no advantage to having a default value for the ball tag attribute. If there is a response to the prompt that would be given frequently, that would be a good choice for the default value.

> ■ **TIP** You could create a title block for your drawings that would use attributes. As the attribute for the drafter's name, you would make the attribute prompt, "Enter drafter's name." For the default value, you would put your own name. If you insert the block into a drawing, the default value within the default angle brackets after the prompt is your own name. You can press the ↵ key to accept the default rather than having to type in your name each time. ■

Attribute Text Options

The attribute uses the same types of options that regular text uses. It can be centered, fit, aligned, and so on, just like any other text. Pick on the box to the right of Justification:. The text justification options pull down. Select the Middle option to position the middle of the text in the center of the ball tag.

Pick: **Middle**

The text style ROMANS is acceptable. You do not need to change this setting. If you had a number of different text styles in your drawing, you could pick on the box to pull down the style options and select a different one. For the ball tag, you will not need to do this.

Set the text height to .125, or 1/8". Use the arrow cursor and pick button to select the box to the right of Height.

Type: **.125** ***(to replace the default size of .20)***

> ■ **TIP** Clicking on Height lets you specify the height either by picking on the screen or typing at the command prompt. ■

Leave the rotation set at 0 degrees for this tutorial, because you do not want the attribute rotated at an angle in the drawing. (Clicking on Rotation lets you set the rotation either by picking from the screen or typing at the command prompt.)

Attribute Insertion Point

You will use the Pick Point option to select the center of the circle from your drawing. The other option is to type the x, y, and/or z coordinates into the appropriate boxes. Pick on Pick Point.

Your drawing returns to the screen. At the command line is the prompt:

Start point: **CEN** ↵

of ***(pick on the edge of the circle)***

Pick: **OK *(to exit the Attribute Definition dialogue box)***

The middle of the text for the tag name appears centered in the circle. The circle and the attribute tag should look like Figure 14.18.

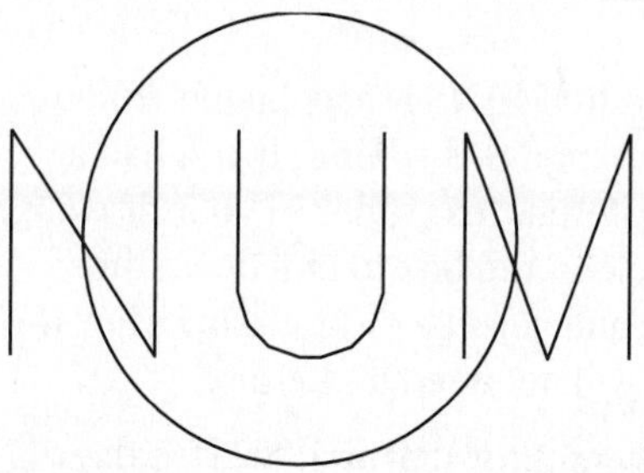

Figure 14.18

Next you will make the attributes for part name (description), material, quantity, and part number. These attributes will be invisible. This way they do not show up and appear crowded in the drawing, but they can still be extracted for use in a spreadsheet or database.

To restart the DDATTDEF command,

Press: ↵

The Attribute Definition dialogue box appears on your screen. Select the Invisible Mode, as shown in Figure 14.19.

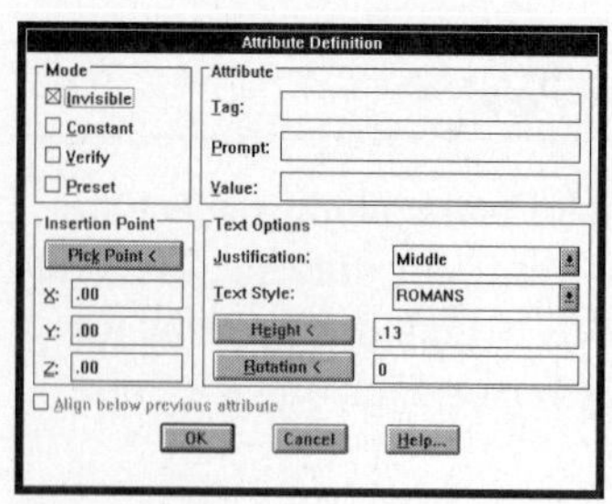

Figure 14.19

Use the dialogue box to create an invisible attribute with the following information:

Tag: **PART**

Prompt: **Please type in part description**

Value: ***(leave this box blank so that there is no default value)***

Justification: Left

Text Style: ROMANS

Height: .125

(Your height value is rounded by AutoCAD to .13) When you have entered this information into the dialogue box, you are ready to select the location in the drawing for your invisible attribute.

Pick: **Pick Point**

Your drawing returns to the screen. At the command line is the prompt:

Start point: ***(pick a point to the right of the ball tag circle)***

Pick: **OK *(to exit the Attribute Definition dialogue box)***

The tag name PART should appear at the location you selected.

On your own, use this same method to create the three invisible attributes listed below. Choose Pick Point to locate each of them to the right of the previous attributes.

Tag: **MATL**

Prompt: **Please type in material**

Value: ***(leave blank)***

Justification: Left

Height: .125

Tag: **QTY**

Prompt: **Please type in quantity required**

Value: ***(leave blank)***

Justification: Left

Height: .125

Tag: **PARTNO**

Prompt: **Please type in part number, if any**

Value: ***(leave blank)***

Justification: Left

Height: .125

When you are finished, you should see each of the tags appear in the drawing.

Defining the Block

Now you will make the circle and the attributes into a block. It is important to remember that first you create the shapes for the block and the attributes, and then you define them into a block.

Pick: **BLOCKS *(screen)*, BLOCK**

Block name (or ?): **BALLTAG** (↵)

Insertion base point: **QUA** (↵)

of ***(pick on the left side of the circle to select its left quadrant point)***

Select objects: ***(use Window to pick the circle and the tag names NUM, PART, MATL, QTY, PARTNO)*** (↵)

The circle and the tag names disappear from your screen. Now you can insert the necessary ball tags into the drawing, using the block you have made.

> ■ ***TIP*** You may want to use the WBLOCK command so that the block is available for other drawings. Without WBLOCK, it is only defined in the present drawing. ■

Inserting the Ball Tags

You will use the Leader command to draw the arrows and the lines to the ball tags. Then you will insert block BALLTAG to add the balloons and tag numbers.

You will use Figure 14.20 as your guide as you insert the ball tags.

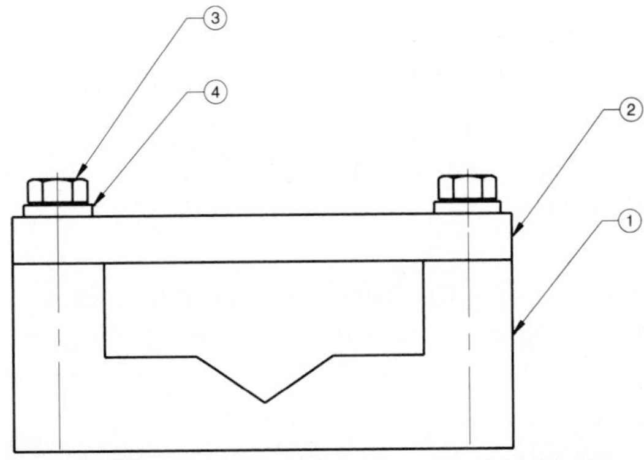

Figure 14.20

On your own, turn ORTHO off by pressing (F8) or picking O from the toolbar, so that it is no longer highlighted.

Pick: **Draw *(menu bar)*, Dimensions, Leader**

Leader start: ***(pick NEAREST from the toolbox)*** (↵)

near to ***(pick a point on the right edge of Part 1; the Nearest mode finds a point on the entity nearest to the center crosshairs)***

To point: ***(pick a point that is above and to the right of Part 1)***

To point: (↵)

Dimension text <>: (↵)

Continue to create the leader lines for Part 2, Part 3 (the hex head), and Part 4 (the washers) on your own. The leader can start anywhere on the edge of the part. Try to pick points and leader line angles that place the callouts in a location in the drawing that provides clear access and easy readability.

> ■ ***TIP*** Because block BALLTAG has its insertion point on the left, you want to draw the leaders towards the right. ■

PARTS LIST				
ITEM NO	DESCRIPTION	MATL	PART NUMBER	QTY
1	CLAMP BASE	1020ST	ADD 1	1
2	CLAMP TOP	1020ST	ADD 2	1
3	.375-16UNCx.125 HEX HEAD	STEEL	ADD 3	2
4	.438x.750x.125 FLAT WASHER	STEEL	ADD 4	2

Figure 14.21

When adding the ball tags, refer to the parts list in Figure 14.21 that shows the information for each part. To add the ball tags, you will turn the OSNAP, Endpoint running mode on:

Pick: **Settings *(menu bar)*, Object Snaps**

Use the dialogue box to select Endpoint (and turn off any other modes that may be on). When you are finished,

Pick: **OK**

Pick: **Draw *(menu bar)*, Insert. . .**

Pick the box labeled Block. . . and select the block BALLTAG from the list. Pick OK. You are returned to the insert prompt at the command line.

Insertion point: ***(pick near the end of the short section of one of the leader lines)***

X scale factor <1>/Corner/XYZ: ↵

Y scale factor (default = X): ↵

Rotation angle <0>: ↵

Please type in material: ***(type in the appropriate material)*** ↵

Please type in tag number: ***(type in the appropriate tag number)*** ↵

Please type in part description: ***(type in the appropriate part description)*** ↵

Please type in part number, if any: ***(type in the appropriate part number)*** ↵

Please type in quantity required: ***(type in the appropriate quantity)*** ↵

The circle and number that you typed appear on your screen. Repeat this process on your own to add the part numbers and type in the information for the remaining parts. When you are done, your drawing should look similar to Figure 14.20.

Changing an Attribute Value

The command DDATTE (Dynamic Dialogue Attribute Edit) is very useful for changing an attribute value. If you have mistyped a value, or you want to change an existing attribute value, use the DDATTE command.

Pick: **EDIT *(screen)*, DDATTE**

Select block: ***(pick on one of the ball tags)***

The Edit Attributes dialogue box pops up on your screen, as shown in Figure 14.22.

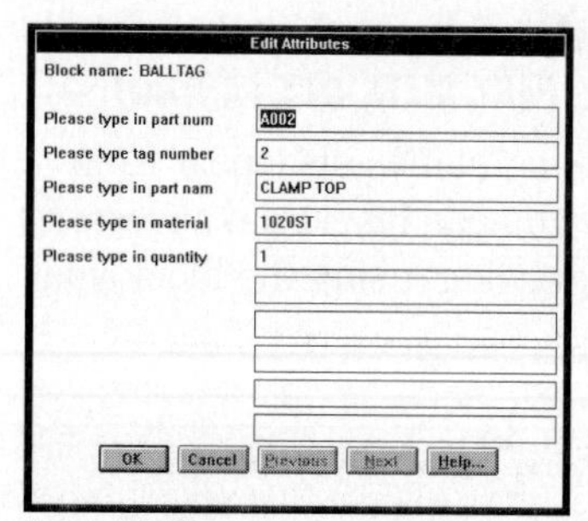

Figure 14.22

It contains the attribute prompt and a box to the right with the value you previously entered. To change the value,

Pick: ***(highlight the value you want to change)***

Type: ***(the new value)***

Pick: **OK *(to exit the dialogue box)***

Save your drawing on your own before you continue.

Attributes are an important feature of AutoCAD and can be used for many applications. Now that you are familiar with this feature, you can use it to add useful attributes to blocks you create in your drawing.

Creating the Parts List

The next task is to create a parts list. The required headings for the parts list are Item, Description, Material, Part No., and Quantity. The item number is the number that appears in the ball tag for the part on the assembly drawing. Sometimes a parts list is created on a separate sheet, but often in a small assembly drawing like the clamp assembly it is included in the drawing. Usually it is positioned near the title block or in the upper right-hand corner of the drawing.

While there is no standard format for a parts list, each company may have its own standard. Dimensions for a parts list can be based loosely on one of the formats recommended in the MIL-15 Technical Drawing Standards, or on ANSI Y14-2M standards for text sizes and note locations in the drawing.

Using Dynamic Data Exchange (DDE)

You can use AutoCAD for Windows Dynamic Data Exchange to send drawing information to other applications, such as the Excel spreadsheet program. In this example you will see how to export the attribute data that you created in the previous steps into Excel. You will then paste information from the spreadsheet into the AutoCAD drawing to create a parts list. Just imagine what other uses DDE will have. You can export the drawing database as well as attributes to other programs. DDE allows you to establish a two-way link so that other programs can also make changes to the drawing database. This allows you to use a spreadsheet or other program to make changes to the drawing database, do parametric modeling, redesign the drawing based on engineering analysis programs, etc.

To see if you have a DDE link to your spreadsheet established,

Pick: **Edit *(menu bar)*, DDE, Dialog**

The dialogue box that appears on your screen allows you to type in the command to run the spreadsheet application. If there is no application established already, you may be able to set it up by typing the command to run the application, including the necessary path.

Pick: ***OK (to exit the dialogue box)***

If you do not have Excel, Lotus 1-2-3, Quatro Pro, for Windows or other software that can use DDE, skip ahead to the Going Further box near the end of this tutorial and use the method described to add a parts list to your drawing.

AutoCAD can export blocks; the entire drawing database; handles, attributes, and tags (using Attribute Filter 1); or just handles and attributes (using Attribute Filter 2) through DDE. To select Attribute Filter 2 as the type of information to export using DDE,

Pick: **Edit *(menu bar)*, DDE, Attribute Filter 2**

The next items selected using DDE will use the Attribute Filter 2 format. This will export the attributes, their handle numbers, and the decimal equivalent of the handle numbers. Now you are ready to export the attribute information to Excel using DDE.

Pick: **Edit *(menu bar)*, DDE, Export Selection Set**

Select objects: ***(pick on each of the ball tags in the drawing)***

Select objects: ↵

...Total 4 rows

You may see the Excel (or other) spreadsheet appear on your screen briefly. If it remains there, just pick in the AutoCAD window and then make the appropriate selections.

> ■ ***TIP*** You may need to close the second AutoCAD session in order to open the spreadsheet. ■

Switching to the Spreadsheet Program

The spreadsheet program that is available to the DDE link is started automatically when you export the selection using DDE. To switch so that the spreadsheet is active,

Press: ALT - ESC ***(until the spreadsheet program is active)***

Your screen should appear similar to Figure 14.23.

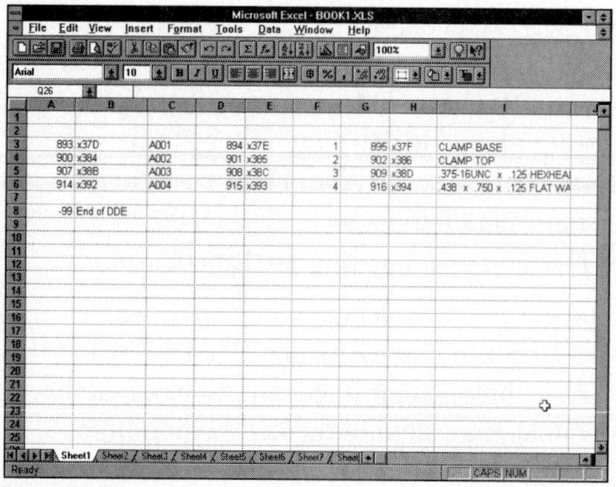

Figure 14.23

The number shown in column A is the decimal equivalent for the handle number of the attribute for the part number for each ball tag. Column B contains the hexadecimal handle number. Column C contains the part number that you entered as an attribute. This is followed in the next two columns by handle numbers and then the ball tag numbers (or item numbers). Columns G and H again contain handle numbers and then the part descriptions, and so on.

On your own, use your knowledge of your spreadsheet program to delete the columns with the handle numbers and create titles for the correct columns. When you are finished with this step, save the spreadsheet file. Then highlight the columns and rows and use the spreadsheet's Edit, Copy command to copy the selection to the Windows clipboard. Press ALT - ESC again until you see your AutoCAD drawing return to the screen.

Pasting from the Clipboard

AutoCAD's drawing editor should be on your screen, with the assembly drawing created earlier in the tutorial. Be sure that you have completed the previous step of highlighting and copying the selection from your spreadsheet to the clipboard. Then,

Pick: **Edit *(menu bar)*, Paste**

The selection that you copied to the Windows clipboard from the spreadsheet is attached to the crosshairs.

Insertion point: ***(select a point near the upper left corner of the drawing area)***

X scale factor/corner/XYZ <1>: ↵

Y scale factor: ↵

rotation angle <0>: ↵

On your own, use the SCALE command to scale down the inserted block of text for the parts list, if necessary. Use MOVE, if needed, to locate the parts list in the upper right of the drawing. Save your drawing.

Your completed assembly drawing should look similar to Figure 14.24.

ITEM NO.	DESCRIPTION	MATERIAL	QUANTITY	PART NO.
1	CLAMP BASE	1020ST	1	A001
2	CLAMP TOP	1020ST	1	A002
3	.375-16UNC x .125 HEXHEAD	STEEL	2	A003
4	.438 x .750 x .125 FLAT WASHER	STEEL	2	A004

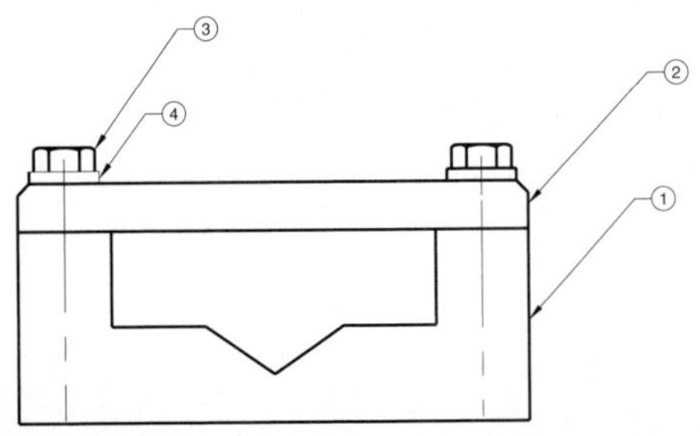

Figure 14.24

Going Further

If you do not have a spreadsheet that is capable of using DDE, then use any Windows compatible word processor or spreadsheet to create the parts list shown in Figure 14.21. Once you have typed in the information for the parts list, highlight all of the text information that you have entered. Select Edit, Copy to copy the selection to the Windows clipboard. Switch back to the AutoCAD program and use Edit, Paste to add the parts list to your AutoCAD drawing.

■ ***TIP*** When creating drawings to export to other programs through such methods as selecting File, Export, and creating a DXF (Drawing Exchange Format) file, it is often a good idea to explode all of the blocks first, because many programs will not be able to translate them. ■

Save and plot your drawing. Close all AutoCAD sessions and any spreadsheet or word processing programs that you may have left open.

You have now completed the clamp assembly drawing and parts list. Exit AutoCAD; you have finished Tutorial 14.

KEY TERMS

assembly drawing
attribute
ball tag
balloon number
block name
block reference
client
detail drawing
exploded view
image
invisible attribute
object linking and embedding
partial section (broken-out section)
parts list
paste
server
visible attribute
working drawings

KEY COMMANDS

Attribute Definition
Attribute Extract
Base
Block
Dynamic Dialogue Attribute Definition
Dynamic Dialogue Attribute Edit
Dynamic Dialogue Insert
Insert
Paste Clip
Write Block

EXERCISES

14.1 Clamping Block

Prepare an assembly drawing and parts list based on the information below. First draw detail drawings of Parts 1 and 2. Join Part 2 to Part 1 using two .500–13UNC×2.50 LONG HEX-HEAD BOLTS. Include .500–13UNC NUTS on each bolt. Locate a .625×1.250×.125 WASHER under the head of each bolt, between Parts 1 and 2, and between Part 1 and the NUT. (Each bolt will have 3 washers and a nut.)

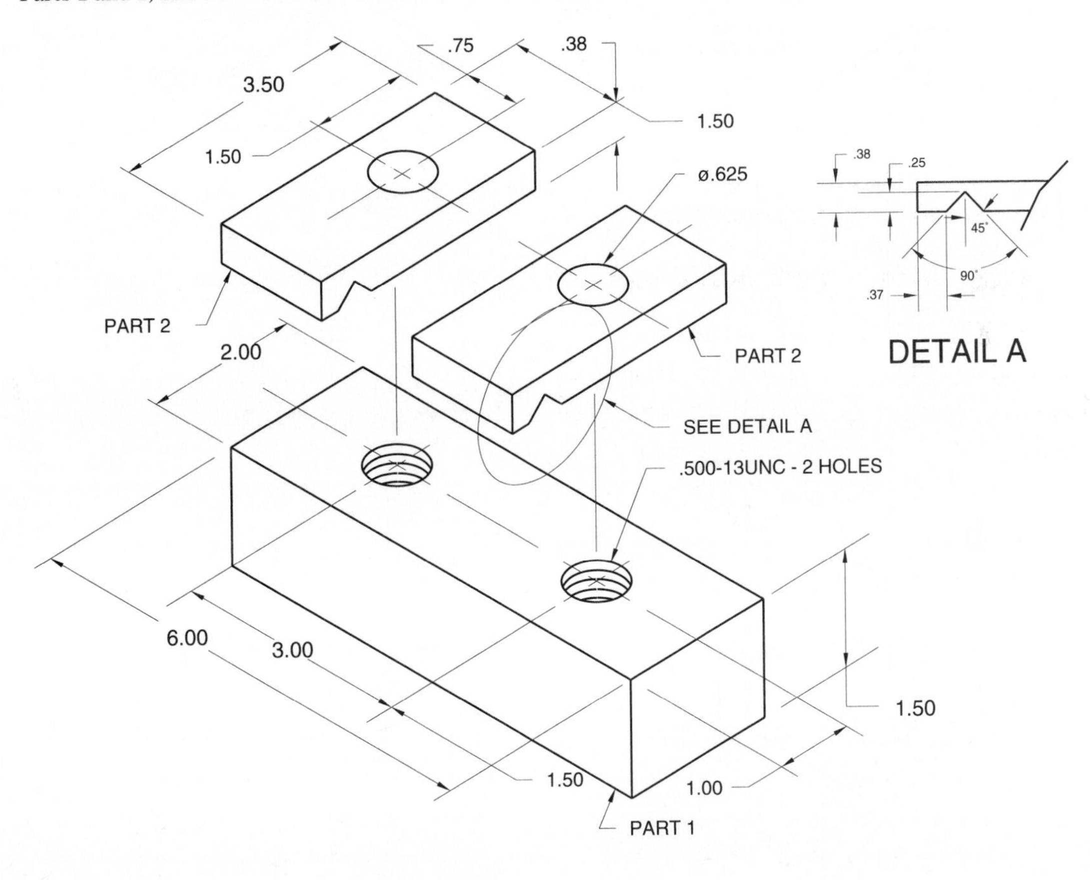

14.2 Pressure Assembly

Prepare an assembly drawing and parts list of the pressure assembly. First, draw detail drawings of the BASE, GASKET, and COVER shown below. Use four .375–16UNC×1.50 HEX-HEAD SCREWS to join the COVER, GASKET, and BASE. The GASKET assembles between the BASE and COVER.

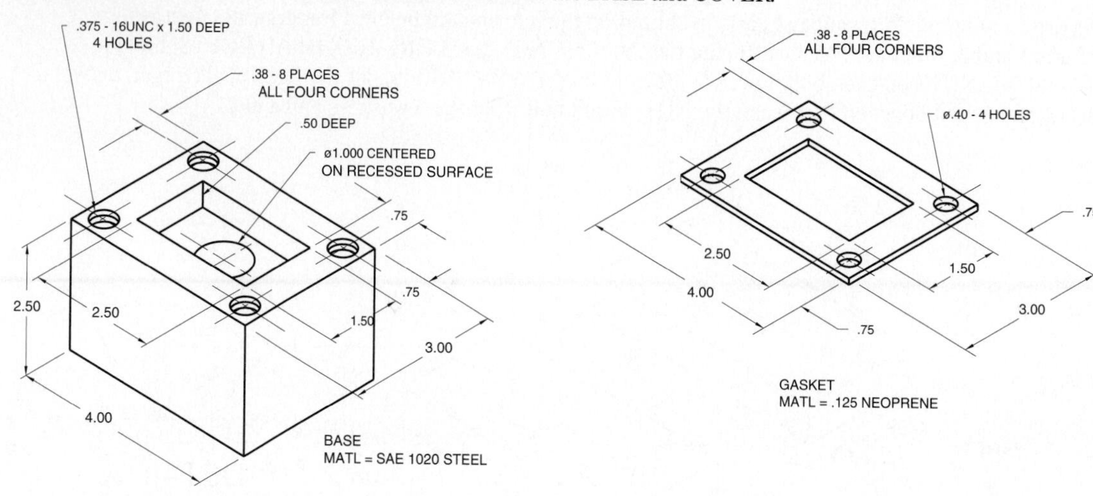

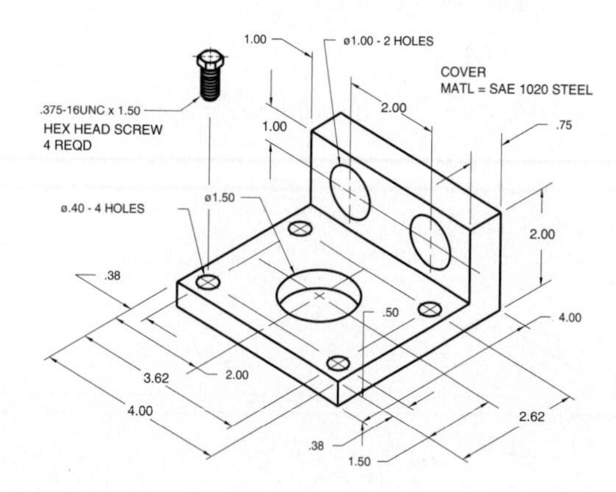

14.3 Hub Assembly

Create an assembly drawing for the parts shown. Use 8 bolts with nuts to assemble the parts.

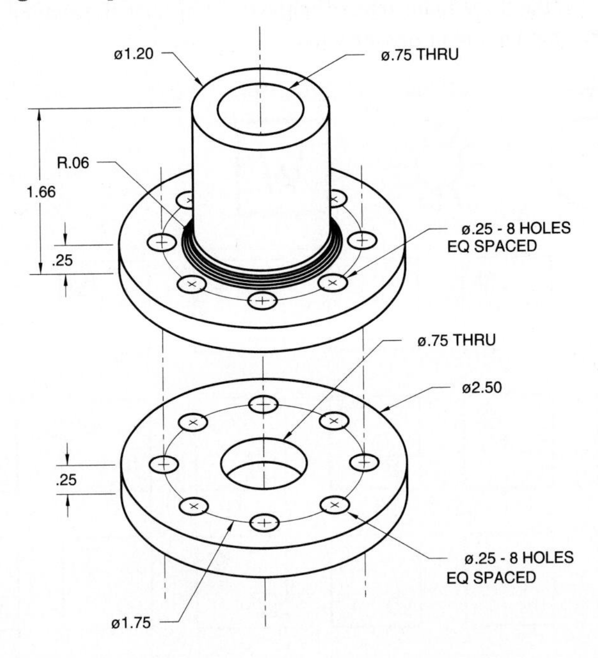

14.4 Piping Symbols

Draw the following piping symbols to scale; the grid shown is 0.2 inches (you do not need to show it on your drawing). Use plines (0.03 wide). Make each symbol a separate block and label it.

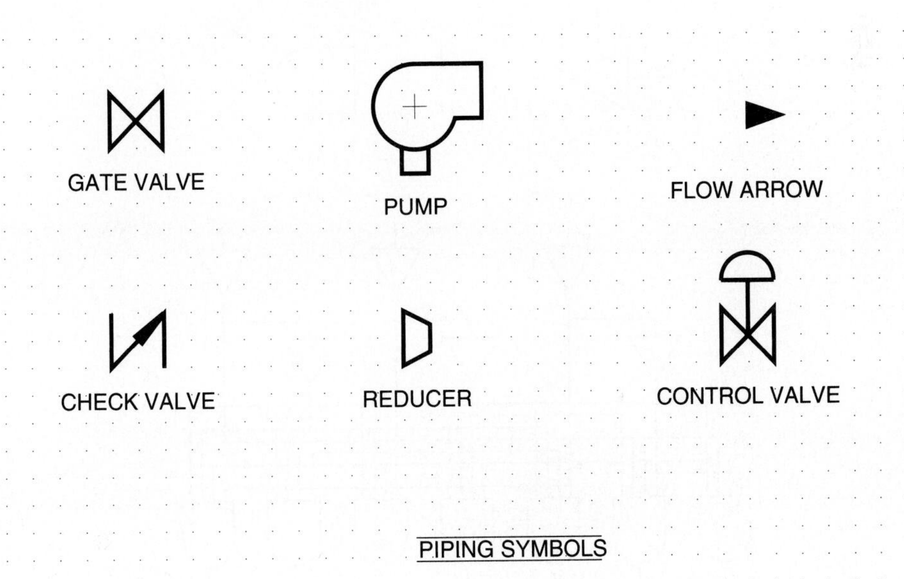

14.5 Utilities Layout

Construct this representation of a group of city blocks' utilities layout (grid spacing is at 0.25). Using plines 0.05 wide, construct and label the three main symbols shown. Then scale the symbols down to 1/4 size, make each one a block, and insert them in the proper location.

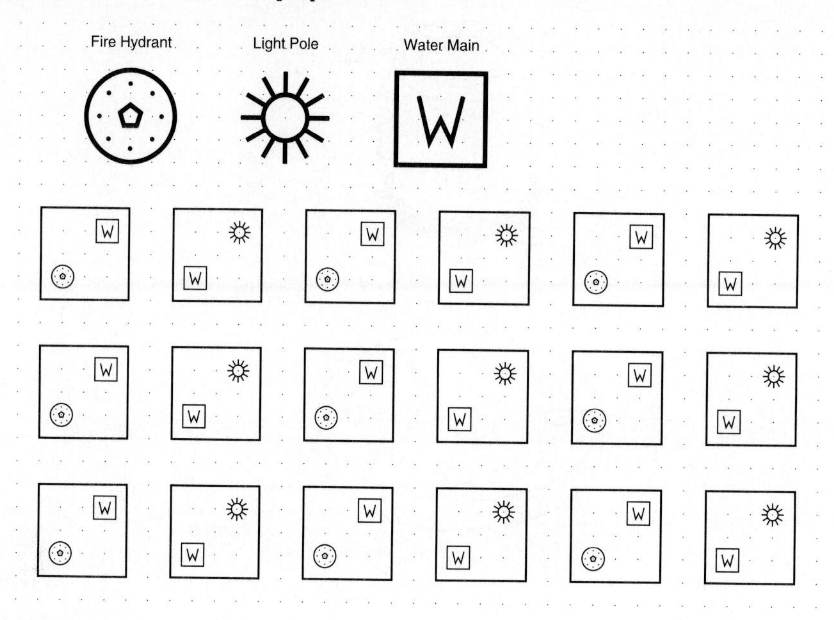

14.6M Decoder Logic Unit

Use blocks to create the NAND gate and INVERTER. Insert the blocks to draw the diagram.

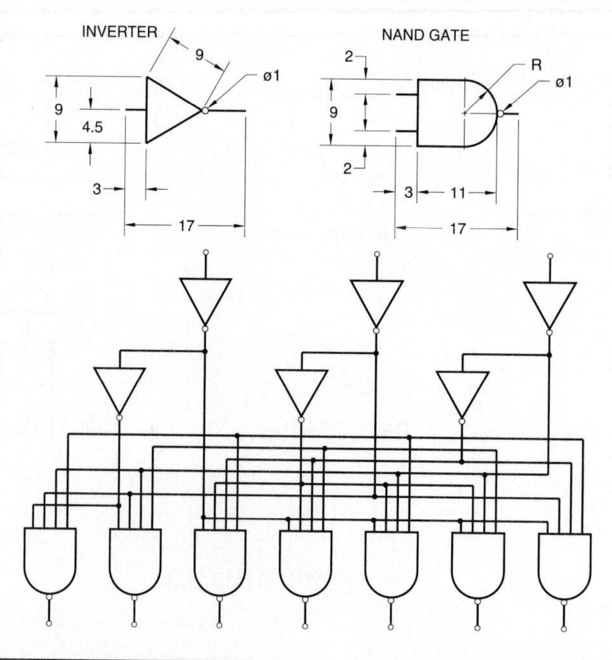

14.7 Turbine Housing Assembly

Create detail drawings for the two parts shown below and save each as a WBLOCK. Insert each block to form an assembly.

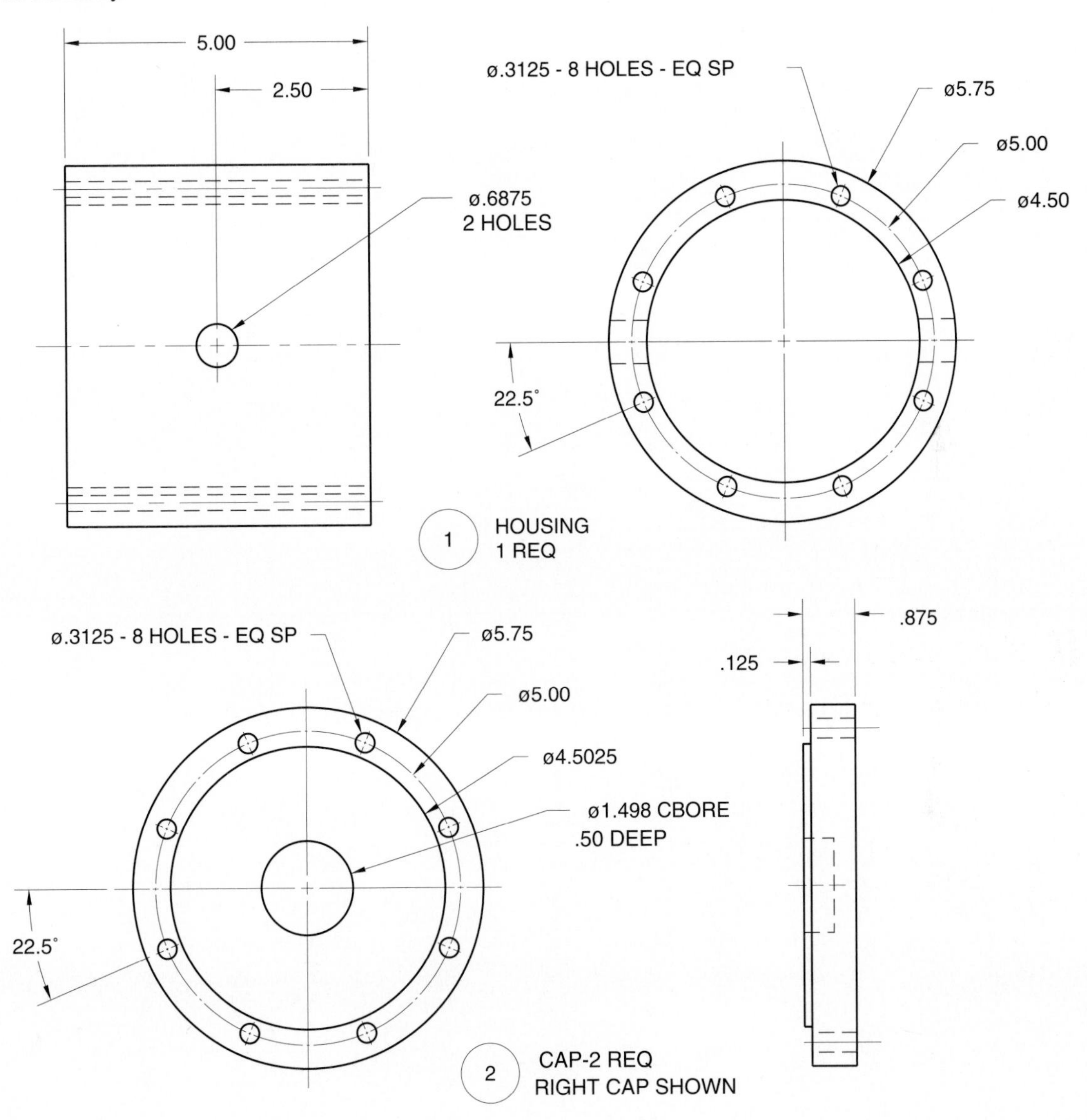

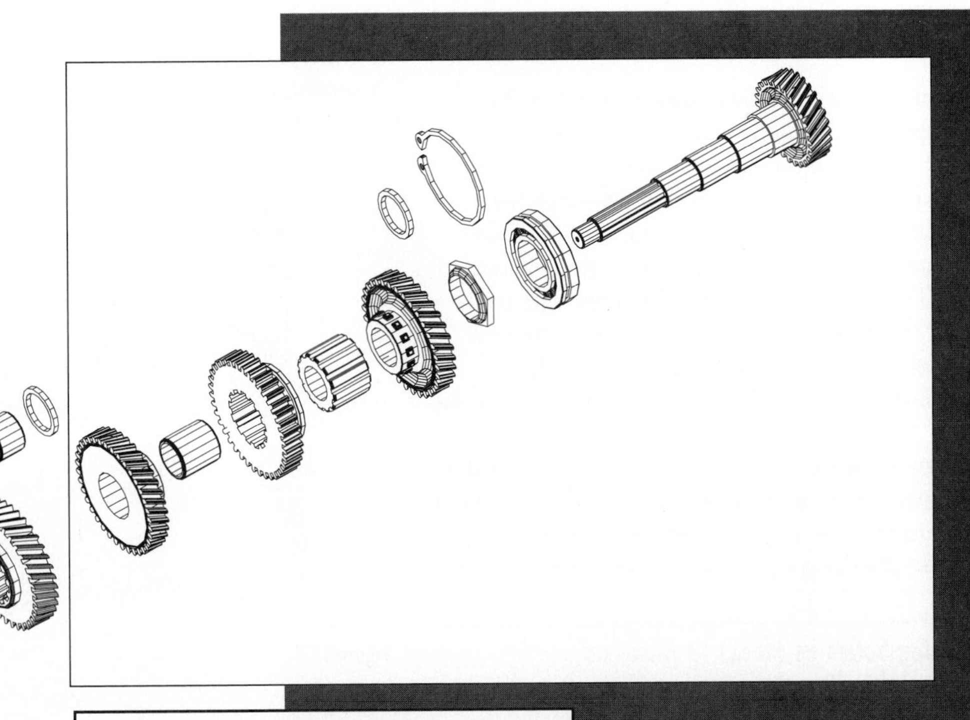

TUTORIAL 15

Creating Assembly Drawings from Solid Models

Objectives

When you have completed this tutorial, you will be able to

1. Load LISP routines to insert and export solid models.
2. Create an assembly drawing from solid models.
3. Use xrefs.
4. Create an exploded isometric.
5. Analyze the mass properties and change the materials of solid models.

Introduction

You have seen in previous tutorials how to create solid models of objects and project 2D views to create dimensioned part drawings. To complete a set of working drawings using solid modeling, you will create an assembly drawing for the clamp, like the one you created in Tutorial 14 using 2D techniques. The parts for the assembly drawing have been created as solids and are included with the data files so you can proceed directly to creating the assembly drawing. Remember that assembly drawings usually do not show dimensions or hidden lines. The purpose of an assembly drawing is to show how the parts go together, not to fully describe the shape and size of each part.

Using Solids as Blocks to Make an Assembly Drawing

In this tutorial you will learn how to use the XREF commands to include part drawings in the assembly. A drawing attached to the assembly drawing using xrefs updates automatically when a change is made to the original part drawing.

You will also learn to insert solids as parts in the assembly. When inserting solids, you must be careful not to use commands that will corrupt the solid model database for the objects you are inserting. Commands such as INSERT and WBLOCK may destroy handle or block information used to keep track of the solid in the drawing database. The AutoCAD program comes with a *LISP* program, called WBLKSOL, to make it easy for you to insert solids.

The parts in Figures 15.1, 15.2, 15.3, and 15.4 are the parts provided with the data files. The insertion points are identified by 0,0 in the drawings.

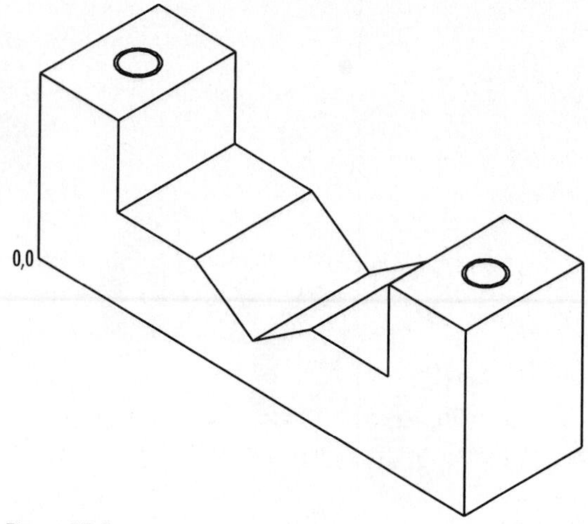

Figure 15.1

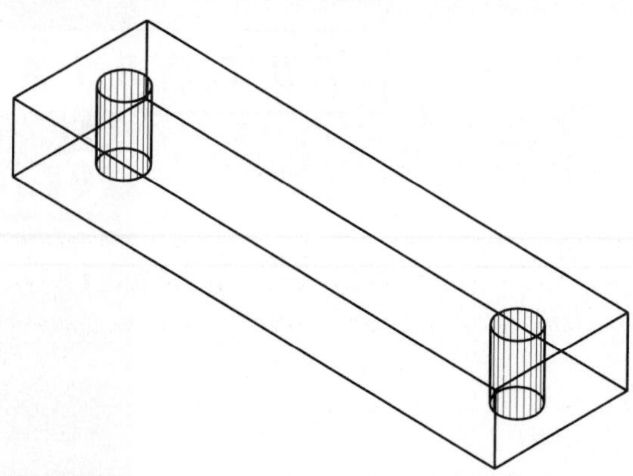

Figure 15.2

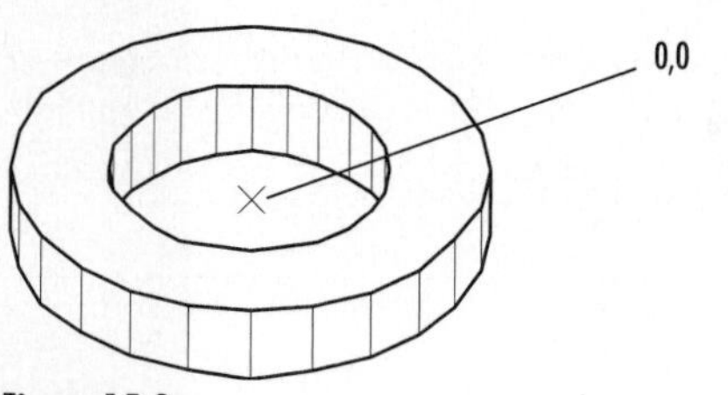

Figure 15.3

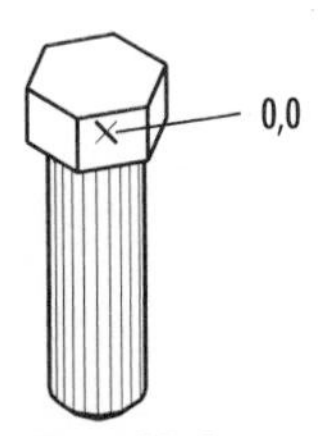

Figure 15.4

Starting

Start AutoCAD from the Autodesk Collection Interface as instructed in Chapter 2. From the AutoCAD drawing editor,

Pick: **File *(menu bar)*, New**

Use the dialogue box to select the prototype drawing called PROT-ISO provided with the data files. Name your new drawing ASMB-SOL. When you have finished,

Pick: **OK *(to exit the dialogue box)***

The AutoCAD drawing editor appears on your screen with the settings from the prototype drawing for 3D isometric views. Your screen should appear similar to Figure 15.5.

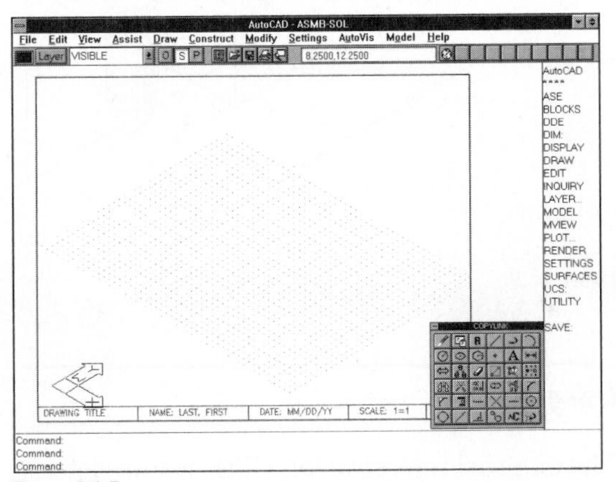

Figure 15.5

Loading Applications and LISP Routines

The File menu bar selection provides an easy way to load application programs that run inside AutoCAD to enhance its capabilities. *AutoLISP* programs can also be loaded this way. Some useful samples are provided with your AutoCAD software. LISP programs have the file extension .LSP. You will use the File, Applications selection from the menu bar to load WBLKSOL.LSP.

Pick: **File *(menu bar)*, Applications**

The Load AutoLISP and ADS Files dialogue box appears on your screen. Refer to Figure 15.6. Pick on the File button to select the LISP program you want to load from the listed files.

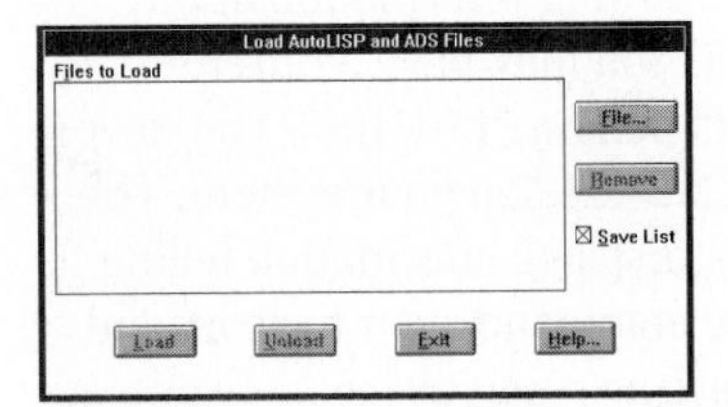

Figure 15.6

The Select LISP/ADS Routine dialogue box pops up on top of the previous dialogue box, as shown in Figure 15.7. Click on the names in the column at the right to select the directory that your AutoCAD, Release 12 files are stored in, usually ACADWIN. If you need to step back to the root directory, click on the c:\ folder. Inside your ACADWIN directory, you will see a subdirectory called SAMPLE. Double-click on the SAMPLE subdirectory to select it. When you have the proper directory selected, using the list of files at the left,

Pick: **WBLKSOL.LSP**

Pick: **OK**

You return to the previous dialogue box.

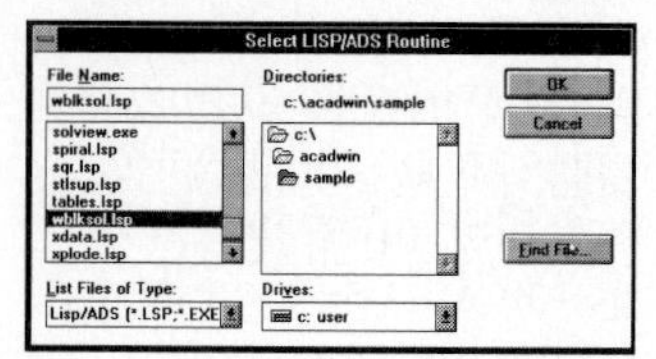

Figure 15.7

The name of the file you selected is listed in the area under the heading Files to Load. Make sure that the name WBLKSOL.LSP is highlighted,

Pick: **Load**

You will see the following information at the command prompt. You may have a different directory listed, depending on where you have loaded the AutoCAD files on your system. The command prompt displays information telling how to invoke the commands you have loaded.

Loading C:\ACADWIN\SAMPLE\WBLKSOL.LSP.

C:WBLKSOL and C:INSRTSOL loaded. Start commands with WBLKSOL and INSRTSOL.

Inserting the Solid Part Drawings

Now you are ready to begin inserting the solids into the assembly drawing. INSRTSOL is like the INSERT command you used in Tutorial 14 except that it does not destroy the solid drawing information.

Command: **INSRTSOL** ↵

The file selection dialogue box for this LISP routine appears on your screen, under the heading Insert Drawing File of Solid, as shown in Figure 15.8. It is a standard file selection dialogue. Use the left- and right-hand columns to select the drawing BASE-3D from the data files that were provided. Pick OK when you are done selecting the file.

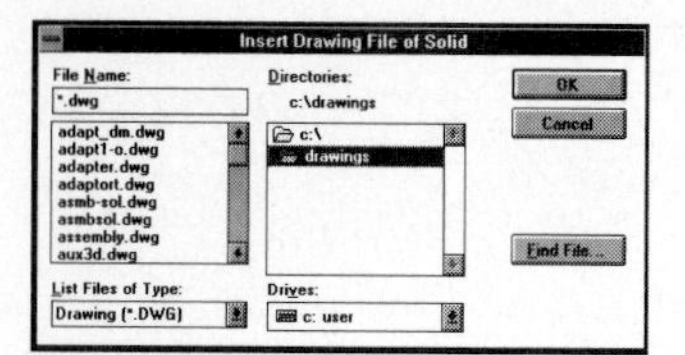

Figure 15.8

You return to the command prompt for the remaining prompts.

Enter insertion point and rotation angle: **0,0** ↵ ↵

The solid model of the clamp base appears in your drawing, as shown in Figure 15.9. (Be sure you pressed ↵ twice.) The part still has all of its solid properties.

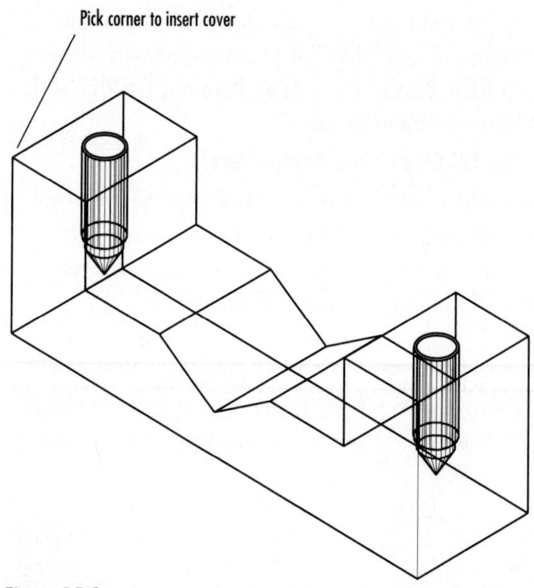

Figure 15.9

Using XREFS

The external reference, or XREF, feature lets you use another drawing without really adding it to your current drawing. The advantage to this is that if you make a change to the referenced drawing, then anywhere it is used in another drawing it is automatically updated.

Like blocks, XREFs can be inserted anywhere in the drawing; they can be scaled and rotated. The XREF command can be selected from the BLOCKS selection on the screen menu. Next, you will attach the cover for the clamp as an XREF. Refer to Figure 15.9 when selecting points.

Pick: **BLOCKS *(screen menu)*, XREF**

?/Bind/Detach/Path/Reload/<Attach>: ↵

Xref to Attach<BASE-3D>: **C:\DRAWINGS\COVER-3D** ↵
(be sure to add the correct drive and directory)

Insertion point: **INT** ↵

of ***(target the intersection of the upper left corner indicated in Figure 15.9; be sure SNAP is turned off to make it easier to select)***

X scale factor <1>/Corner/XYZ: ↵

Y scale factor (default = X): ↵

Rotation angle <0>: ↵

The cover should now appear in your drawing, lined up with the clamp base. Your drawing should appear similar to Figure 15.10.

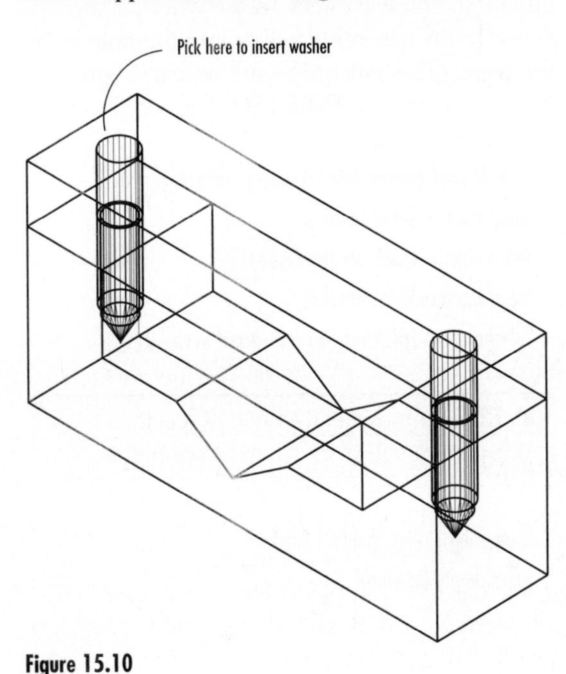

Figure 15.10

Adapting for Architecture

Xrefs are useful in the creation of a set of architectural working drawings. Make your base plan an xref drawing, so that if you need to make changes in the future to the form of your building, all the subsequent drawings will be updated too. Try to include dimensioning and text on these xrefs so that all of this information will be updated. ■

Now you are ready to insert the washers into the assembly. Restart the XREF command by pressing the ↵ key. Turn Snap off to make it easier to select.

Command: ↵

?/Bind/Detach/Path/Reload/<Attach>: ↵

Xref to Attach<COVER-3D>: **C:\DRAWINGS\WASHR-3D** ↵
(be sure to add the correct drive and directory)

Insertion point: **CEN** ↵

of ***(target the top edge of the hole indicated in Figure 15.10)***

X scale factor <1>/Corner/XYZ: ↵

Y scale factor (default = X): ↵

Rotation angle <0>: ↵

Restart the command and insert the washer for the right-hand side of the part on your own. You will see the prompt "Xref to attach <WASHR-3D>:". As WASHR-3D is already the default, press ↵ to position the washer on the other hole, and continue accepting the defaults.

Once you have the washers inserted, your drawing should appear similar to Figure 15.11.

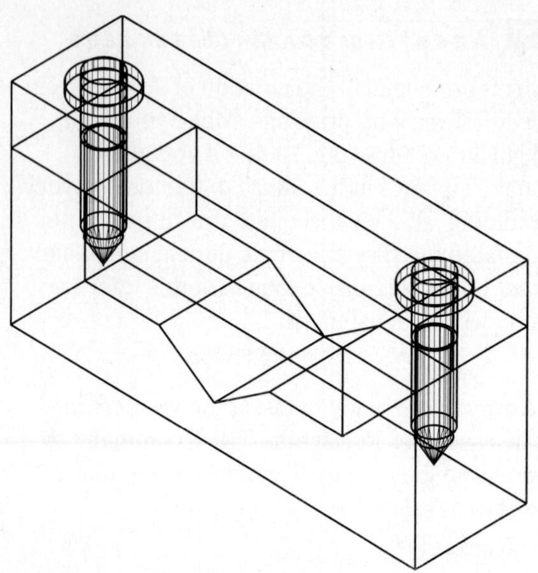

Figure 15.11

Next, you will add the two screws to the assembly to finish inserting the parts you will need. You will use INSRTSOL to insert the two screws, using OSNAP, Center to pick the center of the top surface of the washers as the insertion point and specify rotation angle 0. You will use INSRTSOL, not XREF so that you can use other AutoCAD features like checking interference (SOLINTERF) later in this tutorial.

Command: **INSRTSOL** ↵

The file selection dialogue box appears on your screen. Use it to select the drawing SCREW-3D from the data files that were provided. Pick OK when you are done selecting the file. You return to the command prompt for the remaining prompts.

Enter insertion point and rotation angle: ***(pick CENTER from the toolbox and then pick on the top of the left hole in the washer)*** ↵ ↵

The screw should appear in your drawing. Repeat this process on your own for the right-hand screw. Because you have already inserted a block named SCREW-3D, you will see the message, "SCREW-3D is already a standard block in the current drawing. Insert SCREW-3D? Yes<No>:" This gives you the opportunity to respond No if you do not want to overwrite a block that happens to have the same name in your drawing. In this case it is the same block, so type "Y" to respond Yes you do want to continue to insert the block. Now your drawing should show the parts completely assembled.

Checking for Interference

When you are designing a device, you often want to know if the parts will fit together correctly. You can use AutoCAD's SOLINTERF command to check and see whether two parts overlap. If they overlap, AutoCAD creates a new solid, showing where the two objects were overlapping. You can use this to determine whether the objects are fitting together as intended. You will check to see whether the screw in the assembly will fit into the hole in the base. (This will only work on parts you have inserted with INSRTSOL, not on parts that are inserted as XREFs.)

Pick: **Model *(menu bar)*, Inquiry, Interference**

Select the first set of solids. . .

Select objects: ***(pick on the base)*** ↵

Select the second set of solids. . .

Select objects: ***(pick on the left-hand screw)*** ↵

> ■ ***TIP*** You may need to use ZOOM, Window to select the correct screw. ■

Comparing 1 solid against 1 solid.

Solids do not interfere.

Determining Mass Properties

Using AutoCAD, you can inquire about the *mass properties* of an object. The volume of the object is calculated using an approximation method. The boxed-in outline of the object is broken down into smaller units, based on the setting of the variable called SOLSUBDIV. Into each box, an imaginary ray is fired. If the ray hits inside the object's solid areas, the length of the ray through the solid is determined and that portion is added in to calculate the volume. If the ray does not hit inside the solid boundary of the object, that box is ignored. The higher the value set for SOLSUBDIV, the more boxes the object outline is broken into and the more accurate the volume calculation. However, the higher the value set for SOLSUBDIV, the longer the calculation time.

The other variable that affects the accuracy of the volume calculation and mass properties is SOLDECOMP. SOLDECOMP determines the direction in which the rays are fired. The default is that the rays are fired along the X axis. Depending on the shape of your part, you may get a more accurate calculation if you change this direction. A general rule is that the SOLDECOMP direction should be set along the long axis of the part and towards the more detailed shape.

Pick: **Model *(menu bar)*, Inquiry, Mass Property. . .**

Select objects: ***(pick the clamp base)*** ↵

The Mass Properties dialogue box appears on your screen, as shown in Figure 15.12. Using the dialogue box, you can set the variables, send the results to a file, check the values that are displayed at the top of the box, and change settings and recompute the mass properties.

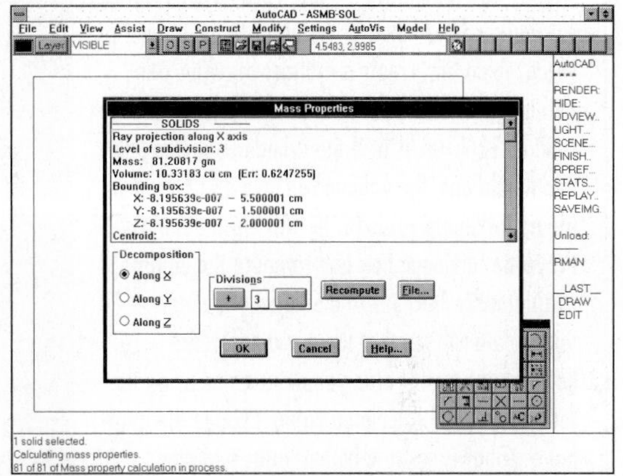

Figure 15.12

To set SOLSUBDIV to a higher number,

Pick: ***(the + (plus) sign to the left of the 3 in the Divisions area to set it to 4)***

Just pick once, to set it to 4, as higher numbers result in a very slow calculation. Notice the error level that is listed after the volume, near the top of the box (Err: 0.624725). Next, pick Recompute and check the error level again:

Pick: **Recompute**

The error level should now be smaller.

Pick: **OK *(to exit the dialogue)***

Going Further

You can check the basic accuracy of the mass properties calculations by creating a solid of a known volume and comparing the mass properties volume calculation determined by AutoCAD to the known value. To do this, create a cylinder of radius one and height one. The formula for the volume of a cylinder is: $V = \pi r^2 h$. If the cylinder is radius one and height one, the volume will be 3.1417, the approximate value for pi. Next, use the Mass Properties dialogue box and compare the volume calculated by AutoCAD to the value you determined. You will see that there is a difference between the exact value you determined using the formula and the calculated value. Change the number of subdivisions to a higher value and pick Recompute. Is the value closer to the calculated value? Try selecting the axis for decomposition so that it is toward the circular shape of the cylinder, and pick Recompute. The value should be closer to the actual value of pi.

Changing the Material

AutoCAD allows you to assign different materials to the solids you create. The default material is mild steel. You will use the Materials Browser to change the material properties assigned to an object.

Pick: **Model *(menu bar)*, Utility, Material. . .**

The Materials Browser dialogue box shown in Figure 15.13 pops up on your screen.

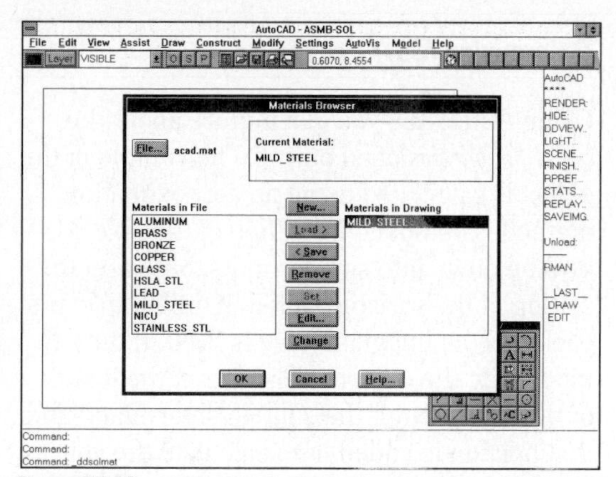

Figure 15.13

Using it, you can create and assign different materials for a part. The materials that are listed at the left are already created for you to use. Picking New shows a dialogue box you can create new materials by specifying their properties. Try this on your own. To change the material of the base to brass instead of the default, mild steel:

Pick: **BRASS *(from the left-hand column)***

Pick: **Change**

After you select Change, you are returned to your drawing so you can select the object.

Pick: ***(the clamp base)*** ↵

The material assigned to the clamp base is now brass.

Use the Mass Properties dialogue box on your own and reanalyze the base now that its material has been changed. You should notice that the mass has changed to reflect the change in materials.

Adapting for Architecture

You will rarely if ever check mass properties of architectural drawings; however, you can use AutoCAD's AREA and DIST commands to quickly extract data from a drawing. The AREA command lets you quickly get information, including the building area in square feet and the perimeter size. Use the DIST command to measure the length, height, and width of objects. The DIST command is important because diagonal measurements are broken into their orthogonal components, for ease of understanding and use. ■

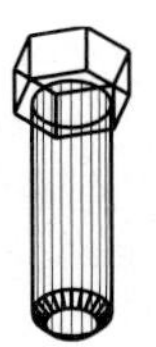

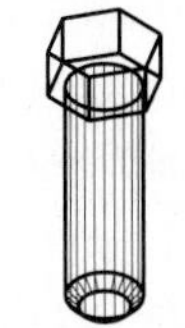

Creating an Exploded Isometric View

Exploded views are often used to show how parts are assembled. You saw an example of an exploded isometric assembly drawing in Tutorial 14. In this tutorial, you will create an exploded view from your assembly drawing by moving the parts you inserted away from each other. In an exploded view, the parts still should align with their assembled positions, so you will move them only along one axis.

Pick: **MOVE *(toolbox)***

Select objects: ***(pick the two screws)*** ↵

Base point or displacement: **0,0,0** ↵

Second point of displacement: **0,0,5** ↵

The screws move up in the drawing and off the view. You will use the ZOOM, Extents command to zoom the view so that the entire drawing fits on the screen.

Pick: **Zoom *(toolbar)***

All/Center/Dynamic/Extents/Left/Previous/Vmax/Window/ <Scale (X/XP)>: **E** ↵

Your drawing should appear similar to Figure 15.14.

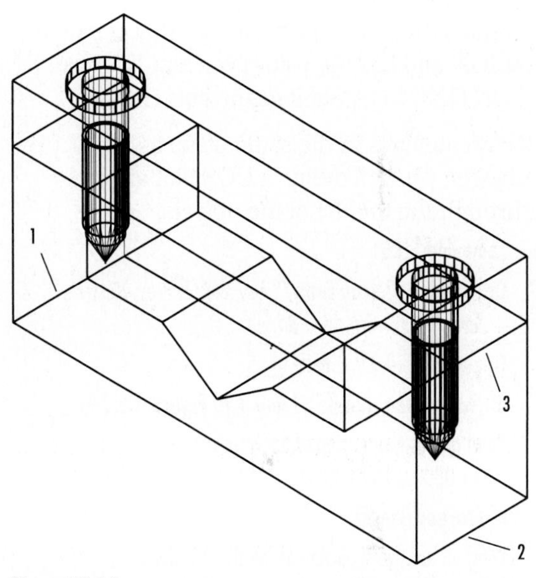

Figure 15.14

Continue with the MOVE command and relocate the washers in line with their present position, but moved 3 units along the Z axis.

Pick: **MOVE *(toolbox)***

Select objects: ***(pick the two washers)*** ↵

<Base point or displacement>: **0,0,0** ↵

Second point of displacement: **0,0,3** ↵

The washers line up below the screws, still in line with the holes on the object. Next, move the clamp cover up 2 units along the Z axis.

Command: ↵
MOVE
Select objects: ***(pick the cover)*** ↵
<Base point or displacement>: **0,0,0** ↵
Second point of displacement: **0,0,2** ↵

When you create an exploded view, it is customary to add thin lines that show how the parts assemble.

Create a new layer on your own that is called ALIGN and has the color cyan and linetype CONTINUOUS. Set it as the current layer.

To create lines in the same plane as the objects, you will define a UCS that aligns through the middle of the objects.

Command: **UCS** ↵
Origin/ZAxis/3point/Entity/View/X/Y/Z/Prev/Restore/
Save/Del/?/<World>: **3** ↵
Origin point <0,0,0>: **MID** ↵
of ***(target the middle of line 1 in Figure 15.14)***
Point on positive portion of the X axis
<1.0000,0.7500,0.0000>: **MID** ↵
of ***(target line 2)***
Point on positive-Y portion of the UCS XY plane
<1.0000,0.7500,0.0000>: **MID** ↵
of ***(target line 3)***

On your own, turn SNAP on if the word Snap is not currently displayed on the toolbar. Draw the lines indicating how the parts align. Use the LEADER command to add the text identifying the parts, or use the ball tag block that you created in Tutorial 14. Be sure to save your drawing.

Your drawing should look like Figure 15.15.

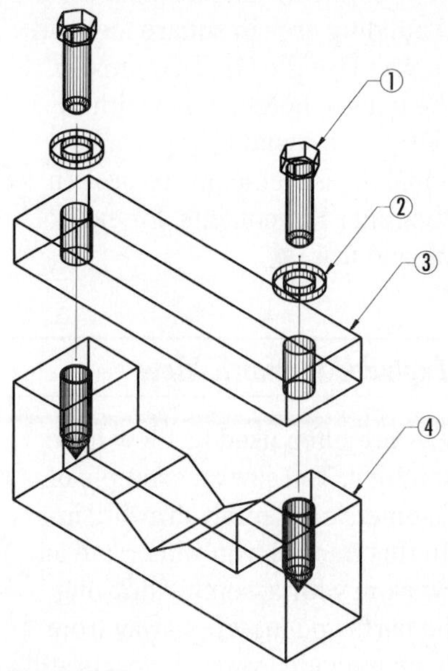

Figure 15.15

Changing an Externally Referenced Drawing (xref)

The major difference between blocks and xref drawings is that xrefs are not really added to the current drawing. A pointer is established to the original drawing (xref) that you attached. If the original drawing is changed, the change is also made in any drawing to which it is attached. Next, you will try this feature by opening drawing COVER-3D and changing its thickness.

Pick: **File *(menu bar)*, Open. . .**

Select drawing COVER-3D as the drawing to open. Pick OK to exit the dialogue box when you have finished making the selection.

The drawing of the cover appears on your screen.

Using SOLCHP

You will use the command SOLCHP to change the thickness of the cover to .5", as shown in Figure 15.16.

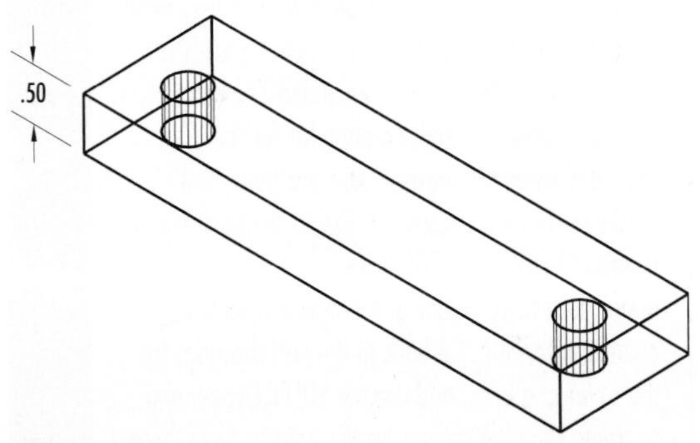

Figure 15.16

Pick: **Model *(menu bar)*, Modify, Change Primitives**
Select object: ***(pick on the edge of the cover)***
Select primitive: ***(pick on the edge of the cover again)***
Color/Delete/Evaluate/Instance/Move/Next/Pick/Replace/Size/eXit<N>: **S** ↵
Length along X axis: <5.5>: ↵
Length along Y axis: <1.5>: ↵
Length along Z axis: <0.75>: **.5** ↵
Color/Delete/Evaluate/Instance/Move/Next/Pick/Replace/Size/eXit<N>: **X** ↵

You will notice that the thickness of the cover has changed to .5. Save the changes to drawing COVER-3D so that they will occur in your assembly drawing.

Now you are ready to open the assembly drawing file and observe that the changes to COVER-3D appear in that drawing also.

Pick: **File *(menu bar)*, Open. . .**

Select drawing ASMB-SOL as the file to open. When you are finished, pick OK to exit the dialogue box.

Drawing ASMB-SOL appears on your screen, as shown in Figure 15.17.

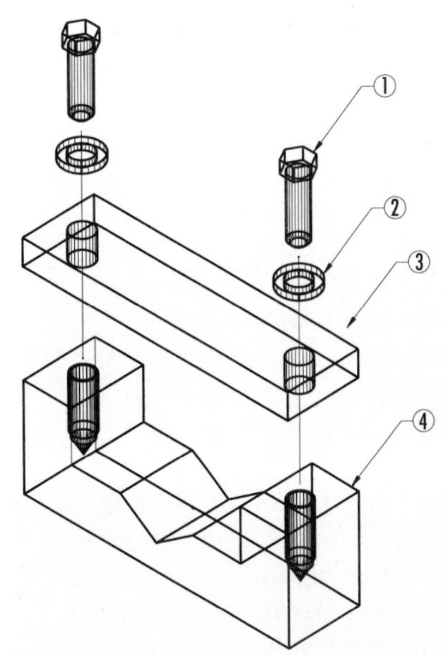

Figure 15.17

The change to the thickness of the cover has been made in the assembly drawing, as shown in Figure 15.17. The changes took place when this drawing was opened and the newly changed xref drawing COVER-3D was loaded into ASMB-SOL, automatically updating the assembly.

Adapting for Architecture

One important area where blocks and xrefs are useful is in the creation of architectural models for rendering or presentation. One problem with these types of models is the tradeoff that must be made between dimensionally accurate objects and model size and efficiency. You can use xrefs and blocks to simplify elements like doors, windows, furniture, and many others, and then later add detail. When you redefine the block or update the xref, your model automatically changes. At this point you can decide what foreground elements need enhancing, and what background elements can remain simple. If you have many symbols for the same thing in a drawing, and only want to alter a few of them, use EXPLODE to make sure the others are not changed. ■

■ ***TIP*** You must keep careful track of your drawings when using xrefs. If you did not intend to change the assembly, but made a change to an xref'd part, the assembly will change. Use SAVEAS and save the changed drawing to a new file name if you want to change an xref'd drawing, but not the assembly. Also, if you are going to send the drawing to someone on a disk, you must make sure to send all xref'd drawings too. Otherwise the recipient will not be able to open the xref'd portions of the drawing. A good way to avoid this problem is to use the XREF, Bind option to link the two drawings. This makes the xref'd drawing a part of the drawing where it is inserted. Also, it prevents you from unintentionally deleting the drawing that is xref'd into another drawing. However, once this has been done, the xrefs will no longer update. To use the XREF, Bind option, after you attach xrefs, choose XREF, Bind, and type the names (separated by commas, but no spaces) of all the xref files you want to bind to your assembly. ■

Going Further

Use the dimensions given in Tutorial 14 to create your own solid models of the parts for this assembly. Save the drawings on your disk. Then use xrefs to insert the parts to create an exploded isometric assembly drawing. Create a parts list for the exploded assembly drawing. Use attributes and blocks to create the parts list. Export the parts list to a spreadsheet, using DDE. Insert the parts list in the upper right-hand corner of the drawing. Save the assembly drawing. Go back to the part drawings for the cover and base, and use the SOLFILL command to create rounded corners on these parts. Save these changes to the drawings. Open the assembly drawing once again and note that the changes you made to the parts are automatically updated in the assembly.

Before surfaces can be hidden or shaded, the surfaces must be defined using the MESH command. When parts are inserted as xrefs they cannot be changed in the assembly drawing. Since the parts which were xref'd into your assembly were not meshed, you must open the original 3D part drawings and use the MESH command to mesh the part and save the file. Then re-open the assembly and use the SHADE command or pick AutoVis, Render from the menu bar. Use the AVE Full selection from the dialogue box and pick Render Scene to shade the objects in your drawing. This makes it easier to visualize the shapes of the parts.

Save your drawing and exit AutoCAD. You have completed Tutorial 15.

KEY TERMS

AutoLISP

LISP

mass properties

KEY COMMANDS

External Reference

Insert Solid

Solid Interference

Solid Mass Properties

Solid Material

Write Block Solid

EXERCISES

15.1 Clamping Block

Prepare assembly and detail drawings, and a parts list based on the information below using solid modeling techniques. Create solid models of Parts 1 and 2. Join Part 2 to Part 1 using two .500–13UNC × 2.50 LONG HEX-HEAD BOLTS. Include .500–13UNC NUTS on each bolt. Locate a .625×1.250×.125 WASHER under the head of each bolt, between Parts 1 and 2, and between Part 1 and the NUT. (Each bolt will have 3 washers and a nut.)

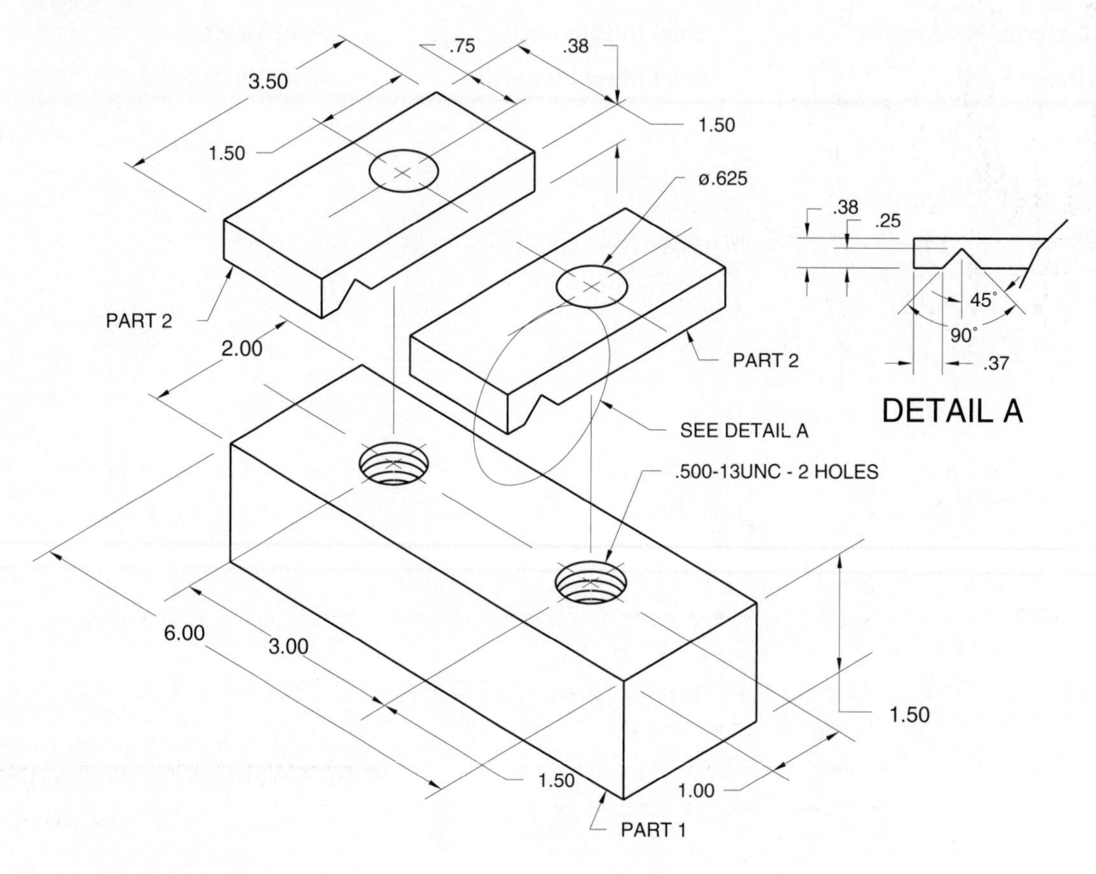

15.2 Pressure Assembly

Prepare assembly and detail drawings, and a parts list of the pressure assembly using solid modeling techniques. Create solid models of the BASE, GASKET, and COVER shown below. Use four .375–16UNC × 1.50 HEX-HEAD SCREWS to join the COVER, GASKET, and BASE. The GASKET assembles between the BASE and COVER.

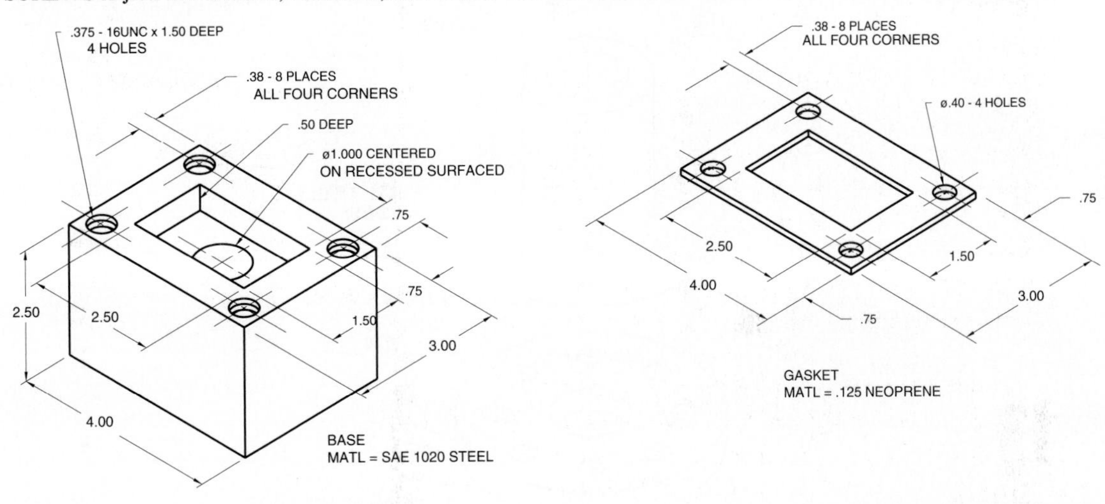

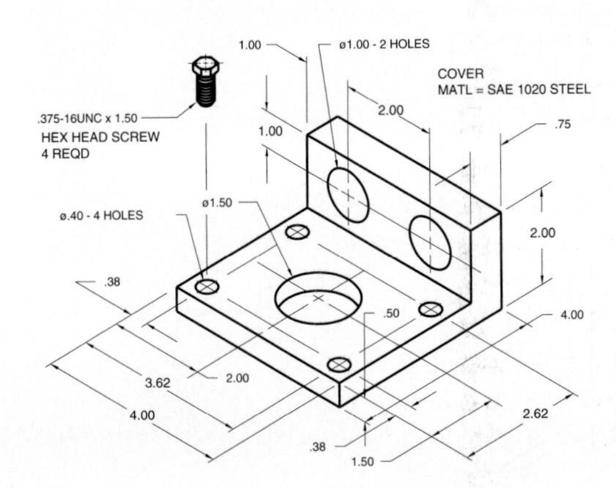

15.3 Hub Assembly

Redraw the following assembly using solid modeling techniques. Experiment with different materials and analyze mass properties.

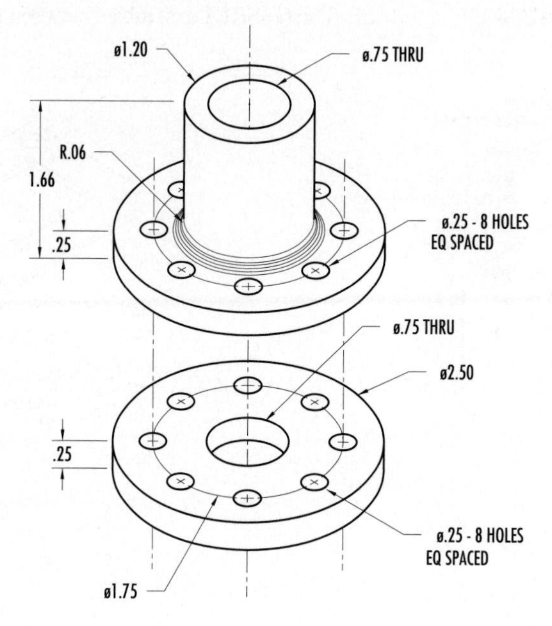

15.4 Staircase

Use solid modeling to generate this staircase assembly detail.

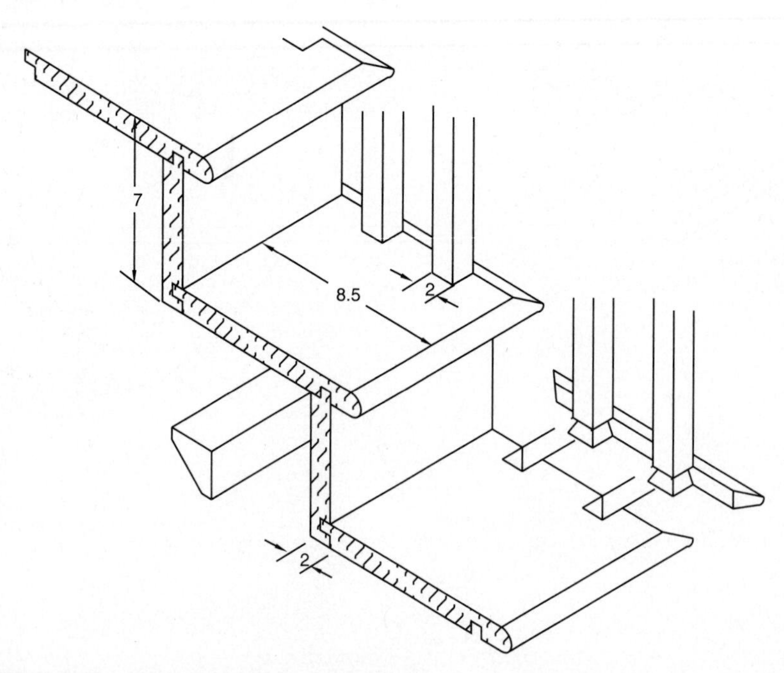

Create an assembly drawing for the parts shown, using solid modeling techniques. Experiment with different materials and analyze mass properties.

 15.5 Geneva Wheel Assembly

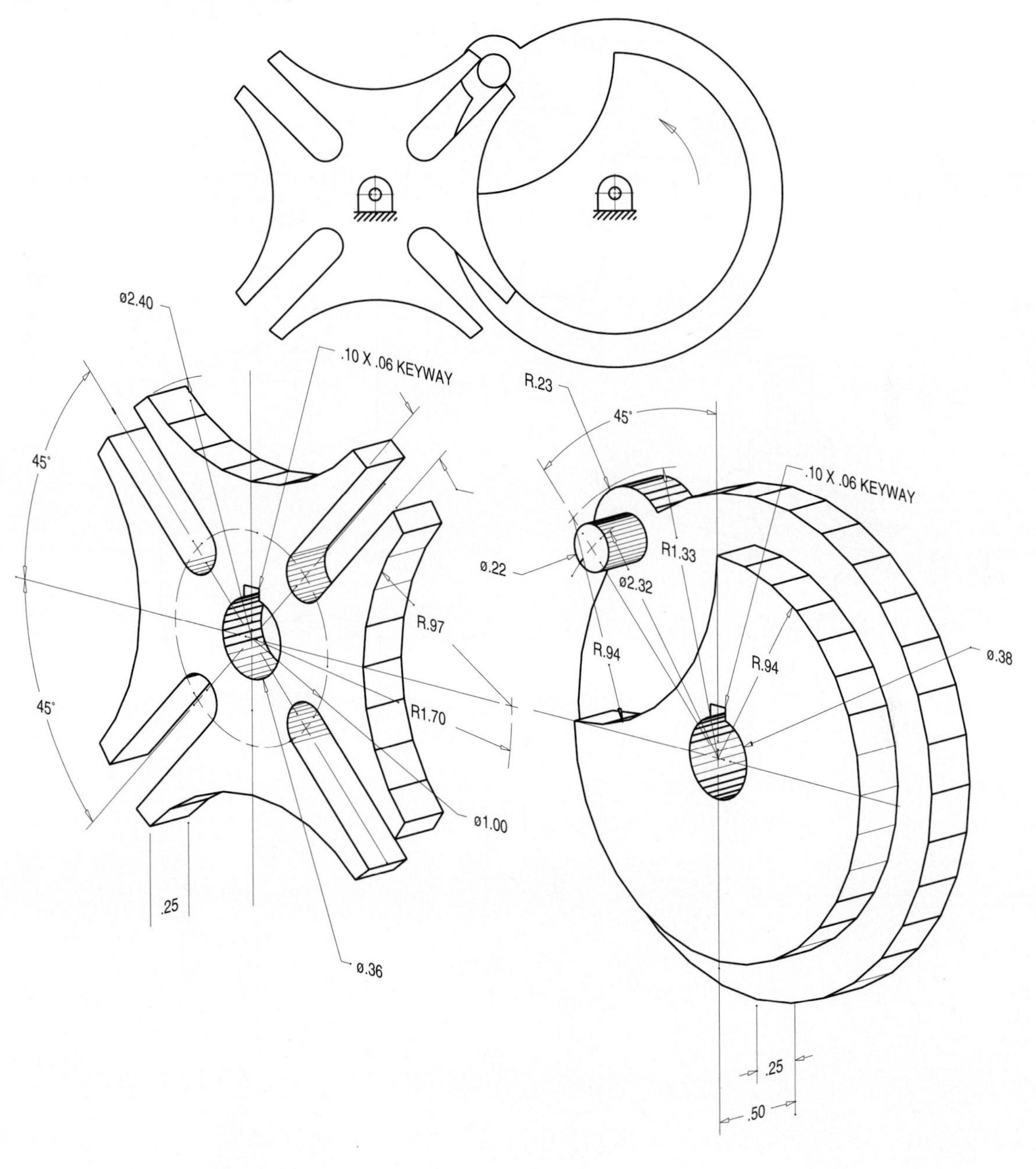

15.6M Universal Joint

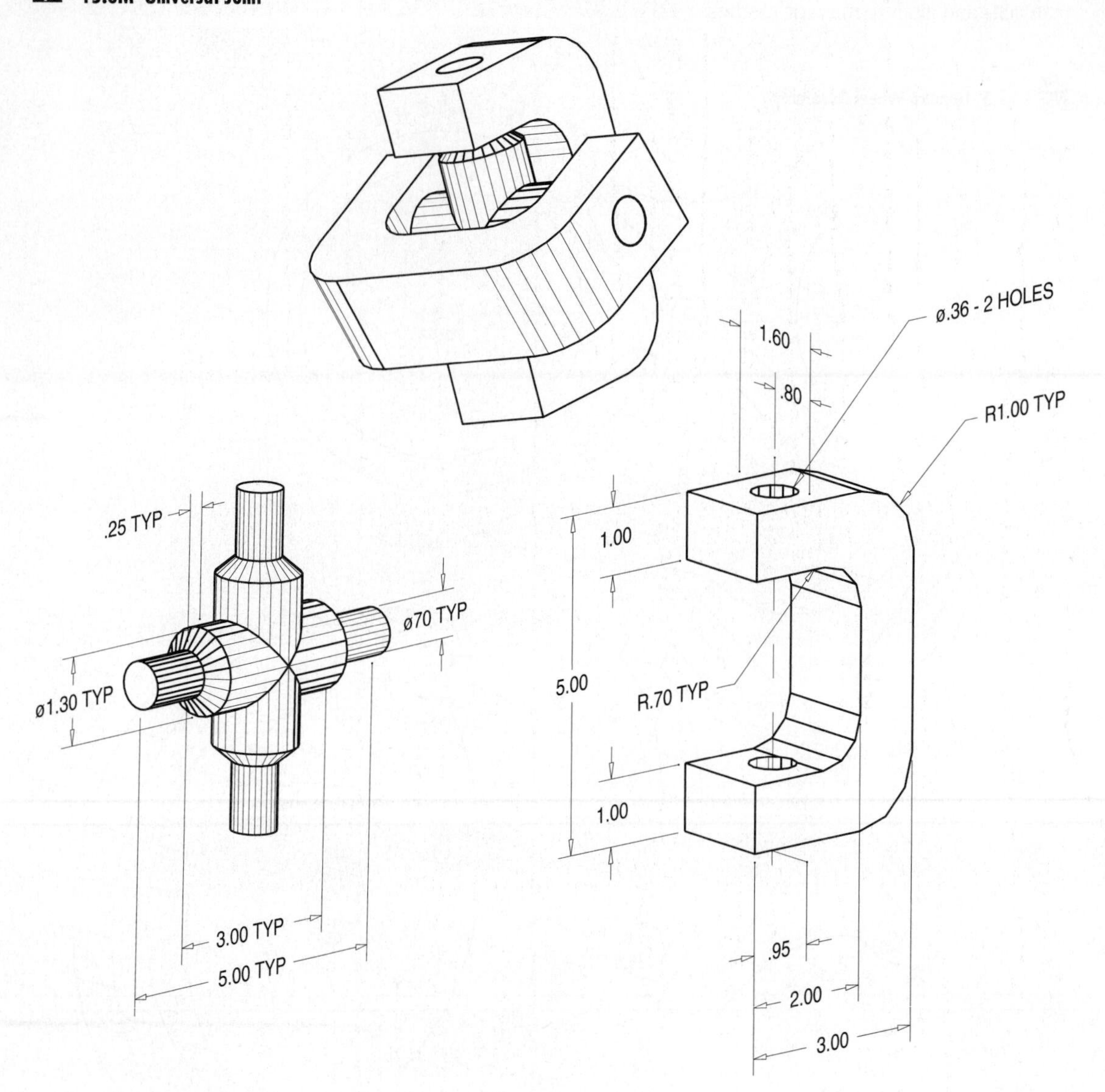

TUTORIAL 16

Rendering with AutoVision

Objectives

When you have completed this tutorial, you will be able to

1. Realistically shade a solid modeled drawing.
2. Set up and use lighting effects.
3. Apply materials and finishes.
4. Save rendered files for quick display.
5. Export to 3D Studio format.

Introduction

AutoVision lets you quickly create *rendered* images of AutoCAD objects, such as solid models like the ones you created beginning in Tutorial 8. Rendering is the process of calculating the lighting effects, color, and shape of an object in a single two-dimensional view. You can also use AutoVision to shade surfaces that were created using AutoCAD's surface modeling commands, which you select under Draw, 3D Surfaces from the menu bar. A rendered view adds greatly to the appearance of the drawing. It makes the object appear more real, and aids in interpretation of the object's shape, especially for those unfamiliar with engineering drawing. Rendered drawings can be used very effectively in creating presentations for clients, managers, salespeople and others.

Rendering is a process that is mathematically complex. When you are using AutoVision or other programs to do rendering, the capabilities of your hardware, such as speed, amount of memory, and the *resolution* of the display are particularly noticeable. The complex rendering calculations demand more hardware performance than just running the AutoCAD program, so you may notice that your system seems slower. Display resolution affects not only the speed with which objects are rendered, but the quality of the rendered appearance as well. The rendered screens shown in this tutorial were created using Super VGA resolution (800 × 600) and 256 colors and AutoCAD's configured WIN ADI display/rendering driver. Better appearance can be gained by rendering to a display using higher resolution and more colors; however, increased resolution and colors take a longer time to render.

In this tutorial you will learn to apply materials, surface maps, and lighting to your drawing and to render views of the object, using AutoVision for Windows. Applying a material to a surface in your drawing gives the surface its color and shininess; it is similar to painting the surface. Materials can also reflect light like a mirror, or be transparent like glass. Adding a surface map is similar to adding wallpaper; surface maps are patterns or pictures that can be applied to the surface of an object. Lighting is used to illuminate the surfaces. Lighting is a very important factor in creating the desired effect in your rendered drawing.

You should have installed and configured AutoVision when you installed AutoCAD. When AutoVision is installed, the word AutoVis replaces Render as an option on the menu bar. If you did not install AutoVision, do so before you begin this tutorial. Refer to Chapter 2, Installing and Configuring Your Software, for instructions on how to install and configure AutoVision.

Launch AutoCAD with AutoVision. If you need help, review the AutoCAD for Windows section of Chapter 3, in Part 1, Getting Started.

Using AutoVision

Next you will open the drawing ASMB-SL1 from the data files provided with your AutoCAD software. You will use AutoVision to render this solid model drawing so that it appears realistically shaded on your screen.

Pick: **File *(menu-bar)*, Open**

Use the dialogue box to select ASMB-SL1 from the data files in the DRAWINGS directory. When you have the correct file selected,

Pick: **OK *(to exit the dialogue box)***

The drawing ASMB-SL1 appears on your screen, as shown in Figure 16.1. Notice the AutoVis menu selection on the menu bar.

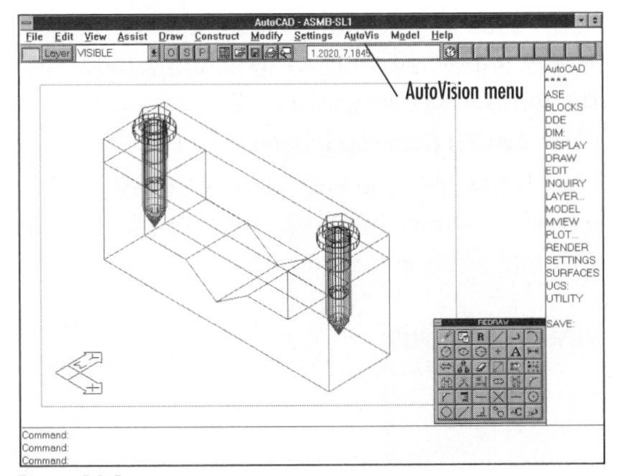

Figure 16.1

Before you use AutoVision to render objects that were created using AutoCAD AME, you should load the AME modeler. Otherwise, AutoVision may not be able to shade and render the object correctly. To load AME,

Pick: **Model *(menu bar)*, Utility, Load Modeler**

No modeler is loaded yet. Both AME and Region Modeler are available.

Autoload Region/<AME>: ↵

Pick: **AutoVis *(menu bar)***

The AutoVision menu selections pull down from the menu bar, as shown in Figure 16.2.

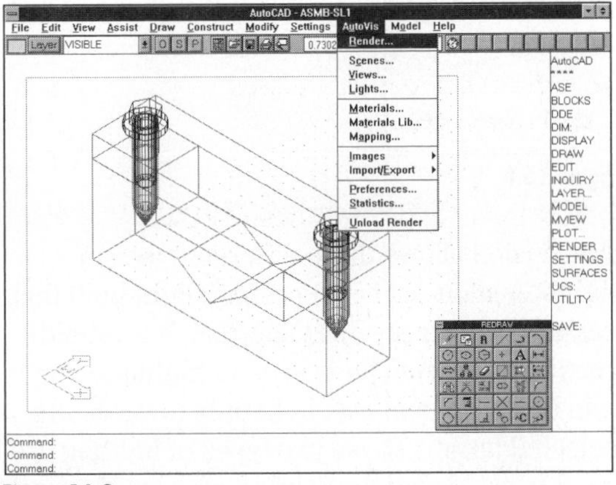

Figure 16.2

The Render option that you see at the top of the AutoVision pull-down menu uses a dialogue box to allow you to select rendering options.

Pick: **Render**

You will see AutoVision's Render dialogue box appear on your screen, as shown in Figure 16.3. Under Rendering Type you should see AVE Full. This, along with AVE Quick, makes up the standard AutoCAD rendering commands that you have used in previous tutorials. The circle to the left of the word AutoVision is filled in solidly, indicating that it is the default selection. The selection AutoVis Raytrace uses a *ray tracing* algorithm to produce rendered images that have *reflections*, *refractions*, and detailed shadows. Leave the AutoVision button selected.

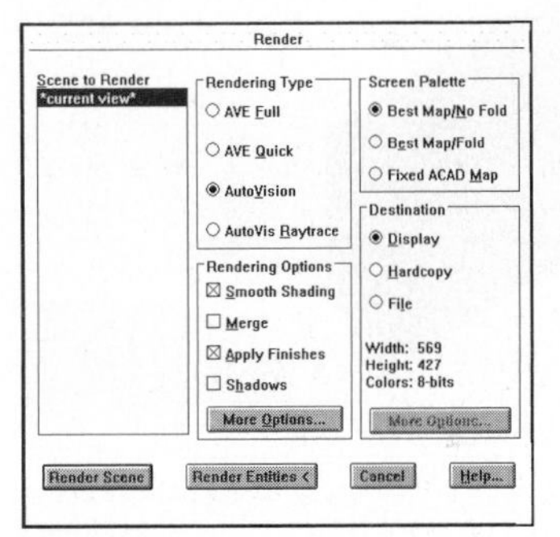

Figure 16.3

Check to see that Display is selected under the heading Destination. The Destination selection allows you to send the rendered output to either the display or to a hardcopy output device or file. You want to have the drawing rendered to your display, or screen.

Check to see also that Apply Finishes and Smooth Shading are turned on under Rendering Options. If you do not select Smooth Shading, meshed surfaces will appear faceted (made up from flat surfaces). Selecting

Apply Finishes tells AutoVision to apply materials to objects. In the scene you will render, since you have not selected any finishes yet, the AutoCAD Color Index (ACI) will be used, giving your shaded objects a color similar to their original AutoCAD color. Later, when you apply materials to the surfaces of the objects in your drawing, selecting Apply Finishes will cause the surfaces to be rendered with the material appearance, not the AutoCAD color.

Pick: **Render Scene**

Your drawing is rendered to the display. It should appear similar to Figure 16.4.

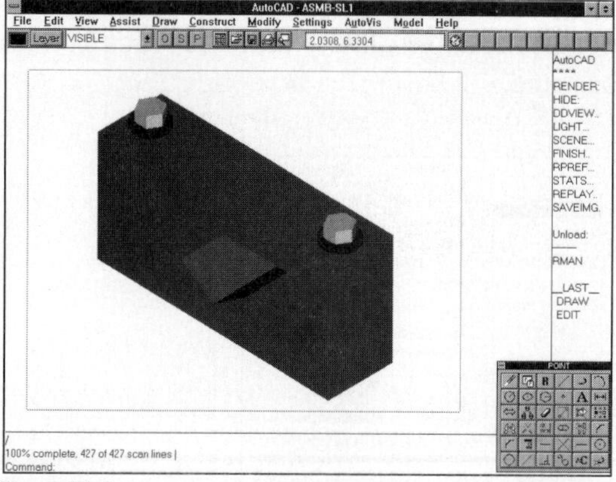

Figure 16.4

Adding Lights

Notice that some of the surfaces blend into one another and are hard to see. This is because you have not set up any lighting in the drawing. The default lighting in the drawing is one distant light, which is placed as though it were lighting the drawing from over your shoulder. It has an *ambient* light intensity of 0.30, which is not very much illumination. You can make your rendered drawing look better by using AutoVision to add additional lights. Lighting is very important in order to achieve good-looking rendering results.

Pick: **AutoVis *(menu bar)*, Lights**

The Lights dialogue box appears on your screen, as shown in Figure 16.5. You will use it to create lighting for your drawing.

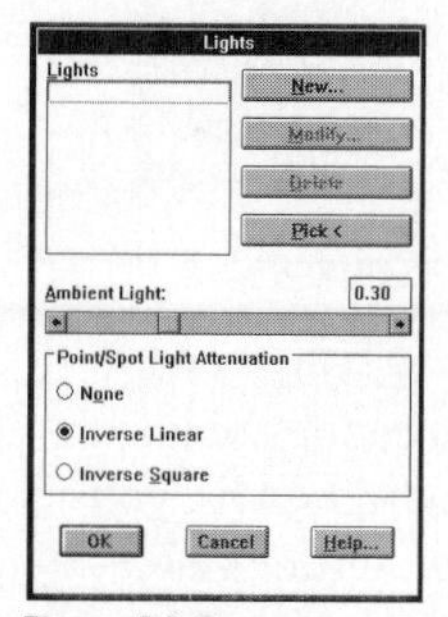

Figure 16.5

To create a new light for the drawing,

Pick: **New *(from the upper right corner of the Lights dialogue box)***

The New Light Type dialogue box appears on your screen to allow you to select the type of light you will add to the drawing. Figure 16.6 shows this dialogue box.

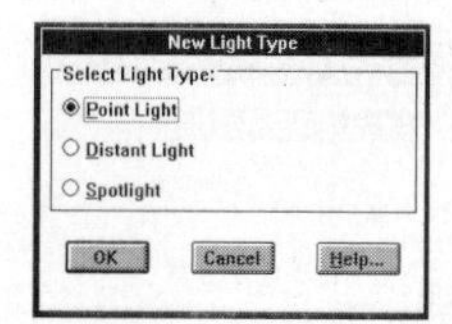

Figure 16.6

AutoVision allows three different types of lights. A *point light* is like a bare light bulb that casts light in every direction (i.e., it is omnidirectional). A *spotlight* is used to highlight certain key areas and cast light only towards the selected target. These two types of lighting are used to create indoor lighting effects. The final type of lighting is distant light, which is like sunlight. AutoVision provides a sun angle calculator feature that is particularly useful in architectural applications. You will learn how to use the sun angle calculator later in this tutorial. First, you will add a point light to your drawing. Because it is the default, it is already selected.

Pick: **OK *(to continue)***

The New Point Light dialogue box appears, as shown in Figure 16.7. You will use this dialogue box to name the new light and select the features that determine its appearance, such as intensity (brightness), color, and its location in the drawing. You will name the light FILL because you are using it to fill the area where your object is with more lighting.

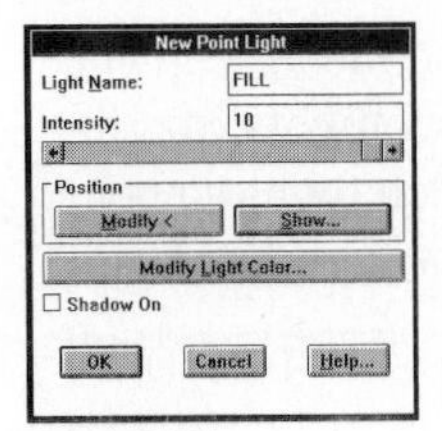

Figure 16.7

Type: **FILL *(in the text box to the right of Light Name:)***

Next you will position the light in your drawing. AutoVision places a block as a symbol in your drawing to represent the light.

Pick: **Modify *(under the heading Position)***

You are returned to your drawing. You can position the light by picking a location from the screen; however, for this example you will type in the coordinates for the light. It is difficult to position the light by picking from the screen because you are selecting only the x and y coordinates. (You can use point filters and then set the z location, if you desire. Use HELP to find out more about point filters.) When specifying the coordinates for the light position, remember not to position it too close to the object.

Enter light location <current>: **–3,–10,5** ↵

You return to the New Point Light dialogue box.

Pick: **Show**

The Show. . . selection shows you the coordinates of the light's location. This allows you to check to see whether you have made an error, or to identify the coordinates for lights that were placed previously or located by picking from the screen.

Pick: **OK *(to exit the dialogue box)***

Next you will adjust the *intensity* or brightness of the light. You can think of this as the wattage of the bare light bulb (a 100-watt bulb in the location is brighter than a 60-watt bulb). You will type the value in the box provided. You can also use the slider bar to adjust the intensity of the light.

Select: ***(highlight the value in the box for Intensity)***

Type: **10**

You could use the Modify Light Color. . . selection from the dialogue box to select a different color for the light. Setting the light to a yellowish color will give a warmer effect, like indoor lamps. For this example you will leave it white.

Pick: **OK *(to exit the New Point Light dialogue box)***

You return to the Lights dialogue box.

Pick: **OK *(to exit the dialogue box)***

Now you are ready to use AutoVision's RENDER command to see the effect of the added point light to your drawing.

Pick: **AutoVis *(menu bar),* Render**

The Render dialogue box that you used earlier appears on your screen. Make sure that the rendering type selected is AutoVision and that Smooth Shading is selected under Rendering Options. The destination for the rendered drawing should be the display, so that you will see it on your screen. When you have made sure that these selections are chosen,

Pick: **Render Scene**

The added lighting should improve the appearance of your rendered drawing so that it looks like Figure 16.8.

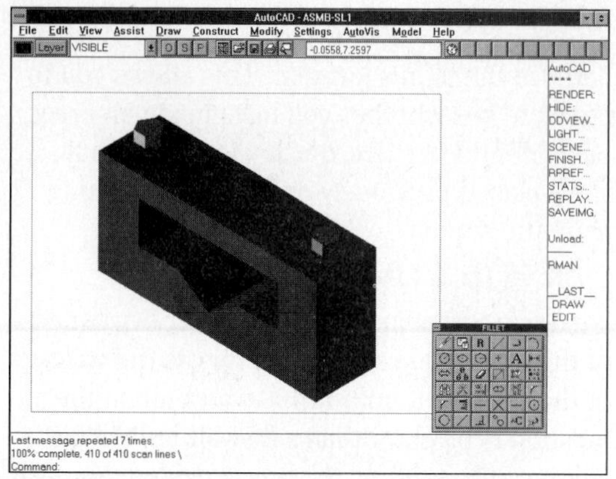

Figure 16.8

The right-hand surface of the object is still not lighted very well; not much light is striking that surface. Next you will add a spotlight behind the object to light that surface and provide highlights in the drawing.

Pick: **AutoVis *(menu bar)*, Lights**

You will use the Lights dialogue box once again to add a new light.

Pick: **New**

From the New Light Type dialogue box,

Pick: **Spotlight**

Pick: **OK**

The New Spotlight dialogue box shown in Figure 16.9 appears on your screen. You will use it to name and select the attributes for the spotlight.

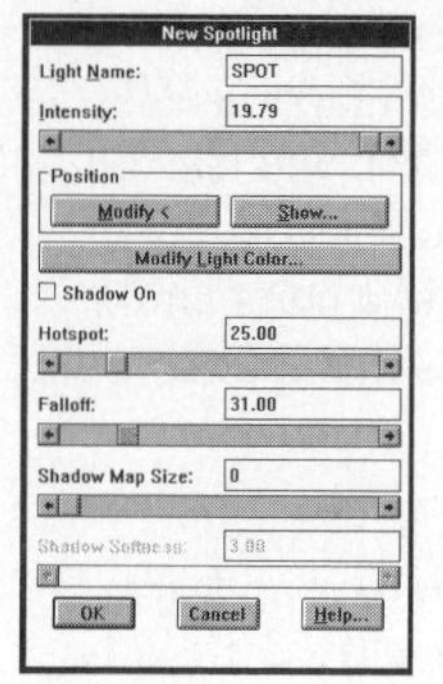

Figure 16.9

Type: **SPOT *(in the text box to the right of Light Name:)***

Set the intensity for the spotlight by moving the slider bar to a setting near 9.00, or type that value in the box to the right of Intensity:.

Now you are ready to position the light in your drawing. When positioning spotlights, you first specify the target toward which they will point. Then you give the location for the light. Under the heading Position,

Pick: **Modify**

Press ↵ to accept the current location for the target (near the center of the object), then type in the location for the light at the next prompts:

Enter light target <current>: ↵

Enter light location <current>: **14,4,6** ↵

The New Spotlight dialogue box returns to your screen. Next, you will set the *falloff* and *hotspot* for the spotlight. Falloff is the angle of the cone of light from the spotlight. Hotspot is the angle of the cone of light for the brightest area of the beam. The angles for the falloff and hotspot must be between 0 and 160 degrees. AutoVision will not allow you to set Hotspot to a greater value than Falloff.

On your own, use the slider bar to set the value for Hotspot to 25 and the value for Falloff to 31. For now, leave Shadow Map Size set to zero. When you are finished setting these values, pick OK to exit the New Spotlight dialogue box and then pick OK once again to exit the Lights dialogue box.

You return to the AutoCAD drawing editor. You will use the Render dialogue box to render your drawing again to see the effect of adding the spotlight to the drawing.

Pick: **AutoVis *(menu bar)*, Render**

Check the settings in the dialogue box to make sure that they are the same ones you have used before in this tutorial and then:

Pick: **Render Scene**

The drawing is rendered to your screen and should appear similar to Figure 16.10. Notice the bright area of the spotlight beam, which you set using Hotspot. The size of the entire circle of light from the spotlight is determined by the setting you entered for Falloff.

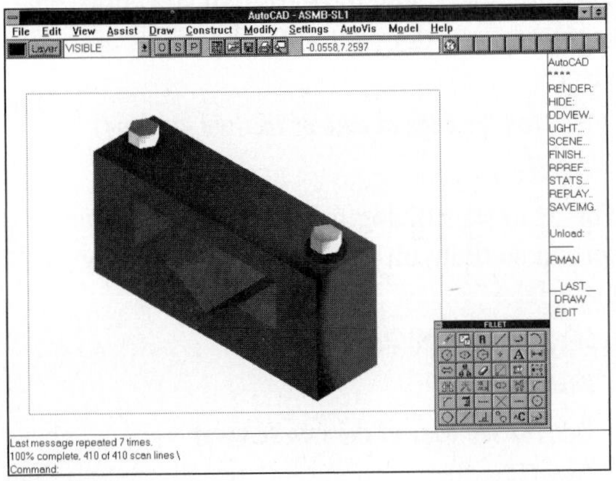

Figure 16.10

Choosing Materials

Your rendered drawing can also be improved by selecting or creating realistic-looking materials for the objects in your drawing. You can either use the materials that are provided or create your own materials, using AutoVision. As with lights, a block is added in the drawing representing the material. To add materials,

Pick: **AutoVis *(menu bar)*, Materials**

The Materials dialogue box appears on your screen. You will use it to select materials from the Materials Library for the objects in your drawing. A single block or solid object in the drawing can only have one material assigned. This is usually not a problem in engineering drawings, because you typically make each separate part in an assembly a separate object or block in the drawing. Remember not to use Boolean operators to union together parts that you want to assign different materials.

To select from the library of pre-made materials,

Pick: **Materials Library *(from the lower right corner of the dialogue box)***

The Materials Library dialogue box shown in Figure 16.11 appears on your screen. You will choose materials for your assembly drawing from the list of materials shown in the right-hand side of the dialogue box.

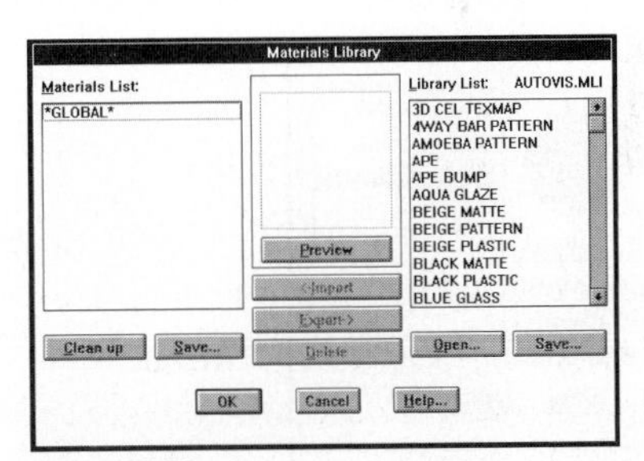

Figure 16.11

Use the scroll bar or pick on the upward- or downward-pointing arrow to scroll through the list of materials until you see the selection BRASS VALLEY, which you will use for the washers in the assembly drawing. Position the cursor over the name BRASS VALLEY and press the pick button to select it. The material you have selected becomes highlighted in the list.

Many of the materials dialogues allow you to preview the selection to see approximately what the material will look like. This saves time in case you do not want to use the particular material once you see it, or your system is not capable of displaying it. Remember that rendering a complex drawing can be time-consuming. Use the Preview function to see what the material will look like before you decide to use it.

Pick: **Preview**

The material you selected is shown applied to a spherical shape in the Preview box, as you see in Figure 16.12.

■ ***Warning:*** If you do not see it, you may not have set the variable for AVEMAPS before you started Windows, or perhaps your system cannot display the colors being used. If this happens, refer to Chapter 2, Installing and Configuring Your Software, or check with your technical support person. ■

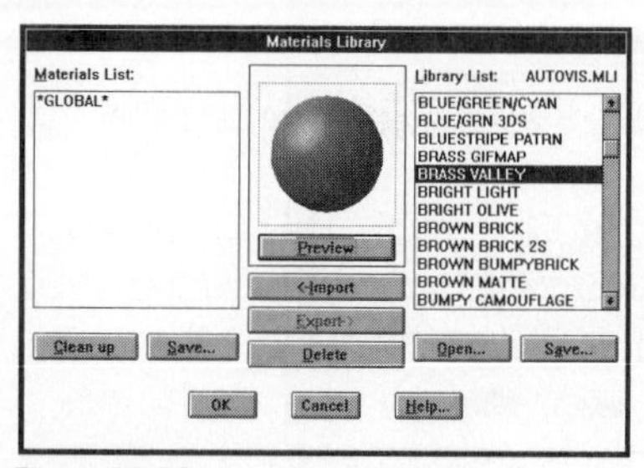

Figure 16.12

Once you have previewed the material, you will import it so that it is available for use in your drawing.

Pick: **Import**

The selected material is shown in the Materials List at the left of the dialogue box. Now you are ready to select another material.

Now highlight the material named GRAY MATTE from the list of materials at the right of the dialogue box. If you want to preview it, do so. Then pick Import to make the material available for use in the current drawing. Its name is added to the list at the left. Select the final material you will use, GRAY SEMIGLOSS, from the list at the right. Use the Preview option to see what the material will look like. Pick Import to add GRAY SEMIGLOSS to the list of materials you will use. When you have finished importing the materials,

Pick: **OK *(to exit the Materials Library dialogue box)***

You return to the Materials dialogue box, where you will select to attach the materials to the objects in your drawing.

Select: **BRASS VALLEY *(from the list of materials at the left of the dialogue box)***

Pick: **Attach**

You are returned to your drawing to allow selection of the objects, in this case the two washers. If you accidentally select something else, use the Remove option to take it out of the selection set. If you have trouble selecting, try to pick on an edge, not in the center of an object.

Pick: ***(on the edge of each of the two washers)***

Press: ↵

The Materials dialogue box returns to your screen so that you may continue attaching materials.

Select: **GRAY SEMIGLOSS**

Pick: **Attach**

Pick: ***(on the edge of the two screws)***

Press: ↵

Next, attach the material GRAY MATTE to the base and cover of the assembly.

Select: **GRAY MATTE**

Pick: **Attach**

Pick: ***(on the edge of the base and the cover)***

Press: ↵

Pick: **OK *(to exit the dialogue box)***

Now that you are finished selecting the materials, you will render the drawing once again in order to see the results of the changes you have made.

Pick: **AutoVis *(menu bar)*, Render**

Accept the same defaults that you have been using previously.

Pick: **Render Scene**

Your drawing should now show the new materials. It should look similar to Figure 16.13.

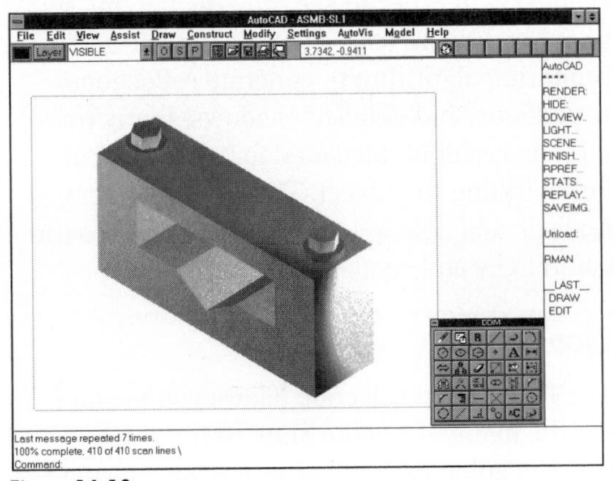

Figure 16.13

You can also use AutoVision to create your own materials. Next you will create a material to look like steel to use for the base and cover of the assembly.

Pick: **AutoVis *(menu bar)*, Materials**

When the Materials dialogue box appears,

Pick: **New *(from the right-hand side of the dialogue box)***

The New Standard Material dialogue box shown in Figure 16.14 appears on your screen.

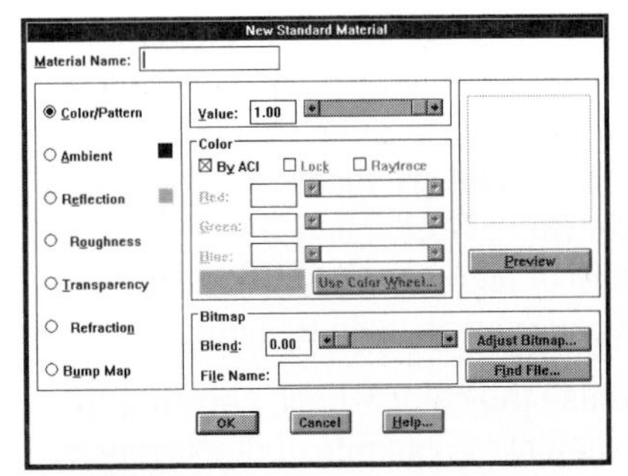

Figure 16.14

Type: **STEEL *(in the text box to the right of Material Name:)***

At the left of the dialogue box are the various qualities, or material attributes. They are Color/Pattern, Ambient, Reflection, Roughness, Transparency, Refraction, and Bump Map. These are the attributes that you can control to create materials with different appearances. In general, these qualities tell how the surface or material responds when light strikes it. To change these attributes, pick in the circle to the left of the attribute for which you want to set the values. Below is a description of the function of each attribute.

Color/Pattern

This selection determines the color for the material. The default selection for color is By ACI (AutoCAD Color Index), which results in the object being rendered in the color assigned to its lines in the AutoCAD model. You saw this when you rendered the assembly for the first time and the objects were shown in the original layer colors. If you deselect By ACI under Color, you can use the slider bars in that section of the dialogue box to set how much of each color of light is used to make up the material color. As you move the slider bars, the resulting color is shown in the empty box at the bottom of the Color area. This is called the color *swatch*. Keep in mind that colors on your computer screen are made of the primary colors of light (Red, Green, and Blue), not the primary colors of pigment (Red, Blue, and Yellow) that you may be used to using.

You can also use the color wheel, showing the colors your monitor is capable of displaying, to select the color. Or you may want to start from the color wheel and then adjust the slider bars for Red, Green, and Blue to achieve the final color.

In addition, you can use a bit map (a pattern or picture), such as a scanned image or drawing created with a paint-style program, instead of just solid color. To do this, use the Bitmap section and type the name of the bitmap file in the box to the right of File Name:.

Ambient

This selection allows you to set the color for the object's shadow. You can use the same color controls as discussed above.

Reflection

This selection allows you to adjust the color of the material's reflective highlight. When ray tracing is selected, you can specify the value for the material's reflectivity from 0, where it does not reflect any light, to 1, where it is perfectly reflective, like a mirror.

Roughness

Roughness lets you specify the surface *roughness* of the material. This is also related to reflectivity. The lower the surface roughness, the more reflective the surface will be. Change the value and use Preview to see how roughness changes the size of the material's highlight.

Transparency

The settings for *transparency* allow you to make objects that are clear, like glass, or somewhat clear, like colored liquids. Keep in mind that objects that are completely transparent, so that you do not even see them in the drawing when they are rendered, still take time to render.

Refraction

This control is only used with transparent objects. Refraction is the amount that light is bent when entering and leaving a transparent object. You must use AutoVision's Raytrace rendering in order to see the effect of this setting. Ray tracing uses a more sophisticated rendering algorithm to generate reflections, refractions, and detailed shadows. In ray tracing, the result is calculated for each "ray" of light striking the object. This produces very realistic and detailed effects, but increases the complexity and rendering time.

Bump Map

The Bump Map selection allows you to enter the file name of a *bump map*. Bump maps convert the color intensity or grayscale information to heights, to give the appearance that features are raised above the surface, like embossed letters.

Next you will select the attributes for the steel material you are going to create.

Pick: ***(the circle to the left of Color/Pattern if it is not already filled in)***

Pick: ***(in the small square to the left of By ACI to turn it off, so that no X appears in the box)***

Use the slider bars to adjust the colors for Red, Green, and Blue so that Red and Green are each set to a value of .88 and Blue is set to .80. Notice how the color swatch changes as you move the slider bars. The resulting color should be gray. Preview the result.

Next you will make the surface somewhat reflective and assign a small value for surface roughness, so that the material will appear like steel.

Pick: ***(the circle to the left of Reflection)***

Use the slider bar to set the value for reflection to .65. Then,

Pick: ***(the circle to the left of Roughness)***

Set the value for roughness to .30.

To see the results of your selections on the material being created,

Pick: **Preview**

Your screen should appear similar to Figure 16.15.

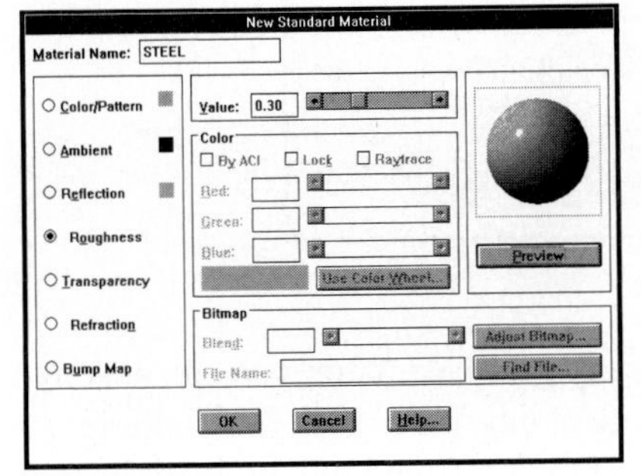

Figure 16.15

Pick: **OK** ***(to exit the dialogue box)***

Enter new material location <current>: ↵

You will return to the Materials dialogue box. Next you will attach this material to the base and cover in the assembly drawing in place of GRAY MATTE. To do this, use the dialogue box on your own to select the material STEEL that you created and attach it to the base and cover. When you have attached the material, pick OK to exit the dialogue box. Then select the AutoVision Render command and render the drawing to the display.

Saving and Replaying an Image File

Because it can take a long time to render a complex drawing, you may want to save an image, or bitmapped file, of the screen so that you can call it up quickly. The selection Image found under AutoVision on the menu bar saves and replays image files.

Pick: **AutoVis** ***(menu bar),*** **Images**

The selections Save Image and Replay Image pop out from the Image menu item.

Pick: **Save Image**

The Save Image dialogue box appears on your screen, as shown in Figure 16.16.

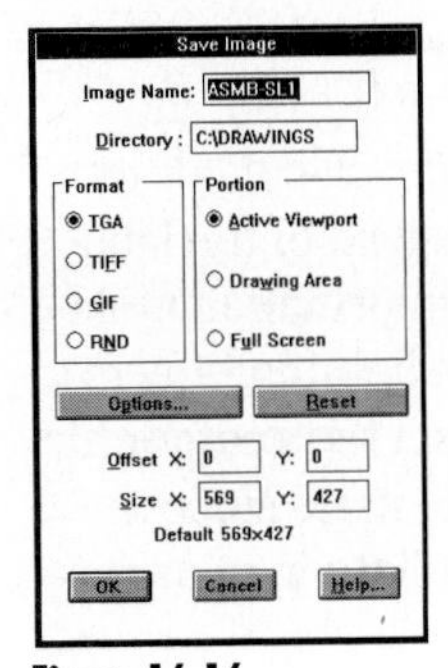

Figure 16.16

You can use the dialogue box to save in any of the following formats: TGA (TARGA), TIFF, GIF, and RND. If you have a paint-style program that uses one of these formats, you may be able to edit and print the saved image file. These formats can often also be used to insert the drawing into a word processing program. You can use the Portion options to select the portion of the drawing that you want to capture in the file, and you can change the name and directory for the file. To save the image file using the defaults,

Pick: **OK**

The file is saved with the extension .TGA, .TIF, .GIF, or .RND, depending on the format you selected. To replay a file,

Pick: **AutoVis *(menu bar)*, Image, Replay Image. . .**

Pick: **OK *(in the dialogue box that appears)***

Use the Replay Image dialogue box that appears to select the file that you just saved. Notice that it draws on the screen in a much shorter time than it takes to render the drawing.

Using the Sun Angle Calculator

The sun angle calculator is particularly useful in architectural drawings for showing the different effects that sunlight has on the rendered scene during different times of the day and year. You can use the sun angle calculator to easily figure these effects, instead of the laborious process of looking the information up in tables and adding the correct lighting effects to your drawing. You can even set the geographic location by picking it from the map. Since the sun will be added as a distant light in your rendered drawing,

Pick: **AutoVis *(menu bar)*, Lights**

Pick: **New**

Pick: **Distant Light**

Pick: **OK**

The New Distant Light dialogue box shown in Figure 16.17 appears on your screen.

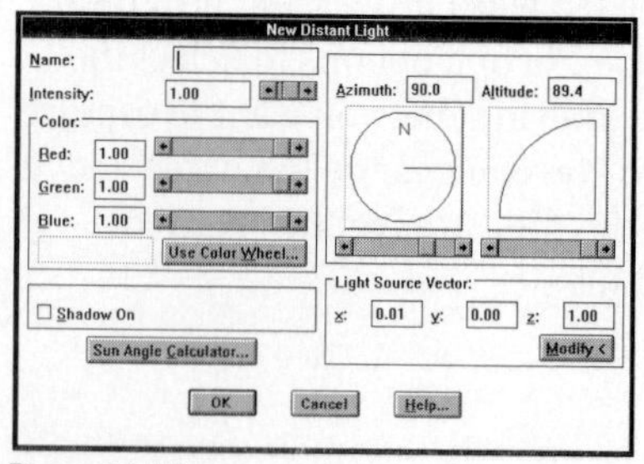

Figure 16.17

Type: **SUN *(in the empty box to the right of Name:)***

You can use the slider bars or the color wheel to set the color for the distant light. Leave it white for now, as the sun usually casts white light, which is composed of the full spectrum of light colors. The area at the right of the dialogue box allows you to specify the azimuth and altitude for the sun if you wish. You will use the sun angle calculator and let it determine these values for you.

Pick: **Sun Angle Calculator**

The Sun Angle Calculator dialogue box is shown in Figure 16.18.

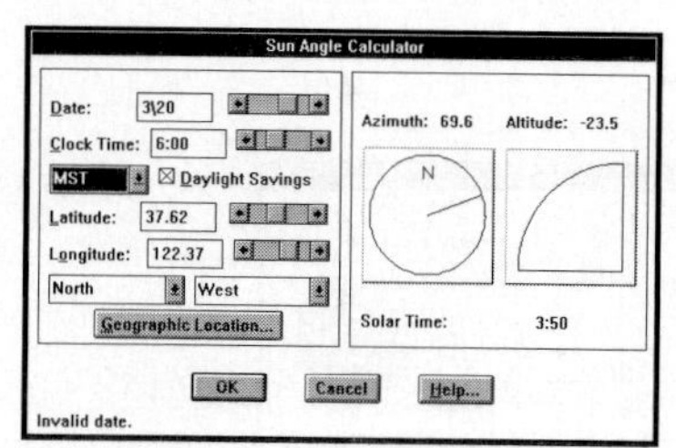

Figure 16.18

Using the sun angle calculator, you can specify the date, time of day, time zone, and latitude and longitude to determine the angle of the sun.

Set the date to March 20 (3/20) and the clock time to 6:00 hours (6 o'clock a.m.) MST on your own. Turn Daylight Savings on by picking in the box to its left so that an X is displayed in the box.

Next you will specify the geographic location, because it works with date and time of day to determine the angle of the sun.

Pick: **Geographic Location**

The Geographic Location dialogue box shown in Figure 16.19 appears on your screen.

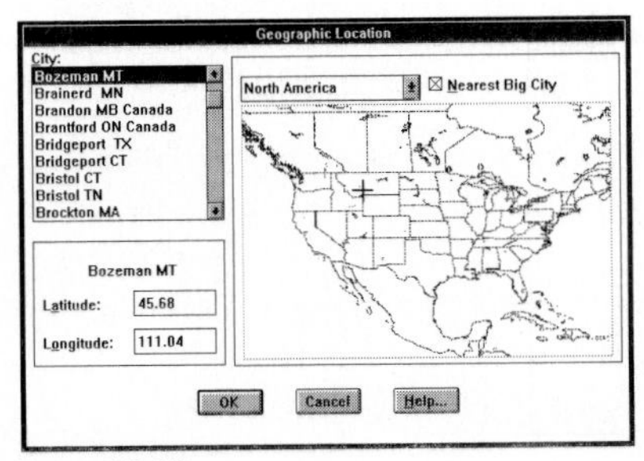

Figure 16.19

Move the cursor over the map until it is positioned as you see in Figure 16.19 and press the pick button. Notice that Bozeman, MT (cultural Mecca and center of the universe) appears as the nearest big city in the list at the left. Below, the latitude and longitude for Bozeman are displayed. You can also scroll down the list of cities to make a selection. Position the cursor over the words North America to the upper left of the map area and

Pick: ***(on the words North America)***

A list of the other continents pulls down, as shown in Figure 16.20. You can use the scroll bar to select from the other continents. The major cities of other continents are stored in the database and can be selected by picking from the map or by scrolling down the list of cities.

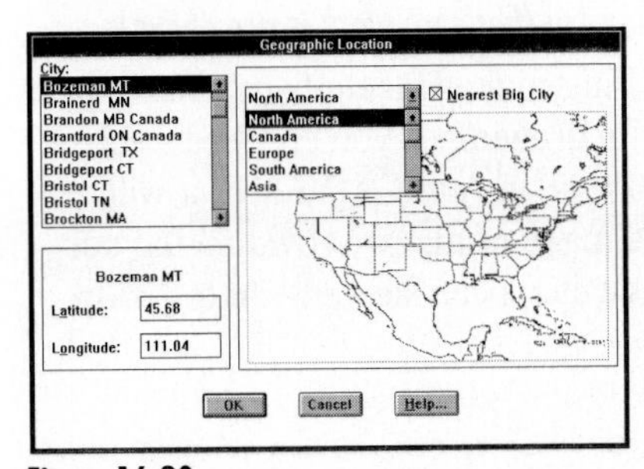

Figure 16.20

Do not change the continent selection at this time. Leave it set to North America.

Pick: ***OK (to exit the Geographic Location dialogue box)***

Pick: ***OK (to exit the Sun Angle Calculator dialogue box)***

Pick: ***OK (to exit the New Distant Light dialogue box)***

Pick: ***OK (to exit the Lights dialogue box)***

Your drawing returns to the screen. Now you will render the drawing again to see the part as though the sun were shining on it at 6:00 a.m. on March 20 in Bozeman, Montana.

On your own, render the drawing and notice the effect of the sunlight. Then select AutoVision, Lights. . . and pick SUN as the light you want to modify. Change the time of day to 4:00 p.m. (The time-of-day-clock is a 24-hour clock.) Render the drawing again and notice the change. Although this assembly is not an architectural drawing, you can see what a great advantage the sun angle calculator is for architectural uses. You can also use it to evaluate the suitability of a site for solar power, and other heat transfer analysis.

Exporting to 3D Studio

You can use the materials and lights that you have created in 3D Studio, Autodesk's 3D animation program. AutoVision will also allow you to apply smoothing in 3D Studio, so that faceted surfaces are shown smoothed. Now you are ready to *export* your drawing in 3D Studio format. You will *import* your drawing into 3D Studio and learn to add 3D animation effects in the next tutorial.

■ ***Warning:*** AutoCAD's AME entities are not converted to 3D Studio format and will not import correctly unless they have been meshed. ■

You will use the AME MESH command to mesh the objects to ensure that they export correctly to 3D Studio. Make sure that AME is loaded and then,

Pick: **Model *(menu bar)*, Display, Mesh**

Select objects: ***(window the solids making up the assembly)***

Select objects: ↵

Pick: **AutoVis *(menu bar)*, Import/Export, 3DS Out...**

Select objects: **ALL** ↵

Select objects: ↵

A dialogue box for naming your 3D Studio output file appears on your screen, as shown in Figure 16.21.

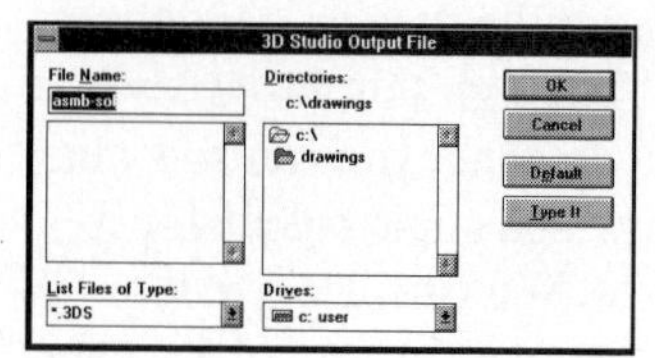

Figure 16.21

Use the dialogue box to select the directory and name your drawing file on your own. The file extension .3DS will be assigned to your file. When you are finished naming the file, pick OK to exit the dialogue box.

When you exit the file naming dialogue box, the 3D Studio File Export Options dialogue shown in Figure 16.22 appears on your screen. You will use it to set the method that 3D Studio should use to determine individual objects, and the smoothing and welding to be done.

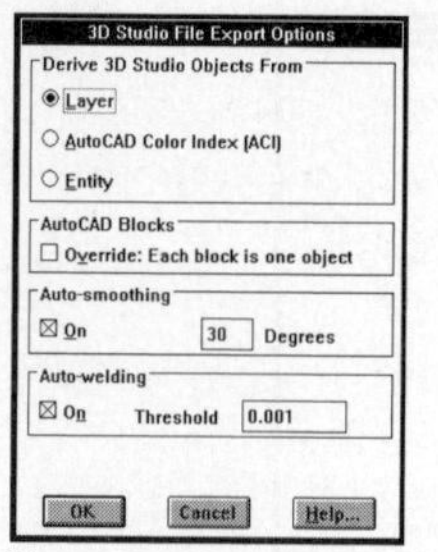

Figure 16.22

3D Studio can determine which entities are individual objects and can therefore be moved and animated separately from one another by three methods. If you select the Layer option, each entity that you want to have as a separate 3D Studio object must be on its own layer in the drawing. This method works quite well if the entities are on separate layers. (It is easy to change the layer of an entity, using AutoCAD's CHPROP command, if they are not on separate layers.) Assigning objects by AutoCAD Color Index creates the object from entities that have the same AutoCAD color. Choosing by Entities creates individual objects from the same type of entity in the drawing. Arcs, lines, and polylines must have a non-zero thickness in order to be exported as 3D Studio objects.

Pick: **Entity *(from the selections available in the dialogue box)***

Pick: **Override *(so that each block is one object)***

Auto-smoothing makes faceted surfaces appear smooth in the drawing. If you create an object, such as a sphere, in AutoCAD AME, it will appear to be made of many individual flat surfaces (i.e., it will appear faceted). AutoVision and 3D Studio have the ability to make such an object appear to be smooth and round, like a ball. When Auto-smoothing is turned on, the setting in the Degrees area specifies the maximum number of degrees for smoothing; in other words, surfaces that meet with an angle greater than the number of degrees specified will not be smoothed. 30 degrees is the default.

Leave Auto-smoothing turned on and the angle set to 30 degrees.

Auto-welding joins vertices that are no farther apart than the specified *threshold value* into one vertex. This simplifies complex geometry so that it is quicker to animate and render in 3D Studio. As in AutoVision, the complexity of the objects and the demands of the lighting and shading can make rendering and animating slow. Simplifying the drawing in this way can improve the speed of rendering and animating in 3D Studio. For the assembly drawing, multiple vertices are not close together, so this will not have an effect.

Leave Auto-welding turned on and the threshold value set to .001.

Pick: ***OK (to export the assembly drawing to 3D Studio format)***

Your computer will take a moment to process the file and export it into 3D Studio format. When it is finished, you are ready to exit AutoCAD and continue to the next tutorial where you will learn to use 3D Studio to add exciting animation to your drawing.

KEY TERMS

ambient
bump map
export
falloff
hotspot
import
intensity
point light
ray tracing
reflection
refraction
rendered
resolution
roughness
spotlight
swatch
threshold value
transparency

KEY COMMANDS

3D Studio Out
Lights
Materials
Render
Replay Image
Save Image
Scenes
Views

EXERCISES

16.1

Retrieve one or more of the following files: Exercise 8.4 (Chess Piece), Exercise 9.4 (Rod Holder), Exercise 9.6 (Gear), and Exercise 11.5 5M (Shaft). Produce at least three different renderings of each object, varying the type, location, intensity, and color of the light, and experimenting with different materials.

16.2

Retrieve your file from Exercise 15.4 and render the stairs using wood materials and a point light source.

16.3

Retrieve your file from Exercise 8.8. This bridge design will be used around the world, so use the sun angle calculator to create renderings of this bridge at it would appear at 8:30am in London, 11:45am in Beijing, 2:00pm in Sydney, and 5:20pm in Rio de Janeiro on May 26.

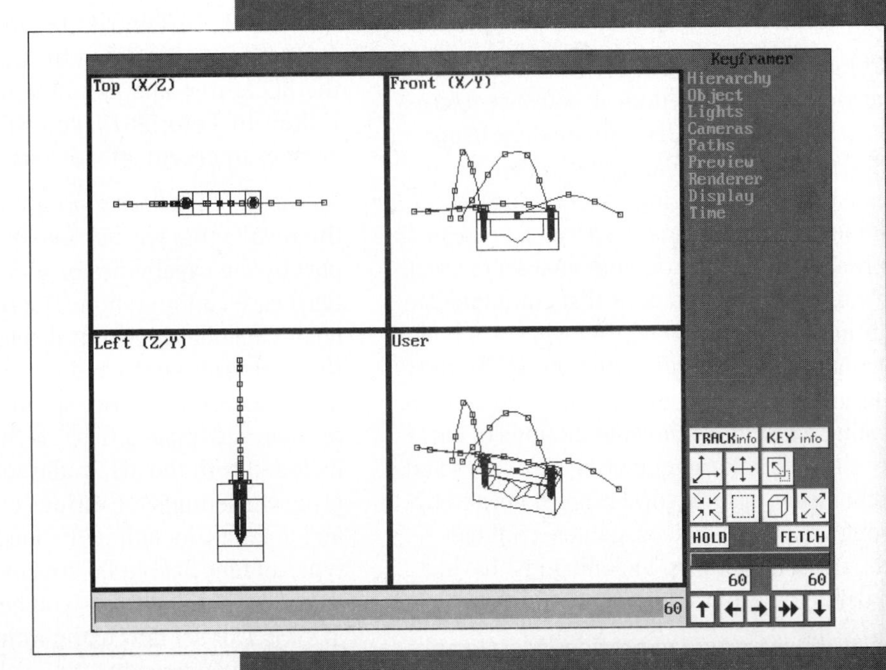

TUTORIAL 17

Basic Animation with 3D Studio

Objectives

When you have completed this tutorial, you will be able to

1. Import the assembly drawing into 3D Studio.
2. Set up and use drawing aids.
3. Render your project to the screen.
4. Use 3D Studio's Keyframer to move objects.
5. Create an animated FLI file.
6. Lengthen the animation.
7. Add keys for rotation.
8. Add a background.
9. Save and load your projects.

Introduction

Throughout this manual, you have learned to apply a variety of Autodesk software to create 2D drawings and 3D solid models, using AutoCAD, and to add lights and materials to create realistic renderings, using AutoVision. When you are working on a project, you can apply all of these tools in combination to create drawings and presentations that communicate your ideas. In this tutorial, you will learn how to animate 3D drawings, using the 3D Studio program. Among the uses for 3D Studio are creating *animations* showing motions of parts and assemblies for engineering processes and mechanisms, architectural renderings and fly-throughs, training videos, games, commercials, and many others, including just having fun using the program.

The 3D Studio program provides tools to animate motion, rotation, scaling (size), and even changes to the shapes of objects in your drawing. You can create objects in 3D Studio using the *2D Shaper* and the *3D Lofter*, and you can add lighting effects and materials using the *3D Editor* portion of the program. The *Materials Editor* lets you create your own materials, similar to AutoVision. 3D Studio is a standalone program. It does not require AutoCAD or AutoVision in order to run. However, it can import AutoCAD drawing geometry.

In this tutorial, you will learn the basics of the 3D Editor and the Keyframer by creating an animation using the assembly drawing from Tutorial 16. You will learn to animate the 3D parts in the assembly so that they move, rotate, and assemble themselves on the screen. In Tutorial 18, you will learn to create geometry using the 2D Shaper and the 3D Lofter, and to add lights with the 3D Editor. In Tutorial 19, you will animate the camera to create a fly-through of a building.

As with any rendering program, the quality of the results that you achieve is determined in part by the capabilities of your computer's hardware configuration. The resolution and color capabilities of your display, as well as the processor speed and the amount of memory available, affect the speed and quality of rendered images. The file 3DS.SET that is included with the 3D Studio software contains program settings for various configurations and defaults, including the locations for the types of files 3D Studio creates. You must store the files in the locations you have specified in 3DS.SET or set new paths with the Configure option. If you need to, edit 3DS.SET with a text editor and specify the correct locations for your files and type of display.

Starting 3D Studio

Load and start 3D Studio from the Autodesk Collection Interface as instructed in Chapter 2. 3D Studio's 3D Editor Program Module should appear on your screen, as shown in Figure 17.1.

■ ***Warning:*** 3D Studio does not run inside Windows. You may need to make changes to your computer's configuration in order to run 3D Studio. Review the section in this book on configuring 3D Studio if you cannot get the program to run. ■

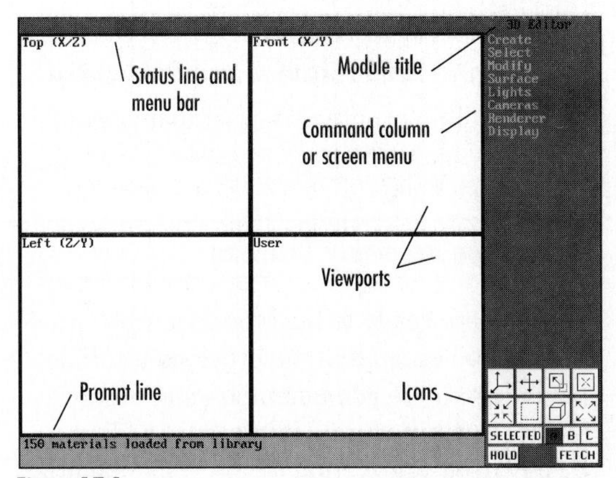

Figure 17.1

The 3D Studio 3D Editor screen is similar in many ways to AutoCAD's drawing editor. It contains several basic parts.

The Prompt Line: The prompt line appears near the bottom of the screen. It is important to pay attention to this area, because this is where 3D Studio prompts you if you need to enter information or make selections.

Module Title: 3D Studio has 5 basic modules, or parts where you can perform certain tasks. The Module Title area shows you which of these modules is active. The five program modules and their basic purposes are listed below:

Module Name	Function Key	Used to
2D Shaper	F1	create 2D geometry
3D Lofter	F2	loft (extrude) or revolve 2D primitives into 3D shapes
3D Editor	F3	create basic 3D shapes, apply materials and patterns to surfaces, add lights and camera, and render single scenes
Keyframer	F4	add animation
Materials Editor	F5	create new materials and change existing ones

The 3D Editor is the active program module when you start 3D Studio. You can switch to a different program module by pressing its function key or by selecting from Program on the menu bar.

Command Column: The command column, like the screen menu in AutoCAD, shows the available commands for the current module. Most of the items you select from the command column cause a further list of selections to appear below the item picked.

Viewports: The viewports contain views of your 3D Studio objects, similar to AutoCAD viewports. The default arrangement of views is the top view in the upper left viewport, the front view in the upper right viewport, the left view in the lower left viewport, and an isometric view in the lower right viewport. The top, front, and left views are labeled in the viewports. You can arrange the views differently, using the Viewports selection from the Views menu bar.

Icons: The icons let you quickly select commonly used commands from the lower right-hand area of the screen. The icons are different, depending on what program module you are using. When you are in the 3D Editor, the icons let you change the zoom magnification and the viewing direction. Figure 17.2 shows the icons, labeled with the functions they perform. You will learn more about the HOLD and FETCH functions (which allow you to store and retrieve your stored steps as you work) and the other icons later in the tutorial.

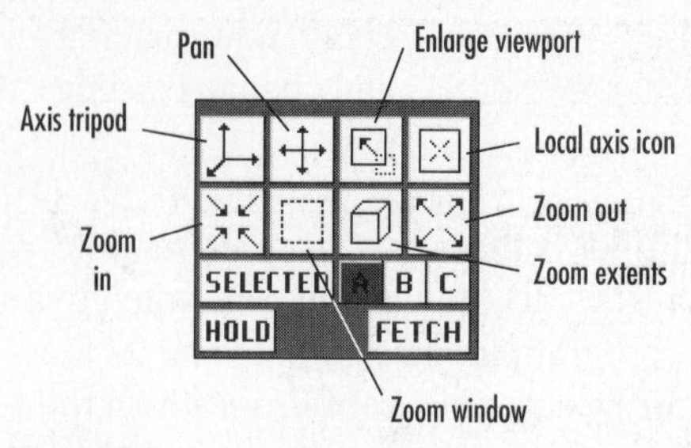

Figure 17.2

Status Line and Menu Bar: The menu bar selections appear when you position the cursor in the area above the viewports. To select a menu item, position the cursor over it and press the pick button, just as you do when using AutoCAD. When you are working in a viewport, this area also shows a status line, showing coordinates and other information.

Now that you are familiar with the basic areas of the screen, you will reset 3D Studio.

Resetting 3D Studio

When starting out, it is a good idea to reset the program to use the defaults. This way you can be sure that the program will behave as you expect and that settings you are not using in this drawing will not be active. Reset is located on the menu bar under the File selection. The File menu selections are shown in Figure 17.3.

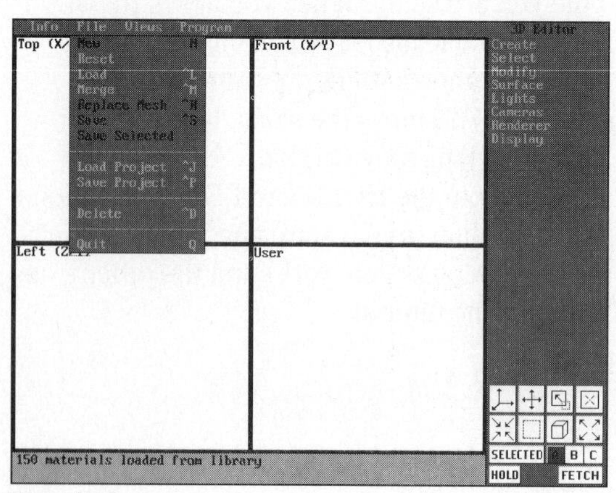

Figure 17.3

Pick: **File *(menu bar),* Reset**

Pick: **Yes *(to reset 3D Studio to its default settings)***

The 3D Studio program is reset to its default settings.

Loading the Assembly Drawing

Now you are ready to load the assembly drawing that you created in the previous tutorials into 3D Studio to add animation and other effects. In other words, bring it to life! You already used AutoVision to add some materials and lighting to the assembly drawing file and then exported it to 3D Studio's .3DS format. 3D Studio can also import AutoCAD .DXF files (created using the AutoCAD DXFOUT command) and .FLM files (created using the AutoCAD FILMROLL command).

Pick: **File *(menu bar),* Load**

A dialogue box similar to the one shown in Figure 17.4 appears on your screen. You will use it to select the mesh file ASMB-SOL that you exported from AutoVision in the last tutorial (or you can use the data file ASMB-SL1 that was provided with the data files that came with your software). The datafiles will be stored in the directory C:\3DS2\PROJECTS, where you loaded them during the Getting Started section.

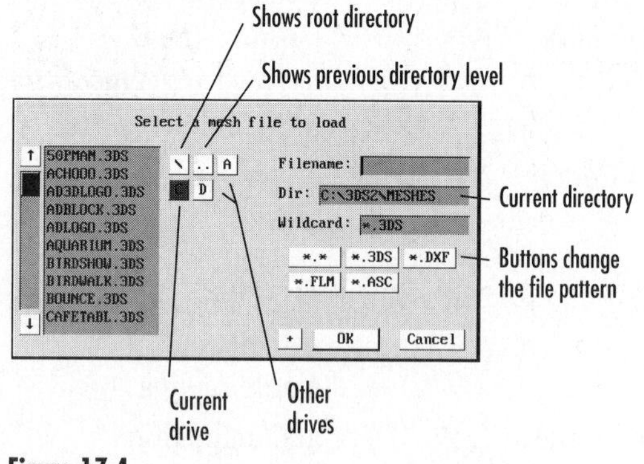

Figure 17.4

Depending on the paths and defaults you have set in the file 3DS.SET, your dialogue box may be slightly different than Figure 17.4. Use the buttons to the right of the list of files to select a different directory if your file is not shown on the list. Selecting the box with the backward slash displays the files from the root directory. Picking the .. (double dot) selection moves you one directory level closer to the root directory. The remaining buttons allow you to select from the drives on your system. To open a directory displayed in the list at the left, pick on the directory name.

Use the buttons and the list at the left to select the directory (probably C:\3DS2\PROJECTS) where your file ASMB-SOL.3DS is stored, or use AMSB-SL1.3DS from the data files. When you have selected the file so that its name appears in the box at the right of the dialogue box to the right of Filename:, pick OK to exit the dialogue box.

When you have successfully opened your file, you should see the assembly drawing on your screen, as shown in Figure 17.5.

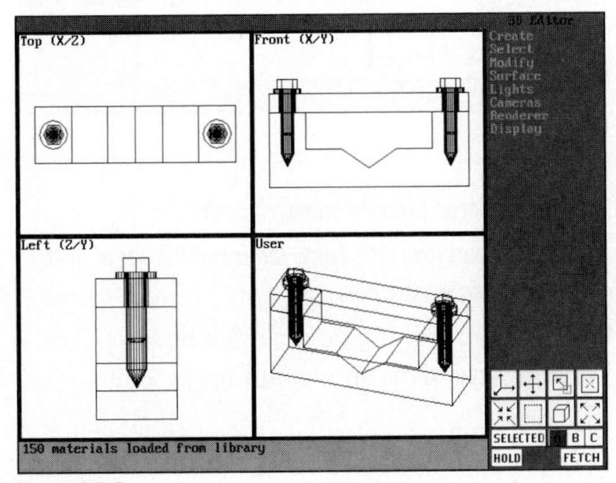

Figure 17.5

The 3D Editor

3D Studio's 3D Editor allows you to create basic 3D geometry; add materials, lights, and cameras; and render and view single scenes. You will add the material CHROME GIFMAP to the base and cover of the assembly. In the previous tutorial you created a material, using the AutoVision materials editor, but because user-defined materials from AutoVision don't transfer to 3D Studio, you will need to select a different material. If you were to render the drawing now, the base and cover would appear black.

There are two steps to applying a material to an object: first you must choose the material from a material library (or create one in the Materials Editor, similar to the way you did using AutoVision); then you select the Assign command and select the object to which the material will be assigned.

Notice that submenu selections do not replace the root page of the menu, as they do in AutoCAD. Instead, they appear near the bottom of the screen menu. Submenu selections remain on the screen once they have been picked, so that they can be picked directly a second time, without your having to pick down through the entire menu sequence. The entire sequence is listed in this tutorial to help you in case you are lost.

Pick: **Surface *(screen menu)*, Material, Choose**

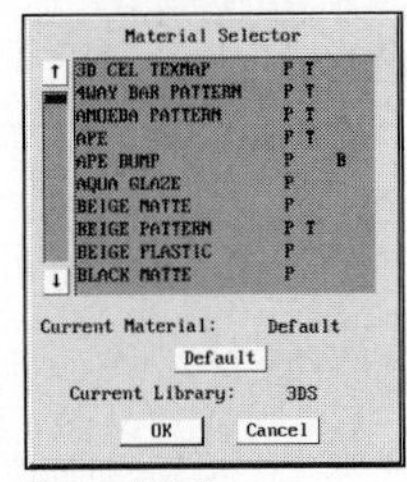

Figure 17.6

Use the dialogue box shown in Figure 17.6 to select the material CHROME GIFMAP. Pick on the downward pointing arrow along the left side of the dialogue box to scroll the list of materials until you see CHROME GIFMAP and then pick so that it is highlighted. When you are finished selecting,

Pick: **OK *(to exit the dialogue box)***

Next you will apply the selected material to the object, using the Surface, Materials, Assign, Object selections and then picking on the objects that you want to make chrome. You may have to pick inside the viewport once to make it active before you can start selecting the object.

Pick: **Surface *(screen menu)*, Material, Assign, Object**

Select object to make CHROME GIFMAP: ***(pick the base in the lower right viewport)***

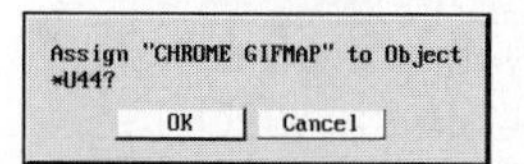

Figure 17.7

When a dialogue box like the one in Figure 17.7 appears on the screen, verifying that you want to assign the material to the object you have selected, pick OK. Notice that in this case the object name is *U44; yours may be named differently. Each object in 3D Studio is assigned a name. Later, in Tutorial 18, you will create 3D objects using 3D Studio, and assign names to the objects. When you import a file, such as ASMB-SOL, the names are generated for you. You can rename the objects to give them more meaningful names if you wish by picking Modify, Object, Attributes in the 3D Editor and using the dialogue box that appears to specify a new name.

Pick: **OK**

Pick: ***(the cover in the lower right viewport)***

Pick: **OK**

Rendering a Scene to the Display

3D Studio is similar to AutoVision in that it renders, or displays, the objects using lighting and materials to show a realistic effect on the screen. As with AutoVision, you can also render an individual scene to the display, disk, or a hardcopy device. You will render the assembly drawing to the screen so that you can see how your objects and materials look in 3D Studio. The selections you will make from the screen menu are shown in Figure 17.8. The prompt, "Select object to make CHROME GIFMAP:" will still be active in the command line, but will be canceled when you choose a new command.

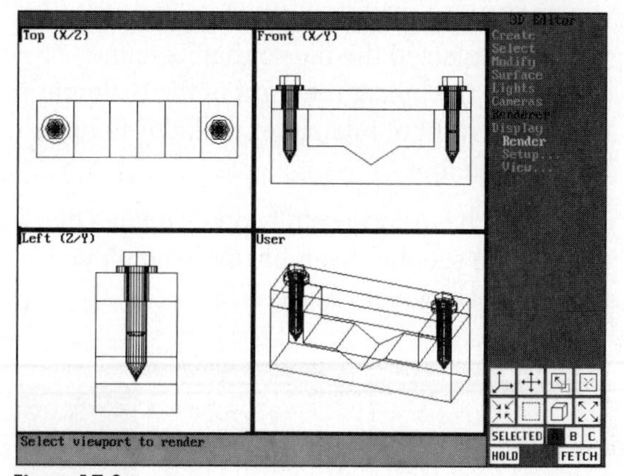

Figure 17.8

Pick: **Renderer *(screen menu)*, Render**

Select viewport to render: ***(pick the isometric view in the lower right viewport)***

The Render Still Image dialogue box appears on your screen, as shown in Figure 17.9.

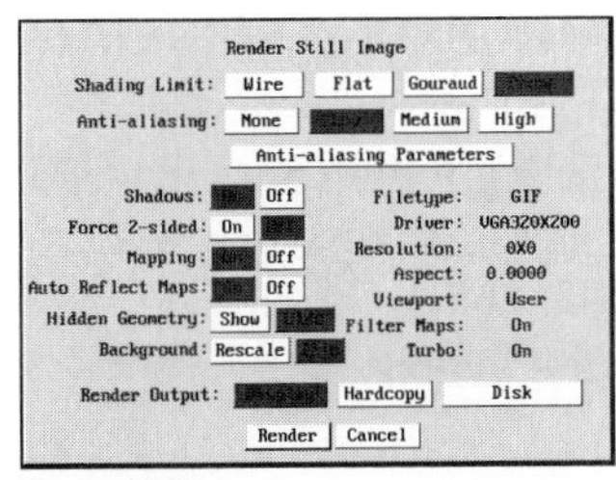

Figure 17.9

For now, accept the default settings in the dialogue box. Make sure that Display is selected as the method for Render Output, so that the rendered drawing will appear on your screen. When you are finished checking these settings,

Pick: **Render**

to start the process of rendering the scene. While the calculations for the rendered scene are being made, the dialogue box shown in Figure 17.10 appears on your screen, showing a bar being filled in from left to right to depict the percentage completed. You can press the (ESC) key to cancel the rendering process, or press the spacebar to see the drawing being rendered to the screen.

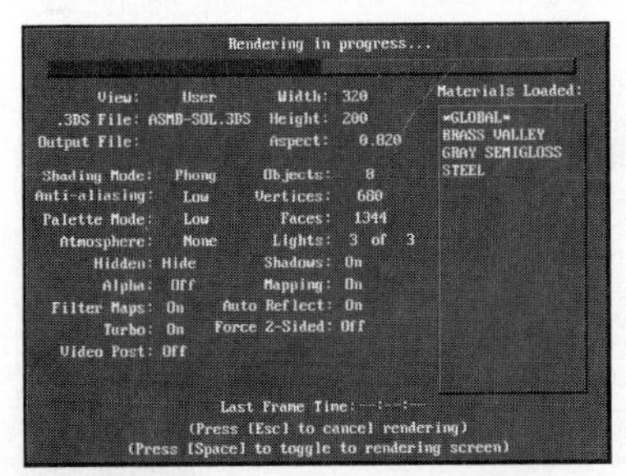

Figure 17.10

When the process is completed, the rendered view of the assembly should appear on your screen, similar to Figure 17.11.

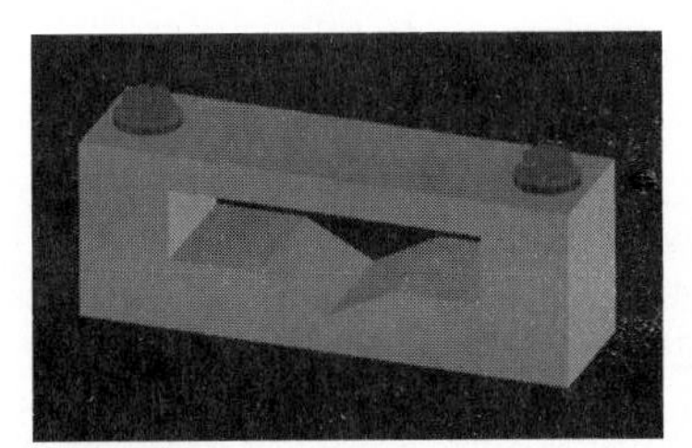

Figure 17.11

3D Studio renders the drawing to a separate rendering screen. When you are finished looking at the rendered drawing, press the pick button on the mouse to return to the 3D Studio Editor.

Next you will set up a grid and snap to help you move the parts of the object away from their assembled positions. In order to create an animation of the parts becoming assembled, you will start with them in their unassembled positions.

Using Drawing Aids

Like AutoCAD, 3D Studio allows you to set up GRID and SNAP to make it easy to create and modify your drawing. You will set up the grid, snap, and extents, or drawing area, using the Drawing Aids dialogue box selected from the Views menu.

Pick: ***Views (menu bar),*** **Drawing Aids**

> ■ ***TIP*** You can select many menu items by typing their hot-key combinations. Notice that the Drawing Aids selection on the Views menu shows the key combination ^-A. To quickly select the drawing aids, press (Ctrl) and the A key simultaneously. ■

3D Studio's drawing aids dialogue box appears on your screen. See Figure 17.12.

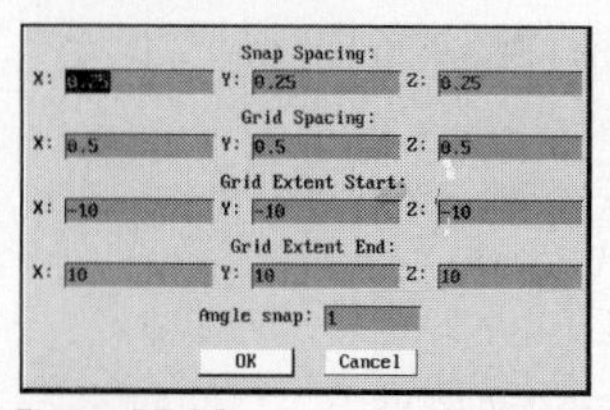

Figure 17.12

Using the cursor to pick the entry to change, and typing in the new values, set the X, Y, and Z snap spacing to .25, the grid spacing to .5, and the Grid Extent start at –10 and end at +10. You can also use (TAB) to move between the entries. Set Angle snap to 1. When you are finished making these selections, pick OK to exit the dialogue box.

> ■ ***TIP*** To quickly transfer the snap spacing for X, Y, and Z, first set the X value and then pick on the letter Y and the letter Z under the Snap Spacing area. To use the same grid spacing as the snap, pick on the title, Grid Spacing. ■

You will return to the 3D Studio Editor. Next, you will zoom out on the top view of the drawing to give yourself more room for moving the objects apart. You will use the zoom out icon, the far right icon in the bottom row of icons at the lower right corner of the screen (shown in Figure 17.13) to zoom out in the top view.

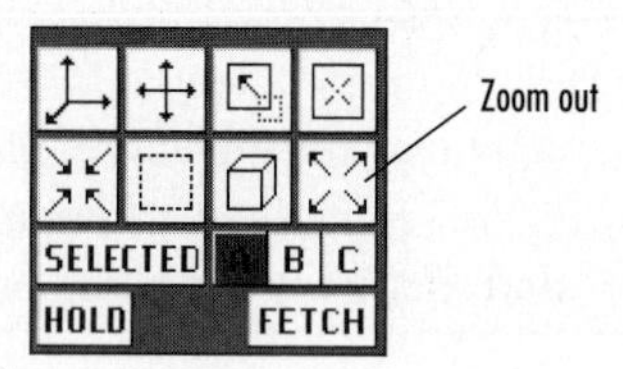

Figure 17.13

Pick: ***(inside the upper left viewport, showing the top view of the object, to make it active)***

Pick: ***(twice on the zoom out icon shown in Figure 17.13)***

Now you will turn on the grid and snap that you set up using Drawing Aids. This will make it easier for you to line things up when you move them. The menu options are toggle switches, similar to the toolbar buttons in AutoCAD.

Pick: **Views *(menu bar)*, Use Snap**

Pick: **Views *(menu bar)*, Use Grid**

> ■ ***TIP*** You can also quickly toggle Snap and Grid by typing "S" and "G" respectively. You do not have to press (↵) afterwards. ■

Repeat these steps on your own for the upper right and lower left viewports. Zoom out only once and turn on the grid and snap. Zoom out once on the lower right viewport. The grid and snap will not work in the User view; they are grayed out on the Views menu when the User viewport is active.

When you have zoomed out and turned on GRID and SNAP, your screen should look like Figure 17.14.

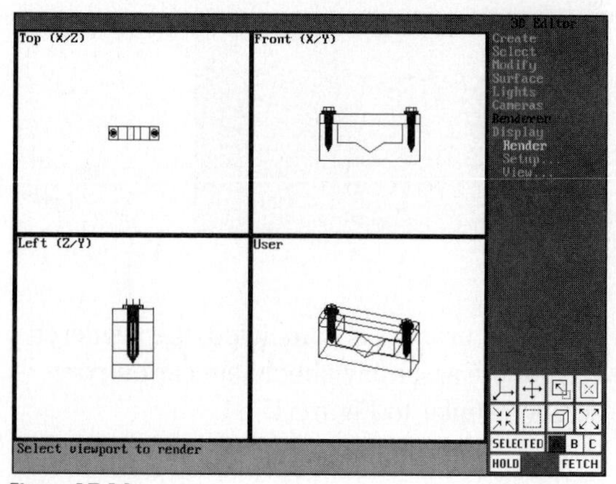

Figure 17.14

To enlarge a single viewport to make it easier to work in a single view, use the enlarge viewport icon (the third from the left in the top row of icons). Be sure the top left viewport is still active.

Pick: **Enlarge viewport icon**

The upper left (top) viewport should fill your screen.

Now you are ready to move the objects apart, so you can animate their assembly later.

Pick: **Modify *(screen menu)*, Object, Move**

The cursor changes to a four-way arrow. Use this cursor to select and reposition the object. In the prompt area, shown in Figure 17.15, you are prompted to select an object to move. To the right of your command line, you are given the option of constraining the cursor to vertical or horizontal motion (like ORTHO) by holding down (TAB), or of cloning an object (like COPY) by holding down (SHIFT), as you pick. You will pick once on the object to select it, then move the object to its new location and press the pick button again to place it there.

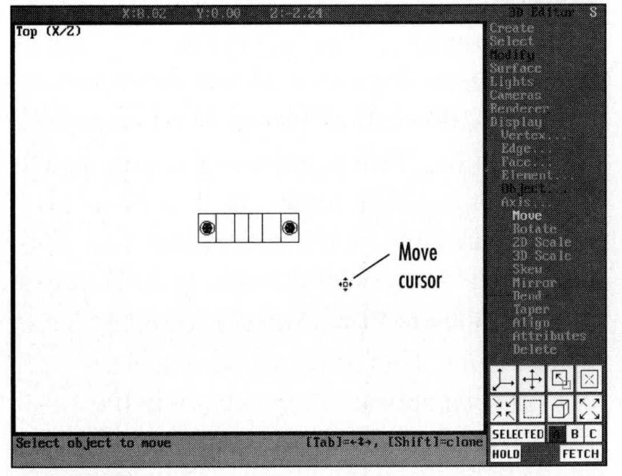

Figure 17.15

Select object to move: ***(pick on the top cover)***

Reposition the object near the right of the view and:

Press: ***(the pick button to place the top cover at that location)***

Repeat this process on your own until you have moved each of the objects apart so that they line up as shown in Figure 17.16. In order to place the washers and screws correctly, you may have to turn off Snap and use the Zoom, Window icon to enlarge the area you are working in so that you can see clearly to align the parts.

■ ***TIP*** If all of the objects do not fit in your viewport, pick the Zoom Extents icon (shaped like a cube and third from the left in the bottom row of icons) from the lower right of the screen to show all of the drawing objects in the viewport. Refer to Figure 17.12 if you are not sure which icon to use. ■

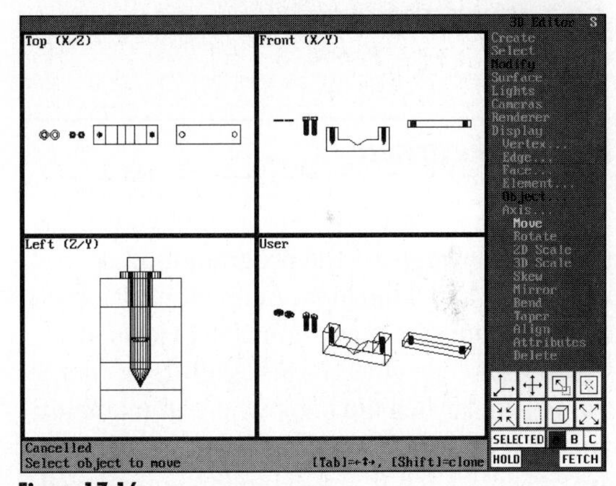

Figure 17.16

Saving a Project File

Before you continue, you will save your project so that you do not lose your work. Also, it is useful to save as you go along so that if you make an error, you can restore the previous project file and start from that point. You will use the file you save again. Before saving, return to four viewports by picking the enlarge viewport icon (third from the left in the top row) again.

Pick: **Enlarge viewport icon**

Pick: **File *(menu bar)*, Save**

Use the dialogue box you see in Figure 17.17 to save your file. Save your project file in the \3DS2\PROJECTS directory. Name your project file ASSMB2.3DS. 3D Studio locates files, meshes, and other files in the directories set up in the 3DS.SET file. In general, you should save to the default directories so that the parts of your file can be found by the 3D Studio program.

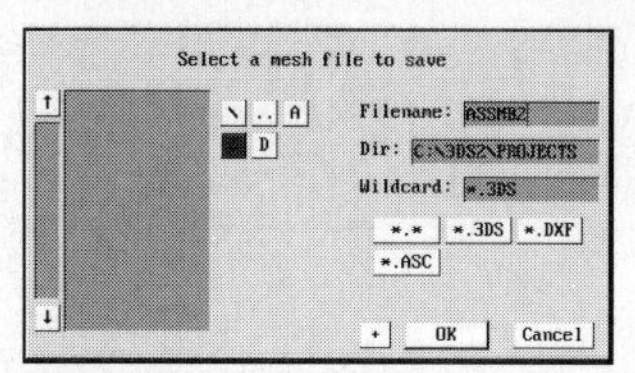

Figure 17.17

Using the Keyframer

Now you are ready to add motion to your drawing. The *Keyframer* is the program module where you add animation. Animations are created by rendering many individual views in which the scene changes just slightly in each frame, similar to a flip book where you quickly flip the pages so that it looks as if the objects are moving. Each frame of motion is rendered individually and when the frames are played in a series, it appears that the objects are moving. About 30 individual frames per second are required to animate motion so that objects appear to move smoothly. The Keyframer module is used to move, rotate, scale, squash, and *morph* (change the shape of) the objects in your drawing at a particular frame. You will create a one-second animation, showing the objects assembling, using the Keyframer.

Pick: **Program *(menu bar)*, Keyframer**

> ■ ***TIP*** You can also press (F4) to quickly change to the Keyframer. ■

The Keyframer menu appears at the right side of the screen; refer to Figure 17.18. Notice that Keyframer has now replaced 3D Editor as the module title. To animate the objects in your drawing, first you will select the frame where a particular motion is to take place, and then you will specify what happens to the object at that frame. You do not need to specify exactly what the object will look like in every frame; all you need to do is move to a particular frame and change the object in that frame. In other words, you create a *key* for that frame, showing what you want to happen. 3D Studio will fill in the steps in between for you, a process called *tweening*. The Keyframer has several basic parts:

The Drawing Area: The drawing area is in the center of the screen, containing viewports showing the objects; it is similar to the 3D Editor.

The Status Line: The status line at the top of the screen displays context-sensitive information, such as coordinates and rotation angles.

Prompt Line/Frame Slider: The prompt line at the bottom of the screen displays information and prompts for input; the same area functions as the frame slider to specify the frame of the animation in which you are working.

Icon Panel: This panel shows a new set of icons that appear when you are in the Keyframer. You will learn more about their use in this part of the tutorial. They are:

TRACK Info: You can pick this icon and then the object to display the *track* for an object.

KEY Info: You can pick this icon and then the object to display the key information for the object.

HOLD and FETCH Icons: These icons store and retrieve your work. Pick HOLD to store your work in its present state; pick FETCH to restore your work as it was when you picked HOLD last. (This is very useful because there is no UNDO command.)

Segment Bar: This bar shows the total number of frames in the animation, with the active segment shown highlighted. A white bar shows the current frame. The active segment of an animation is the portion of a larger animation you have selected to work on. Defining a smaller active segment makes it easier to work on a large animation. To do this, use the command sequence Time, Define Segment or click in the Segment Bar. You are starting with 30 frames in the animation and the entire animation is in the active segment.

Current Frame Field: This field shows which frame is current. Click in this area to use the Go To Frame dialogue box to select a different frame.

Total Frames Field: This field displays the total number of frames in the animation, regardless of which segment is active. The default is 30 frames (starting from frame 0). Click in this field to change the number of frames in the animation. You can have up to 32000 frames in the Keyframer. If necessary, you can link several animations together after they are rendered to create longer animations.

Playback Icons: These icons appear as a series of arrows. The double arrow plays the wireframe of the animation in a continuous loop; the up arrow moves you to the first frame in the active segment; the left arrow moves you back one frame; the right arrow moves you forward one frame; and the down arrow moves you to the last frame of the active segment.

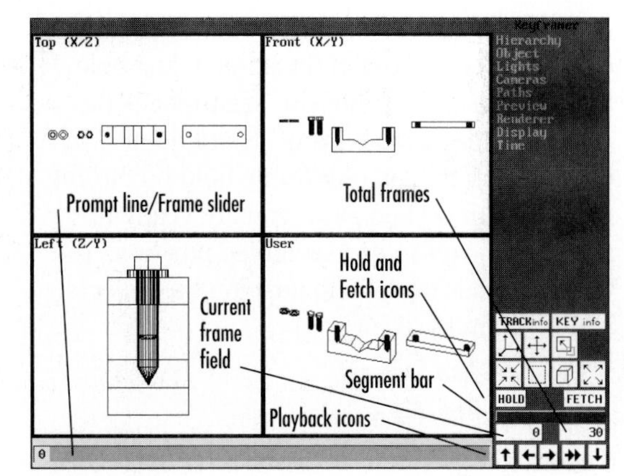

Figure 17.18

Using HOLD and FETCH

Before you move the objects, you will pick the HOLD icon to store your work at its present point. This way, if you move an object to the wrong location, you can use FETCH to restore you to the point where you picked HOLD.

Pick: **HOLD**

Next, you will use the frame slider to move to frame 8 of the animation, where you will move the objects.

Move: ***(the cursor below the viewports, to the bottom of the screen)***

Notice that a strip with the number zero at the left appears along the bottom of the screen. This strip is the *frame slider*. It shows the current frame highlighted. The starting frame for an animation is frame 0. Making a change to an object in frame 0 changes the actual object in your drawing. Making a change in any other frame just changes the appearance of the object for that frame, and does not change your drawing. Next you will change to frame 8 and move the cover so that it is on top of the base in that frame. Use the right arrow to move to frame 8.

Pick: ***(until the frame displayed in the box just above the right arrow displays 8)***

You should now be at frame 8. Move the cursor to the bottom of the screen, just below the viewports, and check to see that 8 is displayed as the current frame, 8 should also be displayed in the current frame field box to the right of your screen. Now you are ready to move the cover to its assembled position. You will turn Snap on to help position the objects when you move them.

Type: ***S (to turn Snap on)***

Pick: **Object** ***(screen menu)***

The available options for animating objects appear on the screen menu. These are shown on the screen menu in Figure 17.19. From the list of options that appear,

Pick: **Move** ***(screen menu)***

When you are in the MOVE command, the same four-way cursor you saw in the 3D Editor is used. Remember, you can constrain the movement to horizontal or vertical by pressing the (TAB) key. Pressing (SHIFT) clones the object. To start with, you will just move the objects horizontally.

Press: (TAB) ***(until the move cursor changes to a horizontal cursor)***

Select object to move: ***(pick on the lower left corner of the top cover in the upper left viewport)***

The arrow cursor is replaced with the object you are moving.

Pick: ***(the lower left corner of the assembly base)***

The cover moves to the selected location so that it is in its assembled position, as shown in Figure 17.19.

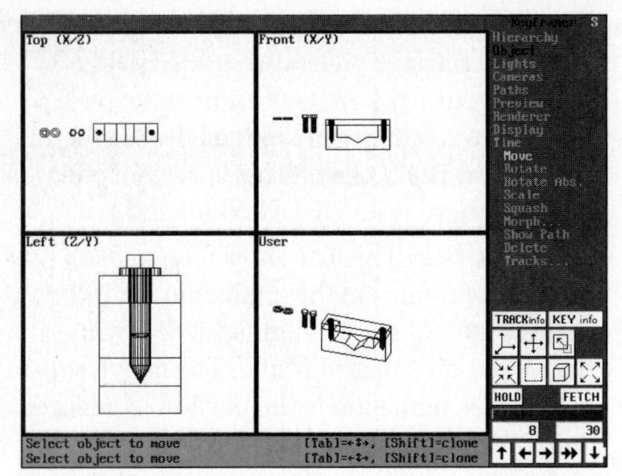

Figure 17.19

■ ***TIP*** If you select the wrong object to move, you can deselect it by pressing the right mouse button. If you move the object to the wrong location, pick FETCH to restore your work to the way it was when you picked HOLD and then try it again. ■

Next, you will move the right-hand washer and then the left-hand washer in frame 16 of the animation.

On your own, use the HOLD command to store your work at its present point. Use the methods you learned above to set the current frame to 16. Once you have completed this step, move the right-hand washer and then the left-hand washer to their assembled positions in the drawing. Use Snap to help you line the objects up correctly, or use the zoom in icon or Zoom Window and enlarge your view so that you can clearly see where they are positioned. Refer to Figure 17.20.

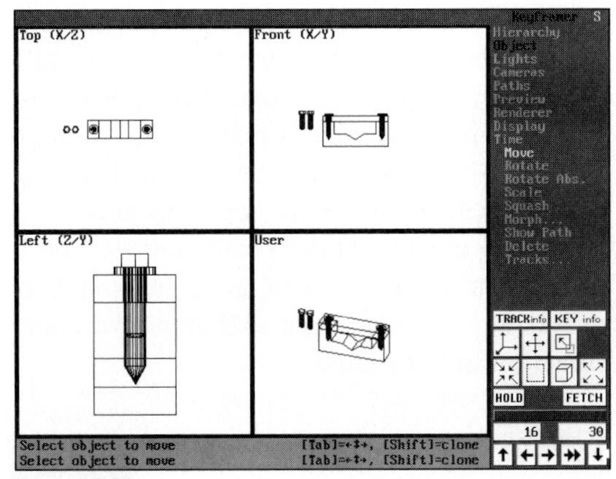

Figure 17.20

The final step before you render this animation is to move the screws into position in frame 24.

Use HOLD once again to store your work at its present point. Now set the current frame to 24 and move the screws into their assembled positions. When you have finished this step, the assembly should be completely put together.

Now you are ready to make a preview of the animation. Previews do not show the parts with the correct colors and patterns, but rather as shades of gray. This saves time in rendering the drawing, and if you do not like the result, you can make a change to the key frames without having spent the time it would take to render the entire animation with materials shown correctly.

Pick: **Preview *(screen menu)*, Make**

Select viewport to Preview: ***(pick twice in the user viewport)***

The Make Preview dialogue box appears on your screen, as shown in Figure 17.21. You can select to make a preview that shows Faces (shaded surfaces), Faces + Lines (shaded surfaces with contrasting lines for the edges), or Lines (edges only, like a wireframe). Pick Faces + Lines. Picking Numbers imprints the frame number in the upper left corner of each frame, so that you can keep track if you want to change something. For now, leave this set to No. You can also set the accuracy for how hidden surfaces are shown and whether to render one or both sides of a surface. Leave these set to the defaults. You use the Frames: area to select the portion of your animation you want to preview, and whether to use every frame in the preview or only every *n*th frame. (Leave these set to the defaults.) Finally, you can choose the size and resolution for the preview. Again, leave these set to the defaults. It takes less time to create a preview using a lower resolution; however, the appearance is poorer. When you have finished making these selections,

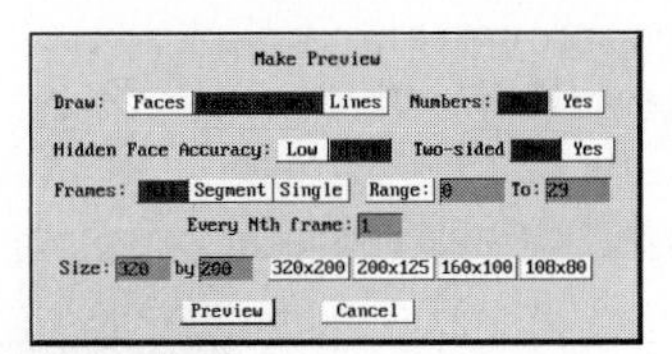

Figure 17.21

Pick: **Preview**

The objects are rendered to the screen, one step at a time; notice that the washers do not appear to be brass, but are shown gray. The preview renders your project without the materials in order to save time. Once each step has been rendered, the animation will continue to play at a faster rate. When you are finished viewing the preview, press the right mouse button.

What happened? The parts where shown moving together, but the movement of each part was in a straight line. The screws slid right through the base to their locations. Moving the screws up and then into position would improve the way this animation looks. You will edit the paths and change the keys so that the objects move into position without going through each other.

First, you will enlarge the user view. The user view should already be active.

Pick: **Enlarge viewport icon**

Pick: **Paths *(screen menu)*, Show-Hide**

Select object to show or hide path: ***(pick on the right-hand screw)***

Select object to show or hide path: ***(pick on each of the washers, the other screw, and the cover)***

The paths for those objects should appear in the viewport, as shown in Figure 17.22. Notice that frame 3 is shown in Figure 17.22 and the subsequent figures. Your objects will be positioned differently, depending on which frame you are showing. To change the frame, pick on the right-pointing arrow to move ahead a frame or the left-pointing arrow to move back a frame. You can step through your animation one frame at a time by doing this.

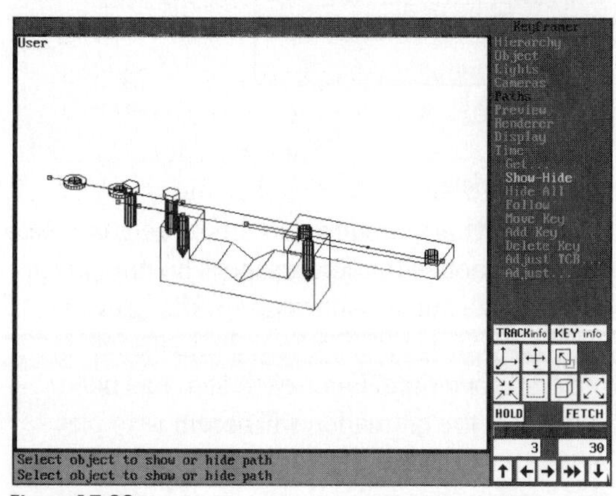

Figure 17.22

You will return to four viewports and then enlarge the front view so that you can edit the paths so that the objects do not pass through one another.

Pick: **Enlarge viewport icon *(to show 4 views)***

Pick: ***(in the Front view)***

Pick: **Enlarge viewport icon**

The front view of the assembly is enlarged, as shown in Figure 17.23, so that the viewport fills the entire viewport area. Notice that the paths of motion are still shown, although it may be hard to see the ones that are lying underneath others. The highlighted boxes that appear along the paths are the keys that tell 3D Studio how the object should appear in a particular frame. Presently there are keys only at the beginning and end of each path. You will add more keys, so that you can move the object up as it moves to its location, so that parts do not pass through one another.

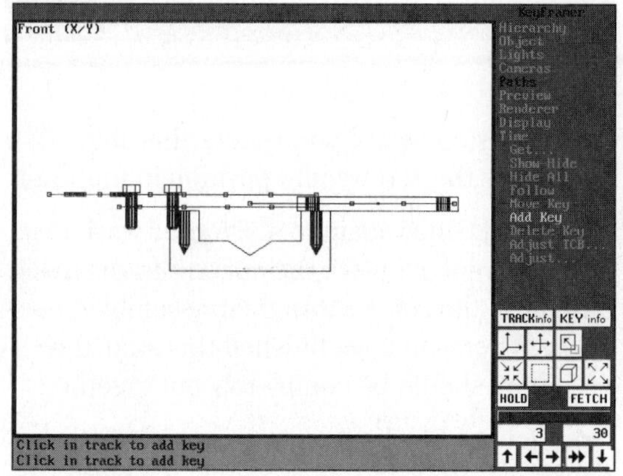

Figure 17.23

Pick: **Add Key *(screen menu)***

Click in track to add key: ***(pick on the white dots along each path and pick to add a key about every 2 or 3 dots)***

Key boxes appear at the locations you have picked. When you have finished adding keys, you will move them to change the object's path of motion. (You may need to move some keys and then return to add keys to paths that are currently obscured.)

Use HOLD to store your work on your own before continuing.

Pick: **Move Key *(screen menu)***

Press: (TAB) ***(if necessary to change the move cursor)***

Click on key to move it: ***(pick on the key second from the end on the path from the cover)***

Move the key up to approximately the location shown in Figure 17.24.

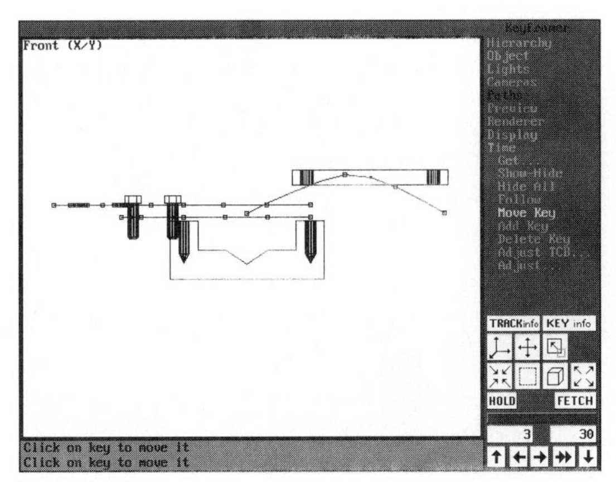

Figure 17.24

On your own, continue moving the added keys until the paths of motion for the washers, screws, and the cover appear similar to Figure 17.25. (It is shown at Frame 0.) When you have finished, pick the enlarge viewport icon again to toggle back to four viewports.

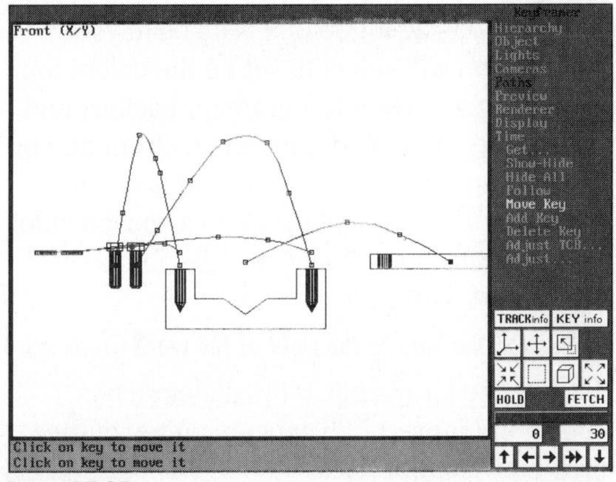

Figure 17.25

Use the method you have learned to save your project file. Name it ASSMB3. Giving your file a new name will allow you to return to the file you started with, if you have a problem or want to use the original file for some purpose.

Now you are ready to render your animation and then play it back.

Pick: **Renderer *(screen menu)*, Render**

Select viewport to render: ***(pick twice in the user viewport)***

The Render Animation dialogue box appears on your screen. You will use the default settings and render the animation to disk.

Pick: **Disk *(from the lower right corner of the dialogue box)***

Pick: **Render *(from the bottom left corner of the dialogue box)***

3D Studio supports rendering to different types of animation files, giving you a variety of playback options. The .FLI format is the same one used by Autodesk Animator. Animation files rendered with the .FLI format always use the resolution 320 × 200. This gives a poorer-quality image, but one that renders quickly and that most hardware can display. Files using the .FLC format, which is used by Autodesk Animator Pro, can be any resolution. These files will take better advantage of hardware capabilities, but take longer to render. You will save your animation as an .FLI file so that you can play it back later. Use the dialogue box that appears to specify the file name ASSMB3.FLI (the default suggested by 3D Studio) for your animation. The three-letter extension .FLI will automatically be added when *.FLI is picked as the file type. The default directory is \3DS2\IMAGES, on your hard drive. Pick OK to proceed and render the animation to the specified file.

The Render animation box appears on the screen, similar to the one shown when you made the preview.

Press: **spacebar *(if you want to see the frames rendered step by step to the screen)***

When the animation is finished rendering, the Keyframer returns to your screen. You will now view the animation.

Pick: **View *(screen menu)*, Image**

The View Image File dialogue box shown in Figure 17.26 appears.

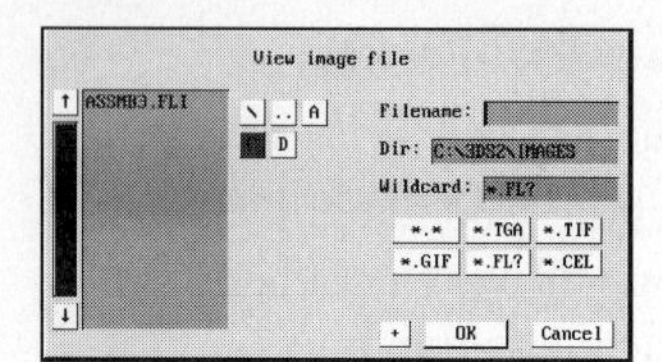

Figure 17.26

Pick: ***.FL? *(for the file pattern)***

Pick: **ASSMB3 *(from the list at the left of the dialogue box)***

Pick: **OK *(to view the animation you created)***

When you are finished viewing the animation, press the right mouse button to return to the Keyframer. Call your friends over to see what a glorious thing you have created in about an hour! Next, you will continue to improve the animation by adding a background, making it longer, and adding rotation to the screws as they drop into place.

You will use the 3D Editor menu to add a background to your scene. To select the 3D Editor program module,

Pick: **Program *(menu bar),* 3D Editor**

Pick: **Renderer *(screen menu),*** Setup, Background

The Background Method dialogue box shown in Figure 17.27 appears on your screen. Using this dialogue box, you can select to have a solid background of any color, a gradient background using three colors that blend from one to the next, or a *bitmapped* pattern, showing a pixel-drawn image of some sort, as the background.

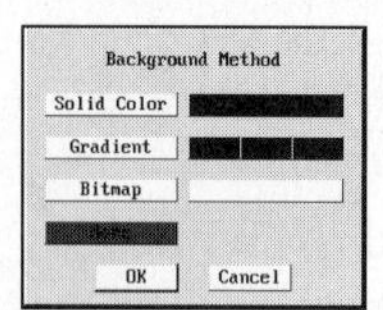

Figure 17.27

To specify the color for a solid background,

Pick: ***(on the bar to the right of the words Solid Color)***

The dialogue box shown in Figure 17.28 appears on your screen. You will use it to define the solid color for the background to add to your scene.

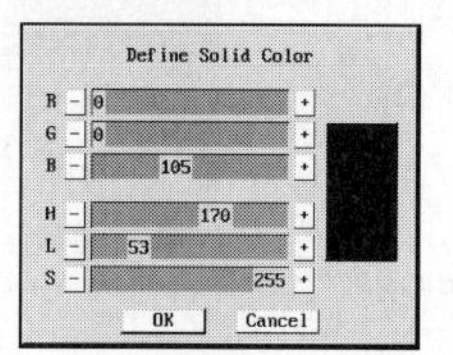

Figure 17.28

Use the slider bar and set the color for blue to 105; this will give you a dark shade of blue as the background color. The slider bars labeled H, L, and S (hue, luminance, and saturation) can be used to change the appearance of the color.

Pick: **OK**

The previous dialogue box returns to your screen. You will select to set up the colors for a gradient background. A gradient background uses three colors and then blends from one to the next so that your background is shaded one color at the top, blends into a second color in the middle, and finally changes into a third color at the bottom.

Pick: ***(on the bars to the right of the word Gradient)***

The Define Gradient Colors dialogue box shown in Figure 17.29 appears on top of the previous dialogue box.

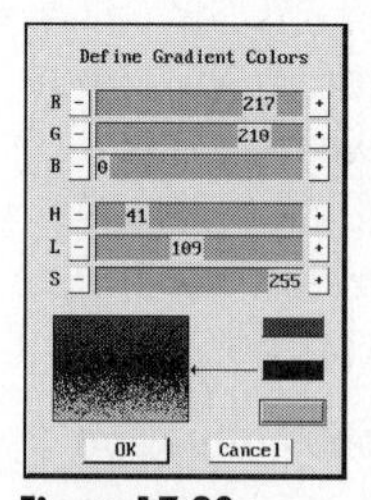

Figure 17.29

You will use the dialogue box to select the colors for the top, middle, and bottom regions of the background. In the lower portion of the dialogue box, you will see a larger square with three bars to the right of it. The middle bar shows an arrow pointing to the larger box. The large box will show you a representation of your gradient background. The three boxes to the right represent the colors for the top, middle, and bottom of the background. First set the color for the top of the background.

Pick: ***(on the top of the three boxes to the right of the large square)***

Increase the slider bar for red to set the color for the top box to a shade of red. When you have completed this step,

Pick: ***(on the middle of the three boxes, the one with the arrow pointing to the large box)***

Increase the slider bar for blue to set the color for the middle box to a shade of blue. Then,

Pick: ***(on the bottom box)***

Use the slider bars for red and green to create a shade of yellow for the bottom of the background.

When you have finished selecting all three colors, you should see the large box filled in with the top portion red, then blending into blue in the middle and yellow at the bottom of the box. When you are pleased with the selection of colors,

Pick: **OK** ***(to return to the previous dialogue box)***

Pick: ***(the bar to the right of Bitmap from the dialogue box)***

The dialogue box shown in Figure 17.30 appears. You will use it to select from the bitmapped files that are provided with 3D Studio to use as backgrounds. In order for 3D Studio to find bitmapped files, they should be located in the \3DS2\MAPS directory or the location you have specified in the 3DS.SET file.

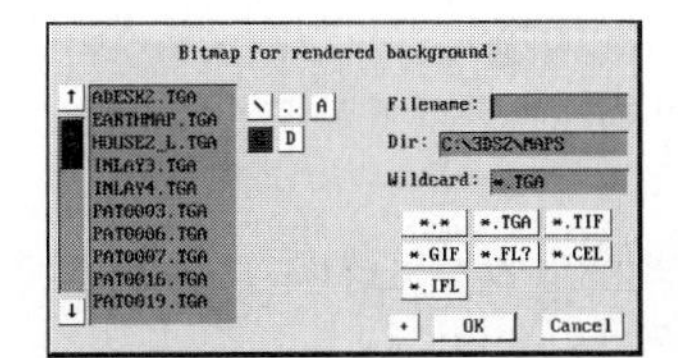

Figure 17.30

Pick: **EARTHMAP.TGA** ***(from the list of files at the left of the dialogue box)***

Pick: **OK**

You return to the Background Method dialogue box. Now you have set up three different backgrounds. You are ready to render your scene to the display to see what they will look like with your assembly drawing. To use the bitmapped background,

Pick: **Bitmap** ***(so that the bar with the word Bitmap becomes highlighted)***

Pick: **OK** ***(to exit the dialogue box)***

You are returned to the 3D Editor module. Next you will render the scene to the display so that you can see your drawing with the bitmapped background. The addition of the background will cause 3D Studio to take longer to render the scene than it did previously.

Pick: **Renderer** ***(screen menu),*** **Render**

Select viewport to render: ***(pick twice in the lower right-hand viewport)***

Make sure that Display is the only Render Output choice highlighted for the rendered scene.

Your drawing is rendered to the screen, showing the bitmapped background of the Earth. Perhaps this background provides too much distraction and takes away from the appearance of the object.

On your own, select Renderer, Setup, Background and choose the gradient background. When you have it selected, render the scene to the display again. When you have observed the result, return to the 3D Editor and choose the solid background. Render the still scene again to see the solid background.

Leave the solid background selected. Now you will use the Keyframer module to lengthen the animation that you created in the last tutorial. Then you will add rotation to the screws so that they appear to twist themselves down into the holes in the base.

Pick: **Program *(menu bar)*, Keyframer**

Keyframer appears at the top right corner of the screen, indicating that it is the current module.

Increasing the Number of Frames

Think back to the animation you created earlier in the tutorial. When you rendered the entire animation of 30 frames, it only took one second to play, which meant that you could not see each motion clearly because the speed was too great. Now you will increase the number of frames in the animation so that it will play for a longer period of time and the motion won't be so hurried.

Pick: ***(on the number 30 in the bottom right of your screen)***

The dialogue box shown in Figure 17.31 appears on your screen. It allows you to set the number of frames that you will use in the animation.

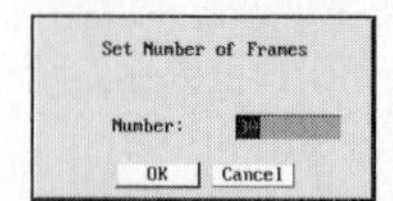

Figure 17.31

Replace the value 30 with the value 60 and pick OK to exit the dialogue box. Pick on the right end of the slide at the bottom of your screen, as shown in Figure 17.32. Notice that the number of frames of animation shown in the bar across the bottom of the screen goes up to 60.

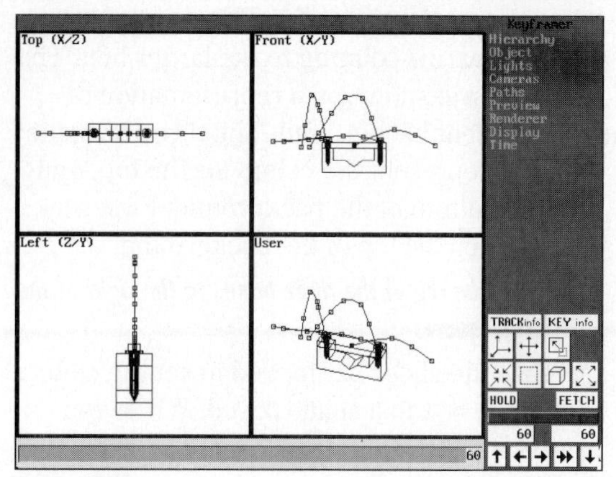

Figure 17.32

The number of frames in the animation is now set to 60 instead of 30, so when rendered, it will last for 2 seconds instead of one second. The number of frames per second determines whether the motion of the object appears smooth. If the number of frames per second is too low (less than 12), the objects will appear as a series of still frames. Most television uses 30 frames per second, although the PAL television standard is 25 frames per second. Movies are shown with 24 frames per second. Next, you will change the animation so that the action takes place over 60 frames (2 seconds of animation).

To play wireframe of the current animation to see the effect of increasing the length,

Pick: ***(in the lower right viewport)***

Pick: ***(on the double right-pointing arrows)***

Notice that all of the movement takes place in the first 30 frames. You have not created any new movement for the new frames that you added. Next, you will make changes to the keys so that the motions of the objects are stretched out over a longer period of time.

Press: ***(the right mouse button to quit playing)***

Next, use the HOLD button on your own to store your work so that you can use FETCH to return to this point if you make an error.

Using Track Info

Picking on the Track info icon and then selecting on an object in your drawing will display the transformation track for that object. A *transformation* of an object can include any of the following: moving, scaling, rotating, squashing, or morphing the object. You will use the transformation tracks to lengthen the animation so that all of the movement does not take place in the first 30 frames.

Pick: ***(the Track info icon from the lower right corner of the screen)***

Select object to see TRACK info: ***(pick the cover)***

The Track Info box appears on your screen, as shown in Figure 17.33.

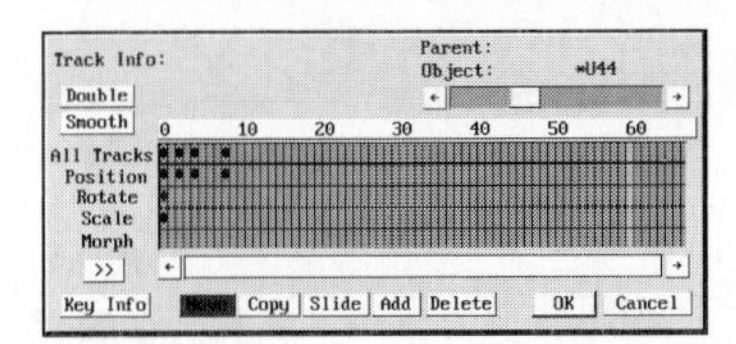

Figure 17.33

The upper right-hand area shows the name of the object, in this case *U44. Your object may be named differently if you are using your own file.

The central area shows the track information. Each frame is represented as a vertical box listed below the frame numbers. Keys showing the transformations of the object are represented by a black dot in the frame where they take place. There are separate tracks for position, rotation, scaling, and morphing, because each of these can take place in any particular frame. (In other words, you could move an object and rotate it in the same frame.)

You will use the Slide function shown near the bottom of the screen to slide the keys over so that the motion of the cover does not end in frame 8, but continues to frame 34, as shown in Figure 17.34. Key 1 has a special function and usually is left in frame 0. If you move key 1, you are actually moving the drawing in the 3D Editor. The movement keys you have in your project may differ somewhat from the figure, as you added keys by picking on the path and you may have added your keys to a different frame.

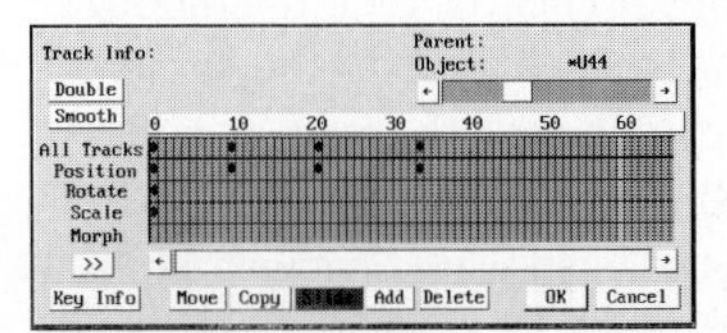

Figure 17.34

Pick: ***(the box near the bottom of the Track Info box marked Slide)***

Click on key to move it and all subsequent keys: ***(pick on the second key from the left in the all tracks row)***

Slide the key over to the right so that it appears in frame 9. All of the keys to the right of the one you are sliding will move with it. Click on the key farthest to the right and slide it over to frame 34.

Pick: **Smooth *(from the upper left of the tracks area)***

Smoothing the Motion

At the prompt, pick Yes to indicate that you do want 3D Studio to smooth the motions for the object. *Smoothing* the motion will result in some of the keys being moved. Smoothing evens out the motion so that the apparent speed of the object as it moves is uniform;

otherwise, the object may appear to start out fast and then slow down, or display other jerky motion.

Pick: **OK *(to exit Track Info)***

If you want, use Preview, Make and preview the animation shown in the lower right viewport. Notice that the cover now slides over to its location during 34 frames. This does not look too good now, because it passes through the other parts. Next, you will change their movement transformation keys so that they move more slowly also.

Use Track Info again to change the motion transformation keys for the right-hand screw so that its motion ends at frame 58 instead of frame 24, as it does presently. Pick to smooth the motion for that track. Then do the same for the left-hand screw. Change the keys for the washers so that their motion ends at key 48. Smooth their motion also. Use Preview, Make to check the result.

Rendering

Now you are ready to render the drawing with the lengthened motion. This will take longer to render because of the added motion.

Pick: **Renderer *(screen menu),* Render**

Select viewport to render: ***(pick the lower right viewport)***

Check to see that Phong rendering is the method selected and that Disk is highlighted at the bottom right corner of the dialogue box. *Phong shading* calculates a color for each pixel in the object which generally results in more color and shading variation and therefore more realism in the rendered scene. *Gourard shading* calculates a color for each vertex on the object and then blends the shading between each pair of vertices to determine the color for the pixels in each flat polygon which makes up the object. The colors of the vertices at the ends of an edge are averaged and the resulting color is used for the color of the edge. Gourard shading is less realistic than Phong shading, but also takes less time to calculate. Choosing *Flat shading* causes each side of a polygon to be shaded a single color. Flat shading is generally the least realistic effect but takes less time to render than Phong or Gourard shading. It is beneficial to render test images using Flat shading to save time and also when rendering objects composed of flat surfaces where the shading effects are not dramatic.

■ ***TIP*** It is often useful to render first with Flat shading selected to produce initial images. Then switch to Gourard shading for better results. Finally, try Phong shading to produce the most realistic images. Starting with the simplest rendering algorithm and then moving in steps to the most complex will save you time since you will not have to wait for images to be rendered realistically when you are still in the process of making changes to the animation. ■

You will render the animation to a file on disk so that you can play it back later. When you have checked these settings,

Pick: **Render *(the box at the lower left of the dialogue box)***

Use the dialogue box to specify the file name ASSMB-60.FLI and pick OK to start the rendering process. The calculations to render all 60 frames will take a bit of time. Have a cup of coffee while you are waiting, or read your manuals. When the rendering calculations are finished, you return to the Keyframer. Now you are ready to play back the animation to see what you have created.

Pick: **Renderer *(screen menu),* View, Image**

Pick: ***.FL?**

Pick: **ASSMB-60.FLI** ***(from the list of files)***

Pick: **OK**

Notice that the file plays for a longer time and it is easier to see the motions because they do not happen so quickly. When you are finished, press the pick button to return to the Keyframer.

Adding a Rotation Key

Having the screws rotate as they descend into the holes will make your animation of the assembly more interesting. You will add a key to the transformation track for the two screws, so that they rotate as well as move into their assembled positions.

Use the frame slider to move to frame 58, so that you can specify the amount of rotation the screws should exhibit by the time this frame is reached. To use the frame slider, pick near the bottom right of the screen below the viewports. On your own, move the position of the cursor or use the single arrows to move from one frame to the next until frame 58 is selected as the current frame.

Now you are ready to specify the ending rotation you want the screws to have when they reach this frame. 3D Studio will spread the rotation out between the first key and the ending key for the sequence. You will use rotation about the object's own axis instead of relative to some other point in the scene. (Using Rotate Abs., or absolute rotation, rotates the object about an axis system perpendicular to an active orthographic or User view instead of about its own axis.)

■ ***TIP*** Pressing (ALT) while clicking on the object to rotate, updates its existing keys but does not create a new key. Pressing (SHIFT) while clicking on the object to rotate creates an instance copy of the object in the new position like you used when pressing (SHIFT) during the Move command to create a copy. ■

Pick: **Object** ***(screen menu),*** **Rotate**

Select object to rotate: ***(pick the right-hand screw)***

Move the cursor around and notice that the boxed-in shape of the object rotates on the screen, as shown in Figure 17.35.

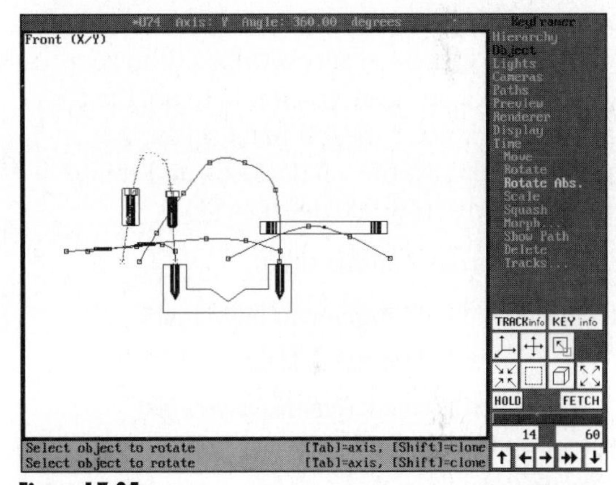

Figure 17.35

Press (TAB) to select a different axis of rotation. Try pressing (TAB) and then moving the mouse so you can see about which axis the object will rotate. Press (TAB) again to select the next axis of rotation, and move the mouse so you can see the effect. You want the screws to rotate around their vertical axis, in this case the Y axis.

Press: (TAB) ***(until the vertical axis of the screw is selected; notice the status line near the top of the screen)***

Use the pointing device to continue to specify the rotation for the object until you see the value Angle: 900 degrees in the status line readout. You may have to move the mouse, pick it up and move it to where you started, and then move it again several times to reach 900 degrees.

Press: ***(pick button to accept 900 degrees as the amount of rotation)***

Repeat this process on your own for the left-hand screw, first setting the current frame number to 52. Since the left-hand screw has less distance to travel, it will probably look better in the animation if its motion has ended before the right-hand screw's does. If necessary, go back and use Track info to set the last motion key for the left-hand screw to frame 52. Choose the vertical axis and rotate the left-hand screw 900 degrees also.

Save your project at this time.

To preview the changes you have made,

Pick: **Preview *(screen menu)*, Make**

Select viewport to preview: ***(pick the lower right viewport)***

Pick: **Preview *(from the lower left corner of the dialogue box)***

Notice that the rotation has been added to the movement of the screws. You have completed this tutorial. Save your project and exit 3D Studio.

Going Further

Pick Renderer, Setup, Background and add a background in the Keyframer, as you did using the 3D Editor. If you like the effect, use the Renderer to render the animation to a file that you can play back. You can use the animation player program named AAPLAY.exe, found in the \3DS2 directory, to play your animations on computers that do not have 3D Studio loaded. The AAPLAY program is small enough to fit on a single floppy disk. To run the program, exit to DOS and then change to the directory \3DS2. Type "AAPLAY" and press (↵) to start the program. To load your animation, pick File, FLI Load and select your file. Pick the double arrow near the bottom center of the screen to play the animation. To change the speed, use the arrows at the bottom right of the screen or the slider bar located between them. To quit playing the animation, press the right mouse button. Pick Player, Quit to exit the program.

KEY TERMS

- 2D Shaper
- 3D Lofter
- 3D Editor
- animation
- bitmapped
- Flat shading
- Gourard shading
- gradient
- key
- Keyframer
- Materials Editor
- morph
- paths
- Phong shading
- smooth
- tracks
- transformation
- tween

KEY COMMANDS

- Add Key
- Bitmap
- Drawing Aids
- Enlarge Viewport
- Fetch
- Grid
- Hold
- Load
- Material
- Move Key
- Move Object
- Preview
- Render
- Reset
- Rotate Object
- Save
- Show/Hide Path
- Snap
- Track Info
- View Image
- Zoom Extents
- Zoom Out

EXERCISES

17.1

Retrieve your file from Exercise 9.6. Export the gear using DXFOUT. Use 3D Studio to make three copies of the gear and animate them to show them meshing with each other.

17.2

Retrieve your file from Exercise 15.5. Use AutoVision to export a 3D Studio file. Animate the motion of the geneva wheel assembly.

17.3

Retrieve your file from Exercise 15.6M and export it to a 3D Studio. Animate the movement range of the universal joint.

17.4

Retrieve the rendered chess piece from Exercise 16.1 and export it to 3D Studio. Create a chessboard setting and animate all of the allowable moves for that piece from the square on which you have located it. Create additional pieces and animate a game.

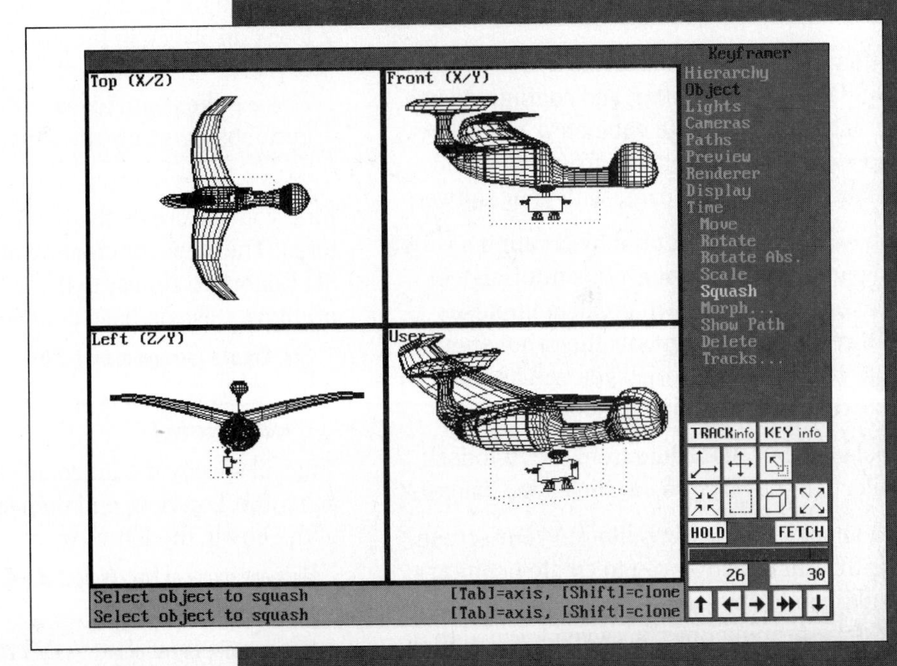

TUTORIAL 18

Creating Geometry in 3D Studio

Objectives

When you have completed this tutorial, you will be able to

1. Create basic 3D shapes.
2. Import meshed objects.
3. Create shapes with the 2D Shaper.
4. Loft shapes with the 3D Lofter.
5. Create animations with squash and morph keys.
6. Add lights to your scenes.

Introduction

In this tutorial you will learn to use 3D Studio's 2D Shaper and 3D Lofter, and continue to use the 3D Editor to create geometry. You will also learn to import objects from the World Creating Toolkit that came with your software.

You will begin this tutorial by creating a robot. As you are going through this tutorial, feel free to try out your own creative impulses with regard to exactly how the robot should look. Later in the tutorial, you will animate your robot transporting to a space ship.

Load and start 3D Studio from the Autodesk Collection Interface as instructed in Chapter 2.

You should see the 3D Editor on your screen. The 3D Editor allows you to create geometry in addition to applying materials to surfaces and transforming objects, as you learned to do in Tutorial 17. First you will create some basic 3D primitive shapes for your robot. You will draw a box for its torso, a cylinder for its neck, a sphere for its head, and two cones for its legs.

To make it easier to create the robot, use the Drawing Aids dialogue box on your own to set up the snap to .25, the grid to 1, Grid Extents from –10 to 10 for all axes, and Angle snap to 1 degree. Refer to Tutorial 17 if you need to review drawing aids. Turn on Grid and Snap in each viewport by picking the viewport and then pressing G and then S. (You cannot turn them on in the user viewport.) As you are working, use the status line, which indicates the current cursor location, to help you locate and size features of the robot.

Press: ***(the right mouse button to pick the zoom extents icon)***

Press: ***(the right mouse button to pick the zoom out icon)***

> ■ ***TIP*** Right picking on the various zoom icons displayed in the lower right corner of the screen zooms all of the viewports. Picking the zoom icons with the left mouse button zooms only the active viewport. ■

First you will create the box for the robot's torso. The steps for creating objects with the 3D Editor are similar to those for creating AME primitives, as you have done in past tutorials.

Pick: **Create *(screen menu)*, Box**

Pick: ***(in the Top view in the upper left viewport to make it active)***

You will specify the diagonal corners of a box, using the Top view, and then specify the height of the box in the left view.

Place one corner of box: ***(select X:–4.00, Y:0.00, Z:–4.00)***

Place opposite corner of box: ***(select the relative coordinates shown, X:6.00, Y:0.00, Z:5.00)***

Click in viewport to define length of box: ***(pick in the Left view)***

Specify the height for the box as follows:

Click in viewport to define length of box: ***(pick: X:0.00, Y:7.00, Z:1.00)***

Length: ***(pick a point below the first point so that the length displayed at the top of the screen is 7.00)***

> ■ ***TIP*** You may need to use PAN or ZOOM so that you can select the appropriate points. ■

A dialogue box appears on your screen, similar to the one shown in Figure 18.1. Use it to name the object BODY, and press ↵ or pick Create after you have entered the name.

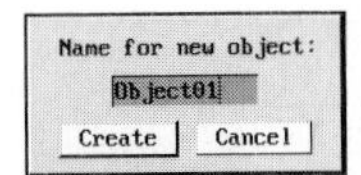

Figure 18.1

■ *TIP* On your own, pick HOLD to save your work in the hold buffer when you successfully complete a step. This way it can be restored with the FETCH button, if necessary. Remember that 3D Studio does not have an UNDO command. ■

Next, you will add a cylinder for the robot's neck. Cylinders can be either faceted or smooth. The selection Values allows you to choose more faces and segments for the cylinder; the default is set to 6. (Setting Values is similar to setting the SOLWDENS variable in AutoCAD.)

Pick: **Create *(screen menu)*, Cylinder, Smoothed**

Pick: ***(in the upper left viewport to make the Top view active)***

Place center of 6-side, 1-segment smoothed cylinder: ***(pick X:–1.00, Y:0.00, Z:–1.50 as the center for the cylinder)***

Set radius: ***(pick so that the status line at the top of the screen shows Radius 0:.75 Angle: 0)***

Click in viewport to define length of cylinder: ***(pick in the Left viewport to make it active)***

Pick: **X:0.00, Y:0.00, Z: –1.50**

Length: ***(pick to specify Length: 1.50)***

Use the dialogue box that appears to name the cylinder NECK and press ↵. When you are finished with this step, your drawing should appear similar to Figure 18.2.

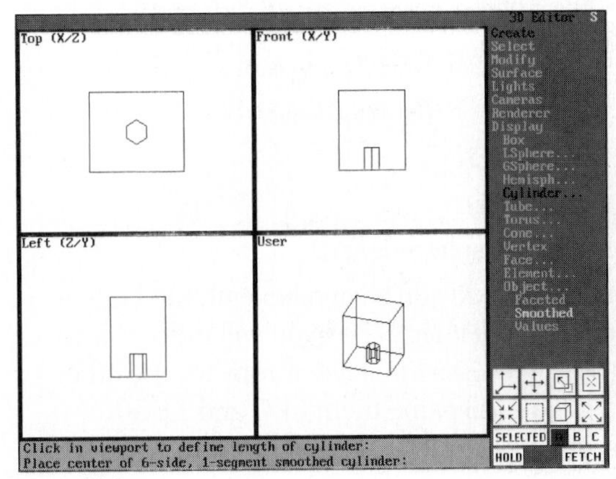

Figure 18.2

You will use Move from the Modify screen menu to move part NECK so that it is on top of part BODY.

Pick: **Modify *(screen menu)*, Object, Move**

Select object to move: ***(pick on NECK in the Left view)***

Move object NECK straight up until it is on top of the body. Use the snap to help you line things up.

■ *TIP* Remember that you can press TAB to constrain movement so that it is only vertical or horizontal, as you did in Tutorial 17. Look at the shape of the arrow cursor to determine in which directions movement is possible. ■

Next you will add a sphere for the robot's head. The 3D Editor allows you to create two types of spheres. The LSPHERE command produces a sphere with faces that are arranged like a globe with lines of latitude and longitude. GSPHERE produces a sphere with triangular faces arranged like a geodesic dome. You will use the LSPHERE command.

Pick: **Create *(screen menu)*, LSphere, Smoothed**

Place center of 16-segment smoothed LSphere: ***(pick in the upper left viewport to make the Top view active)***

Type: **–1** ↵ ***(for the X value)***

Type: **10.25** ↵ ***(for the Y value)***

Type: **–1.5** ↵ ***(for the Z value)***

Radius: **1.75** ↵

Angle: **0** ↵

Name the sphere HEAD.

Next you will add a cone beneath the body to act as the left leg. Then you will move it with SHIFT depressed to make a copy for the other leg. You will name them LEG and LEG01.

Pick: **Create *(screen menu)*, Cone, Smoothed**

Place Center of 16-side smoothed cone:

Type: **–2.75** ↵ ***(for the X value)***

Type: **–4** ↵ ***(for the Y value)***

Type: **–1.5** ↵ ***(for the Z value)***

Base radius: **1** ↵

Top radius: **.5** ↵

Angle: **0** ↵

Click in viewport to define length of cone: ***(pick in the lower left viewport to make the Left view active)***

Pick: ***(X:0.00, Y:0.00, Z:–1.50)***

Length: ***(pick so that the length is 4.00)***

Name the object LEG and press ↵. Now you will use the Modify, Object, Move command and press SHIFT to create a copy and move it for the other leg.

Pick: **Modify *(screen menu)*, Object, Move**

Select object to move: ***(pick in the upper right viewport to make the Front view active)***

Select object to move: ***(hold down* SHIFT *and pick the leg)***

Move it to the right side below the body. When the dialogue box appears, accept the default to name the object LEG01. When you are finished, the robot should look similar to Figure 18.3.

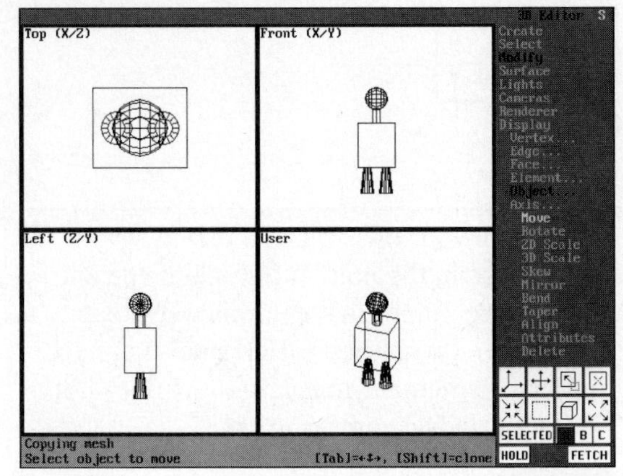

Figure 18.3

To save your work,

Pick: **File *(menu bar)*, Save**

Use the dialogue box shown in Figure 18.4 to save the drawing to the file name ROBOT. Save your drawing in the default directory, C:\3DS2\MESHES.

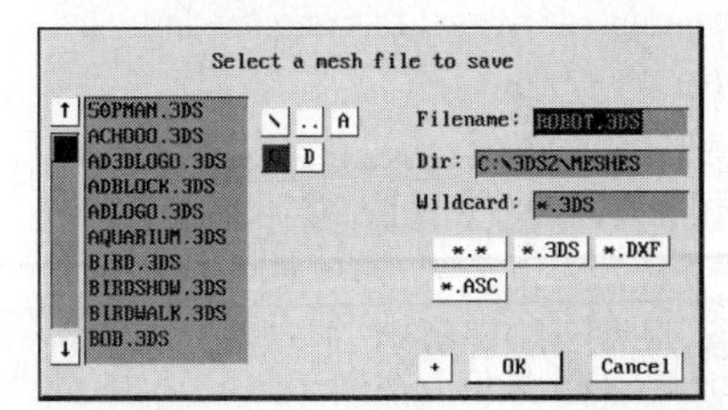

Figure 18.4

Next you will import the mesh file EYEBALL from the \3DS2\MESHES directory and copy it to form the eyes.

Pick: **File *(menu bar)*, Merge**

The dialogue box shown in Figure 18.5 appears on your screen. Pick on the selections Cameras, Lights, and Animation to unselect them so that they are no longer highlighted, leaving only Mesh objects highlighted, as shown in the figure.

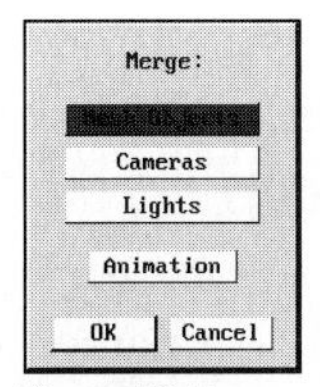

Figure 18.5

Pick: **OK**

to proceed to the next portion of the dialogue, where you will select the file to merge. The select files dialogue appears on your screen, as shown in Figure 18.6.

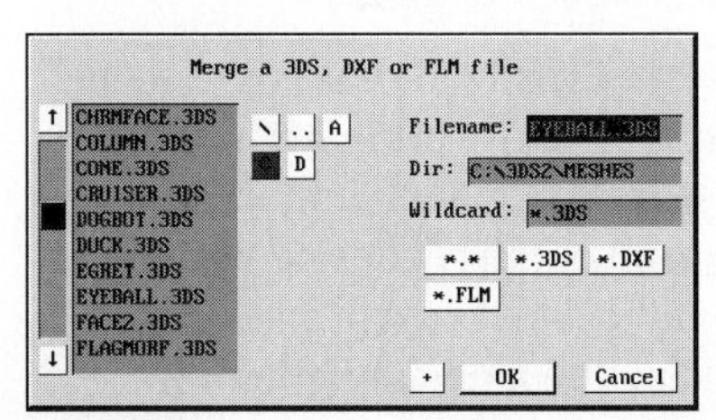

Figure 18.6

Use it to select the file EYEBALL from the list of files at the left. Once you have selected EYEBALL, pick OK. A new dialogue box appears, showing you the objects that were part of the mesh file. In this case there is only one object, EYEBALL. Pick that item to highlight it as the object to merge and then pick OK. Refer to Figure 18.7.

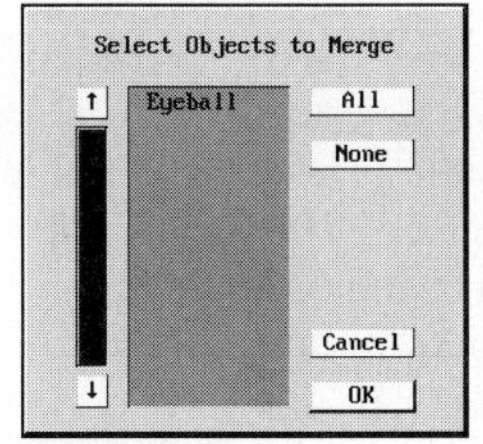

Figure 18.7

When you have merged EYEBALL, your drawing should look like Figure 18.8.

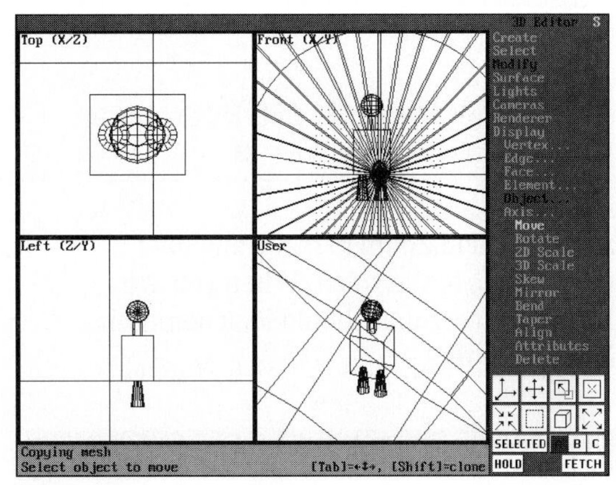

Figure 18.8

The EYEBALL appears in your drawing, but it is HUGE! (A terrifyingly huge eyeball. . .argghh!) You will scale it down to fit the robot. 3D Studio is often easier to use when you create objects large scale. When importing other mesh files, you will often have to change their scale to make them work with the size of objects in your current drawing.

Pick: **Modify *(screen menu)*, Object, 3D Scale**

Select object to scale: ***(pick the enormous EYEBALL)***

Scale: ***(pick 1% by rolling the mouse)***

Select object to scale: ***(pick the EYEBALL again)***

Scale: ***(pick 20% by rolling the mouse)***

On your own, use the Modify, Object, Move selection and move the eye into position at the front left of the robot's head. (Use Zoom as needed.) Use the Left and Top views to place and copy your robot's eyeball as it appears in Figure 18.9. Then use the Move command again, this time holding down SHIFT so that the eye is copied as it is moved, and make a second eye at the other side of the head. When the dialogue box appears, accept the default to name the second eyeball EYEBALL01.

> ■ ***TIP*** To refresh your display, pick Views (menu bar), Redraw All to redraw all of the viewports. Pick Views, Redraw to redraw only the current viewport. ■

Use Move and Zoom to make any final adjustments to the robot. When you are finished, your robot should look something like Figure 18.9.

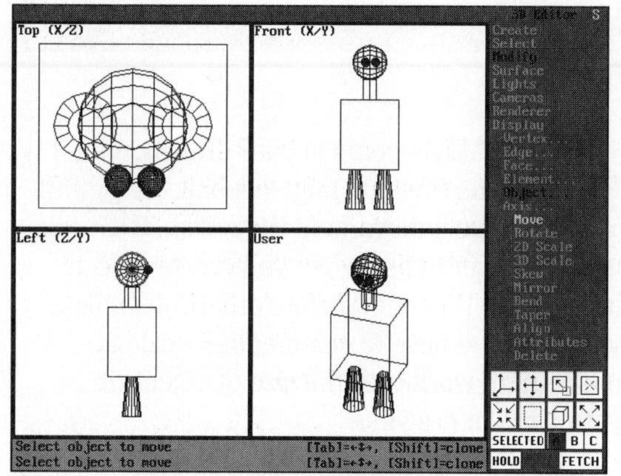

Figure 18.9

Now you are ready to select materials for the surfaces of the robot, as you did for the base and cover in Tutorial 17.

Pick: **Surface *(screen menu)*, Material, Choose**

Use the dialogue box shown in Figure 18.10 to select BLUE METALIC. You will need to scroll the list of materials to show BLUE METALIC, then pick on its name to select it.

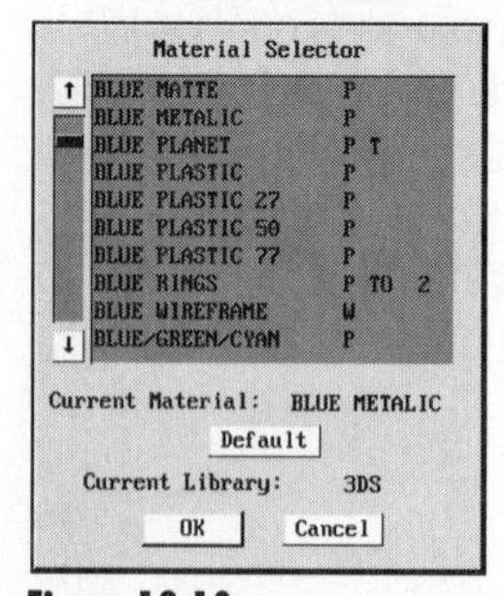

Figure 18.10

Pick: **OK *(to exit the dialogue box)***

Pick: **Surface *(screen menu)*, Material, Assign, Object**

Select object to make BLUE METALIC: ***(pick BODY)***

as the object to which the material is to be applied. A dialogue box appears with the name of the object you have selected. If you have the correct object selected,

Pick: **OK *(in response to the dialogue box)***

On your own, select materials and apply them to NECK, HEAD, LEG and LEG01. Do not apply any materials to EYEBALL and EYEBALL01, because they already have materials assigned to them.

Now you are almost ready to render the scene to see the results of your work. First you should increase the amount of light in the scene, or the result of the rendering will be dark and difficult to see. You will add more light by increasing the ambient light level.

Pick: **Lights *(screen menu)*, Ambient**

Use the slider bars to change the ambient light level so that the dialogue box looks like Figure 18.11.

Pick: **OK *(to exit dialogue box)***

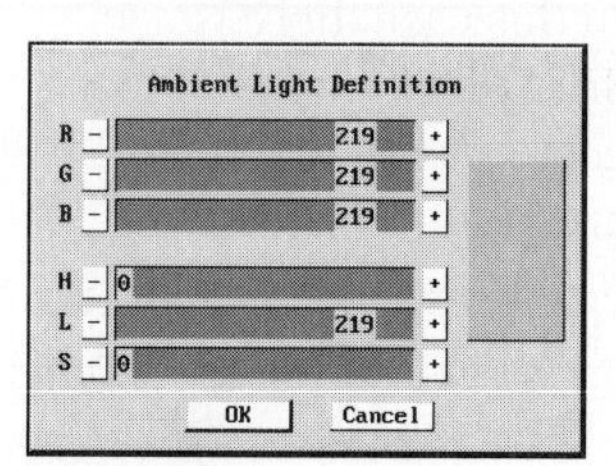

Figure 18.11

Now you are ready to render the scene to the display to see what the robot looks like with the materials added.

Pick: **Renderer *(screen menu)*, Render**

Select viewport to render: ***(pick twice in the user view)***

Pick Render to accept the defaults in the dialogue box to render the robot model to the screen. It should appear similar to Figure 18.12.

Figure 18.12

Press: ***(the right mouse button to exit the rendered view)***

On your own, use File, Save and save your work to the default file name, ROBOT.

In the next steps you will use the 2D Shaper to create an irregular shape and then use the 3D Lofter to extrude it along a helical path to form some unusual arms for the robot. Using 3D Studio, you can create a wide variety of shapes that you cannot create with AutoCAD. You can export these shapes into AutoCAD if you wish by picking File, Save and then the *.DXF button to export a .DXF file.

You will get a brief introduction to the 2D Shaper and the 3D Lofter in the next portion of this tutorial. Experiment with these tools on your own to create many varied shapes. To select the 2D Shaper program module,

Pick: **Program *(menu bar)*, 2D Shaper**

Pick: **Views *(menu bar)*, Drawing Aids**

On your own, set Snap to .125. The other drawing aids should already be: Grid, 1; Grid Extents, –10 to 10 for all axes; and Angle snap, 1 degree. Turn on Snap and Grid to assist in creating your 2D shape. When you have finished turning on Grid and Snap, pick Zoom Extents.

Pick: **Create *(screen menu)***

Notice the types of 2D entities you can create using the 2D Shaper. Again, these are similar to the AutoCAD Draw menu items.

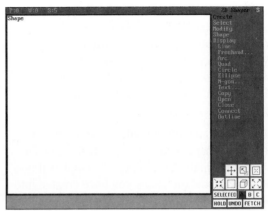

Figure 18.13

You will select the Line command and draw a closed figure similar to the one in Figure 18.14. First, Zoom up an area that is about 1 grid unit square on your own to assist you in creating the shape and size that will work as an arm for the scale of the robot you have drawn.

Pick: **Create *(screen menu)*, Line**

Click to create or insert line vertex: ***(pick points 1–12 from Figure 18.14 in order on the snap spacing)***

Press: ***(right mouse button to end the command)***

Pick: **Close**

Select polygon to close: ***(pick on any of the lines)***

The final line segment, from 12 back to 1, is added to the drawing so that it looks like Figure 18.14.

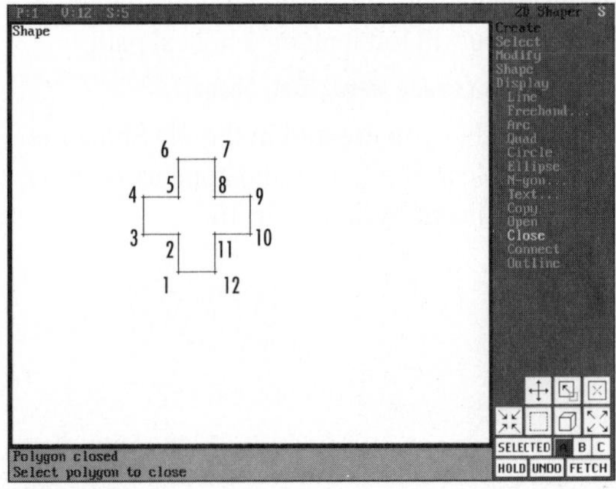

Figure 18.14

You can modify the shape of the polygon you created in the 2D Shaper in a variety of ways. You can change it to a curve with the selection Modify, Linear, Curve. You can use the points you selected as a spline and shape it by moving the vertices. You can skew it (similar to stretching it at an angle).

Before you can loft the polygon you created into a 3D shape, you must specify it as the current shape in the 2D Shaper. This makes it possible to import the shape you have created into the 3D Lofter, which is a separate program module. To make this polygon the current shape,

Pick: **Shape *(screen menu)*, Assign**

Select polygon(s) to assign as shape: ***(pick the polygon you created)***

It becomes highlighted, telling you that it is the current shape in the Shaper. Now you are ready to move to the 3D Lofter, where you will extrude the shape.

Pick: **Program *(menu bar)*, 3D Lofter**

Notice that the screen menu for the 2D Shaper is replaced with the screen menu for the 3D Lofter. The arrangement of the viewports has changed to show a large view of the shape and smaller views for the top, front, and user views. The line with tick marks, shown in the top and user views and as a point view in the front view, is the current path, a straight line. First you will get the shape that you created in the Shaper and then you will loft it along a helical path.

Pick: **Shapes *(screen menu)*, Get, Shaper**

The shape that you created in the 2D Shaper is now available to the Lofter and appears on your screen, as shown in Figure 18.15.

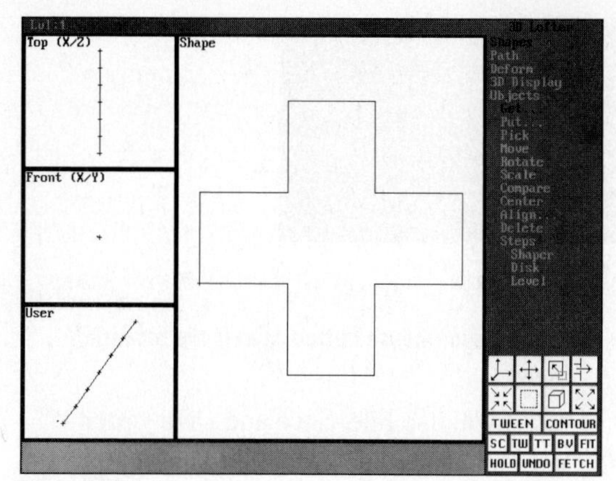

Figure 18.15

Pick: **HOLD *(to store your current work in the hold buffer)***

Next you will change the path so that it is shaped like a helix, and then you will loft it.

Pick: **Paths *(screen menu)*, Helix**

The Helix Path Definition dialogue box appears on your screen, as shown in Figure 18.16. You will use it to define the shape of a helix that will act as the path of extrusion. Use the techniques you have learned to change the dialogue box so that its settings match Figure 18.16.

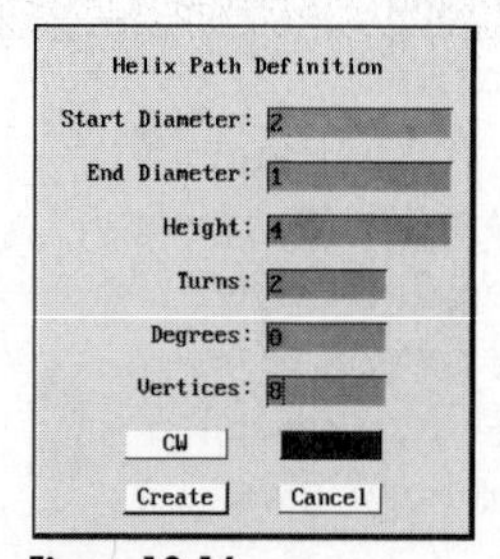

Figure 18.16

When you have finished making the changes to the dialogue box,

Pick: **Create**

Use the dialogue box that appears to select that you will import just mesh objects, not cameras, lights, or animation. Pick OK when you have deselected the items you do not want to import. Use the next dialogue box to change the path to the drive that contains your 3D Studio program files on the CD-ROM, where the sample files from the World Creating Toolkit are stored (usually D:\). Select the directory SAMPLES, the subdirectory MESHES, and the file SPACESHP.3DS from the list of files. When you have the file selected, pick OK.

Now you are ready to select which objects from this file you want to merge. You will pick the button All to the right of the list of objects shown in the dialogue box.

Pick: **All**

All of the objects have asterisks preceding their names to show they are selected.

Pick: **OK**

The spaceship is imported into the drawing. Like the eyeball, its scale is too large for the scale of this project. You will use the right mouse button to pick Zoom Extents so that you can see the objects clearly in all viewports.

Pick: **Zoom extents icon *(with the right mouse button)***

You need to scale the ship down so that it will fit the scale of your robot. Before doing this, however, you will select all four objects that make up the spaceship; otherwise, you will have to scale each part individually. To avoid this, you will use the Select, Crossing option and make a selection set. Then you can scale the selection.

Pick: **Select *(screen menu)*, Object, Crossing**

Use the top view and make a crossing box that crosses all four pieces of the spaceship (both wings, the tail section, and the front section). Be sure not to select the little robot. The items become highlighted, indicating that they are selected.

Pick: **Modify *(screen menu)*, Object, 3D Scale**

Pick: **SELECTED button *(from the lower right corner of the screen, above HOLD)***

Select object to scale: ***(pick in the center of the ship)***

Scale the ship down to 20% of its original size.

Pick: **Zoom extents icon *(using right mouse button)***

The spaceship should be scaled down. On your own, use the Move command with the SELECTED button to position the ship above the robot, so that your drawing appears like Figure 18.22.

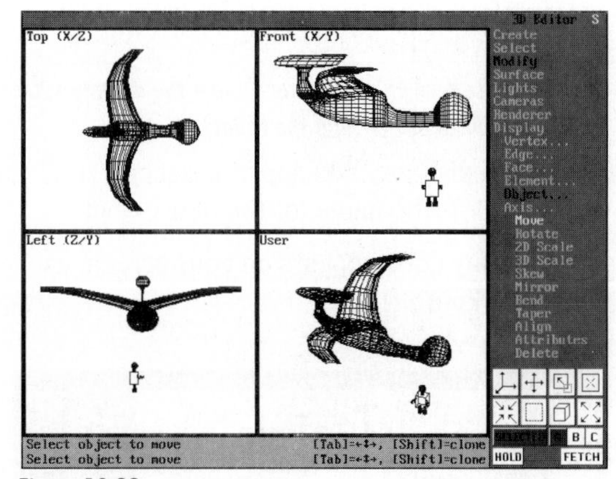

Figure 18.22

Now add a material for the spaceship and a spotlight to illuminate it from above on your own. Then render the scene to the display to see your lighting effects. When you are finished, save your work as ROBOT2. (Remember to change to the appropriate directory.)

Now you are ready to add animation to the scene, using the Keyframer. You will animate the robot walking to where it is just below its ship and then transport it up to the ship. To animate the robot walking, you will use a *dummy*. A dummy appears as a dotted cube in the Keyframer. It is an object to which you can link other objects in order to animate them as a group, yet still retain control over their separate parts. You will link the parts of the robot as *child* objects to the *parent* dummy object. If the parent object is moved, all of the child objects follow that same motion; however, moving a child does not move the parent. This way you can move the robot and all of its parts toward the spaceship, while moving parts of the robot independently.

Pick: **Program *(menu bar)*, Keyframer**

The Keyframer becomes the active module. You will use the Hierarchy option to create the dummy object.

Pick: **Hierarchy *(screen menu)*, Create Dummy**

Place center of dummy cube: ***(pick in the center of the robot's body)***

Move mouse to adjust dummy size: ***(make the dummy cube just a little larger than the robot)***

When the dialogue box appears, accept Dummy01 as the name for the new object.

The dummy cube appears on your screen, as shown in Figure 18.23.

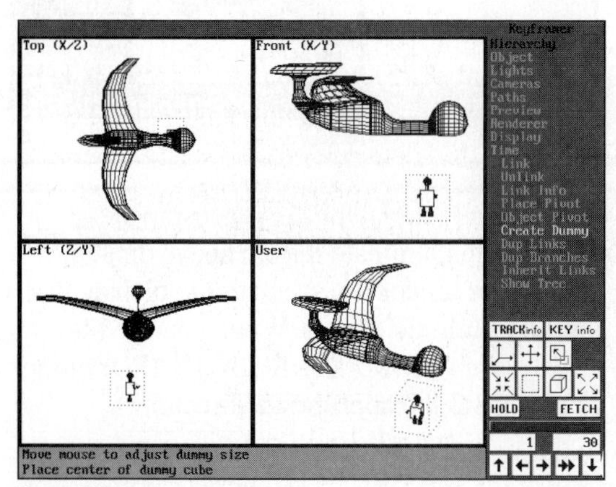

Figure 18.23

Now you will link the objects so that they can be moved in groups in the Keyframer. First, link the eyes to the head. This way you can rotate the head in the Keyframer and the eyes will move with it.You will need to Zoom to pick the eyeballs easily.

Pick: **Hierarchy *(screen menu)*, Link**

Select child object: ***(pick the left eye)***

"EYEBALL" selected.

Now select parent object: ***(pick the head)***

Linking "EYEBALL" to "HEAD"

Select child object: ***(pick the right eye)***

"EYEBALL01" selected

Now select parent object: ***(pick the head)***

Linking "EYEBALL01" to "HEAD"

On your own, continue the Link command and link the head, neck, body, left and right legs and arms to the dummy cube. Link the robot's spotlight, too, if you wish, so it moves with the robot. Save your work; reuse the file name ROBOT2.

You will next make a short animation, where the robot transports to its ship. Pick to make the front view active.

Pick: **Frame 7 *(as the current frame to animate)***

Pick: **Object *(screen menu)*, Move**

Select object to move: ***(pick on the dummy cube)***

Drag the dummy cube over to the left, as you see in Figure 18.24, until it is below the ship.

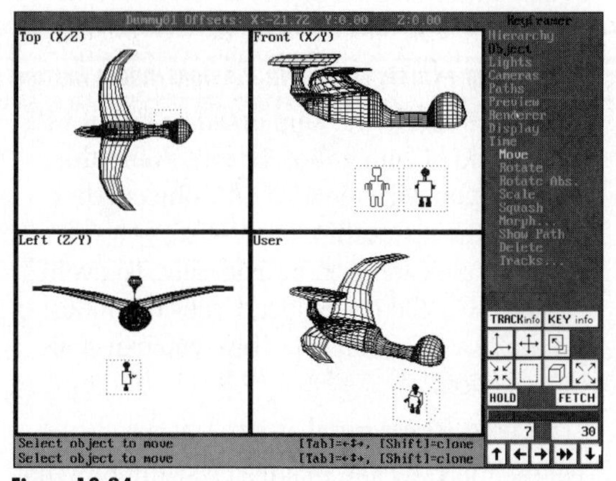

Figure 18.24

Now you will move to frame 3 of the animation, where you will rotate the robot's head and legs. Use the front view.

Pick: **Frame 3**

Pick: **Object *(screen menu)*, Rotate**

Select object to rotate: ***(pick the head)***

Press TAB until the Y axis is selected and then move the mouse until the status line shows 30 degrees of rotation. Press the mouse button.

Select object to rotate: ***(pick the right leg)***

Press TAB until the Z axis is selected and then move the mouse until the status line shows about 30 degrees of rotation. Press the mouse button.

Select object to rotate: ***(pick the left leg)***

Press TAB until the Z axis is selected and then move the mouse until the status line shows about 30 degrees of rotation. Press the mouse button.

On your own, move to frame 5 and add more rotation keys for your robot. Then pick the view you want to see and press the double right-facing arrow to play the frames in sequence. Notice how the robot moves with the dummy, and also how its individual parts move to make it look as though the robot is walking and moving its head.

Now the robot is ready to transport to the ship. First you will move to the frame just before the one where it will transport to the ship, and copy the keys so that its position does not change until you are ready. Because 3D Studio's Keyframer adds the in-between steps for you, the frame just before the one where you want an action to start should contain a key; otherwise, the transformation will be tweened from the last key to the new one.

Pick: **Track info**

Select object to see TRACK info: ***(pick the dummy cube)***

Use the dialogue box to copy the keys from frame 7 to frame 9 on your own.

Pick: **OK *(to exit the Track Info dialogue box)***

Next you will use the frame slider to make frame 24 the active frame.

Pick: **Frame 24**

Now you will add a movement key to move the robot up to the ship. Again, you will animate the dummy object and the robot's parts will follow.

Pick: **Object *(screen menu)*, Move**

Select object to move: ***(pick the dummy cube)***

Move the dummy cube straight up until it just touches the bottom of the ship.

But it seems that a failure on board the spaceship caused the hatch to be left closed. The poor robot will be flattened against the hatch by the force of the transport beam. You will use the Squash transformation on the dummy object so that the robot is squashed against the ship. Before adding the key for Squash, copy the scale key from frame 0 to frame 24 on your own, using Track info.

The Squash Transformation

The Squash command is similar to Scale in AutoCAD or 3D Studio, except that the apparent volume of the object remains constant. While you are squashing along one axis, the other two axes are scaling in the opposite direction to maintain the volume.

Pick: **Frame 26**

Pick: **Object *(screen menu)*, Squash**

Select object to squash: ***(pick the dummy cube)***

Move the mouse so that the dummy becomes thin and flat, as shown in Figure 18.25. Press TAB to select the X axis if necessary.

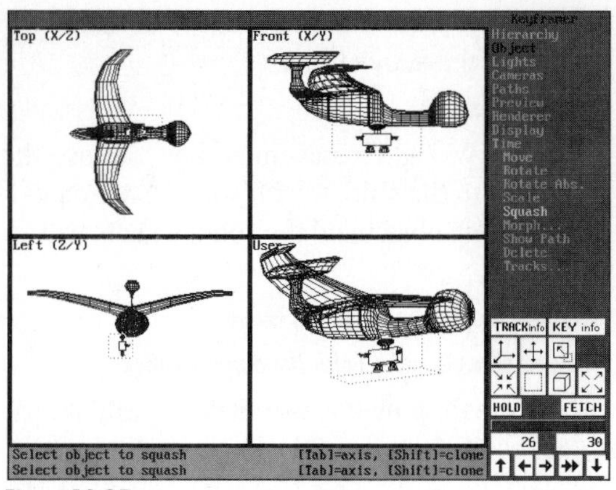

Figure 18.25

When you squash the dummy, it squashes about the center of the cube. On your own, use the Move command to move the dummy so that it is touching the ship in frame 26. Then move to frame 28 and repeat this process to squash and move the dummy a bit further. Add a motion key in frame 30 to move the squashed robot back to ground level. Add a background and then render the animation to a file. Play back your animation. If you need help, refer to Tutorial 17.

Morphing the Ship

Next you will use the Morph transformation to metamorphose one object into another. In order to do this, you must have two objects with exactly the same number of vertices. There are essentially two ways to get objects with the same number of vertices: you can use the 2D Shaper and 3D Lofter to create objects, making sure that you start with a certain number of vertices in the Shaper and set exactly the same number of segments in the Lofter, or you can make a copy of the object you want to morph and then edit the shape of the copy until it looks like the second object. This is generally the easier method. In the next steps you will copy the ship in the 3D Editor and make it into the shape of a bird. Then you will return to the Keyframer to morph the ship into the bird. You will return to the 3D Editor to copy the ship and change the shape of the copy.

Pick: **Program *(menu bar)*, 3D Editor**

To copy the object, you will hold down SHIFT and use the selected set of objects (which should still be set to the four parts of the spaceship).

Pick: **Modify *(screen menu)*, Objects, Move**

Pick: **SELECTED**

Press: SHIFT

Pick on the ship and move the copy to the lower left of the ship in the front view.

The message shown in Figure 18.26 appears on your screen.

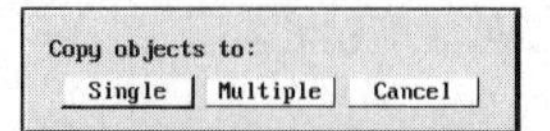

Figure 18.26

Pick: **Single**

Specify the name BIRD for the object that you will create with the move. If needed, pick on Zoom Extents with the right mouse button to zoom all of the views. When you have completed the above steps, your screen should look similar to Figure 18.27.

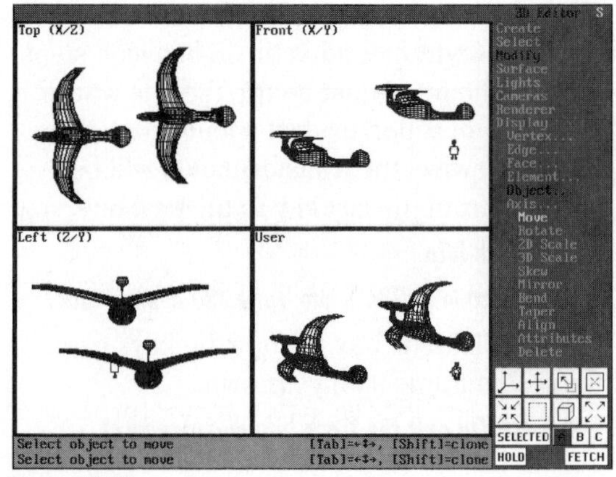

Figure 18.27

Next you will join the four parts of the spaceship to create one object.

Pick: **Create *(screen menu)*, Object, Attach**

Select object to attach: ***(pick on the front part of the ship)***

Object OBJECT01 selected, now select base object to attach it to: ***(pick on the tail portion of the ship)***

On your own, repeat these steps to attach the two wings to the tail portion of the ship.

Now deselect the ship.

Pick: **Select *(screen menu)*, Object, Deselect C**

Make a crossing box that crosses the entire ship. It will be deselected and no longer highlighted.

On your own, enlarge the user view to show the front portion of the bird object that you created, so that it appears similar to Figure 18.28.

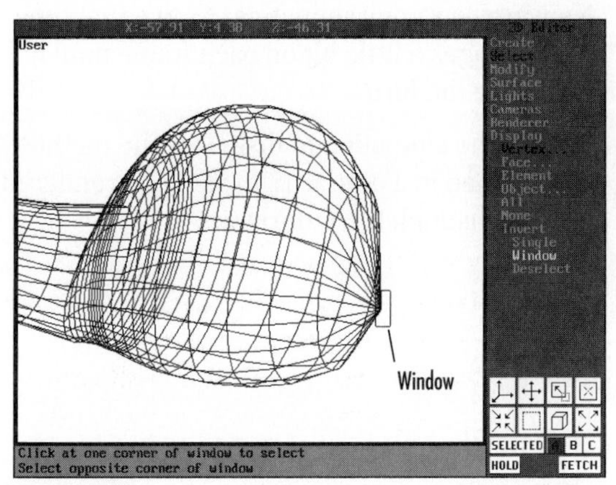

Figure 18.28

Next you will edit the vertices that make up the front portion so that it appears more like a bird's head. To edit several vertices at once, you will make a selection set first and then use the Move command to move all of the vertices. Otherwise, it will be difficult to move each one correctly; there are more than a thousand vertices making up this object.

Pick: **Select *(menu bar)*, Vertex, Window**

Make a small window around the rightmost vertices, as you see in Figure 18.28. They will become selected. Then you will move them to the right to make a beak.

Pick: **HOLD *(so that if you make a mistake you can restore the hold buffer)***

Pick: **Modify *(screen menu)*, Vertex, Move**

Select Vertex to move:

Pick: **SELECTED**

Pick: ***(near the existing right point)***

A box is drawn on your screen, representing the moved vertices. Locate it a little to the right of the last pick and:

Press: **Pick button**

The result should look like Figure 18.29.

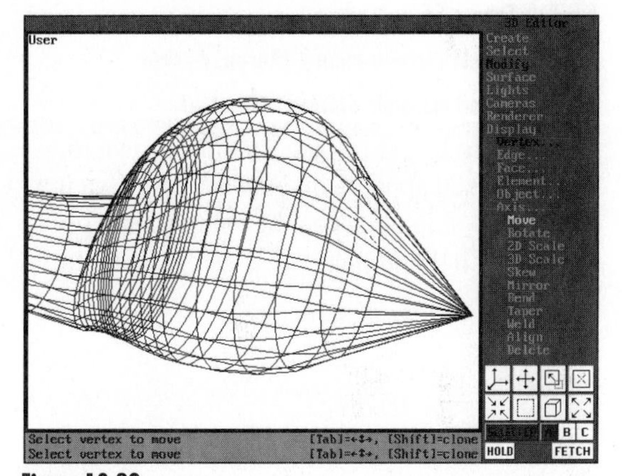

Figure 18.29

If you like the result, pick HOLD again. If not, pick FETCH and start again.

Repeat this process on your own to edit the vertices so that the object looks like a bird. You may need to switch and work in various viewports until you achieve the results you want. As you are working, save your file whenever you have created something that you are satisfied with. Use HOLD as you work to store your work in its present state so that you can restore the hold buffer with FETCH if you are unhappy with the results of a step. Alternatively, you can use the file BIRD.3DS that is provided with the data files and merge it into your drawing, using the method you learned at the beginning of the tutorial.

Now you should have two similar objects, the ship and the bird. You are ready to move to the Keyframer and morph the ship into a bird.

Make the Keyframer active and add another 30 frames to the animation on your own. You will not want to see the bird object in your animation, so you will use the Display, Hide command to hide it.

Pick: **Display *(screen menu)*, Hide Object**

Select object to hide: ***(pick on the bird object)***

The bird object becomes hidden.

Pick: **Frame 55**

Pick: **Object *(screen menu)*, Morph, Assign**

Select object to morph: ***(pick on the ship)***

A dialogue box similar to the one shown in Figure 18.30 appears on your screen. Use it to select the ship object as the thing to morph (OBJECT04) and pick BIRD as the thing to morph to.

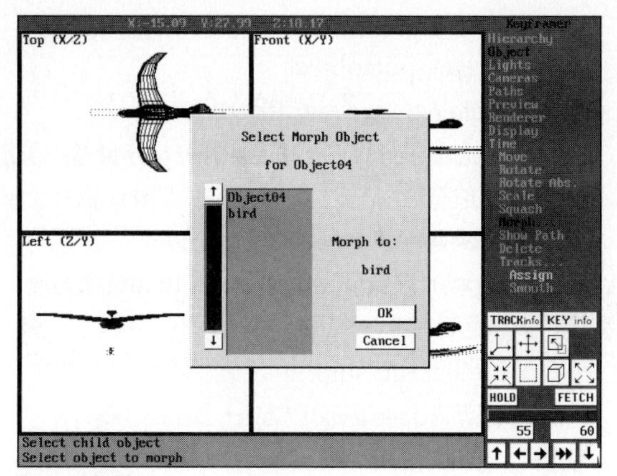

Figure 18.30

Copy the morph key from the first frame over to frame 32 so that the morph sequence doesn't start until after the squashing is done.

Now preview your animation. Notice that the ship changes a little bit on each frame until it looks like the bird.

Render the animation to disk. Use the method you learned in Tutorial 17 to view the rendered file. This completes Tutorial 18.

KEY TERMS

child
dummy
parent
squash

KEY COMMANDS

3D Scale
Ambient
Attach Object
Box
Center Shape
Cone
Create Dummy
Cylinder
Gsphere
Helix
Hide
Line
Link
Lsphere
Make Object
Merge
Morph Object
Select
Shape Assignment
Shaper
Spot
Squash Object

EXERCISES

18.1

Use 3D Studio to create a model of the solar system and animate the motions of the planets.

18.2

Use 3D Studio to create and animate a pinball game.

18.3

Use 3D Studio to design a fantasy chess set. Use the morphing techniques you learned to morph the pieces from one appearance to another. Animate a chess play where the pieces change shape.

18.4

Create a threaded screw in 3D Studio and export it using DXF format from 3D Studio to AutoCAD. Open a new AutoCAD drawing and use the DXFIN command to import the threaded screw into AutoCAD.

TUTORIAL 19

Camera Animation with 3D Studio

Objectives

When you have finished this tutorial, you will be able to

1. Create and move a camera.
2. Create a motion path.
3. Use the Tape tool to measure distance.
4. Set up and use object hierarchies.
5. Calculate the appropriate length of an animation.
6. Scale the timing of an entire animation.
7. Modify the quality of motion produced by splines.
8. Move a keyframe's position in time and space.
9. Copy keyframes.
10. Scale the duration of segments of an animation.

Introduction

"The nature and power of conceptual tools available to the designer determine in no small measure what [he/she] can accomplish."

- Tom Heath from *Method in Architecture*

Since before the building of the pyramids, architects have employed drawings and 3D models as conceptual and presentation tools. Drawings are employed at the conceptual stage of design, where frequent changes need to be made, and benefit from being easily replicated and transported. Physical models are more effective for depicting 3D relationships, but cannot be easily modified or transported, and are restricted in their ability to provide a sense of scale and interior. Neither drawings nor physical models are very good at representing dynamic situations.

3D Studio is able to combine for the architect many of the benefits of drawings with the advantages of physical models. In addition, 3D Studio enables the architectural designer to explore dynamic situations in a programmed manner through the power of the animated fly-through.

Three-dimensional fly-throughs are quickly becoming standard practice in architectural design, and required for effective presentation. This type of animation involves "flying" a "camera" along a path through a 3D computer model of an existing, proposed, or reconstructed building. Fly-throughs enable the architect and client to sample and consider various design solutions, using a format that is dynamic, visually effective, and easily modified.

This tutorial will focus on how to create an architectural fly-through using 3D Studio. Though this tutorial is geared toward architects, the techniques it explains are general and can be applied in a wide variety of disciplines, as can 3D Studio itself.

Starting

Begin 3D Studio from the Autodesk Collection Interface as you were instructed in Chapter 2.

Pick: **File *(menu bar)*, Reset**

A dialogue box appears, warning you that Reset will replace all data in all program modules.

Pick: **Yes**

Pick: **File, Load Project**

Select the file named FLY-THRU.PRJ that was provided with the data files that came with your software. The data files will be stored in C:\3DS2\PROJECTS where you loaded them during Getting Started.

Pick: **OK**

A dialogue box appears, warning you that loading a project file will erase any existing data (such as objects, lights, etc.).

Pick: **Yes**

> ■ ***TIP*** To the right of Load Project in the File menu are the characters ^J. To use this shortcut press Ctrl-J (^ is a conventional notation for the control key in computer literature). Several operations in 3D Studio have keyboard equivalents, and it is worth your time to memorize them. ■

Your screen should look like Figure 19.1.

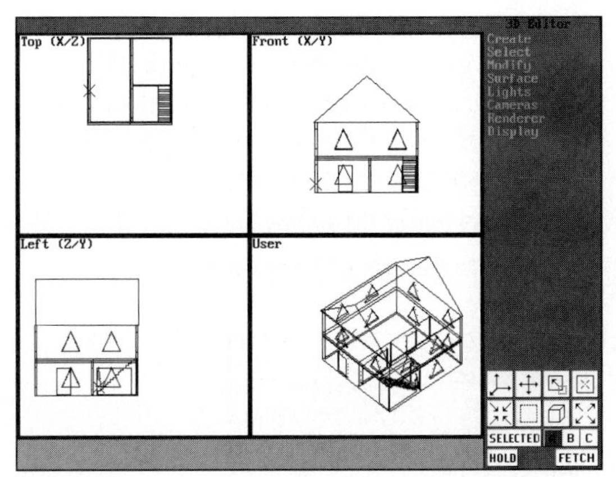

Figure 19.1

The structure that you just loaded was created using 3D Studio, and was designed to contain as little data as possible (hence the triangular windows). This is so that it can be more quickly rendered for the purposes of this tutorial.

Move the cursor around the screen, and look at the status line at the top of the screen. Note that the coordinates of the cursor are displayed in architectural units, as shown in Figure 19.2. (Your values will probably be different.)

Figure 19.2

You specify the type of unit used by 3D Studio with the Unit Setup command on the Views menu bar, similar to using the UNITS command in AutoCAD.

Pick: **Views *(menu bar)*, Unit Setup**

The Measurement Unit Selection dialogue box will appear on your screen as shown in Figure 19.3. You can use it to change the type of units and the unit precision like you have done in AutoCAD. For now exit the dialogue box without changing any of the settings.

Pick: **OK *(to exit the dialogue box)***

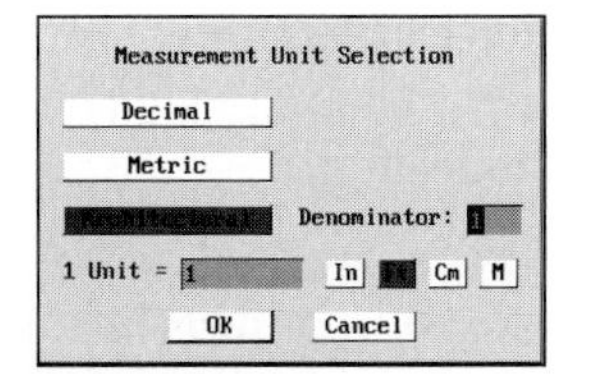

Figure 19.3

Creating a Camera

The primary components of a simple fly-through are the building, the camera, and the path the camera follows during the animation. The building, with a single light source, has already been provided for you. For this tutorial, you will first need to create a camera.

In 3D Studio, a camera is a special type of object that possesses particular attributes, characteristics, and components. The anatomy of a camera includes the camera itself and its target, as shown in Figure 19.4.

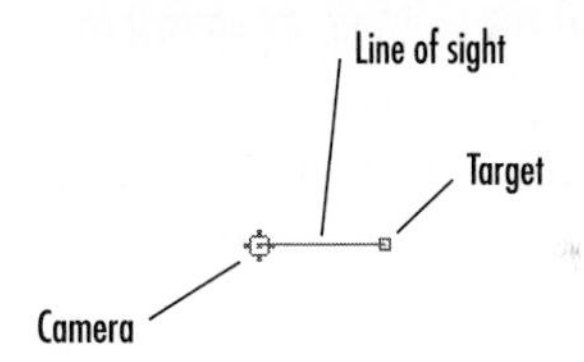

Figure 19.4

When you create a camera, you first place the camera itself in space, and then place its target. 3D Studio treats the camera and its target as two separate but connected entities. The target is necessary to specify where the camera is pointing. The line between the camera and the target is the camera's line of sight.

A camera and its target can be positioned in space, just like regular objects. However, they cannot be rotated, only "rolled," which involves treating the line of sight as a rotation axis. The camera's restricted rotation capacity will become an issue later, when you are further along in setting up your animation.

For the purposes of this tutorial, you will create your camera in the top view. On your own, make sure that the top view is active by picking in that viewport.

Pick: **Cameras *(screen menu)*, Create**

Place Camera: ***(pick a point at approximately X:15' Y:0' Z:–30', as shown in Figure 19.5)***

Don't worry about precision now. You will see in a little bit how to place your camera precisely.

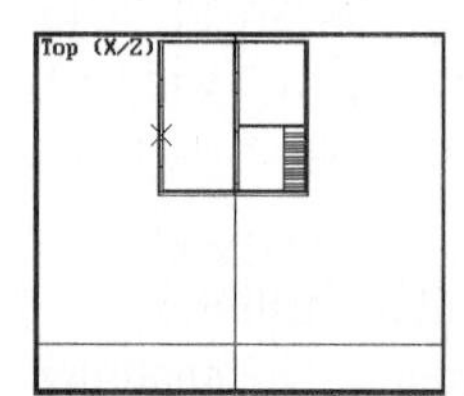

Figure 19.5

Now place camera's target: ***(pick a point in the positive Z axis in the middle of the building, as shown in Figure 19.6)***

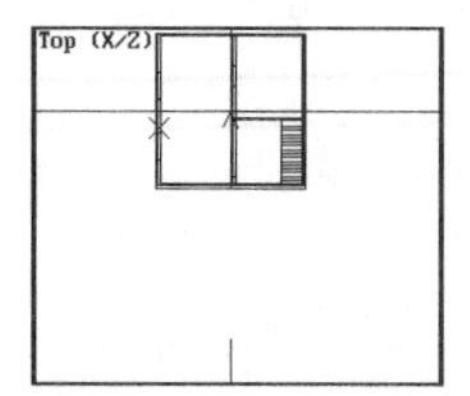

Figure 19.6

The Camera Definition dialogue box appears, as shown in Figure 19.7. Using this dialogue box, you can specify your camera's name to distinguish it from other cameras you may want to create (you can have more than one camera in a scene). You can also change the default lens and show the camera's cone, which helps in determining the extent of your camera's field of view (FOV).

You will select the 35mm lens from Stock Lenses to get a wider field of view (FOV is a function of lens size) and you will select On to the right of Show Cone, so that the camera's FOV is displayed graphically.

Pick: **35mm *(under the section Stock Lenses)***

Pick: **On *(to the right of Show Cone)***

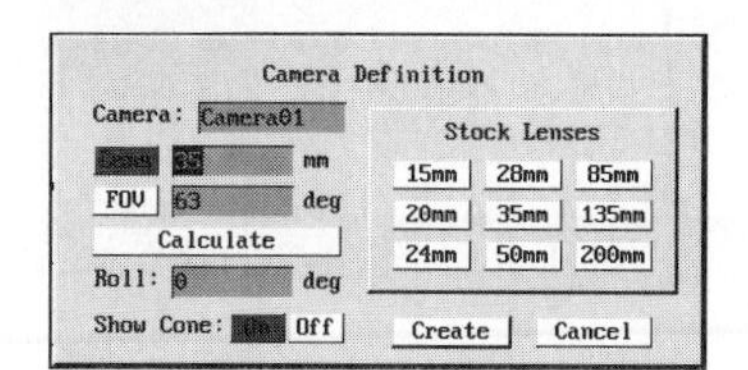

Figure 19.7

Pick: **Create**

A camera is displayed, along with its cone, in each of the four viewports. However, none of the viewports show you what the camera sees. To see the building from the camera's point of view, you need to set one of the available views to the camera view. You will change the front view to the camera view. First make the front view active, and then press the C key. Your screen should look similiar to Figure 19.8.

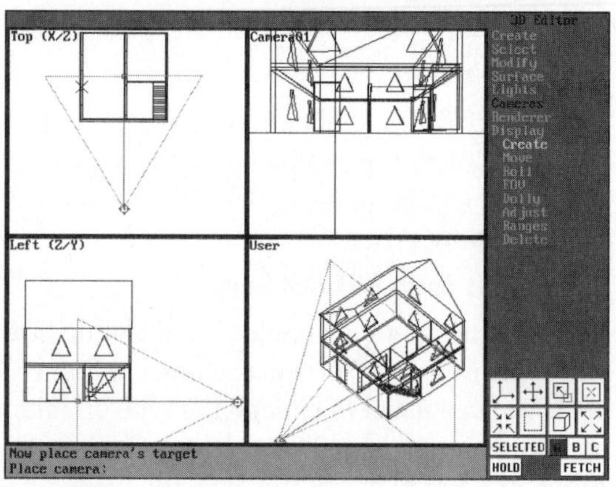

Figure 19.8

■ **TIP** You can use the keyboard to quickly switch the active viewport from one view to another. F stands for front view, K for back, T for top, B for bottom, L for left, R for right, C for camera, and U for user-defined isometric view. ■

Moving the Camera

The current camera view only gives us a worm's-eye view of the building. This can be addressed by moving either the camera or its target. For this tutorial, you will move the target. On your own, make the left view active, because this is the view you will work in to move the camera.

Pick: **Cameras *(screen menu),* Move**

Select camera or target to move ***(click on the camera's target)***

Note that the camera, the target, and the line of sight connecting them turn yellow. Move the target straight up the Y axis about 20'. Note the change in the camera viewport. Your screen should look like Figure 19.9.

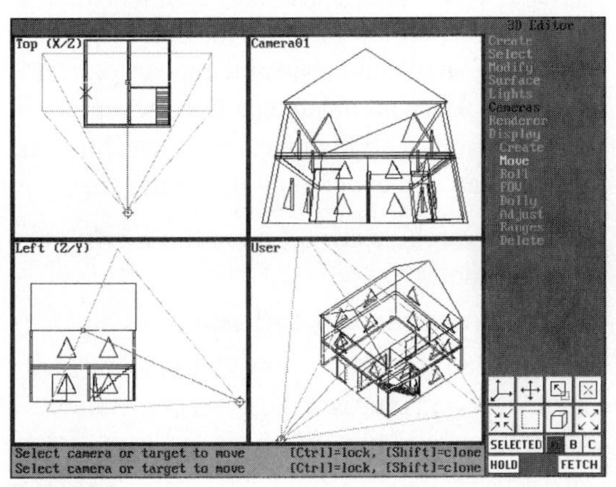

Figure 19.9

■ **TIP** You can move the camera and its target separately, or you can move them together by holding down Ctrl and then clicking either the camera or its target. ■

Precise Placement of the Camera

There is a way to place your camera precisely. First, you will delete the existing camera. While it is possible to have more than one camera, deleting the first one will avoid any possible confusion while you complete this tutorial.

Pick: **Cameras *(screen menu),* Delete**

Select camera to delete ***(pick the camera or its target in the left view)***

A dialogue box appears, asking whether or not to delete Camera01.

Pick: **Yes**

Note that the camera view has gone blank, and the viewport's label has changed to "No view defined." You will now create another camera, specifying precisely where you want it placed.

Pick: **Cameras *(screen menu),* Create**

Place Camera: ***(press the 1 key on the keyboard)***

Note that Camera X:1 appears in the status line at the top of the screen, as shown in Figure 19.10. Press the 5 key and then press ↵. When you press ↵, the value 15 is set for the X position of the camera.

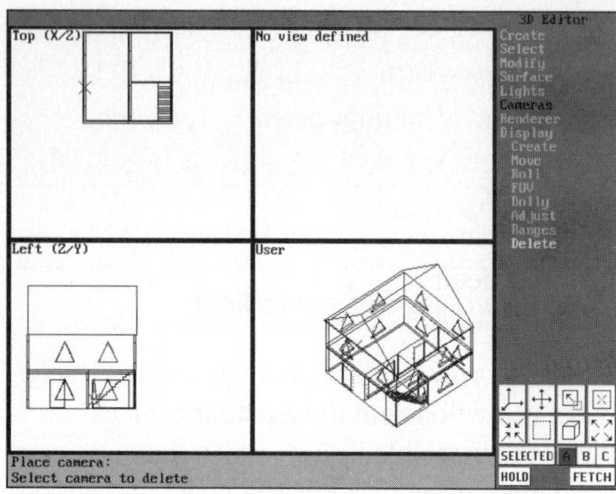

Figure 19.10

On your own, use the keyboard to set the Y and Z values for the camera's position to 5 and –30, respectively. Set the X, Y, and Z values for the camera's target to be 15, 5, and –20, respectively. Select the 35mm lens for the camera from the Camera Definition dialogue box, and turn the Show Cone setting to On. Set the undefined viewport to the camera view.

■ ***TIP*** Whenever a command appears in the prompt line with a colon (:) after it, that means that you can enter values for that command from the keyboard. Press (ESC) to return to picking points with the mouse while the command is active. ■

Note that even though the target does not reach the building as before, it can still be seen in the camera view. This is because the camera and its target still describe a line of sight that contains the building.

Object Hierarchies and Dummy Objects

Cameras are restricted in how they can be rotated. To get around this, you can attach the camera to another object that has full freedom of rotation, like attaching a camera to a tripod. This tripod object can, in turn, be attached to another object, which can serve as a kind of sled. While the sled is moving along a motion path, the tripod can be rotating, so that the camera attached to it is being pointed in different directions. Because the camera is attached to the tripod, which in turn is attached to the sled, the camera's movement is determined by the movement of the sled. The linkage of the camera to the tripod object, and the linkage of the tripod to the sled object, is called an *object hierarchy.*

Using object hierarchies, as you did when linking the parts of the robot in Tutorial 19, is an extremely powerful method for constructing complex animations. An example of a simple object hierarchy would be a small sphere linked to a large sphere. In this case, the large sphere is the parent, and the small sphere is the child. Whatever movement is applied to the large sphere is passed on to the small sphere. For instance, if the large sphere is rotated around a vertical axis passing through the center of the object, the small sphere would appear to orbit its parent. A parent object can have several children. Even a child object can have children. However, an object can only have one parent.

Object hierarchies are set up in the Keyframer program module.

Pick: **Program *(menu bar)*, Keyframer**

Change the upper right viewport to show the Front view on your own. Your screen should look similar to Figure 19.11.

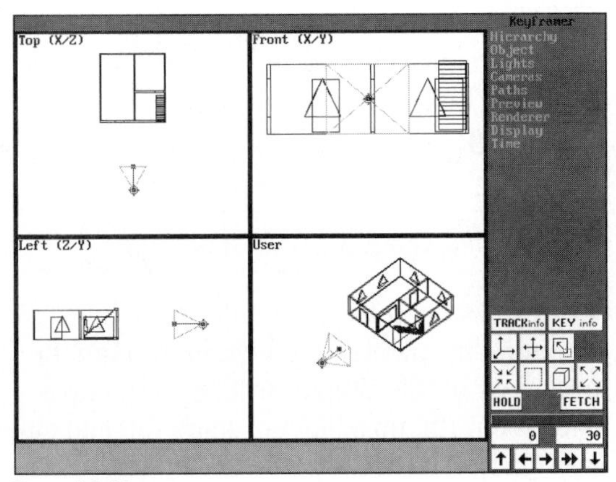

Figure 19.11

You will need to create an object hierarchy like the one described above, so that your camera can be oriented properly during the fly-through. However, you don't want to actually include a tripod and sled in the rendering of your animation. Instead, you will use dummy objects, as you learned in Tutorial 18.

First, you will create a dummy object that you will use as a tripod for your camera. You will work in the top view, so make that the active viewport.

Pick: **Hierarchy *(screen menu)*, Create Dummy**

Place center of dummy cube ***(pick on the camera)***

Move mouse to adjust dummy size ***(pick so that the top edge of the dummy box is about halfway between the camera and its target, as shown in Figure 19.12)***

When the dialogue box appears, name the object TRIPOD.

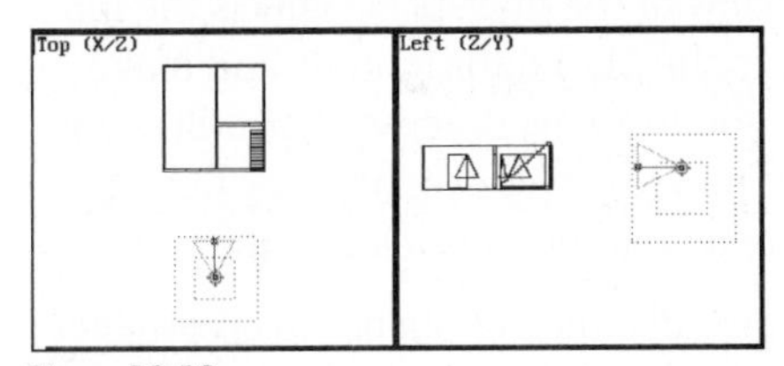

Figure 19.12

Now create a second, larger dummy on your own, as shown in Figure 19.12, and name it SLED.

Linking Objects

You now need to link the camera and the dummy objects together in the proper sequence.

First, let's inspect the current status of hierarchies in your scene.

Pick: **Hierarchy *(screen menu)*, Show Tree**

The Object Attachment Tree dialogue box appears, as shown in Figure 19.13. This dialogue box lists all the objects in the current scene, including those that are hidden. Objects that are linked as children to another object are listed below their parents, with the child object's name indented. None of the object names listed in the dialogue box are indented, indicating that there are no object hierarchies currently set up.

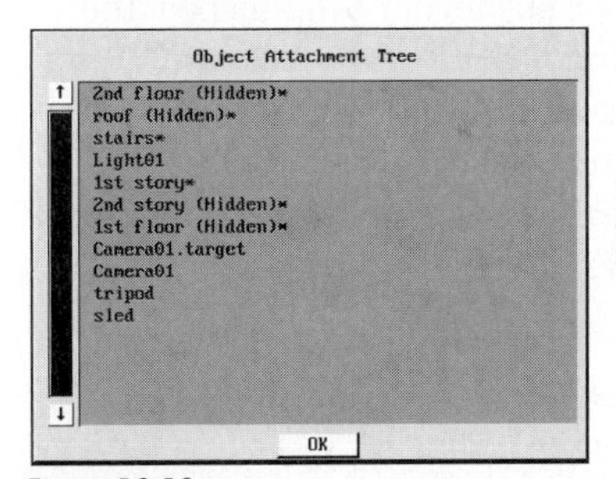

Figure 19.13

Pick: **OK *(to exit the Object Attachment Tree dialogue box)***

You will now link your objects together to form your object hierarchies. When linking objects, you will always begin with the child. It doesn't matter which viewport you work in, as long as you can see all of the objects.

Pick: **Hierarchy *(screen menu)*, Link**

Select child object ***(pick on the camera)***

"Camera01" selected: Now select parent object ***(pick on the TRIPOD dummy object)***

Linking "Camera01" to "TRIPOD"

Pick: **Hierarchy *(screen menu)*, Show Tree**

Note that Camera01 is listed below TRIPOD, and is indented, as shown in Figure 19.14. Note also that the camera's target is **not** linked. It is necessary for you to specifically link the camera target to the tripod as well.

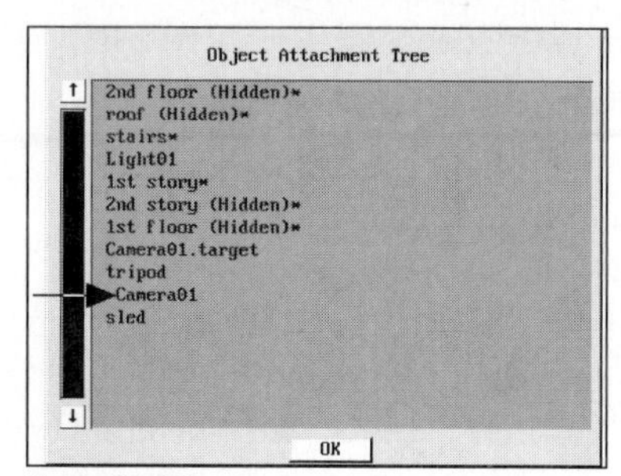

Figure 19.14

Pick: **OK**

Link the camera target to TRIPOD, and link TRIPOD to SLED, on your own. Inspect the Object Attachment Tree box to see the results of your efforts and ensure that your hierarchy is set up properly. It should look like Figure 19.15.

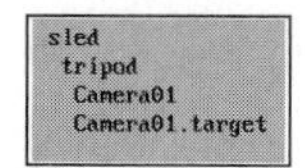

Figure 19.15

You will now test the results of your object hierarchy. First, save the current scene to the hold buffer so that you can restore it later.

Pick: **Hold**

On your own, change your upper right viewport to show the Camera view.

Now, move and/or rotate the sled around, then rotate and/or move the tripod around (dummy objects are manipulated in the same manner as regular objects). When you are finished experimenting, restore the scene to its previous state, using the FETCH function.

Pick: **FETCH**

Creating the Camera's Animation Path

Next, you will create an architectural fly-through that takes the camera in through the front door of this simple structure (1), into a back room (2), up a flight of stairs (3), and out into the middle of the second story (4), which is a single open room. Figure 19.16 shows the path your animation will follow as you fly through the first floor.

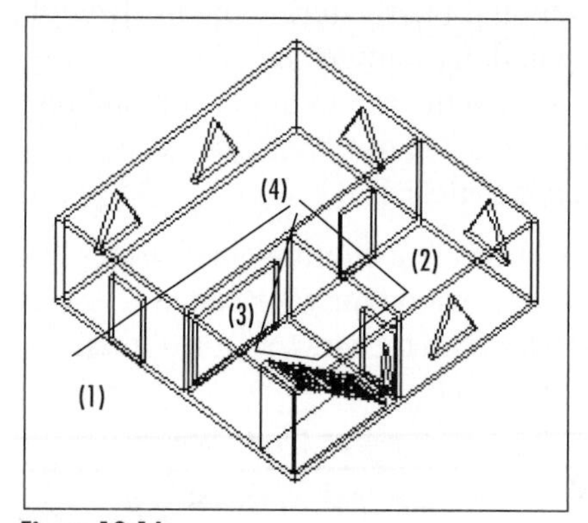

Figure 19.16

You will use the three-dimensional model loaded into 3D Studio as a guide in creating your path. You first need to select the view in the 3D Editor program module that provides the best view of the floor plan. This is the top view. Go to the 3D Editor module and make sure that the top view is active. You will see in a little bit how you will use this view to help you create a path for your animation.

You will now use the 2D Shaper to create the path your fly-through will follow.

Pick: **Program *(menu bar)*, 2D Shaper**

You will now display the floor plan of the 3D module as a guide for creating your animation path.

Pick: **Display *(screen menu)*, 3D Display, Choose**

Since your fly-through begins by entering the first story, you only need to display that part of the structure.

Pick: **1st story**

Pick: **OK**

Pick: **Display *(screen menu)*, 3D Display, On**

A top view of the part of the model named 1st story should be displayed in the shape viewport, as shown in Figure 19.17.

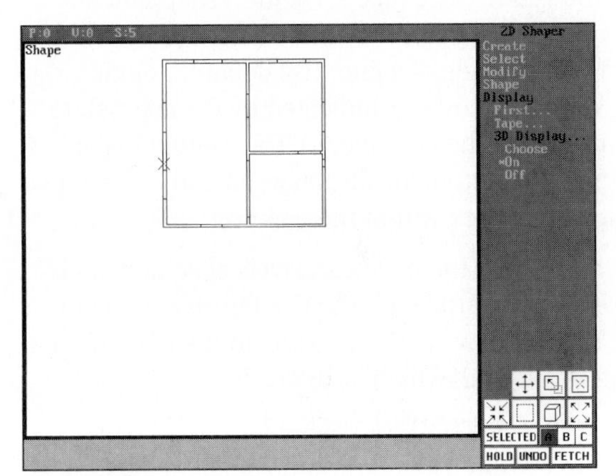

Figure 19.17

The 3D Display in 2D Shaper displays data using whichever view is active in the 3D Editor. This is why you made sure that the top view was active before you switched to the 2D Shaper. The 1st story is displayed in the 2D Shaper for purposes of reference only; the data cannot be modified in this program module.

Drawing the Path

You will now use the 2D Shaper's Line tool to create an open shape that will be used as the basis of the path that your camera will follow for the fly-through.

Pick: **Create *(screen menu)*, Line**

Click to create or insert Line vertex:

You could now use the mouse to draw a line. Note, however, that the command ends with a colon, indicating that you can enter the coordinates using the keyboard, enabling you to achieve a higher degree of precision.

On your own, create a four-sided, open shape whose vertexes are located at the X, Y coordinates specified in Table 19.1. Enter the coordinate values the same way you entered values for the camera's position. When you are finished, press (ESC).

Table 19.1

X	*Y*
Point 1: 9'	–30'
Point 2: 9'	20'
Point 3: 27'	20'
Point 4: 27'	2'
Point 5: 15'	16'
To stop:	press (ESC)

After you have finished, your screen should look similar to Figure 19.18.

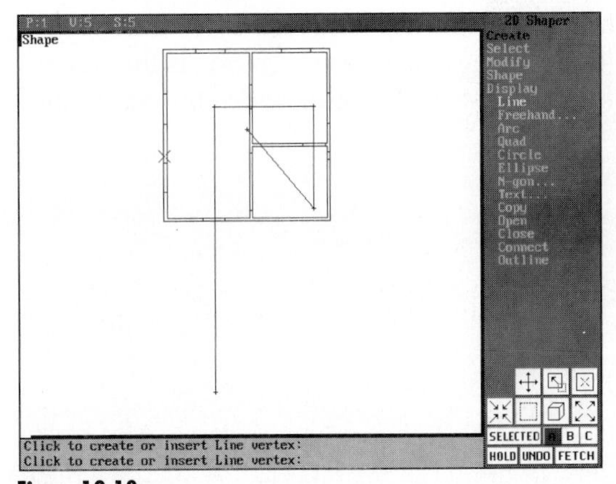

Figure 19.18

■ ***TIP*** The coordinates listed in Table 19.1 were arrived at by moving the cursor around the viewport to approximate positions, noting the coordinate values displayed in the status line at the top of the screen, and then rounding the values to the nearest foot. ■

It will be helpful to you to know the shape's dimensions when you are using it as an animation path. This is because the duration of your animation will be largely determined by the distance that the camera needs to travel, which in turn will be determined by the length of the shape's sides. The 2D Shaper module has a tape measure tool that you can use to determine the length of each side of the shape.

Pick: **Display *(screen menu)*, Tape, Find**

This function fits and places the tape measure into the current viewport.

Pick: **OK**

A horizontal green line appears in the middle of the viewport, as shown in Figure 19.19. This is your tape measure tool. Note that the length and angle of the tape measure are displayed in the status line at the top of the screen. You can determine a line's length by aligning the ends of the tape with the endpoints of the line. The length of the tape measure (which is the same length as the line) is displayed in the status line.

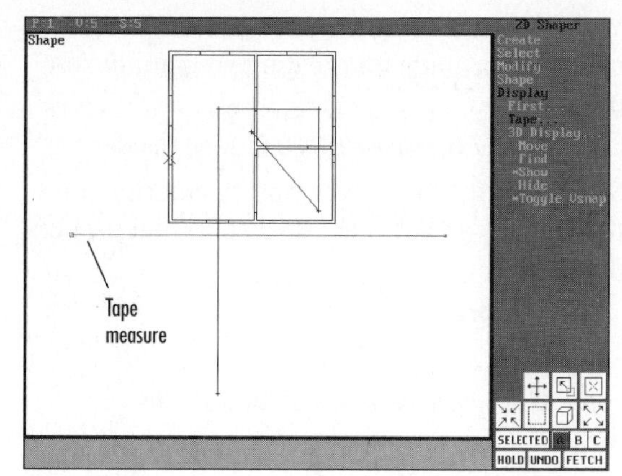

Figure 19.19

You can use the tape's Toggle Vsnap function to help you align the ends of the tape measure with the ends of a line. (By default, Toggle Vsnap is active, as indicated by the asterisk to the left of the command.) The Toggle Vsnap function automatically snaps an end of the tape to any vertex within the pickbox.

The size of the pickbox area is specified in pixels, and set through the Configure command. You will now set the pickbox to the maximum size allowed, which is 16 pixels.

Pick: **Info *(menu bar)*, Configure**

The Program Configuration dialogue box appears. The third item from the top is a slider bar, which you use to specify the size, in pixels, of the pickbox. Drag the slider all the way to the right so that the pickbox size is 16 pixels, as shown in Figure 19.20.

Pick: **OK**

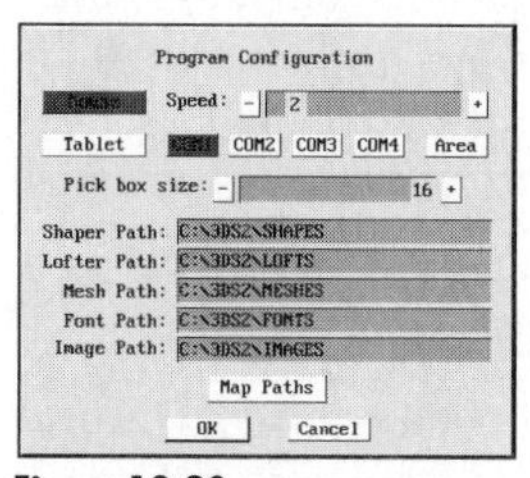

Figure 19.20

Now you will align the ends of the tape measure with the ends of the long, vertical side of the shape you just created, as shown in Figure 19.21.

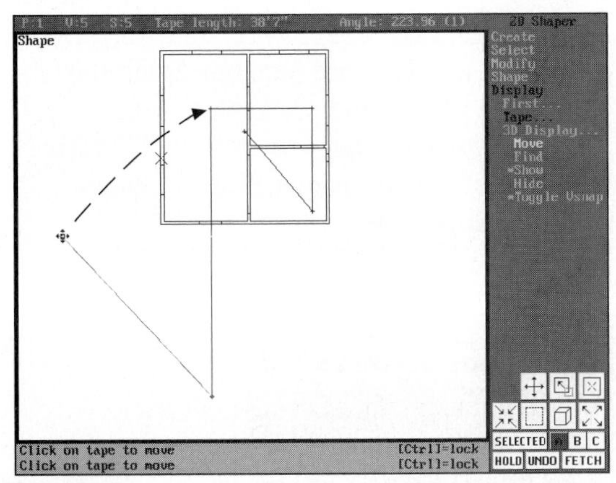

Figure 19.21

Pick: **Display *(screen menu)*, Tape, Move**

Click on the tape to move ***(pick the right end of the tape measure and drag it close to the first vertex of the shape)***

The end of the tape measure should snap onto the vertex.

Click on the tape to move ***(pick the left end of the tape measure and snap it onto the second vertex)***

The status line indicates that the tape length is 50 feet.

Use the tape measure tool to measure the lengths of the other sides of the shape on your own. The lengths of the sides of the shape should be 50', 18', 18', and 18'5" (as shown in Figure 19.22), for a total length of 104 feet, 5 inches. This information will come in handy later when you calculate the duration of your animation.

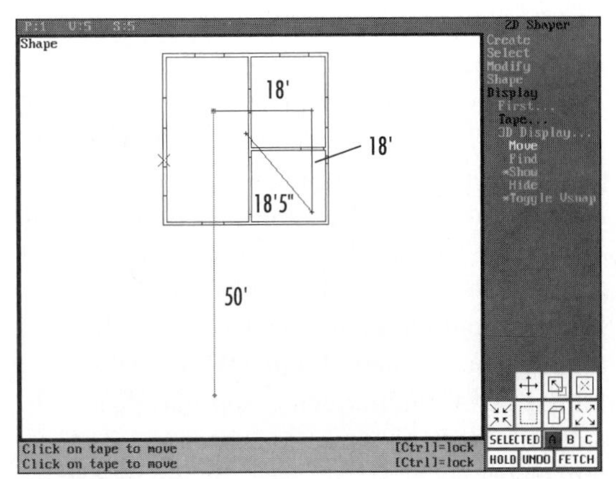

Figure 19.22

■ ***TIP*** You may have noticed that some of the lines of the shape have disappeared. Don't worry, they're still there. The lines were erased as a result of moving the tape measure around, and just need to be redrawn. To refresh and redraw the display, press (SHIFT)-~. ■

You will use the 2D shape you have created as a motion path that your camera will follow during the course of the animation. However, the path will not be assigned directly to the camera. Instead, the path will be assigned to the dummy object named SLED. Those objects that are attached to SLED, such as the tripod, the camera, and the camera target, will follow the sled as it follows the motion path.

Basic Concepts of Keyframe Computer Animation

Before you proceed, it might be a good time to review some basic animation concepts.

As you learned in Tutorial 17, animation involves the depiction of change over time. The change can be change in position, rotation, scale, etc. The depiction consists of a series of pictures, each representing a step in a transformation or change. When these pictures, called *frames*, are displayed in proper sequence and at an adequate speed, called *frame rate*, the illusion of smooth motion is achieved. For this tutorial, you will use a frame rate of thirty frames per second, which is appropriate for output to video (film uses a frame rate of 24 frames per second).

On your own, switch to the Keyframer module. By default, the Keyframer is set to 30 frames.

The four basic elements of any keyframe animation are:

1. The keyframes themselves
2. The order or sequence of keyframes
3. Timing (i.e., number of frames) between keyframes
4. The nature of the transformation between keyframes

The first element of a keyframe animation is the individual keyframes themselves. A keyframe is a declaration of some condition or set of conditions. A condition might be a specific position in space, or rotation value, light intensity, surface color, etc. You specify the conditions set for individual keyframes, and 3D Studio creates animation by calculating the transformation from one keyframe to another.

Let's see what, if any, keyframe information is set for SLED (since it is the object you will attach the path to).

Pick: **Track info**

Select object to see TRACK info ***(pick SLED)***

The Track Info dialogue appears, as shown in Figure 19.23, indicating which frames are set as keyframes for SLED. Note that there is a black "key dot" at frame 0 only; no other frames have been set as keyframes.

■ ***TIP*** You need more than one keyframe to create a transition. Otherwise, your animation would comprise a series of identical frames, and no transformation or change would happen. ■

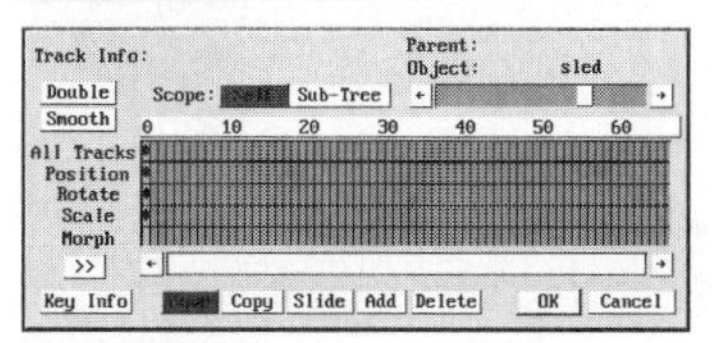

Figure 19.23

Pick: **OK**

You are now ready to assign the shape as a path to SLED. You will use the Paths menu in the screen menu to get the shape currently loaded in the 2D Shaper module, and assign it to SLED. The Paths menu can also be used to manipulate the path after it has been assigned.

Pick: **Paths *(screen menu)*, Get. . ., Shaper**

Select object to apply path ***(pick SLED)***

The Get Path dialogue box appears. Select Yes to relocate the object to the beginning of the path, as shown in Figure 19.24.

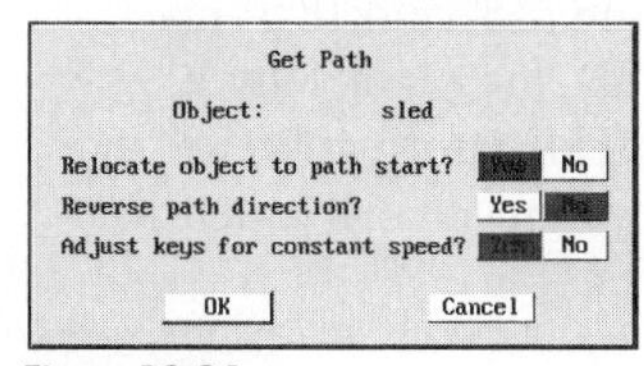

Figure 19.24

Pick: **OK**

You have assigned the shape in the 2D Shaper to SLED. You can show the path to see the assignment more clearly.

Pick: **Paths *(screen menu)*, Show-Hide**

Select object to show or hide path ***(pick SLED)***

The square white dots on the path represent keyframes. The yellow dots on the path represent locations at frames that are not keyframes; these locations are the result of interpolation between the keyframes. The duration of the path is equal to the number of frames in the current animation *segment*. For example, the default Keyframer setting is for a thirty-one-frame segment, beginning with frame 0 and ending at frame 30.

Bring up the Track Info box for SLED again on your own. Note that there are now five position keyframes set for SLED, which corresponds to the number of vertices in the shape you made in the Shaper.

The second element of keyframe animation is the order of keyframes. Let's say that one keyframe specifies that an aircraft is on the ground, and another specifies that the aircraft is in the air. Depending on the order that the keyframes are arranged in, the animation produced from these keyframes will show an aircraft either taking off or landing.

The order of SLED's keyframes corresponds to the order of the vertices in the shape that is being used as SLED's animation path.

Pick: **OK *(to close dialogue box)***

Modifying the Motion of the Sled

Try moving the bar in the frame slider at the bottom of the screen back and forth. Observe the movement of SLED and its children as they follow the path. Note that the camera does not orient itself properly to correspond to the direction of its movement. You can fix this using 3D Studio's Follow function.

Pick: **Paths *(screen menu)*, Follow**

Click on object or path to follow ***(pick SLED)***

The Follow Path dialogue box appears. Select No for Bank. The Bank option will cause the sled and its children to tilt as they turn a corner. While this may be desirable in some cases, such as for aircraft, it is not appropriate for this tutorial.

Pick: **OK**

Again, slide the bar in the frame slider at the bottom of the screen back and forth. The camera now orients itself properly. Actually, SLED is orienting itself as a result of the Follow operation, and its children, including the camera, are following it. The Follow operation will not work on the camera by itself.

Bring up the Track Info box for SLED again on your own. There are now several rotation keyframes set for SLED. These are a result of the Follow operation (only keyframes that contain position data are represented in the viewports as small white boxes on the path).

Now it's time to make a preview of the animation you have created so far. You will render your previews in wireframe, because this mode renders fastest.

First, make the camera view active, since it is the view you want to preview.

Pick: **Preview *(screen menu)*, Make**

Select viewport to Preview ***(pick the camera viewport)***

Pick: **Preview *(bottom left button in the dialogue box)***

You will notice right away that the animation is much too fast! Press the right button to stop the preview (you can also press ESC to stop the preview).

Changing the Timing of the Animation

The third element of keyframe animation is timing. Timing is determined by the amount of time, i.e., number of frames, it takes to complete a transformation from one keyframe to another. Picking up on the earlier example, let's say your first keyframe has the aircraft in the air, and the second keyframe has the aircraft on the ground. If you set the keyframes 15 frames apart in your animation, the transformation will occur in one-half second, and the aircraft will appear to crash. If you set the keyframes 150 frames, or 5 seconds, apart, the aircraft will appear to make a controlled landing.

Review Figure 19.22. Note that the total length of the path, rounded to the nearest foot, is 104 feet. To travel this distance at, say, 10 miles per hour takes about 7.1 seconds, which equals 213 frames of animation:

5,280 feet per mile * 10 = 52,800 feet

52,800 feet / 3600 seconds in an hour =
  14.6 feet per second

104 feet /14.6 feet per second = 7.1 seconds

7.1 seconds * 30 frames per second of
  animation = 213 frames

If you simply added frames to the animation, as you did in Tutorials 17 and 18, the path would still keep its duration of 30 frames, and the characters would stand idle for the remaining 183 frames of the animation. You need to scale the motion to fit into 213 frames.

Pick: **Time *(screen menu)*, Scale Segment**

The Scale Segment Length dialogue box appears. Scale the current segment length to 213 frames, as shown in Figure 19.25.

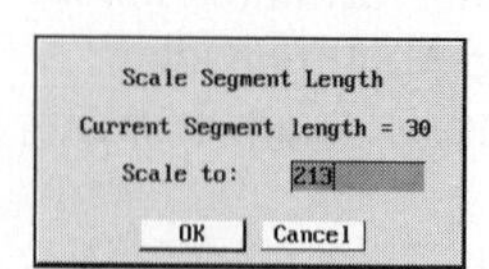

Figure 19.25

Pick: **OK**

Note that the number of yellow dots on the path, which represent the individual frames (not keyframes), has increased dramatically. Your path looks more like a yellow line than a red line now.

Make another preview, using the camera view, on your own.

Using Hierarchy to Change Altitude

The motion path is a two-dimensional figure that doesn't allow the camera to fly up the staircase to the second story. One way to fix this would be to move the fourth and fifth keyframes up 10 feet, to the second floor. This might be reasonable with only two keyframes to move, but could become complicated with many more than that. Also, the second keyframe is too far from the staircase; your camera would begin moving up too soon in the animation. You can fix this by adding one more object to your object hierarchy, linking the sled to it as a child, and using the new object to control the vertical movement of SLED.

Create another dummy object next to the sled on your own, as seen in Figure 19.26. Call this object V_SLIDER (the V stands for "vertical"). Link SLED to V_SLIDER as its child.

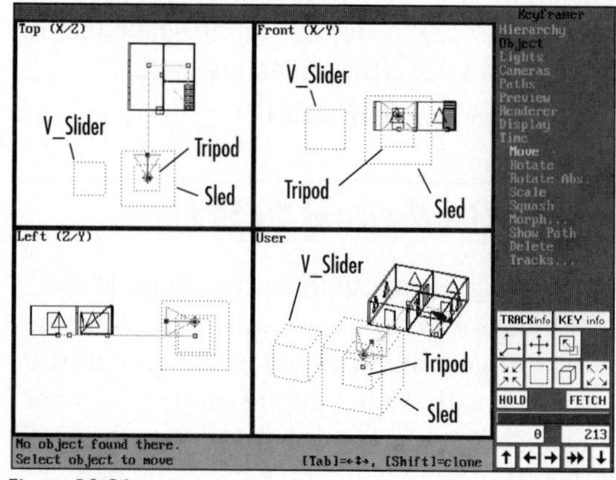

Figure 19.26

Move the frame slider at the bottom of the screen to a point in the animation just before the camera reaches the stairs, about frame 150. V_SLIDER will stay in its original position.

You are now going to create a position keyframe for V_SLIDER at the current frame, which is frame 150.

Pick: **Key Info**

Click on V_SLIDER.

The Key Info dialogue box appears. Unlike the Track Info box, which gives very general information about an object over the duration of the entire animation, the Key Info box provides detailed information about an object at a specific keyframe. The box also provides you with the ability to manipulate certain attributes of the object, such as its position, rotation, and scale, and to modify the qualities of its motion, such as easing, tension, etc.

Pick: **Create Key *(at the bottom of the Key Info dialogue box)***

You have created a new keyframe for V_SLIDER at the current frame and at the current position. The Key Info dialogue box should look like the one shown in Figure 19.27. Your position numbers may be slightly different.

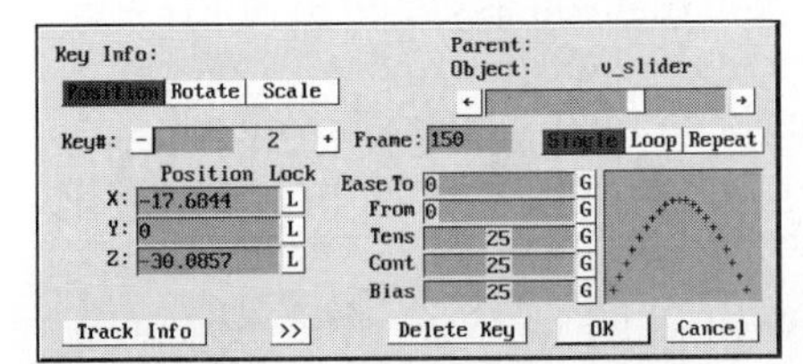

Figure 19.27

Pick: **OK**

Now slide the frame slider so that the animation is at a point where the camera is below the top of the stairs. This should be about frame 177.

You are now going to move V_SLIDER up vertically about ten feet. The sled and all of its children will move up with it.

Pick: **Object *(screen menu)*, Move**

Select object to move

Working in the left viewport, press TAB until the cursor changes to an icon with two arrowheads, one pointing up, the other down, as shown in Figure 19.28. This means that only vertical movement is allowed.

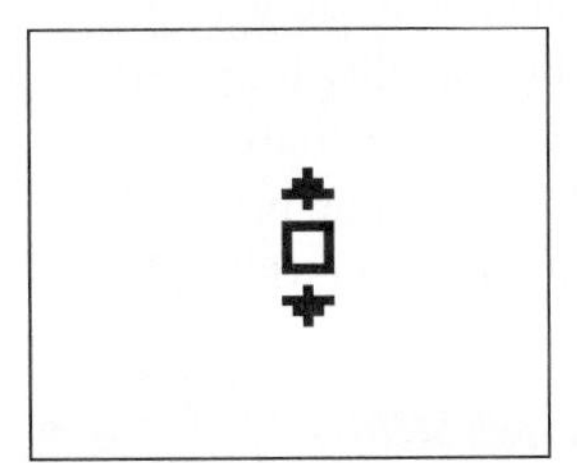

Figure 19.28

Click on V_SLIDER and drag it up approximately 10 feet, as indicated by the status line at the top of the screen.

Note that the part of the SLED's animation path that occurs after frame 177 has slid up 10 feet, while the part that occurs before frame 150 stays put. The part of the path occurring between frames 150 and 177 is "ascending" the staircase.

Make another preview, using the camera view.

> ■ ***TIP*** It would be a good idea to save the work you have done so far. Save your work as a project file named BACKUP.PRJ. You will need to use the File, Save Project command instead of the File, Save command. ■

Non-Linear Interpolation

The motion path is very linear, and the changes in direction are uncomfortably severe. You can fix this using 3D Studio's built-in spline functions. This brings us to the fourth element of keyframe animation, which is the nature of the transformation between keyframes.

Computers use a process called *interpolation* to calculate the transformation from one keyframe to another. The simplest form of interpolation involves dividing the transformation mathematically into equal increments. This process is called *linear* interpolation and may result in unnatural or robotic movement. 3D Studio incorporates spline functions into the interpolation process in order to give a smoother and more natural quality to the transformation. In some cases, as you shall see, the spline feature of 3D Studio may produce unwanted results, and need to be modified.

Pick: **Key Info**

Click on object to see KEY info ***(pick SLED)***

The Key Info dialogue for SLED appears. Make sure the Position button is active, as shown in Figure 19.29. (You may have a different frame number and X,Y, and Z values; don't worry about it right now.)

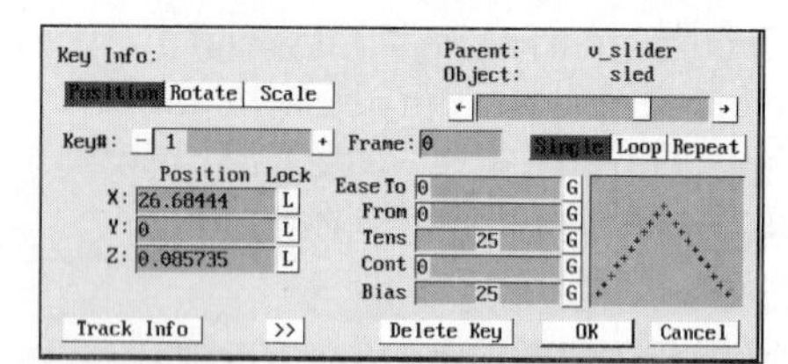

Figure 19.29

In the lower right corner of the Key Info dialogue box is a small window that graphically depicts the form of the transition, or interpolation, from one keyframe to the next (see Figure 19.30). The lower left-hand corner represents a point halfway to the preceding frame, the red tick mark represents the current frame, and the lower right-hand corner represents a point halfway to the following frame. The black tick marks indicate the form of the transition.

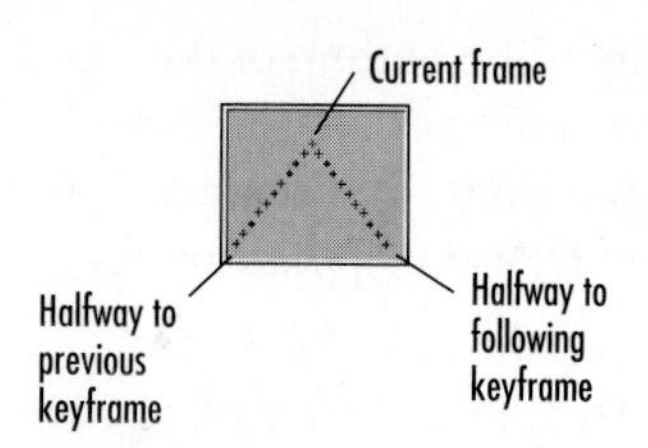

Figure 19.30

Typically, when a keyframe is created, 3D Studio assigns a curve, or spline, to it in order to create more naturalistic motion. 3D Studio provides three parameters that control this splining function: Tension (Tens), Continuity (Cont), and Bias. *Tension* refers to the attack of the spline toward a keyframe. *Continuity* refers to continuity between the slopes of the splines going into and out of the keyframe. *Bias* controls on which side of the keyframe splining occurs. Since Tension, Continuity, and Bias control the nature of interpolation, not movement, they can be applied to a wide range of transformations.

> ■ ***TIP*** You must have at least three keyframes for the spline controls to work. ■

Since the path that you assigned to SLED was created using the Line tool in the 2D Shaper module, its keyframes were automatically set for linear interpolation. Therefore, you need to invoke the splining function manually.

Drag the Cont slider halfway to the right until Cont is set to 25, and click on the G button to the right of the slider, as shown in Figure 19.31. (The G button stands for "global" and applies the settings to all of SLED's existing position keyframes.) Note the effect moving the slider has on the graphic to the right of the sliders.

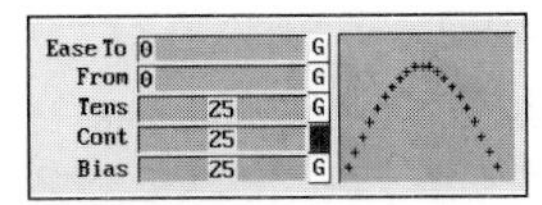

Figure 19.31

Pick: **OK**

On your own, make the Top viewport active. Then expand the active viewport (which should be the top view) so that it is the only viewport displayed.

Moving a Keyframe's Position in Space

The path now contains nice, smooth arcs. As a result of these arcs, however, the path comes too close to the walls when passing through the doorways, as shown in Figure 19.32.

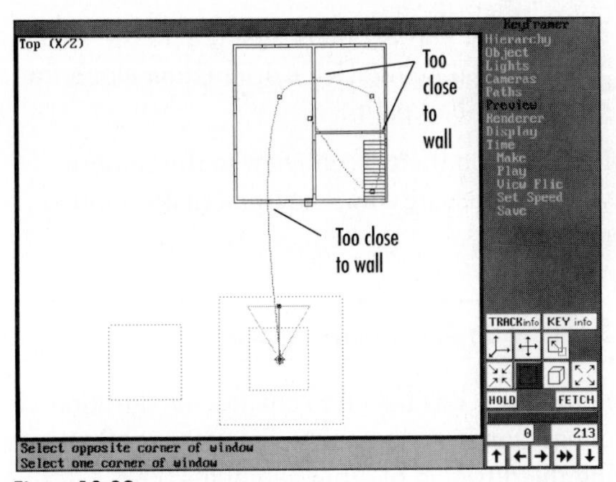

Figure 19.32

You will fix this by moving some keyframe's position in space. By moving a keyframe, what you are really doing is moving the position in space of the associated object at that frame in the animation. You will use two methods to move a keyframe's position in space: the first using the mouse, and the second using the Key Info dialogue box. On your own, make the Top view active

Pick: **Paths *(screen menu)*, Move Key**

Click on key to move it

Press (TAB) until the cursor indicates freedom of movement in all directions. Click on the second keyframe of SLED's motion path, and move it approximately 2 feet to the right in X and –3 feet in Z, as indicated by the status line at the top of the screen, and as shown in Figure 19.33.

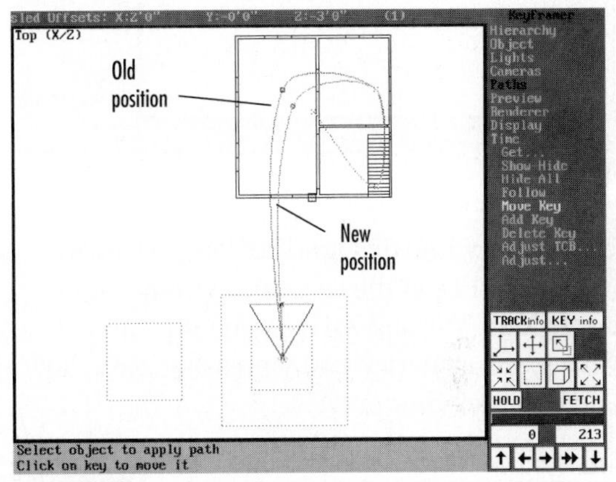

Figure 19.33

Another way to move a keyframe that has a higher degree of precision is to use the Key Info dialogue box; however, you lose the interactivity of moving it using the mouse.

Pick: **Key Info**

Click on object to see KEY info ***(pick the third keyframe of SLED's motion path)***

The Key Info dialogue box for SLED at frame 142 should appear. Let's say that you know that you want to move over about 3' in a negative X direction. The current position in X of SLED at frame 142 should be approximately 44.26595. You need to subtract 3' from the current position, giving a new position of 41.26595.

Place the cursor in the X Position field and click the left mouse button once. Type in "41.26595" and press (↵).

The third keyframe should move over to the left, as shown in Figure 19.34.

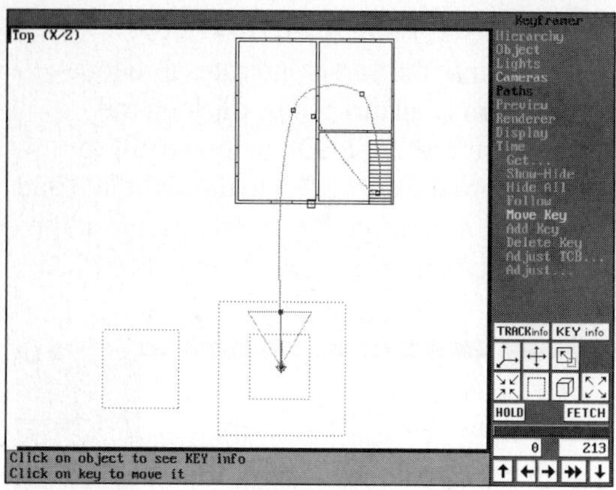

Figure 19.34

Use the Key Info dialogue box on your own to place SLED, at the second keyframe, at precisely X:28, Y:0, and Z:47. Switch the current view to the camera view by pressing the C key, and make another preview.

Moving a Keyframe's Position in Time

So far, the camera moves slowly into the structure, and then zips around into the back room. Let's say that you want to shorten the amount of time it takes to travel from the first keyframe (frame 0) to the second keyframe (frame 99), and lengthen the amount of time it takes to travel from the second keyframe to the third keyframe (frame 143). However, you do not want to change the position in space of any keyframe. You can achieve this by shifting the second keyframe's position in time, not space, so that it occurs earlier in the animation. This takes time from the segment of the animation occurring between the first and second keyframe, and adds it to the segment occurring between the second and third keyframe. You will use the Paths menu in the screen menu to achieve this.

Change the current view to the top view by pressing the T key.

Pick: **Paths *(screen menu)*, Adjust, Key Time**

Click on key to move in time ***(pick the second keyframe of the motion path)***

Note that the keyframe's position in time (specified in frames) is indicated as frame 99 in the status line at the top of the screen.

Drag the mouse to the left. The keyframe itself will not move in space! Note that the keyframe's position in time, as indicated in the status line at the top of the screen, moves closer to the beginning of the animation (which is frame 0).

Drag the mouse to the left until the keyframe becomes frame 70. Click the left mouse button to set the new keyframe time.

Note that, unlike the Move Key command, this operation changes the keyframe's position in time, not in space.

Reapply the Paths, Follow function to the sled. This will update the sled's orientation along the newly modified path.

Next, switch the current view to the camera view by pressing the C key, and make another preview.

Defining an Animation Segment

Sometimes it is useful to change the duration of one portion of an animation without affecting the duration of other segments. For instance, let's say that you want to slow the animation between the second and fourth keyframes, without affecting the beginning of the animation. You need to define the portion of the animation between the second and fourth keyframes as the current animation segment and then scale it.

Change the current view to the top view by pressing the T key.

Slide the frame slider at the bottom of the screen to determine the frame number of the second and fourth keyframes. You do this by moving the slider so that the sled passes over the keyframes. When the sled turns white, that means that there is a position key value set for SLED at that frame; the frame number is indicated in the status line at the top of the screen. The second keyframe should be set at 70 and the fourth at 177.

■ ***TIP*** You can also use the Track Info dialogue box to find out which frames are set as keyframes. ■

You will define the current animation segment as the set of frames beginning at frame 70 (the second keyframe) and ending at frame 177 (the fourth keyframe). The frames from 0 to 69, and those from 178 to 213 (the end of the animation), will not be part of the new animation segment.

Pick: **Time *(screen menu)*, Define Segment**

The Define Active Segment dialogue box appears. Set Start: to 70 and End: to 177, as shown in Figure 19.35.

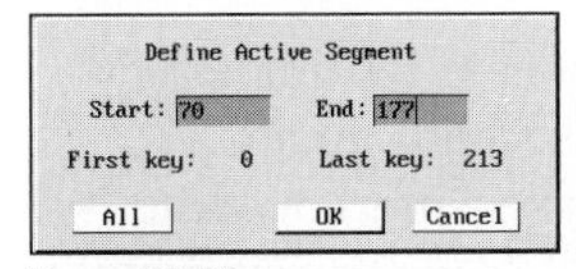

Figure 19.35

Pick: **OK**

The beginning and ending segments of your animation disappear (as shown in Figure 19.36), and the frame slider at the bottom of the screen goes from frame 70 to 177.

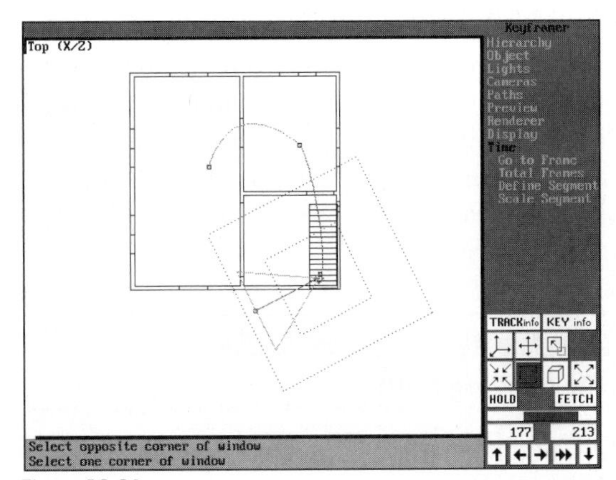

Figure 19.36

Scaling an Animation Segment

In order to slow down the current segment of animation, you have to increase the number of frames in the segment. This is done by *scaling* the segment. Let's say that you want to add three seconds to the current segment. You will do this by increasing the number of frames in the segment by 90 frames. (Current segment length = 107 frames) + (3 seconds x 30 frames per second = 90 frames) = 197 frames.

Pick: **Time *(screen menu)*, Scale Segment**

The Scale Segment Length dialogue box appears. Add 90 to the current segment length, which is 107 frames. Set Scale to: to 197, as shown in Figure 19.37.

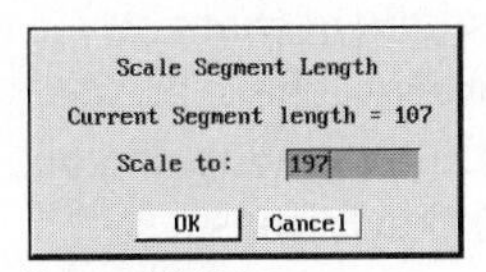

Figure 19.37

Pick: **OK**

Reapply the Follow function to SLED and make another preview, using the camera view. Note that the preview only contains that part of the animation included in the current segment, as specified in the Frames: field of the Make Preview dialogue box. Set the field to All and remake your preview.

Inserting Keyframes and Scaling the New Segments

An animation segment does not need to begin and end exactly on keyframes. However, it is a good idea to begin and end segments at keyframes if you plan to scale the segment. This is because the scaling operation requires keyframes as beginning and ending points. If there are no keyframes in the current animation segment, 3D Studio will use keyframes that are outside the current segment, probably with unwanted results.

What should you do if you want to scale a portion of the animation that does not begin or end precisely on a keyframe? The answer is to create your own keyframes where you need them. Let's say that around 170, you want the camera to stop and pan around the back room for about five seconds.

Set the viewport to the top view, using the T key. Define the current segment as beginning at frame 170 and ending at frame 171.

You now have a two-frame segment that you can scale to 150 frames. However, there are no keyframes at either end of this segment, so you will have to make them both keyframes.

Make sure the frame slider at the bottom of the screen is set to frame 170.

Pick: **Key Info**

Click on object to see KEY info ***(pick SLED)***

Make sure that the Position button is selected. Note that frame 170 is not a keyframe; the position values for this frame are the result of interpolation between the preceding and following keyframes. However, you can turn this frame into a keyframe.

Pick: **Create Key**

You have just created a position keyframe for SLED at frame 170. Now you want to copy this keyframe to frame 171. You will use the Track Info dialogue box to do this.

Pick: **Track Info *(at the bottom left of the dialogue box)***

Note that the current frame, 170, is indicated in the Track Info dialogue box with a vertical light blue line. You want to copy SLED's position setting at frame 170 to frame 171.

Pick: **Copy *(at the bottom of the Track Info dialogue box)***

Click on the position dot at frame 170. Drag the copied keyframe setting to frame 171.

Pick: **OK**

The current animation segment now begins and ends with a keyframe. Note that since frame 171 is a copy of frame 170, both keyframes contain identical information. This will be significant as you continue to create this rotation.

Scale the current segment to 150 frames, giving it a duration of five seconds. Frame 171 becomes frame 320. Make a preview of the entire animation from the camera view. Note the five-second pause about halfway into the animation. This pause is a result of the fact that the two adjacent keyframes, frame 170 and frame 320 (formerly frame 171), specify the same position in space. Therefore, there is no motion between these frames.

Removing Unsightly Splining

Or almost no motion. There is, in fact, a slight drifting of the camera during the pause. This is caused by 3D Studio's built-in splining functions, and is the result of having two consecutive keyframes with the same position in space. As mentioned earlier, 3D Studio's built-in splining functions can sometimes cause unwanted results. In this case, a *loop* was created in the path of the sled between frames 170 and 320, as shown in Figure 19.38 (which is an extreme closeup).

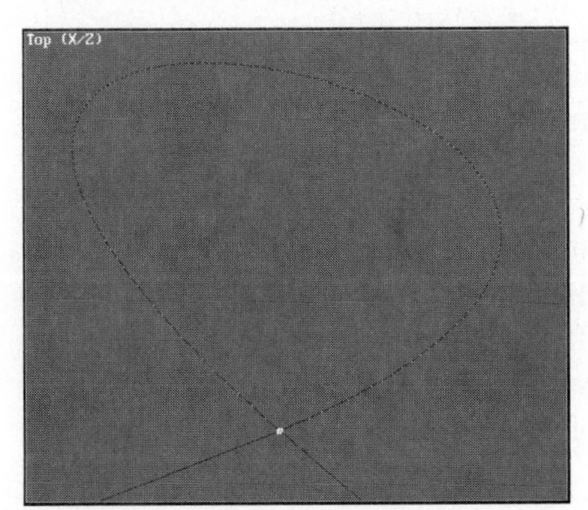

Figure 19.38

You can fix this problem by modifying the Bias parameters of these two keyframes. As was mentioned above, Bias controls on which side of a keyframe splining occurs. You can use this control so that there is no splining between frames 170 and 320. This will remove the loop in SLED's motion path. You will also set the Ease parameters for these frames to smooth out the stop and start of motion caused by this segment.

Make sure the frame slider is set all the way to the left to frame 170, and bring up the Key Info box for SLED on your own. You should be at key# 3, frame 170.

Move the Bias slider all the way to the left, setting this parameter to 0, as shown in Figure 19.39. Also, set the Ease To value for this frame to 50.

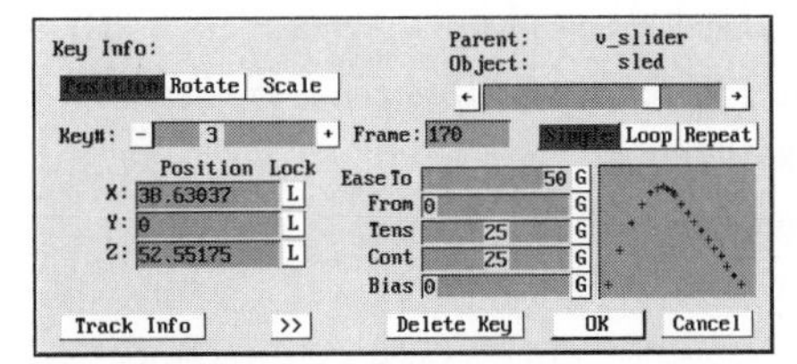

Figure 19.39

Click on the + of the Key# slider so that you are at key# 4, frame 320.

Move the Bias slider all the way to the right, setting this parameter to 50. Also, set the Ease From value for this frame to 50.

Pick: **OK**

Use Time, Define Segment to show the whole path before you continue. Since you have added more keyframes to SLED's path, redo the Follow Path operation for this object.

Changing the Children

Remember, the whole point of creating this pause in the animation was to give yourself time to rotate the camera so that it pans around the room. Unfortunately, cameras cannot be rotated in 3D Studio, and you cannot rotate the sled because this might conflict with the rotation values resulting from the Follow Path operation performed earlier. Instead, you will rotate the tripod that the camera is attached to. This in turn will rotate the camera.

Go to frame 170. You are now going to make a rotation keyframe for TRIPOD at frame 170.

Pick: **Key Info**

Click on TRIPOD. By default, the Key Info dialogue box displays information pertaining to the object's position. However, you want to create keyframes that control the tripod's rotation. For this purpose, you need to set the Key Info box to display rotation information.

Pick: **Rotate *(in the upper left corner of the Key Info dialogue box)***

Pick: **Create Key**

Pick: **OK**

Go to frame 320. Set the current view to the top view.

Pick: **Object *(screen menu)*, Rotate**

Select object to rotate ***(pick TRIPOD)***

Press TAB until the status line at the top of the screen indicates that you are rotating around the Y axis.

Drag the mouse to the right until TRIPOD has been rotated around the Y axis by about 360 degrees, as indicated by the status line. Since the camera is a child of the tripod, the camera also rotates.

Click the left mouse button to set the rotation.

Going Further

Try and make it so that the camera looks up the staircase as it climbs the stairs. You will need to have a keyframe near the bottom and the top of the stairs, where the camera is looking straight ahead. You will also need to create two more keyframes, about one-third and two-thirds of the way up the stairs, where the camera (i.e., TRIPOD) is tilted, looking up. When you have finished, make a preview of the animation from the camera's point of view.

Rendering Your Animation

You will now create and save to disk a fully rendered version of your animation. Rendering a 3D computer animation can take a great deal of time. There are several factors that can affect how long it takes to fully render a complete animation: hardware configuration, software settings, and the complexity of the scene being rendered. The 3D model used for this tutorial was designed to contain as few faces as possible, so that it could be quickly rendered. Some of the software settings that affect the amount of time it takes to render an animation include the resolution of the rendered frames, what display algorithm is used (wireframe, flat, gouraud, or phong), anti-alias settings, etc. Generally speaking, anything that enhances the quality of the final image will add to the amount of time needed to render that image. The hardware issues that will affect the length of time needed to render a frame include type of processor and processor speed, amount of memory, speed of hard disks, etc.

■ ***TIP*** A good way to estimate how long it will take to render an animation is to render a few frames from different parts of the animation, figure out their average rendering time (maybe add a second or two for overhead), and multiply that time by the number of frames in your total animation. This method is not meant to be precise, just approximate. ■

As you learned in Tutorial 17, 3D Studio can create two different types of animation files, .FLI and .FLC. Both types of files contain 256 colors. The difference between them is that the resolution of .FLI files cannot exceed 320 pixels by 200 pixels, while .FLC files are resolution independent. 3D Studio creates .FLI files by default. In order to create and play high-resolution .FLC files in 3D Studio, you need to install whatever drivers are appropriate for the display board installed in your computer. For now, you will render to .FLI files, using the default resolution of 320 X 200 pixels.

Before you begin rendering, you will unhide the rest of the structure so that it will be included in the final rendering.

Pick: **Display *(screen menu)*, Unhide. . ., All**

Save your project on your own before continuing. Now you will render the animation.

Pick: **Renderer *(screen menu)*, Render**

Click the mouse in the camera viewport. The Render Animation dialogue box appears. You will set the Shading Limit to Flat and Anti-aliasing to Low.

Pick: **Flat *(at the middle top of the dialogue box)***

Pick: **Low *(just below the Flat button)***

Pick: **Render *(at the bottom of the dialogue box)***

The Save File dialogue box appears, just as it did when you rendered .FLI files in Tutorial 17. Name your file FLY-THRU.FLI and save it in the default directory (this should be \3DS2\IMAGES on your hard drive).

Going Further

The animation takes you up to the second floor, and stops there rather unceremoniously. Apply what you have learned so far and build onto the end of this animation. Below are some suggestions:

Change the timing of the camera's climb up the stairs and movement out into the second floor to make them both more leisurely.

Create a fully rendered .FLC file of your fly-through.

Have the camera stop in the middle of the second floor and do a pan around the room.

Add a path onto the end of the animation that flies the camera out of a window on the second story. Have the camera look back at the structure as it flies out.

After you have flown the sled, tripod, and camera out the window and placed them in space, finish the animation by sliding the V_SLIDER object downward as it rotates about its Y axis. This will cause its children objects to spiral downwards. Reorient the camera so that it is always looking at the structure.

KEY TERMS

bias	interpolation	scaling
continuity	linear	segment
frame	loop	tension
frame rate	object hierarchy	

KEY COMMANDS

3D Display	Follow	Scale Segment
Create Camera	Get	Show Tree
Define Segment	Key Time	Tape
Delete Camera	Move Camera	

EXERCISES

19.1

Retrieve your file from Exercise 9.3. Create a fly-through of the office layout.

19.2

Retrieve one of your rendered bridges from Exercise 16.3. Create a valley for it to span and put traffic on the bridge (use cars from the World Creating Toolkit). Make an animation from the point of view of a traffic helicopter flying past.

19.3

Use the RULESURF command in AutoCAD to create a surface mesh for the railroad bed site plan for Challenge Exercise 6. Export the site to 3D Studio and use camera animation to show the site.

19.4

Retrieve the assembly drawing from Tutorial 16 and animate the camera flying around the assembled object.

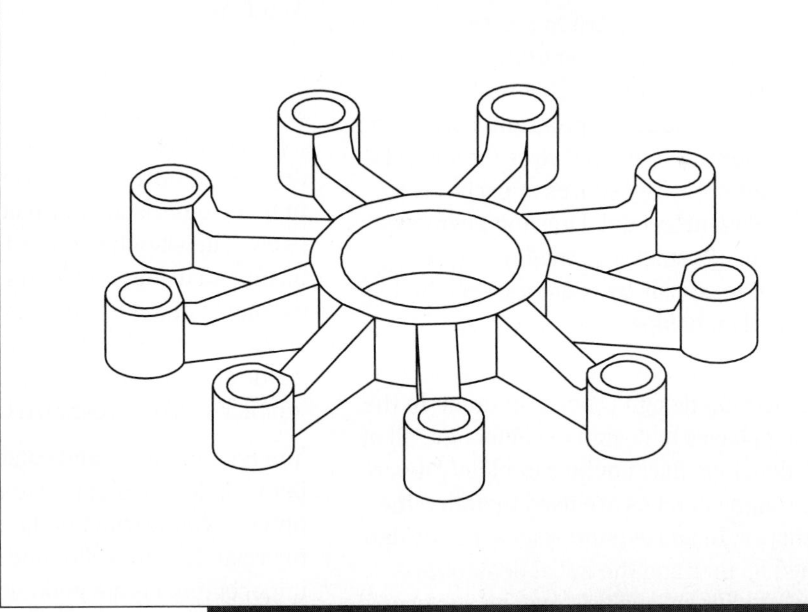

TUTORIAL 20

Introduction to AutoCAD Designer

Objectives

When you have completed this tutorial, you will be able to

1. Create models of parts parametrically, using AutoCAD Designer.
2. Sketch initial part shapes.
3. Add constraints to define part geometry.
4. Add parametric dimensions to control part size.
5. Create 3D parts from sketched geometry.
6. Change dimensions and update the size of 2D profiles and 3D features.
7. Use equations linking part geometry.
8. Generate correctly drawn orthographic drawings automatically.
9. Analyze mass properties.

Introduction

In this tutorial you will learn to create 3D solid models and engineering drawings using AutoCAD Designer. AutoCAD Designer is a *parametric* solid modeling program. Parametric modeling allows you to input sizes for and relationships between the features of parts, creating an "intelligent" model. Drawing geometry created using parametric modeling can be updated automatically by changing specified sizes and relationships.

As you are working through this tutorial, keep the engineering design process in mind. In the beginning phases of design development, all of the relationships may not be completely determined; rough sketches are used to define the basic shapes. In subsequent stages, the design is refined further and the initial designs are updated. Additional analysis may be performed to determine the suitability of different design alternatives. When the final design is determined, drawings are produced to specify the information necessary to manufacture the part.

The process of parametric modeling parallels the engineering design process. In the initial stages, you roughly define shapes and sizes in the model by specifying *constraints*, which define relationships between the elements that create the model, such as perpendicularity, tangency, parallelism and others. You add dimensions specifying the sizes of the drawing elements. As in the design process, as new information becomes available, you can change the sizes and relationships. You can evaluate the mass properties of the model and use the resulting information in making design decisions. AutoCAD Designer automatically updates the model by interpreting the size and constraint parameters. The process of defining the constraints that will be used to build the model is central to the parametric modeling process.

When you are using AutoCAD Designer, initially you sketch rough shapes, using AutoCAD's line, pline, circle, and arc tools. In a process similar to that of a colleague interpreting your rough sketch, AutoCAD Designer adds constraints to the rough sketch by applying rules, such as that lines within four degrees of horizontal or vertical are intended to be true horizontal or true vertical, respectively. The sketch is turned into a 3D *feature* using extrusion, revolution, or *sweeping* (like extrusion along a path curve), similar to the way you created solid models, starting in Tutorial 8. Features are the simpler 3D building blocks from which parts are created.

You next combine and establish relationships between features to create parts. Unlike the process you learned in the preceding tutorials to create 2D and solid models, where it was important to create geometry to exact sizes in order to have a useful database, AutoCAD Designer allows you to easily resize features and add and change constraints defining the relationships between features of the part. You can also specify equations relating various features of the model.

When the part is designed to your satisfaction, you use AutoCAD Designer to automatically generate dimensioned orthographic views, sections, and auxiliary views directly from the model. Because of the "intelligence" built in through the parametric modeling process, fully dimensioned orthographic views can be generated from the model, with hidden lines shown correctly. If you make a change to the model, the orthographic views update automatically.

Generated Layers in AutoCAD Designer

AutoCAD Designer runs within AutoCAD, so many of the commands that you have learned previously in this tutorial guide will still be useful to you when creating parametric models.

As with the AME module, some commands cannot be used without corrupting the parametric model database. AutoCAD Designer generates layers for storage of the AutoCAD Designer database and work planes, axes, and points. These layers are named ADP_FRZ, ADP_WORK, ADPLNDSP, ADAXISDSP, and ADPTDSP. Changing the contents of these layers can corrupt the AutoCAD Designer database.

■ ***Warning:*** Information for the AutoCAD Designer database is stored in the layer ADP_FRZ, and other layers starting with ADP. Leave these layers frozen and do not edit their contents. Making changes to these layers can corrupt the parametric modeling database. Model information is stored in the drawing as BLOCK entities. Do not use commands that will corrupt or destroy block information, such as the EXPLODE command or HANDLES OFF. It is always a good idea to save your work often; if you use SAVEAS and save to a new name, you can restore the previous file if you make an error that you cannot correct easily. ■

Starting

Before you begin, make sure that you have installed and configured AutoCAD Designer. AutoCAD Designer runs inside the DOS version of AutoCAD, not the Windows version. If you have not installed AutoCAD Designer or do not have the DOS version of AutoCAD installed, refer to the section of Part 1, Chapter 2 on installing and configuring AutoCAD Designer. If you have not set up your AutoCAD program so that the AutoCAD Designer menu is automatically loaded, see the section on configuration in Chapter 2.

Launch the DOS version of AutoCAD, making sure that the AutoCAD Designer module is loaded. You should see the AutoCAD drawing editor on your screen. Designer replaces Model on the pull-down menu. Verify that you have the Designer pull-down menu available. Move the mouse so that the crosshairs on the drawing screen bump up against the top of the drawing area. The pull-down menu selections appear along the top of the screen. The Designer pull-down menu should appear at the far right of the pull-down menu items, as shown in Figure 20.1. (AutoVis may appear in place of the Render pull-down menu if it was installed.)

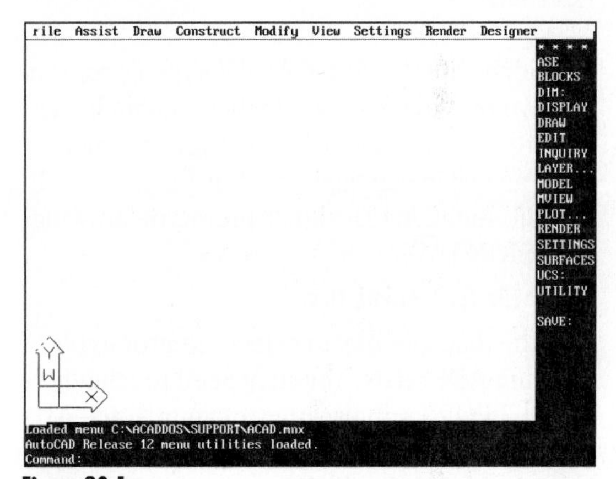

Figure 20.1

The part you will create in this tutorial, shown in Figure 20.2, is a clevis, a common mechanical device used for attachment.

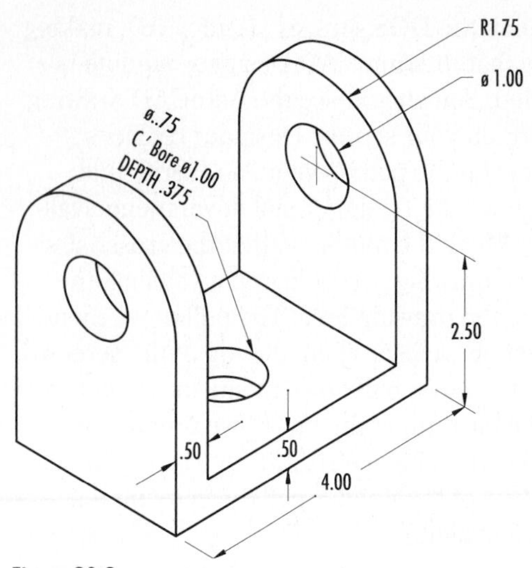

Figure 20.2

Provided with the AutoCAD Designer program are two prototype drawings that contain basic settings useful in AutoCAD Designer, which you can use in starting new drawings. You will use the AutoCAD Designer prototype drawing ADESIGN.DWG.

Pick: **File *(pull-down)*, New**

Use the dialogue box to select the prototype drawing ADESIGN. You may need to change to the SUPPORT subdirectory of your AutoCAD directory in order to select it. Type "CLEVIS" for the new file name. When you are finished, pick OK to exit the dialogue box and return to the AutoCAD drawing editor.

On your own, create a new layer named CLEVIS. Assign it the color blue and set it as the current layer.

Creating Geometry as a Sketch

Using AutoCAD Designer, you can enter the basic shapes very roughly. In the process of constraining the sketch, endpoints will be aligned and lines will be straightened. Similar to doing rough sketches early in the design process, you begin by showing the basic shapes and not worrying too much about lining things up perfectly.

Choose a major surface of the object to sketch first. Other, smaller features can be added to the first feature. Starting with a smaller feature may make it more difficult to add the other features, because the first part will act as the *base feature*. The base feature is important because other features are related to it by the constraints you add, and the way the model updates and the ease of adding features is affected by the choice of the base feature.

On your own, use the LINE and ARC commands in AutoCAD to sketch the shapes that make up the rounded shape of the clevis, as shown Figure 20.3. Notice that the lines do not have to be perfectly straight and endpoints do not need to meet exactly. The basic shapes you sketch cannot contain any internal features, such as holes.

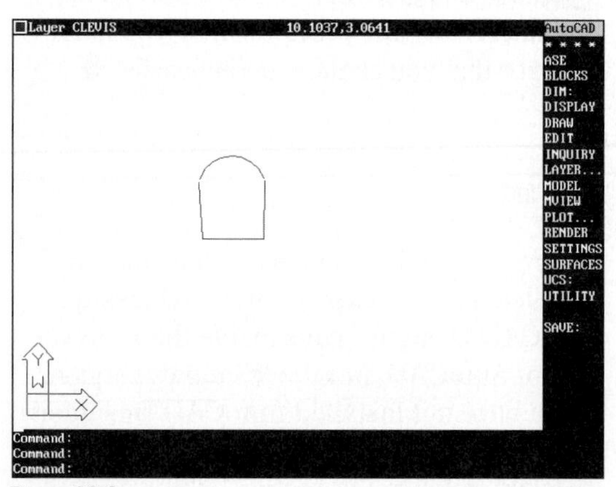

Figure 20.3

In the next steps, you will use AutoCAD Designer to apply constraints that will establish the final relationships between the lines, arcs, and other entities in your part drawing. Later you will refine this shape and then use an extrude command, as in AME modeling, to make a 3D solid feature. You will use AutoCAD Designer to create the hole feature after the initial feature is created.

Setting AutoCAD Designer Variables

You can use the Designer Settings dialogue box to control the constraints that are applied in solving your sketch. You will select the Designer Settings dialogue box from the pull-down menu.

Pick: **Designer, Settings. . .**

The dialogue box shown in Figure 20.4 appears on your screen. You can use it to set the angular tolerance, the pickbox size, and whether constraints are applied to your geometry. You can also use the Drawing Settings sub-dialogue box to set drawing variables controlling various aspects of the way orthographic drawings are created from the model.

Figure 20.4

The default setting for Rule Mode is on, which tells AutoCAD Designer to apply constraints to realign sketch geometry. Setting the dialogue box so that no X appears in the Rule Mode area of the dialogue box tells AutoCAD Designer not to apply constraints to realign geometry, except for aligning the endpoints of entities. Similarly, Sketch Mode set to on is also the default, which tells AutoCAD Designer to assume that the sketch is inaccurate and to apply constraints to realign sketch geometry. Setting the dialogue box so that no X appears next to Sketch Mode tells AutoCAD Designer to assume your sketch is accurate and not to change the geometry.

The Angular Tolerance area of the dialogue box determines the variation that lines can have before AutoCAD Designer considers them to be horizontal, vertical, parallel, etc. Initially this variable is set to 4 degrees. The size of the AutoCAD pickbox determines whether endpoints that do not touch are considered by AutoCAD Designer to be joining. You can use the Pickbox Size. . . area of the dialogue box to change the pickbox size, or you can zoom in or out on the drawing.

You can also specify the linetypes that you wil use to draw the entities of the sketch, using the Sketch Linetypes area of the dialogue box. Entities drawn with linetypes other than the one specified will be considered construction lines when it is time to apply constraints to solve the sketch. The Constraint Display Size selection in the dialogue box allows you to change the size of the symbols that are used to display constraints on the screen. You will see how to display the constraints later in this tutorial, and if you want to change the size, you can return to this dialogue box.

Do not change any of the settings in the dialogue box at this time.

Pick: **OK *(to exit the dialogue box)***

■ ***TIP*** As you did using AutoCAD, you can use HELP and 'HELP (transparent help) to get information on AutoCAD Designer commands. ■

The Sketch Menu

Selecting Sketch from the Designer pull-down menu causes the Sketch selections, which are used to add information such as constraints and dimensions to your sketches, to appear on your screen. Keep in mind that only one sketch can be active at a time. When using AutoCAD Designer, you create a sketch, constrain it, and make it into a feature by extrusion, revolution, or sweeping. When a feature is complete, you can define a new orientation for the sketch plane and start a new sketch. The new sketch can be linked to the existing feature, using the projected constraint, and then made into a new feature.

The Sketch submenu contains the following selections:

Profile	used to apply constraints to the sketch to create a 2D profile
Path	used to create a constrained *path* for use in sweeping operations
Sketch Plane	used to define the active sketch plane and its orientation
Constraints	used to add, remove, and show the constraints in a sketch
Fix Point	used to change the location of the sketch's fixed point
Add Dimension	used to add dimensions to the active sketch

Menu Names and Designer Commands

You will use the pull-down menus almost exclusively to work with AutoCAD Designer in this tutorial. When you do, the command names echoed in the command prompt area are those that you could type in to use the command. The command names are printed in capital letters inside parentheses following the pull-down menu sequence for the command. (The command name does not appear on the actual pull-down menu.)

Because the Designer menu can only be selected from the menu bar at the top of the screen, *(menu bar)* will not be listed when you are directed to make a selection from the Designer menu. When other AutoCAD commands are used you will still be directed from which menu to select the command.

Creating a Profile

A *profile* is a closed 2D shape that can be extruded, revolved, or swept. AutoCAD Designer solves the active sketch geometry by applying rules to form closed 2D profiles, or cross-sectional shapes. You can create a profile by picking Designer, Sketch, Profile (ADPROFILE) from the pull-down menu. A similar command creates paths of open or closed planar shapes that can be used in sweeping operations to create solids. (A sweeping operation is similar to extrusion, except that the path can be curved, instead of always a straight line.) To create a path, you would pick Designer, Sketch, Path (ADPATH) from the pull-down menu.

ADPROFILE applies the following constraints:

Symbol	***Constraint***
H	Lines sketched nearly horizontal are horizontal.
V	Lines sketched nearly vertical are vertical.
T	Two arcs or an arc, a circle, and a line sketched nearly tangent are tangent.
N	Two arcs or circles whose centers are sketched nearly coincident are concentric.
C	Two lines sketched nearly overlapping along the same line are colinear.
P	Lines sketched nearly parallel are parallel.

L	Lines sketched nearly perpendicular are perpendicular. The lines must be attached for perpendicularity to be inferred automatically.

R	Any arcs and circles sketched with nearly the same radius have the same radius. One of the arcs or circles must include a radius dimension before AutoCAD Designer applies this rule.

none	Objects are attached using endpoints.

none	Objects are attached using the endpoint of one object and the near point of the other object.

Pick: **Designer, Sketch, Profile**

Select objects: ***(use implied crossing to select all of the entities in your sketch)***

Select objects: ↵

The lines and arcs of your sketch are "neatened up" according to the previously listed constraints. You will see a box and Xs marking locations on the sketch. The box indicates that the point enclosed is fixed with respect to the World Coordinate System (WCS). As you add constraints and update your model, this point stays at the same WCS location and the other points are moved to meet the constraint criteria. The Xs mark the locations of temporary points in the sketch that are added as AutoCAD Designer is solving the sketch. Your drawing should appear similar to Figure 20.5.

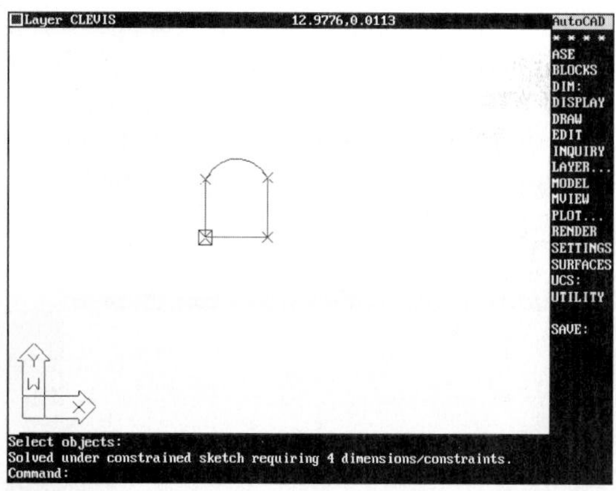

Figure 20.5

> ■ ***TIP*** To select a different point to act as the fixed point for the sketch, select Designer, Sketch, Fix Point or use the command ADFIXPT. Follow the prompts to select a new point to be fixed in the WCS. ■

Showing the Constraints

You can see what constraints AutoCAD Designer has applied to the profile by selecting Designer, Sketch, Constraints, Show (ADSHOWCON) from the pull-down menu. You will not have to select Sketch because the last AutoCAD Designer submenu selection stays active and you picked Sketch in the previous command step. If you did not, you need to pick Sketch after picking Designer. It is listed below in case you have not followed the command sequence exactly.

Pick: **Designer, Sketch, Constraints, Show**

All/Select/Next<eXit>: **A** ↵

The constraints that were applied appear on your screen, as shown in Figure 20.6. Each sketched entity is identified by a number. The constraints are shown by a code letter and number matching the entity to which the constraint applies.

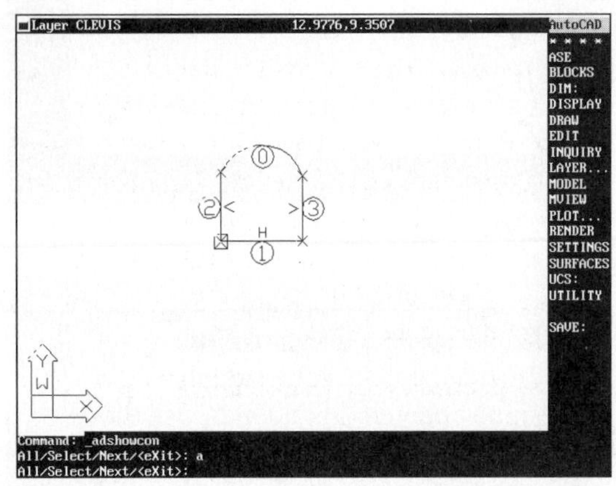

Figure 20.6

Refer to the previous list of constraints to help you interpret the constraints in your drawing. The constraints shown in your drawing may not be exactly the same as shown in the figure, depending on how you created your sketch. When you are finished examining the constraints, press ↵ to end the command. This removes the constraints from your screen.

All/Select/Next<eXit>: ↵

In the next step you will learn to add more constraints to the drawing. This is a very important capability because you can control the geometry in your drawing by controlling the constraints applied. These constraints tell AutoCAD Designer how to control the appearance of the drawing when a change is made to a feature. You can also delete constraints that AutoCAD Designer has created.

You will add two tangent constraints so that the rounded end is tangent to the two vertical lines. If your drawing already has these constraints, you can skip this step. If your lines are not horizontal and vertical, you will need to add those constraints on your own before you add the tangent constraints. To add new constraints,

Pick: **Designer, Sketch, Constraints, Add**

Hor/Ver/PErp/PAr/Tan/CL/CN/PRoj/Joint/XValue/Yvalue/Radius/<eXit>: **T** ↵

Select first item to make tangent: ***(pick on the arc)***

Select second item to be tangent to first: ***(pick on the right vertical line)***

Hor/Ver/PErp/PAr/Tan/CL/CN/PRoj/Joint/Xvalue/Yvalue/Radius/<eXit>: **T** ↵

Select first item to make tangent: ***(pick on the arc)***

Select second item to be tangent to first: ***(pick on the left vertical line)***

Hor/Ver/PErp/PAr/Tan/CL/CN/PRoj/Joint/Xvalue/Yvalue/Radius/<eXit>: ↵

When you have added the constraints, your drawing should look like Figure 20.7.

■ ***TIP*** If you have constraints in your drawing that are incorrect, you can delete them by picking Designer, Sketch, Constraints, Delete (ADDELCON) from the pull-down menu. Picking on the entity from which you want to delete the constraint causes the constraints along that entity to be shown. Next, pick on the symbol for the constraint you want to remove. Press ↵ to end the command. ■

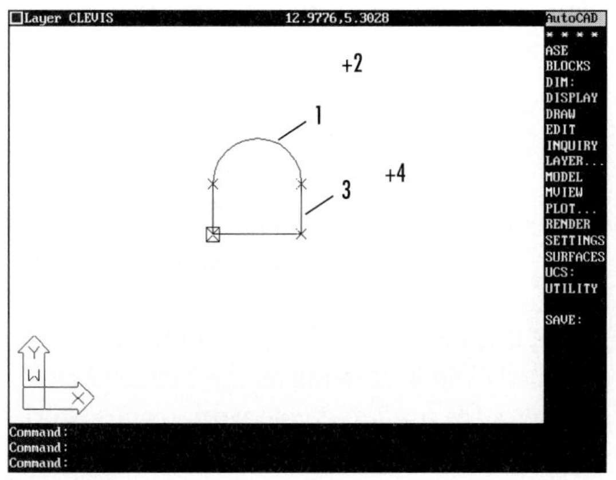

Figure 20.7

Adding Parametric Dimensions

The two additional tangent constraints are added to your drawing. Next you will add parametric dimensions to your drawing by picking Designer, Sketch, Add Dimension (ADPARDIM). The constraints you add control the shape of the part you are creating; the parametric dimensions control the size. Because you already know that the rounded end is tangent to the vertical lines, only two dimensions are necessary to determine the size of the part: the radius of the rounded end and the distance from the horizontal line to the center of the arc (the length of the straight side). If you provide too many constraints or parametric dimensions, you will get a message saying that the drawing is over-constrained. Remember the tutorials on dimensioning: you were reminded not to overdimension drawings because of the confusion that might result, either from the application of tolerance or from giving two different dimensions for the same feature.

When you are adding parametric dimensions to the part, consider carefully the function of the part in the design, and dimension the features accordingly. The dimensions you place can be used to change the size of the sketch and the feature created from it. When you override the default value with a different one as you are dimensioning, your drawing will be updated to match the new value. It will often make sense to locate dimensions from the fixed point, just as you would when creating a fixture to hold the part during inspection. As the fixed point will not move on the WCS, it is a good practice for other locations to be dimensioned from this point.

Pick: **Designer, Sketch, Add Dimension**

Select first item: ***(pick on the rounded end near point 1 in Figure 20.7)***

Select second item or place dimension: ***(pick near point 2)***

Undo/Dimension value <xxxx>: **1.75** ↵

Select first item: ***(pick on the right-hand vertical line identified as point 3)***

Select second item or place dimension: ***(pick near point 4)***

Undo/Hor/Vert/Align/Par/Dimension value <xxxx>: **2.5** ↵

Select first item: ↵

The dimensions appear in your drawing, as shown in Figure 20.8, and the drawing is updated automatically to reflect the sizes that you typed in.

> ■ ***TIP*** Use the PAN and ZOOM commands, if necessary, to move your view on the screen so that you can see the entire drawing. ■

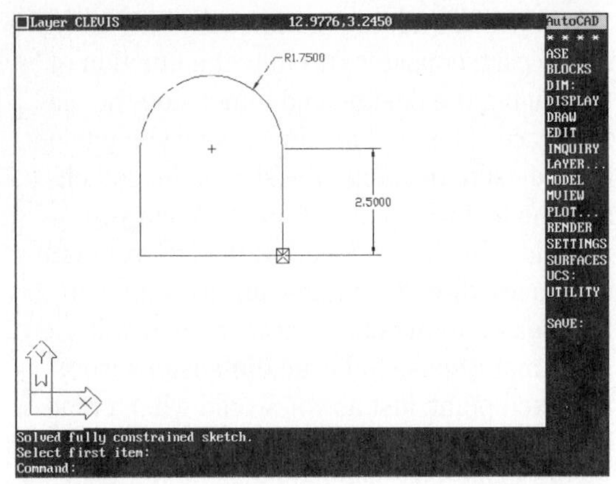

Figure 20.8

Notice the message in the command prompt area says, "Solved fully constrained sketch." This indicates that you do not need any additional dimensions or constraints; the profile is fully defined. Think back to the tutorials on dimensioning. Like the machinist trying to manufacture a part from the dimensions shown, AutoCAD Designer cannot create a 3D solid model if some dimensions are left out. Likewise, if there are too many dimensions, it is confusing and hard to determine how to apply the dimensions.

■ ***TIP*** Pick Change Dimension from the Designer menu to change the values of dimensions after they are added to the sketch. Once you create the object as a 3D solid feature, as you will do in the next step, you must use Edit Feature (ADEDITFEAT) from the Designer menu to change the resulting feature. After changing dimensions or features, you must update the model's appearance, using Designer, Update (ADUPDATE). ■

Creating Features

The Features selection from the pull-down menu contains selections for creating features. AutoCAD Designer allows you to create features by extrusion, revolution, or sweeping a 2D profile. You can also easily add features such as holes, fillets, and chamfers to your model through the specialized commands provided. The final items on the Features submenu are used to create work planes, work axes, and work points. A *work plane* is a parametric plane that can be used to locate the sketch plane or other features. When you create a work plane, you link it to the current feature geometry by an edge, axis, vertex, or surface of the part. This way, features located on the work plane will move and update when the parent feature is moved. A *work axis* is similar to a work plane, except that it is a line at the center line of the cylindrical, conical, or toroidal surface that you select. You can use the work axis to locate other features. A *work point* is a point that you can place to locate holes. You can constrain and dimension the location of the work point on the sketch plane, using the sketch commands you have learned. Work planes, work axes, and work points are all located on the generated layer ADP_WORK. Do not edit the contents of this layer; that may corrupt or destroy your modeling database.

Creating an Extrusion

Now that the profile is fully constrained, you are ready to extrude the profile to form a 3D solid feature. As you saw in Tutorial 8, extrusion is named for the manufacturing process in which material is forced through a shaped opening. In AutoCAD Designer, extrusion is used to give a part profile thickness, thus creating a feature. To extrude the profile, you will pick Designer, Features, Extrude (ADEXTRUDE) from the pull-down menu.

Pick: **Designer, Features, Extrude**

Use the dialogue box that appears on your screen, shown in Figure 20.9, to select the distance to extrude the part. You will leave the other settings at their defaults.

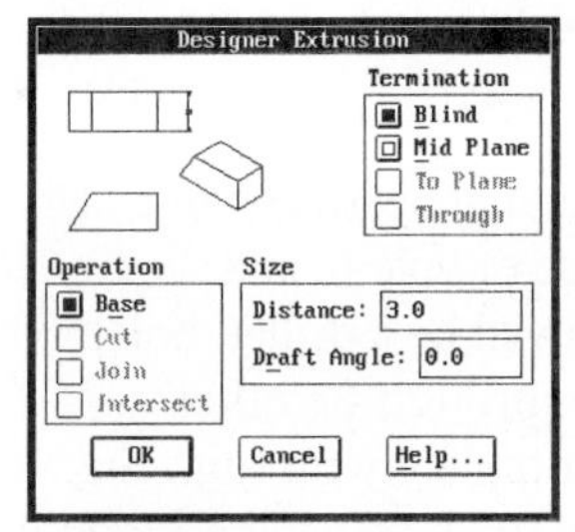

Figure 20.9

Type: **3 *(in the box to the right of Distance)***

Pick: **OK *(to exit the dialogue box)***

The part is extruded, creating a 3D solid. Because you are looking straight down the Z axis, you cannot see the thickness of the part.

Viewing the Part

AutoCAD Designer allows you to change the viewing angle for the part and makes it easy to specify preset views from the pull-down menu by picking Designer, Part Viewing (ADPARTVIEW). You will select isometric viewing so you can see the 3D shape of the part.

Pick: **Designer, Part Viewing, Iso**

Your viewing direction changes so that your screen looks like Figure 20.10.

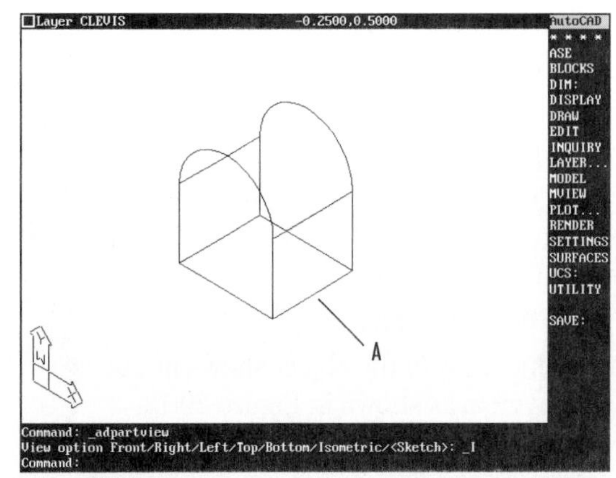

Figure 20.10

Changing 3D Solid Features

To change the dimensions of 2D sketches you would use Designer, Sketch, Change Dimensions (ADMODDIM). To change the dimensions for 3D solid features, you will pick Designer, Edit Feature (ADEDITFEAT) from the pull-down menu.

Pick: **Designer, Edit Feature**

Select feature: ***(pick line A in Figure 20.10)***

The dimensions for the solid appear on the screen, as shown in Figure 20.11.

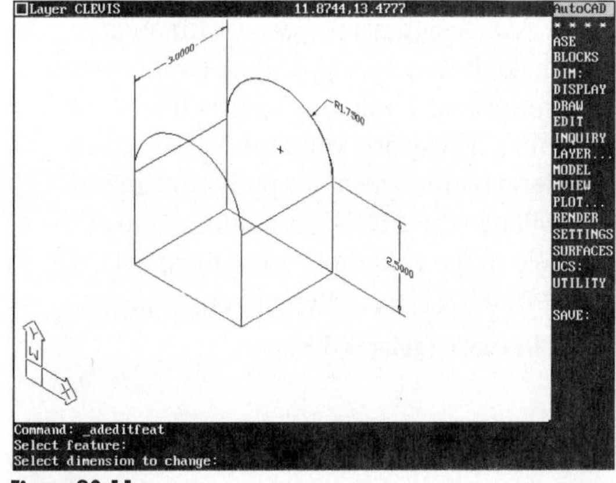

Figure 20.11

Select dimension to change: ***(pick on the 3.0000 dimension)***

New value for dimension <3.0000>: **4.5**

Select dimension to change: ↵

The display remains unchanged until you update it. To select the ADUPDATE command from the pull-down menu,

Pick: **Designer, Update**

The thickness of the object shows in the isometric view, as shown in Figure 20.12.

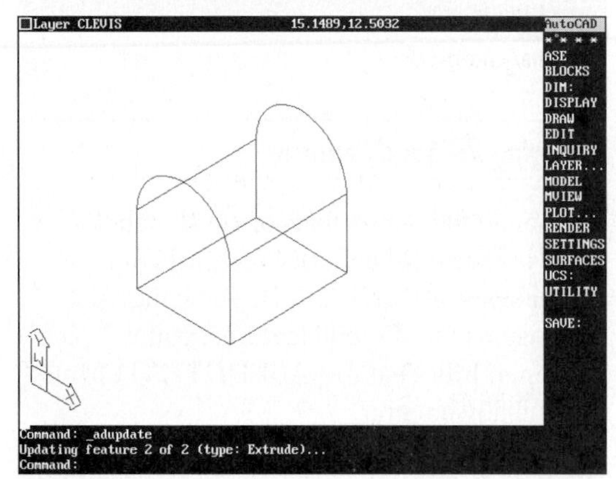

Figure 20.12

Adding the Hole

AutoCAD Designer provides commands that make it easy to add drilled, countersunk, or counterbored holes, as well as fillets and chamfers. These are found on the Features submenu on the Designer pull-down menu. You will use the ADHOLE command to add the hole to the rounded end of the clevis. To select ADHOLE from the pull-down menu,

Pick: **Designer, Features, Hole**

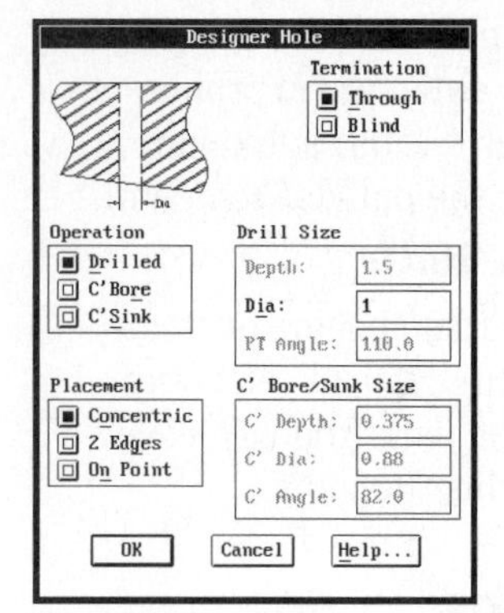

Figure 20.13

Use the dialogue box that appears on your screen to select the type of hole to add. For this part, the operation will be a drilled hole; the termination will be through (in other words, the hole goes completely through the object); the diameter of the hole will be 1; and the placement will be concentric. The options you can use to place the hole in your drawing are locating it from a concentric edge, two edges, or a work point.

When locating the hole from two edges, you are prompted to select entities to define the planar work face where the circular shape of the hole will be located, and then to specify the distance from each of the two edges that you select.

To locate the hole from a work point, you must first have selected by picking Designer, Features, Work Point (ADWORKPT) to place a work point in the drawing. The selected point will then be the center location for the hole.

Locating the hole from a concentric edge will cause you to be prompted to select the work face and then a rounded edge, and then the hole will be located at its center. Selecting the right placement method is important because it will in part determine the way the model will update when changes are made to the dimensions or constraints. Use the techniques you have learned and make the selections so the dialogue box looks like Figure 20.13. When you are finished selecting,

Pick: **OK *(to exit the dialogue box)***

You are returned to the drawing for the following selections.

Select work plane or planar face: ***(pick on the rounded edge)***

Select concentric edge: ***(pick the rounded edge again)***

The hole is added to your model, as shown in Figure 20.14.

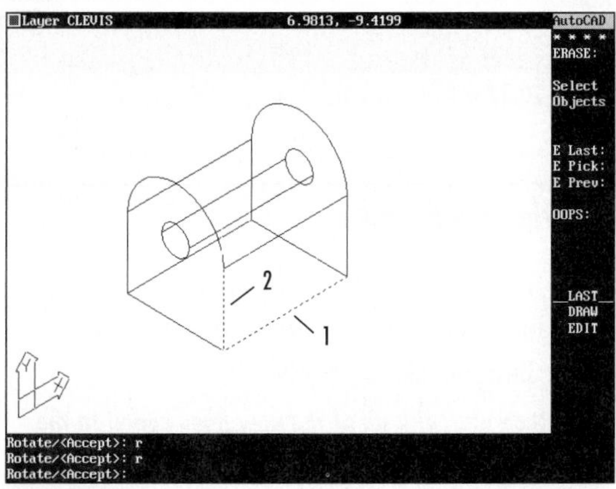

Figure 20.14

Aligning the Sketch Plane

Next you will select a new sketch plane and create a sketch showing the shape of the clevis from that direction. Aligning the sketch plane is much like orienting the User Coordinate System, which you have done in previous tutorials. Only one sketch plane can be active at a time. You will align the sketch plane by picking Designer, Sketch, Sketch plane (ADSKPLN) from the pull-down menu.

Pick: **Designer, Sketch, Sketch plane**

Xy/Yz/Zx/Ucs/<Select work plane or planar face>: ***(pick the line labeled 1 in Figure 20.14)***

Select another edge: ***(pick the line labeled 2)***

X/Y/Z/<Select work axis or straight edge>: ***(pick line 1 again)***

Rotate/<Accept>:**R** ↵

You should now see the UCS icon aligned with lines 1 and 2, as in Figure 20.14. If not, continue to enter "R" and press ↵ to rotate the coordinates. When the UCS icon matches Figure 20.14, accept the position for the plane.

Rotate/<Accept>: ↵

Sketching the Side View

The new sketch plane is now aligned with lines 1 and 2, so that you can draw the clevis as it appears from the side. Once the side view of the clevis is drawn, it can then be extruded and the Boolean intersection of the two extrusions can be found. Using AutoCAD Designer, you can perform both the extrude and intersection operations in a single command step.

Before sketching the side view of the clevis, set the color for entity creation to red so that it is easier to see the new entities added to the drawing. Use the AutoCAD Settings pull-down menu.

Pick: **Settings *(menu bar)*, Entity Modes**

The Entity Creation Modes dialogue box appears on your screen, as shown in Figure 20.15.

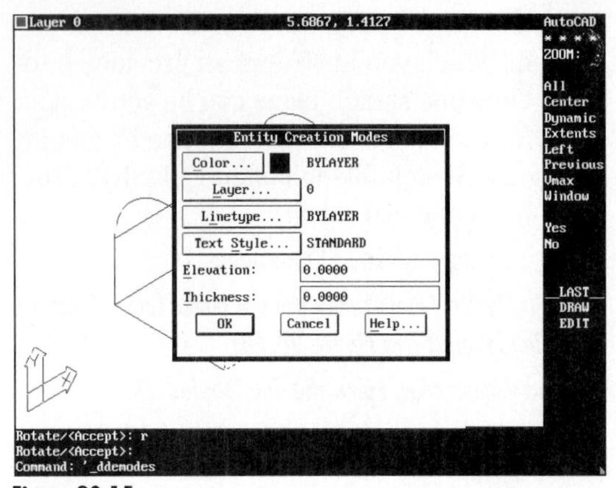

Figure 20.15

The Entity Creation Modes dialogue box can be used to set the color, linetype, and other properties of drawing entities. Usually it is a better practice to set the color using BYLAYER, because then changes to the layer will be reflected in the color of the entity. In this case, however, you will leave the layer set to CLEVIS and change the color for new entities created.

Pick: **Color. . .**

The Select Color dialogue box appears, as shown in Figure 20.16.

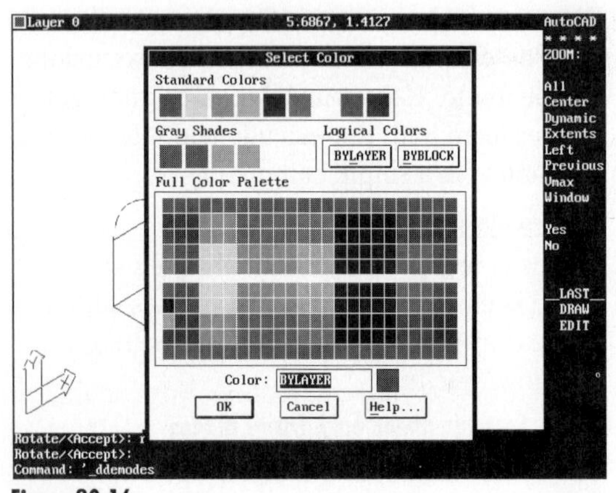

Figure 20.16

Pick: ***Red (color 1 from the top row of the dialogue box)***

Pick: ***OK (to exit the Select Color dialogue box)***

Pick: ***OK (to exit the Entity Creation Modes dialogue box)***

On your own, use the LINE command to sketch the shape you see in Figure 20.17. Do not draw your lines exactly on top of the blue lines of the existing feature, because this will make them hard to select.

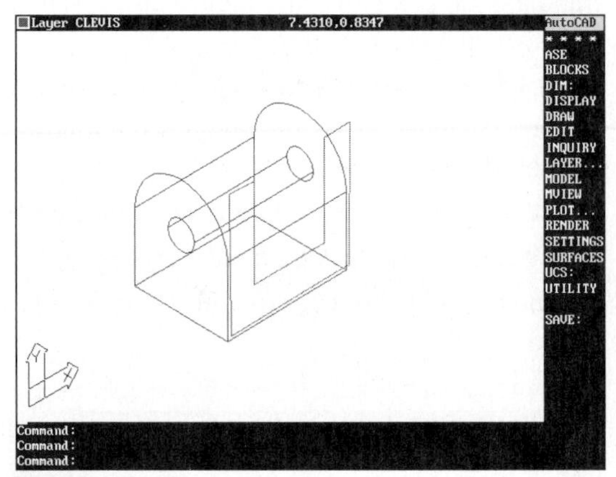

Figure 20.17

Creating the Profile

Next, create a profile from the sketched entities, as you learned earlier in the tutorial.

Pick: **Designer, Sketch, Profile**

Select objects: ***(pick all of the new lines added to the new sketch)***

Select objects: ↵

> ■ ***TIP*** You can use implied crossing to select the objects. If you select the wrong item, you can type “R” at the “Select objects:” prompt and then press ↵ and select the items to remove from the selection set. ■

The lines that you drew are "neatened up" and you may see Xs drawn at the corners. Next, you will use the ADSHOWCON command that you learned earlier to show the constraints that have been added, establishing relationships between the new lines. To select ADSHOWCON from the pull-down menu as you did before,

> *Pick:* **Designer, Sketch, Constraints, Show**
>
> All/Select/Next/<eXit>: **A** ↵
>
> All/Select/Next/<eXit>: ***(when you are finished examining the constraints shown on the screen, press ↵)***

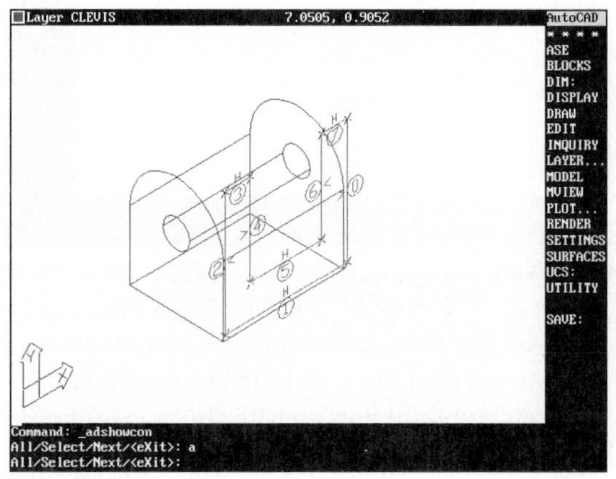

Figure 20.18

The constraints added in the drawing should appear similar to Figure 20.18. Your drawing may not be identical, depending on how you constructed each line. If you do not have horizontal constraints for the four horizontal lines, add them on your own. If your vertical lines do not have vertical constraints, add them also by selecting Designer, Sketch, Constraints, Add.

Next you will add projected constraints for the bottom endpoints of the vertical lines. Adding projected constraints allows you to link the new sketch profile to the existing part. You will also add *colinear* constraints for the bottom line of the sketch and the bottom line of the previous object, and between the two short top horizontal lines.

On your own, zoom the lower right-hand corner of the object, so that your drawing appears similar to Figure 20.19. Your drawing may be slightly different, depending on the actual sketch you created. After you add the constraints in the next steps, your drawing should be the same as the figures.

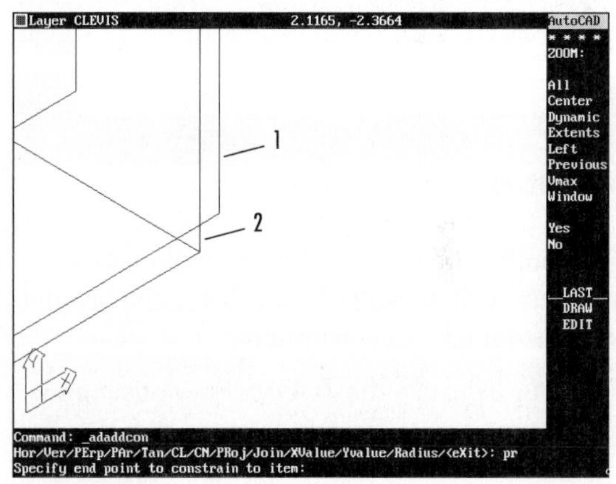

Figure 20.19

> *Pick:* **Designer, Sketch, Constraints, Add**
>
> Hor/Ver/PErp/PAr/Tan/CL/CN/PRoj/Join/XValue/Yvalue/Radius/<eXit>: **PR** ↵
>
> Specify endpoint to constrain to item: ***(pick the vertical red line of the new sketch, labeled 1in Figure 20.19)***
>
> Specify line, arc, or circle to constrain to: ***(pick the vertical blue line 2 on the 3D solid)***

The new line should move to align with the selected line from the solid model. You are returned to the command prompt, where you can continue to add constraints. Next, make the bottom line of the sketch colinear with the bottom line of the solid.

> Hor/Ver/PErp/PAr/Tan/CL/CN/PRoj/Join/XValue/Yvalue/Radius/<eXit>: **CL** ↵

Select first line: ***(pick red line 3 in Figure 20.20)***

Select second line: ***(pick blue line 4)***

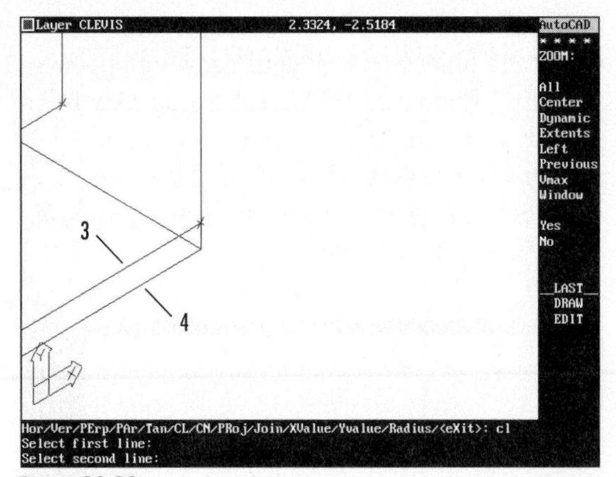

Figure 20.20

The bottom line of the sketch should now be colinear with the solid. You still see the prompt options for adding constraints.

On your own, use the ZOOM, Previous command to return to the previous zoom factor and then zoom the lower left-hand corner of the object. You will need it enlarged so that you can add another projected constraint for the left-hand vertical line in order to line it up with the solid. When you are finished, you should still see the command prompt with the add constraint options. If not, start the command again by pressing ↵.

Hor/Ver/PErp/PAr/Tan/CL/CN/PRoj/Join/XValue/Yvalue/ Radius/<eXit>: **PR** ↵

Specify end point to constrain to item: ***(pick the vertical line of the new sketch)***

Specify line, arc or circle to constrain to: ***(pick the vertical line on the 3D solid)***

Use ZOOM, Previous on your own to return to the original zoom factor so that you can add the colinear constraint for the top two short horizontal lines.

Hor/Ver/PErp/PAr/Tan/CL/CN/PRoj/Join/XValue/Yvalue/ Radius/<eXit>: **CL** ↵

Select first line: ***(pick red line 5 in Figure 20.21)***

Select second line: ***(pick red line 6)***

Hor/Ver/PErp/PAr/Tan/CL/CN/PRoj/Join/XValue/Yvalue/ Radius/<eXit>: ↵

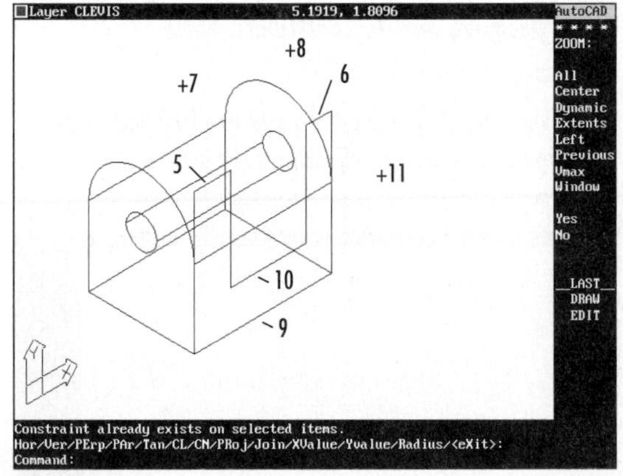

Figure 20.21

Now you are finished adding the constraints. The two vertical lines and the bottom line of the sketch should line up with the corresponding edges of the solid, as shown in Figure 20.21. The short horizontal lines at the top of the object should align with one another.

Dimensioning the New Profile

Next, you will add parametric dimensions to define the size of the object so that it is fully constrained, as you did with the previous profile. You will dimension the height of the profile so that it is equal to the height of the existing feature, using a simple equation.

Pick: **Designer, Sketch, Add Dimension**

Select first item: ***(pick on line 5 in Figure 20.21)***

Select second item or place dimension: ***(pick near point 7)***

Undo/Hor/Vert/Align/Par/Dimension value <xxxx>: **.5** ↵

Select first item: ***(pick on line 6)***

Select second item or place dimension: ***(pick near point 8)***

Undo/Hor/Vert/Align/Par/Dimension value <xxxx>: **.5** ↵

Select first item: ***(pick on line 9)***

Select second item or place dimension: ***(pick on line 10)***

Specify dimension placement: ***(pick near point 11)***

Undo/Hor/Vert/Align/Par/Dimension value <xxxx>: **.5** ↵

Select first item: ↵

> ■ ***TIP*** If you have trouble selecting the lines to dimension use ZOOM, Window to enlarge your work area. When you have finished making the selection use ZOOM, Previous to restore the original zoom factor. ■

When you have finished adding the dimensions, your drawing should look like Figure 20.22.

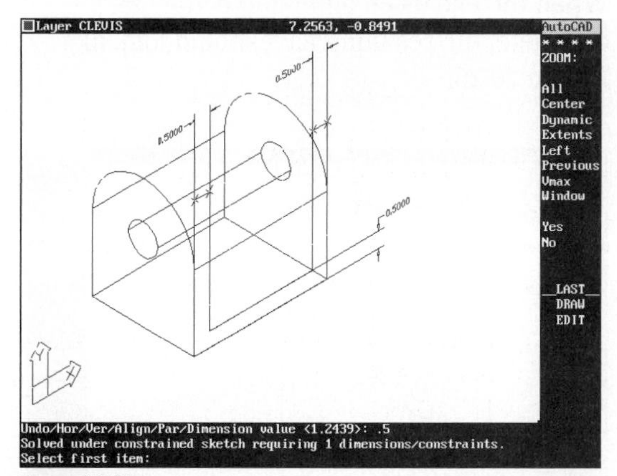

Figure 20.22

AutoCAD Designer assigns a variable to all parametric dimensions. You can change the way the dimensions are displayed by picking Designer, Display, Dim Display from the pull-down menu. This selection activates the command ADDIMDSP. You will use it to display the dimensions as variables, or in other words, in their parametric form.

Pick: **Designer, Display, Dim Display**

Parameters/Equations/<Numeric>: **P** ↵

The dimensions on your screen change to display their variable names (yours may be different), as shown in Figure 20.23.

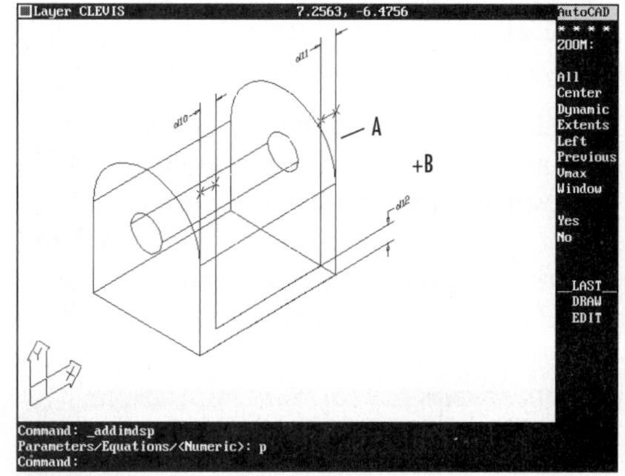

Figure 20.23

Next you will use the selection Designer, Edit Feature to display the dimensions for the previous sketch, so that you can determine the variable names of the rounded end and the height of the sketch. You will add an equation dimension for the height of the current sketch so that it is the height of the first sketch plus the radius of the rounded end.

Pick: **Designer, Edit Features**

Select dimension to change: ***(pick on the rounded end)***

Notice that the parametric dimensions for the previous sketch are now shown. Review your drawing and determine the variable names for the radius of the rounded end (probably d0) and the height of the side (probably d1). Once you have this information, exit the command by pressing Ctrl-C.

Select dimension to change: Ctrl-**C**

Now you will add the equation dimension for the height of the side view sketch. (If your variable names are not the same, substitute the variable names from your drawing in the next step.)

Pick: **Designer, Sketch, Add Dimension**

Select first item: ***(pick on line A)***

Select second item or place dimension: ***(pick near point B)***

Undo/Hor/Vert/Align/Par/Dimension value <xxxx>:
d0+d1 ↵

Select first item: ↵

Your sketch updates so that the height is the same as the height of the original sketch. On your own, change the dimension display back so that the numerical values are shown. When you are finished with this step, your drawing should look similar to Figure 20.24.

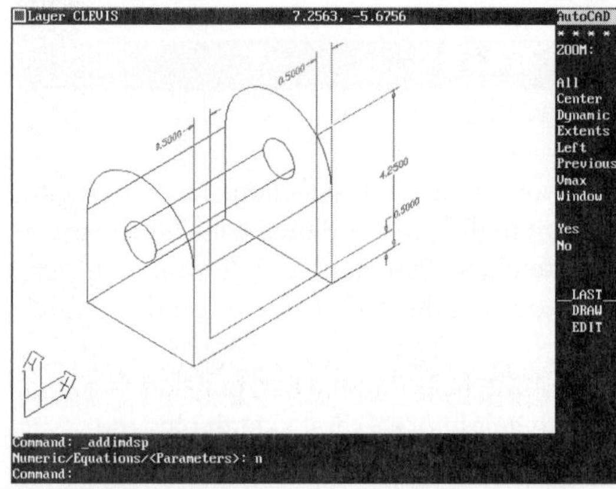

Figure 20.24

Using AutoCAD Designer, you can extrude and find the intersection between two features in the same command step. Next, use the ADEXTRUDE command to extrude the new sketch into a 3D solid object and to find the intersection with the base solid created previously.

Pick: **Designer, Features, Extrude**

Use the dialogue box to select a Through Termination and to select Intersect as the operation.

Pick: **OK**

An arrow appears, indicating the direction in which the extrusion will proceed. If the arrow is pointing in the correct direction, as shown in Figure 20.25, press ↵ to accept. If not, type "DF" ↵ at the prompt to flip the direction and then accept when the arrow is pointing the correct way.

Direction Flip/<Accept>: **DF** ***(if necessary)*** ↵

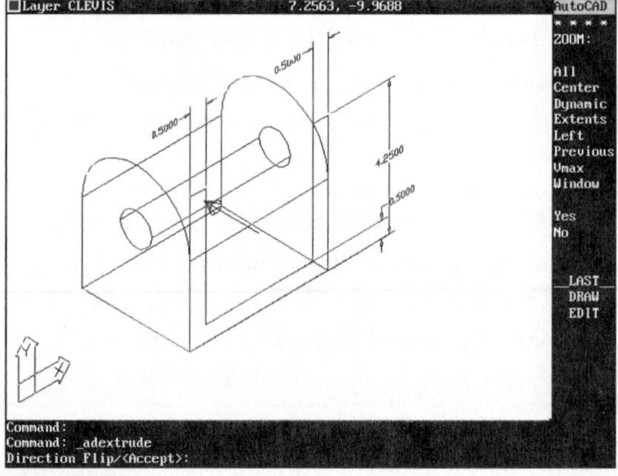

Figure 20.25

When the extrusion and intersection are complete, the resulting part should look like Figure 20.26.

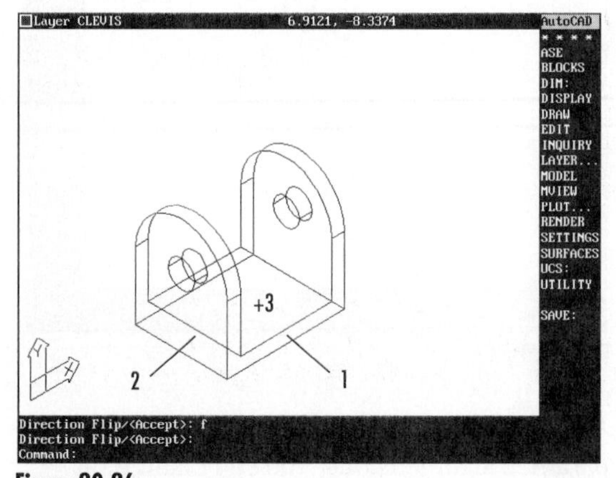

Figure 20.26

Adding the Hole

Now you are ready to add the final hole and then create a multiview orthographic drawing from your model.

Pick: **Designer, Features, Hole**

Use the dialogue box to add a counterbored hole of diameter .75. Use the dialogue box to select so that the hole will be C'Bore with C'Depth 0.375 and C'Dia of 1.00, and will be a Through hole. Select to have the hole located by 2 Edges. When you are finished making these selections,

Pick: **OK *(to exit the dialogue box and place the hole)***

Select first edge: ***(pick on line 1 in Figure 20.26)***

Select second edge: ***(pick line 2)***

Select hole location: ***(place the corner of the box that rubberbands from the lines you selected by picking 3, near the center of the bottom surface of the object)***

Distance from first edge <xxxx>: **1.75** ↵

Distance from second edge <xxxx>: **1.75** ↵

The hole should be added to your model, as shown in Figure 20.27.

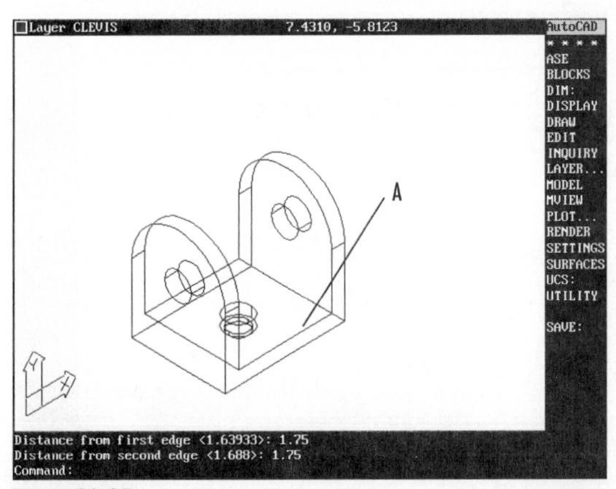

Figure 20.27

Now that the counterbored hole is added, it appears that there is not enough material in the base of the clevis for the depth of counterbore you chose. You will make the base of the clevis thicker. To change the thickness of the base,

Pick: **Designer, Edit Feature**

Select feature: ***(pick on line A in Figure 20.27)***

The dimensions for the side view of the part should appear on your screen.

Select dimension to change: ***(pick the .5 dimension between two bottom surfaces)***

New value for dimension<.5>: ***.75*** ↵

Select dimension to change: ↵

Next you will update the appearance of the model to show the change you have made.

Pick: **Designer, Update**

Your model should now look like Figure 20.28.

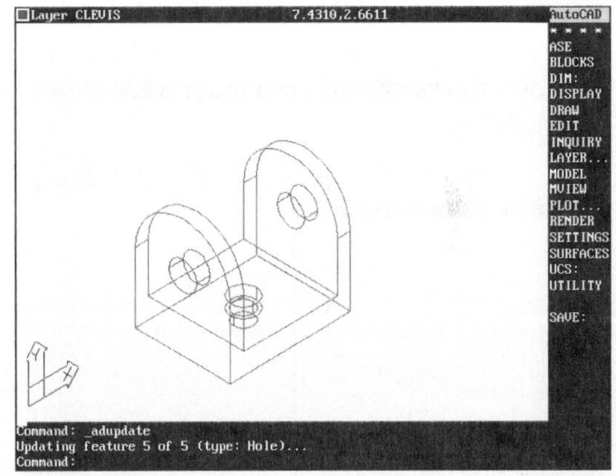

Figure 20.28

Creating a Drawing from the Part

Now you have finished creating the model of the clevis. You are ready to have AutoCAD Designer create the dimensioned multiview orthographic drawing of the part. You create this drawing automatically by picking Designer, Drawing, Create View (ADVIEW).

Before creating the drawing views, you will set the Entity Creation Mode so that colors are determined by layer before you create the drawings. Otherwise, all lines will continue to be drawn with red, regardless of what layer is used. Use the AutoCAD Settings pull-down menu to select the Entity Creation Modes dialogue box.

Pick: **Settings *(menu bar)*, Entity Modes**

Use the dialogue box that appears and pick the Color option. Pick the BYLAYER button. Pick OK twice when you have finished.

To create a drawing from the part,

Pick: **Designer, Drawing, Create View**

The dialogue box shown in Figure 20.29 appears on your screen. You will accept the defaults to create the base view. The base view is the main orthographic view from which the lines of sight for the other orthographic views are established.

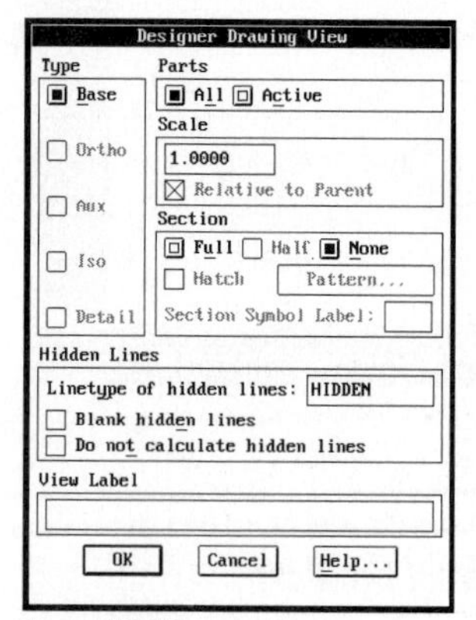

Figure 20.29

Pick: **OK**

You return to the drawing screen.

Xy/Yz/Zx/Ucs/<Select work plane or planar face>: ***(pick lines 1, 2, and 3 in Figure 20.30)***

Rotate/<Accept>: ***(type "R" and press ⏎ until the UCS icon aligns as shown in Figure 20.30)***

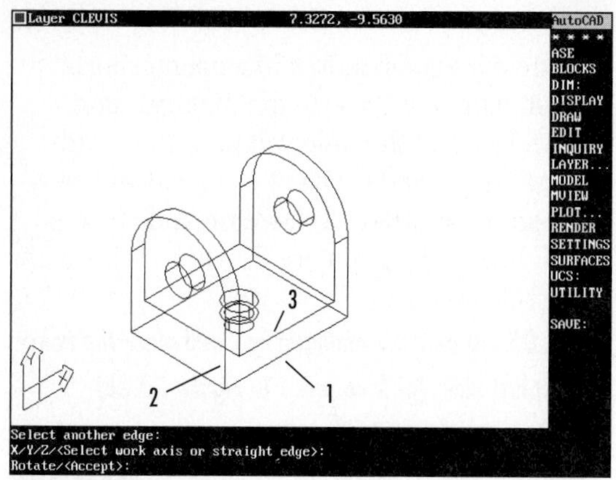

Figure 20.30

You are automatically switched to paper space, where you will specify a location for the view. Your screen should look like Figure 20.31. The title block you see is part of ADESIGN.DWG, the prototype drawing you used to start drawing CLEVIS.

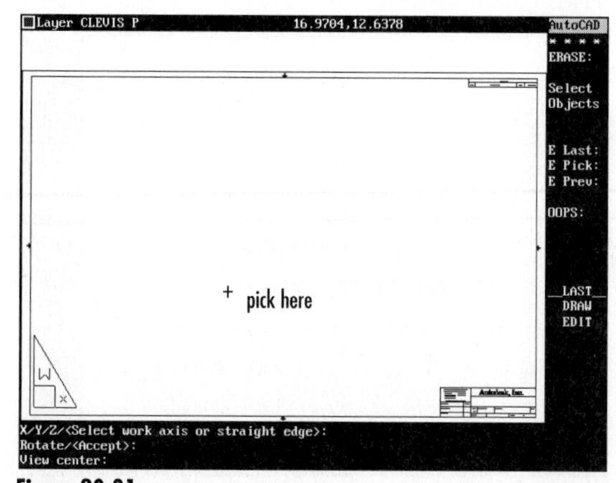

Figure 20.31

View center: ***(pick near the point indicated)***

View center: ⏎

The front view and dimensions for the front view are placed in your drawing, as shown in Figure 20.32. The dimensions may be too small to see clearly. This is because the prototype drawing, ADESIGN.DWG is set up to plot on a sheet of paper that is about 34" by 22" long. If you zoom up on the view you should be able to read the dimensions. You will learn more about changing the appearance of the dimensions in the next section of this tutorial.

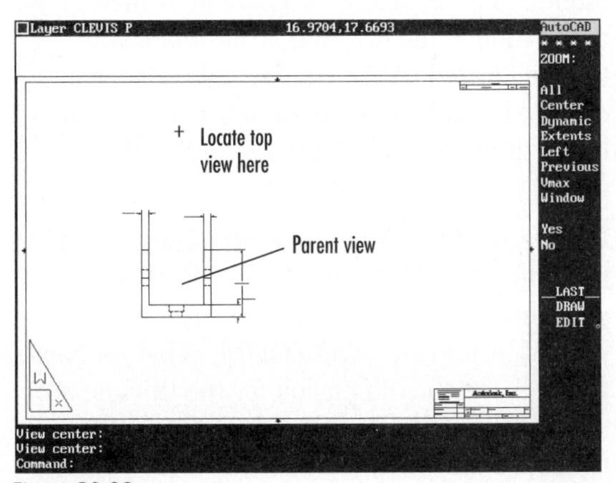

Figure 20.32

Next you will add the top view. To restart the ADVIEW command,

Command: (↵)

This time, select the box to the left of ORTHO in the dialogue box that appears on your screen. When you are finished,

Pick: **OK**

Select parent view: ***(pick in the center of the front view that you just placed)***

Location for orthographic view: ***(pick above the front view, where you want the center of the top view located)***

Location for orthographic view: (↵)

■ ***TIP*** If views overlap, you can move them by picking Designer, Drawing, Move Views. It is easy to move the views around on the sheet at any time, so don't be too concerned about the placement at this point. ■

On your own, repeat this process to create a right-side view. When you are finished, your drawing should look like Figure 20.33.

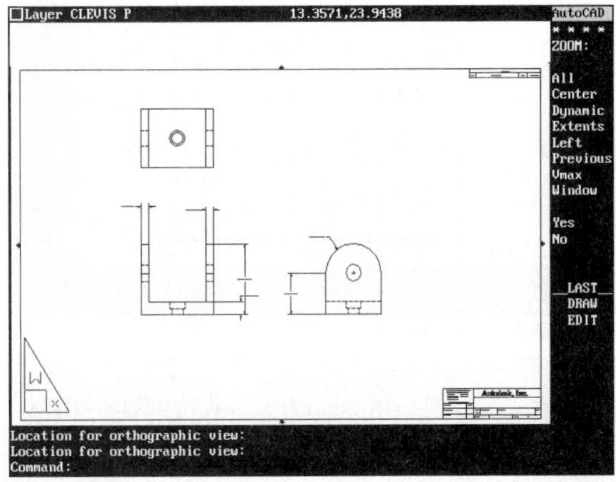

Figure 20.33

Cleaning Up the Dimensions

When dimension views are created automatically, AutoCAD Designer uses the current dimension style for the dimensions it places in the drawing. If there is no dimension style active, a style called ADDIM0 is created. As additional dimension styles are needed, they are created and named ADDIM1, ADDIM2, and so on. If you create a dimension style and make it active before you create drawing views, that dimension style will be used for the dimensions and additional styles will not be created.

You can change the appearance of the dimensions in your drawing two ways. One way is to use the Designer menu selection Drawing, Dimension, Attributes. First you are prompted to select a dimension to modify and the dialogue box shown in Figure 20.34 appears on your screen. You can use the dialogue box to change the appearance of the selected dimension.

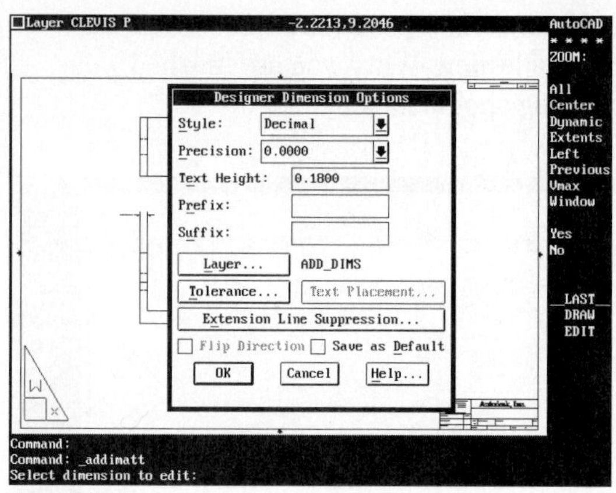

Figure 20.34

The other way to change the appearance of the dimensions is by changing the dimension style characteristics, using the AutoCAD Settings pull-down menu selection, Dimension Style, and then using the dialogue boxes to change the dimension style. Because AutoCAD Designer uses paper space and viewports to create the drawing views, choosing Use paper space scaling and then setting the dimension variables to the sizes you want shown on the plotted drawing usually works well.

AutoCAD Designer also provides commands for moving the dimensions in the drawing, including between drawing views; freezing and thawing individual dimensions; and adding and deleting reference dimensions (ones that do not affect the parametric model).

The Designer, Drawing, Annotation menu selection allows you to create, delete, and move annotation, or text, that is associated with a view (so that if the view moves, so does the note); you can also use this menu to select the Hole Note command to create a standard hole note for the drawing.

On your own, use the commands listed above to clean up the appearance of the dimensions in the drawing.

Bi-directional Associativity

AutoCAD Designer has *bi-directional associativity* between the drawing and the model. In other words, if a change is made to the model, the drawing is automatically updated to reflect the change. Likewise, if a change is made to the parametric dimensions in the drawing, both the drawing and the model update automatically.

Next, you will change one of the dimensions in the drawing so that you can see this effect in your drawing. On your own, enlarge the front view of the clevis, using ZOOM, Window. Next, you will edit the dimension for the thickness of the right side of the clevis by picking Designer, Change Dimension (ADMODDIM).

Pick: **Designer, Change Dimensions**

Select dimension to modify: ***(pick on the .50 dimension for the top right side of the clevis)***

New value for dimension<.50>: **1** ↵

Select dimension to change: ↵

Pick: **Designer, Update**

Your drawing and model are updated to reflect the change. Your screen will briefly show the model and then will return to the drawing where it will show the changed thickness of the right side of the clevis. Your drawing should appear similar to Figure 20.35.

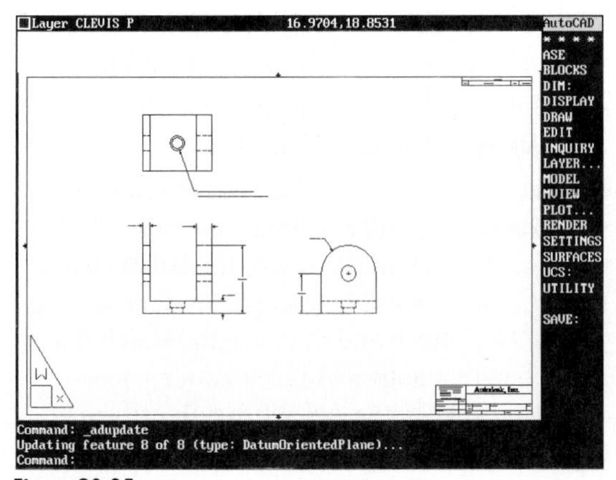

Figure 20.35

To return to the model, you will use the ADMODE command explained in the next section.

Switching between Part and Drawing Mode

The drawing is created in paper space, as were the multiview drawings you created in Tutorial 9. To return to the original part that was created in model space, you will select Designer, Mode (ADMODE) and then type "P" ↵ to select part mode. You can also use this command to return to the drawing by typing "D" ↵ to return to the drawing mode. Now, you will return to the part mode, where you will analyze the mass properties of the part.

Pick: **Designer, Mode**

Part/<Drawing>: **P** ↵

You are returned to your model. Notice that the right side of the clevis is now 1.00 thick.

Examining the Mass Properties

You can examine the mass properties of models created with AutoCAD Designer as you did using AME in the previous tutorials. To do so, you will pick Designer, Utilities, Mass Properties (ADMASSP) from the pull-down menu.

Pick: **Designer, Utilities, Mass Properties**

ALl/Select/<ACtive>: ↵

The Designer Mass Properties dialogue box shown in Figure 20.36 appears on your screen, listing the mass properties information. You can use the Density area of the dialogue box to specify a different density for the material of the part. Pick in the text box to the right of Density and type in a new value, then press ↵. Notice that changing the density changes the mass properties. When you are finished examining the mass properties, pick OK to exit the dialogue box.

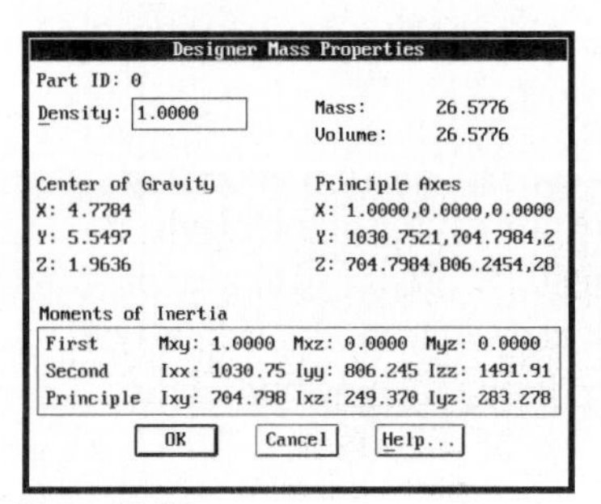

Figure 20.36

Creating a Section View

You will create a work plane and then add a section view of the clevis to your drawing. Use the Features submenu from the Designer pull-down menu and select the Work Plane option to add the work plane. You will pick Planar Parallel to add a parametric work plane and then pick Offset to offset the parallel plane so that it is through the center of the clevis.

Pick: **Designer, Features, Work Plane**

The Designer Work Plane dialogue box shown in Figure 20.37 appears on your screen.

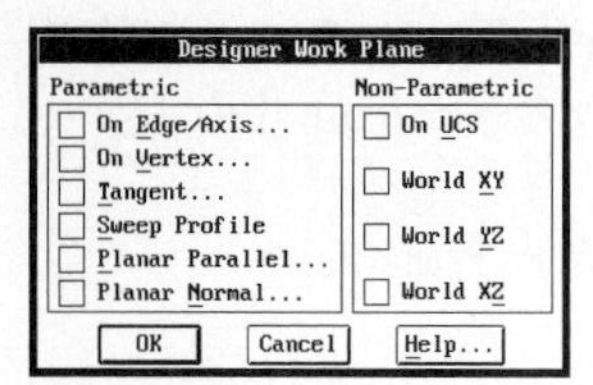

Figure 20.37

Pick: **Planar Parallel *(from the left side of the dialogue box)***

Pick: **Offset**

Pick: **OK**

Pick: **OK**

You will be returned to your drawing; make the following selections. Refer to Figure 20.38.

Xy/Yz/Zx/Ucs/<Select work plane or planar face>: ***(pick line 1)***

Select another edge: ***(pick line 2)***

Offset <1.00>: **1.75** ↵

The work plane appears on your screen. If it appears toward the center of the clevis, as shown in Figure 20.38, press ↵ to accept the position. If it is away from the clevis, type "F" and press ↵ to flip the position of the work plane.

Flip/<Accept>: ↵

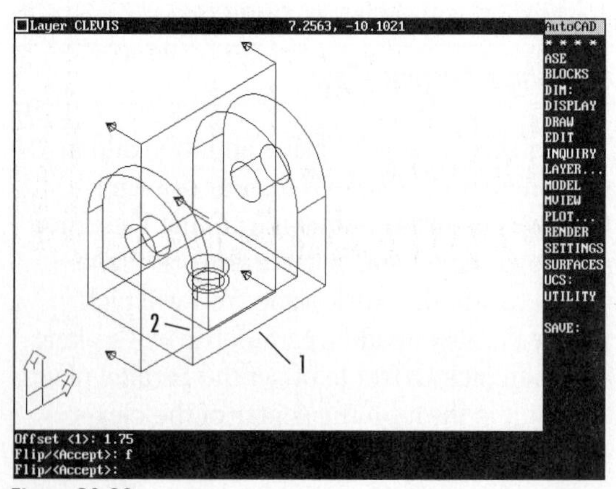

Figure 20.38

To add the section view to your drawing, you will select Designer, Drawing, Create View from the pull-down menu.

Pick: **Designer, Drawing, Create View**

Use the dialogue box that appears to select Ortho and then Full Section as the type of view to add. Pick in the box to the left of Hatch so that hatching will be created for your section view. Pick Pattern and then use the Hatch dialogue box that appears to pick Pattern once again and specify the ANSI31 hatch pattern to use for the hatching. Type "A" in the text box for the Section Symbol label. Type "Section A-A" in the text box for the View Label. Pick OK when you have finished making the selections shown in Figure 20.39. You are returned to the drawing to specify the location for the section view and whether to section through a point you specify on the view or use a work plane.

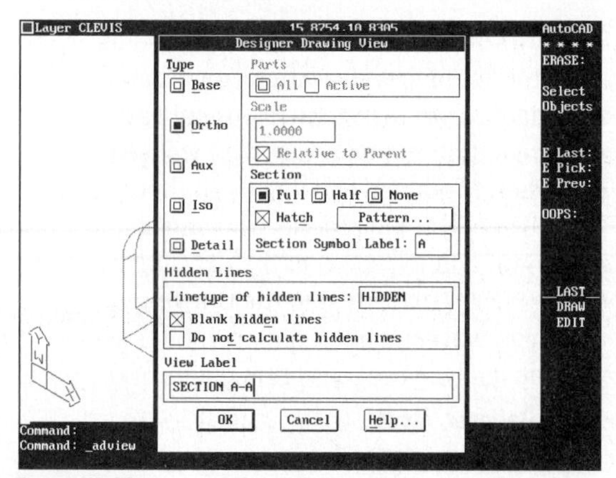

Figure 20.39

Select parent view: ***(pick the top view)***

Location for orthographic view: ***(pick below the front view)***

Location for orthographic view: ↵

Section through point/<Work plane>: ↵

Select work plane in parent view for the section: ***(pick the edge view of the work plane, labeled A, as shown in Figure 20.40)***

The section view is generated automatically and the cutting plane added and labeled in the drawing. Your drawing should appear similar to Figure 20.40.

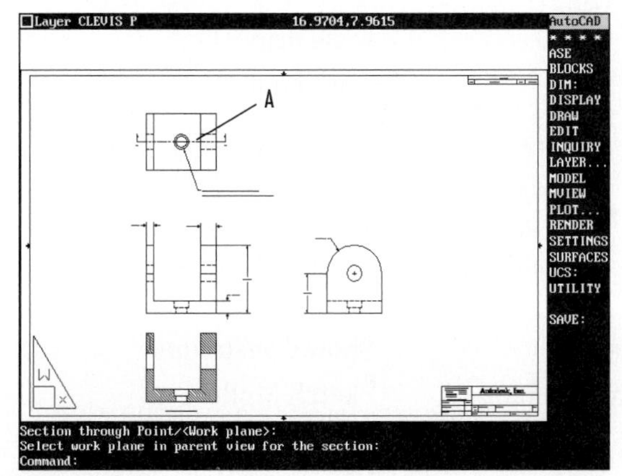

Figure 20.40

You will move the views on the drawing so that they fit on the sheet better.

Pick: **Designer, Drawing, Edit View, Move**

Select view to move: ***(pick the front view)***

View location: ***(position the crosshairs above their current position to move them up to make more room for the section view on the sheet)***

Continue on your own to position the views until they fit on the sheet, as shown in Figure 20.41. To do this efficiently, position the parent view (in this case the front view) first, as its descendants move with it. Then position the remaining views, such as the top, side and section views. Figure 20.41 shows the final drawing.

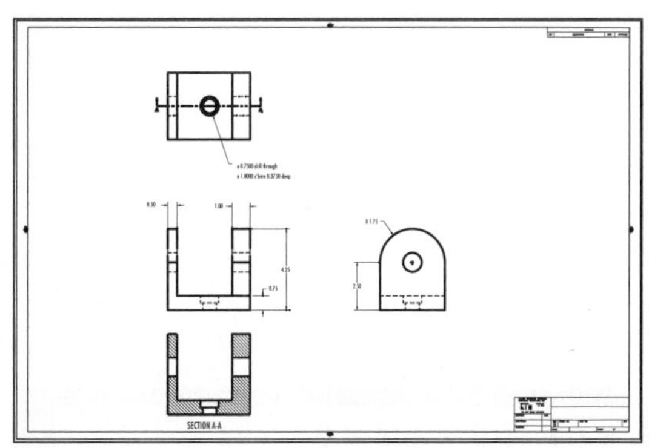

Figure 20.41

Going Further

Use the AutoCAD Plot dialogue box and plot your drawing from paper space. Start a new drawing named BOLT1 and use AutoCAD Designer to create a bolt that will fit through the holes in the rounded end of the clevis. When it is finished, begin another new drawing named ASSM-DS. Select Designer, Utilities, Transfer, Part In to use the ADPARTIN command to import the CLEVIS and the BOLT1 drawings that you created. Analyze the mass properties of the two parts. Make a work plane through the center of the parts to use for creating a section view. Create a section view assembly drawing automatically, using the Designer, Drawing, Create View selection from the pull-down menu.

KEY TERMS

base feature	feature	sweeping
bi-directional associativity	parametric	work axis
colinear	path	work plane
constraints	profile	work point

KEY COMMANDS

Angular Tolerance	Mode	Rule Mode
Delete Constraints	Modify Dimensions	Show Constraints
Dimension Display	Parametric Dimensioning	Sketch Mode
Edit Features	Part In	Update
Extrude	Part Viewing	View
Fix Point	Path	Work Axis
Hole	Pickbox	Work Plane
Mass Properties	Profile	Work Point

EXERCISES

 20.1

Use AutoCAD Designer to create parametric models for the exercises listed below. Create and plot dimensioned part drawings from the parametric model. Analyze the mass properties of the parts. Make design changes on your own and then plot the new drawings.

Ex. 8.1
Ex. 8.2
Ex. 8.3
Ex. 8.4
Ex. 8.5M
Ex. 8.6
Ex. 9.4
Ex. 9.5M
Ex. 9.6
Ex. 9.7
Ex. 9.8
Ex. 10.1
Ex. 10.2M
Ex. 11.2M
Ex. 11.6
Ex. 13.1
Ex. 13.2
Ex. 13.3
Ex. 14.5
Ex. 14.6
Ex. 15.2
Ex. 15.3M
Ex. 15.4M
Ex. 15.5M
Ex. 15.6

 20.2

Create a parametric model of the floorplan from Exercise 7.8. Extrude the walls to create a 3D solid model. Make design changes using the ADEDITFEAT command. Generate the first floor plan drawing.

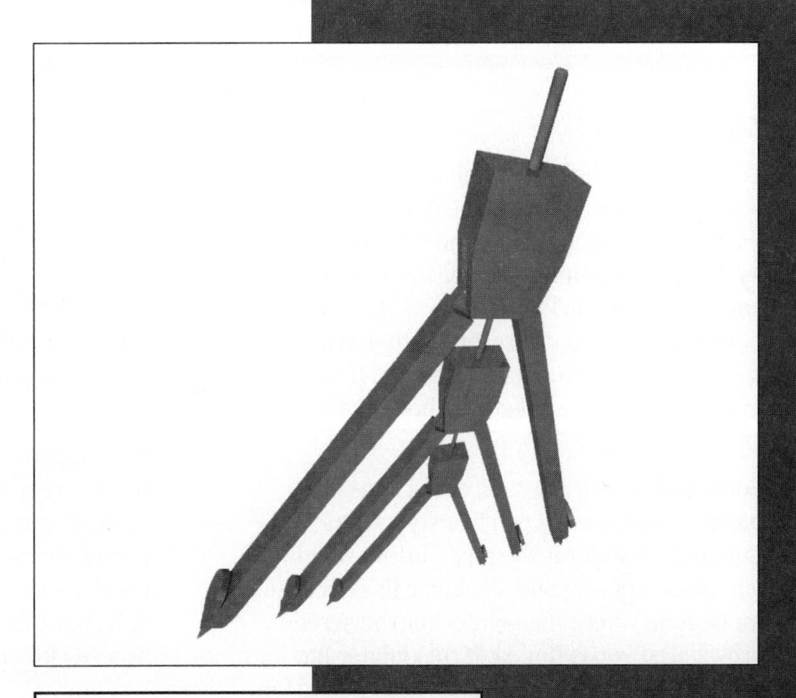

PART THREE

Appendix

Using a Digitizing Tablet

Device Drivers for AutoCAD Release 12

Converting Drawings from Older Versions of AutoCAD

Challenge Exercises

Tablet Operation

You can use a digitizing tablet as a screen pointing device. In the AutoCAD graphics window, crosshairs appear on the screen and move as the tablet's pointer moves. You can define any part of the tablet's surface as the screen pointing area; you can reserve other areas for command entry from tablet menus. If tablet mode is on, you can also use the tablet to trace an existing paper drawing.

Some tablets use a cursor, or puck, as the pointer; others use a pen-like stylus. One button on the pointer is the pick button, which you press to designate a point or to select the menu item where the pointer (or the screen crosshairs) is positioned. If the pointer has more buttons, they are usually assigned to successive items in the AutoCAD button menu.

Configuring Your Tablet Menu

You can use the optional tablet menu, which requires a digitizing tablet and pointing device (stylus or puck only; it will not work with a mouse), in conjunction with the screen menus. The standard AutoCAD tablet template is designed to be used on a digitizing tablet with an active area at least 11 inches square. The tablet template file (TABLET.DWG) is included with your AutoCAD software and can be printed and affixed to your tablet. If your tablet is a different size, plot the template to a scale that fits.

The menu areas and number of rows are specific to the AutoCAD template, so if you have a different template, the configuration may differ. Check your tablet manufacturer's documentation for instructions.

To configure the tablet menu,

1. Attach the template to your tablet so it will not shift during use.
2. In the AutoCAD drawing editor, at the command prompt, enter this series of choices:

Command: **tablet** ↵

Option (ON/OFF/CAL/CFG): **cfg** ↵

Enter number of tablet menus desired (0–4) <0>: **4** ↵

4. You are next asked to pick three points on the template for the first menu area. These points are illustrated in the following diagram (Figure A.1). After picking these points, you are asked for the number of columns and rows, also shown in Figure A.1. AutoCAD prompts you to repeat this process for each of the four menu areas.

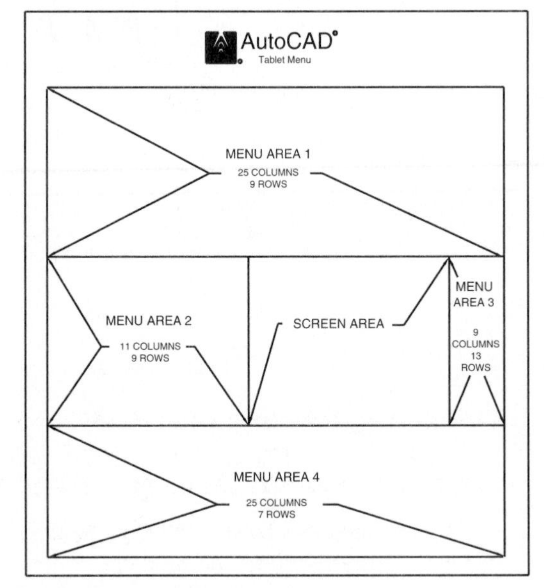

Figure A.1

After you complete the selection of menu areas, AutoCAD prompts you for two points to define the screen area, as shown in the figure above. This completes the configuration of the tablet menu.

Using Tablet Swap

Tablet swap allows you to change the function of each of the four menu areas on the template. Three of the areas are reserved for use by AutoCAD; the fourth can be used for a custom menu or third-party application.

You make a swap by picking one of the four tablet icons just below the lower-right corner of the screen area, at coordinates S19 through S22, as shown in Figure A.2. You can make a swap at any time, even when a command is active. Picking an icon a second time swaps you back to the original menu.

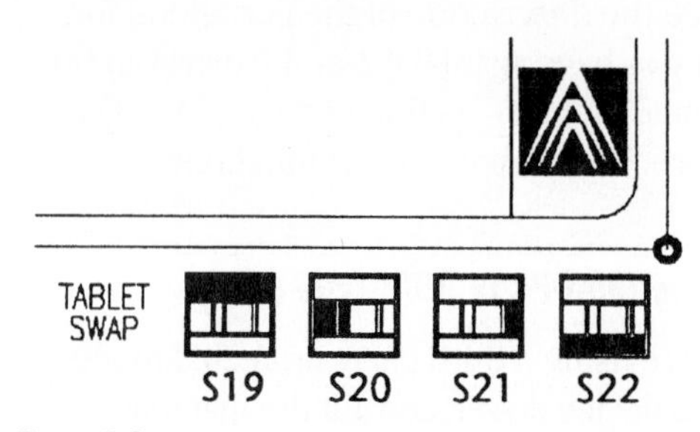

Figure A.2

Icon S19 swaps the top area of the template to a blank menu, eliminating the AME and AutoShade menus. This blank menu area is the same as in previous versions of the AutoCAD template and may be used for personal applications and menu items.

Icon S20 swaps the left area of the template. Zoom and other display commands cancel the command in progress. Vpoint and Dview commands refer to the current User Coordinate System. When you swap back, display commands are transparent, and Vpoint and Dview refer to the World Coordinate System.

Icon S21 swaps the right area of the template. This swap changes units from American to metric.

Icon S22 swaps the bottom area of the template. This swap changes the OSNAP picks (T12–22) to running OSNAP by resetting the OSMODE system variable. When you swap back, the last running OSNAP is the default for OSNAP override.

When a swap is made to load one of these alternate menus, a number (1–4) replaces one of the four stars at the top of the screen menu. To reset all menu areas to their original state, pick the heading AutoCAD above the line of stars.

DEVICE DRIVERS FOR AUTOCAD RELEASE 12

AutoCAD uses Autodesk Device Interface (ADI) device drivers (programs) to communicate with peripheral hardware. Some ADI drivers come with AutoCAD and are included in the list of devices displayed during configuration.

If you want to install and configure a peripheral device that is not listed on the Configuration Menu, you should check the manufacturer's documentation for information about using it with AutoCAD Release 12. In many cases, a device will emulate a supported device and may be configured to run with its driver.

If you want to configure a device for which no driver is listed on the Configuration Menu, and the manufacturer has provided an ADI driver for it, you can select the appropriate ADI interface from the Configuration Menu to communicate with the installed ADI driver. Instructions on how to prepare your system for use with the ADI driver should be included with the ADI driver documentation.

■ ***Warning:*** If you are installing and configuring AutoCAD Release 12 for Windows, you must use version 4.2 ADI device drivers. ADI drivers created for AutoCAD 386 or AutoCAD Release 11 for Windows do not work. ■

If you are installing AutoCAD Release 12 for DOS, you will first need to determine whether your ADI driver is a *protected-mode* or a *real-mode* driver.

Real-Mode ADI Drivers

A real-mode ADI driver is one originally designed to run with earlier versions of AutoCAD (9, 10, or 11). These drivers are .EXE files that you must run *before* starting and configuring AutoCAD. They load into low memory as terminate-and-stay resident (TSR) programs. Most existing real-mode drivers work with AutoCAD Release 12 for DOS.

You should refer to the manufacturer's instructions for installing any ADI driver supplied with a peripheral device. An ADI driver with version number 4.0 is likely to be a real-mode driver; version 4.1 drivers may be real mode or protected mode.

Protected-Mode ADI Drivers

A protected-mode ADI driver (P386 ADI) offers increased performance because it runs in the native 32-bit mode of the 80386 chip, and because the DOS extender handles memory and paging requirements in 32-bit address space. Protected-mode drivers are .EXP files that you must copy to the hard disk before configuring the device in AutoCAD. You must set an environment variable to tell AutoCAD where to look for the driver file. AutoCAD then automatically loads the driver into memory when it starts.

You should refer to the manufacturer's instructions for installing any ADI driver supplied with a peripheral device. ADI drivers with version number 4.2 are likely to be protected mode; version 4.1 drivers may be real mode or protected mode.

Important: ADI 4.1 and 4.0 protected-mode drivers have limited capabilities in AutoCAD Release 12. Dialogue boxes may appear slightly misaligned, sliders may not work properly, and rendering in a viewport is not permitted. See the description of the peripheral for which you have an ADI 4.1 or 4.0 driver in the Technical Support section of your CD-ROM for more information about limitations.

Installing Third-Party ADI Device Drivers

If you are using a third-party protected-mode ADI 4.2 device driver, consult the manufacturer's documentation for installation instructions. However, if you are using an older driver, the instructions might not work with AutoCAD Release 12. If you have problems getting your third-party ADI driver to work, do the following:

- Read the descriptions in the Technical Support section of your CD-ROM pertaining to your device. Find out what has changed and apply those changes to the manufacturer's instructions.
- Contact the driver manufacturer for updated instructions and possibly an updated driver.

Some third-party protected-mode ADI drivers must be installed in a special directory. Some drivers have support files, such as resource, font, or data files, assigned to their own subdirectory. If you have such a driver, do one of the following so that AutoCAD can locate the files and list the drivers in the appropriate configuration menu:

- Leave the driver files where they were installed, and add the driver directory to the ACADDRV path (DOS) or to the AutoCAD device drivers directory setting (Windows).
- Move the driver and the support files to a directory that is already on the ACADDRV path (DOS) or specified by the device drivers directory setting (Windows). You may need to adjust the driver configuration so the driver can find its support files. For example, you might need to set an environment variable that provides the path to the driver's support files.

For information on creating the AutoCAD device drivers directory setting, see "The /d Switch (Drivers Directory)" in "Setting the AutoCAD Environment" (Windows) or "Environment Variables" (DOS) under "Performance" in the Technical Support section of your CD-ROM.

Prefixes for ADI Devices

In Release 12, AutoCAD requires each type of driver to use a name that starts with a special prefix, as shown in Table 1-1. AutoCAD ignores drivers with an incorrect prefix.

Table 1-1. ADI 4.2 Driver Prefixes

Driver	ADI Prefix
Display	ds
Combined rendering and display	rc
Plotter	pl
Digitizer	dg

If your driver is on a specified AutoCAD device drivers directory path and does not appear in the AutoCAD Configuration Menu, rename the driver file using the proper prefix from Table 1-1. For example, for AutoCAD Release 12 for Windows, plotter driver file DRIVER.DLL should be renamed PLDRIVER.DLL. Similarly, for AutoCAD Release 12 for DOS, plotter driver file DRIVER.EXP should be renamed PLDRIVER.EXP.

CONVERTING DRAWINGS FROM OLDER VERSIONS OF AUTOCAD

You can use AutoCAD Release 12 with drawings, slides, and DXF files that were originally produced with an earlier version of AutoCAD. AutoCAD updates are designed so that drawings you create with any version of AutoCAD are readable by the latest version.

AutoCAD Release 12 drawings, slides, and DXF files can be used with AutoCAD Release 11, but not with versions older than Release 11.

In general, files are forward compatible, not backward compatible.

To convert an older drawing, open it as you would any drawing. The drawing is converted automatically and you can begin work. The original, pre-Release 12 drawing is retained, with its file type changed from .DWG to .OLD.

CHALLENGE EXERCISES

Exercise 1: You should be able to complete this after finishing Tutorial 1.

Draw the object shown below. Set LIMITS to –4,–4 and 8,5. Set SNAP to .25 and GRID to .5. The origin (0,0) is to be the center of the left circle. Do not include the dimensions. Use END to save the file.

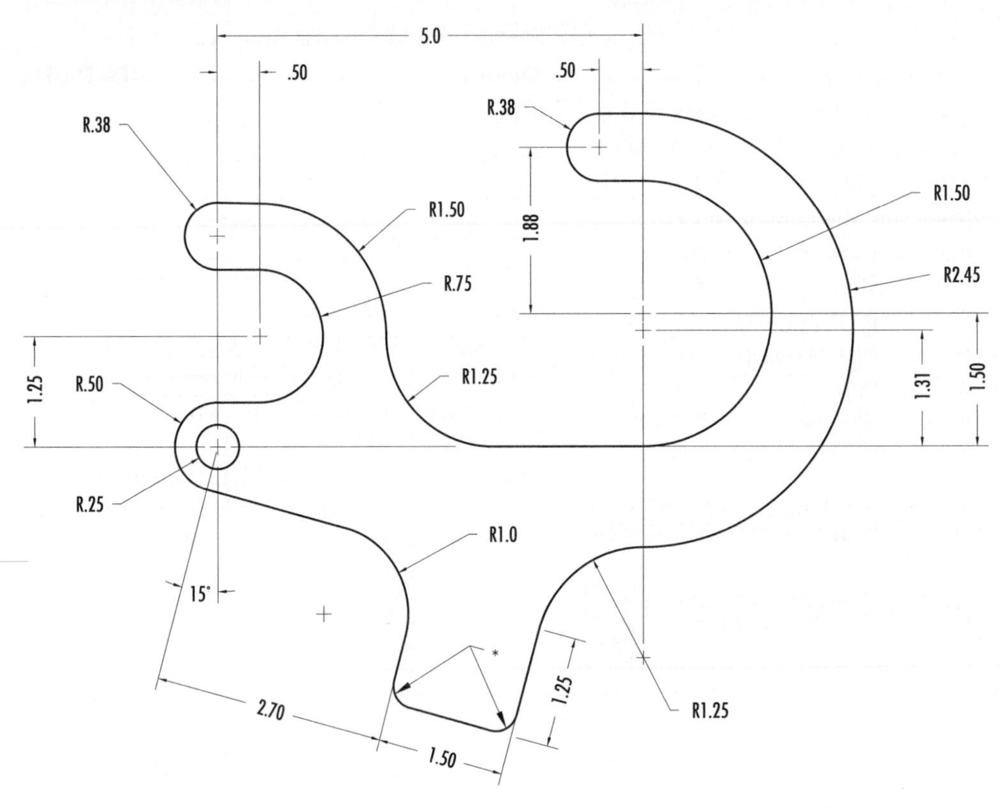

*Corners have R.25

Going Further

Add the dimensions (Tutorial 7). Use PEDIT, Join and then EXTRUDE to give the shape a thickness (Tutorial 8).

Exercise 2: You should be able to complete this after finishing Tutorial 2.

Redraw the window schedule shown below. Experiment with different fonts.

WINDOW SCHEDULE

TYPES: 1 2 3 4 5 6 7 8 9 10

SYM	TYPE	SIZE		MATL FIN	FRAME	FIN SCRN AREA	AREA		VENT	GLAZING		DETAILS				REMARKS
		H	W							MAT'L		H	J	S		
A	1	5'-0"	6'-4"	MTL	ST	MTL	ST	Y	32.5 SF	65 SF						
B	2	5'-5"	7'-4"	MTL	ST	MTL	ST	N		40.5 SF						FIXED GLAZING
C	3	4'-0"	14'-8"	MTL	ST	MTL	ST	N		58.8 SF						FIXED GLAZING
D	4	7'-0"	5'-0"	MTL	ST	MTL	ST	N		70 SF						FIXED GLAZING
E	5	5'-5"	4'-6"	MTL	ST	MTL	ST	N		48.6 SF						FIXED GLAZING
F	6	5'-0"	5'-4"	MTL	ST	MTL	ST	Y	13.3 SF	26.5 SF						
G	7	5'-5"	5'-4"	MTL	ST	MTL	ST	Y	9.9 SF	29.7 SF						
H	8	8'-0"	6'-4"	MTL	ST	MTL	ST	N		100.8 SF						FIXED GLAZING
I	9	5'-6"	6'-4"	MTL	ST	MTL	ST	N		126.1 SF						FIXED GLAZING
J	10	8'-0"	9'-4"	MTL	ST	MTL	ST	Y	24.8 SF	74.4 SF						
K	11	5'-6"	4'-8"	MTL	ST	MTL	ST	N		25.3 SF						FIXED GLAZING
L	12	6'-0"	3'-0"	WD	ST	WD	ST	N		36 SF						FIXED GLAZING
M	13	7'-6"	11'-6"	WD	ST	WD	ST	N		86.3 SF						FIXED GLAZING WITH CURVED GLASS
N	14	10'-0"	8'-0"	MTL	ST	MTL	ST	N		160 SF						FIXED GLAZING
O	15	10'-0"	14'-0'	MTL	ST	MTL	ST	N		140 SF						FIXED GLAZING
P	16	6'-0"	6'-6"	WD	ST	WD	ST	N		32.5 SF						FIXED GLAZING

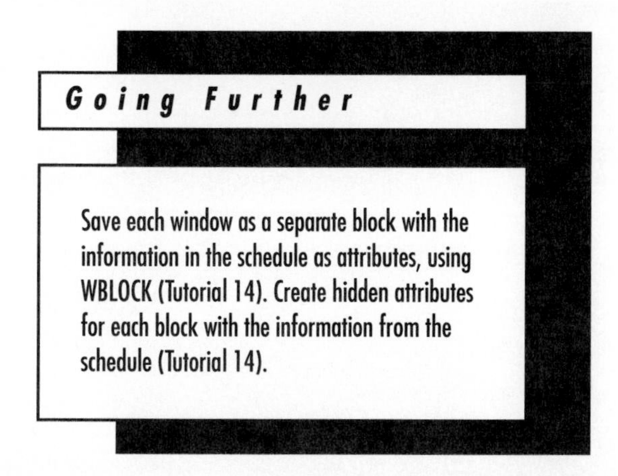

Going Further

Save each window as a separate block with the information in the schedule as attributes, using WBLOCK (Tutorial 14). Create hidden attributes for each block with the information from the schedule (Tutorial 14).

Exercise 3: You should be able to complete this after finishing Tutorial 2.

Draw the object shown below. Set LIMITS to –5,–5 and 150,125. Set SNAP to 1 and GRID to 5. Do not include the dimensions.

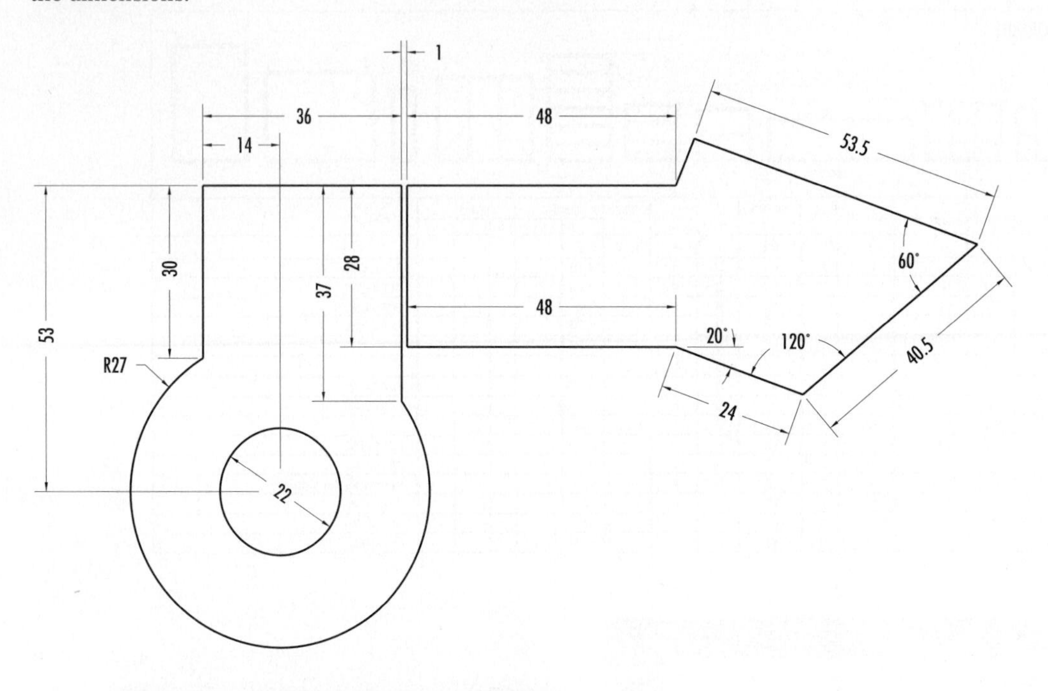

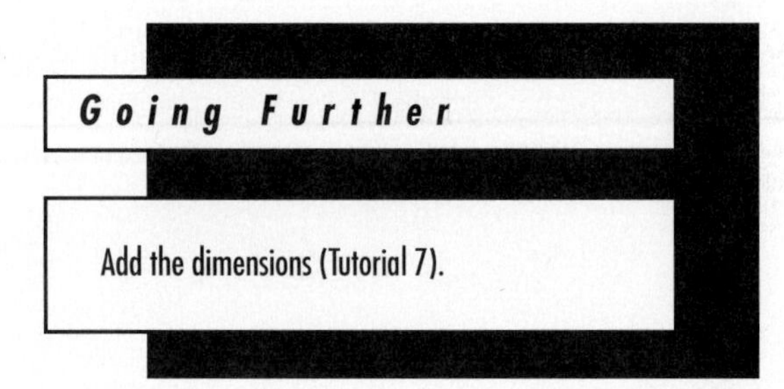

Exercise 4: You should be able to complete this after finishing Tutorial 3.

Draw the architectural framing plan shown below. Do not include the callouts. Use OFFSET to locate the joists.

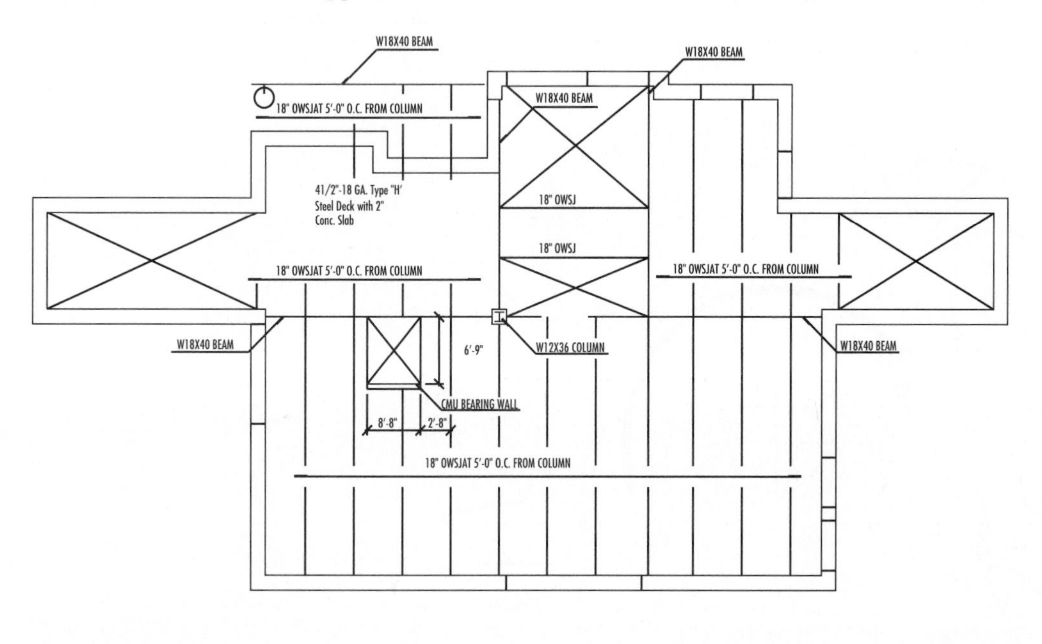

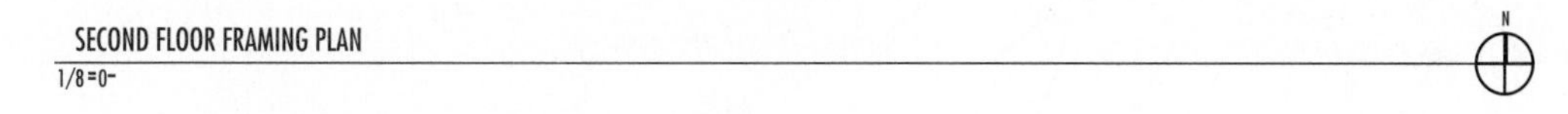

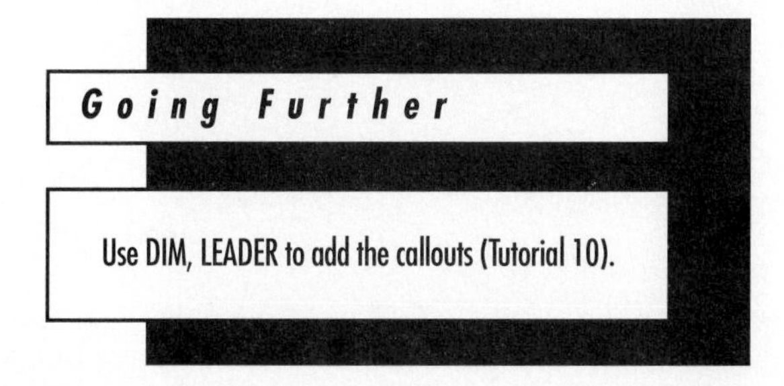

Going Further
Use DIM, LEADER to add the callouts (Tutorial 10).

Exercise 5: You should be able to complete this after finishing Tutorial 3.

Draw the saw blade shown below. Use ARRAY and PLINE. Do not include dimensions. In a separate drawing, experiment with the SOLID command, which allows you to create solid-filled regions; return to the saw blade and add the arrow that shows the blade's rotation.

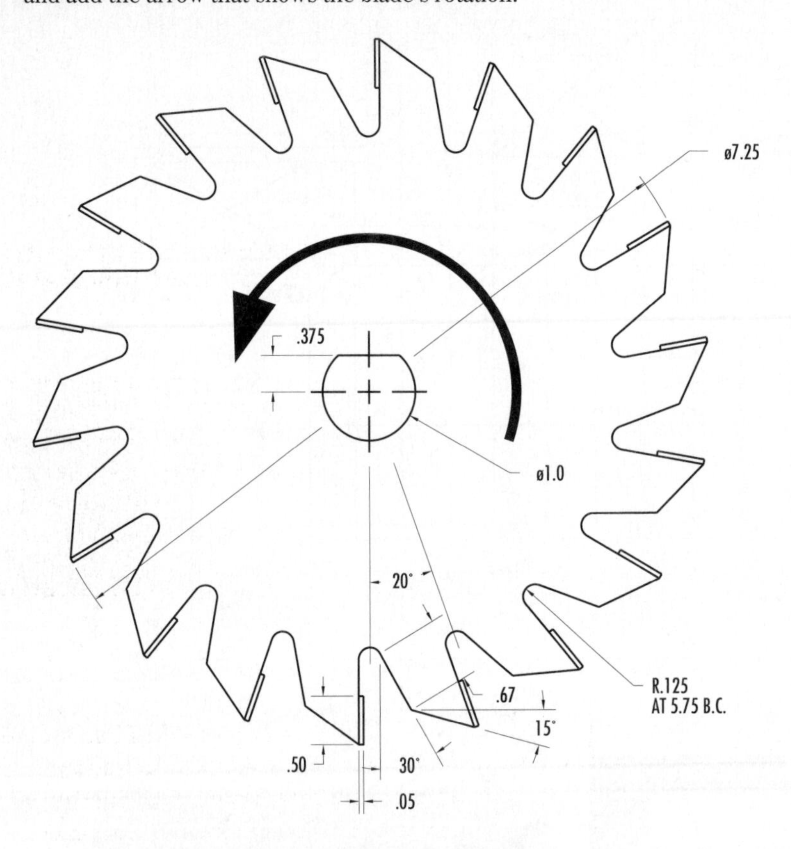

Going Further

Add the dimensions (Tutorial 7). Extrude the saw blade to create a solid (Tutorial 8). Assign materials and create a realistic rendering (Tutorial 16). Animate the spinning saw blade with 3D Studio (Tutorials 17–19).

Exercise 6: You should be able to complete this after finishing Tutorial 3.

Use the information in the file ROCKPLAN.PTS to create the plan and profile drawings for the railroad bed as shown below. The file has the information in the following order: point number, northing (the y coordinate to the north from the reference point), easting (the x coordinate to the east from the last reference point), elevation, and description. Start by locating each point at the northing and easting given. Extrapolate between elevations and draw polylines for the contour lines at 1' intervals. Make the contour lines for 95' and 100' wide, so that they stand out.

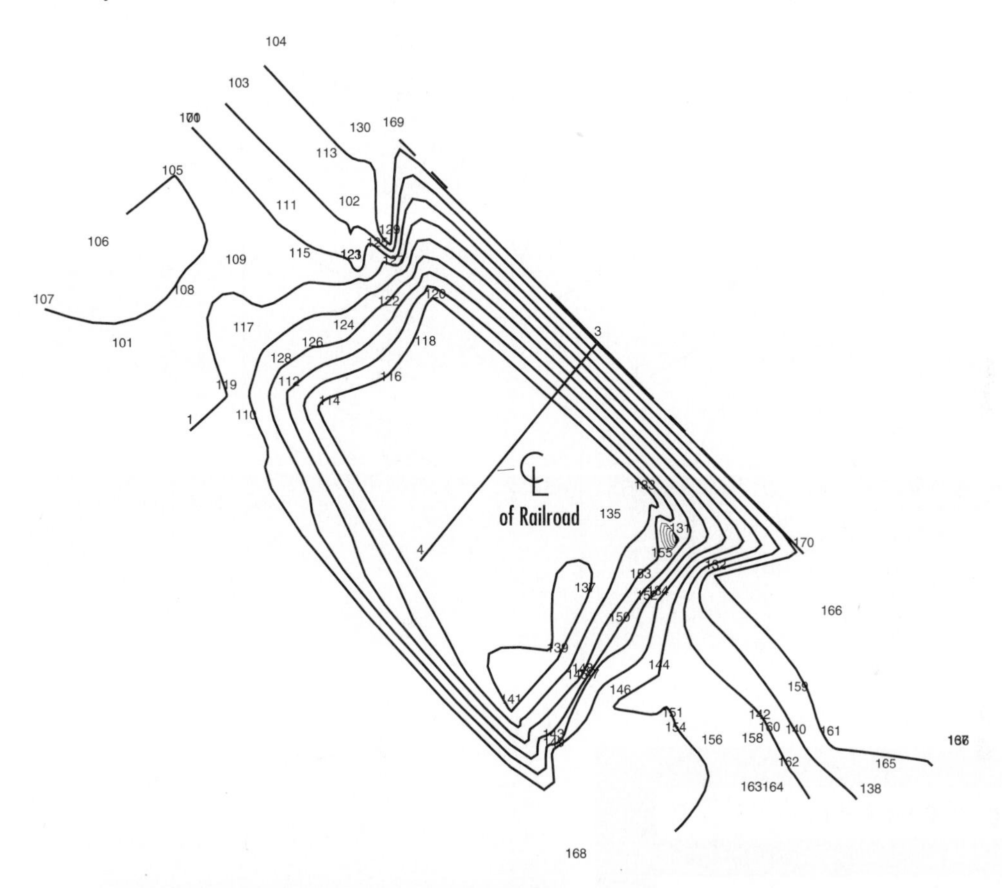

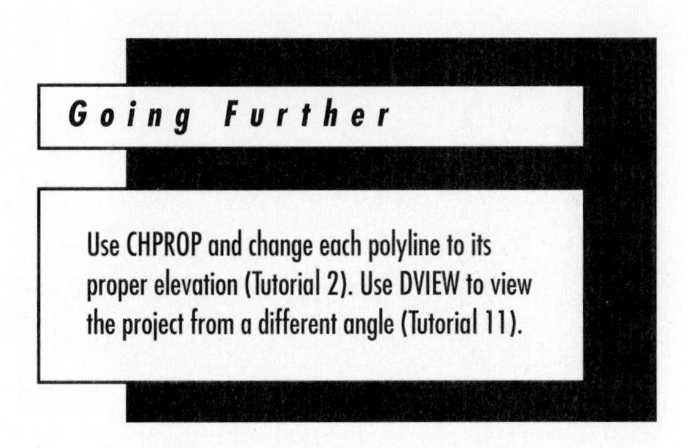

Exercise 7: You should be able to complete this after finishing Tutorial 9.

Create this mechanical part with solid modeling techniques. Do not include the dimensions. You will need to change your UCS several times. Set up several views of the object.

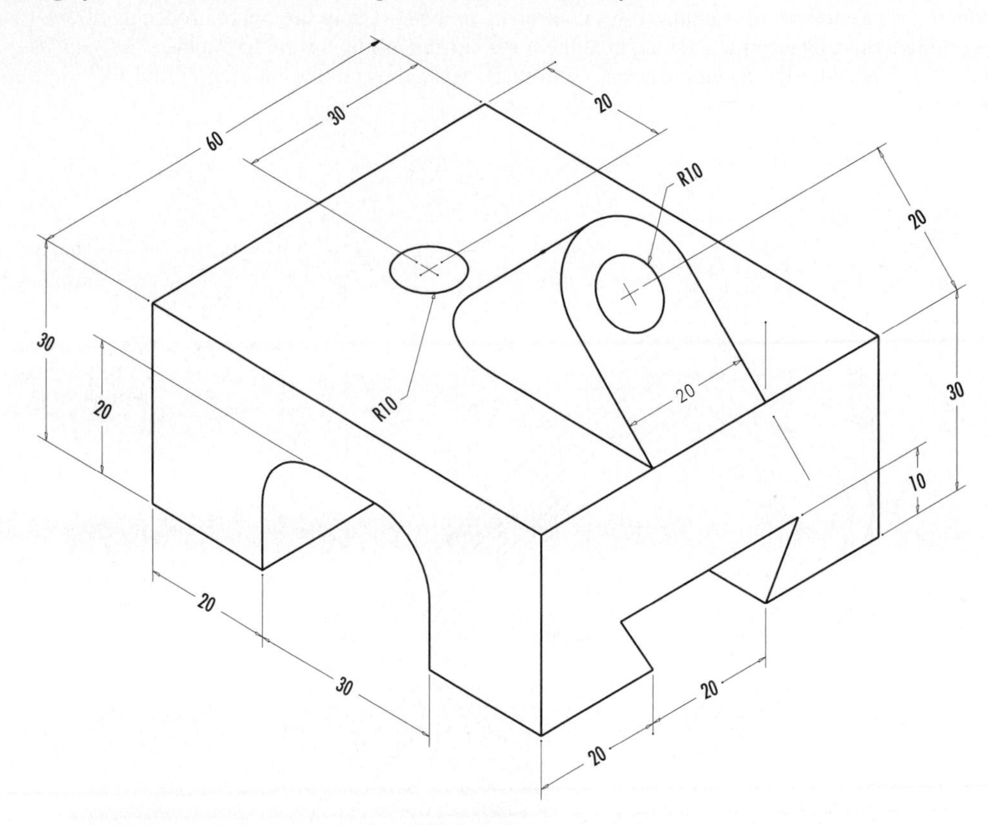

Going Further

Create an auxiliary view of the angled part (Tutorial 12). Add the dimensions (Tutorial 13). Use AutoVision to render the part and export it to 3D Studio (Tutorial 16). Animate it revolving with 3D Studio (Tutorials 17–19)

Exercise 8: You should be able to complete this after finishing Tutorial 9.

Create the object shown below, using solid modeling techniques. Both figures are shown in order that you may better understand the actual object. Do not include the dimensions.

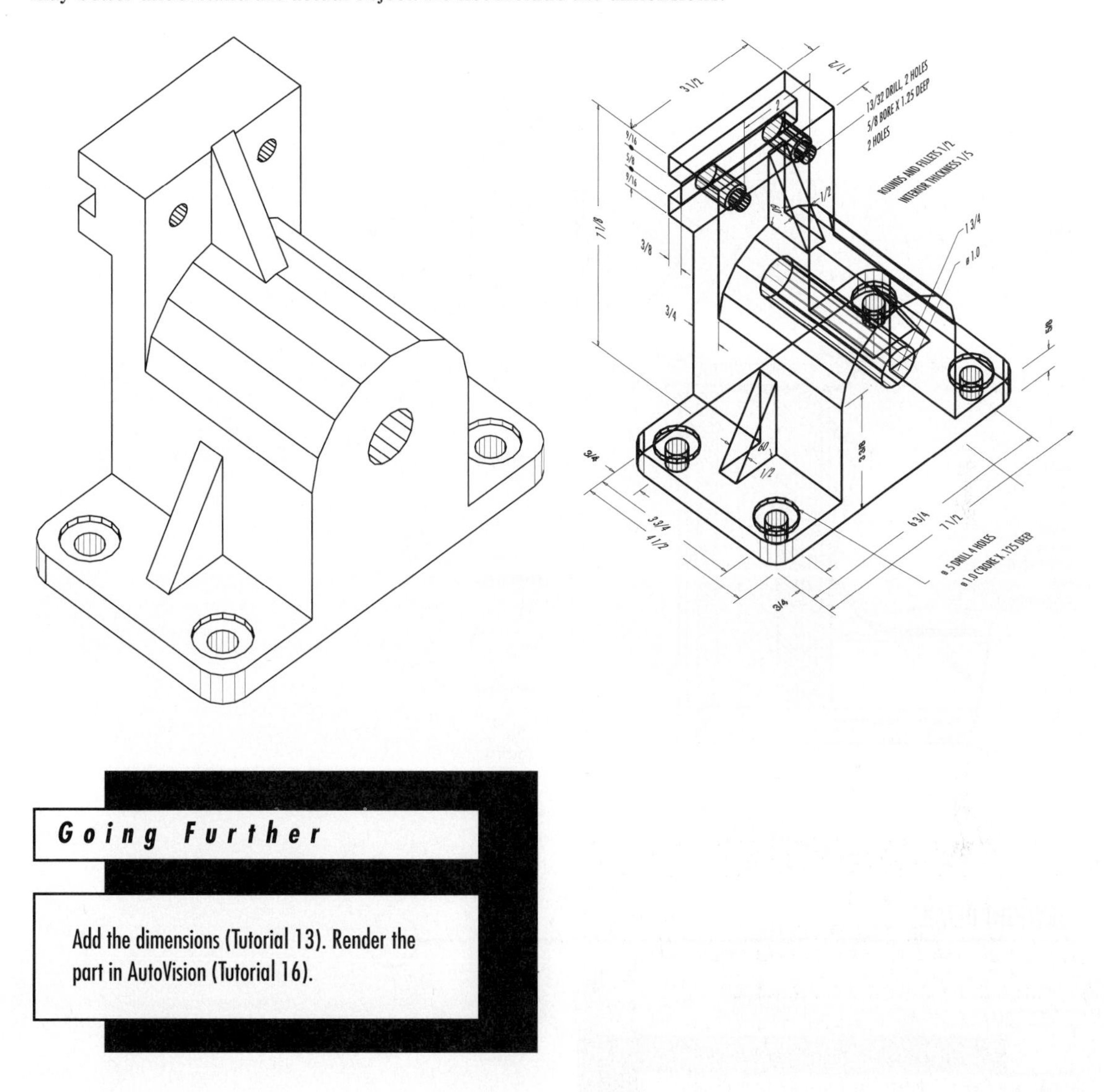

Going Further

Add the dimensions (Tutorial 13). Render the part in AutoVision (Tutorial 16).

Exercise 9: You should be able to complete this after finishing Tutorial 10.

Draw the skylight detail as shown. Use different hatch patterns to denote materials. Use DIM, LEADER to add the callouts.

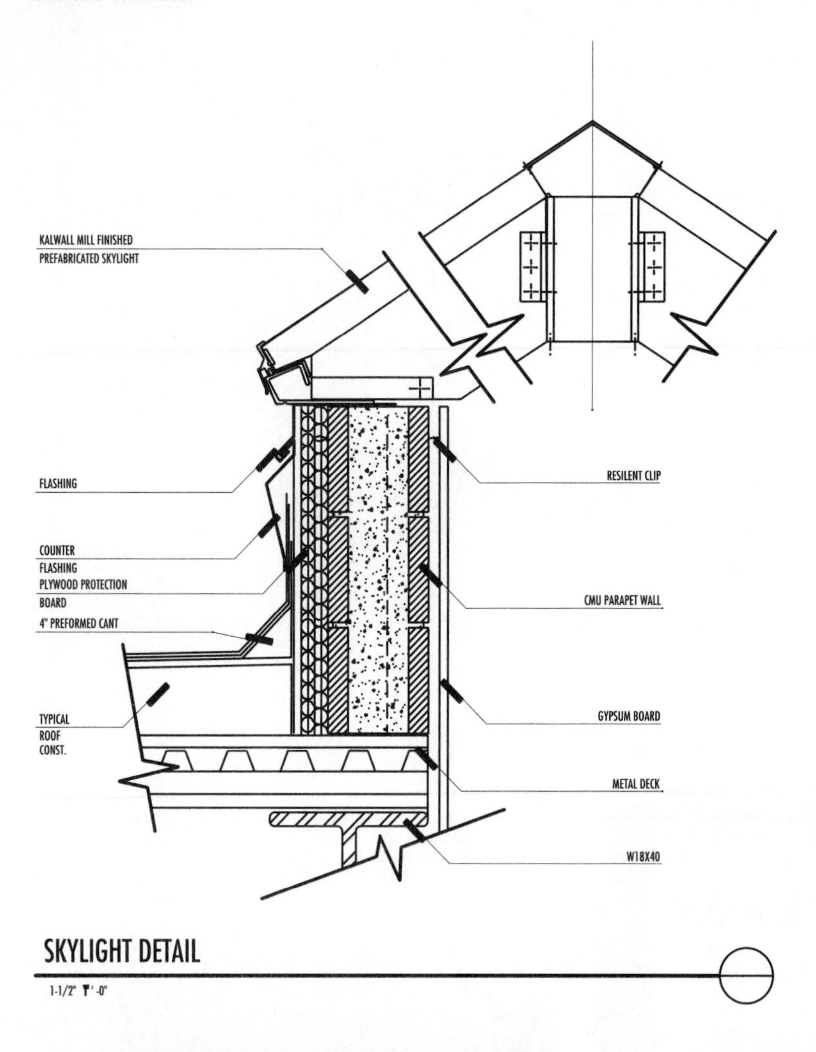

SKYLIGHT DETAIL

1-1/2" = 1'-0"

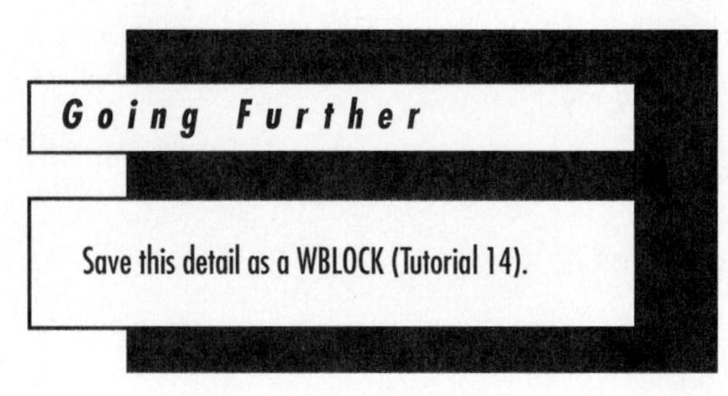

Going Further
Save this detail as a WBLOCK (Tutorial 14).

Exercise 10: You should be able to complete this after finishing Tutorial 11.

Create four views of the object shown below: top, front, half section of the front view, and an isometric.

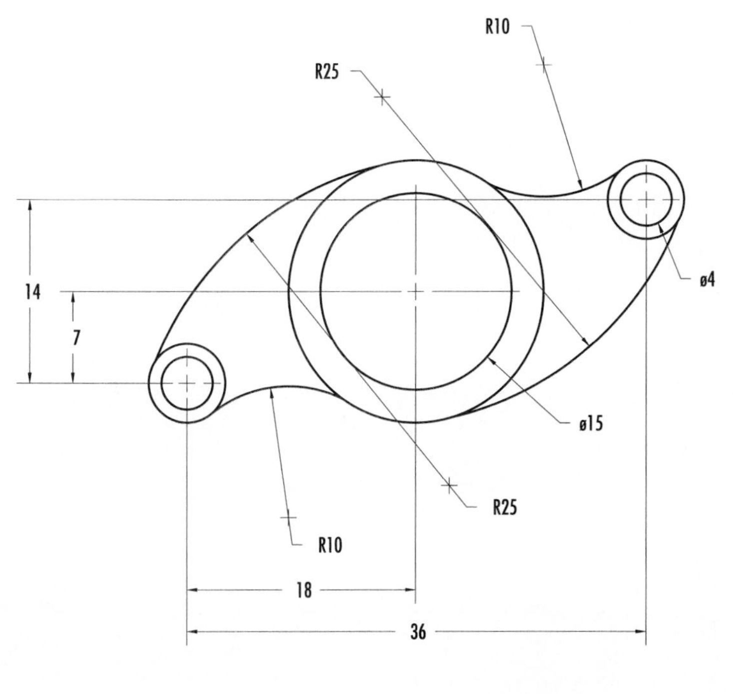

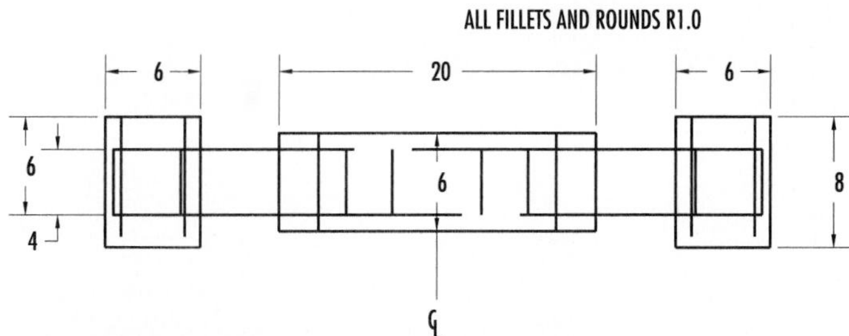

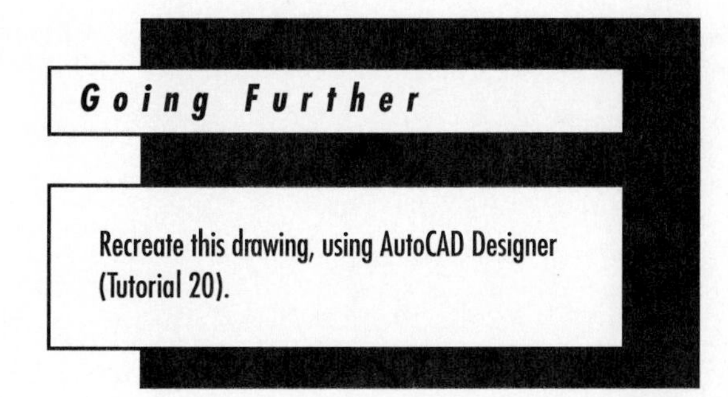

Going Further

Recreate this drawing, using AutoCAD Designer (Tutorial 20).

GLOSSARY OF KEY TERMS

2D Shaper The 3D Studio module used to create two-dimensional geometry.

3D Editor The 3D Studio module used to create basic three-dimensional shapes, apply materials and patterns to surfaces, add lights and camera, and render single scenes.

3D Lofter The 3D Studio module used to loft (extrude) or revolve two-dimensional primitives into three-dimensional shapes.

absolute coordinates The exact location of a specific point in terms of distances and/or angles from a fixed point of origin.

alias A short name that can be used to activate a command; you can customize command aliases by editing the file ACAD.PGP.

aligned dimensioning A method of aligning dimension text that places the dimension value at the same orientation as the dimension line.

ambient The overall amount of light that exists in the environment of a rendered scene.

angle brackets A value that appears in angle brackets < > is the default option for that command, which will be executed unless it is changed.

animation The illusion of movement on the screen, created by showing multiple, slightly different images in rapid sequence.

aperture A type of cursor resembling a small box placed on top of the crosshairs; used to select objects in Object Snap mode.

architectural units Drawings made with these units are drawn in feet and fractional inches.

aspect ratio The relationship of an object's three dimensions to each other; if your circles look like ovals, you need to correct the aspect ratio of your display.

assembly drawing Shows how the parts of an item fit together.

associative dimensioning Dimensioning where each dimension is inserted as a group of drawing entities relative to the points selected in the drawing. If the drawing is scaled or stretched, the dimension values automatically update.

attribute Text information associated with a block.

AutoLISP A programming language that allows you to customize AutoCAD functions.

auxiliary view An orthographic view of an object using a direction of sight other than one of the six basic views (front, top, right-side, rear, bottom, left-side).

ball tag A circled number identifying each part shown in an assembly drawing; also called a balloon number.

balloon number A circled number identifying each part shown in an assembly drawing; also called a ball tag.

base feature In AutoCAD Designer, the main feature of a drawing, from which other features are calculated based on the constraints put on the model.

base grip The selected grip, used as the base point for hot grip commands.

baseline dimensioning A dimensioning method in which each successive dimension is measured from one extension line or baseline.

basic view One of the six standard views of an object: front, top, right side, rear, bottom, or left side.

bias Controls on which side of the keyframe splining occurs in 3D Studio.

bi-directional associativity Describes the link between the drawing and the model in AutoCAD Designer. If a change is made to the model, the drawing is automatically updated to reflect the change; if a change is made to the parametric dimensions in the drawing, both the drawing and the model update automatically.

bilateral tolerances Tolerances specified by defining a nominal dimension and the allowable range of deviation from that dimension, both plus and minus.

bitmapped An image stored as a pattern of tiny individual dots.

blipmarks Little crosses that appear on the screen, indicating where the cursor has been clicked.

block A set of entities that have been grouped together to act as one, and can be saved and used in other drawings.

block name Identifies a particular block of entities.

block reference A particular insertion of a block into a drawing (blocks can be inserted more than once).

Boolean operators Find the union (addition), difference (subtraction), and intersection (common area) of two or more sets.

boss A turret-like shape, raised slightly above a surface, that can be machined without machining the entire surface. Typically used to provide a bearing surface for a bolt or nut.

broken-out section (partial section) A view that shows only part of an object in section.

bump map Converts color intensity or grayscale information to heights to give the appearance that features are raised above the surface, like embossed letters.

buttons A method of selecting options by picking in a defined area of the screen resembling a box or push button.

chained (continued) dimensioning A dimensioning method in which each successive dimension is measured from the last extension line of the previous dimension.

chamfer A straight line segment connecting two otherwise intersecting lines. Machining term for angled surfaces usually used to eliminate a sharp edge between two intersecting surfaces.

child An object attached to a parent object; if the parent object is moved, all of the child objects follow that motion, but if the child object is moved, the rest do not follow.

chord length The straight line distance between the start point and the end point of an arc.

circular view A view of a cylinder in which it appears as a circle (looking into the hole).

circumscribed Drawn around the outside of a base circle.

client An application that receives information from another application.

colinear Lying on the same straight line.

command aliasing The creation and use of alternative short names for commands, such as LA for LAYER.

command prompt area One to three lines of text below the drawing editor that indicate the status of commands and prompt for user input.

constraints Relationships between the elements that make up a model, such as perpendicularity, tangency, or parallelism.

construction plane The XY plane at the current elevation; the base plane where an object will be drawn unless you override it by providing the axis coordinate. Some solid modeling commands let you define a construction plane during a command.

continued (chained) dimensioning A dimensioning pattern in which each successive dimension is given from the last extension line of the previous dimension.

continuity Refers to connections between the slopes of the splines going in to and out of the keyframe in 3D Studio.

coordinate system locator An icon to help you visually refer to the current coordinate system.

coordinate values Used to identify the location of a point, using the Cartesian coordinate system. x represents the horizontal position on the X axis, and y represents the vertical position on the Y axis. In a three-dimensional drawing, z represents the depth position on the Z axis.

counterbored Having a second hole, wider than but not as deep as the first hole around which it is drilled, usually to allow the head of a bolt or nut to fit below the surface of the object.

countersunk Having a hole with tapered edges to match the shape of flat-head screws and bolts.

crosshairs (cursor) A mark that shows the location of the pointing device in the graphics area of the screen; used to draw, select, or pick menu items. The appearance of the cursor may change, depending on the command or option selected.

crosshatching The practice of filling an area with a pattern to differentiate it from other components of a drawing.

current layer The layer you are working on. New drawing entities are always created in the layer that is current.

cursor (crosshairs) A mark that shows the location of the pointing device in the graphics area of the screen; used to draw, select, or pick menu items. The appearance of the cursor may change, depending on the command or option selected.

customize To change the toolbar, toolbox, and other aspects of the program to show those commands and functions that you want them to.

cutting edges Drawing entities used to define the portions to be removed when trimming an object.

cutting plane Defines where part of a solid model is to be removed.

cutting plane line Defines the location on the object where the sectional view is taken.

default directory The DOS directory to which AutoCAD will save all drawing files unless instructed otherwise.

default option The value that AutoCAD will use unless you specify otherwise; appears in <> brackets after a prompt.

detail drawing Shows the shape, dimensions, tolerances, and materials necessary to create a single part.

diameter symbol ∅ Indicates that the value is a diameter.

difference The area or volume formed by subtracting one region or solid model from another.

dimension line Drawn between extension lines with an arrowhead at each end; indicates how the stated dimension relates to the feature on the object.

dimension style A group of dimension features saved as a set.

dimension value The value of the dimension being described (how long, how far across, etc.); placed near the midpoint of the dimension line.

dimension variables (dim vars) Features of dimensions can be altered by the user; you control the features by setting the variables.

dimensions Describe the sizes and locations of a part or object so that it can be manufactured.

distance across the flats A measurement of the size of a hexagon from one flat side to the side opposite it.

drag To move an object on the screen and see it at the same time, in order to specify the new size or location.

dummy An object to which you can link other objects in order to animate them as a group, yet still retain control over their separate parts.

edge view A line representing the edge of a surface.

engineering units Drawings made with these units are drawn in feet and decimal inches.

entities Separate elements such as lines, arcs, circles, text, and so forth that help make up a drawing.

exploded view An assembly drawing that shows the parts separately, but in line with the positions in which they would be assembled.

export To save a file from one application as a different file type for use by another application.

extension line Relates a dimension to the feature it refers to.

extrusion Creates a long three-dimensional strip with the shape of a closed two-dimensional shape, as if material had been forced through a shaped opening.

falloff The angle of the cone of light from a spotlight.

feature Any definable aspect of an object — a hole, a surface, etc.

file extension The part of a file name that is composed of a period, followed by 1 to 3 characters, and that helps to identify the file.

fillet An arc of specified radius that connects two lines, arcs, or circles, or a rounded interior corner on a machined part.

flat shading A shading method that colors each polygon making up an object a single color.

floating Refers to the toolbox's ability to be moved to any location on the screen.

foreshortened Appears smaller than actual size, due to being tipped away from the viewing plane.

fractional units Drawings made with these units express lengths less than 1 as fractions (e.g., 15 3/4).

frame A picture representing one step in a transformation or change.

frame rate The speed at which the individual pictures that make up an animated sequence are displayed; a faster rate makes a smoother animation.

full section A sectional view showing an object cut in half along its center line.

generated hatch Hatching produced by AutoCAD for you in commands such as SOLSECT.

generated hidden lines Hidden lines that AutoCAD automatically creates on new, separate layers in response to certain commands; the layer names start with PH.

generated visible lines Lines that AutoCAD automatically creates on new, separate layers in response to certain commands; the layer names start with PV.

globe Used to select the direction for viewing a three-dimensional model.

Gourard shading A shading method that calculates a color for each vertex on the object and then blends the shading between each pair of vertices to determine the color for the pixels in each flat polygon that makes up the object. The colors of the vertices at the ends of an edge are averaged and the resulting color is used for the color of the edge.

grab To pick and hold on to an entity with the pointing device in order to move it on the screen.

gradient A pattern that blends from one color to another.

graphics area The central part of the screen, which is used to create and display drawings.

grayed When an option appears on the screen in light gray rather than black, it means that the command cannot be used under current circumstances.

grid Regularly spaced dots covering an area of the graphics display screen to aid in drawing.

handle A distinct number assigned to each drawing entity that helps AutoCAD to store tree structure information for solid models in the drawing database.

hidden line Represents a surface that is not directly visible because it is behind or beneath another surface.

highlight A change of color around a particular command or object, indicating that it has been selected and is ready to be executed or worked on in some way.

hot grips A method for editing an already drawn entity using only the pointing device, without needing to use the menus or keyboard.

hotspot The angle of the cone of light for the brightest area of the beam of a spotlight.

image A way of storing a graphic image as a pattern of tiny individual dots; also called a bitmap.

implied windowing mode When this mode is activated, the first corner of a box is started when you select a point on the screen that is not on an entity in the drawing. If the box is drawn from left to right, a window is formed that selects everything that is entirely enclosed in the box. If the box is drawn from right to left, everything that partially crosses as well as items fully enclosed by the box are selected. Implied windowing can be turned on and off under the Settings, Selection Settings pull-down menu.

import To open and use a file created by a different application than the one being used.

inclined Slanted at an angle; a surface that is perpendicular to one of the three principal views and tipped away from the other principal views.

inscribed Drawn inside a base circle.

intensity The brightness level of a light source.

interpolation The calculation of an intermediate step, given the start and end points.

intersection The point where two lines or surfaces meet, or the area shared by overlapping regions or solid models.

invisible attribute Text information associated with a block that is not displayed on the screen but can still be extracted for use in a spreadsheet or database.

isocircle An isometric ellipse that represents a circle in an isometric view.

isometric axis An axis defined by three lines 120 degrees apart; used in isometric views.

key In 3D Studio, the defined position, rotation, scale, or other transformations for an object in an animation sequence, which indicates the beginning or ending appearance of the animated object.

Keyframer The 3D Studio module that adds animation to a scene.

layer A method of separating drawing entities so that they can be viewed individually or stacked like transparent acetates, allowing all layers to show. Used to set color and linetype properties for groups of drawing entities.

leader line A line from a note or radial dimension that ends in an arrowhead pointing at the feature.

limit tolerances Tolerances specified by defining an upper and lower allowable measurement.

limiting element The outer edge of a curved surface.

linear Moving in a straight line from one point to the next without deviation.

LISP A type of computer programming language; AutoCAD comes with a specific LISP language called AutoLISP.

loop A section of a program that returns to the same step it went through earlier.

major axis The long axis of symmetry across an ellipse.

mass properties Data about the real-world object being drawn, such as its mass, volume, and moments of inertia.

Materials Editor The 3D Studio module that lets you create new materials and change existing ones.

menu bar The strip across the top of the screen showing the names of the pull-down menus, such as File, Edit, etc.

minor axis The short axis of symmetry across an ellipse.

mirror line A line that defines the angle and distance at which a reversed image of a selected object will be created.

model space The AutoCAD drawing database when an object exists as a three-dimensional entity.

morph An animation process in which an object changes from one shape and appearance to another; from the word polymorphism, meaning being able to assume different forms.

Motion Coordinate System (MCS) Shows the x, y, and z coordinate axis of a selected primitive while it is being moved.

normal surface A surface that is perpendicular to two of the three principal orthographic views and appears at the correct size and shape in a basic view.

noun/verb selection A method for selecting an entity first and then the command to be used on it.

object hierarchy The order in which objects are linked to each other, determining which is the parent object and which is the child.

object linking and embedding A process by which an object (such as text, an image, a spreadsheet, etc.) created in one software application can be incorporated into another software application. A linked object is connected to the original document, and if the original is changed, all linked copies will change as well. An embedded object will remain the same even if the original is changed.

oblique line A line that is neither parallel nor perpendicular to any of the three principal views.

oblique surface A surface that is neither parallel nor perpendicular to any of the three principal views.

options The choices associated with a particular command or instruction.

orthographic view A two-dimensional drawing used in representing a three-dimensional object. A minimum of two orthographic views are necessary to show the shape of a three-dimensional object, because each view shows only two dimensions.

overall dimensions The widest measurements of a part; needed by manufacturers to determine how much material to start with.

override mode When the desired OSNAP mode must be selected during each command it is to be used for.

paper space A mode that allows you to arrange, annotate, and plot different views of a model in a single drawing, as you would arrange views on a piece of paper.

parametric A modeling method that allows you to input sizes for and relationships between the features of parts. Changing a size or relationship will result in the model being updated to the new appearance.

parent An object to which a child object is attached; if the parent object is moved, all of the child objects follow that motion, but if the child object is moved, the rest do not follow.

partial auxiliary view An auxiliary view that shows only the desired surfaces.

partial section (broken-out section) A view that shows only part of an object in section.

parts list Provides information about the parts in an assembly drawing, including the item number, description, quantity, material, and part number.

paste To insert information that was originally created in another part of the file or in a different file.

paths The direction of motion for objects being animated or swept.

Phong shading A shading method that calculates a color for each pixel in the object, which generally results in more color and shading variation, and therefore more realism, in the rendered scene.

plan view The top view or view looking straight down the Z axis toward the XY plane.

plus/minus tolerances Another name for variance tolerances.

point light A light source similar to a bare light bulb that casts light in every direction.

polar array A pattern created by repeating objects over and over in a circular fashion.

polar coordinates In AutoCAD, the location of a point, defined as a distance and an angle from another specified point, using the input format @DISTANCE<ANGLE.

polygon A closed shape with sides of equal length.

polyline A series of connected entities (lines or arcs) that are treated as a single entity also called pline.

precedence When two lines occupy the same space, precedence determines which one is drawn. Continuous lines take precedence over hidden lines, and hidden lines take precedence over center lines.

primitives Basic shapes that can be joined together or subtracted from each other to form more complex shapes.

profile A two-dimensional view of a three-dimensional model; or a closed 2D shape that can be extruded, revolved, or swept.

project To transfer information from one view of an object to another by aligning them and using projection lines.

projection lines Horizontal lines that stretch from one view of an object to another to show which line or surface is which.

prototype drawing A drawing saved with certain settings that can be used as the basis for starting new drawings.

pull-down menu A menu of commands that appears when the menu heading is picked from the top menu bar.

quadrant point Any of the four points that mark the division of a circle or arc into four segments: 0, 90, 180, and 270 degrees.

ray tracing The method of calculating shading by tracking reflected light rays hitting the object. Both AutoVision and 3D Studio use the Phong algorithm to perform ray tracing to produce realistic shading.

real-world units Units in which drawings in the database are drawn; they should always be drawn at the size that the real object would be.

rectangular array A pattern created by repeating objects over and over in columns and rows.

rectangular view A view of a cylinder in which it appears as a rectangle (looking from the side).

reference surface A surface from which measurements are made when creating another view of the object.

reflection The degree to which a surface bounces back light.

refraction The degree to which an object changes the angle of light passing through it.

regenerate To recalculate from the drawing database a drawing display that has just been zoomed or had changes made to it.

relative coordinates The location of a point in terms of the X and Y distance, or distance and angle, from a previously specified point @X,Y.

rendering The process of calculating the lighting effects, color, and shape of an object in a single two-dimensional view.

resolution Refers to how sharp and clear an image appears to be and how much detail can be seen; the higher the resolution, the better the quality of the image. This is determined by the number of colors and pixels the computer monitor can display.

revolution Creating a three-dimensional object by sweeping a two-dimensional polyline, circle, or region about a circular path to create a symmetrical solid that is basically circular in cross-section.

root page The original standard screen menu column along the right side of the screen, accessed by picking the word AutoCAD at the top of the screen.

roughness The apparent texture of a surface. The lower the surface roughness, the more reflective the surface will be.

round A convex arc, or a rounded external corner on a machined part.

running mode When the current OSNAP mode is automatically used any time a command calls for the input of a point or selection.

runout The point where a rounded edge blends into (become tangent to) the surface of the object.

scale factor The multiple or fraction of the original size of a drawing entity or linetype at which it is displayed.

scaling To change something's size by multiplying or dividing it (twice the original size, one-third the original size, etc.).

scientific units Drawings made with these units are drawn in exponential notation.

screen menu The list of available commands in the column along the right edge of the drawing screen.

sectional lines Show surfaces that were cut in a sectional view.

sectional view A type of orthographic view that shows the internal structure of an object; also called a cutaway view.

segment One piece of something (e.g., a line, an animation sequence) with distinct start and end points.

selection set All of the objects chosen to be affected by a particular command.

server An application that provides information to another application.

slider bar The area in between the arrows at the ends of a scroll box; used to scroll text up and down quickly.

smooth A process that evens out the motion of an animated object so that the apparent speed of the object as it moves is uniform.

solid modeling A type of three-dimensional modeling that represents the volume of an object, not just its lines and surfaces; this allows for analysis of the object's mass properties.

spotface A circular shallow hole cut into a surface just deep enough to create a smooth surface; usually surrounding another hole.

spotlight A light source used to highlight certain key areas and cast light only toward the selected target.

squash To change an object while maintaining its apparent volume; when one axis is compressed, the other two axes scale in the opposite direction to maintain the volume.

submenu A list of available options or commands relating to an item chosen from a menu.

surface modeling A type of three-dimensional modeling that defines only surfaces and edges so that the model can be shaded and have hidden lines removed; resembles an empty shell in the shape of the object.

swatch An area that shows a sample of the color or pattern currently selected.

sweeping Extrusion along a non-linear path rather than a straight line.

target area The square area on an Object Snap aperture, in which at least part of the entity to be selected must fit.

tension Refers to the attack of the spline toward a keyframe in 3D Studio.

tessellation To cover a surface with a grid or lines, like a mosaic. Tessellation lines are displayed on a curved surface to help you visualize it; the number of tessellation lines determines the accuracy of surface area calculations.

threshold value Determines how close vertices must be in order to be automatically welded during the rendering process.

tiled viewports If more than one viewport is created, they cannot overlap. They must line up next to each other, like tiles on a floor.

tolerance The amount that a manufactured part can vary from the specifications laid out in the plans and still be acceptable.

toolbar The strip across the top of the screen showing layer information, cursor coordinates, and icons for certain commands, such as OPEN, PRINT, and SAVE.

toolbox The palette of command icons that can be moved around on the screen.

tracks The method by which 3D Studio records the position, rotation, scaling, and morphing of an object being animated; there is a separate track for each transformation.

transformation Moving, scaling, rotating, squashing, or morphing an object.

transparency A quality that makes objects appear clear, like glass, or somewhat clear, like colored liquids.

transparent command A command that can be selected while another command is operating.

tree structure The organization pattern of the database for solid models; the original definitions of each primitive are stored in a previous "branch" of the tree, which makes it easier to change the model and requires less computer storage space.

tween To automatically calculate the steps needed for a complete animation sequence, given only the start and end points.

typing cursor A special cursor used in dialogue boxes for entering text from the keyboard.

UCS icon Indicates the current coordinate system in use and the direction in which the coordinates are being viewed in 3D drawings.

unidirectional dimensioning The standard alignment for dimension text, which is to orient the text horizontally.

unilateral tolerances Tolerances specified by defining a nominal dimension and the allowable range of deviation from that dimension, where either the plus or minus value is zero.

union The area or volume formed by adding two regions or solid models together.

units AutoCAD can draw figures using metric, decimal, scientific, engineering, or architectural measurement scales. These are set with the UNITS command.

User Coordinate System (UCS) A set of x, y, and z coordinates whose origin, rotation, and tilt are defined by the user. You can create and name any number of User Coordinate Systems.

variance tolerances Tolerances specified by defining a nominal dimension and the allowable range of deviation from that dimension; includes bilateral and unilateral tolerances.

vector A directional line. Also, a way of storing a graphic image as a set of mathematical formulas.

viewpoint The direction from which you are viewing a three-dimensional object.

viewport A "window" showing a particular view of a three-dimensional object.

virtual screen A file containing only the information displayed on the screen. AutoCAD uses this to allow fast zooming without having to regenerate the original drawing file.

visible attribute Text information associated with a block that is displayed on the screen.

Windows Control Box A box that appears in the upper left corner of a window that controls closing and resizing the window.

wireframe modeling A type of three-dimensional modeling that uses lines, arcs, circles, and other entities to represent the edges and other features of an object; so called because it looks like a sculpture made from wires.

work axis In AutoCAD Designer, a parametrically defined line at the center line of a cylindrical, conical, or toroidal surface that can be used to define other features.

work plane In AutoCAD Designer, a parametrically defined plane attached to a feature of the model that you can use to define other features.

work point In AutoCAD Designer, a parametrically located point that can be placed to define the location of holes.

working drawings A set of drawings that provides all the information needed to manufacture and assemble an item, including the detail drawings, assembly drawing, and parts list.

World Coordinate System (WCS) AutoCAD's system for defining three-dimensional model geometry using x, y, and z coordinate values; the default orientation is a horizontal X axis with positive values to the right, a vertical Y axis with positive values above the X axis, and a Z axis that is perpendicular to the screen and has positive values in front of the screen.

AUTOCAD COMMAND SUMMARY

This is a list of the AutoCAD Release 12 commands used in these tutorials. If you are looking for a command that operates within a dialogue box, look under "Dynamic Dialogue." Dimension Variables are listed separately.

Name/Icon	Definition	Menu Bar	Screen Menu	Command:
Angular	Dimensions an angle.	Draw, Dimensions, Angular	DIM, Angular	DIM ↵ ANGULAR
Arc	Draws arcs in a drawing.	Draw, Arc	DRAW, ARC	A or ARC
Area	Finds the area and perimeter of a closed plane surface.	Assist, Inquiry, Area	INQUIRY, AREA	AREA
Array	Copies an object multiple times to create a regularly spaced rectangular or circular pattern.	Construct, Array	EDIT, ARRAY	ARRAY
Attribute Definition	Creates attribute text entities from the command prompt.	N/A	BLOCKS, ATTDEF	ATTDEF
Attribute Extract	Extracts attribute data from a drawing.	N/A	UTILITY, ATTEXT	ATTEXT
Base	Specifies the insertion point for a block or drawing.	N/A	BLOCKS, BASE	BASE
Baseline	Measures next dimension from one extension line.	Draw, Dimensions, Linear, Baseline	DIM, next, Baseline	DIM ↵ BASELINE
Block	Groups a set of entities together so that they are treated as one object.	Construct, Block	BLOCKS, BLOCK	BLOCK
Boundary Hatch	Automatically fills the area you select with a pattern.	Draw, Hatch. . .	DRAW, BHATCH	BHATCH
Break	Removes or breaks part of an entity or circle.	Modify, Break	EDIT, BREAK	BREAK

Name/Icon	Definition	Menu Bar	Screen Menu	Command:
Calculator	Calculates mathematical expressions.	Assist, Calculator	N/A	CAL or 'CAL if in the middle of executing another command.
Center Marks	Draws center marks.	Draw, Dimensions, Radial, Center Mark	DIM, next, Center	DIM ↵ CENTER
Chamfer	Draws a straight line segment (called a chamfer) between two given lines.	Construct, Chamfer	EDIT, CHAMFER	CHAMFER
Change Properties	Changes the properties of an object.	N/A	EDIT, CHPROP	CHPROP
Circle	Draws circles of any size.	Draw, Circle	DRAW, CIRCLE, select options for radius and diameters.	C or CIRCLE
Continue	Adds the next chained dimension, measured from the last dimension.	Draw, Dimensions, Linear, Continue	DIM, next, Continue	DIM ↵ CONTINUE
Copy	Copies an existing shape from one area on the drawing to another area.	Construct, Copy	EDIT, COPY	CP or COPY
Diameter	Adds center marks to a circle when providing its diameter dimension.	Draw, Dimensions, Radial, Diameter	DIM, Diameter	DIM ↵ DIAMETER
Dimension Style	Shows the current dimension style.	Settings, Dimension Style. . .	DIM, Dim Styl, Dimstyle	DIMSTYLE
Dimensions	Places AutoCAD into dimensioning mode.	Draw, Dimensions	DIM	DIM
Distance	Reads out the value for the distance between two selected points.	Assist, Inquiry, Distance	INQUIRY, DIST	DIST

Name/Icon	Definition	Menu Bar	Screen Menu	Command:
Divide	Places points or blocks along an entity to create segments.	Construct, Divide	EDIT, DIVIDE	DIVIDE
Donut	Draws concentric filled circles or filled circles.	Draw, Donut	DRAW, DONUT	DONUT
Double Line	Draws double lines.	Draw, Line, Double Lines	N/A	DLINE
Drawing Exchange File Out	Exports a drawing to a file of type DXF so that another application can use it.	File, Import/Export, DXF Out...	UTILITY, DXF/DXB, DXFOUT	DXFOUT
Dynamic Dialogue Attribute Definition	Creates attribute text entities using a dialogue box.	Draw, Text, Attributes, Define...	BLOCKS, ATTDEF, Dialogue	DDATTDEF
Dynamic Dialogue Attribute Edit	Edits attribute values.	Draw, Text, Attributes, Edit...	EDIT, DDATTE	DDATTE
Dynamic Dialogue Change Properties	Uses a dialogue box to change the properties of an object.	Modify, Change, Properties	N/A	DDCHPROP
Dynamic Dialogue Dimension Style	Controls dimension styles.	Settings, Dimension Style...	N/A	DDIM
Dynamic Dialogue Edit Text	Allows you to edit text inside a dialogue box.	N/A	EDIT, DDEDIT	DDEDIT
Dynamic Dialogue Insert	Places blocks or other drawings into a drawing via a dialogue box.	Draw, Insert...	N/A	DDINSERT
Dynamic Text	Adds text to a drawing.	Draw, Text, Dynamic	DRAW, DTEXT	DTEXT

Name/Icon	Definition	Menu Bar	Screen Menu	Command:
Dynamic View	Changes the 3D view of a point.	View, Set View, Dview	DISPLAY, DVIEW	DVIEW
Ellipse	Used to draw ellipses.	Draw, Ellipse	DRAW, ELLIPSE	ELLIPSE
End	Saves current drawing file under name specified at beginning and returns you to the operating system.	N/A	UTILITY, next, END	END
Erase	Erases entities from drawing.	Modify, Erase	EDIT, ERASE	E or ERASE
Explode	Separates blocks or dimensions into component entities so that they are no longer one group and can be edited.	Modify, Explode	EDIT, EXPLODE	EXPLODE
Extend	Extends the length of an existing entity to meet a boundary.	Modify, Extend	EDIT, next, EXTEND	EXTEND
External Reference	Adds one drawing inside another, linking them so that changes appear in both drawings.	File, Xref	BLOCKS, XREF	XREF
Extrude	Extrudes a two-dimensional shape into a three-dimensional object.	Model, Extrude	MODEL, SOLEXT	EXTRUDE, or SOLEXT, or EXT
Fillet	Connects lines, arcs, or circles with a smoothly fitted arc.	Construct, Fillet	EDIT, next, FILLET	FILLET
Grid	Displays a grid of dots at desired spacing on the screen.	Settings, Drawing Aids. . ., Grid	SETTINGS, GRID	GRID, or toggle off and on with F7
Handles	Controls the use of handles in solid models.	N/A	SETTINGS, HANDLES	HANDLES

Name/Icon	Definition	Menu Bar	Screen Menu	Command:
Hatch	Fills the boundary defined by the user with a hatch pattern.	N/A	DRAW, HATCH	HATCH
Help	Displays information explaining commands and procedures.	Help	****, HELP	HELP or ?, or 'HELP or '? if in the middle of executing another command
Hide	Removes hidden lines from 3D surface representation.	Render, Hide	RENDER, HIDE	HIDE
Horizontal	Dimensions objects with a horizontal dimension line.	Draw, Dimensions, Linear, Horizontal	DIM, Horizntl	DIM ↵ HORIZONTAL
Identify	Finds the coordinates of any point on the screen.	Assist, Inquiry, ID Point	INQUIRY, ID	ID
Insert	Places blocks or other drawings into a drawing via the command line.	N/A	BLOCKS, INSERT	INSERT
Insert Solid	An AutoLISP command that inserts solid model files into a drawing.	N/A	N/A	INSRTSOL
Intersect	Forms a new solid from the area common to two or more solids or regions.	Model, Intersect	MODEL, SOLINT	SOLINT
Isometric Plane	Controls which isometric drawing plane is active: left, top, or right.	Settings, Drawing Aids. . ., Isometric Snap/Grid	SETTINGS, DDRMODES, Isometric Snap/Grid	ISOPLANE, or toggle with Ctrl-E
Layer	Creates layers and controls layer color, linetype, and visibility.	Settings, Layer Control. . .	LAYER. . .	LA or LAYER

Name/Icon	Definition	Menu Bar	Screen Menu	Command:
Leader	Creates leader lines for identifying lines and dimensions.	Draw, Dimensions, Leader	DIM, Leader	DIM ↵ LEADER
Limits	Sets up the size of the drawing.	Settings, Drawing Limits	SETTINGS, LIMITS	LIMITS
Line	Draws straight lines of any length.	Draw, Line	DRAW, LINE	L or LINE
Linetype	Changes the pattern used for new lines in the drawing.	Settings, Entity Modes. . ., Linetype. . .	SETTINGS, LINETYP	LINETYPE
Linetype Scale	Changes the scale of the linetypes in the drawing.	N/A	SETTINGS, next, LTSCALE	LTSCALE
List	Provides information on an entity, such as the length of a line.	Assist, Inquiry, List	INQUIRY, LIST	LIST
Measure	Marks segments of a chosen length on an object by inserting points or blocks.	Construct, Measure	EDIT, next, MEASURE	MEASURE
Mesh	Generates the surface mesh of a model.	Model, Display, Mesh	MODEL, DISPLAY, SOLMESH	MESH, or SOLMESH
Mirror	Creates mirror images of shapes.	Construct, Mirror	EDIT, next, MIRROR	MIRROR
Model Space	Enters model space.	View, Model Space	MVIEW, MSPACE	MS or MSPACE
Move	Moves an existing shape from one area on the drawing to another area.	Modify, Move	EDIT, next, MOVE	M or MOVE
MV Setup	Helps set up drawing views using a LISP program.	View, Layout, MV Setup	N/A	MVSETUP
Mview	Creates viewports.	View, Mview	MVIEW	MVIEW
New Drawing	Sets up the screen to create a new drawing.	File, New. . .	UTILITY, next, NEW. . .	NEW

Name/Icon	Definition	Menu Bar	Screen Menu	Command:
New Text	Edits dimension text.	Modify, Edit Dimensions, Dimension Text, Change Text	DIM, Edit, Newtext	DIM (↵) NEWTEXT
Object Snap	Finds locations on chosen entities based on drawing geometry.	Settings, Object Snap. . .	SETTINGS, next, OSNAP, or if in override mode, **** and the OSNAP mode	OSNAP
Offset	Draws entities parallel to a given entity.	Construct, Offset	DRAW, OFFSET	OFFSET
Oops	Restores erased entities.	Modify, Erase, Oops!	EDIT, ERASE, OOPS	OOPS
Open Drawing	Loads a previously saved drawing.	File, Open. . .	UTILITY, next, OPEN. . .	OPEN
Ortho [O]	Restricts movement to only horizontal and vertical.	Settings, Drawing Aids. . ., Ortho	SETTINGS, next, ORTHO	ORTHO, or toggle on and off with (F8)
Pan	Moves the drawing around on the screen without changing the zoom factor.	View, Pan	DISPLAY, PAN	P or PAN
Paper Space [P]	Enters paper space when TILEMODE is set to 0.	View, Paper Space	MVIEW, PSPACE	PS or PSPACE
Paper Space Linetype Scale	Causes the paper space LTSCALE factor to be used for every viewport.	N/A	N/A	PSLTSCALE
Paste Clip	Places entities from the Windows Clipboard into the drawing using the Insert command.	Edit, Paste	N/A	PASTECLIP
Plan	Creates a view looking straight down along the Z axis to see the XY coordinates.	View, Set View, Plan View	DISPLAY, PLAN	PLAN

Name/Icon	Definition	Menu Bar	Screen Menu	Command:
Plot	Prints or plots a drawing.	File, Print/Plot. . .	PLOT. . .	PLOT
Polyedit	Changes various features of polylines.	Modify, Polyline Edit	EDIT, next, PEDIT	PEDIT
Polygon	Draws regular polygons with 3 to 1024 sides.	Draw, Polygon	DRAW, next, POLYGON	POLYGON
Polyline	Draws a series of connected entities (lines or arcs) that are treated as a single entity called a polyline.	Draw, Polyline	DRAW, next, PLINE	PLINE
Primitives	Creates a basic solid model shape.	Model, Primitives. . .	MODEL, PRIMS.	DDSOLPRM, or SOLBOX, BOX, SOLCONE, CONE, SOLCYL, CYL, SOLSPHERE, SHPERE, SOLTORUS, TORUS, SOLWEDGE, WEDGE
Purge	Removes unused items from the drawing database.	N/A	UTILITY, PURGE	PURGE
Quick Save	Saves a drawing to the existing default file name.	File, Save	UTILITY, next, QSAVE. . .	QSAVE
Quit	Exits AutoCAD with the option not to save your changes, and returns you to the operating system.	File, Exit AutoCAD	UTILITY, next, QUIT	QUIT
Radius	Adds centermarks to an arc when providing its radius dimension.	Draw, Dimensions, Radial, Radius	DIM, Radius	DIM ↵ RADIUS
Rectangle	Creates rectangular shapes.	Draw, Rectangle	N/A	RECTANG

Name/Icon	Definition	Menu Bar	Screen Menu	Command:
Redo	Reverses the effect of the most recent UNDO command.	Edit, Redo	EDIT, next, UNDO, REDO	REDO
Redraw	Removes excess blipmarks added to the drawing screen and restores objects partially erased while you are editing other objects.	View, Redraw	DISPLAY, REDRAW	R or REDRAW
Redraw All	Redraws all viewports at once.	View, Redraw All	DISPLAY, REDRALL	REDRAWALL
Regenerate	Recalculates the display file in order to show changes.	N/A	DISPLAY, REGEN	REGEN
Regenerate All	Regenerates all viewports at once.	N/A	DISPLAY, REGNALL	REGENALL
Render	Produces a realistically shaded 2D view of a 3D model.	Render, Render	RENDER, RENDER	RENDER
Revolve	Creates a three-dimensional object by sweeping a two-dimensional polyline, circle or region about a circular path to create a symmetrical solid.	Model, Revolve	MODEL, SOLREV	REVOLVE, or SOLREV, or REV
Rotate	Rotates all or part of an object.	Modify, Rotate	EDIT, next, ROTATE	ROTATE
Rotate 3D	Rotates an object in a 3D coordinate system.	Modify, Rotate 3D	EDIT, next, ROTATE, 3D	ROTATE3D
Save	Saves a drawing using Quick Save (if chosen from menu bar) or Save As (if chosen from command prompt).	File, Save...	N/A	SAVE

Name/Icon	Definition	Menu Bar	Screen Menu	Command:
Save As	Saves a drawing, allowing you to change its name or location.	File, Save As. . .	UTILITY, next, SAVE AS. . .	SAVEAS
Save Time	Controls how often a file is automatically saved.	N/A	N/A	SAVETIME
Scale	Changes the size of an object in the drawing database.	Modify, Scale	EDIT, next, SCALE	SCALE
Shade	Creates a shaded view of a model.	Render, Shade	DISPLAY, SHADE	SHADE
Snap S	Limits cursor movement on the screen to set intervals so entities can be placed at precise locations easily.	Settings, Drawing Aids. . ., Snap	SETTINGS, next, SNAP	SNAP, or toggle off and on with F9
Solid Chamfer	Creates chamfers on solid models.	Model, Modify, Chamfer Solids	MODEL, MODIFY, SOLCHAM	SOLCHAM
Solid Change Primitive	Changes, deletes, or moves a primitive.	Model, Modify, Change Primitives	MODEL, MODIFY, SOLCHP	SOLCHP
Solid Cut	Cuts off part of a solid.	Model, Modify, Cut Solids	MODEL, MODIFY, SOLCUT	SOLCUT
Solid Delete Entity	Controls whether an entity is automatically deleted after being extruded, revolved, or solidified.	Model, Setup, Variables. . ., Entity Delete	MODEL, SETUP, SOLVAR, Delent	SOLDELENT
Solid Feature	Creates a copy of any face or edge of a solid object.	Model, Display, Copy Feature	MODEL, DISPLAY, SOLFEAT	SOLFEAT
Solid Fillet	Creates fillets on solid models.	Model, Modify, Fillet Solids	MODEL, MODIFY, SOLFILL	SOLFILL

Name/Icon	Definition	Menu Bar	Screen Menu	Command:
Solid Interference	Shows where two solid objects overlap.	Model, Inquiry, Interference	MODEL, INQUIRY, NTERF	SOLINTERF
Solid List	Lists information about the selected object.	Model, Inquiry, List Objects	MODEL, INQUIRY, SOLLIST	SOLLIST
Solid Mass Properties	Inquires about the mass properties of a solid object.	Model, Inquiry, Mass Property. . .	MODEL, INQUIRY, SOLMASSP	SOLMASSP
Solid Material	Specifies the material an object is made of.	Model, Utility, Material. . .	MODEL, UTILITY, SOLMAT	SOLMAT
Solid Profile	Creates a two-dimensional profile of a model for plotting.	Model, Display, Profile Solids	MODEL, DISPLAY, SOLPROF	SOLPROF
Solid Purge	Removes unused entities from the solid model database.	Model, Utility, Purge Objects	MODEL, UTILITY, SOLPURG	SOLPURGE
Solid Section	Creates a section through a solid model and generates hatching.	Model, Display, Section Solids	MODEL, DISPLAY, SOLSECT	SOLSECT
Solid Separate	Separates joined primitives.	Model, Modify, Separate	MODEL, MODIFY, SOLSEP	SOLSEP
Solid User Coordinate System	Aligns a User Coordinate System with the edge or face of a solid.	Model, Utility, SolUCS	MODEL, UTILITY, SOLUCS	SOLUCS
Solid View	An ADS application that establishes the viewing direction for your model.	N/A	N/A	SOLVIEW
Solid Wire Density	Controls the appearance and accuracy of three-dimensional shapes through the number of tessellation lines.	Model, Display, Set Wire Dens.	MODEL, DISPLAY, SOLWDENS	SOLWDENS

Name/Icon	Definition	Menu Bar	Screen Menu	Command:
Status	Shows the dimension variables and their current settings.	N/A	DIM, next, Status	DIM ⏎ STATUS
Stretch	Stretches the entities selected.	Modify, Stretch	EDIT, next, STRETCH	STRETCH
Style	Lets you create new text styles and modify existing ones.	Draw, Text, Set Style...	SETTINGS, next, STYLE	STYLE
Subtract	Removes the set of a second solid or region from the first set.	Model, Subtract	MODEL, SOLSUB	SUBTRACT, or SOLSUB, or SUB
Text Screen	Switches from the graphics screen to the text screen.	Edit, Text Window	N/A	TEXTSCR, or toggle with F2
Tilemode	When set to 1, allows creation of tiled viewports in model space; when set to 0, enables use of paper space.	View, Tilemode	MVIEW, TILEMOD	TILEMODE
Toolbox	Resizes or removes the toolbox.	N/A	N/A	TOOLBOX
Trim	Removes part of an entity at its intersection with another entity.	Modify, Trim	EDIT, next, TRIM	TRIM
Undo	Reverses the effect of previous commands.	Assist, Undo	UNDO	U (undoes one step) or UNDO
Union	Adds two separate sets of solids or regions together to create one solid model.	Model, Union	MODEL, SOLUNION	UNION, or SOLUNION
Units	Controls the type and precision of the values used in dimensions.	Settings, Units Control...	SETTINGS, next, UNITS	UNITS

Name/Icon	Definition	Menu Bar	Screen Menu	Command:
Update	Updates the dimensions based on changes to the dimension styles and variables.	Modify, Edit Dims, Update Dimensions	DIM, Edit, Update	DIM ↵ UPDATE
User Coordinate System	Creates a user-defined coordinate system.	Settings, UCS	UCS	UCS
User Coordinate System Follow	Generates a plan view of the current UCS in a viewport whenever you change the UCS.	N/A	UCS, Follow	UCSFOLLOW
User Coordinate System Icon	Repositions and turns on and off the display of the UCS icon.	Settings, UCS, Icon	SETTINGS, next, UCSICON	UCSICON
Vertical	Dimensions objects with a vertical dimension line.	Draw, Dimensions, Linear, Vertical	DIM, Vertical	DIM ↵ VERTICAL
View	Saves views of an object to be plotted, displayed, or printed.	View, Set View, Named View. . .	DISPLAY, VIEW	VIEW
View Resolution	Controls "fast zoom" mode and sets resolution for circle and arc generation.	N/A	DISPLAY, VIEWRES	VIEWRES
Viewpoint	Establishes different directions from which to view the xyz coordinate system.	View, Set View, Viewpoint	DISPLAY, VPOINT	VPOINT
Viewport Layer	Controls the visibility of layers within specific viewports.	View, Mview, Vplayer	MVIEW, VPLAYER	VPLAYER
Write Block	Saves a block as a separate file so that it may be used in other drawings.	N/A	BLOCKS, WBLOCK	WBLOCK

Name/Icon	Definition	Menu Bar	Screen Menu	Command:
Write Block Solid	An AutoLISP command that creates a WBLOCK file of a solid object.	N/A	N/A	WBLKSOL
Zoom	Resizes areas of the drawing on the screen.	View, Zoom	DISPLAY, ZOOM	Z or ZOOM

AUTOCAD DIMENSION VARIABLES SUMMARY

This is a list of the AutoCAD Release 12 Dimension Variables used in these tutorials.

Name	Definition	Settings, Dimension Style...	DIM DimVARS	Command or DIM:
DIMALT	Allows alternate units to be shown simultaneously, such as inches and metric units.	Text Format...	dimalt	DIMALT
DIMALTF	Controls conversion of one unit into the other when showing alternate units.	Text Format...	dimaltf	DIMALTF
DIMASO	Controls associative dimensioning.	N/A	dimaso	DIMASO
DIMASZ	Sets the size of the arrow.	Arrows...	dimasz	DIMASZ
DIMCEN	Controls center marks.	Extension Lines...	dimcen	DIMCEN
DIMCLRD	Sets the color of dimension lines.	Colors...	dimclrd	DIMCLRD
DIMCLRE	Sets the color of extension lines.	Colors...	dimclre	DIMCLRE
DIMCLRT	Sets the color of dimension text.	Colors...	dimclrt	DIMCLRT
DIMEXE	Controls the length of extension lines beyond dimension lines.	Extension Lines...	next, dimexe	DIMEXE
DIMLFAC	Adjusts the dimension length values when scaling in paper space.	Text Format...	next, dimlfac	DIMLFAC
DIMSCALE	Controls the scale of all dimension features at once.	Features...	next, dimscale	DIMSCALE
DIMSE1 or DIMSE2	Controls whether the first and/or second extension lines are visible.	Extension Lines...	next, dimse1, or dimse2	DIMSE1 or DIMSE2

Name	Definition	Settings, Dimension Style. . .	DIM DimVARS	Command or DIM:
DIMTAD	Controls whether text appears above the dimension line.	Text Location. . .	next, next, dimtad	DIMTAD
DIMTFAC	Controls the height of tolerance text.	Text Location. . .	next, next, dimtfac	DIMTFAC
DIMTIH	Controls whether the text inside a dimension is horizontal.	Text Location. . .	next, next, dimtih	DIMTIH
DIMTIX	Controls whether the text is inside the extension lines.	Text Location. . .	next, next, dimtix	DIMTIX
DIMTOH	Controls whether the text outside a dimension is horizontal.	Text Location. . .	next, next, dimtoh	DIMTOH
DIMTOL	Generates plus/minus tolerances.	Text Format. . .	next, next, dimtol	DIMTOL
DIMTVP	Adjusts text placement relative to text height.	Text Location. . .	next, next, dimtvp	DIMTVP
DIMTXT	Controls the height of text.	Text Location. . .	next, next, dimtxt	DIMTXT
DIMZIN	Suppresses leading zeroes in dimensions.	Text Format. . .	next, next, dimzin	DIMZIN

AUTOVISION COMMAND SUMMARY

This is a list of the AutoVision commands used in Tutorial 16.

Name	Definition	AutoVis	Command:
3D Studio Out	Saves a file formatted for use in 3D Studio.	Import/Export, 3DS Out. . .	3DSOUT
Lights	Controls the light sources in rendered scenes.	Lights. . .	LIGHT
Materials	Controls the material a rendered object appears to be made of, and allows the creation of new materials.	Materials. . .	RMAT
Render	Controls the creation of a realistically shaded 2D view of a 3D model.	Render. . .	RENDER
Replay Image	Displays a saved image.	Images, Replay Image. . .	REPLAY
Save Image	Creates a bitmapped version of a rendered image for quick reference.	Images, Save Image. . .	SAVEIMG
Scenes	Saves and recalls named scenes, making it easier to quickly change to a different viewpoint and lighting.	Scenes. . .	SCENE
Views	Uses a dialogue box to select saved views.	Views. . .	DDVIEW

3D STUDIO COMMAND SUMMARY

This is a list of the 3D Studio commands used in Tutorials 17 through 19. Similar command names may appear under several different menus and have similar or different effects; the list below reflects only those variations used in these tutorials and is not meant as a complete list of all options available.

Name/Icon	Description	Program Module(s)	Menu
3D Display	Allows 3D data to be displayed in 2D Shaper.	2D Shaper	Display, 3D Display. . .
3D Scale	Changes the size of a 3D object.	3D Editor	Modify, Object, 3D Scale
Add Key	Adds a key to an animation path.	Keyframer	Paths, Add Key
Ambient	Controls the amount of light in a scene overall.	3D Editor	Lights, Ambient
Attach Object	Joins separate objects into one.	3D Editor	Create, Object, Attach
Bitmap	Sets up a bitmap for use as a background to a scene.	3D Editor	Renderer, Setup, Background
Box	Creates a 3D box.	3D Editor	Create, Box
Center Shape	Centers a shape on a path.	3D Lofter	Shapes, Center
Cone	Creates a 3D cone.	3D Editor	Create, Cone. . .
Create Camera	Creates a camera.	3D Editor, Keyframer	Cameras, Create
Create Dummy	Creates a dummy object.	Keyframer	Hierarchy, Create Dummy
Cylinder	Creates a 3D cylinder.	3D Editor	Create, Cylinder. . .
Define Segment	Defines which sequence of frames make up the current segment of animation.	Keyframer	Time, Define Segment
Delete Camera	Deletes a camera.	3D Editor, Keyframer	Cameras, Delete
Drawing Aids	Sets up your drawing.	2D Shaper, 3D Editor, 3D Lofter, Keyframer	Views, Drawing Aids
Enlarge Viewport	Changes the size of a viewport.	2D Shaper, 3D Editor, 3D Lofter, Keyframer	N/A
Fetch FETCH	Restores the drawing as it was the last time Hold was selected.	2D Shaper, 3D Editor, 3D Lofter, Keyframer	N/A

Name/Icon	Description	Program Module(s)	Menu
Follow	Orients an object along a motion path.	Keyframer	Paths, Follow
Get	Gets a path and assigns it to an object.	Keyframer	Paths, Get. . .
Grid	Toggles the grid on and off.	2D Shaper, 3D Editor, 3D Lofter, Keyframer	Views, Use Grid
Gsphere	Creates a sphere made up of triangles like a geodesic dome.	3D Editor	Create, Gsphere. . .
Hide	Hides an object.	Keyframer	Display, Hide
Hold HOLD	Stores your work so that you can return to the chosen settings.	2D Shaper, 3D Editor, 3D Lofter, Keyframer	N/A
Key Time	Changes the frame number associated with a keyframe.	Keyframer	Paths, Adjust, Key Time
Line	Creates a line.	2D Shaper	Create, Line
Link	Creates hierarchical links between objects.	Keyframer	Hierarchy, Link
Load	Opens a file of the type appropriate to the module.	2D Shaper, 3D Editor, 3D Lofter, Keyframer	File, Load
Lsphere	Creates a sphere made up of longitude and latitude lines.	3D Editor	Create, Lsphere. . .
Make Object	Creates an object based on the parameters you set.	3D Lofter	Objects, Make
Material	Allows you to choose and apply materials to objects.	3D Editor	Surface, Material. . .
Merge	Adds the contents of one file to another.	2D Shaper, 3D Editor, 3D Lofter, Keyframer	File, Merge
Morph Object	Sets up a morphing sequence.	Keyframer	Object, Morph
Move Camera	Moves a camera.	3D Editor, Keyframer	Cameras, Move
Move Key	Changes the position associated with a keyframe.	Keyframer	Paths, Move Key
Move Object	Moves an object on the screen.	3D Editor, Keyframer	3DE: Modify, Object, Move; K: Object, Move

Name/Icon	Description	Program Module(s)	Menu
Preview	Shows an unrendered version of an animation so that it can be checked quickly.	Keyframer	Preview
Render	Displays an object with realistic lights, materials, and textures.	3D Editor, Keyframer	Renderer, Render
Reset	Resets 3D Studio to use default values.	2D Shaper, 3D Editor, 3D Lofter, Keyframer	File, Reset
Rotate Object	Causes objects to rotate.	3D Editor, Keyframer	3DE: Modify, Object, Rotate; K: Object, Rotate
Save	Saves your work as the appropriate file type.	2D Shaper, 3D Editor, 3D Lofter, Keyframer	File, Save
Scale Segment	Modifies the duration of a segment of animation.	Keyframer	Time, Scale Segment
Shape Assignment	Specifies the current shape to use.	2D Shaper	Shape, Assign
Shaper	Imports an object from 2D Shaper to 3D Lofter.	3D Lofter	Shapes, Get
Show Tree	Shows a hierarchy of linked objects.	Keyframer	Hierarchy, Show Tree
Show/Hide Path	Toggles whether the animation path is visible.	Keyframer	Paths, Show-Hide
Snap	Toggles snap on and off.	2D Shaper, 3D Editor, 3D Lofter, Keyframer	Views, Use Snap
Spot	Controls spot lights in a rendering.	3D Editor	Lights, Spot. . .
Squash Object	Shortens the shape of an object along one dimension only, lengthening the other two to preserve the original volume.	Keyframer	Object, Squash
Tape	Tape measure tool.	2D Shaper	Display, Tape. . .
Track Info TRACKinfo	Displays the track and transformation information of an animated object.	Keyframer	N/A

Name/Icon	Description	Program Module(s)	Menu
View Image	Displays a rendered animation.	Keyframer	View, Image
Zoom Extents	Shows the entire drawing on the screen.	2D Shaper, 3D Editor, 3D Lofter, Keyframer	N/A
Zoom Out	Reduces the size of the drawing on the screen.	2D Shaper, 3D Editor, 3D Lofter, Keyframer	N/A

AUTOCAD DESIGNER COMMAND SUMMARY

This is a list of the AutoCAD Designer commands used in Tutorial 20.

Name	Description	Designer	Command:
Angular Tolerance	Controls the tolerance angle for constraints.	Settings. . ., Angular Tolerance	ADSKANGTOL
Delete Constraints	Deletes constraints from the active sketch.	Sketch, Constraints, Delete	ADDELCON
Dimension Display	Changes the display mode without affecting the drawing.	Display, Dim Display	ADDIMDSP
Edit Features	Displays and modifies the dimension values of an active part's features.	Edit Feature	ADEDITFEAT
Extrude	Creates an extruded solid from the active sketch.	Features, Extrude. . .	ADEXTRUDE
Fix Point	Locates the immovable point on the active sketch; other geometry moves relative to it.	Sketch, Fix Point	ADFIXPT
Hole	Creates a hole in the active part.	Features, Hole. . .	ADHOLE
Mass Properties	Lists mass properties.	Utilities, Mass Properties	ADMASSPROP
Mode	Controls whether Part or Drawing mode is in effect.	Mode	ADMODE
Modify Dimensions	Allows you to modify dimension values.	Change Dimension	ADMODDIM
Parametric Dimensioning	Allows you to dimension the active sketch.	Sketch, Add Dimension	ADPARDIM
Part In	Reads parts from another file into the current one.	Utilities, Transfer, Part In. . .	ADPARTIN
Part Viewing	Changes the view orientation in Part mode.	Part Viewing	ADPARTVIEW
Path	Defines the motion of Sweep features.	Sketch, Path	ADPATH
Pickbox	Sets the size of the pickbox.	Settings, Pickbox Size. . .	PICKBOX

Name	Description	Designer	Command:
Profile	Applies constraints to turn a sketch into a shape that can be extruded, revolved, or swept.	Sketch, Profile	ADPROFILE
Rule Mode	Controls whether constraints are applied automatically.	Settings. . ., Rule Mode	ADRULEMODE
Show Constraints	Displays the constraint symbols on the active sketch.	Sketch, Constraints, Show	ADSHOWCON
Sketch Mode	Controls whether a sketch is interpreted as precise or rough.	Settings. . ., Sketch Mode	ADSKMODE
Update	Regenerates the active part or drawing using any new dimension values.	Update	ADUPDATE
View	Creates a view of a solid model.	Drawing, Create View. . .	ADVIEW
Work Axis	Creates a line at the center line of a cylindrical, conical, or toroidal surface that can be used to define other features.	Features, Work Axis	ADWORKAXIS
Work Plane	Creates a plane that can be used to define other features.	Features, Work Plane. . .	ADWORKPLN
Work Point	Creates work points used for locating holes.	Features, Work Point	ADWORKPT

ART CREDITS

Figures A.1 and A.2, Chapter 1, 2, and 3 openers, Part 2 opener, and Tutorial 1, 2, 3, 4, 5, 9, 10, 11, and 20 openers courtesy Autodesk, Inc.

Challenge Exercises 2, 4, and 9, Tutorial 19 opener, and all "Adapting for Architecture" tips by Kyle Tage

Images in "CAD and the Design Process" courtesy of Autodesk, Inc., 3D Systems, and David S. Cohn

Exercises 1.2, 1.3, 1.6, 1.7, 2.3, 2.4, 3.2, 3.3, 3.5, 3.6, 3.7, 4.4, 4.5, 4.6, 4.7, 5.5, 5.6, 5.7, 6.6, 6.7, 7.1, 7.2, 7.3, 7.6, 7.7, 8.5, 8.6, 9.4, 9.6, 9.7, 9.8, 11.3, 11.4, 11.5, 11.6, 13.7, 14.3, 14.6, 14.7, 15.3, 15.5, and 15.6 by the Spocad Centers of the Gonzaga University School of Engineering

Exercises 1.9, 2.6, 2.7, 9.2, 10.4, 10.5, 10.6, 12.6, 14.4 and 14.5 by Karen L. Coen-Brown, Engineering Mechanics Department, University of Nebraska-Lincoln

Exercises 7.4, 7.5, 8.1, 8.2, 8.3, 10.7, 10.9, and 13.6 by Tom Bryson, University of Missouri-Rolla

Tutorial 7, 12, and 13 openers by James H. Earle

Exercises 5.4 and 6.8, and Tutorial 6 opener by Kim Manner, Department of Mechanical Engineering, University of Wisconsin-Madison

Exercise 8.4 and Tutorial 8 opener by Mary Ann Koen, University of Missouri-Rolla

Exercises 11.1 and 11.2 by John S. Walker, Program Coordinator-CADD, Essex Community College, Baltimore, MD

Tutorial 15 opener by Doug Baese

Exercise 9.1 by Kevin Berisso

Tutorial 16 opener by David S. Cohn

Exercise 3.4 by D. Krall, Norfolk State University

Tutorial 14 opener by Torian Roesch

INDEX

ART CREDITS

Figures A.1 and A.2, Chapter 1, 2, and 3 openers, Part 2 opener, and Tutorial 1, 2, 3, 4, 5, 9, 10, 11, and 20 openers courtesy Autodesk, Inc.

Challenge Exercises 2, 4, and 9, Tutorial 19 opener, and all "Adapting for Architecture" tips by Kyle Tage

Images in "CAD and the Design Process" courtesy of Autodesk, Inc., 3D Systems, and David S. Cohn

Exercises 1.2, 1.3, 1.6, 1.7, 2.3, 2.4, 3.2, 3.3, 3.5, 3.6, 3.7, 4.4, 4.5, 4.6, 4.7, 5.5, 5.6, 5.7, 6.6, 6.7, 7.1, 7.2, 7.3, 7.6, 7.7, 8.5, 8.6, 9.4, 9.6, 9.7, 9.8, 11.3, 11.4, 11.5, 11.6, 13.7, 14.3, 14.6, 14.7, 15.3, 15.5, and 15.6 by the Spocad Centers of the Gonzaga University School of Engineering

Exercises 1.9, 2.6, 2.7, 9.2, 10.4, 10.5, 10.6, 12.6, 14.4 and 14.5 by Karen L. Coen-Brown, Engineering Mechanics Department, University of Nebraska-Lincoln

Exercises 7.4, 7.5, 8.1, 8.2, 8.3, 10.7, 10.9, and 13.6 by Tom Bryson, University of Missouri-Rolla

Tutorial 7, 12, and 13 openers by James H. Earle

Exercises 5.4 and 6.8, and Tutorial 6 opener by Kim Manner, Department of Mechanical Engineering, University of Wisconsin-Madison

Exercise 8.4 and Tutorial 8 opener by Mary Ann Koen, University of Missouri-Rolla

Exercises 11.1 and 11.2 by John S. Walker, Program Coordinator-CADD, Essex Community College, Baltimore, MD

Tutorial 15 opener by Doug Baese

Exercise 9.1 by Kevin Berisso

Tutorial 16 opener by David S. Cohn

Exercise 3.4 by D. Krall, Norfolk State University

Tutorial 14 opener by Torian Roesch